Hotels and
Bed & Breakfast 2006

Guide to inspected properties
Great Britain & Ireland

First published 2005
Copyright © RAC 2005

Published by BBC Worldwide Limited
Room 1065, Woodlands, 80 Wood Lane,
London W12 0TT
Telephone: 020 8433 2000
Fax: 020 8433 3754

ISBN 0-563-49329-1

Publisher: Adam Waddell
Associate Publisher: Simon Carrington
Sales Manager: Rob Wicker
Sales Executives: Geoff Owen, Romy Tennant
Publishing Assistant: Karen Fisher Pollard

Editorial, production and repro: Thalamus Publishing
Jim Greatorex Davies, Warren Lapworth, Matthew Uffindell, Franco Frey

Cartographic Production: Mapworld, David Fryer
Pixel Cartography, Hilary Austin

Maps: Reproduced by permission of Ordnance Survey on behalf of HMSO.
© Crown Copyright 2005. All rights reserved. Licence number 100022382

Printed and bound in Spain by Cayfossa-Quebecor, Barcelona

Visually impaired readers should contact RAC (contact details below) to discuss the alternative formats in which the information contained in this Guidebook can be provided.

RAC Motoring Services
RAC Hotels
1 Forest Road
Feltham
Middlesex
TW13 7RR

Contents

Regions

Your guide to reassurance starts here

Someone, somewhere, once coined the phrase "Sometimes, it's better to travel than to arrive."

That person obviously didn't have an RAC Hotels and Bed & Breakfast guide to hand. Because if you want to know exactly what accommodation awaits you at the end of a journey, this definitive guide is essential. Just as it has been for over 100 years.

You'll find thousands of hotels and bed and breakfasts in this guide. From historic castles, to luxury hotels, to family run bed & breakfasts. RAC accommodation has been regularly inspected and rated by an RAC Hotel Inspector to exacting standards.

Accommodation is classified within our ratings scheme – Stars for hotels, Diamonds for bed & breakfasts. With the very best properties given one or more of RAC's prestigious awards for excellence.

Whether you're looking for a picture book cottage set in rolling downs miles away from it all, or a five star hotel in the heart of town, you'll find it and everything else in between, in this guide.

If you want to be certain that your expectations on setting off, will be what greets you when you arrive, you'll find this painstakingly researched guide as invaluable as ever.

RAC ratings and awards are designed to tell you exactly what we experienced at each property to help you make the right choice.

And using the guide is so simple...

– Accommodation is ordered by region, so places are easy to find

– Award-winning properties are listed at the beginning of each regional section so you know where to look first for accommodation for special occasions

– Includes Ordnance Survey maps that have RAC accommodation pinpointed, so you can see the nearest places to stay around your planned destination

– Symbols and abbreviations are used throughout for quick reference and to give you all the information you need at a glance

– Thousands of hotels and bed & breakfasts are listed in this one book, making it the one-stop source for all your accommodation needs.

Over a century of experience in hotels

Starting handle. Red flag. Rug. Gauntlets. The Royal Automobile Club Handbook.

Just over 100 years ago, the check list above was as essential to motorists as having a wheel on each corner of the car.

Especially the Royal Automobile Club Handbook which was the forerunner to this guide.

Nothing's changed.

This 2006 RAC Hotels and Bed & Breakfast Guide follows the same successful principals as that first edition;

Accuracy. Fairness. Honesty. Ease of use. Reliability.

Summer Lodge, Evershot, Dorset

Getting the most out of this guide (and your stay)

All it takes is five simple steps to use this guide.

Step 1

Select which region you would like to visit from the map on the Contents page. Each region is colour coded throughout the guide to make it easy to locate.

Step 2

The map at the beginning of each region shows where RAC inspected hotels and bed & breakfasts are located in that region. Choose the town or village where you would like to stay. Alternatively all locations are listed alphabetically on pages 652-677.

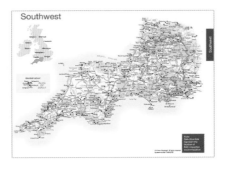

Step 5

We've introduced a 'Map Reference' heading under each accommodation's listing to help you find its location (locations marked with a blue dot) on the Ordnance Survey maps included at the end of this guidebook (pg 634-651).

The Location Index (pg 652-677) now lists all the accommodation in that location, along with the Map References to help you locate them on the Ordnance Survey maps, and page numbers to help you find their listings in the guidebook.

Step 3

After the region map is a list of RAC's award winning properties in that area if you're looking for somewhere special.

Step 4

All accommodation is listed by rating (high to low) in alphabetical order. Symbols and abbreviations are explained fully on the next page. If you know the name of the accommodation but are unsure of its exact location, refer to pages 678-692 for an index of all accommodation by name.

centre. Turn left
left, turn right at traffic
next left into Sydney Pl
Map ref: Bath 3 F1

A guide to everything that's waiting for you

This quick guide shows you what the listings mean. An explanation of the symbols is shown overleaf.

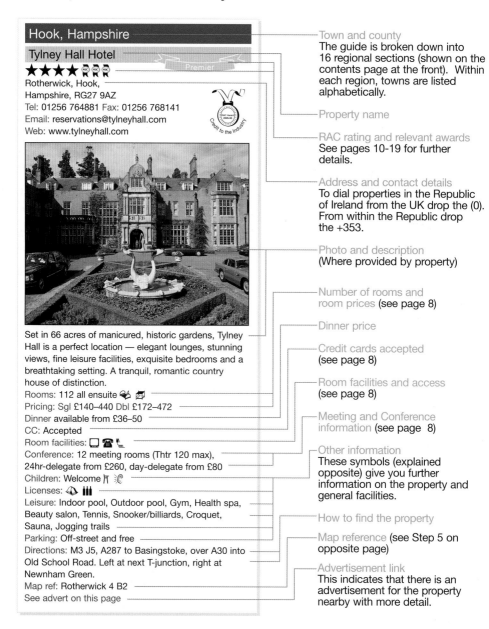

Hook, Hampshire ——— Town and county
The guide is broken down into 16 regional sections (shown on the contents page at the front). Within each region, towns are listed alphabetically.

Tylney Hall Hotel ——— Property name

★★★★ 🏵🏵🏵 *Premier* ——— RAC rating and relevant awards
See pages 10-19 for further details.

Rotherwick, Hook,
Hampshire, RG27 9AZ ——— Address and contact details
Tel: 01256 764881 Fax: 01256 768141
Email: reservations@tylneyhall.com
Web: www.tylneyhall.com

To dial properties in the Republic of Ireland from the UK drop the (0). From within the Republic drop the +353.

Photo and description
(Where provided by property)

Set in 66 acres of manicured, historic gardens, Tylney Hall is a perfect location — elegant lounges, stunning views, fine leisure facilities, exquisite bedrooms and a breathtaking setting. A tranquil, romantic country house of distinction.

Rooms: 112 all ensuite 🏊 🚗 ——— Number of rooms and room prices (see page 8)

Pricing: Sgl £140–440 Dbl £172–472

Dinner available from £36–50 ——— Dinner price

CC: Accepted ——— Credit cards accepted (see page 8)

Room facilities: 📺 ☎ 🔌 ——— Room facilities and access (see page 8)

Conference: 12 meeting rooms (Thtr 120 max), 24hr-delegate from £260, day-delegate from £80 ——— Meeting and Conference information (see page 8)

Children: Welcome 🍴 ☕ ——— Other information
These symbols (explained opposite) give you further information on the property and general facilities.

Licenses: ♿ 🎿

Leisure: Indoor pool, Outdoor pool, Gym, Health spa, Beauty salon, Tennis, Snooker/billiards, Croquet, Sauna, Jogging trails

Parking: Off-street and free

Directions: M3 J5, A287 to Basingstoke, over A30 into Old School Road. Left at next T-junction, right at Newnham Green. ——— How to find the property

Map ref: Rotherwick 4 B2 ——— Map reference (see Step 5 on opposite page)

See advert on this page ——— Advertisement link
This indicates that there is an advertisement for the property nearby with more detail.

What the ★⛺☎🥄🐴♞'s mean

Ratings

For further information please see pages 10-14

★ Hotel classification from 1 to 5 stars. Townhouse classification from 4 to 5 stars.

♦ Guest Accommodation rating (B&Bs, guest houses, farmhouses and inns) from 1 to 5 Diamonds.

Travel Accommodation and Restaurant with Rooms denoted by names only.

✚ Property classification unconfirmed (see page 13).

Awards

For further information please see pages 14-19

 Gold Ribbon Award

 Blue Ribbon Award

 White Ribbon Award

Little Gem Little Gem Award

♞ Dining Award (1 to 5 quality grades)

✻ Sparkling Diamond Award

☙ Warm Welcome Award

⬈ Hotel Group of the Year Award

⬈ Credit to the Industry Award

Room facilities

🛏 Family bedrooms sleeping four or more persons

🛏 Four-poster beds available

⊗ Non-smoking rooms available. Some properties are 100% non-smoking. Please enquire in advance.

▯ TV in all rooms

☎ Telephone in all rooms

☕ Tea/coffee-making facilities in all rooms

⌨ Computer connection available

❄ Air conditioning in all rooms

Children

🐴 Supervised crèche facility

🔊 Baby listening service

🍴 Children's meal menus

Licensing information

⫯⫯⫯ Licensed for the sale of alcohol

⚏ Licensed for the performance of wedding ceremonies

Prices

Sgl Rate for single room with breakfast

Dbl Rate for double/twin room with breakfast (based on two people sharing)

Note:
All room and meal prices quoted are approximate, include VAT and are based on what hoteliers have told us they expect to charge for 2006. Meeting and Conference rates are shown exclusive of VAT and are approximate. Prices can vary by season so please check before booking. Cancellation policies, terms and conditions may apply. Please check when booking.

Payment methods

Major credit cards are accepted where indicated. Where credit cards are not accepted, cash or cheques with a cheque guarantee card are accepted. Please check at the time of booking.

Disabled Access

RAC does not inspect for disabled access at its Hotels and Guest Accommodation. For information on disabled access at any property listed in this guide book please contact the property directly. Alternatively, for recommendations on RAC and other accommodation inspected for accessibility based on the National Accessible Scheme ratings, you can contact Tourism for All (details below) which specialises in providing details of suitable properties.

Tourism for All
The Hawkins Suite
Enham Place, Enham Alamein
Andover
Hampshire SP11 6JS

Tel 0845 124 9971
www.tourismforall.org.uk

Why you can trust us

The moment you arrive at a hotel or guest accommodation with an RAC rating, you can start to relax. Confident in the levels of hospitality and comfort waiting for you.

That rating means that the property has been put through its paces by one of our team of experienced and highly qualified Inspectors.

Inspectors who don't know the meaning of the words 'near enough is good enough'.

Why trust our Inspectors?

Every RAC Inspector knows the hospitality industry inside out based on first hand experience of working in the industry themselves.

They know what to look for, and where to look for it. They know the increasing levels of expectation customers have and that second best is nowhere.

How an inspection works

All RAC properties are inspected on an annual basis. Inspectors arrive unannounced so to the staff and owners, he or she is another guest to be made welcome.

And while no one will have any idea of who they are when they arrive, if service and standards aren't up to scratch, the owners or management certainly will the following day. Working to strict, coordinated, standards every Inspector carries out a comprehensive assessment of every aspect of the property and its customer service. From speed and friendliness of checking in, to the temperature of breakfast toast and freshness of your morning coffee.

Following their stay, the Inspector will have a detailed discussion about the inspection with the owner or manager to help them build on existing strengths, or address weaknesses.

Our Inspectors then provide a written report of their findings. These reports are amongst the most influential in the business and are relied on by hoteliers to provide the information required to raise standards.

RAC Inspectors provide hoteliers with comprehensive feedback on their stay.

We take the guesswork out of choosing a place to stay

When it comes to choosing somewhere to stay, nothing beats words of recommendation from someone you trust.

Someone who's stayed there, eaten there. Our ratings help you find exactly what you're looking for.

Ratings are only awarded as a result of an overnight stay by an RAC Inspector following strict quality guidelines and evaluating standards on your behalf. And you needn't worry that our Inspectors will get special treatment, as they stay in the hotels as normal guests. The hotelier is only aware who our Inspectors are on the following morning when they provide feedback on their stay.

Here's a brief summary of what you can expect to find at a property with an RAC rating.

Hotel

One star hotels offer you a clean and comfortable place to stay with courteous service. They include a dining area and most of the bedrooms will have a television and ensuite bath or shower room. Last orders for dinner are no earlier than 6.30pm.

Hotel

Two star hotels have at least one restaurant open to residents for breakfast and dinner with a wider range of food and drink. Rooms should be comfortable, ensuite, well equipped and include a television. Last orders for dinner are no earlier than 7.00pm.

Rosevine Hotel, St Mawes, Cornwall

★ ★ ★ Hotel

At three star hotels you should find a receptionist, more spacious lounges, a restaurant and bar and professional staff who'll respond to your requests promptly and efficiently. All rooms should be ensuite and offer extras such as remote-control television, hairdryer, direct-dial telephone, toiletries and room service. Fax or email services should also be available for business travellers. Last orders for dinner no earlier than 8.00pm.

★ ★ ★ ★ Hotel

These hotels pride themselves on offering excellent accommodation and top quality cuisine. Services from professional staff include porterage, dry cleaning and 24-hour reception and room service. There will be at least one restaurant offering an extensive choice of dishes and fine wines. Rooms will be spacious and well furnished with remote control television and direct-dial telephone. Ensuite bathroom including fixed shower and high quality toiletries. Last orders for dinner no earlier than 9.00pm.

★ ★ ★ ★ ★ Hotel

You can expect the very best of everything at these hotels. A doorman will greet you on arrival and there should be a full concierge service. Luxurious and spacious rooms will offer every modern amenity and include many extra touches such as bathrobes. Highly professional staff should be multilingual and offer impeccable service at all times. There will be at least one restaurant offering the highest quality cuisine and fine wines, with a range of drinks and cocktails served in the bar or lounge. Last orders for dinner no earlier than 10.00pm.

Mandeville Hotel, London

Townhouse Accommodation

A Townhouse is ideal if you prefer a central town or city location with greater privacy and a more personal level of service than hotels. Luxuriously furnished bedrooms and suites include room service rather than formal dining rooms. Townhouses are usually well served by restaurants in the area and fall broadly into the four and five star classification.

Restaurant with Rooms

Usually a local or national destination for eating out, most of these properties have less than 12 bedrooms, with public areas limited to the restaurant itself. Whilst no star rating is given, you can expect the overall quality normally associated with a two star hotel.

Guest Accommodation

The term Guest Accommodation includes bed & breakfasts, guest houses, farmhouses and inns. These usually have fewer facilities and public rooms than hotels, but often make up for it in their friendliness of service and homely atmosphere.

Guest Accommodation is graded at five levels of quality with one Diamond representing the simplest type of accommodation and five Diamonds being the most luxurious.

The beautiful landscape of Renvyle House Hotel, Clifden, Co. Galway

The Diamond rating is awarded upon inspection, based on every aspect of the property, from the quality of the meals to the friendliness of service, the furnishings and decor to the cleanliness and levels of comfort. The minimum you can expect to find is:

- A comfortable, well fitted room with sufficient storage and seating.
- Bedding and towels changed at least once a week during your stay.
- Tasty, well-presented meals (where served), including a cooked breakfast (unless otherwise advertised).
- Professional service and a properly prepared bill.

Travel Accommodation

Budget or lodge accommodation is popular in major cities and often conveniently located close to main roads, airports and motorways. Bedrooms should be ensuite, well-fitted and provide consistent standards. Many are geared up for business travellers and include meeting rooms.

Awaiting inspection

If a property has only recently joined the RAC scheme and was awaiting inspection at the time this guide went to print, it will carry this symbol. This symbol means the accommodation's rating is unconfirmed.

Today's Special.
And tomorrow. And...

While we can't take you through the menu, this RAC guide can take you to the best places for dining out.

No self-respecting gourmet would be without it.

RAC Dining Award

Little wonder RAC Dining Awards are among the most coveted and respected in the catering industry.

Being awarded one announces that the restaurant you've arrived at, has itself arrived.

RAC Dining Awards are hard earned. And only awarded following an overnight stay, so our Inspectors can experience breakfast, the quality of room service and an evening meal.

When considering if a hotel or bed & breakfast is up to the high standards demanded for an RAC Dining Award, our Inspectors also take into consideration the wine list, the ambience, the service, and the knowledge and helpfulness of those serving you.

RAC Dining Awards recognises five ascending levels of quality as shown below:

This level of Award recognises establishments providing tasty, carefully prepared food using fresh ingredients, served in a warm and friendly atmosphere.

Here you can expect more imaginative cuisine from quality ingredients together with a real degree of technical skill. These properties should be licensed (residential and restaurant) to serve alcohol.

At this level you should enjoy cooking to a high national standard, an imaginative menu and first class ingredients. Dishes should offer flavour and flair. The surroundings are sophisticated with professional service.

At this level you can expect to enjoy innovative and exciting cuisine prepared by a highly accomplished chef. Dishes should be faultlessly presented and the surroundings luxurious, resulting in an excellent meal.

At this top level you will experience intense, daring and exciting food flavours with dishes cooked to perfection. Menus may be innovative or classic using luxury ingredients and impeccably served by highly trained staff. Top chefs receiving this Award are likely to be at the cutting edge of their profession, creating a truly memorable dining experience.

Chocolate temptation at Renvyle House Hotel

The very good. The excellent. The unforgettable

The RAC Awards shown on this page are not handed out lightly. When you find an establishment displaying any one of them, you'll have found accommodation that not only meets, but goes beyond the exacting standards set by RAC.

Where you see a Ribbon or Little Gem Award, you should expect and receive exceptional quality and service in every aspect of your stay. These awards are given annually, not given for life. They are reviewed and reassessed by us to ensure a constant level of excellence. You deserve no less. Be the occasion an anniversary, a birthday, a well-deserved break, or just because you want to. Whatever the reason, this guide will help you find days and nights you'll never forget.

Gold Ribbon Award

Our Gold Ribbon Premier Award is exactly that. An award for the very best. Awarded only to Hotels, Townhouses and Restaurants with Rooms that offer and accept nothing less than the finest. Winners of a Gold Ribbon Award offer a truly exceptional experience in comfort, cuisine, customer care and service.

Blue Ribbon Award

Our Blue Ribbon Award recognises excellent Hotels, Townhouses and Restaurants with Rooms. These establishments strive for, and achieve, excellence in all aspects of comfort, cuisine, service and overall quality. Winners of the Blue Ribbon Award offer a level of commitment and service that ensure guests enjoy first class standards and a memorable stay.

White Ribbon Award

This new Award is given to Hotels, Townhouses and Restaurants with Rooms that are commended for achieving high standards of hospitality, comfort, service and cuisine. We're convinced that when guests stay in an RAC White Ribbon establishment, they will be impressed by the commitment, enthusiasm, and warmth of service.

Little Gem Award

Little Gem

Presented to bed & breakfasts, guest houses, farmhouses and inns, an RAC Little Gem Award recognises exactly what its name implies. Accommodation in smaller establishments whose hospitality and standards sparkle. Personally owned and managed, Little Gem Award properties offer superb standards and a real home from home.

Sparkling Diamond Award

You should expect excellent standards in cleanliness, hygiene and guest comfort at properties given this Award.

Warm Welcome Award

As the name implies, you should feel very much at home from the moment you arrive and throughout your stay at these friendly and hospitable properties.

The pursuit of excellence, rewarded

At RAC we believe that sheer hard work and a determination to set ever higher standards in the hotel industry, should not go unrecognised.

To that end, RAC Hotel Group Awards are presented to hotel groups who through that sheer hard work and determination, set the standard for others to aspire to.

Groups who put their customers first. Who deliver what the customer wants every day and night.

Credit to the Industry Award

This Award is given to the small independent hotel group, which, despite the challenges faced by the hotel industry, has made a big commitment to investing in quality. The winning hotel group will have set new standards of excellence with staff that go the extra mile to give customers an unbeatable stay.

For 2006 the winner of the Credit to the Industry Award is Elite Hotels.

Hotel Group of the Year Award

This Award is given for consistency of approach and standards across the group, so that you can expect the same high quality at each of its hotels. The Hotel Group of the Year Award is made to a hotel group judged to have given customers the most consistent standards of service and customer care across the board.

For 2006 the winner of the Hotel Group of the Year Award is Brend Hotels.

Look out for the Group Award symbols on the hotel entries throughout the guide to see the hotels within each award-winning group on the next page.

Ashdown Park Hotel & Country Club, Forest Row

Credit to the Industry Award

Elite Hotels

Ashdown Park Hotel
& Country Club, Forest Row

The Grand Hotel, Eastbourne

Tylney Hall Hotel, Hook

Tylney Hall Hotel, Hook

Hotel Group of the Year Award

Brend Hotels

Barnstaple Hotel, Barnstaple

Belmont Hotel, Sidmouth

Carlyon Bay Hotel, St. Austell

Devon Hotel, Exeter

Park Hotel, Barnstaple

Royal & Fortescue Hotel, Barnstaple

Royal Duchy Hotel, Falmouth

Royal Hotel, Bideford

Saunton Sands Hotel, Saunton

Victorial Hotel, Sidmouth

The Imperial Hotel, Barnstaple

Royal Duchy Hotel, Falmouth

Devon Hotel, Exeter

To be avoided at all costs.

Call:1740*
from your mobile.

Call 1740 from your mobile for up to the
minute news of tail-backs, bottlenecks
and accidents on the road ahead.

always there

RAC Housekeeper of the Year Award 2006

Step forward the people from behind the scenes. For too long the housekeeping professionals of the hospitality industry have been its unsung heroes. RAC Hotels has changed that with our Housekeeper of the Year Award for 2006.

Above: Anke Neugebauer of The Knightsbridge, London, winner of the Award in 2006

RAC Inspectors have scoured the UK and Ireland looking for those dedicated individuals who make such a difference to a guest's stay. From family run establishments to major hotel chains. It wasn't easy. But after much debate, and a lot of tough decision making, our congratulations go to the winner Anke Neugebauer (pictured above) at 4 Star Townhouse, The Knightsbridge in London.

RAC Industry Star Awards

These very personal Awards recognise individuals in the hotel industry who've shown dedication, commitment and a unique quality that makes them stand out from their peers. The winners of these Awards are individuals working in RAC Hotels who have really made a difference to the business and have brought customer service to a new high.

The winners of these prestigious awards for 2006 are:

Hotelier of the Year –	Debbie Taylor, The Balmoral, Edinburgh
Hotel Chef of the Year –	Craig Munro, Culloden House Hotel, Inverness
Concierge of the Year –	Michael de Cozar, The Ritz, London
Receptionist of the Year –	Una Smyth, Hastings Slieve Donard Hotel, Newcastle, Co. Down
Waiter / Waitress of the Year –	Mohammed Hossain, Killashee House Hotel, Naas, Co. Kildare
Bar Person of the Year –	Ken Cracknell, The Nare Hotel, Veryan-in-Roselan, Cornwall
Chambermaid of the Year –	Maureen Chapman, Kettering Park Hotel & Spa, Kettering

Greater London Map (GL)

In this section you will find some of London's most prestigious hotels.
On the following pages a map of Central London and a list of all RAC
inspected accommodation in the London area will help you find the ideal
place to stay.

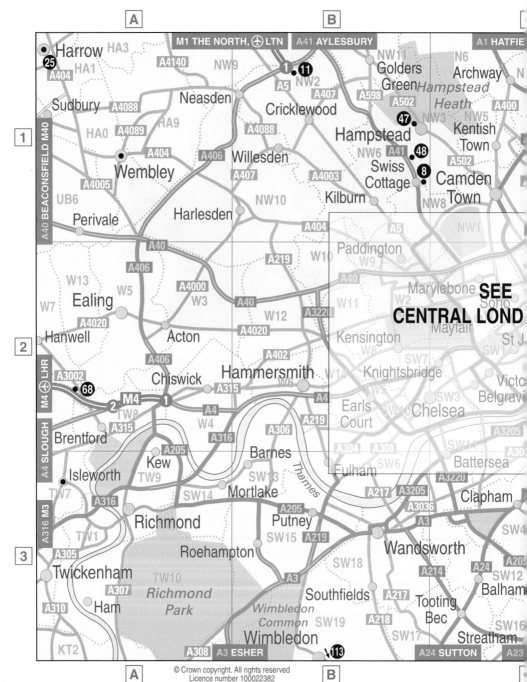

For accommodation name index see pages 24–25

Note: Dark blue numbered dots represent the location of RAC inspected accommodation

London

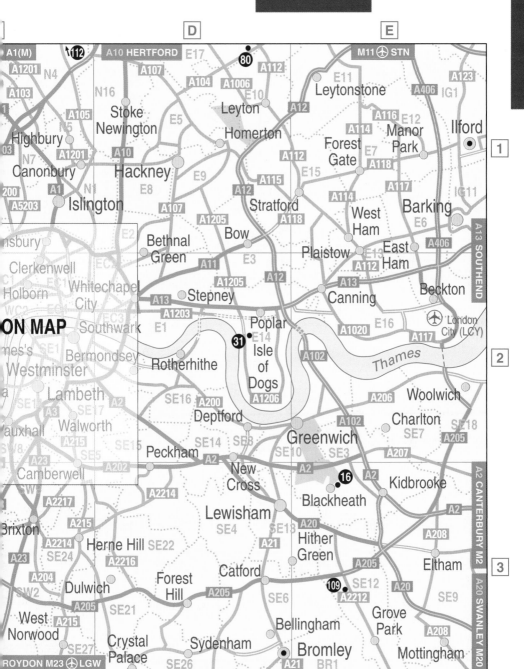

Central London Map (CL)

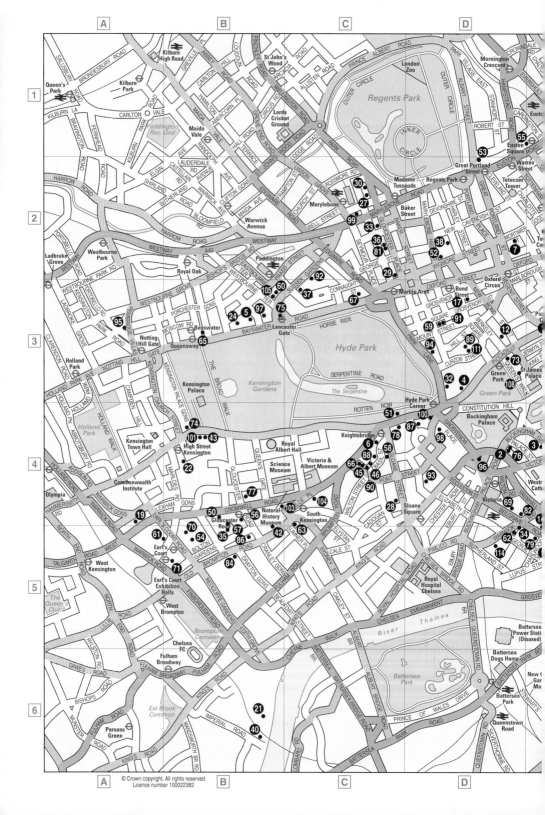

Note: Dark blue numbered dots represent the location of RAC inspected accommodation

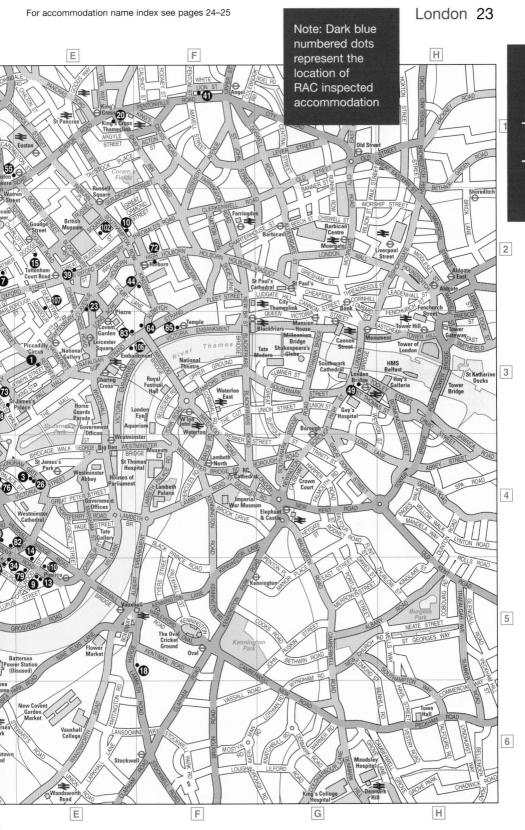

London

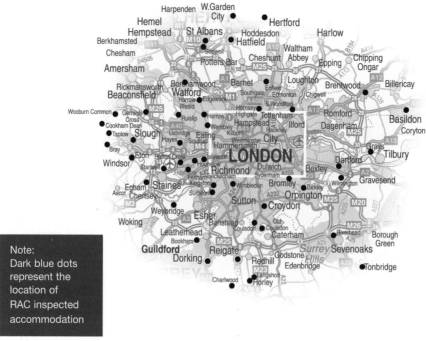

Note:
Dark blue dots represent the location of RAC inspected accommodation

How the index works

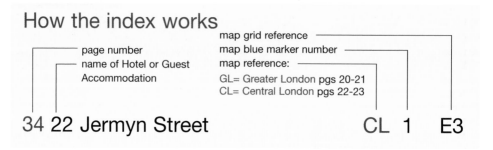

page number

name of Hotel or Guest Accommodation

map grid reference

map blue marker number

map reference:
GL= Greater London pgs 20-21
CL= Central London pgs 22-23

34 22 Jermyn Street   CL   1   E3

Index of London Accommodation

London

London

Award winners

To help you choose somewhere really special for your stay,

Gold Ribbon Hotels

Premier

Athenaeum Hotel & Apartments

Claridge's

The Connaught

The Stafford

we've listed all RAC Award-winning properties in London.

Gold Ribbon Townhouses

Premier

		pg
41	★★★★★	34
51 Buckingham Gate	★★★★★	34
Charlotte Street Hotel	★★★★★	34
Covent Garden Hotel	★★★★★	35
Knightsbridge Hotel	★★★★	44
The Milestone Hotel & Apartments	★★★★★	36
The Soho Hotel	★★★★★	36

Blue Ribbon Hotels

Excellent

		pg
One Aldwych	★★★★★	30
Renaissance Chancery Court	★★★★★	31
Royal Garden Hotel	★★★★★	31
The Bentley Kempinski	★★★★★	32
The Chesterfield Hotel Mayfair	★★★★	42
The Goring	★★★★★	33

51 Buckingham Gate

Charlotte Street Hotel

Covent Garden Hotel

Knightsbridge Hotel

Blue Ribbon Townhouses

White Ribbon Hotels

The Capital Hotel

The Pelham Hotel

Mandeville Hotel

Rubens at The Palace

London

London

Claridge's

★★★★★ 💂💂💂 *Premier*

Brook Street, Mayfair, London, W1A 2JQ
Tel: 020 7629 8860 Fax: 020 7499 2210
Email: info@claridges.co.uk
Web: www.claridges.co.uk
Rooms: 203 all ensuite 🖨 🚭
Pricing: Sgl £505–529 Dbl £588–670
Dinner available from £55
CC: Accepted
Room facilities: 🖵 ☎ 📞 ❄
Access: ⏢
Conference: 8 meeting rooms (Thtr 260 max),
day-delegate from £75
Children: Welcome 🍴
Dogs: Assistance dogs only
Licenses: ◁ 🍾
Leisure: Gym, Health spa, Beauty salon
Directions: Between Hyde Park and Bond Street,
closest Underground Bond Street or Green Park.
Map ref: Central London 17 D3

Conrad London

★★★★★ 💂💂

Chelsea Harbour, London, SW10 0XG
Tel: 020 7823 3000 Fax: 020 7351 6525
Email: londoninfo@conradhotels.com
Web: www.conradlondon.com

Set in the heart of Chelsea Harbour on the marina's
edge, just seconds from the King's Road, Conrad
London is the destination at which to experience
luxurious waterside living, with many of the 160
spacious and contemporary suites offering superb
marina and river views. The hotel boasts an award
winning restaurant, excellent conference facilities, a
health club and serene luxury.
Rooms: 160 all ensuite 🚭
Pricing: Sgl £190.35–366.60 Dbl £204.45–380.70
Dinner available from £27–35
CC: Accepted
Room facilities: 🖵 ☎ 🍵 📞 ❄
Access: ⏢
Conference: 14 meeting rooms (Thtr 250 max),
24hr-delegate from £260, day-delegate from £70

Children: Welcome 🍴
Dogs: Welcome
Licenses: ◁ 🍾
Leisure: Indoor pool, Gym, Health spa, Beauty salon
Parking: Off-street
Directions: A4; then Earl's Court Road going south.
Right into King's Road, left down Lot's Road and hotel
is straight ahead over roundabout.
Map ref: Central London 21 B6

Four Seasons Hotel Canary Wharf

★★★★★ 💂💂💂 *Premier*

Westferry Circus, Canary Wharf, London, E14 8RS
Tel: 020 7510 1999 Fax: 020 7510 1998
Email: res.canarywharf@fourseasons.com
Web: www.fourseasons.com
Rooms: 142 all ensuite 🍽 🚭
Pricing: Sgl £395–455 Dbl £435–495
Dinner available from £35–45
CC: Accepted
Room facilities: 🖵 ☎ 📞 ❄
Access: ⏢
Conference: 4 meeting rooms (Thtr 210 max),
day-delegate from £85
Children: Welcome 🍴 ⚮
Dogs: Welcome
Licenses: ◁ 🍾
Leisure: Indoor pool, Gym, Health spa,
Beauty salon, Tennis
Parking: Off-street
Directions: Leave A13 following signs to Canary Wharf,
Isle Of Dogs and Westferry Circus. Hotel off 3rd exit of
Westferry Circus roundabout.
Map ref: Central London 31 D2

Four Seasons Hotel London

★★★★★ 💂💂💂 *Premier*

Hamilton Place, Park Lane, London, W1A 1AZ
Tel: 020 7499 0888 Fax: 020 7493 1895/6629
Email: fsh.london@fourseasons.com
Web: www.fourseasons.com
Rooms: 219 all ensuite 🚭
Pricing: Sgl £399–1903.50 Dbl £486.63–1927
Dinner available from £33.50
CC: Accepted
Room facilities: 🖵 ☎ 📞 ❄
Access: ⏢
Conference: 6 meeting rooms (Thtr 400 max),
day-delegate from £84
Children: Welcome 🍴 ⚮
Dogs: Welcome
Licenses: ◁ 🍾
Leisure: Gym
Parking: Off-street
Directions: Set back from Park Lane in Hamilton Place.
Closest tubes are Hyde Park Corner and Green Park.
Well situated for Victoria and Paddington stations.
Map ref: Central London 32 C2

Mandarin Oriental Hyde Park

★★★★★★ 🛎🛎🛎 *Premier*

66 Knightsbridge, London, SW1X 7LA
Tel: 020 7235 2000 Fax: 020 7235 2001
Email: molon-reservations@mohg.com
Web: www.mandarinoriental.com

Situated in the heart of Knightsbridge, this luxurious London hotel combines Mandarin Oriental's legendary service with sumptuous rooms, two award-winning restaurants, Foliage and The Park, a buzzing bar and exclusive spa.
Rooms: 200 all ensuite 🖥 🛇
Pricing: Dinner available from £35–50
CC: Accepted
Room facilities: 🖵 ☎ 📞 ❄
Access: ⊫
Conference: 6 meeting rooms (Thtr 250 max), day-delegate from £85
Children: Welcome 🪑
Licenses: 🔔 ♟
Leisure: Gym, Health spa
Parking: Off-street
Directions: Just off the A4, the hotel is located directly opposite Harvey Nichols, in the heart of Knightsbridge.
Map ref: Central London 51 C4

Are the bells ringing?

Getting married? Congratulations! Look for the wedding bells symbol which shows hotels licensed for civil ceremonies.

One Aldwych

★★★★★★ 🛎🛎 *Excellent*

1 Aldwych, London, WC2B 4RH
Tel: 020 7300 1000 Fax: 020 7300 1001
Email: reservations@onealdwych.com
Web: www.onealdwych.com

Brilliant contemporary interiors, two buzzing restaurants – Axis and Indigo – the happening Lobby Bar, an original art collection, thoughtful unpretentious service and an enviable location... just some of the reasons to stay at the award-winning One Aldwych. Bedrooms have the latest movie systems, CD players, wireless broadband internet access, televisions in the bathrooms and pure bath products. Some of the suites have a private gym, terrace or dining room. Fresh fruit and flowers are delivered daily. At weekends guests can relax in the luxurious screening room and take in a movie, or rejuvenate in the state-of-the-art gym and 18m pool with underwater music.
Rooms: 105 all ensuite 🛇
Pricing: Sgl £241–489 Dbl £265–536
Dinner available from £35
CC: Accepted
Room facilities: 🖵 ☎ 📞 ❄ Access: ⊫
Conference: 6 meeting rooms (Thtr 60 max), day-delegate from £79
Children: Welcome 🪑 Licenses: 🔔 ♟
Leisure: Indoor pool, Gym, Health spa, Beauty salon
Directions: At the point where The Aldwych meets The Strand, opposite Waterloo Bridge and close to Covent Garden.
Map ref: Central London 64 F3

Renaissance Chancery Court

★★★★★ 🏨🏨🏨 *Excellent*

252 High Holborn, London, WC1V 7EN
Tel: 020 7829 9888 Fax: 020 7829 9889
Email: sales.chancerycourt@renaissancehotels.com
Web: www.renaissancechancerycourt.com

RENAISSANCE.
CHANCERY COURT
LONDON

Voted "one of the top 5 business hotels in the UK" by the Conde Nast Traveller Awards. 356 light and airy guest rooms and suites, exclusive club floor, meeting facilities, destination restaurant, Pearl, and an award-winning spa.
Rooms: 356 all ensuite 🛏 ⊗
Pricing: Dinner available from £13
CC: Accepted
Room facilities: 📺 ☎ 🖥 📞 ❄
Access: ♿
Conference: 13 meeting rooms (Thtr 435 max), day-delegate from £89
Children: Welcome ♨
Licenses: 🍷 ♂♂♂
Leisure: Gym, Health spa, Beauty salon
Directions: By the Underground exit Holborn station to the right. Hotel is 200m on right.
Map ref: Central London 72 F2

Ritz Hotel

★★★★★ 🏨🏨🏨🏨 *Premier*

150 Piccadilly, London, W1J 9BR
Tel: 020 7493 8181 Fax: 020 7493 2687
Email: enquire@theritzlondon.com
Web: www.theritzlondon.com
Rooms: 133 all ensuite ⊗
Pricing: Sgl £411.25–481.73 Dbl £575.75–658
Dinner available from £60
CC: Accepted

Room facilities: 📺 ☎ 📞 ❄
Access: ♿
Conference: 2 meeting rooms (Thtr 60 max), 24hr-delegate from £399, day-delegate from £75
Children: Welcome ♨ ⅀
Licenses: 🍷 ♂♂♂
Leisure: Gym, Beauty salon
Parking: Off-street
Directions: Located on Piccadilly, next to Green Park, a few steps from Bond Street. From Victoria station, north on Victoria Line to Green Park. Ritz 100 yards away.
Map ref: Central London 73 D3

Royal Garden Hotel

★★★★★ 🏨🏨🏨🏨 *Excellent*

2-24 Kensington High Street, London, W8 4PT
Tel: 020 7937 8000 Fax: 020 7361 1991
Email: sales@royalgardenhotel.co.uk
Web: www.royalgardenhotel.co.uk

Situated in the heart of Kensington, overlooking Hyde Park and Kensington Gardens, The Royal Garden Hotel offers contemporary accommodation, three bars, two restaurants, health club and 24-hour business centre.
Rooms: 396 all ensuite 🛏 ⊗
Pricing: Sgl £335–468 Dbl £424–489
Dinner available from £25
CC: Accepted
Room facilities: 📺 ☎ 📞 ❄
Access: ♿
Conference: 12 meeting rooms (Thtr 550 max), day-delegate from £80
Children: Welcome ♨ ⅀
Licenses: 🍷 ♂♂♂
Leisure: Gym, Health spa, Beauty salon
Parking: Off-street
Directions: On Kensington High Street (A315), between Kensington Church Street and Kensington Palace Gardens.
Map ref: Central London 74 B4

Sheraton Park Tower

★★★★★★ ⛨⛨⛨

101 Knightsbridge, London, SW1X 7RN
Tel: 020 7235 8050 Fax: 020 7235 8231
Email: central.london.reservations@sheraton.com
Web: www.sheraton.com/parktower
Rooms: 280 all ensuite ⊗
Dinner available CC: Accepted
Room facilities: ▢ ☎ ⚏ ❄
Access: ♿
Conference: 4 meeting rooms (Thtr 80 max)
Children: Welcome ⸙
Licenses: ⚏⚏⚏ Leisure: Gym
Parking: Off-street
Directions: Located in the heart of Knightsbridge, next to Harvey Nichols. The nearest Underground station is Knightsbridge.
Map ref: Central London 78 C4

Swissôtel The Howard, London

★★★★★ ⛨⛨⛨

Temple Place, London, WC2R 2PR
Tel: 020 7836 3555 Fax: 020 7379 4547
Email: ask-us.london@swissotel.com
Web: www.london.swissotel.com

Central location with magnificent river views, stretching from the London Eye to Tower Bridge. Luxurious 5-star hotel offering access to major business areas as well as shopping and cultural attractions.
Rooms: 189 (12 ensuite) ⊗
Pricing: Sgl £160–590 Dbl £160–590 Dinner available
CC: Accepted
Room facilities: ▢ ☎ ⊙ ⚏ ❄
Access: ♿
Conference: 2 meeting rooms (Thtr 120 max), day-delegate from £85
Children: Welcome ⸙ Dogs: Assistance dogs only
Licenses: ⚐ ⚏⚏ Leisure: Use of Cannon's Health Club for special fee of £10
Parking: Off-street
Directions: By car take the M4 towards central London, direction City. Hotel is located off the embankment. Underground: Temple.
Map ref: Central London 85 F3

The Bentley Kempinski

★★★★★ ⛨⛨⛨⛨ Excellent

27-33 Harrington Gardens, London, SW7 4JX
Tel: 020 7244 5555 Fax: 020 7244 5566
Email: info@thebentley-hotel.com
Web: www.thebentley-hotel.com
Rooms: 64 all ensuite ⚏ ⊗
Dinner available
CC: Accepted
Room facilities: ▢ ☎ ⚏ ❄ Access: ♿
Conference: 4 meeting rooms (Thtr 60 max), 24hr-delegate from £430, day-delegate from £80
Children: Welcome
Dogs: Welcome
Licenses: ⚏⚏
Leisure: Health spa, Beauty salon
Directions: Five minutes walk Gloucester Road, Station Road, Cromwell Road westbound, left at Gloucester Road, 2nd right into Harrington Gardens.
Map ref: Central London 86 B5

The Berkeley

★★★★★ ⛨⛨⛨⛨ Premier

Wilton Place, London, SW1X 7RL
Tel: 020 7950 5490 Fax: 020 7950 5480
Email: info@the-berkeley.co.uk
Web: www.the-berkeley.com
Rooms: 214 all ensuite ▨ ⊗
Pricing: Sgl £458–505 Dbl £541–671
Dinner available from £60
CC: Accepted
Room facilities: ▢ ☎ ⚏ ❄
Access: ♿
Conference: 6 meeting rooms (Thtr 250 max), day-delegate from £75
Children: Welcome ⸙
Licenses: ⚐ ⚏⚏
Leisure: Indoor pool, Gym, Health spa, Beauty salon
Parking: Off-street
Directions: 200 yards down Knightsbridge from Hyde Park Corner, on left-hand side.
Map ref: Central London 87 D4

The Connaught

★★★★★ ⛨⛨⛨ Premier

Carlos Place, Mayfair, London, W1K 2AL
Tel: 020 7499 7070 Fax: 020 7495 3262
Email: info@the-connaught.co.uk
Web: www.the-connaught.com
Rooms: 92 all ensuite
Pricing: Sgl £387–453 Dbl £517–577
Dinner available from £50
CC: Accepted
Room facilities: ▢ ☎ ⚏ ❄ Access: ♿
Conference: 2 meeting rooms
Children: Welcome
Licenses: ⚏⚏ Leisure: Gym
Directions: Between Berkeley and Grosvenor Squares. Nearest Underground stations are Bond Street and Green Park.
Map ref: Central London 91 D3

The Dorchester

★★★★★★ 🎀🎀🎀 *Premier*

Park Lane, London, W1A 2HJ
Tel: 020 7629 8888 Fax: 020 7409 0114
Email: reservations@thedorchester.com
Web: www.thedorchester.com

Ranked one of the world's best, The Dorchester exudes unparalled levels of service, luxury and style. Located opposite Hyde Park, and minutes from London's famous theatre and shopping districts, The Dorchester remains one of the world's most desirable places to stay.
Rooms: 250 all ensuite 🖼 ⊗
Pricing: Sgl £401.50–472 Dbl £502–607
Dinner available from £39.50
CC: Accepted
Room facilities: ⬜ ☎ 📞 ❄
Access: |↕|
Conference: 9 meeting rooms (Thtr 500 max)
Children: Welcome �🍴
Licenses: ◁ 👯
Leisure: Gym, Health spa, Beauty salon
Parking: Off-street
Directions: The Dorchester is located on Park Lane, opposite Hyde Park, approximately halfway between Marble Arch and Hyde Park Corner.
Map ref: Central London 94 D3

The Goring

★★★★★★ 🎀🎀🎀 *Excellent*

Beeston Place, Grosvenor Gardens, London, SW1W 0JW
Tel: 020 7396 9000 Fax: 020 7834 4393
Email: reception@goringhotel.co.uk
Web: www.goringhotel.co.uk

The finest 5-star privately owned hotel in London, two minutes from Buckingham Palace. The award-winning dining room is famous for the best British food in the capital and the Garden Bar is the ideal place to meet friends. Each of the 71 bedrooms is luxuriously appointed.
Rooms: 71 all ensuite 🐾 ⊗
Pricing: Sgl £211–323 Dbl £258–382
Dinner available from £35 CC: Accepted
Room facilities: ⬜ ☎ 📞 ❄ Access: |↕|
Conference: 4 meeting rooms (Thtr 80 max),
day-delegate from £62.50
Children: Welcome �🍴 ɝ
Licenses: ◁ 👯 Leisure: Complimentary membership of nearby health club Parking: Off-street
Map ref: Central London 96 D4

The Landmark London

★★★★★★ 🎀🎀 *Premier*

222 Marylebone Road, London, NW1 6JQ
Tel: 020 7631 8222 Fax: 020 7631 8080
Email: reservations@thelandmark.co.uk
Web: www.landmarklondon.co.uk

The Landmark London, awarded Best Hotel in London three times, ranks among the finest of the Capital's establishments, combining British elegance and grandeur.
Rooms: 299 all ensuite 🐾 🖼 ⊗
Pricing: Sgl £370–1800 Dbl £395–1825
Dinner available from £32 CC: Accepted
Room facilities: ⬜ ☎ 📞 ❄ Access: |↕|
Conference: 10 meeting rooms (Thtr 380 max),
day-delegate from £85
Children: Welcome �🍴 Licenses: ◁ 👯
Leisure: Indoor pool, Gym, Health spa, Beauty salon
Parking: Off-street
Directions: In front of Marylebone main line station and Underground, also fronting Marylebone Road near Madame Tussaud's. Easy access to M40 and M4.
Map ref: Central London 99 C2

The Lanesborough

★★★★★★ ℛℛℛℛ Premier

Hyde Park Corner, London, SW1X 7TA
Tel: 020 7259 5599 Fax: 020 7259 5606
Email: info@lanesborough.com
Web: www.lanesborough.com
Rooms: 95 all ensuite 🖨 ⊗
Dinner available CC: Accepted
Room facilities: ▢ ☎ 🔌 ❄
Access: ⏐↑↑
Conference: 6 meeting rooms (Thtr 100 max)
Children: Welcome ⅋
Dogs: Welcome
Licenses: ⟁ ⅙⅙⅙
Leisure: Gym, Health spa
Parking: Off-street
Directions: Follow signs to Hyde Park Corner.
Map ref: Central London 100 D4

The Savoy

★★★★★★ ℛℛℛℛ Premier

The Strand, London, WC2R 0EU
Tel: 020 7950 5492 Fax: 020 7950 5482
Email: info@the-savoy.co.uk
Web: www.the-savoy.com
Rooms: 263 all ensuite 🐾 ⊗
Dinner available
CC: Accepted
Room facilities: ▢ ☎ 🔌 ❄
Access: ⏐↑↑
Conference: 10 meeting rooms (Thtr 500 max)
Children: Welcome ⅏ ⅋
Licenses: ⟁ ⅙⅙⅙
Leisure: Indoor pool, Gym, Health spa, Beauty salon
Parking: Off-street
Directions: Between Aldwych and Trafalgar Square on The Strand. Nearest Underground stations Charing Cross and Covent Garden.
Map ref: Central London 106 E3

22 Jermyn Street
Townhouse

★★★★★ Excellent

22 Jermyn Street, St James's, London, SW1Y 6HL
Tel: 020 7734 2353 Fax: 020 7734 0750
Email: office@22jermyn.com
Web: www.22jermyn.com
Rooms: 18 all ensuite 🐾
CC: Accepted
Room facilities: ▢ ☎ 🔌 ❄ Access: ⏐↑↑
Conference: 4 meeting rooms (Thtr 8 max)
Children: Welcome ⅏ ⅋ Dogs: Welcome
Licenses: ⅙⅙⅙
Leisure: Indoor pool, Gym, Health spa, Beauty salon
Parking: Off-street
Directions: From Hyde Park Corner take the underpass leading to Piccadilly. Turn right onto Duke Street, left into King Street onto St James' Square. Take left again at Charles II Street. Left into Lower Regent Street and left again on Jermyn Street.
Map ref: Central London 1 E3

41
Townhouse

★★★★★ ℛℛ Premier

41 Buckingham Palace Road, London, SW1W 0PS
Tel: 020 7300 0041 Fax: 020 7300 0141
Email: book41@rchmail.com
Web: www.41hotel.com
Rooms: 20 all ensuite ⊗
Pricing: Sgl £225–395 Dbl £245–445
Dinner available from £27.50
CC: Accepted
Room facilities: ▢ ☎ 🖨 🔌 ❄ Access: ⏐↑↑
Conference: 1 meeting room (Thtr 10 max),
24hr-delegate from £350, day-delegate from £70
Children: Welcome ⅏ ⅋ Dogs: Welcome
Licenses: ⅙⅙⅙
Directions: 3 minutes walk from Victoria station and connection for Gatwick Rail Express. Opposite the Royal Mews, Buckingham Palace.
Map ref: Central London 2 D4

51 Buckingham Gate
Townhouse

★★★★★ ℛℛ Premier

51 Buckingham Gate, London, SW1E 6AF
Tel: 020 7769 7766 Fax: 020 7233 5014
Email: info@51-buckinghamgate.co.uk
Web: www.51-buckinghamgate.com
Rooms: 82 all ensuite 🐾
Pricing: Sgl £407.75 Dbl £427.75
Dinner available from £45 CC: Accepted
Room facilities: ▢ ☎ 🖨 🔌 ❄ Access: ⏐↑↑
Conference: 2 meeting rooms,
day-delegate from £86
Children: Welcome ⅏ ⅋
Licenses: ⟁ ⅙⅙⅙ Leisure: Gym, Health spa, Beauty salon, Spa relaxation area Parking: Off-street
Directions: From Victoria Street, turn left into Buckingham Gate. A short walk from Buckingham Palace and St James's Park Station.
Map ref: Central London 3 E4
See advert on following page

Charlotte Street Hotel
Townhouse

★★★★★ ℛℛ Premier

15-17 Charlotte Street, London, W1T 1RJ
Tel: 020 7806 2000 Fax: 020 7806 2002
Email: charlotte@firmdale.com
Web: www.firmdalehotels.com
Rooms: 52 all ensuite 🐾 🖨 ⊗
Pricing: Sgl £247.63 Dbl £277.88–371.88
Dinner available from £25 CC: Accepted
Room facilities: ▢ ☎ 🔌 ❄ Access: ⏐↑↑
Conference: 5 meeting rooms (Thtr 67 max)
Children: Welcome ⅏
Licenses: ⅙⅙⅙ Leisure: Gym
Directions: From Oxford Street, turn into Rathbone Place, which leads onto Charlotte Street.
Hotel is on left.
Map ref: Central London 15 E2

Covent Garden Hotel
Townhouse

★★★★★ ⭑⭑ *Premier*

10 Monmouth Street, London, WC2H 9HB
Tel: 020 7806 1000 Fax: 020 7806 1100
Email: covent@firmdale.com
Web: www.firmdalehotels.com
Rooms: 58 all ensuite 🛏 📠 ⊘
Pricing: Sgl £264.75 Dbl £335.63–394.38
Dinner available from £25 CC: Accepted
Room facilities: 🖵 ☎ 📞 ✳
Access: |↕|
Conference: 5 meeting rooms (Thtr 53 max)
Children: Welcome ⼉
Licenses: ⅲ
Leisure: Gym, Health spa, Beauty salon
Directions: Nearest tube is Covent Garden. Walk to the
end of Neal Street (opposite tube) and turn left onto
Monmouth Street. Hotel is on right.
Map ref: Central London 23 E2

Draycott Hotel
Townhouse

★★★★★

26 Cadogan Gardens, London, SW3 2RP
Tel: 020 7730 6466 Fax: 020 7730 0236
Email: reservations@draycotthotel.com
Web: www.draycotthotel.com

A perfect balance of luxury, service, privacy and
location. At the very centre of fashionable London.
Combining the grandeur of the past with the luxuries
and conveniences of today.
Rooms: 35 all ensuite 🛏 📠 ⊘
Pricing: Sgl £141–160 Dbl £178–300
CC: Accepted
Room facilities: 🖵 ☎ 📞 ✳ Access: |↕|
Conference: 1 meeting room (Thtr 12 max),
day-delegate from £85
Children: Welcome ⼉
Dogs: Welcome
Licenses: ⅲ
Directions: From M4, follow signs to Central London.
After Natural History Museum, road veers left,
becoming Brompton Road. Take fourth right turn at
lights into Beauchamp Place. Turn right into Cadogan
Square and fifth left into Cadogan Gardens.
Map ref: Central London 28 C4

The Capital Hotel
Townhouse

★★★★★ 🏨🏨🏨🏨 **Excellent**

Basil Street, Knightsbridge, London, SW3 1AT
Tel: 020 7589 5171 Fax: 020 7225 0011
Email: reservations@capitalhotel.co.uk
Web: www.capitalhotel.co.uk

The Capital is unique, a jewel set in the heart of
Knightsbridge, each of its 49 air-conditioned suites
and bedrooms is individually designed, subtly
luxurious and supremely comfortable.
Rooms: 49 all ensuite 🛏️
Pricing: Sgl £205.63–229.13 Dbl £252.63–323.13
Dinner available from £48–115
CC: Accepted
Room facilities: ▢ 🕻 ☎ ❄
Access: |↕|
Conference: 2 meeting rooms (Thtr 30 max),
day-delegate from £85
Children: Welcome
Licenses: ⛓
Parking: Off-street
Directions: Heading west along A4 turn left after
Harrods, into Brompton Place then left again and
straight into Basil Street.
Map ref: Central London 88 C4

The Milestone Hotel & Apartments
Townhouse

★★★★★ 🏨🏨🏨 **Premier**

1 Kensington Court, Kensington, London, W8 5DL
Tel: 020 7917 7727/1000 Fax: 020 7917 1010 /1133
Email: bookms@rchmail.com
Web: www.milestonehotel.com
Rooms: 57 all ensuite 🛏️ 🚭
Pricing: Sgl £320–330 Dbl £350–370
Dinner available CC: Accepted
Room facilities: ▢ ☎ 🖥 🕻 ❄ Access: |↕|
Conference: 2 meeting rooms (Thtr 30 max),
24hr-delegate from £245, day-delegate from £55
Children: Welcome ᚼ ☕
Dogs: Welcome
Licenses: ⬧ ⛓
Leisure: Indoor pool, Gym
Directions: Directly opposite Kensington Palace and
adjacent to Hyde Park. The Milestone is 400 yards
from High Street Kensington Underground station.
Map ref: Central London 101 B4

The Soho Hotel
Townhouse

★★★★★ 🏨🏨 **Premier**

4 Richmond Mews, off Dean Street, London, W1D 3DH
Tel: 020 7559 3000 Fax: 020 7559 3003
Email: soho@firmdale.com
Web: www.firmdalehotels.com
Rooms: 91 all ensuite 🛏️ 🚭
Pricing: Sgl £295.13 Dbl £331.75–384.63
Dinner available from £25 CC: Accepted
Room facilities: ▢ ☎ 🕻 ❄ Access: |↕|
Conference: 5 meeting rooms (Thtr 100 max)
Children: Welcome ᚼ
Licenses: ⛓
Leisure: Gym, Health spa, Beauty salon
Directions: Travelling east along Oxford Street turn
right into Soho via Dean Street and then right into
Richmond Buildings.
Map ref: Central London 107 E2

Athenaeum Hotel & Apartments

★★★★ 🏨🏨🏨 **Premier**

116 Piccadilly, London, W1J 7BJ
Tel: 020 7499 3464 Fax: 020 7493 1860
Email: info@athenaeumhotel.com
Web: www.athenaeumhotel.com

The Athenaeum offers a warm welcome, luxurious
interiors, 21st century entertainment & technology and
exceptional levels of personalised service. With 157
elegant rooms, suites and apartments, we pride
ourselves on being your home away from home.
Rooms: 157 all ensuite 🛏️ 🚭
Pricing: Sgl £199–750 Dbl £199–750
Dinner available from £18
CC: Accepted
Room facilities: ▢ ☎ 🖥 🕻 Access: |↕|
Conference: 3 meeting rooms (Thtr 70 max),
24hr-delegate from £265, day-delegate from £65
Children: Welcome ᚼ Licenses: ⬧ ⛓
Leisure: Gym, Health spa, Beauty and hair salon
Directions: Located on Piccadilly in the heart of
Mayfair overlooking Green Park. Nearest tube is Green
Park or Hyde Park Corner.
Map ref: Central London 4 D3

Berners Hotel

★★★★★ ®®

Berners Street, London, W1A 3BE
Tel: 020 7666 2000 Fax: 020 7666 2001
Email: berners@berners.co.uk
Web: www.jjwhotels.com
Rooms: 216 all ensuite 🐾 ⊛
Pricing: Sgl £225–255 Dbl £430–490
Dinner available from £16.95
CC: Accepted
Room facilities: ▢ ☎ ⊘ 📞 Access: ↕
Conference: 4 meeting rooms (Thtr 150 max),
day-delegate from £75
Children: Welcome ⻖ Dogs: Assistance dogs only
Licenses: ⚓ ⵜ
Directions: Located just off Oxford Street opposite
Wardour Street and between Oxford Circus and
Tottenham Court Road Underground stations.
Map ref: Central London 7 D2

Copthorne Tara Hotel London Kensington

★★★★

Scarsdale Place, Wrights Lane, Kensington,
London, W8 5SR
Tel: 020 7872 2000 Fax: 020 7937 7100
Email: reservations.tara@mill-cop.com
Web: www.copthornehotels.com

MILLENNIUM
HOTELS AND RESORTS

MILLENNIUM HOTELS
COPTHORNE HOTELS

Set just off Kensington High Street, this hotel offers
access to some of the best shops and attractions in
London. A short walk to Kensington Palace. Weekend
rates available.
Rooms: 834 all ensuite 🐾 ⊛
Pricing: Sgl £115 Dbl £125
Dinner available from £19 CC: Accepted
Room facilities: ▢ ☎ ⊘ 📞 ✲
Access: ↕
Conference: 10 meeting rooms (Thtr 380 max),
24hr-delegate from £205, day-delegate from £65
Children: Welcome ⻖
Licenses: ⵜ Parking: Off-street
Directions: M4 East Central London on to A4 over
Hammersmith Flyover. Cromwell Road left before
Cromwell Hospital into Marloes Road.
Map ref: Central London 22 B4

Crowne Plaza London – St James

★★★★★ ®®

45-51 Buckingham Gate, London, SW1E 6AF
Tel: 020 7834 6655 Fax: 020 7630 7587
Email: sales@cplonsj.co.uk
Web: www.london.crowneplaza.com
Rooms: 342 all ensuite ⊛
Pricing: Sgl £316.13 Dbl £332.63
Dinner available from £20 CC: Accepted
Room facilities: ▢ ☎ ⊘ 📞 ✲ Access: ↕
Conference: 20 meeting rooms (Thtr 180 max),
day-delegate from £86
Children: Welcome ⻖ Licenses: ⚓ ⵜ
Leisure: Gym, Health spa, Beauty salon, Games room,
Spa relaxation area Parking: Off-street
Directions: From Victoria Street, turn left into
Buckingham Gate. A short walk from Buckingham
Palace and St James's Park Station.
Map ref: Central London 26 E4

Harrington Hall

★★★★★ ®®

5-25 Harrington Gardens, London, SW7 4JW
Tel: 020 7396 9696 Fax: 020 7396 9090
Email: sales@harringtonhall.co.uk
Web: www.harringtonhall.co.uk
Rooms: 200 all ensuite ⊛
Dinner available CC: Accepted
Room facilities: ▢ ☎ ⊘ 📞 ✲ Access: ↕
Conference: 9 meeting rooms (Thtr 200 max),
24hr-delegate from £235, day-delegate from £75
Children: Welcome ⻖
Licenses: ⵜ Leisure: Gym
Directions: 100 yards from Gloucester Road
Underground station (Piccadilly, Circle and District
lines). One mile from M4 and A4.
Map ref: Central London 35 B5

Jurys Clifton Ford Hotel and Health Club

★★★★ ®

47 Welbeck Street, London, W1G 8DN
Tel: 020 7486 6600 Fax: 020 7486 7492
Email: cliftonford@jurysdoyle.com
Web: www.jurysdoyle.com

🎩JURYS DOYLE
H O T E L S

Rooms: 255 all ensuite ⊛
Pricing: Sgl £112–264 Dbl £129–280
Dinner available from £31.50
CC: Accepted
Room facilities: ▢ ☎ ⊘ 📞 ✲ Access: ↕
Conference: 8 meeting rooms (Thtr 120 max),
24hr-delegate from £259, day-delegate from £80
Children: Welcome ⻖
Licenses: ⚓ ⵜ
Leisure: Indoor pool, Gym, Health spa, Beauty salon
Directions: From Bond Street tube station walk right
towards Debenhams department store. Welbeck Street
is perpendicular to the back of the store.
Map ref: Central London 38 D2

Jurys Gt. Russell Street Hotel
★★★★★ 🖩🖩
16-22 Great Russell Street, London, WC1B 3NN
Tel: 020 7347 1000 Fax: 020 7347 1001
Email: bookings@jurysdoyle.com
Web: www.jurysdoyle.com

JURYS DOYLE
HOTELS

Rooms: 169 all ensuite 🖚
Pricing: Sgl £121–264 Dbl £138–280
Dinner available from £31.50
CC: Accepted
Room facilities: ▢ ☎ ☕ 🕿 ❄
Access: ⌊⇡
Conference: 12 meeting rooms (Thtr 300 max),
24hr-delegate from £287, day-delegate from £87
Children: Welcome 🍴
Directions: Exit 3 from Tottenham Court Road tube
station, walk past Dominion Theatre and turn right into
Great Russell Street.
Map ref: Central London 39 E2

Jurys Kensington Hotel
★★★★
109-113 Queen's Gate, South Kensington,
London, SW7 5LR
Tel: 020 7589 6300 Fax: 020 7581 1492
Email: bookings@jurysdoyle.com
Web: www.jurysdoyle.com

JURYS DOYLE
HOTELS

Rooms: 173 all ensuite 🖚
Pricing: Sgl £100–248 Dbl £117–265
Dinner available from £20
CC: Accepted
Room facilities: ▢ ☎ ☕ 🕿 ❄
Access: ⌊⇡
Conference: 3 meeting rooms (Thtr 80 max),
24hr-delegate from £231, day-delegate from £71.40
Children: Welcome 🍴
Licenses: ♦♦♦
Parking: Off-street
Directions: Located 13 miles/21 km from London
Heathrow. South Kensington tube (District Line) 5
minutes walk. Victoria station 1½ miles/2 km.
Map ref: Central London 42 B5

Kingsway Hall
★★★★ 🖩🖩
Great Queen Street, Covent Garden,
London, WC2B 5BX
Tel: 020 7309 0909 Fax: 020 7309 9696
Email: reservations@kingswayhall.co.uk
Web: www.kingswayhall.co.uk
Rooms: 170 all ensuite 🖚
Dinner available
CC: Accepted
Room facilities: ▢ ☎ ☕ 🕿 ❄
Access: ⌊⇡

Conference: 11 meeting rooms (Thtr 150 max)
Children: Welcome
Licenses: ♦♦♦
Leisure: Gym
Directions: Turn left onto Kingsway from Holborn
Underground then right onto Great Queen Street. Hotel
is adjacent to New Connaught Rooms.
Map ref: Central London 44 F2

London Bridge Hotel
★★★★ 🖩
8-18 London Bridge Street, London, SE1 9SG
Tel: 020 7855 2200 Fax: 020 7855 2233
Email: sales@london-bridge-hotel.co.uk
Web: www.londonbridgehotel.com

Elegant four-star hotel. 138 air-conditioned bedrooms
and suites with excellent facilities. Meeting rooms, two
fine restaurants, bar, gymnasium and three luxury
serviced apartments. Close to many exciting tourist
attractions.
Rooms: 138 all ensuite ♨ 🖚
Pricing: Sgl £99–285 Dbl £99–298
Dinner available from £25
CC: Accepted
Room facilities: ▢ ☎ ☕ 🕿 ❄
Access: ⌊⇡
Conference: 5 meeting rooms (Thtr 100 max),
24hr-delegate from £266, day-delegate from £64
Children: Welcome
Licenses: ♦♦♦
Leisure: Gym, Sauna, Solarium
Directions: Directly opposite London Bridge station.
Rail and Underground links — Jubilee and Northern
lines, nearest motorway M11.
Map ref: Central London 49 G3

London Marriott Kensington
★★★★ 🖩🖩
147 Cromwell Road, Kensington, London, SW5 0TH
Tel: 0800 221222 Fax: 0870 400 7366
Email: events.kensington@marriotthotels.co.uk
Web: www.marriott.co.uk/lonlm
Rooms: 216 all ensuite ♨ 🖚
Pricing: Sgl £148–250 Dbl £148–562
Dinner available from £20
CC: Accepted

Room facilities: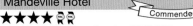
Access: |↓↑|
Conference: 9 meeting rooms (Thtr 200 max),
24hr-delegate from £225, day-delegate from £69
Children: Welcome ⟊
Dogs: Assistance dogs only
Licenses: ⚐ ⋔
Leisure: Indoor pool, Gym
Parking: Off-street
Directions: Situated on the A4 Cromwell Road, only 30
minutes from Heathrow, close to Earl's Court and
Gloucester Road Underground stations.
Map ref: Central London 50 B4

Mandeville Hotel

★★★★★ ®®   ⟅ Commended ⟆

8-14 Mandeville Place, London, W1U 2BE
Tel: 020 7935 5599 Fax: 020 7935 9588
Email: info@mandeville.co.uk
Web: www.mandeville.co.uk
Rooms: 142 all ensuite ⊛
Pricing: Sgl £165 Dbl £185 Dinner available
CC: Accepted
Room facilities: ▢ ☎ ☏ ❄
Conference: 1 meeting room (Thtr 35 max),
day-delegate from £70
Children: Welcome 12yrs min age
Licenses: ⋔
Directions: Only minutes away from Bond Street
Underground station. Cross Oxford Street. Five
minutes walk along St James Street.
Map ref: Central London 52 D2

Melia White House

★★★★★ ®

Albany Street, Regent's Park, London, NW1 3UP
Tel: 020 7391 3000
Email: melia.white.house@solmelia.com
Web: www.solmelia.com
Rooms: 581 all ensuite ⊛
Dinner available
CC: Accepted
Room facilities: ▢ ☎ ☏ ❄
Access: |↓↑|
Conference: 9 meeting rooms (Thtr 150 max)
Children: Welcome ⽊
Licenses: ⚐ ⋔
Leisure: Gym
Parking: Off-street
Directions: Located within walking distance of Great
Portland Street, Regent's Park and Euston
Underground stations. 10 minutes from Paddington
and Euston main railway stations.
Map ref: Central London 53 D2

Millennium Bailey's Hotel London Kensington

★★★★★ ®®

140 Gloucester Road, Kensington, London, SW7 4QH
Tel: 020 7373 6000 Fax: 020 7370 3760
Email: reservations.baileys@mill-cop.com
Web: www.millenniumhotels.com

MILLENNIUM
HOTELS AND RESORTS

MILLENNIUM HOTELS
COPTHORNE HOTELS

This elegant hotel has a townhouse feel to it and
enjoys a prime location opposite Gloucester Road tube
station. Air-conditioned bedrooms are smartly
appointed and thoughtfully equipped, particularly the
club rooms which have DVD players. Public areas
include a stylish contemporary restaurant and bar.
Guests may also use the facilities at its adjacent,
larger sister hotel.
Rooms: 211 all ensuite ⊛
Pricing: Sgl £115–180 Dbl £120–305
Dinner available from £15.95
CC: Accepted
Room facilities: ▢ ☎ ☏ ☏ ❄
Access: |↓↑|
Conference: 21 meeting rooms (Thtr 500 max),
24hr-delegate from £195, day-delegate from £75
Children: Welcome ⟊
Dogs: Assistance dogs only
Licenses: ⋔
Parking: Off-street
Directions: Opposite Gloucester Road Underground
station serviced by Piccadilly, Circle and District lines.
40 mins to London Heathrow and Gatwick airports.
Map ref: Central London 56 B4

Are the bells ringing?

Getting married? Congratulations!
Look for the wedding bells symbol
which shows hotels licensed for
civil ceremonies.

Millennium Gloucester Hotel London Kensington

★★★★

4-18 Harrington Gardens, London, SW7 4LH
Tel: 020 7331 6195 Fax: 020 7835 1854
Email: reservations.gloucester@mill-cop.com
Web: www.millenniumhotels.com

Situated in the heart of Kensington, a fashionable area of West London. Close to Hyde Park, Earl's Court and some of London's most famous museums and Harrods. Weekend rates are also available.
Rooms: 610 all ensuite 🍴 ⊗
Pricing: Sgl £148–250 Dbl £163–265
Dinner available from £18.50–55
CC: Accepted
Room facilities: ▢ ☎ ☐ ☍ ❄ Access: |↓↑
Conference: 21 meeting rooms (Thtr 500 max), 24hr-delegate from £380, day-delegate from £89
Children: Welcome ♣
Dogs: Assistance dogs only
Licenses: ◔ ♟♟
Leisure: Gym
Parking: Off-street
Directions: Next to Gloucester Road Underground station served by Piccadilly, Circle and District lines. 40 minutes to London Heathrow airport.
Map ref: Central London 57 B4

Millennium Hotel London Knightsbridge

★★★★ ☺☺☺

17 Sloane Street, Knightsbridge, London, SW1X 9NU
Tel: 020 7235 4377 Fax: 020 7235 3705
Email: reservations.knightsbridge@mill-cop.com
Web: www.millenniumhotels.com

Chic hotel situated on Sloane Street, London's fashionable neighbourhood, surrounded by elegant shops and stores minutes from Harrods. Contemporary Mju restaurant featuring Pacific Rim cuisine. Smart, sophisticated bar serving drinks and cocktails.
Rooms: 222 all ensuite 🍴 ⊗
Pricing: Sgl £129–247 Dbl £153–270
Dinner available from £25
CC: Accepted
Room facilities: ▢ ☎ ☐ ☍ ❄
Access: |↓↑
Conference: 4 meeting rooms (Thtr 120 max), 24hr-delegate from £278, day-delegate from £78
Children: Welcome ♣ ☕
Dogs: Assistance dogs only
Licenses: ♟♟
Directions: Knightsbridge tube station is a two-minute walk from the Millennium Knightsbridge or follow the A4 signs to Knightsbridge.
Map ref: Central London 58 C4

The big sleep

As part of our comprehensive inspection process, RAC Inspectors investigate the comfort of the beds.

"Here!"

Need a pet friendly property? Look out for 'Dogs welcome' in our listings.

Millennium Hotel London Mayfair

★★★★★ 👥👥

Grosvenor Square, Mayfair, London, W1K 2HP
Tel: 020 7629 9400 Fax: 020 7629 7736
Email: reservations.mayfair@mill-cop.com
Web: www.millenniumhotels.com

MILLENNIUM
HOTELS AND RESORTS

MILLENNIUM HOTELS
COPTHORNE HOTELS

The luxurious and traditional Millennium Hotel London Mayfair, just 5 minutes walk away from the shopping areas of Oxford Street and Bond Street. Diners may sip a cocktail in the trendy Turner's Bar before moving to Brian Turner Mayfair to sample traditional English dishes prepared with the finest produce.
Rooms: 348 all ensuite 🚭
Pricing: Sgl £130–250 Dbl £180–280
Dinner available from £30
CC: Accepted
Room facilities: 📺 ☎ 🍵 📞 ❄ Access: |↓↑
Conference: 10 meeting rooms (Thtr 450 max), 24hr-delegate from £300, day-delegate from £85
Children: Welcome �🪑
Dogs: Assistance dogs only
Licenses: ◈ ♙♙♙
Leisure: Gym
Parking: Off-street
Directions: Situated on Grosvenor Square near Park Lane and Oxford Street, nearest Underground stations Bond Street and Green Park.
Map ref: Central London 59 D3

Royal Lancaster Hotel

★★★★ 👥👥👥

Lancaster Terrace, London, W2 2TY
Tel: 020 7262 6737 Fax: 020 7724 3191
Email: book@royallancaster.com
Web: www.royallancaster.com
Rooms: 416 all ensuite 🚭
Pricing: Dbl £326.23–414.35
Dinner available from £15
CC: Accepted
Room facilities: 📺 ☎ ☎ ❄ Access: |↓↑
Conference: 14 meeting rooms (Thtr 1400 max), day-delegate from £72
Children: Welcome �🪑
Licenses: ♙♙♙ Parking: Off-street
Directions: Adjacent to Lancaster Gate Underground, Paddington main line station (Heathrow Express terminus) and Underground 5 minutes' walk. A40 1 mile.
Map ref: Central London 75 B3

Rubens at The Palace

Commended

★★★★ 👥👥👥

39 Buckingham Palace Road, London, SW1W 0PS
Tel: 020 7834 6600 Fax: 020 7233 6037
Email: bookrb@rchmail.com
Web: www.rubenshotel.com
Rooms: 172 all ensuite 🛏 🚭
Pricing: Sgl £195 Dbl £245
Dinner available from £15.50
CC: Accepted
Room facilities: 📺 ☎ 🍵 📞 ❄ Access: |↓↑
Conference: 8 meeting rooms (Thtr 90 max), 24hr-delegate from £240, day-delegate from £65
Children: Welcome �🪑 ☕
Dogs: Welcome
Licenses: ♙♙♙
Directions: 3 minute walk from Victoria train station and connection for Gatwick Rail Express. Opposite the Royal Mews, Buckingham Palace.
Map ref: Central London 76 D4

Rydges Kensington Plaza

★★★★ 👥

61 Gloucester Road, Kensington, London, SW7 4PE
Tel: 020 7584 8100 Fax: 020 7823 9175
Email: rydges_kensington@rydges.com
Web: www.rydges.com
Rooms: 89 all ensuite 🍴 🚭
Pricing: Sgl £80–100 Dbl £120–145
Dinner available from £14.50–19.50
CC: Accepted
Room facilities: 📺 ☎ 🍵 📞 Access: |↓↑
Conference: 2 meeting rooms (Thtr 45 max), 24hr-delegate from £165, day-delegate from £49
Children: Welcome �🪑
Licenses: ◈ ♙♙♙
Parking: Off-street
Directions: Two minutes walk from Gloucester Road Underground station, near the corner of Gloucester Road and Cromwell Road.
Map ref: Central London 77 B4

The Chesterfield Hotel Mayfair

★★★★ ☺☺ **Excellent**

35 Charles Street, Mayfair, London, W1J 5EB
Tel: 020 7491 2622 Fax: 020 7491 4793
Email: bookch@rchmail.com
Web: www.chesterfieldmayfair.com
Rooms: 110 all ensuite ☺ ☒ ☻
Pricing: Sgl £140–264 Dbl £160–381
Dinner available from £19.95–24.95
CC: Accepted
Room facilities: ☐ ☎ ☺ ☚ ☀ Access: ⌊↑
Conference: 6 meeting rooms (Thtr 120 max),
24hr-delegate from £275, day-delegate from £75
Children: Welcome ☐ ☺
Dogs: Welcome Licenses: ☺ ☷
Directions: Green Park Station turn left, down Berkeley
Street to Berkeley Square. Go left for Charles Street.
Map ref: Central London 89 D3

The Halkin

★★★★ ☺☺☺ **Premier**

Halkin Street, Belgravia, London, SW1X 7DJ
Tel: 020 7333 1000 Fax: 020 7333 1100
Email: res@halkin.como.bz
Web: www.halkin.como.bz

Discrete, contemporary hotel, with attentive and
personalised service. Stylish bedrooms and suites are
equipped to the highest standard offering every
conceivable extra. Award-winning restaurant Nahm
offers exciting Thai cuisine.
Rooms: 41 all ensuite
Pricing: Sgl £255–863 Dbl £255–863
Dinner available from £49.50 CC: Accepted
Room facilities: ☐ ☎ ☚ ☀ Access: ⌊↑
Conference: 1 meeting room (Thtr 36 max),
day-delegate from £85
Children: Welcome ☺ Licenses: ☷
Directions: Located between Belgrave Square and
Grosvenor Place. Access via Chapel Street into
Headfort Place and left into Halkin Street.
Map ref: Central London 98 D4

The Montague on the Gardens

★★★★ ☺☺ **Commended**

15 Montague Street, London, WC1B 5BJ
Tel: 020 7637 1001 Fax: 020 7637 2516
Email: bookmt@rchmail.com
Web: www.montaguehotel.com
Rooms: 99 all ensuite ☺ ☒ ☻
Pricing: Sgl £165–220 Dbl £195–265
Dinner available from £15.50
CC: Accepted
Room facilities: ☐ ☎ ☺ ☚ ☀
Access: ⌊↑
Conference: 7 meeting rooms (Thtr 120 max),
24hr-delegate from £220, day-delegate from £68
Children: Welcome ☐ ☺
Dogs: Welcome
Licenses: ☺ ☷
Leisure: Gym, Sauna, Steam shower
Directions: Located in Montague Street just off Russell
Square, close to British Museum. 5 minutes' walk from
Russell Square Underground.
Map ref: Central London 102 E2

The Rembrandt

★★★★

11 Thurloe Place, Knightsbridge, London, SW7 2RS
Tel: 020 7589 8100 Fax: 020 7225 3476
Email: rembrandt@sarova.co.uk
Web: www.sarova.com
Rooms: 195 all ensuite ☻
Pricing: Sgl £105–190 Dbl £105–215
Dinner available CC: Accepted
Room facilities: ☐ ☎ ☺ ☚
Access: ⌊↑
Conference: 14 meeting rooms (Thtr 200 max),
24hr-delegate from £230, day-delegate from £76
Children: Welcome ☐ ☺
Licenses: ☺ ☷
Leisure: Indoor pool, Gym, Health spa, Beauty salon
Directions: Follow A4 (Cromwell Road) into Central
London. The Rembrandt is opposite Victoria & Albert
Museum. Nearest tube South Kensington.
Map ref: Central London 104 C4

"I do!"

Want a honeymoon hotel? Look
for our Gold, Blue, and White
Ribbon Award winning hotels.

London

The Stafford

★★★★★

St James's Place, London, SW1A 1NJ
Tel: 020 7493 0111 Fax: 020 7493 7121
Email: info@thestaffordhotel.co.uk
Web: www.thestaffordhotel.co.uk

Charming, small, luxurious hotel with exquisite private dining rooms, including 350-year-old working cellars. Individually furnished rooms include the world-famous carriage house rooms. Offers outstanding service and traditional elegance.
Rooms: 81 all ensuite
Pricing: Sgl £325–700 Dbl £345–800
Dinner available from £43.50
CC: Accepted
Room facilities: 🖵 ☎ 📞 ❄
Access: ⬆
Conference: 5 meeting rooms (Thtr 30 max)
Children: Welcome
Licenses: 🔥 ♨
Directions: Just off St James's Street close to Pall Mall and Piccadilly.
Map ref: Central London 108 D3

Washington Mayfair Hotel

★★★★

5 Curzon Street, Mayfair, London, W1J 5HE
Tel: 020 7499 7000 Fax: 020 7495 6172
Email: info@washington-mayfair.co.uk
Web: www.washington-mayfair.co.uk.
Rooms: 171 all ensuite
Dinner available
CC: Accepted
Room facilities: 🖵 ☎ 🍵 📞 ❄
Access: ⬆
Conference: 3 meeting rooms (Thtr 120 max)
Children: Welcome
Dogs: Welcome
Licenses: ♨
Leisure: Gym
Directions: Five minutes' walk from Green Park station. West along Piccadilly, right into Clarges Street; Curzon Street is at the end.
Map ref: Central London 111 D3

Dorset Square Hotel
Townhouse

★★★★

39 Dorset Square, Marylebone, London, NW1 6QN
Tel: 020 7723 7874 Fax: 020 7724 3328
Email: reservations@dorsetsquare.co.uk
Web: www.dorsetsquare.co.uk

A lovingly restored Regency townhouse, ideal for those who know how to enjoy the good things in life... quality, style and very individual service. The experience is timeless, elegant and uniquely English. Located in Marylebone, we are close to Regent's Park, West End theatres and financial areas of the city.
Rooms: 37 all ensuite
Pricing: Sgl £180.25–368.25 Dbl £278.25–384
Dinner available from £19.50
CC: Accepted
Room facilities: 🖵 ☎ 📞 ❄
Access: ⬆
Conference: 1 meeting room (Thtr 12 max), 24hr-delegate from £225, day-delegate from £65
Children: Welcome
Licenses: ♨
Leisure: Use of LA Fitness gym for £12.50 for a day pass
Parking: Off-street
Directions: Nearest Underground station is Baker Street. Or, proceed from M40 onto A40 (Euston Road). Take left-hand lane off flyover. Turn left on Gloucester Place. Dorset Square Hotel is first left.
Map ref: Central London 27 C2

Kensington House Hotel
Townhouse
★★★★ Excellent

15-16 Prince of Wales Terrace, London, W8 5PQ
Tel: 020 7937 2345 Fax: 020 7368 6700
Email: reservations@kenhouse.com
Web: www.kenhouse.com

Contemporary townhouse restored to its original 19th century elegance. Stylish, modern interiors. Rooms are light and airy with good facilities. The Tiger Bar offers anything from coffee to a three-course meal.
Rooms: 41 all ensuite ⊗
Pricing: Sgl £99–150 Dbl £135–195
Dinner available from £9.95
CC: Accepted
Room facilities: ☐ ☎ ☺ ☏ Access: ⌊↿
Children: Welcome ⱦ
Licenses: ⵜ
Directions: Just off Kensington High Street, corner of Prince of Wales Terrace and Victoria Road close to Underground and Victoria station.
Map ref: Central London 43 B4

Knightsbridge Hotel
Townhouse
★★★★ Premier

10 Beaufort Gardens, London, SW3 1PT
Tel: 020 7584 6300 Fax: 020 7584 6355
Email: knightsbridge@firmdale.com
Web: www.firmdalehotels.com
Rooms: 44 all ensuite ⊗
Pricing: Sgl £190.75–202.50 Dbl £240.50–334.50
CC: Accepted
Room facilities: ☐ ☎ ☏ ❄
Access: ⌊↿
Children: Welcome
Licenses: ⵜ
Directions: Beaufort Gardens is just off Brompton Road, in between Harrods and Beauchamp Place.
Map ref: Central London 45 C4

Number Sixteen
Townhouse
★★★★ Excellent

16 Summer Place, South Kensington, London, SW7 3EG
Tel: 020 7589 5232 Fax: 020 7584 8615
Email: sixteen@firmdale.com
Web: www.firmdalehotels.com
Rooms: 42 all ensuite ⊗ ⊛
Pricing: Sgl £124.63–165.75 Dbl £225.75–319.75
CC: Accepted
Room facilities: ☐ ☎ ☏ ❄ Access: ⌊↿
Conference: 1 meeting room
Children: Welcome
Licenses: ⵜ
Leisure: Garden
Directions: Summer Place is the first left on Old Brompton Road from South Kensington tube station.
Map ref: Central London 63 C4

Parkes Hotel Limited
Townhouse
★★★★

41 Beaufort Gardens, Knightsbridge, London, SW3 1PW
Tel: 020 7581 9944 Fax: 020 7581 1999
Email: info@parkeshotel.com
Web: www.parkeshotel.com

Fully refurbished and situated in a quiet tree-lined cul-de-sac 100 metres from Harrods. Parkes Hotel provides modern business facilities including wireless ADSL with luxurious, comfortable surroundings and marble bathrooms.
Rooms: 33 all ensuite ⊗
Pricing: Sgl £240 Dbl £305–511.13
CC: Accepted
Room facilities: ☐ ☎ ☏ ❄ Access: ⌊↿
Children: Welcome
Licenses: ⵜ
Directions: Off Brompton Road, Knightsbridge, 100 metres from Harrods.
Map ref: Central London 66 C4

The Pelham Hotel
Townhouse

★★★★ ♔♔
15 Cromwell Place, London, SW7 2LA
Tel: 020 7589 8288 Fax: 020 7584 8444
Email: pelham@firmdale.com
Web: www.firmdalehotels.com
Rooms: 50 all ensuite ♨ 🖨 ⊛
Pricing: Sgl £193.75 Dbl £246.50–328.75
Dinner available from £25
CC: Accepted
Room facilities: ▢ ☎ ✆ ❄
Access: |⊥|
Conference: 2 meeting rooms (Thtr 10 max)
Children: Welcome ♀
Licenses: ⛊
Directions: Opposite South Kensington tube station.
Map ref: Central London 103 B4

The Royal Park Hotel
Townhouse

★★★★
3 Westbourne Terrace, Lancaster Gate, Hyde Park,
London, W2 3UL
Tel: 020 7479 6600 Fax: 020 7479 6601
Email: info@theroyalpark.com
Web: www.theroyalpark.com
Rooms: 48 all ensuite 🖨 ⊛
CC: Accepted
Room facilities: ▢ ☎ ✆
Access: |⊥|
Conference: 1 meeting room (Thtr 10 max)
Children: Welcome
Licenses: ⛊
Parking: Off-street
Directions: Located 2 minutes walk from Paddington
Station with Heathrow Express, main line and
Underground. Located north side of Hyde Park.
Map ref: Central London 105 B3

Basil Street Hotel
★★★
Basil Street, Knightsbridge, London, SW3 1AH
Tel: 020 7581 3311 Fax: 020 7581 3693
Email: info@thebasil.com
Web: www.thebasil.com
Rooms: 80 all ensuite ♨ ⊛
Pricing: Sgl £150–190 Dbl £170–250
Dinner available from £25
CC: Accepted
Room facilities: ▢ ☎ ✆
Access: |⊥|
Conference: 4 meeting rooms (Thtr 30 max),
24hr-delegate from £231, day-delegate from £55
Children: Welcome ♀
Dogs: Welcome
Licenses: ⛊
Directions: One-minute walk from Knightsbridge
Underground Station. The hotel is located between
Harrods and Sloane Street.
Map ref: Central London 6 C4

Bonnington Hotel, London
★★★
92 Southampton Row, London, WC1B 4BH
Tel: 020 7242 2828 Fax: 020 7831 9170
Email: res@bonnington.com
Web: www.bonnington.com

Opened in 1911 by Lord Strathcona, the newly
refurbished Bonnington offers superior quality
bedrooms. Ideally situated for London's major
attractions and public transport, it is perfect for leisure
and business.
Rooms: 247 all ensuite ♨ ⊛
Pricing: Sgl £80–145 Dbl £110–175
Dinner available from £9–25
CC: Accepted
Room facilities: ▢ ☎ ⊚ ✆ ❄ Access: |⊥|
Conference: 14 meeting rooms (Thtr 250 max),
24hr-delegate from £165, day-delegate from £45
Children: Welcome ♀
Licenses: ⛊ Leisure: Fitness room
Directions: Nearest tube station: Holborn for Piccadilly
and Central lines, less than five minutes' walk. See
hotel website for more details.
Map ref: Central London 10 E2

Relax & smell the coffee

Fresh coffee,
chilled juices for
breakfast. RAC's
team of qualified
Inspectors check
them both.

Jurys Inn Chelsea

★★★

Imperial Road, Imperial Wharf, London, SW6 2GA
Tel: 020 7411 2200 Fax: 020 7411 2444
Email: bookings@jurysdoyle.com
Web: www.jurysinns.com

JURYS DOYLE
HOTELS

Rooms: 172 all ensuite ♨ ⊗
Pricing: Sgl £70–100 Dbl £78–109
Dinner available from £16.95–18
CC: Accepted
Room facilities: ▢ ☎ ◔ ☍ ✳
Access: |↓↑
Conference: 4 meeting rooms (Thtr 12 max),
24hr-delegate from £150, day-delegate from £45
Children: Welcome ♁
Licenses: ♦♦♦
Parking: Off-street
Directions: Alight Earl's Court Underground; exit Earl's
Court Road; board C3 bus outside Barclays Bank
which takes you directly to Jurys Inn Chelsea.
Map ref: Central London 40 B6

Jurys Inn Islington

★★★

60 Pentonville Road, Islington, London, N1 9LA
Tel: 020 7282 5500 Fax: 020 7282 5511
Email: bookings@jurysdoyle.com
Web: www.jurysinns.com
Seasonal closure: 24-26 December

JURYS DOYLE
HOTELS

Rooms: 229 all ensuite ♨ ⊗
Pricing: Sgl £126–139 Dbl £136–145
Dinner available from £18
CC: Accepted
Room facilities: ▢ ☎ ◔ ☍ ✳
Access: |↓↑
Conference: 2 meeting rooms (Thtr 50 max),
24hr-delegate from £190, day-delegate from £65
Children: Welcome ♁
Licenses: ♦♦♦
Directions: Located 25 miles from London Heathrow
Airport. London City 15 miles. Euston main line 15
mins walk and Angel tube 3 mins walk.
Map ref: Central London 41 F1

Quality Hotel Westminster

★★★

82-83 Eccleston Square, London, SW1V 1PS
Tel: 020 7834 8042 Fax: 020 7630 8942
Email: enquiries@hotels-westminster.com
Web: www.choicehotelseurope.com
Rooms: 107 all ensuite ♨ ▱ ⊗
Pricing: Sgl £129–145 Dbl £147–180
Dinner available from £14.95
CC: Accepted
Room facilities: ▢ ☎ ◔ ☍ ✳

Access: |↓↑
Conference: 5 meeting rooms (Thtr 120 max),
24hr-delegate from £173, day-delegate from £51.50
Children: Welcome ♁ ℃
Dogs: Welcome
Licenses: ♦♦♦
Directions: Situated close to Victoria rail, coach and
tube stations.
Map ref: Central London 69 D4

Strand Palace Hotel

★★★

372 The Strand, London, WC2R 0JJ
Tel: 020 7379 4737 Fax: 020 7936 2077
Email: reservations@strandpalacehotel.co.uk
Web: www.strandpalacehotel.co.uk

Located near to Covent Garden, South Bank,
Whitehall, theatres and major tourist attractions. There
are four bars, two restaurants and extensive
conference facilities. Major refurbishment has and will
be taking place.
Rooms: 785 all ensuite ⊗
Pricing: Sgl £85–150 Dbl £95–180
Dinner available from £12.95–20
CC: Accepted
Room facilities: ▢ ☎ ◔ ☍ Access: |↓↑
Conference: 7 meeting rooms (Thtr 200 max),
24hr-delegate from £180, day-delegate from £60
Children: Welcome ♁ ℃
Licenses: ♦♦♦
Directions: Situated on The Strand in the heart of
theatreland. 5 minutes walk from Charing Cross or
Covent Garden Underground stations.
Map ref: Central London 83 E3

Sleep easy
Rest assured. Our com-
prehensive inspection
process includes
checking beds are
comfortable.

The Gresham Hyde Park

★★★

66 Lancaster Gate, London, W2 3NZ
Tel: 020 7262 5090 Fax: 020 7723 1244
Email: info@gresham-hydeparkhotel.com
Web: www.gresham-hotels.com

The Gresham Hyde Park has been substantially enhanced in recent years and offers a fresh, modern environment in a superb location. All bedrooms air-conditioned. Breakfast, light snacks and evening meals available.
Rooms: 188 all ensuite ⊛
Pricing: Sgl £95–200 Dbl £95–200
Dinner available from £14.50–250
CC: Accepted
Room facilities: ▢ ☎ ☺ ☏ ✳
Access: ⌊↑
Conference: 1 meeting room (Thtr 35 max), 24hr-delegate from £125, day-delegate from £35
Children: Welcome
Licenses: ♦♦♦
Leisure: Gym
Directions: Located on Lancaster Gate off Bayswater Road, 1 mile from Marble Arch in between Lancaster Gate Underground and Queensway Underground (Central line).
Map ref: Central London 97 B3

"Stay!"

Need a pet friendly property? Look out for 'Dogs welcome' in our listings.

Clarendon Hotel

★★

8-16 Montpelier Row, Blackheath, London, SE3 0RW
Tel: 020 8318 4321 Fax: 020 8318 4378
Email: relax@clarendonhotel.com
Web: www.clarendonhotel.com

18th Century Georgian Hotel situated overlooking Blackheath Common and the World Heritage Site of Royal Greenwich.
Rooms: 181 all ensuite ⊛ ⊞ ⊛
Pricing: Sgl £80–90 Dbl £90–100
Dinner available from £22.50
CC: Accepted
Room facilities: ▢ ☎ ☺ ☏
Access: ⌊↑
Conference: 8 meeting rooms (Thtr 120 max), 24hr-delegate from £130, day-delegate from £39
Children: Welcome ⍟
Dogs: Welcome
Licenses: ◬ ♦♦♦
Leisure: Games room
Parking: Off-street and free
Directions: Situated just off the A2 on Blackheath. Close to major motorways (M2/M25/M11/A20) — M25 junctions 2, 3 and 27.
Map ref: Greater London 16 E3

Brown's Hotel

🔶 Awaiting inspection

Albemarle Street, Mayfair, London, W1S 4BP
Tel: 020 7493 6020 Fax: 020 7493 9381
Email: reservations.brownshotel@rfhotels.com
Web: www.roccofortehotels.com
Rooms: 117 all ensuite ⊛ ⊛
Pricing: Sgl £350 Dbl £460–670
Dinner available from £42.90
CC: Accepted
Room facilities: ▢ ☎ ☏ ✳
Access: ⌊↑
Conference: 6 meeting rooms (Thtr 65 max), day-delegate from £85
Children: Welcome ⍟
Dogs: Assistance dogs only
Licenses: ◬ ♦♦♦
Leisure: Gym, Health spa
Directions: From Hyde Park Corner into Piccadilly, then left into Albemarle Street.
Map ref: Central London 12 D3

L'Hotel

28 Basil Street, Knightsbridge, London, SW3 1AS
Tel: 020 7589 6286 Fax: 020 7823 7826
Email: reservations@lhotel.co.uk
Web: www.lhotel.co.uk

Under the same ownership as the Capital Hotel next door, this is a very comfortable, cosy and stylish home from home full of personal touches and very friendly, caring staff.
Rooms: 12 all ensuite
Pricing: Dbl £182.12–199
Dinner available from £15–22 CC: Accepted
Room facilities: Access: |↓↑|
Children: Welcome Dogs: Welcome
Licenses: ♦♦♦
Leisure: Agreement with local 5-star hotel for gym use
Parking: Off-street
Directions: Central location in exclusive part of London. Knightsbridge Underground a short walk away, Harrods store next door. Quiet and safe neighbourhood.
Map ref: Central London 46 C4

Best Western Swiss Cottage Hotel

♦♦♦♦

4 Adamson Road, Swiss Cottage, London, NW3 3HP
Tel: 020 7722 2281 Fax: 020 7483 4588
Email: reservations@swisscottagehotel.co.uk
Web: www.swisscottagehotel.co.uk
Rooms: 59 all ensuite ♨ ⊛
Pricing: Sgl £65–110 Dbl £69–130 CC: Accepted
Room facilities: ☐ ☎ ☕ ☏ Access: |↓↑|
Conference: 2 meeting rooms (Thtr 40 max), 24hr-delegate from £125, day-delegate from £35
Children: Welcome
Licenses: ♦♦♦
Parking: Off-street and free

Directions: Swiss Cottage Underground station (Jubilee line); use Exit no.2 to Eton Avenue. The hotel is a two-minute walk.
Map ref: Greater London 8 B1

Comfort Inn Central London

♦♦♦♦

87 South Lambeth, London, SW8 1RN
Tel: 020 7735 9494 Fax: 020 7735 1001
Email: stay@comfortinnvx.co.uk
Web: www.comfortinnvx.co.uk
Rooms: 94 all ensuite CC: Accepted
Room facilities: ☐ ☎ ☕ Access: |↓↑|
Conference: 3 meeting rooms (Thtr 60 max)
Children: Welcome
Licenses: ♦♦♦
Leisure: Gym
Map ref: Central London 18 F5

Four Seasons Hotel

173 Gloucester Place, Regent's Park, London, NW1 6DX
Tel: 020 7724 3461 Fax: 020 7402 5594
Email: fourseasonshotel@btconnect.com
Web: www.4seasonshotel.co.uk
Rooms: 16 all ensuite ♨ ⊛ CC: Accepted
Room facilities: ☐ ☎ ☏
Children: Welcome
Map ref: Central London 30 D3

Hart House Hotel

51 Gloucester Place, London, W1U 8JF
Tel: 020 7935 2288 Fax: 020 7935 8516
Email: reservations@harthouse.co.uk
Web: www.harthouse.co.uk
Rooms: 15 all ensuite ♨ ⊛
Pricing: Sgl £70–79 Dbl £89–110 CC: Accepted
Room facilities: ☐ ☎ ☕ ☏
Children: Welcome ☕
Directions: Just off Oxford Street, behind Selfridges. Close to Marble Arch and Baker Street Underground stations.
Map ref: Central London 36 C2
See advert on opposite page

Hyde Park Radnor

♦♦♦♦

7-9 Sussex Place, Hyde Park, London, W2 2SX
Tel: 020 7723 5969 Fax: 020 7262 8955
Email: hydeparkradnor@btconnect.com
Web: www.hydeparkradnor.com
Rooms: 36 all ensuite
Pricing: Sgl £50–65 Dbl £70–90 CC: Accepted
Room facilities: ☐ ☎ ☕
Access: |↓↑|
Children: Welcome
Map ref: Central London 37 C3

Langorf Hotel and Apartments

◆◆◆◆

20 Frognal, Hampstead, London, NW3 6AG
Tel: 020 7794 4483 Fax: 020 7435 9055
Email: info@langorfhotel.com
Web: www.langorfhotel.com

The Langorf Hotel has now established itself as one of the leading townhouse hotels in London. It has been recognised for its quality and friendly service by several awards and inclusions in many well known guidebooks.
Rooms: 46 all ensuite ✎
Pricing: Sgl £70–90 Dbl £80–110
CC: Accepted
Room facilities: ☐ ☎ ☺ ✉

Access: ♿
Children: Welcome ☺
Licenses: ♦♦♦
Parking: Off-street
Directions: 3 miles north of Oxford Street. 3 miles south of M1 Junction 1. Off the A41 Finchley Road.
Map ref: Greater London 48 B1

MIC Hotel and Conference Centre

◆◆◆◆

81-103 Euston Street, London, NW1 2EZ
Tel: 020 7380 0001 Fax: 020 7387 5300
Email: reception@micentre.com
Web: www.micentre.com
Rooms: 28 all ensuite ✎
Pricing: Sgl £85–130 Dbl £85–130
Dinner available from £15–25
CC: Accepted
Room facilities: ☐ ☎ ☺ ✉ ❋ Access: ♿
Conference: 14 meeting rooms (Thtr 150 max), 24hr-delegate from £175, day-delegate from £32
Children: Welcome ♇
Licenses: ♦♦♦
Directions: Euston mainline, 2 minutes' walk. Euston tube, 2 minutes. Central location. 20 minutes from Paddington. Buses 10, 73, 7, 30, 394, 68, 91, 168, 253. A40, A506-A1.
Map ref: Central London 55 D1

Primrose House

56 Boston Gardens, Brentford, London, TW8 9LP
Tel: 020 8568 5573
Email: information@primrosehouse.com
Web: www.primrosehouse.com
Rooms: 3 (2 ensuite)
Pricing: Sgl £40–50 Dbl £55–65
CC: Accepted
Room facilities:
Children: Welcome
Parking: Off-street and free
Directions: A4 to Boston Manor Road (A3002), north to Boston Gardens, turn left. Underground Piccadilly line, right from Boston Manor station.
Map ref: Greater London 68 A2

St George Hotel

49 Gloucester Place, London, W1U 8JE
Tel: 020 7486 8586 Fax: 020 7486 6567
Email: reservations@stgeorge-hotel.net
Web: www.stgeorge-hotel.net
Rooms: 19 (17 ensuite)
Pricing: Sgl £75–105 Dbl £95–150
CC: Accepted
Room facilities:
Conference: 1 meeting room (Thtr 20 max)
Children: Welcome
Licenses:
Directions: 10 minutes walk from either Marble Arch or Baker Street Underground stations.
Map ref: Central London 81 C2

The Claverley Hotel

13-14 Beaufort Gardens, Knightsbridge, London, SW3 1PS
Tel: 020 7589 8541 Fax: 020 7584 3410
Email: reservations@claverleyhotel.co.uk
Web: www.claverleyhotel.co.uk
Rooms: 30 (27 ensuite)
Pricing: Sgl £70–120 Dbl £120–195
CC: Accepted
Room facilities:
Access:
Children: Welcome
Directions: Exit Knightsbridge tube at Brompton Road. Third street on the left past Harrods.
Map ref: Central London 90 C4

Are the bells ringing?

Getting married? Congratulations! Look for the wedding bells symbol which shows hotels licensed for civil ceremonies.

The Darlington Hyde Park

111-117 Sussex Gardens, London, W2 2RU
Tel: 020 7460 8800 Fax: 020 7460 8828
Email: darlinghp@aol.com
Web: www.darlingtonhotel.co.uk
Seasonal closure: 23-27 December

Charming, clean, comfortable hotel situated on a tree lined avenue, offering personalised service from friendly staff. Just five minutes walk from Hyde Park, Paddington Station and the Heathrow Express Train.
Rooms: 39 all ensuite
Pricing: Sgl £65–95 Dbl £90–150
CC: Accepted
Room facilities:
Access:
Conference: 1 meeting room (Thtr 4 max)
Children: Welcome
Licenses:
Directions: In the centre of Sussex Gardens halfway between Edgware Road and Lancaster Gate, five minutes walk from Paddington station.
Map ref: Central London 92 C2

The Diplomat Hotel

2 Chesham Street, Belgravia, London, SW1X 8DT
Tel: 020 7235 1544 Fax: 020 7259 6153
Email: diplomat.hotel@btinternet.com
Web: www.btinternet.com/~diplomat.hotel

A true gem in the heart of Belgravia. A safe, excellent, exclusive location with its easy access, comfort and personal service, it really is a "home from home".
Rooms: 26 all ensuite

Pricing: Sgl £95–115 Dbl £125–170
Dinner available from £6 CC: Accepted
Room facilities:
Access:
Children: Welcome
Licenses:
Directions: Victoria, Knightsbridge and Sloane Square Underground stations all within 10 minutes walk.
Map ref: Central London 93 D4

The Summerfield Tavern

♦♦♦♦

60 Baring Road, Lee, London, SE12 0PS
Tel: 020 8857 9247 Fax: 020 8857 9247
Email: thesummerfield@aol.com
Web: www.summerfieldtavern.co.uk
Rooms: 4 all ensuite
Pricing: Sgl £45 Dbl £60 CC: Accepted
Room facilities:
Children: Welcome
Licenses:
Leisure: Games room
Directions: Summerfield Tavern is just off A205 South Circular road, on the A2212 within a short drive of the A2, A20 and M25.
Map ref: Greater London 109 E3

Windermere Hotel

♦♦♦♦

142-144 Warwick Way, Victoria, London, SW1V 4JE
Tel: 020 7834 5163 Fax: 020 7630 8831
Email: reservations@windermere-hotel.co.uk
Web: www.windermere-hotel.co.uk

Bed & Breakfast of the year – London Tourism Awards 2003. "The Windermere Hotel gives guests all the intimacy of a family run operation with all the professionalism of a large hotel". An ideal location, within minutes' walk of Buckingham Palace, Westminster Abbey and Tate Britain. All rooms are individually designed and include king, queen, double, twin and family rooms. A scrumptious English breakfast and gourmet dinner is served in the relaxed atmosphere of our licensed restaurant, the Pimlico Room. Parking available. The Windermere has been recognised as offering a "quality value experience" in London.
Rooms: 22 (20 ensuite)
Pricing: Sgl £69–99 Dbl £79–145
Dinner available from £14.50
CC: Accepted
Room facilities:
Conference: 1 meeting room (Thtr 20 max)
Children: Welcome
Licenses:
Directions: Turn left opposite Victoria coach station, take first right into Hugh Street. Proceed along to Alderney Street. Hotel is directly opposite on corner of Alderney Street and Warwick Way.
Map ref: Central London 114 D5

Averard Hotel

♦♦♦

10 Lancaster Gate, Hyde Park, London, W2 3LH
Tel: 020 7723 8877 Fax: 020 7706 0860
Email: sales@averard.com
Web: www.averard.com

Perfectly located, friendly family hotel in an interesting Victorian building with original public rooms and period style paintings, sculptures and other features.
Rooms: 52 all ensuite
Pricing: Sgl £25–35 Dbl £70–85
CC: Accepted
Room facilities: Access:
Children: Welcome
Dogs: Welcome
Licenses:
Directions: From Lancaster Gate Underground station, turn right onto Bayswater Road, cross main traffic lights. After Swan pub, turn right to Lancaster Gate.
Map ref: Central London 5 B3

Blades Hotel

 ◆◆◆

122 Belgrave Road, Victoria, Westminster,
London, SW1V 2BL
Tel: 020 7976 5552 Fax: 020 7976 6500
Email: info@blades-hotel.co.uk
Web: www.blades-hotel.co.uk
Rooms: 16 all ensuite ❤ ⊛
Pricing: Sgl £60 Dbl £75 CC: Accepted
Room facilities: ▢ ⌂
Children: Welcome Dogs: Assistance dogs only
Directions: Close to St George's Square, two minutes
walk from Pimlico tube station, ten minutes walk from
Victoria rail, coach and tube station. Ten minutes by
taxi to Waterloo Station – Eurostar.
Map ref: Central London 9 E5

Brent X Hotel

 ◆◆◆

165 Preston Hill, Kenton, Harrow, London, HA3 9UY
Tel: 020 8904 9394 Fax: 020 8904 1155
Email: info@brentxhotel.com
Web: www.brentxhotel.com
Rooms: 19 (17 ensuite)
Pricing: Sgl £42–50 Dbl £55–60
CC: Accepted
Room facilities: ▢ ☎ ⌂
Conference: 1 meeting room (Thtr 12 max)
Children: Welcome Dogs: Assistance dogs only
Parking: Off-street
Directions: From Preston Road (Metropolitan line) turn
left, ignore first main roundabout, continuing straight,
turn right on roundabout. Start of Preston Hill. From
Kingsbury (Jubilee line) take the mall from Kingsbury
roundabout which turns into Preston Hill.
Map ref: Greater London 11 B1

Comfort Inn King's Cross

 ◆◆◆

2-5 St Chad's Street, King's Cross,
London, WC1H 8BD
Tel: 020 7837 1940 Fax: 020 7278 5033
Email: info@comfortinnkingscross.co.uk
Web: www.comfortinnkingscross.co.uk
Rooms: 53 all ensuite ⊛
CC: Accepted
Room facilities: ▢ ☎ ⌂ ☏ Access: |↓↑
Children: Welcome
Directions: Kings Cross station go to street level,
McDonalds on right, walk up Gray's Inn Road, take
third turning on your right into St Chad's Street.
Map ref: Central London 20 E1

Craven Gardens Hotel

 ◆◆◆

16 Leinster Terrace, London, W2 3EU
Tel: 020 7262 3167 Fax: 020 7262 2083
Email: sales@cravengardenshotel.co.uk
Web: www.cravengardenshotel.co.uk
Rooms: 43 all ensuite

CC: Accepted
Room facilities: ▢ ☎ ⌂ Access: |↓↑
Children: Welcome
Licenses: �
Directions: Nearest Underground Lancaster Gate/
Queensway (Central line), Bayswater (Circle/District
lines). Nearest main line station Paddington.
Map ref: Central London 24 B3

Crescent Hotel

 ◆◆◆

58-62 Welldon Crescent, Harrow,
Middlesex, HA1 1QR
Tel: 020 8863 5491 Fax: 020 8427 5965
Email: jivraj@crsnthtl.demon.co.uk
Web: www.crsnthtl.demon.co.uk
Rooms: 21 (16 ensuite) ❤
Pricing: Sgl £35–45 Dbl £50–60 CC: Accepted
Room facilities: ▢ ☎ ⌂
Children: Welcome
Licenses: ♦♦♦
Parking: Off-street and free
Directions: Conveniently located for M25, M1, M40,
A40. Just off A312 five minutes from Harrow-on-the-
Hill Underground. Please refer to website for details.
Map ref: Greater London 25 A1

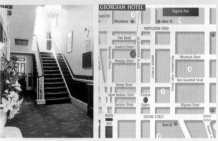

Georgian Hotel

◆◆◆

87 Gloucester Place, London, W1U 6JF
Tel: 020 7935 2211 Fax: 020 7486 7535
Email: georgianhotel@btconnect.com
Web: www.londoncentralhotel.com
Rooms: 19 all ensuite 🐟 ⊗
Pricing: Sgl £75–80 Dbl £90–95
CC: Accepted
Room facilities: ❑ ☎ ⊿
Access: |↕
Children: Welcome 5yrs min age
Directions: Central location near Baker Street tube and Oxford Street. Ideal for West End and shopping close to Marylebone and Paddington stations.
Map ref: Central London 33 C2
See advert on opposite page

La Gaffe

◆◆◆🐟☞

107-111 Heath Street, Hampstead, London, NW3 6SS
Tel: 020 7435 8965 Fax: 020 7794 7592
Email: info@lagaffe.co.uk
Web: www.lagaffe.co.uk

La Gaffe is a welcoming family run hotel with charm and character. Located in historic Hampstead, twelve minutes from the West End. The hotel boasts an award winning Italian Restaurant.
Rooms: 18 all ensuite 🐟 ⬚ ⊗
Pricing: Sgl £75 Dbl £95
Dinner available from £10
CC: Accepted
Room facilities: ❑ ☎ ⊿
Children: Welcome ⊓
Licenses: ♦♦♦
Directions: Hotel 3 minutes from Hampstead Underground, three miles from King's Cross and 18 miles from Heathrow.
Map ref: Greater London 47 B1

Mitre House Hotel

◆◆◆

178-184 Sussex Gardens, Hyde Park,
London, W2 1TU
Tel: 020 7723 8040 Fax: 020 7402 0990
Email: reservations@mitrehousehotel.com
Web: www.mitrehousehotel.com

Founded in 1962, the Grade II listed building has been extensively modernised over the years. Reception provides left luggage facilities and free security boxes. The Plantation Bar overlooks a pleasant garden square.
Rooms: 70 all ensuite 🐟 ⊗
CC: Accepted
Room facilities: ❑ ☎
Access: |↕
Children: Welcome ⅈ€
Licenses: ♦♦♦
Parking: Off-street and free
Directions: One block north of Hyde Park, Paddington Station and buses to major sights. Heathrow Express to airport in 15 mins is also one block away.
Map ref: Central London 60 B3
See advert on following page

My Place Hotel

◆◆◆

1-3 Trebovir Road, Kensington, London, SW5 9LS
Tel: 020 7373 0833 Fax: 020 7373 9998
Email: reception@myplacehotel.co.uk
Web: www.myplacehotel.co.uk
Rooms: 50 all ensuite 🐟
Pricing: Sgl £49–100 Dbl £69–135
CC: Accepted
Room facilities: ❑ ☎
Access: |↕
Conference: 1 meeting room (Thtr 50 max),
24hr-delegate from £145, day-delegate from £39
Children: Welcome
Licenses: ♦♦♦
Directions: M4 becomes A4 (West Cromwell Road). Turn right into Earl's Court Road. Take the third turning on the right. By tube: Piccadilly line/District line to Earl's Court Underground.
Map ref: Central London 61 A5

New England Hotel

◆◆◆

20 St George's Drive, Victoria, London, SW1V 4BN
Tel: 020 7834 8351 Fax: 020 7834 9000
Email: racstay@newenglandhotel.com
Web: www.newenglandhotel.com

Privately owned hotel renowned for its blend of warm, friendly hospitality and high standards in a fantastic London location. It boasts an enviably high level of repeat business and pleasure clientele. Close to Buckingham Palace, Big Ben and all major attractions.
Rooms: 23 all ensuite 🛏 🚭
CC: Accepted
Room facilities: 🖥 ☎ 🔌
Access: ⬆
Children: Welcome
Parking: Off-street
Directions: From Victoria Station go onto Wilton Road and turn right at the Warwick Way junction. Straight then second left onto St George's Drive and the New England is on your left. See map on website.
Map ref: Central London 62 D5

See advert on opposite page

Park Lodge Hotel

◆◆◆

73 Queensborough Terrace, Bayswater, London, W2 3SU
Tel: 020 7229 6424 Fax: 020 7221 4772
Email: parklodgehotel@btconnect.com
Web: www.hotelparklodge.com
Rooms: 29 all ensuite
Pricing: Sgl £45–55 Dbl £55–65
CC: Accepted
Room facilities: 🖥 ☎ 🌀
Access: ⬆
Directions: Nearest tube stations are Queensway or Bayswater, 10 mins walk from Paddington main line station, Park Lodge Hotel off Bayswater Road over looking Hyde Park.
Map ref: Central London 65 B3

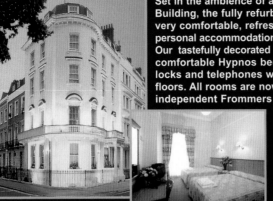

Sidney Hotel London-Victoria

◆◆◆

68/76 Belgrave Road, Victoria, London, SW1V 2BP
Tel: 020 7834 2738 Fax: 020 7630 0973
Email: reservations@sidneyhotel.com
Web: www.sidneyhotel.com
Rooms: 81 all ensuite ⊗
Pricing: Sgl £60–84 Dbl £75–104 CC: Accepted
Room facilities: ▢ ☎ ⊙ ☍ Access: ⊬
Conference: 1 meeting room (Thtr 30 max)
Children: Welcome Licenses: ⋔
Directions: Centrally situated near Victoria Station, from station take Wilton Road, go straight to third traffic lights, turn left, hotel situated on your right. Map ref: Central London 79 E5
See advert on following page

Swiss House Hotel

◆◆◆

171 Old Brompton Road, South Kensington,
London, SW5 0AN
Tel: 020 7373 2769 Fax: 020 7373 4983
Email: recep@swiss-hh.demon.co.uk
Web: www.swiss-hh.demon.co.uk
Rooms: 15 (14 ensuite) ⊗
Pricing: Sgl £60–80 Dbl £95–125 CC: Accepted
Room facilities: ▢ ☎ ⊙ Children: Welcome ⌬
Directions: From M4 turn right into Earl's Court Road. Down the road, turn left onto Old Brompton Road and hotel is situated after the first set of lights on the right.
Map ref: Central London 84 B5

The Gate Hotel

◆◆◆

6 Portobello Road, Pembridge Road End,
London, W11 3DG
Tel: 020 7221 0707 Fax: 020 7221 9120
Email: bookings@gatehotel.com
Web: www.gatehotel.com
Rooms: 7 all ensuite ⊗
Pricing: Sgl £55–75 Dbl £75–99 CC: Accepted
Room facilities: ▢ ☎ ⊙ ☍
Children: Welcome
Directions: Five minutes walk from Notting Hill Gate Underground tube station.
Map ref: Central London 95 A3

The Victoria Inn London

◆◆◆

65-67 Belgrave Road, Victoria,
London, SW1V 2BG
Tel: 020 7834 0182/6721 Fax: 020 7931 0201
Email: info@victoriainn.co.uk
Web: www.victoriainn.co.uk
Rooms: 43 all ensuite
CC: Accepted
Room facilities: ▢ ☎ ⊙ Access: ⊬
Children: Welcome
Directions: From Victoria Station, take Wilton Road, turn left into Belgrave Road; hotel is on the left after 500m.
Map ref: Central London 110 E5

White Lodge Hotel

◆◆◆

1 Church Lane, Hornsey, London, N8 7BU
Tel: 020 8348 9765 Fax: 020 8340 7851
Email: info@whitelodgehornsey.co.uk
Web: www.whitelodgehornsey.co.uk
Rooms: 16 (8 ensuite)
Pricing: Sgl £34–36 Dbl £44–52 CC: Accepted
Room facilities: ▢ ▣
Children: Welcome 🎄 Dogs: Assistance dogs only
Directions: A406 follow sign to Bounds Green then Hornsey High Road and Church Lane off Tottenham Lane, N8.
Map ref: Greater London 112 C1

Carlton Hotel

◆◆

90 Belgrave Road, Victoria, London, SW1V 2BJ
Tel: 020 7976 6634 Fax: 020 7821 8020
Email: info@cityhotelcarlton.co.uk
Web: www.cityhotelcarlton.co.uk
Rooms: 18 all ensuite
Pricing: Sgl £49–59 Dbl £59–69 CC: Accepted
Room facilities: ▢ ☎ ▣ ⚲ Children: Welcome
Parking: Off-street
Directions: From Victoria station take Wilton Road, turn left into Belgrave Road; hotel is about 500 metres on the right, 8 minutes walk from Victoria station.
Map ref: Central London 13 E5

Central House Hotel

◆◆

39 Belgrave Road, Victoria, London, SW1V 2BB
Tel: 020 7834 8036 Fax: 020 7834 1854
Email: info@centralhousehotel.co.uk
Web: www.centralhousehotel.co.uk
Rooms: 54 (53 ensuite)
Pricing: Sgl £50–55 Dbl £55–80 CC: Accepted
Room facilities: ▢ ☎ ▣ Access: ♿
Children: Welcome
Dogs: Assistance dogs only
Directions: From Victoria Underground or railway station take Wilton Road exit. Turn right to Denbigh Street across Warwick Street. At the end of Denbigh Street take first left to Belgrave Road. Hotel is on left.
Map ref: Central London 14 E5

Edward Lear Hotel

◆◆

30 Seymour Street, Marble Arch, London, W1H 7JA
Tel: 020 7402 5401 Fax: 020 7706 3766
Email: edwardlear@aol.com
Web: www.edlear.com
Rooms: 31 (4 ensuite)
Pricing: Sgl £39.50–60 Dbl £49.50–89
CC: Accepted
Room facilities: ▢ ☎ ▣
Children: Welcome
Map ref: Central London 29 C2

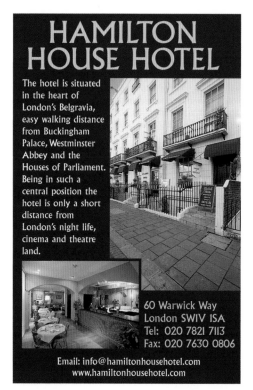

HAMILTON HOUSE HOTEL

The hotel is situated in the heart of London's Belgravia, easy walking distance from Buckingham Palace, Westminster Abbey and the Houses of Parliament. Being in such a central position the hotel is only a short distance from London's night life, cinema and theatre land.

60 Warwick Way
London SW1V 1SA
Tel: 020 7821 7113
Fax: 020 7630 0806

Email: info@hamiltonhousehotel.com
www.hamiltonhousehotel.com

Hamilton House Hotel

60 Warwick Way, Victoria, London, SW1V 1SA
Tel: 020 7821 7113 Fax: 020 7630 0806
Email: info@hamiltonhousehotel.com
Web: www.hamiltonhousehotel.com
Rooms: 42 (40 ensuite)
Room facilities:
Children: Welcome
Directions: The hotel is situated about five minutes walk, at the back of Victoria station, around the corner from Belgrave Road.
Map ref: Central London 34 D5
See advert on this page

Merlyn Court Hotel

2 Barkston Gardens, London, SW5 0EN
Tel: 020 7370 1640 Fax: 020 7370 4986
Email: london@merlyncourthotel.com
Web: www.merlyncourthotel.com
Rooms: 17 (11 ensuite)
Pricing: Sgl £40–55 Dbl £70–80 CC: Accepted
Room facilities:
Children: Welcome
Dogs: Welcome
Directions: Near Kensington Gardens off Cromwell Road. Easy links to motorways and rail stations. West End 15 minutes, Heathrow direct line.
Map ref: Central London 54 B5

Parkwood Hotel

4 Stanhope Place, London, W2 2HB
Tel: 020 7402 2241 Fax: 020 7402 1574
Email: prkwd@aol.com
Web: www.parkwoodhotel.com
Rooms: 16 (12 ensuite)
Pricing: Sgl £35.50–70 Dbl £49.50–89 CC: Accepted
Room facilities: Children: Welcome
Directions: Marble Arch nearest tube station.
Map ref: Central London 67 C3

Ramsees Hotel

32-36 Hogarth Road, Earl's Court, London, SW5 0PU
Tel: 020 7370 1445 Fax: 020 7244 6835
Email: ramsees@rasool.demon.co.uk
Web: www.ramseeshotel.com
Rooms: 67 (56 ensuite)
Pricing: Sgl £38–42 Dbl £50–55 CC: Accepted
Room facilities: Access:
Children: Welcome
Directions: From A4, turn down Earl's Court Road. At Lloyd's Bank on left, turn down Hogarth Road.
Map ref: Central London 70 B5

Rasool Court Hotel

19/21 Penywern Road, Earl's Court, London, SW5 9TT
Tel: 020 7373 8900 Fax: 020 7244 6835
Email: rasool@rasool.demon.co.uk
Web: www.rasoolcourthotel.com

Located in the heart of Earl's Court. The hotel provides the basic needs, comfort and convenience that you can expect with its prime location, within easy reach of the West End and all major attractions.
Rooms: 58 (48 ensuite)
Pricing: Sgl £25–42 Dbl £45–57
CC: Accepted
Room facilities:
Access:
Children: Welcome
Directions: A4 towards central London; then turn onto Earl's Court Road. Underground station on right, take next right onto Penywern Road.
Map ref: Central London 71 B5

London

Stanley House Hotel

19-21 Belgrave Road, Victoria, London, SW1V 1RB
Tel: 020 7834 5042/7292 Fax: 020 7834 8439
Email: cmahotel@aol.com
Web: www.affordablehotelsonline.com

Located in the City of Westminster, off Buckingham
Palace Road. Railways: Victoria Station, easy
connection to Gatwick, Heathrow, Luton and Stansted
airports. Buses: Victoria bus terminal. Underground:
Victoria Coach Station, coaches to all cities in
UK/Europe. Facilities: Colour TV, D/D telephones,
hairdryers, tea & coffee, drinks available 24 hours from
vending machine. Rates: Triple room from £75 (inc.
ensuite), Quad from £25 per person (inc. ensuite),
shower & WC supplement £10/room. Excellent
location, clean & comfortable accommodation,
affordable budget rates.
Rooms: 44 (38 ensuite)
Pricing: Sgl £35–45 Dbl £45–55 CC: Accepted
Room facilities: 🖵 ☎
Children: Welcome 5yrs min age
Directions: 4/5 minutes walk behind Victoria train/tube
station.
Map ref: Central London 82 D4

Wimbledon Hotel

♦♦

78 Worple Road, Wimbledon, London, SW19 4HZ
Tel: 020 8946 9265 Fax: 020 8946 9265
Web: www.wimbledonhotel.com
Rooms: 14 (11 ensuite)
Pricing: Sgl £55–65 Dbl £65–75 CC: Accepted
Room facilities: 🖵 ☎ ☕
Children: Welcome
Parking: Off-street and free
Directions: From M25, take A3 to London, Kingston.
Take Wimbledon exit, turn left at next traffic lights,
keep to right in U-turn.
Map ref: Greater London 113 B3

Comfort Inn Kensington
Travel Accommodation

22/32 West Cromwell Road, Kensington,
London, SW5 9QJ
Tel: 020 7373 3300 Fax: 020 7835 2040
Email: enquiries@hotels-kensington.com
Web: www.hotels-kensington.com
Rooms: 125 all ensuite ⊗
Pricing: Sgl £115.50–126.50 Dbl £137.50–165
CC: Accepted
Room facilities: 🖵 ☎ ☕ ☏ ❄
Access: ♿
Conference: 1 meeting room (Thtr 70 max),
24hr-delegate from £147, day-delegate from £45
Children: Welcome
Licenses: ⦙⦙⦙
Directions: Located on West Cromwell Road.
Continuation of A4(M) main arterial road into London
from West.
Map ref: Central London 19 A4

Sleeping Beauty Motel
Travel Accommodation

543 Lea Bridge Road, Leyton, London, E10 7EB
Tel: 020 8556 8080 Fax: 020 8556 8080
Rooms: 95 all ensuite ♿ 🖨 ⊗
CC: Accepted
Room facilities: 🖵 ☎ ☕
Access: ♿
Children: Welcome
Licenses: ⦙⦙⦙
Leisure: Gym
Parking: Off-street and free
Directions: Ten minutes' walking distance from
Walthamstow Central Underground station.
Map ref: Greater London 80 D1

Southeast

Note:
Dark blue dots represent the location of RAC-inspected accommodation

Award winners

To help you choose somewhere really special for your stay, we've listed here all RAC Award-winning properties in this region.

Gold Ribbon Award

Premier

Alexander House Hotel, Gatwick Airport

Ashdown Park Hotel & Country Club, Forest Row

Cliveden House, Taplow

Gravetye Manor Hotel, East Grinstead

Blue Ribbon Award

Excellent

Danesfield House Hotel and Spa, Marlow

Eastwell Manor, Ashford

The Feathers, Woodstock

St Michael's Manor, St Albans

White Ribbon Award

Commended

Little Gem Award

Little Gem

Pier at Harwich, Harwich

New Park Manor Hotel, Brockenhurst

May Cottage, Andover

Penfold Gallery Guest House, Steyning

Southeast

Abingdon, Oxfordshire

Abingdon Four Pillars

★★★

Marcham Road, Abingdon, Oxfordshire, OX14 1TZ
Tel: 01235 553456 Fax: 01235 554117
Email: abingdon@four-pillars.co.uk
Web: www.four-pillars.co.uk
Rooms: 62 all ensuite 🐾 🅰️
Pricing: Dinner available from £17.95
CC: Accepted
Room facilities: 🖥️ ☎️ 🍵 📞
Conference: 7 meeting rooms (Thtr 140 max)
Children: Welcome 🍴 🎠
Licenses: 🔷 🚹 Parking: Off-street and free
Directions: From A34 take junction for A415 towards
Abingdon. At Abingdon, hotel is on right of roundabout.
Map ref: Abingdon 4 B2

Aldershot, Hampshire

Potters International Hotel

★★★

1 Fleet Road, Aldershot, Hampshire, GU11 2ET
Tel: 01252 344000 Fax: 01252 311611
Email: reservations@pottersinthotel.com
Web: www.pottersinthotel.com
Rooms: 100 all ensuite 🐾 🅰️
Pricing: Sgl £90–120 Dbl £100–140
Dinner available from £17.50 CC: Accepted
Room facilities: 🖥️ ☎️ 🍵 📞 Access: ⚿
Conference: 11 meeting rooms (Thtr 400 max),
24hr-delegate from £165, day-delegate from £45
Children: Welcome 🍴 Dogs: Assistance dogs only
Licenses: 🚹 Leisure: Indoor pool, Gym, Health spa,
Beauty salon, Snooker/billiards
Parking: Off-street and free
Directions: M3 Junction 4, follow Farnborough signs.
Straight across 4th roundabout onto dual carriageway
towards Farnham on A325. Take first slip road, turn
right at bottom for Fleet Road. 500 yards, sharp left
just before bend.
Map ref: Aldershot 4 C3

Alfriston, East Sussex

The Star Inn

★★★🛏️

High Street, Alfriston, East Sussex, BN26 5TA
Tel: 01323 870495 Fax: 01323 870922
Email: bookings@star-inn-alfriston.com
Web: www.star-inn-alfriston.com
Rooms: 37 all ensuite 🐾 🅰️
Dinner available CC: Accepted
Room facilities: 🖥️ ☎️ 🍵 📞
Conference: 1 meeting room (Thtr 30 max)
Children: Welcome 🍴 Dogs: Welcome
Licenses: 🚹 Parking: Off-street and free
Directions: Located in the centre of Alfriston, which is
accessed via the A27 between Brighton and
Eastbourne. Map ref: Alfriston 5 D4

Alton, Hampshire

Alton Grange Hotel

★★★★🛏️🛏️

London Road, Alton, Hampshire, GU34 4EG
Tel: 01420 86565 Fax: 01420 541346
Email: info@altongrange.co.uk
Web: www.altongrange.co.uk
Seasonal closure: 23 December to 3 January
Rooms: 30 all ensuite 🐾 📠 🅰️
Pricing: Sgl £85–105 Dbl £105–120
Dinner available from £28–35 CC: Accepted
Room facilities: 🖥️ ☎️ 🍵 📞
Conference: 5 meeting rooms (Thtr 80 max),
24hr-delegate from £150, day-delegate from £39
Children: Welcome 5yrs min age 🎠
Dogs: Welcome
Licenses: 🔷 🚹
Leisure: Membership of local health club available
Parking: Off-street and free
Directions: Leave M3 at junction 4. Take A331 then
A31 in Farnham/Winchester direction. Turn right after 7
miles at roundabout (signed B3004 to Alton/Bordon).
Hotel is 350 yards on left.
Map ref: Alton 4 C3

Andover, Hampshire

May Cottage   Little Gem

◆◆◆◆ ✂️ 🍷

Thruxton, near Andover, Hampshire, SP11 8LZ
Tel: 01264 771241 Fax: 01264 771770
Email: info@maycottage-thruxton.co.uk
Web: www.maycottage-thruxton.co.uk
Rooms: 3 all ensuite 🅰️
Pricing: Sgl £45–55 Dbl £65–80
Room facilities: 🖥️ 🍵
Children: Welcome
Leisure: Snooker/billiards
Parking: Off-street and free
Directions: From A303, take turning marked 'Thruxton
(village only)'. May Cottage is located almost opposite
The George Inn.
Map ref: Thruxton 4 B3
See advert on following page

Bourne Valley Inn

◆◆◆

St Mary Bourne, near Andover, Hampshire, SP11 6BT
Tel: 01264 738361 Fax: 01264 738126
Email: bournevalley@wessexinns.fsnet.co.uk
Rooms: 9 all ensuite
Pricing: Dinner available from £7 CC: Accepted
Room facilities: 🖥️ ☎️ 🍵
Conference: 1 meeting room (Thtr 100 max)
Children: Welcome 🍴
Licenses: 🚹 Leisure: Games room
Parking: Off-street and free
Directions: Off the A343 Newbury to Andover road in
main village.
Map ref: St Mary Bourne 4 B3

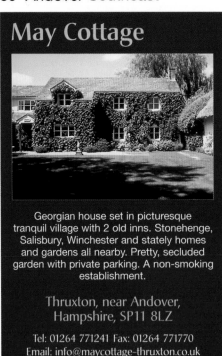

Ashford, Kent

Eastwell Manor

★★★★ ♔♔♔ Excellent

Eastwell Park, Boughton Lees,
Ashford, Kent, TN25 4HR
Tel: 01233 213000 Fax: 01233 635530
Email: enquiries@eastwellmanor.co.uk
Web: www.eastwellmanor.co.uk

Enjoy luxury combined with history at this magnificent manor house in Kent, set within beautiful grounds. Award-winning restaurant, excellent leisure facilities including indoor and outdoor pools and beauty salon.
Rooms: 62 all ensuite 🛁 🖥
Pricing: Sgl £190–365 Dbl £220–395
Dinner available from £38.50
CC: Accepted
Room facilities: 📺 ☎ 🍵 🔌
Access: ♿
Conference: 7 meeting rooms (Thtr 180 max), 24hr-delegate from £195, day-delegate from £65
Children: Welcome 🪑 Dogs: Welcome
Licenses: 🍷 👯
Leisure: Indoor pool, Outdoor pool, Gym, Health spa, Beauty salon, Tennis
Parking: Off-street and free
Directions: Take left hand road at roundabout J9/M20 into Trinity Road, follow over four roundabouts, turn left at lights onto A251. Hotel is approx 1 mile on left at bottom of hill after bend.
Map ref: Eastwell Park 4 E3
See advert on this page

London Beach Hotel and Golf Club
★★★
Ashford Road, St Michaels, Tenterden,
Ashford, Kent, TN20 6SP
Tel: 01580 766279 Fax: 01580 763884
Email: enquiries@londonbeach.com
Web: www.londonbeach.net
Seasonal closure: 24 December to 2 January
Rooms: 26 all ensuite 🛁 🖥 🚫
Dinner available
CC: Accepted
Room facilities: 📺 ☎ 🍵 🔌
Access: ♿
Conference: 5 meeting rooms (Thtr 100 max)
Children: Welcome

Licenses:
Leisure: Golf, Fishing
Parking: Off-street and free
Directions: Junction 9 on M20. Follow signs for
Tenterden. Continue through Bethersden and
High-Halden. Hotel one mile before Tenterden.
Map ref: St Michaels 5 E3

Croft Hotel
◆◆◆◆

Canterbury Road, Kennington,
Ashford, Kent, TN25 4DU
Tel: 01233 622140 Fax: 01233 635271
Email: crofthotel@btconnect.com
Web: www.crofthotel.com
Rooms: 26 (23 ensuite) 🐾 🚭
Pricing: Dinner available from £15
CC: Accepted
Room facilities: 🖵 ☎ 🍵 📞
Conference: 2 meeting rooms (Thtr 25 max),
24hr-delegate from £85, day-delegate from £25
Children: Welcome ⼑ 🍼
Dogs: Welcome
Licenses: 🕴
Parking: Off-street and free
Directions: From M20 Junction 9 or 10, follow A28
signs to Canterbury. Croft Hotel is on right.
Map ref: Kennington 5 E3

Aylesbury, Buckinghamshire

Hartwell House Hotel Restaurant and Spa
★★★★ 🦐🦐🦐 *Premier*

Oxford Road, near Aylesbury,
Buckinghamshire, HP17 8NL
Tel: 01296 747444 Fax: 01296 747450
Email: info@hartwell-house.com
Web: www.hartwell-house.com
Rooms: 46 all ensuite 🖨 🚭
Pricing: Sgl £165 Dbl £270
Dinner available from £46
CC: Accepted
Room facilities: 🖵 ☎ 📞
Access: 🛗
Conference: 4 meeting rooms (Thtr 60 max),
24hr-delegate from £265, day-delegate from £95
Children: Welcome 8yrs min age
Dogs: Welcome
Licenses: 🍷 🕴
Leisure: Indoor pool, Gym, Health spa, Beauty salon,
Tennis, Fishing
Parking: Off-street and free
Directions: In Aylesbury, take A418 towards Oxford.
Hartwell House is 2 miles along this road on the
right-hand side.
Map ref: Aylesbury 4 C1

Poletrees
◆◆◆

Poletrees Farm, Ludgershall Road, Brill,
near Aylesbury, Buckinghamshire, HP18 9TZ
Tel: 01844 238276 Fax: 01844 238276
Email: poletrees.farm@virgin.net
Web: www.country/accom.co.uk

This family farm provides comfortable ensuite bed and
breakfast in cottages, fully heated, providing lunches,
peace and quiet. Central to Oxford, Milton Keynes,
Bicester, Thames and National Trust properties.
Rooms: 4 all ensuite 🐾 🚭
Pricing: Sgl £35–40 Dbl £60–70
CC: Accepted
Room facilities: 🖵 🍵
Children: Welcome
Licenses: 🍷
Parking: Off-street and free
Map ref: Brill 4 B1

Banbury, Oxfordshire

The Unicorn Inn
◆◆◆◆ 🍴🚭 ☕

Market Place, Deddington, Banbury,
Oxfordshire, OX15 0SE
Tel: 01869 338838 Fax: 01869 338592
Web: www.unicorninn.net
Rooms: 5 all ensuite 🚭
Pricing: Sgl £55–58 Dbl £65–71
Dinner available from £6.95
CC: Accepted
Room facilities: 🖵 🍵
Conference: 2 meeting rooms
Children: Welcome ⼑
Licenses: 🕴
Leisure: Aunt Sally game
Directions: M40 Junction 10 A43E, half mile turn left,
Aynho turn left to Deddington.
Map ref: Deddington 4 B1

Fresh coffee, chilled juices for breakfast.
RAC's team of qualified Inspectors
check them both.

Basildon, Essex

Chichester Hotel

★★★

Old London Road, Wickford, Basildon,
Essex, SS11 8UE
Tel: 01268 560555 Fax: 01268 560580
Email: info@chichester-hotel.com
Web: www.chichester-hotel.com
Rooms: 33 all ensuite ⊛
Pricing: Sgl £55.70–68.65 Dbl £61.65–85.65
Dinner available from £10.75
CC: Accepted
Room facilities: ▢ ☎ ♒ ✆
Licenses: ♟ Parking: Off-street and free
Directions: Exit M25 at Junction 29. Turn east on A127
(signposted Southend on Sea). After 13 miles, turn
north on the A1245, after 1 mile turn west on the A129,
after ¼ mile turn right at hotel sign.
Map ref: Wickford 5 E2

Campanile Hotel
Travel Accommodation

A127 Southend Arterial Road, Pipps Hill, Basildon,
Essex, SS14 3AE
Tel: 01268 530810 Fax: 01268 286710
Email: basildon@envergure.co.uk

Campanile hotels offer comfortable and convenient
budget accommodation and a traditional French-style
Bistro providing freshly-cooked food for breakfast,
lunch and dinner. All rooms ensuite with tea/coffee
making facilities, DDT and TV with pay-per-view
channels.
Rooms: 97 all ensuite ⊛
Pricing: Sgl £45.90–53.45 Dbl £51.85–59.40
Dinner available from £12.95
CC: Accepted
Room facilities: ▢ ☎ ♒ ✆
Conference: 1 meeting room (Thtr 35 max),
24hr-delegate from £75, day-delegate from £21.50
Children: Welcome ♟ Dogs: Welcome
Licenses: ♟
Parking: Off-street and free
Directions: Exit J29 M25, follow A127 then A176
towards Basildon and Billericay. Left at first
roundabout and also at second, then first left.
Map ref: Basildon 5 E2

Basingstoke, Hampshire

The Basingstoke Country Hotel

★★★★

Scures Hill, Nately Scures, Hook,
Hampshire, RG27 9JS
Tel: 01256 764161 Fax: 01256 768341
Email: basingstokecountry@paramount-hotels.co.uk
Web: www.paramount-hotels.co.uk

PARAMOUNT
GROUP OF HOTELS

Surrounded by mature woodland, this elegant hotel
with a superb leisure club is conveniently located
within a mile of the M3.
Rooms: 100 all ensuite ♋ ⊛
Pricing: Sgl £39–121 Dbl £78–146
Dinner available from £20
CC: Accepted
Room facilities: ▢ ☎ ♒ ✆ ❈
Access: ⌊⌊⌊
Conference: 12 meeting rooms (Thtr 240 max),
24hr-delegate from £199, day-delegate from £72
Children: Welcome ♟
Licenses: ⟁ ♟
Leisure: Indoor pool, Gym, Health spa, Beauty salon
Parking: Off-street and free
Directions: From M3 J5 to Hook. Turn left at T-junction.
Hotel is approximately 200m on the right.
Map ref: Nately Scures 4 B3

The Hampshire Centrecourt

★★★★ ♖

Centre Drive, Great Binfields Road, Chineham,
Basingstoke, Hampshire, RG24 8FY
Tel: 01256 816664 Fax: 01256 816727
Email: hampshirec@marstonhotels.com
Web: www.marstonhotels.com
Rooms: 90 all ensuite ♋ ⊛
Dinner available CC: Accepted
Room facilities: ▢ ☎ ♒ ✆ Access: ⌊⌊⌊
Conference: 12 meeting rooms (Thtr 220 max)
Children: Welcome ♟ ⛀ ✇ Licenses: ⟁ ♟

Leisure: Indoor pool, Gym, Health spa, Beauty salon, Tennis
Parking: Off-street and free
Directions: Leave M3 at Junction 6. Follow A33 for Reading. Turn right at Chineham Centre roundabout. Hotel 1/4 mile on left.
Map ref: Chineham 4 B2

ROMANS COUNTRY HOUSE HOTEL

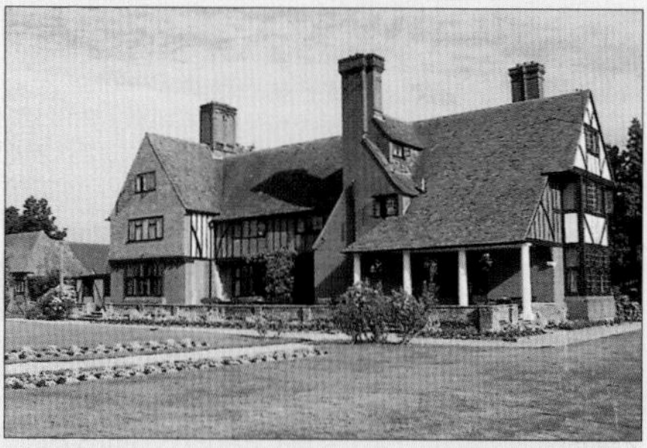

Country House set in the tranquil village of Silchester, ideal for conferences and short break holidays. Gourmet restaurant. Real log fire in the oak panelled lounge. Leisure centre with tennis, gymnasium, sauna and unique outdoor pool heated to a steaming 30°c year round.

LITTLE LONDON ROAD, SILCHESTER, BASINGSTOKE, HAMPSHIRE, RG7 2PN
Tel: 01189 700421
Fax: 01189 700691
Email: romanhotel@hotmail.com
Website: www.bestwestern.co.uk

RAC ★★★ Hotel
RAC Dining Award

Romans Country House Hotel

★★★

Little London Road, Silchester, Basingstoke, Hampshire, RG7 2PN
Tel: 0118 970 0421 Fax: 0118 970 0691
Email: romanhotel@hotmail.com
Web: www.bestwestern.co.uk
Rooms: 25 all ensuite
Pricing: Sgl £85–105 Dbl £105–155
Dinner available from £19.50 CC: Accepted
Room facilities:
Conference: 5 meeting rooms (Thtr 60 max), 24hr-delegate from £130, day-delegate from £40
Children: Welcome Dogs: Welcome
Licenses:
Leisure: Outdoor pool, Gym, Health spa, Tennis
Parking: Off-street and free
Directions: Leave M3 at Junction 6 and follow signs on A340 to Tadley/Aldermarston. At Pamber End, follow hotel signs to Silchester.
Map ref: Silchester 4 B2
See advert on this page

Beaconsfield, Buckinghamshire

The Chequers Inn Hotel & Restaurant

★★

Kiln Lane, Wooburn Common, Beaconsfield, Buckinghamshire, HP10 0JQ
Tel: 01628 529575 Fax: 01628 850124
Email: info@chequers-inn.com
Web: www.thechequersatwooburncommon.co.uk
Rooms: 17 all ensuite
Pricing: Sgl £72.50–99.50 Dbl £77.50–107.50
Dinner available from £24
CC: Accepted
Room facilities:
Conference: 1 meeting room (Thtr 60 max), 24hr-delegate from £150, day-delegate from £40
Children: Welcome
Licenses:
Parking: Off-street and free
Directions: M40 at Junction 2. Follow A40 through Beaconsfield Old Town towards High Wycombe. After 2 miles take turning left (Broad Lane). Hotel is signed and is on this road on left.
Map ref: Wooburn Common 4 C2

Beaulieu, Hampshire

Beaulieu Hotel

★★★

Beaulieu Road, Lyndhurst, Hampshire, SO42 7YQ
Tel: 023 8029 3344 Fax: 023 8029 2729
Email: beaulieu@newforesthotels.co.uk
Web: www.newforesthotels.co.uk
Rooms: 23 all ensuite
Pricing: Sgl £67.50–77.50 Dbl £135–155
Dinner available from £21.50
CC: Accepted
Room facilities:
Conference: 2 meeting rooms (Thtr 250 max), 24hr-delegate from £95, day-delegate from £30
Children: Welcome
Dogs: Welcome
Licenses:
Leisure: Indoor pool
Parking: Off-street and free
Directions: From M27, follow signs to Lyndhurst, then Beaulieu on B3056. Beaulieu Hotel is approximately 3 miles along the road.
Map ref: Lyndhurst 4 B3
See advert on following page

The big sleep

As part of our comprehensive inspection process, RAC Inspectors investigate the comfort of the beds.

Southeast

Master Builders House Hotel

★★★★

Bucklers Hard, Beaulieu, Hampshire, SO42 7XB
Tel: 01590 616253 Fax: 01590 616297
Email: res@themasterbuilders.co.uk
Web: www.themasterbuilders.co.uk
Rooms: 25 all ensuite ⊗
Dinner available
CC: Accepted
Room facilities: ▢ ☎ ⊿
Conference: 2 meeting rooms (Thtr 50 max)
Children: Welcome
Licenses: ⚓ ⣿
Parking: Off-street and free
Map ref: Bucklers Hard 4 B4

Bickley, Kent

Glendevon House Hotel

♦♦♦

80 Southborough Road, Bickley, Kent, BR1 2EN
Tel: 020 8467 2183 Fax: 020 8295 0701
Email: sales@glendevonhotel.co.uk
Web: www.glendevonhotel.co.uk
Seasonal closure: 24-30 December
Rooms: 12 all ensuite ▰ ⊗
Pricing: Sgl £41.95–49.50 Dbl £58.50–71.50
CC: Accepted
Room facilities: ▢ ☎ ⊿ ⌇
Children: Welcome 2yrs min age
Directions: M25 Junction 4, take A21 at Bromley Common. Take a right into Crown Lane at the 2nd mini roundabout. Take a 3rd left to car park.
Map ref: Bickley 5 D2

Bishop's Stortford, Hertfordshire

The Cottage

♦♦♦♦

71 Birchanger Lane, Birchanger, Bishop's Stortford, Hertfordshire, CM23 5QA
Tel: 01279 812349 Fax: 01279 815045
Email: bookings@thecottagebirchanger.co.uk
Web: www.thecottagebirchanger.co.uk
Seasonal closure: Christmas to New Year
Rooms: 15 (13 ensuite) ⊗
Pricing: Sgl £58–60 Dbl £75–80
CC: Accepted
Room facilities: ▢ ⊿
Children: Welcome
Licenses: ⣿
Parking: Off-street and free
Directions: Leave M11 at Junction 8. Take A120 west for 1 mile. Take B1383 north towards Newport and Saffron Waldon, then first right into Birchanger Lane.
Map ref: Birchanger 5 D1

George Hotel

♦♦♦

1 North Street, Bishop's Stortford, Hertfordshire, CM23 2LD
Tel: 01279 504128 Fax: 01279 655135
Email: enquiries@stanstedhotels.net
Web: www.stanstedhotels.net
Rooms: 30 (17 ensuite)
Pricing: Sgl £40–60 Dbl £65–85 Dinner available
CC: Accepted
Room facilities: ▢ ⊿
Children: Welcome
Licenses: ⣿
Parking: Off-street and free
Directions: Take signs to Bishop's Stortford Town Centre. Hotel is in the middle of town centre on the crossroads.
Map ref: Bishop's Stortford 5 D1

Bracknell, Berkshire

Coppid Beech Hotel

★★★★ ☜☜

John Nike Way, Bracknell, Berkshire, RG12 8TF
Tel: 01344 303333 Fax: 01344 301200
Email: welcome@coppid-beech-hotel.co.uk
Web: www.coppidbeech.com
Rooms: 205 all ensuite ☜ ☜
Pricing: Sgl £65–150 Dbl £95–185
Dinner available from £27
CC: Accepted
Room facilities: ☐ ☎ ☜ ☜
Access: ||↑
Conference: 11 meeting rooms (Thtr 320 max),
24hr-delegate from £205, day-delegate from £65
Children: Welcome ☌ ☜
Dogs: Welcome
Licenses: ☜ ☷
Leisure: Indoor pool, Gym, Beauty salon
Parking: Off-street and free
Directions: Leave M4 at Junction 10. Take A329(M) to
Wokingham. After 3 miles take first exit to Coppid
Beech roundabout. Take first exit and in 300 yards the
hotel is on the right.
Map ref: Bracknell 4 C2

Brentwood, Essex

Marygreen Manor Hotel

★★★★ ☜☜

London Road, Brentwood, Essex, CM14 4NR
Tel: 01277 225252 Fax: 01277 262809
Email: info@marygreenmanor.co.uk
Web: www.marygreenmanor.co.uk
Rooms: 44 all ensuite ☷ ☜
Pricing: Sgl £149.50–211.50 Dbl £184–269
Dinner available from £35
CC: Accepted
Room facilities: ☐ ☎ ☜ ☜ ☼
Conference: 7 meeting rooms (Thtr 50 max),
24hr-delegate from £205, day-delegate from £48.75
Children: Welcome ☌ ☜
Licenses: ☜ ☷
Parking: Off-street and free
Directions: Exit the M25 at Junction 28. Take A1023,
after two minutes the hotel is on right.
Map ref: Brentwood 5 D2
See advert on this page

New World Hotel
★★★★

Great Warley Street, Brentwood, Essex, CM13 3JP
Tel: 01277 226418 Fax: 01277 239020
Email: newworldhotel@btinternet.com
Web: www.newworldhotel.co.uk

The Manor House has been owned and managed by the Hilton family for nearly 35 years. Although continually expanded and refurbished, the hotel retains its elegance and character and stands in 10 acres of gardens overlooking natural beauty spots.
Rooms: 68 all ensuite 🛏 📺 ⊗
Pricing: Sgl £69–99 Dbl £89–119
Dinner available from £15.95
CC: Accepted
Room facilities: 🖵 ☎ 🍵 📞
Access: ⬆️
Conference: 5 meeting rooms (Thtr 150 max), 24hr-delegate from £150, day-delegate from £37.50
Children: Welcome ⌐
Licenses: ⚓ 🚻
Leisure: Outdoor pool, Tennis
Parking: Off-street and free
Directions: Junction 29 off M25 onto A127 towards Southend. Leave A127 at first exit (100m) onto B186 to Great Warley. Hotel is approximately 1 mile on left.
Map ref: Brentwood 5 D2

Brighton, East Sussex
(see also Hove)

Old Ship Hotel
★★★★

Kings Road, Brighton, East Sussex, BN1 1NR
Tel: 01273 329001 Fax: 01273 820718
Email: oldshipreservations@paramount-hotels.co.uk
Web: www.paramount-hotels.co.uk

PARAMOUNT
GROUP OF HOTELS

The oldest hotel in Brighton, The Old Ship stands proud on the bustling seafront of this popular UK destination.
Rooms: 152 all ensuite 🛏
Pricing: Sgl £83 Dbl £166
Dinner available from £15 CC: Accepted
Room facilities: 🖵 ☎ 🍵 📞 Access: ⬆️
Conference: 11 meeting rooms (Thtr 300 max), 24hr-delegate from £175, day-delegate from £55
Children: Welcome ⌐ Dogs: Welcome
Licenses: ⚓ 🚻 Parking: Off-street
Directions: From M25 take M23 to Brighton, follow signs for seafront, hotel is centrally located on seafront (Kings) road.
Map ref: Brighton 5 D3

The Royal Pavilion Townhouse Hotel
Townhouse
★★★★

12a Regency Square, Brighton, East Sussex, BN1 2FG
Tel: 01273 722123 Fax: 01273 722293
Email: info@rpthotel.co.uk
Web: www.rpthotel.co.uk
Rooms: 8 all ensuite 📺 ⊗
Dinner available CC: Accepted
Room facilities: 🖵 ☎ 🍵 📞
Conference: 1 meeting room (Thtr 12 max), 24hr-delegate from £150, day-delegate from £50
Licenses: 🚻
Directions: From Brighton seafront turn up Preston Street and right into Regency Square. Follow one-way system around square to 12a.
Map ref: Brighton 5 D3

Imperial Hotel

★★★

First Avenue, Hove, East Sussex, BN2 2GU
Tel: 01273 777320 Fax: 01273 777310
Email: info@imperial-hove.com
Web: www.imperial-hove.com
Rooms: 76 all ensuite
Pricing: Sgl £40–80 Dbl £70–130
Dinner available from £17.50
CC: Accepted
Room facilities: 💻 ☎ ☕ 🔌 Access: ⬆
Conference: 5 meeting rooms (Thtr 110 max),
24hr-delegate from £90, day-delegate from £30
Children: Welcome
Dogs: Assistance dogs only
Licenses: 🍾
Directions: Enter Brighton on A23, proceed to seafront.
Turn right (west) onto A259. First Avenue 1 mile on
right.
Map ref: Hove 5 D3

Kings Hotel

★★★

139–141 Kings Road, Brighton, East Sussex, BN1 2NA
Tel: 01273 820854 Fax: 01273 828309
Email: info@kingshotelbrighton.co.uk
Web: www.kingshotelbrighton.co.uk
Rooms: 84 all ensuite
Dinner available CC: Accepted
Room facilities: 💻 ☎ ☕ 🔌 Access: ⬆
Conference: 4 meeting rooms (Thtr 80 max),
24hr-delegate from £140, day-delegate from £40
Children: Welcome
Licenses: 🍾
Parking: Off-street
Directions: From London or M25, take M23/A23 to
Brighton. Follow signs for the seafront. On reaching
Brighton Pier roundabout take third exit and drive
west. Hotel is opposite West Pier.
Map ref: Brighton 5 D3

Quality Hotel Brighton

★★★

West Street, Brighton, East Sussex, BN1 2RQ
Tel: 01273 220033 Fax: 01273 778000
Email: enquiries@hotels-brighton.com
Web: www.choicehotelseurope.com
Rooms: 138 all ensuite
Pricing: Sgl £114.75–134.75 Dbl £125.75
Dinner available from £13.50
CC: Accepted
Room facilities: 💻 ☎ ☕ 🔌
Access: ⬆
Conference: 8 meeting rooms (Thtr 200 max),
24hr-delegate from £135, day-delegate from £35
Children: Welcome
Licenses: 🍾
Directions: Follow A23 into Brighton until seafront, turn
right at roundabout, second set of lights turn right into
West Street.
Map ref: Brighton 5 D3

Blanch House

◆◆◆◆ ♛♛♛

17 Atlingworth Street, Brighton, East Sussex, BN2 1PL
Tel: 01273 603504 Fax: 01273 689813
Email: info@blanchhouse.co.uk
Web: www.blanchhouse.co.uk
Seasonal closure: Christmas
Rooms: 12 all ensuite
Pricing: Sgl £100–220 Dbl £125–220
Dinner available from £25
CC: Accepted
Room facilities: 💻 ☎ ☕
Conference: 1 meeting room (Thtr 24 max),
day-delegate from £45
Children: Welcome
Dogs: Welcome
Licenses: 🍷 🍾
Leisure: Cocktail bar
Directions: 500 yards from Brighton Pier, just off
Marine Parade.
Map ref: Brighton 5 D3

Cavalaire House

◆◆◆◆

34 Upper Rock Gardens, Brighton,
East Sussex, BN2 1QF
Tel: 01273 696899 Fax: 01273 600504
Email: welcome@cavalaire.co.uk
Web: www.cavalaire.co.uk
Seasonal closure: mid-January to mid-February
Rooms: 10 all ensuite
Pricing: Sgl £39–55 Dbl £65–99
CC: Accepted
Room facilities: 💻 ☕ 🔌
Children: Welcome 5yrs min age
Licenses: 🍾
Parking: Off-street
Directions: Follow signposts to town centre/seafront.
At Brighton Pier roundabout, take A259 Rottingdean.
At second set of lights, turn left into Lower Rock
Gardens. Hotel up hill.
Map ref: Brighton 5 D3

Esteban Hotel

◆◆◆◆

35 Upper Rock Gardens, Brighton,
East Sussex, BN2 1QF
Tel: 01273 681161 Fax: 01273 676945
Email: reservations@estebanhotel.co.uk
Web: www.estebanhotel.co.uk
Rooms: 12 all ensuite
Pricing: Sgl £30–50 Dbl £65–95
Room facilities: 💻 ☕
Children: Welcome
Parking: Off-street
Directions: At the Brighton Pier turn left (Marine
Parade). Turn left at the lights. This road leads to
Upper Rock Gardens.
Map ref: Brighton 5 D3

Fyfield House

26 New Steine, Brighton, East Sussex, BN2 1PD
Tel: 01273 602770 Fax: 01273 602770
Email: info@fyfieldhotelbrighton.com
Web: www.fyfieldhotelbrighton.com
Seasonal closure: Christmas
Rooms: 11 (9 ensuite)
CC: Accepted
Room facilities:
Children: Welcome Dogs: Welcome
Directions: Town centre, at Brighton Pier, take A259
east. Eighth turning into the square, which has a
one-way system.
Map ref: Brighton 5 D3

Genevieve Hotel

18 Madeira Place, Brighton, East Sussex, BN2 1TN
Tel: 01273 681653 Fax: 01273 681653
Email: rac@genevievehotel.co.uk
Web: www.genevievehotel.co.uk
Rooms: 13 all ensuite
Pricing: Sgl £40–60 Dbl £65–115 CC: Accepted
Room facilities:
Directions: From Brighton Pier go east along Seafront
Road A259 (Marine Parade). Madeira Place is the 5th
turning on the left.
Map ref: Brighton 5 D3

Hotel Twenty One

21 Charlotte Street, Marine Parade, Brighton,
East Sussex, BN2 1AG
Tel: 01273 686450 Fax: 01273 695560
Email: the21@pavilion.co.uk
Web: www.smoothhound.co.uk/hotels/21.html
Rooms: 8 all ensuite
Pricing: Sgl £25–35 Dbl £60–115 CC: Accepted
Room facilities:
Directions: From Palace Pier turn left onto A259. After
³/₄ mile, turn left onto Charlotte Street. Hotel Twenty
One is on left-hand side.
Map ref: Brighton 5 D3

Paskins Town House

18/19 Charlotte Street, Brighton, East Sussex, BN2 1AG
Tel: 01273 601203 Fax: 01273 621973
Email: welcome@paskins.co.uk
Web: www.paskins.co.uk
Rooms: 19 (16 ensuite)
Pricing: Sgl £35–55 Dbl £70–140
CC: Accepted
Room facilities:
Children: Welcome Dogs: Welcome
Licenses:
Directions: At Brighton Pier, turn left. Paskins Hotel is
on 11th road on left.
Map ref: Brighton 5 D3

Trouville

11 New Steine, Marine Parade, Brighton,
East Sussex, BN2 1PB
Tel: 01273 697384
Seasonal closure: Christmas and January
Rooms: 8 (6 ensuite)
Pricing: Sgl £35–59 Dbl £69–85 CC: Accepted
Room facilities: Children: Welcome
Licenses:
Directions: Take A23 to Palace Pier. Turn left onto A259.
New Steine is the first square on left, after 300 yards.
Map ref: Brighton 5 D3

4 Seasons

3 Upper Rock Gardens, Brighton, East Sussex, BN2 1QE
Tel: 01273 673574
Email: hotels4seasons@hotmail.com
Web: www.hotel4seasons.co.uk
Rooms: 7 (5 ensuite)
Pricing: Sgl £30–55 Dbl £50–90 CC: Accepted
Room facilities:
Directions: Follow signpost to town centre/seafront. At
Brighton Pier roundabout take A259 Rottingdean. Left
at second lights. Hotel up hill.
Map ref: Brighton 5 D3

Amsterdam Hotel

11-12 Marine Parade, Brighton, East Sussex, BN2 1TL
Tel: 01273 688825 Fax: 01273 688828
Email: info@amsterdam.uk.com
Web: www.amsterdam.uk.com
Rooms: 24 (21 ensuite)
Pricing: Dbl £60–140
Dinner available from £5–20 CC: Accepted
Room facilities:
Conference: 1 meeting room (Thtr 30 max)
Licenses: Leisure: Gym, Mens' sauna and steam room
Directions: On Brighton seafront opposite Brighton Pier
and Sealife Centre.
Map ref: Brighton 5 D3

Brighton Marina House Hotel

8 Charlotte Street, Brighton, East Sussex, BN2 1AG
Tel: 01273 605349 Fax: 01273 679484
Email: rooms@jungs.co.uk
Web: www.brighton-mh-hotel.co.uk
Rooms: 10 (7 ensuite)
Pricing: Sgl £25–50 Dbl £50–89
Dinner available from £19.50 CC: Accepted
Room facilities: Children: Welcome
Parking: Off-street
Directions: At Brighton Pier turn up Marine Parade
(A259). After second traffic lights, take fifth left
(Charlotte Street).
Map ref: Brighton 5 D3
See advert on opposite page

Marina House Hotel

8 Charlotte Street, Brighton BN2 1AG

Tel: 0044 (0) 1273 605349   Fax: 0044 (0) 1273 679484

Email: rooms@jungs.co.uk
Web: www.brighton-mh-hotel.co.uk

Location

*Located off the sea front within
3 minutes walk to the beach.
Our exquisitely appointed rooms offer a
unique and innovative experience in
today's Bed & Breakfast.*

We offer

- *Ensuite rooms with the required comforts*
- *All rooms non-smoking*
- *Rooms with & without breakfast*
- *Free internet access & e-mail facility*
- *Special Sunday - Friday offers*

*We seek to pre-empt the needs of our guests as
we look to offer customer service at its best as*

"We consider our Guests to be a Valuable asset"

Eastern Style Room

French 4-poster Room

You will love our romantic rooms

Tudor Style Room

Yummy Breakfast

*After sleeping in our exquisite beds, you
will love our yummy breakfast. We cater
for Vegan, Vegetarian, Continental and the
full English.*

*Please call us for more information or take
a look at our web site for a new and unique
experience in today's Bed and Breakfast.*

Tudor Room – balcony

*Tariff: £25.00 to £50
per person per night.*

Pine Room

Budgies Guest House

7 Madeira Place, Brighton, East Sussex, BN2 1TN
Tel: 01273 683533 Fax: 01273 683533
Email: budgiesghouse@aol.com
Web: www.budgiesghouse.com
Seasonal closure: January
Rooms: 9 all ensuite ⊗
Pricing: Sgl £30–50 Dbl £50–85
Room facilities: ⬚ ☕ ☎
Children: Welcome
Directions: 5 minutes walking distance from Brighton
Pier towards east off A259. 20 minutes walk from
Brighton train station.
Map ref: Brighton 5 D3

Colson House Guest House

17 Upper Rock Gardens, Brighton, East Sussex, BN2 1QE
Tel: 01273 694922 Fax: 01273 694922
Email: info@colsonhouse.co.uk
Web: www.colsonhouse.co.uk
Rooms: 8 all ensuite ⊞ ⊗
Pricing: Sgl £30–45 Dbl £60–90
CC: Accepted
Room facilities: ⬚ ☕
Children: Welcome 12yrs min age
Directions: Follow signs to seafront and turn left at
Brighton Pier then left again at next traffic lights.
Map ref: Brighton 5 D3

Malvern Hotel

◆◆◆

33 Regency Square, Brighton, East Sussex, BN1 2GG
Tel: 01273 324302 Fax: 01273 324285
Email: info@themalvernhotel.com
Web: www.themalvernhotel.com
Rooms: 12 all ensuite ⊗
CC: Accepted
Room facilities: ⬚ ☎ ☕ ☎
Conference: 2 meeting rooms (Thtr 24 max)
Children: Welcome
Dogs: Welcome
Directions: Check website for details.
Map ref: Brighton 5 D3

Marine View

24 New Steine, Brighton, East Sussex, BN2 1PD
Tel: 01273 603870 Fax: 01273 603870
Email: mvbrighton@aol.com
Web: www.mvbrighton.co.uk
Rooms: 10 (8 ensuite)
Room facilities: ⬚ ☕
Children: Welcome
Directions: A23 to sea front, left at roundabout 300
metres along sea front, left into New Steine, first
garden square.
Map ref: Brighton 5 D3

The Garth

28 Cornwall Gardens, Brighton, East Sussex, BN1 6RJ
Tel: 01273 561515 Fax: 01273 561515
Email: m.edward81@ntlworld.com
Rooms: 3 ⊗
Pricing: Sgl £30–40 Dbl £60–70
Room facilities: ⬚ ☕
Children: Welcome 5yrs min age
Directions: A23 into Brighton becomes London Road;
after 1 mile turn left into Varndean Road; Cornwall
Gardens is first right.
Map ref: Brighton 5 D3

The Lanes Hotel

◆◆◆

70-72 Marine Parade, Brighton, East Sussex, BN2 1AE
Tel: 01273 674231 Fax: 01273 674230
Email: thelanes@mistral.co.uk
Web: www.laneshotel.co.uk
Rooms: 34 all ensuite ☕ ⊞ CC: Accepted
Room facilities: ⬚ ☎ ☕ Access: ⬚
Children: Welcome Licenses: ⬚
Parking: Off-street and free
Directions: The Lanes Hotel is about 500m east of
Brighton Pier along Marine Parade.
Map ref: Brighton 5 D3

Alvia Hotel

 New for 2006

36 Upper Rock Gardens, Brighton, East Sussex, BN2 1QF
Tel: 01273 682939 Fax: 01273 626287
Web: www.alviahotel.co.uk
Rooms: 10 (9 ensuite) ⊞ ⊗
Pricing: Sgl £18–55 Dbl £60–140 CC: Accepted
Room facilities: ⬚ ☕ Children: Welcome 3yrs min age
Parking: Off-street and free
Directions: From pier go east along Marine Parade.
Turn left into Lower Rock Gardens Road which then
becomes Upper Rock Gardens.
Map ref: Brighton 5 D3

Broadstairs, Kent

Fayreness Hotel

★★★

Marine Drive, Kingsgate, Broadstairs, Kent, CT10 3LG
Tel: 01843 868641 Fax: 01843 608750
Email: fayreness@btinternet.com
Web: www.fayreness.com
Rooms: 29 all ensuite ☕ ⊗
Dinner available CC: Accepted
Room facilities: ⬚ ☎ ☕ ☎
Conference: 1 meeting room (Thtr 40 max)
Children: Welcome ⬚ Dogs: Welcome Licenses: ⬚ ⬚
Leisure: Games room Parking: Off-street and free
Directions: From M2/A299 follow directions for
Broadstairs then Kingsgate. Hotel is situated at the
bottom of Kingsgate Avenue.
Map ref: Broadstairs 5 F2

Bay Tree Hotel

◆◆◆◆

12 Eastern Esplanade, Broadstairs, Kent, CT10 1DR
Tel: 01843 862502 Fax: 01843 860589
Rooms: 11 all ensuite ⊛
Pricing: Sgl £37–41 Dbl £74–82
Dinner available from £23
CC: Accepted
Room facilities: ▯ ☕
Children: Welcome 10yrs min age
Licenses: ♦♦♦
Leisure: Library
Parking: Off-street and free
Directions: Situated on clifftop Eastern Esplanade.
Follow main road through town, turning right into
Rectory Road on leaving Broadstairs.
Map ref: Broadstairs 5 F2

Brockenhurst, Hampshire

Balmer Lawn

★★★

Lyndhurst Road, Brockenhurst, Hampshire, SO42 7ZB
Tel: 01590 623116 Fax: 01590 623864
Email: info@balmerlawnhotel.com
Web: www.balmerlawnhotel.com
Rooms: 55 all ensuite ⊛ ▱ ⊛
Dinner available CC: Accepted
Room facilities: ▯ ☎ ☕ ☏
Access: ⊥↥
Conference: 7 meeting rooms (Thtr 100 max)
Children: Welcome ↟ ⊱ Dogs: Welcome
Licenses: ⟁ ♦♦♦
Leisure: Indoor pool, Outdoor pool, Gym, Tennis
Parking: Off-street and free
Directions: West on M27. Exit J1, take A337 through
Lyndhurst toward Brockenhurst. Hotel is 4 miles on
left. Turn left on B3055.
Map ref: Brockenhurst 4 B4

New Park Manor Hotel

★★★

Lyndhurst Road, New Forest, Brockenhurst,
Hampshire, SO42 7QH
Tel: 01590 623467 Fax: 01590 622268
Email: info@newparkmanorhotel.co.uk
Web: www.newparkmanorhotel.co.uk
Rooms: 24 all ensuite ▱ ⊛
Dinner available
CC: Accepted
Room facilities: ▯ ☎ ☕ ☏
Conference: 5 meeting rooms (Thtr 120 max)
Children: Welcome ↟ ⊱ Dogs: Welcome
Licenses: ⟁ ♦♦♦
Leisure: Outdoor pool, Tennis, Riding
Parking: Off-street and free
Directions: Leave M27 at Junction 1. Follow A337 to
Lyndhurst and Brockenhurst. Hotel sign and private
drive on right midway between Lyndhurst and
Brockenhurst.
Map ref: Brockenhurst 4 B4

Watersplash Hotel

★★

The Rise, Brockenhurst, Hampshire, SO42 7ZP
Tel: 01590 622344 Fax: 01590 624047
Email: bookings@watersplash.co.uk
Web: www.watersplash.co.uk
Rooms: 23 (19 ensuite) ⊛ ▱ ⊛
Pricing: Sgl £60–82 Dbl £82–126
Dinner available from £24
CC: Accepted
Room facilities: ▯ ☎ ☕ ☏
Conference: 2 meeting rooms (Thtr 60 max),
24hr-delegate from £120, day-delegate from £30
Children: Welcome ↟ ⊱ Dogs: Welcome
Licenses: ♦♦♦
Leisure: Outdoor pool, Snooker/billiards
Parking: Off-street and free
Directions: Exit M27 West junction 1. A337 to
Lyndhurst onto Brockenhurst. Entering Brockenhurst
take Grigg Lane then Sway Road. Turn right after Esso
garage into The Rise.
Map ref: Brockenhurst 4 B4

Little Heathers Guest House

◆◆◆◆

13 Whitemoor Road, Brockenhurst,
Hampshire, SO42 7QG
Tel: 01590 623512
Email: littleheathers@msn.com
Web: www.newforest.demon.co.uk/littleheathers.htm
Seasonal closure: 25-26 December
Rooms: 3 (2 ensuite) ⊛
Pricing: Sgl £30–40 Dbl £60–65
Room facilities: ▯ ☕ Children: Welcome
Parking: Off-street and free
Directions: From A337 turn right into Meerut Road,
right into Rhinefield Road, fourth left into Oberfield
Road, left into Whitemoor Road.
Map ref: Brockenhurst 4 B4

Bromley, Kent

Bromley Court Hotel

★★★

Bromley Hill, Bromley, Kent, BR1 4JD
Tel: 020 8461 8600 Fax: 020 8460 0899
Email: enquiries@bromleycourthotel.co.uk
Web: www.bw-bromleycourthotel.co.uk
Rooms: 114 all ensuite ⊛ ⊛
Pricing: Sgl £85–107 Dbl £95–120
Dinner available from £17.95–19.95 CC: Accepted
Room facilities: ▯ ☎ ☕ ☏ Access: ⊥↥
Conference: 9 meeting rooms (Thtr 150 max),
24hr-delegate from £150, day-delegate from £39
Children: Welcome ↟ ⊱ Licenses: ⟁ ♦♦♦
Leisure: Gym, Health spa, Steam room
Parking: Off-street and free
Directions: Exit J4 M25, A21 to Bromley use Kentish
Way to London Road A21. Private Drive off Bromley
Hill opposite Volkswagen showroom.
Map ref: Bromley 5 D2

Avis Hotel

◆◆◆

33 Roadway Road, Bromley, Kent, BR1 3JP
Tel: 020 8460 6311 Fax: 020 8290 1312
Email: reservations@avishotel.co.uk
Web: www.avishotel.co.uk
Rooms: 20 all ensuite 🦽 📠 ⊗
Pricing: Sgl £41.95–49.50 Dbl £58.50–85 CC: Accepted
Room facilities: ▢ ☎ 🍵 ⬍
Children: Welcome 2yrs min age
Parking: Off-street and free
Directions: M25 Junction 4 A21 to Bromley Town. Near
Bromley North from Tweedy Road turn right into
Sherman Road that leads to Roadway.
Map ref: Bromley 5 D2

Burley, Hampshire

Moorhill House Hotel

★★★🕊

Burley, near Ringwood, Hampshire, BH24 4AH
Tel: 01425 403285 Fax: 01425 403715
Email: moorhill@newforesthotels.co.uk
Web: www.newforesthotels.co.uk
Rooms: 31 all ensuite 🦽 📠
Pricing: Sgl £67.50–77.50 Dbl £135–155
Dinner available from £21.50 CC: Accepted
Room facilities: ▢ ☎ 🍵 🍵
Conference: 3 meeting rooms (Thtr 120 max),
24hr-delegate from £95, day-delegate from £30

Children: Welcome 🎋 ⅔℃ Dogs: Welcome
Licenses: 🍸 🎵 Leisure: Indoor pool, Gym, Sauna,
Croquet Parking: Off-street and free
Directions: From M27, take A31 and follow signs to Burley.
Go through village up hill, Moorhill House is on the right.
Map ref: Burley 4 A4
See advert on this page

Cadnam, Hampshire

Bartley Lodge Hotel

★★★🕊

Lyndhurst Road, Cadnam, Hampshire, SO40 2NR
Tel: 023 8081 2248 Fax: 023 8081 2075
Email: bartley@newforesthotels.co.uk
Web: www.newforesthotels.co.uk
Rooms: 31 all ensuite 🦽 📠
Pricing: Sgl £67.50–77.50 Dbl £135–155
Dinner available from £21.50 CC: Accepted
Room facilities: ▢ ☎ 🍵
Conference: 3 meeting rooms (Thtr 120 max),
24hr-delegate from £95, day-delegate from £30
Children: Welcome 🎋 ⅔℃ Dogs: Welcome
Licenses: 🍸 🎵
Leisure: Indoor pool, Gym, Tennis, Sauna
Parking: Off-street and free
Directions: From M27 exit at junction 1, left at first round-
about, then right at second, Bartley Lodge is on the left.
Map ref: Cadnam 4 B3
See advert on this page

Camberley, Surrey

Camberley Guest House

◆◆◆◆

116 London Road, Camberley, Surrey, GU15 3TJ
Tel: 01276 24410 Fax: 01276 65409
Seasonal closure: Christmas
Rooms: 5 all ensuite
Pricing: Sgl £55 Dbl £80
CC: Accepted
Room facilities: □ ☎ ☺
Conference: 1 meeting room (Thtr 10 max)
Children: Welcome
Parking: Off-street and free
Directions: Situated on main A30, running parallel to
M3. From London, take exit 3, from south coast take
exit 4. Hotel in town centre of Camberley.
Map ref: Camberley 4 C2

Chelmsford, Essex

Atlantic Hotel

★★★

New Street, Chelmsford, Essex, CM1 1PP
Tel: 01245 268168 Fax: 01245 268169
Email: info@atlantichotel.co.uk
Web: www.atlantichotel.co.uk
Seasonal closure: 24 December to 2 January
Rooms: 59 all ensuite
Pricing: Sgl £50–185.95 Dbl £50–196.90
Dinner available from £20–35
CC: Accepted
Room facilities: □ ☎ ☺ 🔌 ❄
Conference: 3 meeting rooms (Thtr 15 max),
24hr-delegate from £120, day-delegate from £30
Children: Welcome
Licenses: ♙♙♙ Leisure: Gym, Beauty salon
Parking: Off-street and free
Directions: From railway station turn into Victoria Road.
At traffic lights, turn left into New Street, hotel is on right.
Map ref: Chelmsford 5 E1

County Hotel

★★★

29 Rainsford Road, Chelmsford, Essex, CM1 2PZ
Tel: 01245 455700 Fax: 01245 492762
Email: sales@countyhotel-essex.co.uk
Web: www.countyhotel-essex.co.uk
Rooms: 61 all ensuite
Dinner available CC: Accepted
Room facilities: □ ☎ ☺ 🔌
Conference: 5 meeting rooms (Thtr 150 max)
Children: Welcome 🥢
Licenses: ♙♙♙
Parking: Off-street and free
Directions: From M25 Junction 28, take A12 to
Chelmsford. From town centre, take road to rail
station. Pass station, under bridge, hotel on left after
traffic lights.
Map ref: Chelmsford 5 E1

Chichester, West Sussex

Millstream Hotel

★★★★
Commended

Bosham Lane, Bosham, Chichester,
West Sussex, PO18 8HL
Tel: 01243 573234 Fax: 01243 573459
Email: info@millstream-hotel.co.uk
Web: www.millstream-hotel.co.uk

Beautifully-appointed country hotel dating from 1701,
set in a picturesque sailing village. Bar, sitting-room,
restaurant and a bedroom designed for wheelchair
access, all on ground floor. Locally renowned award-
winning restaurant.
Rooms: 35 all ensuite
Pricing: Sgl £85–110 Dbl £139–159
Dinner available from £29
CC: Accepted
Room facilities: □ ☎ ☺ 🔌
Conference: 1 meeting room (Thtr 40 max),
24hr-delegate from £120, day-delegate from £30
Children: Welcome 🥢
Licenses: ♙♙♙
Parking: Off-street and free
Directions: From Chichester or Havant take the A259
to Bosham. From Swan roundabout follow brown signs
south to hotel.
Map ref: Bosham 4 C4

Southeast

The Horse and Group

◆◆◆◆

East Ashling, Chichester, West Sussex, PO18 9AX
Tel: 01243 575339 Fax: 01243 575560
Email: horseandgroomea@aol.com
Web: www.thehorseandgroomchichester.com
Rooms: 11 all ensuite
Pricing: Sgl £35–50 Dbl £55–75
Dinner available from £8–16
CC: Accepted
Room facilities:
Children: Welcome
Dogs: Welcome
Licenses:
Parking: Off-street and free
Directions: A27 Chichester take A259 (Bosham)
second right Salthill Road, left at top (B2178) to East
Ashling. Pub on left.
Map ref: East Ashling 4 C3
See advert on this page

The Vestry

◆◆◆◆

23 Southgate, Chichester, West Sussex, PO19 1ES
Tel: 01243 773358 Fax: 01243 530633
Email: info@the-vestry.com
Web: www.the-vestry.com
Rooms: 11 all ensuite
Pricing: Sgl £65 Dbl £75–95
Dinner available from £5–25 CC: Accepted
Room facilities:
Children: Welcome
Licenses: Parking: Off-street
Directions: From the A27 join the Chichester ring road
and follow signs for Southgate. The Vestry is on South
Street.
Map ref: Chichester 4 C3

Clacton-on-Sea, Essex

The Sandrock Hotel

◆◆◆

1 Penfold Road, Marine Parade West,
Clacton-on-Sea, Essex, CO15 1JN
Tel: 01255 428215 Fax: 01255 428215

Rooms: 9 all ensuite
Dinner available
CC: Accepted
Room facilities:
Children: Welcome
Dogs: Welcome
Licenses:
Parking: Off-street and free
Directions: Take A120 to Clacton. Turn right at the
seafront. The Sandrock Hotel is in the second turning
on the right, past pier.
Map ref: Clacton-on-Sea 5 E1

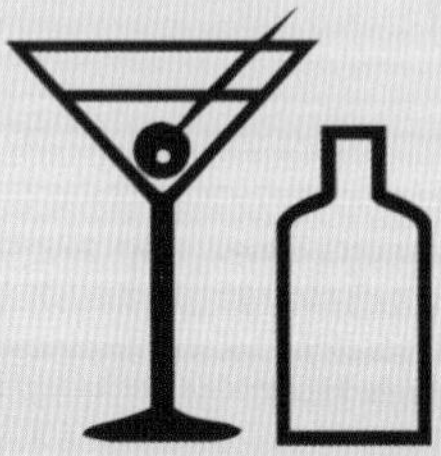

Colchester, Essex

Five Lakes Resort
★★★★ ☻☻

Colchester Road, Tolleshunt Knights, Maldon,
Essex, CM9 8HX
Tel: 01621 868888 Fax: 01621 869696
Email: enquiries@fivelakes.co.uk
Web: www.fivelakes.co.uk

Modern four-star resort set in 320 acres of Essex
countryside which offers some of the finest and most
extensive health, leisure and golf facilities in the east of
England.
Rooms: 194 all ensuite ☻ ☻ ☻
Pricing: Sgl £75–123.95 Dbl £85–183
Dinner available from £18.50
CC: Accepted
Room facilities: ☐ ☎ ☺ ☜
Access: ⌊↥
Conference: 18 meeting rooms (Thtr 2000 max),
24hr-delegate from £195, day-delegate from £65
Children: Welcome ☂ ☻
Dogs: Assistance dogs only
Licenses: ☻ ☻
Leisure: Indoor pool, Gym, Health spa, Beauty salon,
Tennis, Golf, Games room, Snooker/billiards,
Hairdressers, Squash, Badminton, Fitness studio,
Sauna, Steam room, Spa bath
Parking: Off-street and free
Directions: Take Junction off A12 for Kelvedon, then
follow brown tourist signs for approximately six miles
to Five Lakes Resort.
Map ref: Tolleshunt Knights 5 E1

Relax & smell the coffee

Fresh coffee, chilled juices
for breakfast. RAC's team
of qualified Inspectors
check them both.

De Vere Arms

★★★★ ☻☻☻

53 High Street, Earls Colne,
Colchester, Essex, CO6 2PB
Tel: 01787 223353 Fax: 01787 223365
Email: info@deverearms.com
Web: www.deverearms.com

Rooms: 9 all ensuite ☻
Pricing: Sgl £80–110 Dbl £95–160
Dinner available from £23–35
CC: Accepted
Room facilities: ☐ ☎ ☺ ☜
Children: Welcome
Licenses: ☻
Parking: Off-street and free
Directions: From A120 (between M11/A12) follow signs
to Earls Colne (B1024), left at mini roundabout (A1124)
into High Street. Hotel is on right.
Map ref: Earls Colne 5 E1

Ramada

★★★

A12/A120 Ardleigh Junction, Old Ipswich Road,
Colchester, Essex, CO7 7QY
Tel: 01206 230900 Fax: 01206 231095
Email: reception@ramadacolchester.co.uk
Web: www.ramadainternational.com

R A M A D A.

Rooms: 50 all ensuite ☻
Pricing: Sgl £69.95–89.95 Dbl £79.90–99.90
Dinner available from £17.50
CC: Accepted
Room facilities: ☐ ☎ ☺ ☜
Conference: 4 meeting rooms (Thtr 80 max),
24hr- delegate from £97.50, day-delegate from £32.50
Children: Welcome ☂
Licenses: ☻
Parking: Off-street and free
Directions: Situated north of Colchester by the
A12/A120 Ardleigh junction.
Map ref: Ardleigh Junction 5 E1

Coulsdon, Surrey

Aries Guest House

♦♦♦♦

38 Brighton Road, Coulsdon, Surrey, CR5 2BA
Tel: 020 8668 5744 Fax: 020 8668 5744
Email: enquiries@arieshouse.co.uk
Web: www.arieshouse.co.uk
Rooms: 6 (2 ensuite) ⊗
Pricing: Sgl £28 Dbl £40–50
CC: Accepted
Room facilities: ▢ ☉
Children: Welcome 7yrs min age ⴕ
Parking: Off-street and free
Directions: Situated on the A23 between Purley and
Coulsdon — 400 yards north of Coulsdon shopping
centre and Smitham rail station.
Map ref: Coulsdon 5 D2

Crowborough, East Sussex

Yew House Bed & Breakfast

♦♦♦♦ ⌇

Crowborough Hill, Crowborough,
East Sussex, TN6 2EA
Tel: 01892 610522
Email: yewhouse@yewhouse.com
Web: www.yewhouse.com
Seasonal closure: Christmas Day

Yew House is a brand new detached property offering
a flexible range of bed and breakfast accommodation.
Yew House has been built with as many green and
eco-friendly features as possible and is just 2 miles
from Ashdown Forest.
Rooms: 4 (2 ensuite) ⤢ ⊗
Pricing: Sgl £35–55 Dbl £55–65
Dinner available from £12
Room facilities: ▢ ☉ ⬥
Conference: 2 meeting rooms (Thtr 6 max)
Children: Welcome ⴕ
Leisure: Books and magazines, Cards and board
games in all rooms
Parking: Off-street and free
Directions: Through Crowborough high street over
roundabout, passing police station. Yew House is one
drive before the turning into Medway Jarvis Brook.
Map ref: Crowborough 5 D3

Plough and Horses

♦♦♦

Walshes Road, Crowborough, East Sussex, TN6 3RE
Tel: 01892 652614 Fax: 01892 652614
Rooms: 15 all ensuite ⤢ ⊗
Dinner available
CC: Accepted
Room facilities: ▢ ☉
Conference: 2 meeting rooms (Thtr 70 max)
Children: Welcome ⴕ
Dogs: Welcome
Licenses: ⵜⵜⵜ
Parking: Off-street and free
Directions: A26 Tunbridge Wells to Crowborough. First
left at Boars Head roundabout. Cross junction with
Crowborough Hill to the end of Tollwood Road.
Map ref: Crowborough 5 D3

Croydon, Surrey

Coulsdon Manor

★★★★★ ⌘ ⌘

Coulsdon Court Road, Old Coulsdon,
Croydon, Surrey, CR5 2LL
Tel: 020 8668 0414 Fax: 020 8668 3118
Email: swallow.coulsdon@swallowhotels.com
Web: www.swallowhotels.com

Manor house in 140 acres of parkland with 18 hole golf
course, convenient for Central London, 2 AA rosette
restaurant. Leisure facilities include: squash, tennis,
gym, sunbed and aerobic studio.
Rooms: 35 all ensuite ⤢ ⊗
Pricing: Sgl £85–149 Dbl £95–160
Dinner available from £30
CC: Accepted
Room facilities: ▢ ☎ ☉ ⬥
Access: ⌊↕
Conference: 11 meeting rooms (Thtr 180 max),
24hr-delegate from £164, day-delegate from £53.50
Children: Welcome ⴕ ⚘ ⚘
Licenses: ⟁ ⵜⵜⵜ
Leisure: Gym, Tennis, Golf, Squash courts,
Aerobics studio
Parking: Off-street and free
Directions: Follow M23 towards Croydon. Drive
through Coulsdon on A23. Turn right into Stoats Nest
Road. Hotel is 1 mile on right.
Map ref: Old Coulsdon 5 D2

Jurys Inn Croydon

★★★

Wellesley Road, Croydon, Surrey, CR0 9XY
Tel: 020 8448 6000 Fax: 020 8448 6111
Email: bookings@jurysdoyle.com
Web: www.jurysinns.com

Rooms: 240 all ensuite 🐾 ⊛
Pricing: Sgl £77–105 Dbl £86.50–115
Dinner available from £17 CC: Accepted
Room facilities: 🖵 ☎ ☕ ✳
Access: ⬆
Conference: 14 meeting rooms (Thtr 100 max),
24hr-delegate from £119, day-delegate from £44
Children: Welcome ⍭
Licenses: ⛉
Directions: Five minute walk to hotel from East
Croydon station.
Map ref: Croydon 5 D2

South Park Hotel

★★

3-5 South Park Hill Road, Croydon, Surrey, CR2 7DY
Tel: 020 8688 5644 Fax: 020 8760 0861
Email: reception@southparkhotel.co.uk
Web: www.southparkhotel.co.uk
Rooms: 32 all ensuite 🐾 ⊛
Pricing: Sgl £50–60 Dbl £60–76
Dinner available from £11.95
CC: Accepted
Room facilities: 🖵 ☎ ☕ ☕
Licenses: ⛉
Parking: Off-street and free
Directions: From A23, take A236 towards Croydon for
1 mile. Straight across roundabout under flyover, then
immediate left into Lower Coombe Street. Through two
sets of lights, over railway bridge to two mini-
roundabouts. Right at the first roundabout into South
Park Hill Road.
Map ref: Croydon 5 D2

Woodstock Hotel

♦♦♦ ✖

30 Woodstock Road, Croydon, Surrey, CR0 1JR
Tel: 020 8680 1489 Fax: 020 8667 1229
Email: woodstockhotel@croydon-surrey.fsworld.co.uk
Web: www.woodstockhotel.co.uk
Seasonal closure: Christmas Day
Rooms: 8 (6 ensuite) ⊛
Pricing: Sgl £45–55 Dbl £75
CC: Accepted
Room facilities: 🖵 ☕
Children: Welcome 4yrs min age
Parking: Off-street and free
Directions: From A232 or A212 at Park Lane
roundabout exit towards South Croydon. Third road off
Park Lane is Woodstock Road.
Map ref: Croydon 5 D2

Dartford, Kent

Rowhill Grange Hotel

★★★★ ⧲⧲⧲   *Excellent*

Wilmington, Dartford, Kent, DA2 7QH
Tel: 01322 615136 Fax: 01322 615137
Email: admin@rowhillgrange.com
Web: www.rowhillgrange.com
Rooms: 38 all ensuite 📂 ⊛
Pricing: Sgl £165–280 Dbl £190–340
Dinner available from £35 CC: Accepted
Room facilities: 🖵 ☎ ☕ ☕ Access: ⬆
Conference: 7 meeting rooms (Thtr 160 max),
24hr-delegate from £150, day-delegate from £45
Children: Welcome 5yrs min age ⍭
Licenses: ⬥ ⛉
Leisure: Indoor pool, Gym, Health spa, Beauty salon
Parking: Off-street and free
Directions: Leave M25 Junction 3 to Swanley. Follow
B2175 through 4 roundabouts to Hextable on B258.
Hotel is 1.5 miles on left opposite garage.
Map ref: Wilmington 5 D2

Campanile Hotel
Travel Accommodation

1 Clipper Boulevard West, Crossways Business Park,
Dartford, Kent, DA2 6QN
Tel: 01322 278925 Fax: 01322 278948
Email: reception.dartford@campanile-hotels.com
Web: www.campanile.com

Campanile hotels offer comfortable and convenient
budget accommodation and a traditional French-style
Bistro providing freshly-cooked food for breakfast,
lunch and dinner. All rooms ensuite with tea/coffee-
making facilities, DDT and TV with Sky channels.
Rooms: 127 all ensuite ⊛
Pricing: Sgl £57.90 Dbl £63.85
Dinner available from £7.50 CC: Accepted
Room facilities: 🖵 ☎ ☕ ☕
Conference: 2 meeting rooms (Thtr 50 max),
24hr-delegate from £75, day-delegate from £21.50
Children: Welcome ⍭
Dogs: Welcome
Licenses: ⛉
Parking: Off-street and free
Directions: From M25 junction 1A until the ferry terminal,
or from Dartford bridge follow signs for ferry terminal.
Map ref: Dartford 5 D2

Southeast

Deal, Kent

Kilgour House

22 Gilford Road, Deal, Kent, CT14 7DJ
Tel: 01304 368311
Rooms: 3 all ensuite
Room facilities: ☐ ☕
Map ref: Deal 5 F3

Dorking, Surrey

Macdonald Burford Bridge Hotel

★★★★ ☸

At the foot of Boxhill, Dorking, Surrey, RH5 6BX
Tel: 0870 4008283 Fax: 01306 880386
Email: burfordbridge@macdonald-hotels.co.uk
Web: www.burfordbridgehotel.com

The Macdonald Burford Bridge Hotel nestles at the
foot of National Trust Box Hill and alongside the River
Mole, an area of natural beauty. This is an ideal venue
for business or pleasure.
Rooms: 57 all ensuite ⊗
Pricing: Dbl £110–180
Dinner available from £28.50
CC: Accepted
Room facilities: ☐ ☎ ☕ ☍ ✳
Conference: 7 meeting rooms (Thtr 200 max),
24hr-delegate from £220, day-delegate from £80
Children: Welcome ♀
Dogs: Welcome
Licenses: ⟁ ♦♦♦
Leisure: Outdoor pool, Heated outdoor pool
Parking: Off-street and free
Directions: Junction 9 of M25, four miles south on A24.
Two miles north of Dorking.
Map ref: Dorking 4 C3

Gatton Manor Hotel Golf & Country Club

★★★★ ☸

Standon Lane, Ockley, Dorking, Surrey, RH5 5PQ
Tel: 01306 627555 Fax: 01306 627713
Email: gattonmanor@enterprise.net
Web: www.gattonmanor.co.uk
Rooms: 18 all ensuite ▱ ⊗
Dinner available
CC: Accepted
Room facilities: ☐ ☎ ☕
Conference: 3 meeting rooms (Thtr 50 max)
Children: Welcome ♀
Licenses: ⟁ ♦♦♦
Leisure: Gym, Health spa, Beauty salon, Tennis, Golf,
Fishing Parking: Off-street
Directions: Situated off A24/A29 between Horsham
and Dorking.
Map ref: Ockley 4 C3

Dover, Kent

Ramada Hotel Dover

★★★

Singledge Lane, Whitfield, Dover, Kent, CT16 3EL
Tel: 01304 821230 Fax: 01304 825576

 RAMADA.

Rooms: 68 all ensuite
Pricing: Sgl £56–105 Dbl £56–105
Dinner available from £7.95–19.95
Room facilities:
Conference: 3 meeting rooms (Thtr 100 max)
Children: Welcome
Licenses:
Leisure: Gym
Parking: Off-street and free
Directions: Towards Dover on A2, take A2 Canterbury bypassing Dover. Through lights, 3 miles after approach Whitfield. Just before roundabout left into Singledge Lane, round the corner into hotel entrance.
Map ref: Whitfield 5 F3
See advert on opposite page

Wallett's Court Country House Hotel & Spa

★★★ 🍴🍴🍴   Commended

Westcliffe, St Margaret's Bay, Dover, Kent, CT15 6EW
Tel: 01304 852424 Fax: 01304 853430
Email: wc@wallettscourt.com
Web: www.wallettscourt.com
Seasonal closure: 24-26 December

Set in the heart of White Cliffs Country, this 17th-Century hotel with highly acclaimed restaurant and spa is simply beautiful. Relaxed and secluded, yet only 3 miles from Dover.
Rooms: 17 all ensuite
Pricing: Sgl £99–119 Dbl £119–159
Dinner available from £35
CC: Accepted
Room facilities:
Conference: 3 meeting rooms (Thtr 30 max), 24hr-delegate from £161, day-delegate from £32.50
Children: Welcome
Licenses:
Leisure: Indoor pool, Gym, Health spa, Beauty salon,

Tennis, Sauna, Steamroom, Croquet lawn, Boules court
Parking: Off-street and free
Directions: From M2/A2 or M20/A20, signs A258 Deal. On A258, first right for Westcliffe, St. Margaret's-at-Cliffe. Hotel 1 mile on right.
Map ref: St Margaret's Bay 5 F3

East Lee (non smoking) Guest House

♦♦♦♦

108 Maison Dieu Road, Dover, Kent, CT16 1RT
Tel: 01304 210176 Fax: 01304 206705
Email: elgh@eclipse.co.uk
Web: www.eastlee.co.uk
Rooms: 4 all ensuite
Pricing: Dbl £50–58
CC: Accepted
Room facilities:
Children: Welcome
Parking: Off-street and free
Directions: Approaching from M20/A20, at York Street roundabout, turn left and proceed straight over next roundabout. Turn right at Dover town hall. At end of street, turn right into Maison Dieu Road.
Map ref: Dover 5 F3

Hubert House Guest and Coffee House

♦♦♦♦

9 Castle Hill Road, Dover, Kent, CT16 1QW
Tel: 01304 202253 Fax: 01304 210142
Email: huberthouse@btinternet.com
Web: www.huberthouse.co.uk
Seasonal closure: January
Rooms: 8 all ensuite
Pricing: Sgl £30–40 Dbl £45–50
Dinner available CC: Accepted
Room facilities:
Children: Welcome
Dogs: Welcome
Licenses:
Parking: Off-street and free
Directions: Situated on the A258 Deal road at the bottom of Castle Hill, close to Dover town centre.
Map ref: Dover 5 F3

Number One Guest House

♦♦♦♦

1 Castle Street, Dover, Kent, CT16 1QH
Tel: 01304 202007 Fax: 01304 214078
Email: res@number1guesthouse.co.uk
Web: www.number1guesthouse.co.uk
Rooms: 3 all ensuite
Pricing: Sgl £30–35 Dbl £46–56
Room facilities:
Children: Welcome
Parking: Off-street
Directions: Just off A20 turn right to castle on corner before Castle Hill. A2 1 mile, 2 minutes from port, 10 minutes from tunnel.
Map ref: Dover 5 F3

Southeast

Pennyfarthing Guest House

◆◆◆◆

109 Maison Dieu Road, Dover, Kent, CT16 1RT
Tel: 01304 205563 Fax: 01304 204439
Email: pennyfarthing.dover@btinternet.com
Web: www.pennyfarthingdover.com
Rooms: 6 (5 ensuite)
Pricing: Sgl £25–27 Dbl £38–42
Room facilities: Children: Welcome
Parking: Off-street and free
Directions: From M20/A20 left at York Street roundabout, proceed straight over next roundabout. Turn first right to end, turn right at lights into Maison Dieu.
Map ref: Dover 5 F3

Sandown

◆◆◆◆

229 Folkestone Road, Dover, Kent, CT7 9SL
Tel: 01304 226807/07769 944434
Email: sandhams@sandown229.wanadoo.co.uk
Rooms: 3 (1 ensuite)
Pricing: Sgl £30 Dbl £40–45
Room facilities:
Children: Welcome
Parking: Off-street and free
Directions: M20, A20, B2011, 2³/₄ miles on right. M2, A2, A20, Eastern Docks, left at roundabout, right at next roundabout, left Folkestone Road (B2011).
Map ref: Dover 5 F3

Tower House

◆◆◆◆

Priory Hill, Dover, Kent, CT17 0AE
Tel: 01304 208212 Fax: 01304 208212
Email: enquiries@towerhouse.net
Web: www.towerhouse.net
Rooms: 2 all ensuite
Pricing: Dbl £46–56
Room facilities:
Children: Welcome
Parking: Off-street
Directions: M20-B2011 to Dover; turn left at roundabout, then third turning left at main traffic lights to top of Priory Hill.
Map ref: Dover 5 F3

Ardmore Private Hotel

◆◆◆

18 Castle Hill Road, Dover, Kent, CT16 1QW
Tel: 01304 205895 Fax: 01304 208229
Email: res@ardmoreph.co.uk
Web: www.ardmoreph.co.uk
Seasonal closure: Christmas
Rooms: 4 all ensuite
Pricing: Dbl £45–60 CC: Accepted
Room facilities: Children: Welcome
Directions: On A258 next to Dover Castle. Follow signs for castle from all roads to Dover. 10 minutes to Channel Tunnel, close to ports.
Map ref: Dover 5 F3

St Martins Guest House

◆◆◆

17 Castle Hill Road, Dover, Kent, CT16 1QW
Tel: 01304 205938 Fax: 01304 208229
Email: res@stmartinsgh.co.uk
Web: www.stmartinsgh.co.uk
Seasonal closure: Christmas
Rooms: 6 all ensuite
Pricing: Sgl £30–35 Dbl £40–52 CC: Accepted
Room facilities:
Children: Welcome
Directions: On the A258. Follow signs to Dover Castle from all roads to Dover. 10 minutes from Channel Tunnel, minutes from ports.
Map ref: Dover 5 F3

Dymchurch, Kent

Waterside Guest House

◆◆◆◆

15 Hythe Road, Dymchurch, Kent, TN29 0LN
Tel: 01303 872253 Fax: 01303 872253
Email: info@watersideguesthouse.co.uk
Web: www.watersideguesthouse.co.uk

Offering the peacefulness of the countryside along with the fun of the seaside, Waterside is an ideal base for exploring Kent and Sussex. Comfortable accommodation, good food and relaxed atmosphere.
Rooms: 5 all ensuite
Pricing: Sgl £32–55 Dbl £45–55
Dinner available from £5
CC: Accepted
Room facilities:
Children: Welcome
Licenses: ▮▮▮
Parking: Off-street and free
Directions: From M20 take Junction 11. Follow signs to Hythe. Turn right onto A259. Guest House approximately 7 miles on right-hand side.
Map ref: Dymchurch 5 E3

"Stay!"

Need a pet friendly property? Look out for 'Dogs welcome' in our listings.

East Grinstead, West Sussex

Gravetye Manor Hotel
★★★★ 🐾🐾🐾

Vowels Lane, near East Grinstead,
West Sussex, RH19 4LJ
Tel: 01342 810567 Fax: 01342 810080
Email: info@gravetyemanor.co.uk
Web: www.gravetyemanor.co.uk

Gravetye Manor is an ivy-clad Elizabethan house in
William Robinson's famous garden and 1,000 acres of
Forestry Commision land. Located 30 miles from Hyde
Park.
Rooms: 18 all ensuite 🖼
Pricing: Sgl £90–160 Dbl £150–325
Dinner available from £35–56
CC: Accepted
Room facilities: ☐ ☎ 📠
Conference: 1 meeting room (Thtr 12 max),
24hr-delegate from £235, day-delegate from £60
Children: Welcome 7yrs min age ⌨
Licenses: ⚖ ⛉
Leisure: Fishing, Croquet
Parking: Off-street and free
Directions: Leave M23 at Exit 10, and take A264
towards East Grinstead. After 2 miles, at roundabout,
take third exit (B2028) towards Turners Hill. Only 20
minutes from Gatwick Airport.
Map ref: East Grinstead 5 D3

Are the bells ringing?

Getting married? Congratulations!
Look for the wedding bells symbol
which shows hotels licensed for
civil ceremonies.

Eastbourne, East Sussex

The Grand Hotel
★★★★★ 🐾🐾🐾 Excellent

King Edward's Parade,
Eastbourne, East Sussex, BN21 4EQ
Tel: 01323 412345 Fax: 01323 412233
Email: reservations@grandeastbourne.com
Web: www.grandeastbourne.com

COUNTRY HOTELS OF DISTINCTION

England's finest resort hotel, The Grand Hotel in
Eastbourne reflects the glories of Victorian
architecture. Recently restored, this magnificent hotel
offers award-winning cuisine, health club and
conscientious, friendly service.
Rooms: 152 all ensuite 🐾 🖼 ⊘
Pricing: Sgl £135–335 Dbl £165–365
Dinner available from £35
CC: Accepted
Room facilities: ☐ ☎ ☕ 📠
Access: ♿
Conference: 17 meeting rooms (Thtr 300 max),
24hr-delegate from £245, day-delegate from £65
Children: Welcome ⋔ 🛏 ⌨
Dogs: Welcome
Licenses: ⚖ ⛉
Leisure: Indoor pool, Outdoor pool, Gym, Health spa,
Beauty salon, Snooker/billiards
Parking: Off-street and free
Directions: Located at west end of Eastbourne
seafront.
Map ref: Eastbourne 5 D4

"Here!"

Need a pet friendly
property? Look out for
'Dogs welcome' in our
listings.

Hydro Hotel

★★★

Mount Road, Eastbourne, East Sussex, BN20 7HZ
Tel: 01323 720643 Fax: 01323 641167
Email: rac@hydrohotel.com
Web: www.hydrohotel.com

An elegant traditional hotel offering the highest standards of cuisine and service. Situated in a unique cliff top garden setting with panoramic sea views.
Rooms: 84 (83 ensuite)
Pricing: Sgl £48–76 Dbl £96–152
Dinner available from £23 CC: Accepted
Room facilities: Access: |↥↧
Conference: 4 meeting rooms (Thtr 175 max)
Children: Welcome Dogs: Welcome
Licenses: Leisure: Outdoor pool, Gym, Beauty salon Parking: Off-street and free
Directions: Proceed along King Edward's Parade to the Grand Hotel. Note sign Hydro Hotel. Proceed up South Cliff and the Hydro Hotel signs are visible.
Map ref: Eastbourne 5 D4

Lansdowne Hotel

★★★

King Edward's Parade, Eastbourne,
East Sussex, BN21 4EE
Tel: 01323 725174 Fax: 01323 739721
Email: reception@lansdowne-hotel.co.uk
Web: www.bw-lansdownehotel.co.uk
Seasonal closure: New Year and Easter
Rooms: 101 all ensuite
Dinner available CC: Accepted
Room facilities:
Access: |↥↧
Conference: 6 meeting rooms (Thtr 120 max)
Children: Welcome
Dogs: Welcome
Licenses:
Leisure: Games room, Snooker/billiards
Parking: Off-street
Directions: M23, A23, A27, A22 or A259 to Eastbourne. Hotel at west end of seafront (B2103) facing Western Lawns.
Map ref: Eastbourne 5 D4

Congress Hotel

★★

31–41 Carlisle Road, Eastbourne,
East Sussex, BN21 4JS
Tel: 01323 732118 Fax: 01323 720016
Web: www.congresshotel.co.uk
Seasonal closure: January to February
Rooms: 62 all ensuite
Pricing: Sgl £32–43 Dbl £64–86
Dinner available from £14
CC: Accepted
Room facilities:
Access: |↥↧
Conference: 1 meeting room (Thtr 70 max)
Children: Welcome
Dogs: Welcome
Licenses:
Leisure: Games room, Snooker/billiards
Parking: Off-street and free
Directions: Opposite Congress Theatre, approx 150 yards from the seafront. Follow signs for 'Theatres'.
Map ref: Eastbourne 5 D4

New Wilmington Hotel

★★

25 Compton Street, Eastbourne,
East Sussex, BN21 4DU
Tel: 01323 721219 Fax: 01323 745255
Email: info@new-wilmington-hotel.co.uk
Web: www.new-wilmington-hotel.co.uk
Seasonal closure: 3 January to 18 February
Rooms: 40 all ensuite
Pricing: Sgl £39.25–46.50 Dbl £68.50–81
Dinner available from £15
CC: Accepted
Room facilities:
Access: |↥↧
Children: Welcome
Licenses:
Directions: Follow signs to sea front, keeping sea on left. At Wilmington Gardens turn right. At end of road turn left.
Map ref: Eastbourne 5 D4

Southeast

Oban

King Edward's Parade, Eastbourne,
East Sussex, BN21 4DS
Tel: 01323 731581 Fax: 01323 721994
Web: www.oban-hotel.co.uk
Seasonal closure: January to February
Rooms: 31 all ensuite
Pricing: Dinner available from £15
CC: Accepted
Room facilities:
Access:
Children: Welcome
Dogs: Welcome
Licenses:
Directions: Go direct to sea front then find hotel
opposite the Wish Tower on the Green.
Map ref: Eastbourne 5 D4

West Rocks Hotel

44-46 Grand Parade, Eastbourne,
East Sussex, BN21 4DL
Tel: 01323 725217 Fax: 01323 720421
Email: westrockshotel@tiscali.co.uk
Web: www.westrockshotel.co.uk
Seasonal closure: January to February
Rooms: 47 (45 ensuite)
Pricing: Dinner available from £15
CC: Accepted
Room facilities:
Access:
Conference: 1 meeting room (Thtr 36 max),
24hr-delegate from £90, day-delegate from £32
Children: Welcome 3yrs min age
Licenses:
Directions: On seafront between the bandstand and
the Wish Tower, 600 yards west from the pier.
Map ref: Eastbourne 5 D4

Gladwyn Hotel

16 Blackwater Road, Eastbourne,
East Sussex, BN21 4JD
Tel: 01323 733142
Email: gladwynhotel@aol.com
Web: www.gladwynhotel.com
Rooms: 10 (8 ensuite)
Pricing: Sgl £26-28 Dbl £52-56
CC: Accepted
Room facilities:
Children: Welcome
Dogs: Welcome
Licenses:
Parking: Off-street and free
Directions: Follow signs to Devonshire Park and
proceed down Hardwick Road to junction with
Blackwater Road. Hotel overlooks Devonshire Park.
Map ref: Eastbourne 5 D4

Sheldon Hotel

9-11 Burlington Place, Eastbourne,
East Sussex, BN21 4AS
Tel: 01323 724120 Fax: 01323 430406
Email: sheldonhotel@tiscali.co.uk
Web: www.thesheldonhotel.co.uk

The Sheldon Hotel is centrally located, 100m from
Eastbourne's prestigious seafront. Walking distance to
all amenities, theatres, conference centre, bathing
beach, restaurants and shopping centre. Hotel's own
large car park.
Rooms: 28 all ensuite
Pricing: Sgl £28-36 Dbl £56-76
Dinner available from £12
CC: Accepted
Room facilities:
Access:
Children: Welcome
Licenses:
Parking: Off-street and free
Directions: Hotel is fifth turning right after the pier,
travelling west. Sheldon Hotel is 150m on left.
Map ref: Eastbourne 5 D4

Sherwood Hotel

7 Lascelles Terrace, Eastbourne,
East Sussex, BN21 4BJ
Tel: 01323 724002
Email: sherwood-hotel@supanet.com
Web: www.sherwood-hotel-eastbourne.co.uk
Rooms: 13 all ensuite
Pricing: Sgl £25-32 Dbl £50-64
Dinner available from £10
CC: Accepted
Room facilities:
Children: Welcome
Dogs: Welcome
Licenses:
Directions: Follow directions to seafront, theatres or
town west. Lascelles Terrace runs between Devonshire
Park and seafront.
Map ref: Eastbourne 5 D4

The Atlanta Hotel

10 Royal Parade, Eastbourne, East Sussex, BN22 7AR
Tel: 01323 730486 Fax: 01323 723228
Email: enquiries@hotelatlanta.co.uk
Web: www.hotelatlanta.co.uk
Rooms: 9 all ensuite
Pricing: Sgl £25–31 Dbl £44–62
Dinner available from £10
CC: Accepted
Room facilities:
Children: Welcome
Licenses:
Directions: The hotel is located on the seafront 350 metres east of the pier between the Glastonbury and Waterfront hotels.
Map ref: Eastbourne 5 D4

Egham, Surrey

Runnymede Hotel & Spa

Windsor Road, Egham, Surrey, TW20 0AG
Tel: 01784 436171 Fax: 01784 436340
Email: info@runnymedehotel.com
Web: www.runnymedehotel.com
Rooms: 180 all ensuite
CC: Accepted
Room facilities:
Access:
Conference: 12 meeting rooms (Thtr 170 max)
Children: Welcome
Licenses:
Leisure: Indoor pool, Gym, Health spa, Beauty salon, Tennis, Snooker/billiards
Parking: Off-street
Directions: Leave M25 at Junction 13. Take A308 to Egham/Windsor. The Runnymede is on the right at the entrance to Runnymede Meadows.
Map ref: Egham 4 C2

Emsworth, Hampshire

Jingles Hotel

77 Horndean Road, Emsworth, Hampshire, PO10 7PU
Tel: 01243 373755 Fax: 01243 375426
Web: www.jingleshotel.co.uk
Rooms: 15 all ensuite
Pricing: Sgl £44.50–59.50 Dbl £69–89
CC: Accepted
Room facilities:
Children: Welcome
Licenses:
Leisure: Gym, Beauty salon
Parking: Off-street and free
Directions: From A259 in Emsworth, head north on the B2148 towards Rowlands Castle for approximately 1 mile.
Map ref: Emsworth 4 C3

Enfield, Middlesex

Royal Chace Hotel

The Ridgeway, Enfield, Middlesex, EN2 8AR
Tel: 020 8884 8181 Fax: 020 8884 8150
Email: reservations@royalchacehotel.co.uk
Web: www.royal-chace.com
Seasonal closure: Christmas Day, Boxing Day & New Years Day

With over 25 years experience of wedding receptions, The Royal Chace Hotel has gained a reputation for its range of function rooms including the splendid Pavilion set in the glorious grounds. A number of bridal suites are also available with four-poster beds, flowers and champagne to bring the day to a perfect end.
Rooms: 92 all ensuite
Pricing: Sgl £99 Dbl £115
Dinner available from £16 CC: Accepted
Room facilities:
Conference: 10 meeting rooms (Thtr 250 max), 24hr-delegate from £155, day-delegate from £55
Children: Welcome   Dogs: Assistance dogs only
Licenses: Leisure: Outdoor pool
Parking: Off-street and free
Directions: Leave M25 at Junction 24. Take A1005 towards Enfield. The Royal Chace Hotel is situated 3 miles along on right-hand side.
Map ref: Enfield 5 D2

The Enfield Hotel

52 Rowantree Road, Enfield, Middlesex, EN2 8PW
Tel: 020 8366 3511 Fax: 020 8366 2432
Email: admin@enfieldhotel.com
Web: www.enfieldhotel.com
Rooms: 34 all ensuite
Pricing: Sgl £45–85 Dbl £65–95
Dinner available from £12.50 CC: Accepted
Room facilities:
Conference: 2 meeting rooms (Thtr 75 max), 24hr-delegate from £110, day-delegate from £27
Children: Welcome
Licenses:
Parking: Off-street and free
Directions: M25 J24, A1005 pass hospital on left, straight across mini roundabout then take 3rd left into Bycullah Road then 2nd left into Rowantree Road.
Map ref: Enfield 5 D2

Fareham, Hampshire

Solent Hotel and Spa
★★★★

Rookery Way, Whiteley, Fareham, Hampshire, PO15 7AJ
Tel: 01489 880000 Fax: 01489 880007
Email: solent@shirehotels.com
Web: www.shirehotels.com

SHIRE
HOTELS

A haven of peace and quiet, Solent Hotel indulges in rest and relaxation. Cherry wood panelling, terracotta tiles and deep pile rugs create a warm and homely feeling. With 17 meeting rooms the Solent Hotel is also well equipped to host your training course or sales conference. Spa treatments from spring 2006.
Rooms: 111 all ensuite
Pricing: Sgl £88–150 Dbl £126–170
Dinner available from £28.50 CC: Accepted
Room facilities: ☐ ☎ ☺ ✎ ❄ Access: ⇑
Conference: 17 meeting rooms (Thtr 200 max),
24hr-delegate from £170, day-delegate from £59
Children: Welcome ⅙ Licenses: ⬥ ⅲ
Leisure: Indoor pool, Gym, Tennis, Activity studio
Parking: Off-street and free
Directions: Leave M27 at Junction 9 to Whiteley. Turn left at first roundabout. Hotel on your right.
Map ref: Whiteley 4 B3

TravelRest – Avenue House Hotel
♦♦♦

22 The Avenue, Fareham, Hampshire, PO14 1NS
Tel: 01329 232175 Fax: 01329 232196
Web: www.travelrest.co.uk
Rooms: 19 all ensuite
Pricing: Sgl £50–60 Dbl £50–70 CC: Accepted
Room facilities: ☐ ☎ ☺ ✎
Conference: 1 meeting room (Thtr 30 max),
24hr-delegate from £75, day-delegate from £12.50
Children: Welcome Dogs: Welcome
Parking: Off-street and free
Directions: M27 Junction 9 (signposted Fareham West), A27 to Fareham. After 2 miles Fareham College on right, hotel 300 yards on left.
Map ref: Fareham 4 B3

Farnborough, Hampshire

Falcon Hotel
★★★

68 Farnborough Road, Farnborough,
Hampshire, GU14 6TH
Tel: 01252 545378 Fax: 01252 522539
Email: hotel@falconfarnborough.com
Web: www.falconfarnborough.com
Rooms: 30 all ensuite
Pricing: Sgl £55–105 Dbl £65–110
Dinner available from £13.50–250
CC: Accepted
Room facilities: ☐ ☎ ☺ ✎
Conference: 1 meeting room (Thtr 25 max),
24hr-delegate from £125, day-delegate from £35
Children: Welcome ⅙ ✶
Licenses: ⬥ ⅲ Parking: Off-street and free
Directions: On A3225 Aldershot side of Farnborough town centre at the junction of aircraft Esplanade and Farnborough Road.
Map ref: Farnborough 4 C2

Amber Lodge
♦♦♦

101 Victoria Road, Farnborough,
Hampshire, GU14 7PP
Tel: 01252 371889 Fax: 01252 541880
Web: www.amberlodge.net
Rooms: 9 (7 ensuite) ☺
Pricing: Sgl £30–45 Dbl £50–65
CC: Accepted
Room facilities: ☐ ☺
Children: Welcome 3yrs min age
Parking: Off-street and free
Directions: M3 J4, A331 Farnborough. A325 Farnborough/Hawley, B3014 Victoria Road Cove/town centre. Over three mini-roundabouts. Lodge 50 yards on right.
Map ref: Farnborough 4 C2

Farnham, Surrey

Bishop's Table Hotel
★★★★

27 West Street, Farnham, Surrey, GU9 7DR
Tel: 01252 710222 Fax: 01252 733494
Email: welcome@bishopstable.com
Web: www.bishopstable.com
Seasonal closure: 23 December to 6 January
Rooms: 17 all ensuite
Pricing: Sgl £107.50–117.50 Dbl £117.50–140
Dinner available from £24–40 CC: Accepted
Room facilities: ☐ ☎ ☺ ✎
Conference: 2 meeting rooms (Thtr 20 max),
24hr-delegate from £180, day-delegate from £45
Licenses: ⅲ
Directions: Take M3 Junction 4, follow 'Birdworld' signs and Farnham town centre signs. Located next door to library.
Map ref: Farnham 4 C3

Beech Cottage

The Avenue, Rowledge, Farnham, Surrey, GU10 4BD
Tel: 01252 795383
Map ref: Rowledge 4 C3

Fleet, Hampshire

Lismoyne Hotel

Church Road, Fleet, Hampshire, GU51 4NE
Tel: 01252 788585 Fax: 01252 811761
Email: sales@lismoynehotel.com
Web: www.lismoynehotel.com
Rooms: 62 all ensuite 🛏 🖫 ⊗
CC: Accepted
Room facilities: 💻 ☎ 🖥 🕾
Conference: 4 meeting rooms (Thtr 170 max)
Children: Welcome ⅓ Licenses: ⚓ 🚻
Leisure: Gym
Parking: Off-street
Directions: Leaving M3 at J4a, take the A3013 and
follow the signs for Fleet. Once over the railway bridge
continue on the A3013 for approx ³/₄ mile before
turning right into Church Road. The hotel is ¼ mile
down on the left, just past the church.
Map ref: Fleet 4 C3

Forest Row, East Sussex

Ashdown Park Hotel & Country Club

★★★★★ 🏵🏵
Premier
Wych Cross, Forest Row,
East Sussex, RH18 5JR
Tel: 01342 824988 Fax: 01342 826206
Email: reservations@ashdownpark.com
Web: www.ashdownpark.com

COUNTRY HOTELS OF DISTINCTION

A stunning 186-acre country house hotel, Ashdown
Park offers log fires, gourmet cuisine, fine wines,
panoramic views, golf, beautiful bedrooms and a
luxurious country club. Ideal for relaxation and pure
indulgence.

Rooms: 106 all ensuite 🖫 ⊗
Pricing: Sgl £135–335 Dbl £165–365
Dinner available from £35 CC: Accepted
Room facilities: 💻 ☎ 🕾 Access: 🔒
Conference: 16 meeting rooms (Thtr 160 max),
24hr-delegate from £235, day-delegate from £72
Children: Welcome ⅓ ❋
Licenses: ⚓ 🚻
Leisure: Indoor pool, Gym, Health spa, Beauty salon,
Tennis, Golf, Games room, Snooker/billiards
Parking: Off-street and free
Directions: M23 J10. A264 to East Grinstead, A22 to
Eastbourne through Forest Row on A22 for 2 miles. At
Wych Cross turn left to Hartfield. Ashdown Park is ³/₄
mile on the right.
Map ref: Wych Cross 5 D3

Frimley Green, Surrey

Lakeside International Hotel

★★★
Wharf Road, Frimley Green, Surrey, GU16 6JR
Tel: 01252 838000 Fax: 01252 837857
Email: international@lakesidecomplex.com
Web: www.lakesidecomplex.com
Rooms: 98 all ensuite 🛏 ⊗
Pricing: Dinner available from £19 CC: Accepted
Room facilities: 💻 ☎ 🕾 🕾 Access: 🔒
Conference: 5 meeting rooms (Thtr 130 max),
24hr-delegate from £165, day-delegate from £45
Children: Welcome ⅓
Licenses: ⚓ 🚻
Leisure: Indoor pool, Gym, Health spa, Games room,
Snooker/billiards
Parking: Off-street and free
Directions: Leave M3 at Junction 4. Follow signs for
Frimley. Take Church Road for 5 minutes, turn left into
Wharf Road.
Map ref: Frimley Green 4 C2

Gatwick Airport

Copthorne Hotel London Gatwick

★★★★ 🏵🏵
Copthorne Way, Copthorne, West Sussex, RH10 3PG
Tel: 01342 348888 Fax: 01342 348866
Email: sales.gatwick@mill-cop.com
Web: www.copthornehotels.com

Traditional, welcoming country house hotel built around a 16th century farmhouse in 100 acres of gardens. Ideal for many local attractions. Weekend break rates also available.
Rooms: 227 all ensuite 🛏 Ⓢ
Pricing: Sgl £77–190.75 Dbl £87–206.50
Dinner available from £20.50
CC: Accepted
Room facilities: 🖵 ☎ 🕭 📠
Access: |↓↑
Conference: 15 meeting rooms (Thtr 150 max), 24hr-delegate from £175, day-delegate from £55
Children: Welcome 🍴 🍼
Dogs: Welcome
Licenses: 🍷 ♟
Leisure: Indoor pool, Gym, Health spa, Beauty salon, Tennis, Games room
Parking: Off-street
Directions: Leave M23 at Junction 10, taking A264 towards East Grinstead. At first roundabout, take third exit which is the hotel entrance.
Map ref: Copthorne 5 D3

Copthorne Hotel & Resort Effingham Park
★★★★★ ®®
West Park Road, Copthorne, West Sussex, RH10 3EU
Tel: 01342 714994 Fax: 01342 716039
Email: sales.effingham@mill-cop.com
Web: www.copthornehotels.com

Former stately home set in 40 acres of peaceful parkland. Superb leisure facilities including a nine-hole golf course. Close to many local attractions. Weekend break rates also available.
Rooms: 122 all ensuite 🐾 🛏 Ⓢ
Pricing: Sgl £79–145 Dbl £79–145
Dinner available from £25
CC: Accepted
Room facilities: 🖵 ☎ 🕭 📠

Access: |↓↑
Conference: 12 meeting rooms (Thtr 600 max), 24hr-delegate from £175, day-delegate from £75
Children: Welcome 🍴
Licenses: 🍷 ♟
Leisure: Indoor pool, Gym, Beauty salon, Tennis, Golf
Parking: Off-street and free
Directions: Leave M23 at Junction 10, taking A264 towards East Grinstead. At second roundabout, turn left onto B2028. Hotel is on the right.
Map ref: Copthorne 5 D3

Alexander House Hotel
★★★ ®®® Premier
Turners Hill, West Sussex, RH10 4QD
Tel: 01342 714914 Fax: 01342 717328
Email: info@alexanderhouse.co.uk
Web: www.alexanderhouse.co.uk

Beautiful 17th century mansion. 18 luxury ensuite rooms including four-poster suites. Set amidst 175 acres of mature gardens and parkland. Excellent Anglo French cuisine together with impeccable service guarantees a memorable stay.
Rooms: 18 all ensuite 🛏 Ⓢ
Pricing: Sgl £140–385 Dbl £185–400
Dinner available from £39.50–49.50
CC: Accepted
Room facilities: 🖵 ☎ 📠
Access: |↓↑
Conference: 6 meeting rooms (Thtr 100 max), 24hr-delegate from £252, day-delegate from £77
Licenses: 🍷 ♟
Leisure: Indoor pool, Outdoor pool, Health spa, Beauty salon, Tennis, Croquet
Parking: Off-street and free
Directions: At Turners Hill Village take the B2110 to East Grinstead. Alexander House is approx 1½ miles on the left.
Map ref: Turners Hill 5 D3

Southeast

Langshott Manor

★★★ 🇷 🇷 🇷

Langshott, Horley, near Gatwick, Surrey, RH6 9LN
Tel: 01293 786680 Fax: 01293 783905
Email: admin@langshottmanor.com
Web: www.langshottmanor.com

'Europe's most civilised airport hotel' 2 miles from Gatwick Airport. An Elizabethan manor house providing the best in hospitality and cuisine, yet with the most modern services.
Rooms: 22 all ensuite 🗲 ⊗
Pricing: Sgl £150–210 Dbl £190–330
Dinner available from £39 CC: Accepted
Room facilities: ▢ ☎ ⟍
Conference: 3 meeting rooms (Thtr 30 max), 24hr-delegate from £200, day-delegate from £60

Children: Welcome 🍼
Licenses: 🔔 ♨ Leisure: Croquet
Parking: Off-street
Directions: From Horley, take A23 towards Redhill. At roundabout with Shell petrol station, take third exit into Ladbroke Road. Langshott is ³/₄ mile on right.
Map ref: Langshott 5 D3

Stanhill Court Hotel

★★★★ 🇷 🇷 🇷 Commended

Stanhill, Charlwood, Surrey, RH6 0EP
Tel: 01293 862166 Fax: 01293 862773
Email: enquiries@stanhillcourthotel.co.uk
Web: www.stanhillcourthotel.co.uk
Rooms: 15 all ensuite 🗲 ⊗
Pricing: Dinner available from £28
CC: Accepted
Room facilities: ▢ ☎ 🗲
Conference: 7 meeting rooms (Thtr 240 max), 24hr-delegate from £145, day-delegate from £45
Children: Welcome 🍼
Licenses: 🔔 ♨
Leisure: Fishing
Parking: Off-street and free
Directions: M25/J8 6 miles or M25/J7, M23/J9 Gatwick Airport then A23 north signposted at roundabout. Through village, follow brown signs.
Map ref: Charlwood 5 D3
See advert on this page

The Lawn Guest House

30 Massets Road, Gatwick, Horley, Surrey, RH6 7DF
Tel: 01293 775751 Fax: 01293 821803
Email: info@lawnguesthouse.co.uk
Web: www.lawnguesthouse.co.uk

Luxury Victorian house set in a mature garden, five minutes to Gatwick, two minutes to the centre of Horley, and close to mainline rail station. Holiday parking. No smoking.
Rooms: 12 all ensuite
Pricing: Sgl £45–50 Dbl £58 CC: Accepted
Room facilities: Children: Welcome
Dogs: Welcome Parking: Off-street and free
Directions: Exit M23 Junction 9. Follow A23 Redhill. Esso station 3rd exit. 300 yards right Massetts Road. Lawn 550 yards on left.
Map ref: Horley 5 D3

Waterhall Country House

Prestwood Lane, Ifield Wood, Gatwick, Near Crawley, West Sussex, RH11 0LA
Tel: 01293 520002 Fax: 01293 539905
Email: info@waterhallcountryhouse.co.uk
Web: www.waterhallcountryhouse.co.uk
Rooms: 10 all ensuite
Pricing: Sgl £40–50 Dbl £55–75
Dinner available from £7.95 CC: Accepted
Room facilities:
Children: Welcome 12yrs min age Licenses:
Parking: Off-street and free
Directions: Exit J10 M23, A2011 Crawley Avenue. Right at third roundabout into Ifield Avenue. Continue for 2 miles, Prestwood Lane on left.
Map ref: Ifield Wood 5 D3

Gerrards Cross, Buckinghamshire

The Bull Hotel

★★★

Oxford Road, Gerrards Cross,
Buckinghamshire, SL9 7PA
Tel: 01753 885995 Fax: 01753 885504
Email: bull@sarova.co.uk
Web: www.sarova.com

Rooms: 123 all ensuite
Pricing: Sgl £89–210 Dbl £89–210
Dinner available from £15–30 CC: Accepted
Room facilities: Access:
Conference: 10 meeting rooms (Thtr 180 max), 24hr-delegate from £180, day-delegate from £65
Children: Welcome
Dogs: Assistance dogs only
Licenses:
Leisure: Gardens
Parking: Off-street and free
Directions: Leave M40 J2 and follow signs to Gerrards Cross.
Map ref: Gerrards Cross 4 C2

Great Milton, Oxfordshire

Le Manoir Aux Quat'Saisons

★★★★

Premier

Church Road, Great Milton,
Oxford, Oxfordshire, OX44 7PD
Tel: 01844 278881 Fax: 01844 278847
Email: lemanoir@blanc.co.uk
Web: www.manoir.com
Rooms: 32 all ensuite
Pricing: Sgl £275–895 Dbl £275–895
Dinner available from £95 CC: Accepted
Room facilities:
Conference: 1 meeting room (Thtr 30 max)
Children: Welcome Dogs: Welcome
Licenses:
Parking: Off-street and free
Directions: From London, leave M40 at Junction 7. Turn towards Wallingford. Le Manoir is signposted on the right 2 miles further on.
Map ref: Oxford 4 B1

Harrow, Middlesex

Grim's Dyke

★★★★

Old Redding, Harrow Weald, Middlesex, HA3 6SH
Tel: 020 8385 3100 Fax: 020 8954 4560
Email: reservations@grimsdyke.com
Web: www.grimsdyke.com
Seasonal closure: 24-30 December
Rooms: 46 all ensuite
Pricing: Sgl £95–125 Dbl £105–152
Dinner available from £20 CC: Accepted
Room facilities:
Conference: 4 meeting rooms (Thtr 90 max), 24hr-delegate from £160, day-delegate from £51
Children: Welcome
Dogs: Welcome
Licenses:
Parking: Off-street and free
Directions: From north, leave M1 at Junction 5. Take A41 towards A409 Harrow. After garden centre on right, turn right. Hotel is 300 yards on right.
Map ref: Harrow 4 C2

Southeast

QUALITY HARROW HOTEL

One of the few family owned and run hotels around; so for business or pleasure, a very warm welcome awaits you. In addition to our fine facilities, our new Executive wing offers bedrooms with the finest of features — climate control, wireless broadband access, interactive TV to name but a few.

12/22 PINNER ROAD, HARROW, MIDDLESEX, HA1 4HZ

Tel: 020 8427 3435
Fax: 020 8861 1370

Email: info@harrowhotel.co.uk
Web: www.harrowhotel.co.uk

RaC
★★★
Hotel

RAC
Dining
Award

Quality Harrow Hotel

★★★

12/22 Pinner Road, Harrow, Middlesex, HA1 4HZ
Tel: 020 8427 3435 Fax: 020 8861 1370
Email: info@harrowhotel.co.uk
Web: www.harrowhotel.co.uk
Rooms: 78 all ensuite 🍴 🚭 ⊘
Pricing: Sgl £65–120 Dbl £75–135
Dinner available from £14.95–28.5
CC: Accepted
Room facilities: 🖵 ☎ 🍵 🗝
Access: ⥮
Conference: 6 meeting rooms (Thtr 120 max)
Children: Welcome ⍓ ⍵
Licenses: ⟁ ⍦
Parking: Off-street and free
Directions: Situated at junction of A312 and A404 on the A404, leaving Harrow towards Pinner and Rickmansworth.
Map ref: Harrow 4 C2
See advert on this page

Bogarts Bar and Lindal Hotel

★★

2 Hindes Road, Harrow, Middlesex, HA1 1SJ
Tel: 020 8863 3164 Fax: 020 8427 5435
Email: e.j.egan@amserve.net
Rooms: 24 (22 ensuite) 🍴 ⊘
Dinner available
CC: Accepted

Room facilities: 🖵 ☎ 🗝
Children: Welcome 2yrs min age
Licenses: ⍦ Parking: Off-street and free
Directions: Opposite Tesco/Wickes Harrow, off Station Road, 7 mins walk from Harrow on the Hill tube station or Harrow Wealdstone. Three miles from M1 and M40.
Map ref: Harrow 4 C2

Harwich, Essex

Pier at Harwich

★★★★ 🏆🏆

Commended

The Quay, Harwich, Essex, CO12 3HH
Tel: 01255 241212 Fax: 01255 551922
Email: pier@milsomhotels.com
Web: www.milsomhotels.com

On the quay in Harwich Old Town opposite the Ha'penny Pier. The Harbourside restaurant specialises in seafood and has stunning views over the estuaries, while the Ha'penny is a relaxed and informal brasserie. Fourteen stylish bedrooms, many with fine views over the harbour.
Rooms: 14 all ensuite 🍴
Pricing: Sgl £70–120 Dbl £95–170
Dinner available from £25–35 CC: Accepted
Room facilities: 🖵 ☎ 🍵 🗝
Conference: 1 meeting room (Thtr 50 max), 24hr-delegate from £140, day-delegate from £45
Children: Welcome ⍓ Dogs: Assistance dogs only
Licenses: ⟁ ⍦
Parking: Off-street and free
Directions: From A12, follow A120 down to the quay (18 miles). Hotel opposite lifeboat station.
Map ref: Harwich 9 F4

Cliff Hotel

★★

Marine Parade, Dovercourt, Harwich, Essex, CO12 3RE
Tel: 01255 503345 Fax: 01255 240358
Email: reception@cliffhotelharwich.fsnet.co.uk
Web: www.thecliffhotelharwich.co.uk
Rooms: 26 all ensuite
Pricing: Sgl £60–70 Dbl £70–75
Dinner available from £16.50–200 CC: Accepted
Room facilities:
Conference: 2 meeting rooms (Thtr 200 max),
24hr-delegate from £64.75, day-delegate from £24.75
Children: Welcome
Licenses: Leisure: Games room
Parking: Off-street and free
Directions: Leave A120 at Harwich International. At
roundabout take last exit to Dovercourt, then left at
next mini-roundabout. Take 10th turning on right to
seafront, then right 200 yards along.
Map ref: Dovercourt 5 F1

The Tower Hotel

★★

Main Road, Dovercourt, Harwich, Essex, CO12 3PJ
Tel: 01255 504952 Fax: 01255 504952
Email: reception@tower-hotel-harwich.co.uk
Web: www.tower-hotel-harwich.co.uk
Rooms: 13 all ensuite
Pricing: Sgl £56.50–86.50 Dbl £73–113
Dinner available from £5.95–12.95 CC: Accepted
Room facilities:
Conference: 1 meeting room (Thtr 30 max),
24hr-delegate from £100, day-delegate from £60
Children: Welcome Dogs: Assistance dogs only
Licenses:
Parking: Off-street
Map ref: Dovercourt 5 F1

Haslemere, Surrey

Lythe Hill Hotel & Spa

★★★★★ ♔♔♔

Haslemere, Surrey, GU27 3BQ
Tel: 01428 651251 Fax: 01428 644131
Email: lythe@lythehill.co.uk
Web: www.lythehill.co.uk
Rooms: 41 all ensuite
Pricing: Sgl £160–450 Dbl £160–450
Dinner available from £40 CC: Accepted
Room facilities:
Conference: 8 meeting rooms (Thtr 110 max),
24hr-delegate from £199, day-delegate from £60
Children: Welcome
Dogs: Welcome
Licenses:
Leisure: Indoor pool, Gym, Health spa, Beauty salon,
Tennis, Fishing, Games room
Parking: Off-street and free
Directions: Situated one mile east of Haslemere on
B2131.
Map ref: Haslemere 4 C3

Sheps Hollow

♦♦♦

Henley Common, Haslemere, Surrey, GU27 3HB
Tel: 01428 653120 Fax: 01428 648407
Rooms: 3 all ensuite
Pricing: Sgl £40–50 Dbl £80–100
Dinner available from £10–30
Room facilities:
Conference: 1 meeting room (Thtr 25 max)
Children: Welcome
Dogs: Welcome
Leisure: Riding
Parking: Off-street and free
Directions: Sheps Hollow is situated halfway between
Haslemere and Midhurst on the A286.
Map ref: Henley Common 4 C3

The Wheatsheaf Inn

♦♦♦♦ ♔♔

Grayswood Road, Grayswood, Haslemere,
Surrey, GU27 2DE
Tel: 01428 644440 Fax: 01428 641285
Email: thewheatsheef@aol.com
Rooms: 7 all ensuite
Pricing: Sgl £55 Dbl £75
Dinner available from £6.95–15.95 CC: Accepted
Room facilities:
Children: Welcome
Dogs: Welcome
Licenses:
Parking: Off-street and free
Directions: Leave A3 at junction 10 signed Milford
Haven, follow A286 to Haslemere, hotel is in
Grayswood.
Map ref: Grayswood 4 C3

Hastings, East Sussex

Royal Victoria Hotel

★★★

Marina, St Leonards, Hastings,
East Sussex, TN38 0BD
Tel: 01424 445544 Fax: 01424 721995
Email: reception@royalvichotel.co.uk
Web: www.royalvichotel.co.uk
Rooms: 50 all ensuite
Pricing: Sgl £65–110 Dbl £70–150
Dinner available from £19.50
CC: Accepted
Room facilities:
Access:
Conference: 6 meeting rooms (Thtr 150 max),
24hr-delegate from £105, day-delegate from £35
Children: Welcome
Dogs: Welcome
Licenses:
Parking: Off-street and free
Directions: On the A259 seafront, 1 mile west of
Hastings pier. From M25 follow A21 to Hastings, then
right onto seafront.
Map ref: St Leonards 5 E3

Southeast

Eagle House Hotel

12 Pevensey Road, St Leonards,
East Sussex, TN38 0JZ
Tel: 01424 430535 Fax: 01424 437771
Email: info@eaglehousehotel.co.uk
Web: www.eaglehousehotel.co.uk

Town centre hotel with car park. A Victorian house in
period style. All bedrooms ensuite; restaurant
overlooking walled garden. Near the main London
Road, but in a quiet residential area.
Rooms: 19 all ensuite ⊛
Pricing: Sgl £42 Dbl £61
CC: Accepted
Room facilities: ▭ ☎ ☕
Children: Welcome ♀
Licenses: ♦♦♦
Parking: Off-street
Directions: Follow signs to St Leonards, London Road.
At the church opposite office building Ocean House,
turn sharp right into Pevensey Road.
Map ref: St Leonards 5 E3

Hatfield, Hertfordshire

Quality Hotel Hatfield

★ ★ ★

Roehyde Way, Hatfield, Hertfordshire, AL10 9AF
Tel: 01707 275701 Fax: 01707 266033
Email: enquiries@hotels-hatfield.com
Web: www.choicehotelseurope.com
Rooms: 76 all ensuite ⊛ ⊛
Pricing: Dinner available from £18.95
CC: Accepted
Room facilities: ▭ ☎ ☕ ☏
Conference: 11 meeting rooms (Thtr 120 max),
24hr-delegate from £140, day-delegate from £40
Children: Welcome ♀
Dogs: Welcome
Licenses: ♦♦♦
Parking: Off-street and free
Directions: Exit Junction 3 of A1(M). Follow signs for
University of Hertfordshire. Hotel on Roehyde Way, half
mile from junction roundabout.
Map ref: Hatfield (Hertfordshire) 5 D1

Hayes, Middlesex

Shepiston Lodge (Heathrow)

♦♦♦

31 Shepiston Lane, Hayes, Middlesex, UB3 1LJ
Tel: 020 8573 0266 Fax: 020 8569 2536
Email: shepistonlodge@aol.com
Web: www.shepistonlodge.co.uk
Rooms: 22 all ensuite ⊛
Pricing: Sgl £45–50 Dbl £60–65
Dinner available from £6
CC: Accepted
Room facilities: ▭ ☕
Children: Welcome ♀ ⚞
Licenses: ♦♦♦
Parking: Off-street and free
Directions: Exit J4 M4, follow signs for Hayes. 50 yards
from Comfort Inn and Hayes fire station, in Shepiston
Lane.
Map ref: Hayes 4 C2

Hayling Island, Hampshire

Cockle Warren Cottage

♦♦♦♦ ✕ ⚐

36 Seafront, Hayling Island, Hampshire, PO11 9HL
Tel: 023 9246 4961 Fax: 023 9246 4838
Rooms: 5 all ensuite ⚘ ⊞ ⊛
Pricing: Sgl £40–55 Dbl £60–80
CC: Accepted
Room facilities: ▭ ☕
Children: Welcome
Dogs: Welcome
Licenses: ♦♦♦
Leisure: Outdoor pool
Parking: Off-street and free
Directions: On Hayling Island, follow signs to seafront,
passing through Mengham Village. Take road to the left
signed with brown signposts.
Map ref: Hayling Island 4 C4

Redwalls

♦♦♦

66 Staunton Avenue, Hayling Island,
Hampshire, PO11 0EW
Tel: 023 9246 6109
Email: daphne@redwalls66.freeserve.co.uk
Web: www.redwalls.co.uk
Rooms: 3 all ensuite ⊛
Pricing: Sgl £30–35 Dbl £50
Room facilities: ▭ ☕
Parking: Off-street and free
Directions: Follow main road across island signposted
Beachlands. Turn right into seafront road. Staunton
Avenue is fourth on the right.
Map ref: Hayling Island 4 C4

Turanga House

68 West Lane, Hayling Island, Hampshire, PO11 0JL
Tel: 02392 637002 Fax: 02392 637002
Email: rita@turanga-house.co.uk
Web: www.turanga-house.co.uk
Rooms: 3 (2 ensuite) ✑
Pricing: Sgl £30–40 Dbl £45–65
Dinner available from £15 CC: Accepted
Room facilities: ▢ ◳ ☏
Children: Welcome
Dogs: Assistance dogs only
Parking: Off-street and free
Directions: Please call for directions or local map.
Map ref: Hayling Island 4 C4

Heathrow Airport

Renaissance London Heathrow Hotel

★★★★
Bath Road, Hounslow, Middlesex, TW6 2AQ
Tel: 020 8897 6363 Fax: 020 8897 1113
Email: lhrrenaissance@aol.com
Web: www.renaissancehotels.com/LHRBR

Comfortable and relaxing accommodation, some rooms
with spectacular runway views. Plane Spotter break
available. Other services include: Icarus Lounge Bar,
Business Centre, Hairdressers, Bureau de Change,
Concierge, massage treatments and Gift Shop.
Rooms: 649 all ensuite ⊛
Pricing: Sgl £94–180 Dbl £94–180
Dinner available from £23.50 CC: Accepted
Room facilities: ▢ ☎ ◳ ☏ ❄ Access: |↕↕|
Conference: 28 meeting rooms (Thtr 400 max)
Children: Welcome ⴷ
Licenses: ◁◇ ⅲ Leisure: Gym, Sauna, Steam room
Parking: Off-street
Directions: Exit M4, junction 4. Take the 3rd exit off the
roundabout onto Tunnel Road. Turn left onto east ramp
(just before the airport tunnel). Take 2nd exit off Nene
roundabout.
Map ref: Hounslow 4 C2

Jurys Inn Heathrow

★★★
Eastern Perimeter Road, Hatton Cross, Hounslow,
Heathrow, TW6 2SR
Tel: 020 8266 4664 Fax: 020 8266 4665
Email: bookings@jurysdoyle.com
Web: www.jurysinns.com

Rooms: 364 all ensuite
Pricing: Sgl £125 Dbl £135 Dinner available from £15.95
Room facilities: ▢ ☎ ◳ ☏ ❄
Conference: 12 meeting rooms
Children: Welcome
Dogs: Welcome
Parking: Limited car parking
Directions: Located beside Hatton Cross underground
station on Eastern Perimeter Road.
Map ref: Hatton Cross 4 C2

Osterley Park Hotel

★★★
764 Great West Road, Isleworth, Middlesex, TW7 5NA
Tel: 020 8568 9981 Fax: 020 8569 7819
Email: sales@osterleyparkhotel.co.uk
Web: www.osterleyparkhotel.com
Rooms: 60 all ensuite ⊛
Pricing: Sgl £80–105 Dbl £90–133
Dinner available from £20–40
CC: Accepted
Room facilities: ▢ ☎ ◳
Conference: 4 meeting rooms (Thtr 200 max),
24hr-delegate from £135, day-delegate from £37
Children: Welcome ⴷ Dogs: Assistance dogs only
Licenses: ⅲ
Leisure: Beauty salon
Parking: Off-street and free
Directions: J3 M4; follow signs for A4. Pass Osterley
tube station (Piccadilly line); hotel is 1 mile on left.
Map ref: Isleworth 4 C2

St Giles Hotel

★★★
Hounslow Road, Feltham, Middlesex, TW14 9AD
Tel: 020 8817 7000 Fax: 020 8817 7001
Email: book@stgiles.com
Web: www.stgiles.com
Rooms: 300 all ensuite ✑ ⊛
Pricing: Sgl £55–125 Dbl £65–135
Dinner available from £15–25 CC: Accepted
Room facilities: ▢ ☎ ◳ ☏ ❄ Access: |↕↕|
Conference: 10 meeting rooms (Thtr 150 max),
24hr-delegate from £125, day-delegate from £39
Children: Welcome ⴷ
Licenses: ⅲ Leisure: Gym
Parking: Off-street
Directions: Take A312 to Feltham, then A244 to town
centre. Hotel is visible after 600 yards, opposite the
train station.
Map ref: Heathrow Airport 4 C2

Crompton Guest House

◆◆◆

49 Lampton Road, Hounslow, Middlesex, TW3 1JG
Tel: 020 8570 7090 Fax: 020 8577 1975
Email: cromptonguesthouse@btinternet.com
Web: www.cromptonguesthouse.com

Family run guest house near to Heathrow Airport and 20 minutes to Central London. Short and long-term car parking available whilst on holiday/business. Special long-term rates are available.
Rooms: 11 (10 ensuite) ♨
Pricing: Sgl £55–100 Dbl £65–100
Dinner available from £15
CC: Accepted
Room facilities: ▢ ☎ ☕ ☏
Children: Welcome
Parking: Off-street and free
Directions: 50 yards left of Hounslow Central tube underground station (Piccadilly Line), 10 minutes from Junction 3 off the M4 off A3005.
Map ref: Hounslow 4 C2

Henley-on-Thames, Oxfordshire

Thamesmead House Hotel

◆◆◆◆◆ ✳️ ⚐

Remenham Lane, Henley-on-Thames,
Oxfordshire, RG9 2LR
Tel: 01491 574745 Fax: 01491 579944
Email: thamesmead@supanet.com
Web: www.thamesmeadhousehotel.co.uk
Seasonal closure: Christmas
Rooms: 6 all ensuite CC: Accepted
Room facilities: ▢ ☎ ☕ ☏
Conference: 1 meeting room

Children: Welcome 10yrs min age
Licenses: ♛
Parking: Off-street and free
Directions: From M4, junction 8/9, A404(M) to Burchett's Green. Left on A4130, signed Henley 5 miles, turn right by Little Angel pub, house on left.
Map ref: Henley-on-Thames 4 C2

Hertford, Hertfordshire

Salisbury Arms Hotel

★★★ ♟

Fore Street, Hertford, Hertfordshire, SG14 1BZ
Tel: 01992 583091 Fax: 01992 552510
Email: reception@salisbury-arms-hotel.co.uk
Web: www.salisburyarmshotel.co.uk
Rooms: 31 all ensuite ⊗
Pricing: Sgl £44.50–75 Dbl £84–95
Dinner available CC: Accepted
Room facilities: ▢ ☎ ☕ ☏
Conference: 2 meeting rooms (Thtr 40 max)
Children: Welcome ⫝
Licenses: ♛
Parking: Off-street and free
Directions: Situated in the centre of Hertford, off the A414 on Fore Street.
Map ref: Hertford 5 D1

High Wycombe, Buckinghamshire

Clifton Lodge Hotel

◆◆◆

210 West Wycombe Road, High Wycombe,
Buckinghamshire, HP12 3AR
Tel: 01494 440095 Fax: 01494 536322
Email: mail@cliftonlodgehotel.com
Web: www.cliftonlodgehotel.com

A 32 bedroom family-owned hotel with restaurant and bar. Set in 3/4 acre of garden approximately half way between Wycombe and West Wycombe on the A40.
Rooms: 32 (22 ensuite) ♨ 🖥 ⊗
Pricing: Sgl £40–79 Dbl £65–110
Dinner available from £15 CC: Accepted
Room facilities: ▢ ☎ ☕
Conference: 2 meeting rooms (Thtr 20 max)
Children: Welcome ⫝

Licenses:
Parking: Off-street and free
Directions: Clifton Lodge is situated on the A40 West Wycombe Road, 1 mile from the M40 and the centre of High Wycombe.
Map ref: High Wycombe 4 C2

Hitchin, Hertfordshire

Redcoats Farmhouse Hotel

◆◆◆◆

Redcoats Green, near Hitchin, Hertfordshire, SG4 7JR
Tel: 01438 729500 Fax: 01438 723322
Email: sales@redcoats.co.uk
Web: www.redcoats.co.uk
Rooms: 14 (12 ensuite) 🛏 ⊗
Dinner available CC: Accepted
Room facilities: 📺 ☎ 🍵 🐾
Conference: 2 meeting rooms (Thtr 25 max),
day-delegate from £35
Children: Welcome
Dogs: Welcome
Licenses: 🍷 🍴
Parking: Off-street and free
Directions: Leave A1(M) at Junction 8, follow road to village of Little Wymondley. At end of village turn left at roundabout into Blakemore End Road (to Redcoats Green).
Map ref: Redcoats Green 4 C1

Tudor Oaks Lodge

◆◆◆

Taylors Road, Astwick, near Hitchin, Hertfordshire, SG5 4AZ
Tel: 01462 834133 Fax: 01462 834133
Email: tudoroakslodge@aol.com
Web: www.tudoroakslodge.co.uk

15th-century lodge around secluded courtyard. Ensuite rooms, fresh food daily from bar snacks to à la carte. Real Ales.
Rooms: 13 all ensuite 🚭 ⊗
Pricing: Sgl £49.50–59.50 Dbl £62–72
Dinner available from £10–20
CC: Accepted
Room facilities: 📺 ☎ 🍵
Conference: 2 meeting rooms (Thtr 30 max),

24hr-delegate from £90, day-delegate from £50
Children: Welcome 6yrs min age 🍴
Licenses: 🍴
Parking: Off-street and free
Directions: Conveniently placed by the side of the A1, 1 mile north past Junction 10. Within easy reach of Letchworth, Baldock, Stevenage and Hitchin.
Map ref: Astwick 5 D1

Hook, Hampshire

Tylney Hall Hotel

★★★★ 🚩🚩🚩 Premier

Rotherwick, Hook,
Hampshire, RG27 9AZ
Tel: 01256 764881 Fax: 01256 768141
Email: reservations@tylneyhall.com
Web: www.tylneyhall.com

COUNTRY HOTELS OF DISTINCTION

Set in 66 acres of manicured, historic gardens, Tylney Hall is a perfect location — elegant lounges, stunning views, fine leisure facilities, exquisite bedrooms and a breathtaking setting. A tranquil, romantic country house of distinction.
Rooms: 112 all ensuite 🛏 🚭
Pricing: Sgl £140–440 Dbl £172–472
Dinner available from £36–50
CC: Accepted
Room facilities: 📺 ☎ 🐾
Conference: 12 meeting rooms (Thtr 120 max),
24hr-delegate from £260, day-delegate from £80
Children: Welcome 🍴 ☕
Licenses: 🍷 🍴
Leisure: Indoor pool, Outdoor pool, Gym, Health spa, Beauty salon, Tennis, Snooker/billiards, Croquet, Sauna, Jogging trails
Parking: Off-street and free
Directions: M3 J5, A287 to Basingstoke, over A30 into Old School Road. Left at next T-junction, right at Newnham Green.
Map ref: Rotherwick 4 B2

Hounslow, Middlesex

Best Western Master Robert Hotel

★★★

366 Great West Road, Hounslow, Middlesex, TW5 0BD
Tel: 020 8570 6261 Fax: 020 8569 4016
Email: stay@masterrobert.co.uk
Web: www.masterrobert.co.uk
Rooms: 96 all ensuite
Pricing: Sgl £55–69.50 Dbl £65–79.50
Dinner available from £15–30 CC: Accepted
Room facilities:
Conference: 6 meeting rooms (Thtr 130 max),
24hr-delegate from £125, day-delegate from £35
Children: Welcome
Licenses: Leisure: Games room
Parking: Off-street and free
Directions: Exit M25 J15 onto M4. Exit M4 J3. Third
exit A312. A4 towards London, second traffic lights.
Hotel on left.
Map ref: Hounslow 4 C2

Hove, East Sussex
(see also Brighton)

Courtlands Hotel

★★★

15–27 The Drive, Hove, East Sussex, BN3 3JE
Tel: 01273 731055 Fax: 01273 328295
Email: info@courtlandshotel.com
Web: www.courtlandshotel.com
Rooms: 67 all ensuite
Pricing: Sgl £55–67.50 Dbl £90–130
Dinner available from £19.50 CC: Accepted
Room facilities: Access:
Conference: 3 meeting rooms (Thtr 100 max),
24hr-delegate from £80, day-delegate from £30
Children: Welcome
Licenses: Leisure: Indoor pool
Parking: Off-street and free
Directions: From A23 follow signs to Hove. Second
turning at roundabout, follow Dyke Road, then Upper
Drive and The Drive.
Map ref: Hove 5 D3

Langfords Hotel

★★★

Third Avenue, Hove, East Sussex, BN3 2PX
Tel: 01273 738222 Fax: 01273 779426
Email: langfords@pavilion.co.uk
Web: www.langfordshotel.com
Rooms: 60 all ensuite
Dinner available CC: Accepted
Room facilities: Access:
Conference: 6 meeting rooms (Thtr 200 max)
Children: Welcome
Licenses:
Directions: From A23 follow signs to Hove. Turn left on
seafront road (A259). Continue east until you reach
Third Avenue on left.
Map ref: Hove 5 D3

Princes Marine Hotel

★★★

153 Kingsway, Hove, East Sussex, BN3 4GR
Tel: 01273 207660 Fax: 01273 325913
Email: princesmarine@bestwestern.co.uk
Web: www.princesmarinehotel.co.uk
Rooms: 48 all ensuite
Pricing: Sgl £50–75 Dbl £80–160
Dinner available from £17.95
CC: Accepted
Room facilities:
Access:
Conference: 3 meeting rooms (Thtr 80 max),
24hr-delegate from £95, day-delegate from £32
Children: Welcome
Dogs: Welcome
Licenses:
Parking: Off-street and free
Directions: From M23, go straight to sea front. Turn
right at Palace Pier. Continue along main sea front
road. Hotel is 200 yards west of King Alfred swimming
pool. Approx 5 min drive.
Map ref: Hove 5 D3

Hythe, Kent

The Hythe Imperial

★★★★★

Prince's Parade, Hythe, Kent, CT21 6AE
Tel: 01303 267441 Fax: 01303 264610
Email: hytheimperial@marstonhotels.com
Web: www.marstonhotels.com
Rooms: 100 all ensuite
Dinner available
CC: Accepted
Room facilities:
Access:
Conference: 11 meeting rooms (Thtr 220 max)
Children: Welcome
Licenses:
Leisure: Indoor pool, Gym, Health spa, Beauty salon,
Tennis, Golf, Games room, Snooker/billiards
Parking: Off-street and free
Directions: Leave M20 southbound at Junction 11.
Follow A261 to Hythe. When in Hythe follow signs to
Folkestone. Turn right into Twiss Road.
Map ref: Hythe (Kent) 5 E3

Southeast

Stade Court Hotel

★★★

West Parade, Hythe, Kent, CT21 6DT
Tel: 01303 268263 Fax: 01303 261803
Email: stadecourt@bestwestern.co.uk
Web: www.bw-stadecourt.co.uk

Stade Court Hotel sits in a prominent seafront location on the West Parade, easy access to the M20 making it ideal for touring Kent's attractions. Most of the 42 ensuite bedrooms have a sea view and enclosed balcony.
Rooms: 42 all ensuite
Pricing: Sgl £55–67 Dbl £69–87
Dinner available from £12–24
CC: Accepted
Room facilities:
Access:
Conference: 5 meeting rooms (Thtr 60 max),
24hr-delegate from £90, day-delegate from £25
Children: Welcome
Dogs: Welcome
Licenses:
Parking: Off-street and free
Directions: Leave M20 southbound at Junction 11. Follow A261 to Hythe. When in Hythe, turn right into Stade Street (by canal). Hotel fronting the sea.
Map ref: Hythe (Kent) 5 E3

Relax & smell the coffee

Fresh coffee, chilled juices for breakfast. RAC's team of qualified Inspectors check them both.

Icklesham, East Sussex

Manor Farm Oast

◆◆◆◆◆

Workhouse Lane, Icklesham, East Sussex, TN36 4AJ
Tel: 01424 813787 Fax: 01424 813787
Email: manor.farm.oast@lineone.net
Web: www.manorfarmoast.co.uk
Seasonal closure: January

Welcoming 19th century oast house, perfectly located amid orchards in open countryside. Spacious bedrooms are individually styled and include many thoughtful extras to add to guests' comfort. Home-produced dinners are a must.
Rooms: 3 (2 ensuite)
Pricing: Sgl £54–68 Dbl £74–84
Dinner available from £25 CC: Accepted
Room facilities:
Conference: 2 meeting rooms (Thtr 15 max),
day-delegate from £56
Children: Welcome 12yrs min age
Licenses:
Leisure: Croquet
Parking: Off-street and free
Directions: A259 to Rye/Folkestone. Right after Robin Hood pub, down Laurel Lane, right onto Windmill Lane. Signed left into orchards.
Map ref: Icklesham 5 E3

Isle of Wight
(see also Niton Undercliffe and Ventnor)

Burlington Hotel

★★★

Bellevue Road, Ventnor, Isle of Wight, PO38 1DB
Tel: 01983 852113 Fax: 01983 853862
Email: enquiries@burlingtonhotel.freeserve.co.uk
Web: www.burlingtonhotel.uk.com
Seasonal closure: November to March
Rooms: 24 all ensuite
Pricing: Sgl £32–47 Dbl £64–94
Dinner available from £15 CC: Accepted
Room facilities:
Children: Welcome 3yrs min age
Licenses:
Leisure: Outdoor pool, Games room
Parking: Off-street and free
Map ref: Ventnor 4 B4

George Hotel

★★★★ 🏵🏵🏵

Quay Street, Yarmouth, Isle of Wight, PO41 0PE
Tel: 01983 760331 Fax: 01983 760425
Email: res@thegeorge.co.uk
Web: www.thegeorge.co.uk
Rooms: 17 all ensuite 🖨 ⊗
Dinner available CC: Accepted
Room facilities: ▢ ☎
Conference: 1 meeting room (Thtr 30 max),
24hr-delegate from £185, day-delegate from £65
Children: Welcome 10yrs min age
Dogs: Welcome
Licenses: ⚓ ⅲ
Directions: Situated in Yarmouth, between pier and
castle.
Map ref: Yarmouth 4 B4

Keats Green Hotel

★★★

3 Queens Road, Shanklin, Isle of Wight, PO37 6AN
Tel: 01983 862742 Fax: 01983 868572
Email: enquiries@keatsgreenhotel.co.uk
Web: www.keatsgreenhotel.co.uk
Seasonal closure: January to March
Rooms: 33 all ensuite 🐾 ⊗
Pricing: Sgl £42–50 Dbl £84–100
Dinner available from £20 CC: Accepted
Room facilities: ▢ ☎ 🍵 Access: |Ⅱ|
Children: Welcome ⫪ ⋇€
Dogs: Welcome
Licenses: ⅲ
Leisure: Outdoor pool
Parking: Off-street and free
Directions: Driving from Lake take A3055 towards
Ventnor (Queens Road). Hotel is approx 400 yards on left.
Map ref: Shanklin 4 B4

Luccombe Hall Hotel

★★★

Luccombe Road, Shanklin, Isle of Wight, PO37 6RL
Tel: 01983 869000 Fax: 01983 863082
Email: reservations@luccombehall.co.uk
Web: www.luccombehall.co.uk
Rooms: 30 all ensuite 🐾 🖨
Pricing: Sgl £35–55 Dbl £70–150
Dinner available from £29.50
CC: Accepted
Room facilities: ▢ ☎ 🍵
Conference: 1 meeting room (Thtr 10 max)
Children: Welcome ⫪ ⋇€
Licenses: ⅲ
Leisure: Indoor pool, Outdoor pool, Gym, Games
room, Sauna, Jacuzzi, Squash, Putting green
Parking: Off-street and free
Directions: From Shanklin, take B3020 towards
Ventnor. Take road towards Luccombe. Turn left at top.
Hotel 100 yards on right.
Map ref: Shanklin 4 B4
See advert on opposite page

Seaview Hotel & Restaurant

★★★★ 🏵🏵

High Street, Seaview, Isle of Wight, PO34 5EX
Tel: 01983 612711 Fax: 01983 613729
Email: reception@seaviewhotel.co.uk
Web: www.seaviewhotel.co.uk
Seasonal closure: 3–4 days Christmas
Rooms: 17 all ensuite 🐾 ⊗
Pricing: Sgl £72–110 Dbl £89–188
Dinner available from £25
CC: Accepted
Room facilities: ▢ ☎ 🍵
Conference: 2 meeting rooms (Thtr 30 max),
24hr-delegate from £125, day-delegate from £28.50
Children: Welcome ⫪ ⋇€
Dogs: Welcome
Licenses: ⅲ
Parking: Off-street and free
Map ref: Seaview 4 B4

Sentry Mead

★★★★ 🏵

Madeira Road, Totland Bay, Isle of Wight, PO39 0BJ
Tel: 01983 753212 Fax: 01983 754710
Email: enq@sentry-mead.co.uk
Web: www.sentry-mead.co.uk
Rooms: 14 all ensuite ⊗
Pricing: Sgl £40–60 Dbl £80–120
Dinner available from £20
CC: Accepted
Room facilities: ▢ ☎ 🍵 📞
Children: Welcome
Dogs: Welcome
Licenses: ⅲ
Parking: Off-street and free
Directions: A3054 to Totland, right at roundabout by
Broadway Inn, continue to end of road, hotel on left.
Map ref: Totland Bay 4 B4

Fernbank Hotel

★★

Highfield Road, Shanklin, Isle of Wight, PO37 6PP
Tel: 01983 862790 Fax: 01983 864412
Email: enquiries@fernbankhotel.com
Web: www.fernbankhotel.com
Seasonal closure: Christmas to New Year
Rooms: 20 all ensuite 🐾 ⊗
Dinner available
CC: Accepted
Room facilities: ▢ ☎ 🍵
Conference: 1 meeting room (Thtr 30 max),
24hr-delegate from £65, day-delegate from £35
Children: Welcome 5yrs min age ⫪
Licenses: ⅲ
Leisure: Indoor pool, Health spa, Games room
Parking: Off-street and free
Directions: On entering Shanklin, follow signs to Old
Village, at traffic lights turn right, third turning left at the
end of road on the left.
Map ref: Shanklin 4 B4

LUCCOMBE HALL
COUNTRY HOUSE HOTEL

Originally built in 1870 as the Summer Home of the Bishop of Portsmouth, this lovely family run hotel commands the best position, best views and the best selection of facilities of any hotel on the Island!! With a magnificent view of the bay, the hotel has direct access to the beach and the Old Village of Shanklin.

Facilities include indoor and outdoor pools, squash court, jacuzzi, gym, sauna, treatment room, table tennis, pool table and extensive gardens with childrens' play area and tea gardens.

The Grand View Restaurant offers fine cuisine with a five course Table D'Hôte menu.

Rooms with seaviews, four poster beds, spa baths and balconies are available.

LUCCOMBE ROAD, SHANKLIN, ISLE OF WIGHT, PO37 6RL
Tel: 01983 869000   Fax: 01983 863082
Email: reservations@luccombehall.co.uk   Website: www.luccombehall.co.uk

Heatherleigh Hotel

★★

17 Queens Road, Shanklin, Isle of Wight, PO37 6AW
Tel: 01983 862503 Fax: 01983 861373
Email: enquiries@heatherleigh.co.uk
Web: www.heatherleigh.co.uk
Seasonal closure: Christmas
Rooms: 6 all ensuite
Pricing: Sgl £30 Dbl £60
Dinner available from £13
CC: Accepted
Room facilities:
Children: Welcome
Licenses:
Parking: Off-street and free
Directions: On entering Shanklin, follow signs for
Beach Lift. Heatherleigh is just 100 yards from cliff
walk and lift.
Map ref: Shanklin 4 B4

Hillside Hotel

★★

Mitchell Avenue, Ventnor, Isle of Wight, PO38 1DR
Tel: 01983 852271 Fax: 01983 855310
Email: rac@hillside-hotel.co.uk
Web: www.hillside-hotel.co.uk
Seasonal closure: Christmas
Rooms: 12 all ensuite
Pricing: Sgl £33 Dbl £66 Dinner available
CC: Accepted
Room facilities:
Children: Welcome 5yrs min age
Dogs: Welcome
Licenses:
Leisure: Tennis
Parking: Off-street and free
Directions: Take B2257 off A3055 at junction between
Leeson Hill and St Bonipace Road — hotel is behind
tennis courts.
Map ref: Ventnor 4 B4

Holliers Hotel

★★

Church Road, Old Village, Shanklin,
Isle of Wight, PO37 6NU
Tel: 01983 862764 Fax: 01983 867134
Email: enquiries@holliers-hotel.com
Web: www.holliers-hotel.com
Rooms: 30 all ensuite
Pricing: Sgl £30–50 Dbl £50–140
Dinner available from £19.95
CC: Accepted
Room facilities:
Children: Welcome
Licenses:
Leisure: Indoor pool, Outdoor pool, Snooker/billiards
Parking: Off-street and free
Directions: Holliers Hotel is situated on the main
A3055.
Map ref: Shanklin 4 B4

Malton House Hotel

★★

8 Park Road, Shanklin, Isle of Wight, PO37 6AY
Tel: 01983 865007 Fax: 01983 865576
Email: couvoussis@maltonhouse.freeserve.co.uk
Web: www.maltonhouse.co.uk
Rooms: 15 all ensuite
Pricing: Sgl £29–32 Dbl £50–56
Dinner available from £10
CC: Accepted
Room facilities:
Children: Welcome
Licenses:
Parking: Off-street
Directions: From Sandown on A3055, enter Shanklin.
At the traffic lights (Hope Road), go straight up hill.
Take third road on the left.
Map ref: Shanklin 4 B4

Melbourne-Ardenlea Hotel

★★

Queens Road, Shanklin, Isle of Wight, PO37 6AP
Tel: 01983 862283 Fax: 01983 862865
Email: melbourne-ardenlea@virgin.net
Web: www.melbourneardenleahotel.co.uk
Seasonal closure: November to February
Rooms: 50 all ensuite
Dinner available CC: Accepted
Room facilities:
Access:
Children: Welcome
Dogs: Welcome
Licenses:
Leisure: Indoor pool, Health spa, Games room
Parking: Off-street and free
Directions: From Sandown, bear left at Fiveways
Crossroads heading towards Ventnor. Hotel is 150
yards on right after passing church spire.
Map ref: Shanklin 4 B4

Montrene

★★

Avenue Road, Sandown, Isle of Wight, PO36 8BN
Tel: 01983 403722 Fax: 01983 405553
Email: montrene@aol.com
Web: www.montrene.co.uk
Seasonal closure: January
Rooms: 41 all ensuite
Pricing: Sgl £41–45 Dbl £82–90
CC: Accepted
Room facilities:
Children: Welcome
Dogs: Welcome
Licenses:
Leisure: Indoor pool, Games room, Snooker/billiards
Parking: Off-street and free
Directions: Travel from Ryde via Brading, under railway
bridge. Keep to left at roundabout. Hotel at end on
right. Look out for yellow sign.
Map ref: Sandown 4 B4

Sandpipers Hotel

 ★★

Entrance through main car park, Freshwater Bay, Isle of Wight, PO40 9QX
Tel: 01983 758500 Fax: 01983 754364
Email: fatcats@btconnect.com
Web: www.sandpipershotel.com
Rooms: 26 all ensuite
Pricing: Sgl £30–60 Dbl £60–160
Dinner available from £6.75–15.95 CC: Accepted
Room facilities:
Conference: 3 meeting rooms (Thtr 60 max),
24hr-delegate from £150, day-delegate from £30
Children: Welcome
Dogs: Welcome
Licenses:
Leisure: Health spa, Games room, Sauna, Jacuzzi, Steam room
Parking: Off-street and free
Directions: Enter Freshwater Bay, drive into main council park. Drive between two brick pillars at the back to enter private car park.
Map ref: Freshwater Bay 4 B4

Villa Mentone

 ★★

11 Park Road, Shanklin, Isle of Wight, PO37 6AY
Tel: 01983 862346 Fax: 01983 862130
Email: enquiry@villa-mentone.co.uk
Web: www.villa-mentone.co.uk
Rooms: 30 all ensuite
Pricing: Sgl £35–45 Dbl £55–60
Dinner available from £15
CC: Accepted
Room facilities:
Conference: 2 meeting rooms (Thtr 80 max),
24hr-delegate from £90, day-delegate from £30
Children: Welcome   Dogs: Welcome
Licenses:
Parking: Off-street and free
Directions: Follow A3055 to Sandown, then Shanklin. Follow Beach Lift signs.
Map ref: Shanklin 4 B4

Aqua Hotel

 ♦♦♦♦

17 The Esplanade, Shanklin, Isle of Wight, PO37 6BN
Tel: 01983 863024 Fax: 01983 864841
Email: info@aquahotel.co.uk
Web: www.aquahotel.co.uk
Rooms: 22 all ensuite
Pricing: Sgl £28–33 Dbl £56–66
Dinner available from £14.95 CC: Accepted
Room facilities:
Children: Welcome
Licenses:
Leisure: Games room
Directions: Turn down Hope Road from Arthurs Hill, North Road or Atherley Road. Drive down to seafront until you arrive at the hotel.
Map ref: Shanklin 4 B4

Country Garden Hotel

 ♦♦♦♦

Church Hill, Totland Bay, Isle of Wight, PO39 0ET
Tel: 01983 754521 Fax: 01983 754521
Email: countrygardeniow@aol.com
Web: www.thecountrygardenhotel.co.uk
Seasonal closure: January to 13 February
Rooms: 16 all ensuite
Pricing: Sgl £43–63 Dbl £86–126
Dinner available from £19.90
CC: Accepted
Room facilities:
Children: Welcome 12yrs min age
Dogs: Welcome
Licenses:
Parking: Off-street and free
Directions: Eight minutes' drive west from Yarmouth.
Map ref: Totland Bay 4 B4

Denewood Hotel

 ♦♦♦♦

7 Victoria Road, Sandown, Isle of Wight, PO36 8AL
Tel: 01983 402980 Fax: 01983 402980
Email: holiday@denewoodhotel.co.uk
Web: www.denewood-hotel.co.uk
Rooms: 14 all ensuite
Pricing: Sgl £27–28 Dbl £54–56
Dinner available from £11.50
CC: Accepted
Room facilities:
Children: Welcome
Dogs: Welcome
Licenses:
Leisure: Health spa
Parking: Off-street and free
Directions: By car take first right from high street. At next T-junction turn left. Denewood is second hotel on left.
Map ref: Sandown 4 B4

Hambledon Hotel

 ♦♦♦♦

11 Queens Road, Shanklin, Isle of Wight, PO37 6AW
Tel: 01983 862403 Fax: 01983 867894
Email: enquiries@hambledon-hotel.co.uk
Web: www.hambledon-hotel.co.uk
Seasonal closure: November to January
Rooms: 12 all ensuite
Pricing: Sgl £26–28 Dbl £52–56
Dinner available from £12
CC: Accepted
Room facilities:
Children: Welcome
Licenses:
Leisure: Free use of nearby leisure centre
Parking: Off-street and free
Directions: Please call to request a map.
Map ref: Shanklin 4 B4

Southeast

Lake Hotel

Shore Road, Lower Bonchurch, Ventnor,
Isle of Wight, PO38 1RF
Tel: 01983 852613
Email: richard@lakehotel.co.uk
Web: www.lakehotel.co.uk
Seasonal closure: November to February
Rooms: 20 all ensuite
Pricing: Sgl £35–40 Dbl £70–80
Dinner available from £10–12
Room facilities:
Children: Welcome 3yrs min age
Dogs: Welcome
Licenses:
Parking: Off-street and free
Directions: The Lake Hotel is situated opposite
Bonchurch Pond, within easy reach of Shanklin.
Map ref: Lower Bonchurch 4 B4

Latton House

Madeira Road, Totland Bay, Isle of Wight, PO39 0BJ
Tel: 01983 754868 Fax: 01983 754868
Email: lattonhouse@aol.com
Web: www.lattonhouse.co.uk
Seasonal closure: Christmas
Rooms: 3 all ensuite
Pricing: Sgl £35–40 Dbl £55–70
Room facilities:
Children: Welcome 12yrs min age
Parking: Off-street and free
Directions: A3054 from Yarmouth ferry terminal
towards Freshwater/Totland. Straight on at first
roundabout, right at next into Madeira Road.
Map ref: Totland Bay 4 B4

Richmond Hotel

23 Palmerston Road, Shanklin,
Isle of Wight, PO37 6AS
Tel: 01983 862874 Fax: 01983 862874
Email: info@richmondhotel-shanklin.co.uk
Web: www.richmondhotel-shanklin.co.uk
Rooms: 9 all ensuite
Pricing: Sgl £27 Dbl £54
Dinner available from £11
CC: Accepted
Room facilities:
Children: Welcome
Licenses:
Parking: Off-street and free
Directions: Turn off Shanklin High Street opposite
Boots. Hotel facing you.
Map ref: Shanklin 4 B4

St Catherine's Hotel

1 Winchester Park Road, Sandown,
Isle of Wight, PO36 8HJ
Tel: 01983 402392 Fax: 01983 402392
Email: stcathhotel@hotmail.com
Web: www.isleofwight-holidays.co.uk
Rooms: 19 all ensuite
Pricing: Sgl £29–35 Dbl £58–70
Dinner available from £14
CC: Accepted
Room facilities:
Children: Welcome
Licenses:
Parking: Off-street and free
Directions: By car from Fishbourne to Sandown, turn
right at mini roundabout up Broadway. St Catherine's
is at top of hill on left, on corner of Broadway and
Winchester Park Road.
Map ref: Sandown 4 B4

St Leonard's Hotel

22 Queens Road, Shanklin, Isle of Wight, PO37 6AW
Tel: 01983 862121 Fax: 01983 868895
Email: info@stleonards-hotel.co.uk
Web: www.stleonards-hotel.co.uk
Rooms: 7 all ensuite
Pricing: Sgl £24–27 Dbl £48–54
Dinner available from £11
CC: Accepted
Room facilities:
Children: Welcome
Licenses:
Parking: Off-street and free
Directions: Approach Shanklin on A3054. At Fiveways
lights take left-hand fork (signed Ventnor). Hotel is on
right after 1/4 mile.
Map ref: Shanklin 4 B4

The Lodge

Main Road, Brighstone, Isle of Wight, PO30 4DJ
Tel: 01983 741272 Fax: 01983 741144
Email: paul@thelodgebrighstone.com
Web: www.thelodgebrighstone.com
Rooms: 7 all ensuite
Pricing: Dbl £28–30
Room facilities:
Children: Welcome
Parking: Off-street and free
Directions: Leave Newport via Carisbrooke. Take
B3323 then B3399 to Brighstone. Proceed through
village, past Three Bishops Pub. The Lodge is 1/2 mile
on left-hand side.
Map ref: Brighstone 4 B4

White House Hotel

◆◆◆◆

Eastcliffe Promenade, Shanklin, Isle of Wight, PO37 6AY
Tel: 01983 862776 Fax: 01983 865980
Seasonal closure: November to December
Rooms: 11 all ensuite ♨
Pricing: Dinner available from £36–42 CC: Accepted
Room facilities: ☐ ☎ ⌕
Children: Welcome ⱦ ⅋
Licenses: ⅲ Parking: Off-street and free
Directions: Shanklin — North Road (main road) turn
into Clarendon Road, drive to top. Turn right into Park
Road, third carpark entrance on left.
Map ref: Shanklin 4 B4

Braemar Hotel

◆◆◆

1 Grange Road, Shanklin, Isle of Wight, PO37 6NN
Tel: 01983 863172 Fax: 01983 863172
Web: www.braemar-hotel.co.uk
Rooms: 11 all ensuite ♨ ⏦
Pricing: Sgl £27 Dbl £54
Dinner available from £11 CC: Accepted
Room facilities: ☐ ⌕
Children: Welcome ⱦ Dogs: Welcome
Licenses: ⅲ Parking: Off-street and free
Map ref: Shanklin 4 B4

Little Span Farm

◆◆◆

Rew Lane, Wroxall, Ventnor, Isle of Wight, PO38 3AU
Tel: 01983 852419 Fax: 01983 852419
Email: info@spanfarm.co.uk
Web: www.spanfarm.co.uk
Rooms: 4 all ensuite ⊛
Pricing: Sgl £22–50 Dbl £44–50
Room facilities: ☐ ⌕
Children: Welcome ⱦ Dogs: Welcome
Parking: Off-street and free
Directions: From B3327 to Wroxall turn into West Street
(by Post Office); drive out into countryside around sharp
bend. Ignore next right turning, first farm on right.
Map ref: Wroxall 4 B4

Shangri-La Hotel

◆◆◆

30 Broadway, Sandown, Isle of Wight, PO36 9BY
Tel: 01983 403672 Fax: 01983 403672
Email: web@shangrilahotel.co.uk
Web: www.shangrilahotel.co.uk
Rooms: 14 (11 ensuite) ♨ ⊛
CC: Accepted
Room facilities: ☐ ⌕
Children: Welcome ⱦ
Licenses: ⅲ
Leisure: Games room
Parking: Off-street and free
Directions: On A3055. Turn left at traffic lights from
Newport Road. Hotel is on right after approx ³/₄ mile.
Map ref: Sandown 4 B4

Isleworth, Middlesex

The Bridge Inn

◆◆

457 London Road, Isleworth, Middlesex, TW7 5AA
Tel: 020 8568 0088 Fax: 020 8568 0088
Email: bridgeinn@btconnect.com
Rooms: 10 (3 ensuite)
Dinner available
CC: Accepted
Room facilities: ☐ ⌕
Children: Welcome
Licenses: ⅲ
Leisure: Games room
Directions: Next to Isleworth mainline station. Bus
routes 237, 235 between Hounslow and Brentford.
Piccadilly Tube Line (Osterley) 21 mins walk.
Map ref: Isleworth 4 C2

Kidlington, Oxfordshire

Bowood House

◆◆◆

238 Oxford Road, Kidlington, Oxfordshire, OX5 1EB
Tel: 01865 842288 Fax: 01865 841858
Email: bowoodhouse@aol.com
Web: www.bowoodhousehotel.co.uk
Seasonal closure: 23 December to 4 January
Rooms: 20 all ensuite ♨ ⊛
Dinner available CC: Accepted
Room facilities: ☐ ☎ ⌕
Conference: 1 meeting room (Thtr 10 max)
Children: Welcome ⱦ
Dogs: Welcome
Licenses: ⅲ
Parking: Off-street and free
Directions: From north M40 exit 9 onto A34 exit
Kidlington. From south M40 exit 8 onto A40 follow
signs Kidlington.
Map ref: Kidlington 4 B1

Kingston-upon-Thames, Surrey

Antoinette Hotel

★★

Beaufort Road, Kingston-upon-Thames, Surrey, KT1 2TQ
Tel: 0870 011 8944 Fax: 0870 011 8944
Email: info@hotelantoinette.co.uk
Web: www.hotelantoinette.co.uk
Rooms: 100 all ensuite ♨ ⊛
Pricing: Sgl £60 Dbl £70
Dinner available from £20 CC: Accepted
Room facilities: ☐ ☎ ⌕ Access: ⅼⅼ
Conference: 8 meeting rooms (Thtr 130 max),
24hr-delegate from £90, day-delegate from £45
Children: Welcome ⱦ
Licenses: ⅲ Parking: Off-street and free
Directions: From Junction 9 of M25 follow A243 to
Kingston and Surbiton. At Surbiton take second right
after railway bridge, left, fourth set lights.
Map ref: Kingston 4 C2

Leatherhead, Surrey

Bookham Grange

★★

Little Bookham Common, Bookham, Leatherhead,
Surrey, KT23 3HS
Tel: 01372 452742 Fax: 01372 450080
Email: bookhamgrange@easynet.co.uk
Web: www.bookham-grange.co.uk
Rooms: 27 all ensuite
Dinner available CC: Accepted
Room facilities:
Conference: 2 meeting rooms (Thtr 80 max),
24hr-delegate from £130, day-delegate from £29.50
Children: Welcome
Dogs: Welcome
Licenses:
Parking: Off-street and free
Directions: Exit 9 of M25 into Leatherhead and A246
towards Guildford. In Bookham, turn right into High Street,
straight on into Church Road and first right after Bookham
Station.
Map ref: Bookham 4 C2

Lymington, Hampshire

Passford House Hotel

★★★

Mount Pleasant Lane, Lymington, Hampshire, SO41 8LS
Tel: 01590 682398 Fax: 01590 683494
Email: sales@passfordhousehotel.co.uk
Web: www.passfordhousehotel.co.uk
Rooms: 50 all ensuite
Pricing: Sgl £60–95 Dbl £80–280
Dinner available from £28.50 CC: Accepted
Room facilities:
Conference: 5 meeting rooms (Thtr 60 max),
24hr-delegate from £140, day-delegate from £40
Dogs: Welcome
Licenses:
Leisure: Indoor pool, Outdoor pool, Gym, Tennis
Parking: Off-street and free
Directions: Exit M27 J1 (west), A337 to Brockenhurst.
After railway bridge and mini roundabout, right at Toll
House Pub and right into Mount Pleasant Lane. Hotel
is 1 mile from garden centre.
Map ref: Lymington 4 B4

Sleep easy

Rest assured. Our
comprehensive
inspection process
includes checking
beds are comfortable.

Stanwell House Hotel

★★★

14–15 High Street, Lymington, Hampshire, SO41 9AA
Tel: 01590 677123 Fax: 01590 677756
Email: sales@stanwellhousehotel.co.uk
Web: www.stanwellhousehotel.co.uk

This charming Georgian Townhouse is friendly, informal
and comfortable. The 28 bedrooms, which include five
suites and a self contained cottage are individually
designed, some with four posters, roll top baths and
dramatic velvets and silks. Dine by candlelight in the
award-winning Bistro or snack in the lofty conservatory
or garden.
Rooms: 28 all ensuite
Pricing: Sgl £42.50–85 Dbl £55–170
Dinner available from £12.50
CC: Accepted
Room facilities:
Conference: 1 meeting room (Thtr 40 max),
24hr-delegate from £125, day-delegate from £30
Children: Welcome
Dogs: Welcome
Licenses:
Directions: Take Junction 1 M27, then A397 Lyndhurst
and Brockenhurst into Lymington High Street, hotel
halfway along.
Map ref: Lymington 4 B4

Glenhurst B&B

86 Wainsford Road, Everton, Lymington,
Hampshire, SO41 0UD
Tel: **01590 644256** Fax: 01590 644256
Email: **a.rose@virgin.net**
Web: **www.newforest-bedbreakfast.co.uk**
Rooms: **3 all ensuite** 🦯
Room facilities: ▢ 🛋
Children: **Welcome** 🌡
Parking: **Off-street and free**
Directions: **From Lymington turn right off A337
signposted Everton village. Take third right onto
Wainsford Road. Proceed ¼ mile to Glenhurst.**
Map ref: **Everton 4 B4**

Rosewood B & B

Rosewood, 45 Ramley Road, Lymington,
Hampshire, SO41 8GZ
Tel: **01590 677970**
Rooms: **2 (1 ensuite)** 🦯
Pricing: Sgl **£25–35** Dbl **£45–50**
Room facilities: ▢ 🛋
Children: **Welcome**
Parking: **Off-street and free**
Directions: **M3 to M27, exit at Junction 1, A337 from
Cadnam to Lymington. Continue on A337 towards
Milford. Turn right before shops to Pennington.
Rosewood is on right after 1 ½ miles.**
Map ref: **Lymington 4 B4**

Lyndhurst, Hampshire

Forest Lodge Hotel

★★★

Pikes Hill, Romsey Road, Lyndhurst,
Hampshire, SO43 7AS
Tel: **023 8028 3677** Fax: 023 8028 2940
Email: **forest@newforesthotels.co.uk**
Web: **www.newforesthotels.co.uk**
Rooms: **28 all ensuite** 🦺 📠 🦯
Pricing: Sgl **£67.50–77.50** Dbl **£135–155**
Dinner **available from £21.50**
CC: **Accepted**
Room facilities: ▢ ☎ 🛋
Conference: **4 meeting rooms (Thtr 120 max),
24hr-delegate from £95, day-delegate from £30**
Children: **Welcome** 🍴 🌡
Dogs: **Welcome**
Licenses: ⚓ 🎋
Leisure: **Indoor pool, Gym, Sauna**
Parking: **Off-street and free**
Directions: **Exit M27 at J1. Take A337, and after
approximately 3 miles turn right into Pikes Hill. Forest
Lodge is on left.**
Map ref: **Lyndhurst 4 B3**
See advert on this page

The
Forest Lodge
Hotel

The Forest Lodge Hotel is situated on the
outskirts of the village of Lyndhurst and still
retains much of its Georgian architecture.

Forest Lodge offers 28 delightfully furnished
bedrooms along with an indoor leisure
facility consisting of swimming pool, sauna
and fitness room.

Pikes Hill, Lyndhurst, Hants SO43 7AS

Tel: 023 8028 3677   Fax: 023 8028 2940
Email: forest@newforesthotels.co.uk
Website: www.newforesthotels.co.uk

Knightwood Lodge

★

Southampton Road, Lyndhurst, Hampshire, SO43 7BU
Tel: **023 8028 2502** Fax: 023 8028 3730
Email: **jackie4r@aol.com**
Web: **www.knightwoodlodge.co.uk**
Rooms: **19 all ensuite** 📠
Pricing: Sgl **£35–50** Dbl **£70–100**
Dinner **available from £17.95**
CC: **Accepted**
Room facilities: ▢ ☎ 🛋
Children: **Welcome** 🍴 🌡
Dogs: **Welcome**
Licenses: 🎋
Leisure: **Indoor pool, Gym, Sauna, Steam room, Spa**
Parking: **Off-street and free**
Directions: **From Junction 1 of M27, take A337 for
Lyndhurst. Turn left at traffic lights in Lyndhurst. Hotel
is ¼ mile along A35 Southampton Road.**
Map ref: **Lyndhurst 4 B3**

"Stay!"

Need a pet friendly
property? Look out for
'Dogs welcome' in
our listings.

Lyndhurst House

 ◆◆◆◆

35 Romsey Road, Lyndhurst, Hampshire, SO43 7AR
Tel: 023 8028 2230
Email: enquiries@lyndhursthousebb.co.uk
Web: www.lyndhursthousebb.co.uk
Rooms: 5 all ensuite
Pricing: Sgl £30–35 Dbl £50–60
Room facilities: Children: Welcome 10yrs min age
Parking: Off-street and free
Directions: M27 Junction 1, A337 to Lyndhurst. Approx
¹/₄ mile inside 30mph limit, on right-hand side, laying
back off road.
Map ref: Lyndhurst 4 B3

Penny Farthing Hotel

 ◆◆◆◆

Romsey Road, Lyndhurst, Hampshire, SO43 7AA
Tel: 023 8028 4422 Fax: 023 8028 4488
Email: stay@pennyfarthinghotel.co.uk
Web: www.pennyfarthinghotel.co.uk
Seasonal closure: Christmas

A cheerful hotel, ideally situated in the village of
Lyndhurst. Offering licensed bar, bicycle store,
comfortable ensuite rooms with colour TV, telephone
and tea/coffee making facilities and large car park.
Ideal base for touring New Forest.
Rooms: 21 all ensuite
Pricing: Sgl £45–78 Dbl £68–98 CC: Accepted
Room facilities: Children: Welcome
Licenses: Parking: Off-street and free
Directions: Leave M27 at Junction 1. Take A337 to
Lyndhurst. Hotel is on left as you enter village.
Map ref: Lyndhurst 4 B3

Temple Lodge

 ◆◆◆◆

2 Queens Road, Lyndhurst, Hampshire, SO43 7BR
Tel: 023 8028 2392 Fax: 023 8028 4910
Email: templelodge@btinternet.com
Web: www.templelodge-guesthouse.com
Rooms: 6 all ensuite
Pricing: Dbl £60–80 CC: Accepted
Room facilities: Children: Welcome 6yrs min age
Parking: Off-street and free
Directions: M27 J2, follow signs to Lyndhurst (A35).
Temple Lodge is on the corner of A35 and Queens Road.
Map ref: Lyndhurst 4 B3

Maidenhead, Berkshire

Monkey Island

 ★★★★

Old Mill Lane, Bray, Maidenhead, Berkshire, SL6 2EE
Tel: 01628 623400 Fax: 01628 784732
Email: info@monkeyisland.co.uk
Web: www.monkeyisland.co.uk
Rooms: 26 all ensuite
Dinner available
CC: Accepted
Room facilities:
Conference: 6 meeting rooms (Thtr 120 max)
Children: Welcome
Licenses:
Leisure: Golf
Parking: Off-street and free
Directions: J8/9 M4 to Maidenhead central, second
exit roundabout Windsor A308, second left Bray
village, right Old Mill Lane. Signposted to hotel.
Map ref: Bray 4 C2

Thames Hotel

 ★★★

Ray Mead Road, Maidenhead, Berkshire, SL6 8NR
Tel: 01628 628721 Fax: 01628 773921
Email: reservations@thameshotel.co.uk
Web: www.thameshotel.co.uk

Idylically situated on the banks of the River Thames.
The hotel has 35 ensuite rooms, many with superb
views of the river.
Rooms: 35 all ensuite
Pricing: Dinner available from £20
CC: Accepted
Room facilities:
Conference: 1 meeting room (Thtr 60 max),
24hr-delegate from £125, day-delegate from £30
Children: Welcome
Licenses:
Parking: Off-street and free
Directions: Leave M4 at Junction 7. Signed to
Maidenhead. Over bridge and turn right at mini
roundabout. Hotel is 200 yards on left.
Map ref: Maidenhead 4 C2

The Inn on The Green
Restaurant with Rooms

The Old Cricket Common,
Cookham Dean, Berkshire, SL6 9NZ
Tel: 01628 482638 Fax: 01628 487474
Email: reception@theinnonthegreen.com
Web: www.theinnonthegreen.com
Rooms: 9 all ensuite
Pricing: Sgl £70–140 Dbl £90–195
Dinner available from £25
CC: Accepted
Room facilities:
Conference: 2 meeting rooms (Thtr 34 max),
24hr-delegate from £185, day-delegate from £55
Children: Welcome
Licenses:
Parking: Off-street and free
Directions: A404(M) Bisham exit. Follow signs
Cookham Dean. Inn is down lane by war memorial in
centre of Cookham Dean.
Map ref: Cookham Dean 4 C2

Clifton Guest House

21 Craufurd Rise, Maidenhead, Berkshire, SL6 7LR
Tel: 01628 620086/623572 Fax: 01628 623572
Email: clifton@aroram.freeserve.co.uk
Web: www.cliftonguesthouse.co.uk
Rooms: 11 (6 ensuite)
Pricing: Sgl £35–55 Dbl £60–65
Dinner available from £10
CC: Accepted
Room facilities:
Children: Welcome
Licenses:
Parking: Off-street
Directions: Leave M4 at Junction 8/9. Follow A308 to
Maidenhead Central and on towards Marlow. Craufurd
Rise is off Marlow Road.
Map ref: Maidenhead 4 C2

Maidstone, Kent

Merzie Meadows   Little Gem

Hunton Road, Near Marden,
Maidstone, Kent, TN12 9SL
Tel: 01622 820500 Fax: 01622 820500
Email: pamela.mumford@onetel.net
Web: www.smoothhound.co.uk/hotels/merzie.html
Rooms: 2 all ensuite
Pricing: Dbl £66–80
Room facilities:
Children: Welcome 15yrs min age
Leisure: Outdoor pool
Parking: Off-street and free
Map ref: Merzie Meadows 5 E3

Ringlestone Inn and Farmhouse Hotel

Ringlestone Hamlet, near Harrietsham,
Maidstone, Kent, ME17 1NX
Tel: 01622 859900 Fax: 01622 859966
Email: bookings@ringlestone.com
Web: www.ringlestone.com
Rooms: 3 all ensuite
Pricing: Sgl £104–135 Dbl £129–150
Dinner available from £7.95
CC: Accepted
Room facilities:
Conference: 3 meeting rooms (Thtr 40 max),
24hr-delegate from £140, day-delegate from £18
Children: Welcome
Licenses:
Parking: Off-street and free
Directions: Exit J8 M20 to A20 south. Take
Hollingbourne turn and go through village to top of the
hill. Turn right at crossroads.
Map ref: Ringlestone 5 E2

The Black Horse Inn

Pilgrims Way, Thurnham, Maidstone, Kent, ME14 3LD
Tel: 01622 737185 Fax: 01622 739170
Email: info@wellieboot.net
Web: www.wellieboot.net

Tucked beneath the steep face of the North Downs on
The Pilgrims Way is The Black Horse Inn, a homely
and welcoming inn adorned with hops and beams,
with an open log fire in winter. There is a network of
footpaths and bridlepaths in the area used by cyclists,
walkers and horses. Six beautiful rooms are in a
separate annexe.
Rooms: 6 all ensuite
Pricing: Sgl £60–70 Dbl £60–80
Dinner available from £6.95–16.95   CC: Accepted
Room facilities:
Children: Welcome
Dogs: Welcome
Licenses:
Parking: Off-street and free
Directions: M20 junction 7 first exit A249 turn right into
Detling village. Opposite Cock Horse public house.
Lane to Thurnham, go 1 mile down Pilgrims Way.
Map ref: Thurnham 5 E2

Southeast

Marlow, Buckinghamshire

Danesfield House Hotel and Spa

★★★★ ♔♔♔   **Excellent**

Henley Road, Marlow, Buckinghamshire, SL7 2EY
Tel: 01628 891010 Fax: 01628 890408
Email: sales@danesfieldhouse.co.uk
Web: www.danesfieldhouse.co.uk

Built at the turn of the century, the hotel stands in 65 acres of grounds overlooking the River Thames. Luxurious extensive spa includes 50 treatments, 20m pool, fitness studio etc.
Rooms: 87 all ensuite ♨ 🛏
Pricing: Sgl £165–215 Dbl £175–260
Dinner available from £43–60
CC: Accepted
Room facilities: 🖵 ☎ ✆
Access: ♿
Conference: 8 meeting rooms (Thtr 100 max), 24hr-delegate from £323, day-delegate from £94
Children: Welcome ♿ ✧
Licenses: ⚓ ♙♙♙
Leisure: Indoor pool, Gym, Health spa, Beauty salon, Tennis, Snooker/billiards, Sauna, Steam room
Parking: Off-street and free
Directions: Leave M4 at Junction 8/9 or M40 at Junction 4 and take A404 to Marlow. Then take A4155 towards Henley.
Map ref: Marlow 4 C2

The Chequers

♦♦♦

51-53 High Street, Marlow, Buckinghamshire, SL7 1BA
Tel: 01628 482053 Fax: 01628 898386
Email: chequers@massivepub.com
Web: www.massivepub.com
Rooms: 5 all ensuite ⊗
Pricing: Sgl £49.95–59.95 Dbl £69.95–79.95
Dinner available from £4.95–19.95
CC: Accepted
Room facilities: 🖵 🛈
Conference: 2 meeting rooms (Thtr 50 max)
Children: Welcome
Licenses: ♙♙♙
Parking: Off-street and free
Directions: On the main High Street in Marlow which is situated off the A40 between Wycombe and Maidenhead.
Map ref: Marlow 4 C2

Milford-on-Sea, Hampshire

Westover Hall Hotel

★★★ ♔♔♔   **Premier**

Park Lane, Milford-on-Sea, Hampshire, SO41 0PT
Tel: 01590 643044 Fax: 01590 644490
Email: info@westoverhallhotel.com
Web: www.westoverhallhotel.com

A grade II listed Victorian mansion on the edge of the New Forest, 200 yards from the beach with stunning uninterrupted views to The Needles and Isle of Wight. Family owned and run with a relaxed, friendly atmosphere.
Rooms: 12 all ensuite ♨ ⊗
Pricing: Sgl £115–165 Dbl £180–230
Dinner available from £38.50 CC: Accepted
Room facilities: 🖵 ☎ 🛈 ✆
Conference: 2 meeting rooms (Thtr 35 max), 24hr-delegate from £165, day-delegate from £45
Children: Welcome ♿ Dogs: Welcome
Licenses: ⚓ ♙♙♙ Parking: Off-street and free
Directions: Leave M27 at Junction 1. Follow A337 via Lyndhurst, Brockenhurst, Lymington, Pennington then Everton where you take B3058 to Milford-on-Sea.
Map ref: Milford-on-Sea 4 B4

Milton Keynes, Buckinghamshire

Quality Hotel & Suites Milton Keynes

★★★

Monks Way, Two Mile Ash, Milton Keynes, Buckinghamshire, MK8 8LY
Tel: 01908 561666 Fax: 01908 568303
Email: enquiries@hotels-milton-keynes.com
Web: www.choicehotelseurope.com
Rooms: 88 all ensuite ♨ 🛏 ⊗
Pricing: Sgl £40–135 Dbl £60
Dinner available from £18.50 CC: Accepted
Room facilities: 🖵 ☎ 🛈 ✆
Conference: 6 meeting rooms (Thtr 120 max), 24hr-delegate from £150, day-delegate from £35
Children: Welcome ♿ Dogs: Welcome
Licenses: ⚓ ♙♙♙
Leisure: Indoor pool, Gym, Health spa
Parking: Off-street and free
Directions: Exit M1 at Junction 14, follow until the A5. Go north and take next exit and follow signs for A422, Two Mile Ash.
Map ref: Milton Keynes 8 C4

Comfort Inn, Milton Keynes North

★★

Open Pastures, Buckingham Road, Deanshanger, Milton Keynes, Buckinghamshire, MK19 6JU
Tel: 01908 262925 Fax: 01908 263642
Email: info@miltonkeyneshotel.com
Web: www.miltonkeyneshotel.com
Rooms: 46 all ensuite
Pricing: Sgl £60–70 Dbl £70–80
Dinner available from £11–15
CC: Accepted
Room facilities: 📺 ☎ 🍵 📞
Conference: 1 meeting room (Thtr 18 max),
24hr-delegate from £90, day-delegate from £30
Children: Welcome
Licenses: 👤👤👤
Parking: Off-street and free
Directions: M1 junction 14 take A509 to Milton Keynes, follow A5 until roundabout showing A422 to Buckingham. Hotel is at Deanshanger on Buckingham Road.
Map ref: Milton Keynes 8 C4
See advert on this page

Swan Revived Hotel

★★★ ®

High Street, Milton Keynes,
Buckinghamshire, MK16 8AR
Tel: 01908 610565 Fax: 01908 210995
Email: info@swanrevived.co.uk
Web: www.swanrevived.co.uk

Former coaching inn modernised to provide 40 comfortable guest rooms, fine à la carte restaurant, conferences for a maximum of 70 and full wedding services. Holders of civil marriage licence.
Rooms: 42 all ensuite 🐾 📼
Pricing: Sgl £50–83.95 Dbl £68–93.95
Dinner available from £16
CC: Accepted
Room facilities: 📺 ☎ 🍵
Access: |↕|
Conference: 2 meeting rooms (Thtr 70 max), 24hr-delegate from £120, day-delegate from £35
Children: Welcome 🪑
Dogs: Welcome
Licenses: ⚓ 👤👤👤
Parking: Off-street and free
Directions: From M1 Junction 14 take A509 to Newport Pagnell (1³/₄ miles). The hotel is on the High Street opposite the post office.
Map ref: Milton Keynes 8 C4

Are the bells ringing?

Getting married? Congratulations! Look for the wedding bells symbol which shows hotels licensed for civil ceremonies.

Campanile Hotel
Travel Accommodation

40 Penn Road, Fenny Stratford, Bletchley,
Milton Keynes, Buckinghamshire, MK2 2AU
Tel: 01908 649819 Fax: 01908 649818
Email: mk@campanile-hotels.com
Web: www.campanile.com

Campanile hotels offer comfortable and convenient
budget accommodation and a traditional French style
Bistro providing freshly-cooked food for breakfast,
lunch and dinner. All rooms ensuite with tea/coffee
making facilities, DDT and TV with Sky channels.
Rooms: 80 all ensuite ⊗
Pricing: Sgl £38.50 Dbl £38.50
Dinner available from £10
CC: Accepted
Room facilities: 🖵 ☎ ☕ ﹂
Conference: 3 meeting rooms (Thtr 50 max),
24hr-delegate from £89, day-delegate from £21.50
Children: Welcome 12yrs min age ⍊
Dogs: Welcome
Licenses: ⫪
Parking: Off-street and free
Directions: Follow A5 south, towards Dunstable. At
Little Chef roundabout, take fourth exit, on right to
Fenny Stratford. Take first left turn.
Map ref: Fenny Stratford 4 C1

New Alresford, Hampshire

Swan Hotel
★★
11 West Street, New Alresford, Hampshire, SO24 9AD
Tel: 01962 732302 Fax: 01962 735274
Email: swanhotel@btinternet.com
Web: www.swanhotelalresford.com
Rooms: 23 all ensuite ❤ ⌨
Pricing: Sgl £45–50 Dbl £70–80
Dinner available from £57.50–110
CC: Accepted
Room facilities: 🖵 ☎ ☕
Conference: 2 meeting rooms (Thtr 60 max)
Children: Welcome ⍊ Dogs: Welcome
Licenses: ⫪
Parking: Off-street
Directions: Situated between Winchester and Alton,
take the A31 and follow signs for Alresford.
Map ref: New Alresford 4 B3

New Milton, Hampshire

Chewton Glen Hotel
★★★★★ 🏠🏠🏠🏠 Premier
Christchurch Road, New Milton,
Hampshire, BH25 6QS
Tel: 01425 275341 Fax: 01425 272310
Email: reservations@chewtonglen.com
Web: www.chewtonglen.com

Chewton Glen is one of the only privately owned
hotels in the UK with RAC 5-Star Rating plus Gold
Ribbon, together with 4 RAC Dining Awards, and voted
Best Country House Hotel in the World by the
American magazine, Gourmet, in 2000.
Rooms: 58 all ensuite
Pricing: Dbl £245–805
Dinner available from £59.50
CC: Accepted
Room facilities: 🖵 ☎ ﹂ ❄
Conference: 5 meeting rooms (Thtr 100 max),
24hr-delegate from £350, day-delegate from £90
Children: Welcome 5yrs min age ⍊
Dogs: Assistance dogs only
Licenses: ⟡ ⫪
Leisure: Indoor pool, Outdoor pool, Gym, Health spa,
Beauty salon, Tennis, Golf, Snooker/billiards,
Hydrotherapy Spa Pool
Parking: Off-street and free
Directions: On A35 from Lyndhurst Drive 10 miles
towards Christchurch. At Hinton turn left for Walkford
following brown tourist signs.
Map ref: New Milton 4 B4
See advert on opposite page

The big sleep

As part of our
comprehensive
inspection process,
RAC Inspectors
investigate the
comfort of the beds.

Southeast

Chewton Glen
THE HOTEL, SPA AND COUNTRY CLUB

Chewton Glen is a splendid country house hotel set in a tranquil landscape of park and woodland ten minutes from the sea. Located 145km from London it was voted Best Country House Hotel in the World by readers of the American Magazine Gourmet and is one of the only privately owned hotels in Britain with RAC 5-star rating plus Gold Ribbon. The hotel's luxurious spa has recently been voted Best Hotel Spa in Europe by the German magazine, Gala. There is a par 3, 9-hole golf course within the grounds and ten 18-hole golf courses within easy reach of the hotel.

Christchurch Road, New Milton, Hampshire BH25 6QS
Tel: 01425 275341 ■ Fax: 01425 272310 ■ reservations@chewtonglen.com ■ www.chewtonglen.com

Newbury, Berkshire

The Vineyard at Stockcross

★★★★★★ 𝕽𝕽𝕽 Premier

Stockcross, Newbury, Berkshire, RG20 8JU
Tel: 01635 528770 Fax: 01635 528398
Email: general@the-vineyard.co.uk
Web: www.the-vineyard.co.uk

The renowned Vineyard at Stockcross is a haven for food and wine lovers. Chef John Campbell offers exciting food matched with a choice of 2,000 wines. Luxury spa.
Rooms: 49 all ensuite
Pricing: Sgl £180–645 Dbl £270–670
Dinner available from £55–75 CC: Accepted
Room facilities: Access:

Conference: 6 meeting rooms (Thtr 100 max), 24hr-delegate from £320, day-delegate from £95
Children: Welcome
Licenses:
Leisure: Indoor pool, Gym, Health spa, Beauty salon, Fishing
Parking: Off-street and free
Directions: Exit J13 M4. Take A34 southbound and take exit to Stockcross. At next roundabout take the second exit. The Vineyard is ¼ mile on right.
Map ref: Stockcross 4 B2

Donnington Valley Hotel & Golf Club

★★★★ 𝕽𝕽

Old Oxford Road, Donnington, Newbury, Berkshire, RG14 3AG
Tel: 01635 551199 Fax: 01635 551123
Email: general@donningtonvalley.co.uk
Web: www.donningtonvalley.co.uk
Rooms: 58 all ensuite
Pricing: Sgl £170–250 Dbl £180–260
Dinner available from £25 CC: Accepted
Room facilities: Access:
Conference: 10 meeting rooms (Thtr 140 max), 24hr-delegate from £185, day-delegate from £65
Children: Welcome
Licenses: Leisure: Golf
Parking: Off-street and free
Directions: Leave M4 at Junction 13. Follow signs for Donnington. Hotel is located on right after 2 miles.
Map ref: Donnington 4 B2

The Furze Bush Inn

★★

Ball Hill, Newbury, Berkshire, RG20 0NQ
Tel: 01635 253228 Fax: 01635 254883
Email: info@furzebushinn.co.uk
Web: www.furzebushinn.co.uk

A traditional country inn set in beautiful countryside just 4 miles from Newbury with easy access to motorway network via A34 bypass. Lovely gardens, delicious restaurant and bar food.
Rooms: 11 all ensuite 🐾
Pricing: Sgl £52–72 Dbl £72–100
Dinner available from £7.50–250 CC: Accepted
Room facilities: 🛏 ☎ 🍵 📞
Conference: 1 meeting room,
24hr-delegate from £75, day-delegate from £20
Children: Welcome 🍴
Licenses: 👥 Leisure: Games room, Snooker/billiards
Parking: Off-street and free
Directions: Take the A343 (Andover) road out of Newbury, take road signposted to Ball Hill on right.
Map ref: Ball Hill 4 B2

Niton Undercliffe, Isle of Wight
(see also Isle of Wight and Ventnor)

Windcliffe Manor Hotel

◆◆◆

Sandrock Road, Niton Undercliffe, near Ventnor,
Isle of Wight, PO38 2NG
Tel: 01983 730215
Email: enquiries@windcliffemanorhotel.com
Web: www.windcliffemanorhotel.com
Seasonal closure: January to February
Rooms: 10 (9 ensuite) 🚭
Pricing: Sgl £25 Dbl £35–40
Dinner available from £20 CC: Accepted
Room facilities: 🛏 ☎ 🍵
Conference: 1 meeting room (Thtr 40 max)
Children: Welcome 5yrs min age Dogs: Welcome
Licenses: 👥
Leisure: Outdoor pool, Games room, Snooker/billiards
Parking: Off-street and free
Directions: Through Niton Village to St Catherine's Road, turn right. Follow road sharp right-hand bend, hotel is on left.
Map ref: Niton Undercliffe 4 B4

Oxford, Oxfordshire

Oxford Spires Four Pillars Hotel

★★★★

Abingdon Road, Oxford, Oxfordshire, OX1 4PS
Tel: 01865 324324 Fax: 01865 324325
Email: spires@four-pillars.co.uk
Web: www.four-pillars.co.uk
Rooms: 115 all ensuite 🐾 🖨 🚭
Dinner available
CC: Accepted
Room facilities: 🛏 ☎ 🍵 📞 Access: ♿
Conference: 14 meeting rooms (Thtr 266 max)
Children: Welcome 🍴 🍼
Licenses: 🍷 👥
Leisure: Indoor pool, Gym, Health spa, Beauty salon, Fishing, Games room
Parking: Off-street and free
Directions: Exit J9 M40, A34 towards Oxford; then A423 turn left; left next roundabout, hotel 1 mile on the right.
Map ref: Oxford 4 B1

Oxford Thames Four Pillars Hotel

★★★★

Henley Road, Sandford-on-Thames, Oxford,
Oxfordshire, OX4 4GX
Tel: 01865 334444 Fax: 01865 334400
Email: thames@four-pillars.co.uk
Web: www.four-pillars.co.uk
Rooms: 60 all ensuite 🐾 🖨 🚭
Dinner available CC: Accepted
Room facilities: 🛏 ☎ 🍵 📞
Conference: 12 meeting rooms (Thtr 160 max)
Children: Welcome 🍴 🍼
Licenses: 🍷 👥
Leisure: Indoor pool, Gym, Health spa, Tennis
Parking: Off-street and free
Directions: J9 M40, A34 towards Oxford. Take A423 exit, then follow A4074 to Sandford. At T-junction, turn right; hotel is on left.
Map ref: Sandford-on-Thames 4 B2

The Oxford Belfry

★★★★

Milton Common, Thame, Oxfordshire, OX9 2JW
Tel: 01844 279381 Fax: 01844 279624
Email: oxfordbelfry@marstonhotels.com
Web: www.marstonhotels.com
Rooms: 130 all ensuite
Dinner available CC: Accepted
Room facilities: Access:
Conference: 19 meeting rooms (Thtr 450 max)
Children: Welcome
Licenses:
Leisure: Indoor pool, Gym, Tennis
Parking: Off-street and free
Directions: Leave M40 northbound at Junction 7. Travelling southbound leave at Junction 8a. Hotel situated on A40, 1½ miles from either junction.
Map ref: Milton Common 4 B1

The Oxford Hotel

★★★★

Godstow Road, Oxford, Oxfordshire, OX2 8AL
Tel: 01865 489988 Fax: 01865 489952
Email: oxfordreservations@paramount-hotels.co.uk
Web: www.paramount-hotels.co.uk

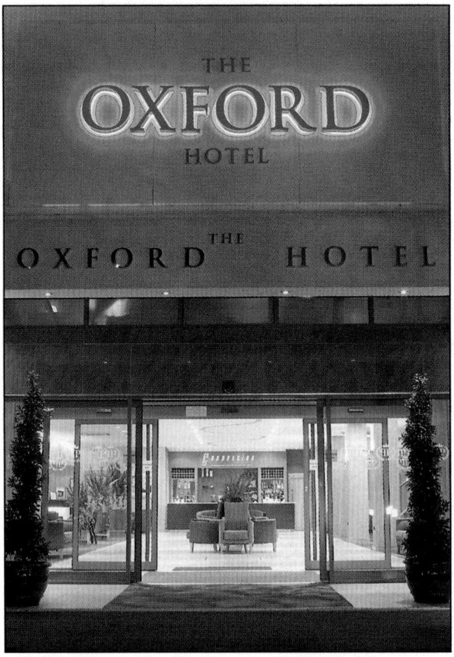

PARAMOUNT
GROUP OF HOTELS

Recently refurbished extensively, this stylish contemporary hotel combines modern comforts and hi-tech facilities with friendly service. Minutes from Oxford City Centre and convenient for The Cotswolds and Blenheim Palace.
Rooms: 168 all ensuite
Pricing: Sgl £83–118 Dbl £116–159
Dinner available from £22.50
CC: Accepted
Room facilities:
Access:
Conference: 27 meeting rooms (Thtr 300 max), 24hr-delegate from £185, day-delegate from £65
Children: Welcome
Licenses:
Leisure: Indoor pool, Gym, Beauty salon
Parking: Off-street
Directions: Exit M40 at junction 8. Following signs for Oxford, A40 and Cheltenham. At third roundabout, take second exit to Wolvercote.
Map ref: Oxford 4 B1

Foxcombe Lodge Hotel

★★

Fox Lane, Boars Hill, Oxford, Oxfordshire, OX1 5DP
Tel: 01865 326326 Fax: 01865 730628
Email: res@foxcombelodge.com
Web: www.foxcombelodge.com
Seasonal closure: 24 December to 8 January
Rooms: 19 all ensuite
Pricing: Sgl £60 Dbl £90–110
Dinner available from £18
CC: Accepted
Room facilities:
Conference: 4 meeting rooms (Thtr 80 max), 24hr-delegate from £105, day-delegate from £25
Children: Welcome
Dogs: Welcome
Licenses:
Leisure: Games room, Snooker/billiards
Parking: Off-street and free
Directions: At Hinksey Hill junction A34/A4142 follow signs for Wootton. At top of hill (½ mile) turn right. Hotel 1 mile on left.
Map ref: Boars Hill 4 B1

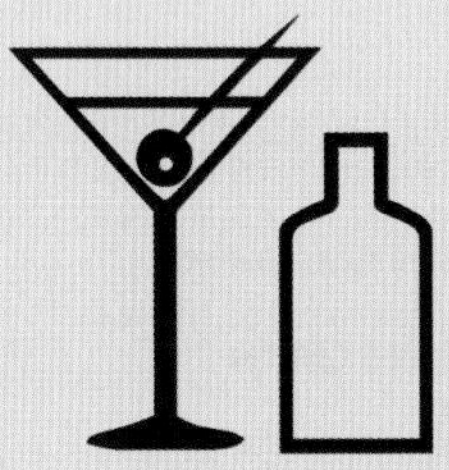

Ice & slice?

RAC's comprehensive inspection means we even check drinks are served the way you want.

Bath Place Hotel

 ◆◆◆◆

4/5 Bath Place, Holywell Street, Oxford,
Oxfordshire, OX1 3SU
Tel: 01865 791812 Fax: 01865 791834
Email: info@bathplace.com
Web: www.bathplace.co.uk

Friendly (awarded RAC Warm Welcome), family-owned
and run hotel comprising a group of 17th century
cottages surrounding a pretty flagstone courtyard.
Centrally located yet nestling in a quiet, historic
backwater of the city. Adjacent to the medieval city
wall. Non-smoking.
Rooms: 14 all ensuite
Pricing: Sgl £82.50–125 Dbl £95–150 CC: Accepted
Room facilities: Children: Welcome
Dogs: Welcome Parking: Off-street and free
Directions: Follow signs to the city centre, Bath Place
is situated off Holywell Street between Mansfield Road
and Broad Street.
Map ref: Oxford 4 B1

Galaxie Hotel

 ◆◆◆◆

180 Banbury Road, Summertown, Oxford,
Oxfordshire, OX2 7BT
Tel: 01865 515688 Fax: 01865 556824
Email: info@galaxie.co.uk
Web: www.galaxie.co.uk
Rooms: 33 (31 ensuite)
Pricing: Sgl £64–72 Dbl £94–115 CC: Accepted
Room facilities: Access:
Conference: 1 meeting room (Thtr 10 max)
Children: Welcome
Parking: Off-street and free
Directions: 1 mile north of city centre.
Map ref: Oxford 4 B1

Marlborough House Hotel

 ◆◆◆◆

321 Woodstock Road, Oxford, Oxfordshire, OX2 7NY
Tel: 01865 311321 Fax: 01865 515329
Email: enquiries@marlbhouse.co.uk
Web: www.marlbhouse.co.uk
Rooms: 17 all ensuite
Pricing: Sgl £73 Dbl £84
CC: Accepted
Room facilities:
Children: Welcome
Licenses:
Parking: Off-street and free
Directions: Located in north Oxford, 6 miles from
Junction 9, M40. 1½ miles from city centre.
Map ref: Oxford 4 B1

Pickwick's Guest House

 ◆◆◆◆

15/17 London Road, Headington,
Oxfordshire, OX3 7SP
Tel: 01865 750487 Fax: 01865 742208
Email: pickwicks@tiscali.co.uk
Web: www.pickwicksguesthouse.co.uk
Seasonal closure: Christmas and New Year

A comfortable guest house with single, double & family
rooms, most ensuite from £30-£80 including English
breakfast and VAT. Private free car parking, small bar,
lounge and garden. Easy access to Oxford City Centre.
Rooms: 15 (13 ensuite)
Pricing: Sgl £30–50 Dbl £70–80
CC: Accepted
Room facilities:
Children: Welcome
Dogs: Welcome
Licenses:
Parking: Off-street and free
Directions: From M40 and Oxford ring road, follow city
centre directions through Headington. Pickwick's is on
the right after 1 mile.
Map ref: Oxford 4 B1

Coach and Horses

 ◆◆◆

Watlington Road, Chislehampton, Oxford,
Oxfordshire, OX44 7UX
Tel: 01865 890255 Fax: 01865 891995
Email: enquiries@coachhorsesinn.co.uk
Web: www.coachhorsesinn.co.uk
Seasonal closure: 26–30 December
Rooms: 9 all ensuite
Pricing: Sgl £53.50–55 Dbl £60–70
Dinner available from £20 CC: Accepted
Room facilities: ▢ ☎ ⊘
Conference: 1 meeting room (Thtr 12 max)
Children: Welcome ⍭
Licenses: ᛙ Leisure: Fishing, Riding
Parking: Off-street
Directions: Situated on the B480 Watlington Road four
miles east of Oxford.
Map ref: Chislehampton 4 B2

River Hotel

 ◆◆◆

17 Botley Road, Oxford, Oxfordshire, OX2 0AA
Tel: 01865 243475 Fax: 01865 724306
Email: reception@riverhotel.co.uk
Web: www.riverhotel.co.uk
Seasonal closure: Christmas and New Year
Rooms: 20 all ensuite
Pricing: Sgl £70–75 Dbl £80–90 CC: Accepted
Room facilities: ▢ ☎ ⊘ ☍
Conference: 1 meeting room (Thtr 30 max)
Children: Welcome 5yrs min age
Licenses: ᛙ
Parking: Off-street and free
Directions: For Botley Road, exit A420 west off ring
road (A34). One mile towards city and rail station.
Hotel on right beside Osney Bridge.
Map ref: Oxford 4 B1

Pagham, West Sussex

Inglenook Hotel

★★★

253–255 Pagham Road, Pagham,
West Sussex, PO21 3QB
Tel: 01243 262495 Fax: 01243 262668
Email: reception@the-inglenook.com
Web: www.the-inglenook.com

Family owned and run, 16th century hotel, restaurant
and free house. Cosy bars with inglenook fireplaces.
Attractive restaurant overlooking and opening onto the
gardens, with seafood specialities. Wedding
ceremonies and receptions, conferences.
Rooms: 18 all ensuite
Pricing: Sgl £50–70 Dbl £90–200
Dinner available from £19.50
CC: Accepted
Room facilities: ▢ ☎ ⊘ ☍
Children: Welcome ⍭
Dogs: Welcome
Licenses: ⚑ ᛙ
Parking: Off-street and free
Directions: Ten minutes from A27, travelling south,
signposted Pagham.
Map ref: Pagham 4 C4

Pevensey, East Sussex

Priory Court Hotel

 ◆◆◆◆

Castle Road, Pevensey, East Sussex, BN24 5LG
Tel: 01323 763150 Fax: 01323 769030
Email: info@priorycourthotel.com
Web: www.priorycourthotel.com
Rooms: 10 (8 ensuite)
Pricing: Sgl £45–60 Dbl £60–85
Dinner available from £15.95–30
CC: Accepted
Room facilities: ▢ ☎ ⊘
Conference: 2 meeting rooms (Thtr 25 max),
24hr-delegate from £150, day-delegate from £99.50
Children: Welcome ⍭
Dogs: Welcome
Licenses: ᛙ
Parking: Off-street and free
Directions: At the roundabout at junction of A27 and
A259, follow sign for Pevensey. Hotel is located
opposite Pevensey Castle on right.
Map ref: Pevensey 5 D3

Portsmouth, Hampshire

Uppermount House Hotel

 ◆◆◆◆

The Vale, off Clarendon Road, Southsea,
Portsmouth, Hampshire, PO5 2EQ
Tel: 023 9282 0456 Fax: 023 9282 0456
Rooms: 16 all ensuite
Pricing: Sgl £32–34 Dbl £55–62
CC: Accepted
Room facilities: ▢ ☎ ⊘ ☍
Children: Welcome ⍭
Licenses: ᛙ
Parking: Off-street and free
Directions: Exit M27; head for D-Day Museum. Turn
down road opposite. Drive over crossroads; right at
T-junction and take first right.
Map ref: Southsea 4 B4

Ramsgate, Kent

Grove End Hotel

♦♦♦

2 Grange Road, Ramsgate, Kent, CT11 9NA
Tel: 01843 587520 Fax: 01843 853666
Email: reservation@groveendhotel.demon.co.uk
Web: www.groveendhotel.demon.co.uk
Rooms: 11 all ensuite ✎
Pricing: Sgl £25 Dbl £50 CC: Accepted
Room facilities: ▯ ▱
Children: Welcome ♯
Parking: Off-street
Directions: Approach Ramsgate along London Road. At the roundabout turn left onto Grange Road. Hotel is 80 metres on left.
Map ref: Ramsgate 5 F2

Reading, Berkshire

Millennium Madejski Hotel Reading

★★★★ ⛫⛫⛫

Madejski Stadium, Junction 11 M4, Reading, Berkshire, RG2 0FL
Tel: 0118 925 3500 Fax: 0118 925 3501
Email: sales.reading@mill-cop.com
Web: www.millenniumhotels.com

Prestigious hotel with superb luxury facilities ideally located in royal Berkshire for business trips and leisure weekends. Nearby attractions include Legoland and Windsor Castle.
Rooms: 140 all ensuite ✎ ⊛
Pricing: Sgl £95–215 Dbl £95–230
Dinner available from £25 CC: Accepted

Room facilities: ▯ ☎ ▱ ☏ ❄ Access: ⇅
Conference: 1 meeting room,
24hr-delegate from £199, day-delegate from £70
Children: Welcome ♯ Dogs: Welcome
Licenses: ⚏ Leisure: Indoor pool, Gym, Health spa
Parking: Off-street and free
Directions: Take the M4 junction 11. Follow the A33 towards Reading. Follow signs to the Madejski Stadium. 1 mile from M4.
Map ref: Reading 4 B2

Kirtons Farm Hotel – Reading

★★★

Pingewood, Reading, Berkshire, RG30 3UN
Tel: 0118 950 0885 Fax: 0118 939 1996
Email: kirtons.farm@mill-cop.com
Web: www.millenniumhotels.com

Rooms: 81 all ensuite ⊛
Pricing: Sgl £85–150 Dbl £95–160
Dinner available from £19.50–30
CC: Accepted
Room facilities: ▯ ☎ ▱ ☏ Access: ⇅
Conference: 14 meeting rooms (Thtr 110 max),
24hr-delegate from £182, day-delegate rate from £58
Children: Welcome ♯
Licenses: ⚐ ⚏
Leisure: Indoor pool, Gym, Tennis, Games room, Snooker/billiards, Water sports
Parking: Off-street and free
Directions: M4 Junction 11, A33 Basingstoke. At first roundabout take third exit, then second right. Follow lane for 3 miles back over motorway.
Map ref: Pingewood 4 B2

Ringwood, Hampshire

Tyrrells Ford Country House Hotel

★★★

Avon, New Forest, Hampshire, BH23 7BH
Tel: 01425 672646 Fax: 01425 672262
Email: tyrrellsfordinfo@aol.com
Web: www.tyrrellsfordhotel.com
Rooms: 16 all ensuite ✎
Pricing: Sgl £65–85 Dbl £150–180
Dinner available from £25 CC: Accepted
Room facilities: ▯ ☎ ▱
Conference: 2 meeting rooms (Thtr 100 max)
Children: Welcome 10yrs min age ♯
Licenses: ⚐ ⚏
Leisure: Arrangement with local sports club
Parking: Off-street and free
Directions: A31 to Ringwood, follow sign for B3347 and Avon, Tyrrells Ford is situated 3 miles from Ringwood on left-hand side at Avon.
Map ref: Avon 4 A3

Ripple-by-Dover

Plough Inn

Church Lane, Ripple-by-Dover, Kent, CT14 8JH
Tel: 01304 360209
Map ref: Ripple 5 F3

Rochester, Kent

Bridgewood Manor

★★★★ ⚄⚅

Bridgewood Roundabout, Walderslade Woods,
Chatham, Kent, ME5 9AX
Tel: 01634 201333 Fax: 01634 201330
Email: bridgewoodmanor@marstonhotels.com
Web: www.marstonhotels.com
Rooms: 100 all ensuite ♨ ⊛
Dinner available CC: Accepted
Room facilities: ▢ ☎ ⌂ ☊ Access: |↓↑
Conference: 11 meeting rooms (Thtr 200 max)
Children: Welcome ⴕ ⅋ Licenses: ⚗ ♠♠♠
Leisure: Indoor pool, Gym, Health spa, Beauty salon,
Tennis, Snooker/billiards
Parking: Off-street and free
Directions: Leave M2 at Junction 3 or M20 at Junction
6. Follow A229 towards Rochester. At Bridgewood
roundabout take third exit.
Map ref: Walderslade 5 E2

Romsey, Hampshire

The Sun Inn

116 Winchester, Romsey, Hampshire, SO51 7JG
Tel: 01794 512255 Fax: 01794 521887
Rooms: 4 (3 ensuite) ⊛ CC: Accepted
Room facilities: ▢ ⌂
Children: Welcome 12yrs min age Licenses: ♠♠♠
Parking: Off-street
Directions: Junction 3 M27 follow road to Romsey, Sun
Inn is on main Winchester road.
Map ref: Romsey 4 B3

Royal Tunbridge Wells, Kent

Spa Hotel

Mount Ephraim, Royal Tunbridge Wells, Kent, TN4 8XJ
Tel: 01892 520331 Fax: 01892 510575
Email: info@spahotel.co.uk
Web: www.spahotel.co.uk
Rooms: 69 all ensuite ♨ 🗺
Pricing: Sgl £104–119 Dbl £148–208
Dinner available from £29.50
CC: Accepted
Room facilities: ▢ ☎ ⌂ ☊
Access: |↓↑
Conference: 6 meeting rooms (Thtr 300 max),
24hr-delegate from £139, day-delegate from £45

Children: Welcome ⴕ 🐎 ⅋
Licenses: ⚗ ♠♠♠
Leisure: Indoor pool, Gym, Beauty salon, Tennis,
Riding
Directions: Leave M25 at Junction 5 and join A21. Take
fourth exit for A26 Royal Tunbridge Wells. Fork right
onto A264. Hotel is ¹/₂ mile on right.
Map ref: Tunbridge Wells 5 D3
See advert on this page

Russell Hotel

★★

80 London Road, Royal Tunbridge Wells,
Kent, TN1 1DZ
Tel: 01892 544833 Fax: 01892 515846
Email: sales@russell-hotel.com
Web: www.russell-hotel.com
Rooms: 25 all ensuite ♨ ⊛
Pricing: Sgl £70–80 Dbl £85–99
Dinner available from £4.95–12.95
CC: Accepted
Room facilities: ▢ ☎ ⌂
Conference: 12 meeting rooms (Thtr 30 max)
Children: Welcome ⴕ ⅋
Licenses: ♠♠♠
Parking: Off-street and free
Directions: In the centre of Royal Tunbridge Wells,
opposite the common on the main London Road.
Map ref: Tunbridge Wells 5 D3

Ruislip, Middlesex

The Barn Hotel

★★★

West End Road, Ruislip, Middlesex, HA4 6JB
Tel: 01895 636057 Fax: 01895 638379
Email: info@thebarnhotel.co.uk
Web: www.thebarnhotel.co.uk
Rooms: 59 all ensuite 🖼 ⊛
Pricing: Sgl £70–125 Dbl £90–240
Dinner available from £22 CC: Accepted
Room facilities: 🖵 ☎ ⊙ ⁌
Conference: 5 meeting rooms (Thtr 80 max),
24hr-delegate from £150, day-delegate from £45
Children: Welcome ♁ Licenses: ⚑ ⛊
Parking: Off-street and free
Directions: A40, exit Ruislip/Polish War memorial, exit
roundabout to Ruislip (A4180, West End Road).
Continue 2 miles, turn right at mini-roundabout.
Map ref: Ruislip 4 C2
See advert in Uxbridge section

Rye, East Sussex

Flackley Ash

★★★

Peasmarsh, Rye, East Sussex, TN31 6YH
Tel: 01797 230651 Fax: 01797 230510
Email: enquiries@flackleyashhotel.co.uk
Web: www.flackleyashhotel.co.uk

Friendly Georgian country house hotel set in beautiful
grounds, candlelit restaurant with fine wines and fresh
local fish. Indoor pool and leisure centre, beauty &
massage, visit local castles and gardens.
Rooms: 45 all ensuite 🥢 🖼
Pricing: Sgl £87–104 Dbl £132–192
Dinner available from £24.50 CC: Accepted
Room facilities: 🖵 ☎ ⊙ ⁌
Conference: 3 meeting rooms (Thtr 100 max),
24hr-delegate from £130, day-delegate from £38
Children: Welcome ♁ ⁌ Dogs: Welcome

Licenses: ⚑ ⛊
Leisure: Indoor pool, Gym, Health spa, Beauty salon
Parking: Off-street and free
Directions: Leave M25 at Junction 5, take A21
signposted Tunbridge Wells. Take A268 towards Rye.
Hotel on left when entering Peasmarsh.
Map ref: Peasmarsh 5 E3

Hope Anchor Hotel

★★★

Watchbell Street, Rye, East Sussex, TN31 7HA
Tel: 01797 222216 Fax: 01797 223796
Email: info@thehopeanchor.co.uk
Web: www.thehopeanchor.co.uk
Rooms: 11 all ensuite 🥢 🖼 ⊛
Dinner available CC: Accepted
Room facilities: 🖵 ☎ ⊙ ⁌
Children: Welcome ♁ ⁌ Dogs: Welcome
Licenses: ⛊
Directions: Drive up Mermaid Street, right into West
Street and right into Watchbell Street.
Map ref: Rye 5 E3

Rye Lodge Hotel

★★★

Hilder's Cliff, Rye, East Sussex, TN31 7LD
Tel: 01797 223838 Fax: 01797 223585
Email: info@ryelodge.co.uk
Web: www.ryelodge.co.uk

Attractive ensuite rooms. Every amenity. Room service
– breakfast in bed! Delicious candlelit dinners in the
elegant marble-floored Terrace Room Restaurant.
Relaxed atmosphere. Indoor swimming pool, spa bath,
sauna – really caring service.
Rooms: 18 all ensuite 🥢 ⊛
Pricing: Sgl £75–110 Dbl £100–200
Dinner available from £29.50 CC: Accepted
Room facilities: 🖵 ☎ ⊙
Children: Welcome ♁ Dogs: Welcome
Licenses: ⛊
Leisure: Indoor pool
Parking: Off-street and free
Directions: Follow town centre signs to Landgate Arch
(ancient monument); continue through Landgate Arch
— hotel is 100 yards on right.
Map ref: Rye 5 E3

The Mermaid Hotel

★★★ ♔♔

Mermaid Street, Rye, East Sussex, TN31 7EY
Tel: 01797 223065 Fax: 01797 225069
Email: mermaidinnrye@btclick.com
Web: www.mermaidinn.com

Experience the unique atmosphere of one of England's
oldest and loveliest inns, ideal for romantic breaks. Our
magnificent AA Rosette restaurant and 'Giants'
fireplace bar offer excellent cuisine, wines and ale.
Rooms: 31 all ensuite ♨ 🚿
Pricing: Dinner available from £37 CC: Accepted
Room facilities: 🖵 ☎
Conference: 2 meeting rooms (Thtr 50 max),
24hr-delegate from £160, day-delegate from £40
Children: Welcome ♁ ⅃ Licenses: ⅙
Parking: Off-street
Directions: Rye is situated on the A259 east of
Hastings, leave M20 at Ashford on the A2070 from A21
take B2089.
Map ref: Rye 5 E3

Jeake's House

17th-century Jeake's House stands on the
most famous cobbled street in Rye's medieval
town centre. Each stylishly restored bedroom
with brass, mahogany or Four-Poster bed
creates a very special atmosphere, combining
traditional elegance with modern comforts.

Breakfast served in
the galleried dining
room is traditional
or vegetarian and
the roaring fire and
timeless
atmosphere will
combine to make
your stay truly
memorable.

There is a
comfortable
drawing room
and book-lined
bar. Private car
park nearby.

RAC
♦♦♦♦♦
Guest
Accommodation

Sparkling
Diamond

Warm
Welcome

Mermaid Street, Rye, East Sussex
TN31 7ET
Tel: 01797 222828 Fax: 01797 222623
Email: stay@jeakeshouse.com
Website: www.jeakeshouse.com

Jeake's House

◆◆◆◆◆ 🖾 ☕

Mermaid Street, Rye, East Sussex, TN31 7ET
Tel: 01797 222828 Fax: 01797 222623
Email: stay@jeakeshouse.com
Web: www.jeakeshouse.com

17th-century Jeake's House stands on the most famous cobbled street in Rye's medieval town centre. Each stylishly restored bedroom with brass, mahogany or four-poster bed creates a very special atmosphere, combining traditional elegance with modern comforts.
Rooms: 11 (10 ensuite) 🖾
Pricing: Sgl £40–80 Dbl £96–120 CC: Accepted
Room facilities: ☐ ☎ ☕
Children: Welcome 7yrs min age Dogs: Welcome
Licenses: 🍶 Parking: Off-street
Directions: Approach Rye from A259 or A2070. Follow town centre signs. From High Street turn right into West Street, which leads to Mermaid Street.
Map ref: Rye 5 E3
See advert on previous page

Relax & smell the coffee

Fresh coffee, chilled juices for breakfast. RAC's team of qualified Inspectors check them both.

White Vine House

◆◆◆◆◆ 🖾 ☕

24 High Street, Rye, East Sussex, TN31 7JF
Tel: 01797 224748 Fax: 01797 223599
Email: info@whitevinehouse.co.uk
Web: www.whitevinehouse.co.uk

Tudor town house in the heart of ancient Rye with comfortable bedrooms, oak beams, stone fireplaces, books and paintings. Excellent breakfasts. Ideal for antique hunting, castles and gardens.
Rooms: 7 all ensuite 🍶 🖾 🚫
Pricing: Sgl £70 Dbl £115
Dinner available from £20–40 CC: Accepted
Room facilities: ☐ ☕
Children: Welcome 🍴 ☕ Licenses: 🍶 🍶
Directions: At Rye follow signs to town centre and enter under Landgate Arch. Follow road into High Street and hotel is on right.
Map ref: Rye 5 E3

Old Borough Arms

◆◆◆◆ 🖾

The Strand, Rye, East Sussex, TN31 7DB
Tel: 01797 222128 Fax: 01797 222128
Email: info@oldborougharms.co.uk
Web: www.oldborougharms.co.uk
Rooms: 9 all ensuite 🍶 🖾 🚫
Pricing: Sgl £35–55 Dbl £70–100
CC: Accepted
Room facilities: ☐ ☕
Children: Welcome 🍴
Licenses: 🍶
Leisure: Olde worlde tea rooms
Parking: Off-street and free
Directions: The hotel is located at the foot of Rye's famous Mermaid Street, opposite the antique centres on the Strand Quay.
Map ref: Rye 5 E3

Saffron Walden, Essex

The Crown House

★★★ R R

Great Chesterford, Saffron Walden, Essex, CB10 1NY
Tel: 01799 530515 Fax: 01799 530683
Web: www.thecrownhouse.com
Rooms: 22 all ensuite 🐶 🖨
Pricing: Sgl £65–74.50 Dbl £84.50–145
Dinner available
CC: Accepted
Room facilities: 🖵 ☎ 🖳 📞
Conference: 2 meeting rooms (Thtr 48 max),
24hr-delegate from £124.50, day-delegate from £27.50
Children: Welcome
Dogs: Welcome
Licenses: 🔱 🍺
Parking: Off-street and free
Directions: Close to M11 Junction 9, on B1383 (old
A11), 1 mile from Stump Cross roundabout.
Map ref: Great Chesterford 5 D1
See advert on this page

Sandwich, Kent

The Blazing Donkey Country Hotel

◆◆◆◆ R

Hay Hill, Ham, Sandwich, Kent, CT14 0ED
Tel: 01304 617362 Fax: 01304 615264
Web: www.blazingdonkey.co.uk
Rooms: 22 all ensuite 🐶 🖨 ⊗
Pricing: Sgl £75–80 Dbl £110–125
Dinner available from £15–30
CC: Accepted
Room facilities: 🖵 ☎ 🖳 📞 ❄
Children: Welcome 🍴 🍼
Dogs: Welcome
Licenses: 🔱 🍺
Parking: Off-street and free
Directions: Take the A256 from A2(M) to village of
Eastry then follow signs. Situated between Dover and
Sandwich.
Map ref: Ham 5 F2

The New Inn

2 Harnet Street, Sandwich, Kent, CT13 9ES
Tel: 01304 612335 Fax: 01304 619133
Email: new.inn@thorleytaverns.com
Web: www.thorleytaverns.com
Rooms: 5 all ensuite ⊚
Pricing: Sgl £49.50 Dbl £79.50
Dinner available from £5.95–11.95
CC: Accepted
Room facilities: ☐ ☎ ☺ ✆
Children: Welcome ⱈ
Dogs: Assistance dogs only
Licenses: ⑪
Parking: Off-street and free
Directions: When leaving M2/M20 follow signs for Ramsgate. Before Ramsgate follow signs for Sandwich, New Inn is in the town centre.
Map ref: Sandwich 5 F2

Sedlescombe, East Sussex

Brickwall Hotel

The Green, Sedlescombe, East Sussex, TN33 0QA
Tel: 01424 870253 Fax: 01424 870785
Email: info@brickwallhotel.com
Web: www.brickwallhotel.com
Rooms: 25 all ensuite ⊛ ⊞ ⊚
Pricing: Sgl £60–65 Dbl £84–90
Dinner available from £19.50–27.50
CC: Accepted
Room facilities: ☐ ☎ ☺
Conference: 1 meeting room (Thtr 40 max)
Children: Welcome ⱈ ✇
Dogs: Welcome
Licenses: ⑪
Leisure: Outdoor pool
Parking: Off-street and free
Directions: The Brickwall Hotel is situated in the village of Sedlescombe on the B2244, 3 miles east of Battle.
Map ref: Sedlescombe 5 E3

Sevenoaks, Kent

Bramber

45 Shoreham Lane, Riverhead,
Sevenoaks, Kent, TN13 3DX
Tel: 01732 457466 Fax: 01732 457466
Rooms: 2 ⊚
Pricing: Sgl £24–26.50 Dbl £40–45
Room facilities: ☐ ☺
Children: Welcome 7yrs min age
Parking: Off-street and free
Directions: A25 Riverhead roundabout towards Maidstone; up a slight incline, then turn first right; Bramber is the middle chalet bungalow and garage on the right.
Map ref: Riverhead 5 D2

Sittingbourne, Kent

Hempstead House

London Road, Bapchild, Sittingbourne, Kent, ME9 9PP
Tel: 01795 428020 Fax: 01795 436362
Email: info@hempsteadhouse.co.uk
Web: www.hempsteadhouse.co.uk
Rooms: 28 all ensuite ⊛ ⊞ ⊚
Pricing: Sgl £75–95 Dbl £85–120
Dinner available from £24.50 CC: Accepted
Room facilities: ☐ ☎ ☺ ✆
Conference: 5 meeting rooms (Thtr 150 max), 24hr-delegate from £145, day-delegate from £45
Children: Welcome ⱈ ⱔ ✇ Dogs: Welcome
Licenses: ⟁ ⑪ Leisure: Outdoor pool
Parking: Off-street and free
Directions: 1½ miles east of Sittingbourne along main A2.
Map ref: Bapchild 5 E2

Beaumont

74 London Road, Sittingbourne, Kent, ME10 1NS
Tel: 01795 472536 Fax: 01795 425921
Email: info@thebeaumont.co.uk
Web: www.thebeaumont.co.uk
Seasonal closure: Christmas and New Year
Rooms: 9 (6 ensuite) ⊞ ⊚
Pricing: Sgl £35–60 Dbl £65–80 CC: Accepted
Room facilities: ☐ ☎ ☺ ✆
Conference: 1 meeting room
Children: Welcome Dogs: Welcome
Parking: Off-street and free
Directions: From M2 or M20, take A249 north towards Sheerness. Take A2 exit, turn right at roundabout and follow A2 for 1 mile towards Sittingbourne.
Map ref: Sittingbourne 5 E2

Slough, Berkshire

Copthorne Hotel Slough Windsor

Cippenham Lane, Slough, Berkshire, SL1 2YE
Tel: 01753 516222 Fax: 01753 516237
Email: sales.slough@mill-cop.com
Web: www.copthornehotels.com

MILLENNIUM
HOTELS AND RESORTS

MILLENNIUM HOTELS
COPTHORNE HOTELS

The perfect location for both business and leisure. London Heathrow 15 miles and in easy reach of Windsor Castle and Legoland. Full details and offers available on website.
Rooms: 219 all ensuite 🛏 🚭
Pricing: Sgl £80–180 Dbl £80–200
Dinner available from £23.75
CC: Accepted
Room facilities: 🖥 ☎ 🍵 🌡 ❄
Access: ♿
Conference: 9 meeting rooms (Thtr 250 max), 24hr-delegate from £225, day-delegate from £75
Children: Welcome �🪑
Licenses: ♙♙♙
Leisure: Indoor pool, Gym, Health spa, Beauty salon
Parking: Off-street
Directions: Exit M4 J6. Follow A355 Slough. Turn left at roundabout. The hotel is on the left.
Map ref: Slough 4 C2

Furnival Lodge

◆◆◆◆ ⌦ 🍷

53-55 Furnival Avenue, Slough, Berkshire, SL2 1DH
Tel: 01753 570333 Fax: 01753 670038
Email: info@furnival-lodge.co.uk
Web: www.furnival-lodge.co.uk
Rooms: 10 all ensuite 🚭
Pricing: Sgl £38–50 Dbl £48–78
CC: Accepted
Room facilities: 🖥
Children: Welcome
Parking: Off-street and free
Directions: M4 Junction 6 or M40 Junction 2 onto A355 Slough. 1.7 miles from M4 and 4.9 miles from M40. Furnival Avenue is adjacent to BP Petrol Station.
Map ref: Slough 4 C2

Southampton, Hampshire

Botleigh Grange Hotel
★★★★ 👓👓

Hedge End, Grange Road, Southampton, Hampshire, SO30 2GA
Tel: 01489 787700 Fax: 01489 788535
Email: enquiries@botleighgrangehotel.co.uk
Web: www.botleighgrangehotel.co.uk
Rooms: 56 all ensuite 🛏 📠 🚭
Dinner available
CC: Accepted
Room facilities: 🖥 ☎ 🍵 📞
Access: ♿
Conference: 8 meeting rooms (Thtr 500 max)
Children: Welcome �🪑
Licenses: ◁ ♙♙♙
Directions: From M27 follow A334 to Botleigh; hotel is 1 mile on the left.
Map ref: Hedge End 4 B3

Jurys Inn Southampton
★★★

1 Charlotte Place, Southampton, Hampshire, SO14 0TB
Tel: +44(0)23 8037 1111 Fax: +44(0)23 8037 1100
Email: bookings@jurysdoyle.com
Web: www.jurysinns.com

🐾JURYS DOYLE
HOTELS

Rooms: 270 all ensuite 🛏 🚭
Pricing: Sgl £150 Dbl £150
Dinner available from £18 CC: Accepted
Room facilities: 🖥 ☎ 🍵 📞 ❄
Access: ♿
Conference: 10 meeting rooms (Thtr 120 max)
Children: Welcome �🪑 Licenses: ♙♙♙
Directions: Jurys Inn Southampton is located in Charlotte Place in the centre of Southampton city, overlooking East Park and close to Southampton Central Rail Station.
Map ref: Southampton 4 B3

Busketts Lawn Hotel
★★

174 Woodlands Road, Woodlands, near Southampton, Hampshire, SO40 7GL
Tel: 023 8029 2272 Fax: 023 8029 2487
Email: enquiries@buskettslawnhotel.co.uk
Web: www.buskettslawnhotel.co.uk

A delightful family-run country house hotel in a two-acre garden set in a quiet forest location. Facilities include a Victorian four-poster suite and a seasonal outdoor pool, with golf and riding nearby.
Rooms: 14 all ensuite 🛏 📠
Pricing: Sgl £45–47.50 Dbl £75–88
Dinner available from £19.50 CC: Accepted
Room facilities: 🖥 ☎ 🍵
Conference: 2 meeting rooms (Thtr 120 max), 24hr-delegate from £97.50, day-delegate from £29.50
Children: Welcome �🪑 Dogs: Welcome
Licenses: ◁ ♙♙♙
Leisure: Outdoor pool
Parking: Off-street and free
Directions: Accessible from J2 M27. Woodlands is a mile from the A35 Ashurst and a mile from A336 Netley Marsh. 15 minutes west from Southampton City Centre.
Map ref: Woodlands 4 B3

Elizabeth House Hotel

42–44 The Avenue, Southampton, Hampshire, SO17 1XP
Tel: 023 8022 4327 Fax: 023 8022 4327
Email: mail@elizabethhousehotel.com
Web: www.elizabethhousehotel.com
Rooms: 27 all ensuite
Pricing: Sgl £57.50 Dbl £67.50
Dinner available from £8
CC: Accepted
Room facilities:
Conference: 1 meeting room (Thtr 40 max),
24hr-delegate from £90, day-delegate from £25
Children: Welcome
Dogs: Welcome
Licenses:
Parking: Off-street and free
Directions: From M3, take A33 towards town centre.
Hotel on left after common but before main traffic lights.
Map ref: Southampton 4 B3

Acacia Lodge Guest House

Providence Hill, Bursledon,
Southampton, Hampshire, SO31 8AT
Tel: 023 8056 1155 Fax: 023 8056 1161
Email: acacialodge1@aol.com
Web: www.theacacialodge.co.uk
Rooms: 9 all ensuite
Pricing: Sgl £35–40 Dbl £55–60
Room facilities:
Children: Welcome
Parking: Off-street and free
Directions: Exit J8 M27; follow signs for Southampton
East and Hamble. Take first exit off roundabout.
Map ref: Bursledon 4 B3

Hunters Lodge Hotel

25 Landguard Road, Shirley,
Southampton, Hampshire, SO15 5DL
Tel: 023 8022 7919 Fax: 023 8023 0913
Email: hunterslodge.hotel@virgin.net
Web: www.hunterslodgehotel.net
Rooms: 14 all ensuite
Pricing: Sgl £40–55 Dbl £65–67.50
CC: Accepted
Room facilities:
Children: Welcome
Dogs: Welcome
Licenses:
Parking: Off-street and free
Directions: North of railway station along Hill Lane.
Landguard Road is fourth turning on your left.
Map ref: Shirley 4 B3

Landguard Lodge

21 Landguard Road, Southampton,
Hampshire, SO15 5DL
Tel: 023 8063 6904 Fax: 023 8063 2258
Email: landguardlodge@141.com
Web: www.landguardlodge.co.uk

This well maintained personally-run property is located
close to the city centre, theatres, university, airport,
docks and ferry terminals. An ideal base for touring the
south. The bedrooms are bright and smartly
decorated; all have modern ensuite shower rooms.
There is a cosy guests' lounge and a sunny breakfast
room.
Rooms: 10 all ensuite
CC: Accepted
Room facilities:
Children: Welcome 5yrs min age
Parking: Off-street and free
Directions: A short walk, north of Southampton Central
Railway Station. Between Hill Lane and Shirley Road.
Location map on request.
Map ref: Shirley 4 B3

"Stay!"

Need a pet friendly property? Look
out for 'Dogs welcome' in our listings.

Southend-on-Sea, Essex

Balmoral Hotel

 ★★

32–36 Valkyrie Road, Westcliff-on-Sea,
Essex, SS0 8BU
Tel: 01702 342947 Fax: 01702 337828
Email: enquiries@balmoralsouthend.com
Web: www.balmoralsouthend.com
Seasonal closure: 24 December to 1 January

Located in a quiet area of Westcliff-on-Sea, the
Balmoral Hotel offers the discerning business traveller
quality accommodaton, high levels of comfort and
service in an environment that is friendly and
welcoming.
Rooms: 32 all ensuite ⊛
Pricing: Sgl £48–90 Dbl £73–120
Dinner available from £13.95
CC: Accepted
Room facilities: ☐ ☎ ⌕
Conference: 1 meeting room (Thtr 10 max)
Children: Welcome ⅄
Dogs: Welcome
Licenses: ⅄⅄⅄
Parking: Off-street and free
Directions: Hotel will send a location map on request.
Easy access from the A127 and the A13.
Map ref: Westcliff-on-Sea 5 E2

Mayflower Hotel

 ◆◆◆

6 Royal Terrace, Southend-on-Sea, Essex, SS1 1DY
Tel: 01702 340489
Web: www.themayflowerhotel.co.uk
Seasonal closure: Christmas
Rooms: 23 (8 ensuite)
Pricing: Sgl £28.20–39.95 Dbl £42.30–54.05
CC: Accepted
Room facilities: ☐ ⌕
Children: Welcome ⅄
Dogs: Welcome
Leisure: Games room
Directions: Along sea front to pier; up Pier Hill into
Royal Terrace; The Mayflower Hotel is on the right.
Map ref: Southend-on-Sea 5 E2

Terrace Hotel

 ◆◆◆⌕

8 Royal Terrace, Southend-on-Sea, Essex, SS1 1DY
Tel: 01702 348143 Fax: 01702 348143
Email: barrick777@freeserve.co.uk
Web: www.theterracehotel.co.uk
Seasonal closure: Christmas
Rooms: 9 (4 ensuite) ⌕ ⌕ ⊛
Pricing: Sgl £28.20–39.95 Dbl £42.30–64.34
CC: Accepted
Room facilities: ☐ ⌕
Children: Welcome
Dogs: Welcome
Directions: Royal Terrace is a one-way street and can
only be approached by vehicle along the seafront via
Pier Hill.
Map ref: Southend-on-Sea 5 E2

The Gleneagles Hotel

 ◆◆◆

5-6 Clifftown Parade, Southend-on-Sea,
Essex, SS1 1DP
Tel: 01702 333635 Fax: 01702 332207
Email: info@thegleneagleshotel.co.uk
Web: www.thegleneagleshotel.co.uk
Rooms: 16 (10 ensuite) ⊛
Pricing: Sgl £27.50–45 Dbl £45–70
CC: Accepted
Room facilities: ☐ ☎ ⌕
Conference: 2 meeting rooms
Children: Welcome
Dogs: Welcome
Licenses: ⅄⅄⅄
Parking: Off-street and free
Directions: A127 across Victoria Plaza roundabout.
Right (lights), right (Churchills), left onto Clarence Road
then turn right. Take second left then left into Clifftown
Parade.
Map ref: Southend-on-Sea 5 E2

Tower Hotel

 ◆◆◆

146 Alexandra Road, Southend-on-Sea,
Essex, SS1 1HE
Tel: 01702 348635 Fax: 01702 433044
Email: enquiries@towerhotelsouthend.co.uk
Web: www.towerhotelsouthend.co.uk
Rooms: 30 all ensuite
CC: Accepted
Room facilities: ☐ ☎ ⌕
Conference: 1 meeting room (Thtr 20 max)
Children: Welcome
Licenses: ⅄⅄⅄
Directions: Turn off A13 into Milton Road, turn left into
Cambridge Road and take third right at mini-
roundabout into Wilson Road. Hotel on right at
crossroads.
Map ref: Southend-on-Sea 5 E2

Southeast

St Albans, Hertfordshire

Sopwell House

Cottonmill Lane, Sopwell, St Albans,
Hertfordshire, AL1 2HQ
Tel: 01727 864477 Fax: 01727 844741
Email: enquiries@sopwellhouse.co.uk
Web: www.sopwellhouse.co.uk

Four star Georgian country house with 129 bedrooms, a choice of restaurants and bars, superb health and beauty facilities and 19 conference and meeting rooms.
Rooms: 129 all ensuite
Pricing: Sgl £113–143 Dbl £197–213
Dinner available from £15.50
CC: Accepted
Room facilities:
Access:
Conference: 19 meeting rooms (Thtr 400 max),
24hr-delegate from £235, day-delegate from £69
Children: Welcome
Dogs: Assistance dogs only
Licenses:
Leisure: Indoor pool, Gym, Health spa, Beauty salon, Hairdressers, Sauna, Steam room, Spa bath
Parking: Off-street and free
Directions: M25 Junction 22, follow A1081 St. Albans, left at traffic lights into Mile House Lane, over mini-roundabout into Cottonmill Lane.
Map ref: Sopwell 4 C1

Quality Hotel St Albans

232-236 London Road, St Albans,
Hertfordshire, AL1 1JQ
Tel: 01727 857858 Fax: 01727 855666
Email: welcome@quality-hotels.net
Web: www.stalbans-hotels.co.uk
Rooms: 81 all ensuite
Pricing: Sgl £49–105 Dbl £69–120
Dinner available from £9–21

CC: Accepted
Room facilities:
Access:
Conference: 5 meeting rooms (Thtr 200 max),
24hr-delegate from £140, day-delegate from £35
Children: Welcome
Licenses:
Leisure: Indoor pool, Gym, Saunarium
Parking: Off-street and free
Directions: Leave M25 at Junction 22. Follow A1081 to St Albans. After 3 miles, hotel is on left-hand side.
Map ref: St Albans 4 C1

St Michael's Manor

Excellent

Fishpool Street, St Albans, Hertfordshire, AL3 4RY
Tel: 01727 864444 Fax: 01727 848909
Email: reservations@stmichaelsmanor.com
Web: www.stmichaelsmanor.com

30 individually styled bedrooms, 7 acres of gardens, 5 minutes walk to town centre, beautiful restaurant. Perfect for weddings, small meetings, romantic breaks. Just 20 minutes from London by train.
Rooms: 30 all ensuite
Pricing: Dinner available from £25
CC: Accepted
Room facilities:
Conference: 3 meeting rooms (Thtr 30 max),
24hr-delegate from £225, day-delegate from £64
Children: Welcome
Licenses:
Parking: Off-street and free
Directions: Leave M25 J21a. Go through Chiswell Green, turn left at King Harry pub. Pass Waitrose on left, right at roundabout and right at next roundabout. Right onto Branch road, left onto Fishpool Street.
Map ref: St Albans 4 C1

Ardmore House Hotel

54 Lemsford Road, St Albans, Hertfordshire, AL1 3PR
Tel: 01727 859313 Fax: 01727 859313
Email: info@ardmorehousehotel.co.uk
Web: www.ardmorehousehotel.co.uk

This beautiful Edwardian residence, which overlooks its splendid gardens, has been tastefully converted to provide comfortable accommodation in a relaxed atmosphere. Only 20 minutes train journey into the heart of London.
Rooms: 40 all ensuite
Pricing: Sgl £50–60 Dbl £65–75
Dinner available from £10.50–250
CC: Accepted
Room facilities:
Conference: 2 meeting rooms (Thtr 60 max), 24hr-delegate from £125, day-delegate from £35
Children: Welcome
Licenses:
Parking: Off-street and free
Directions: M25 Junction 22, A1081 to St Albans. At London Colney roundabout, take A1081 (London Road). Through two sets of traffic lights: right at second mini-roundabout. Hotel 800 yards on right.
Map ref: St Albans 4 C1

St Margaret's at Cliffe, Kent

The Clyffe Hotel

High Street, St Margaret's at Cliffe, near Dover, Kent, CT15 6AT
Tel: 01304 852400 Fax: 01304 851880
Email: stay@theclyffehotel.com
Web: www.theclyffehotel.com
Rooms: 12 all ensuite
Pricing: Sgl £45–55 Dbl £75–85
Dinner available from £18–21
CC: Accepted
Room facilities:
Children: Welcome
Dogs: Welcome
Licenses:
Parking: Off-street and free
Map ref: St Margaret's at Cliffe 5 F3

Stevenage, Hertfordshire

Sleep Inn Baldock
Travel Accommodation

Baldock Services, Junction 10 A1(M)/A509, Baldock, Stevenage, Hertfordshire, SG7 5TR
Tel: 01462 832900 Fax: 01462 832901
Email: enquiries@hotels-baldock.com
Web: www.choicehotelseurope.com
Rooms: 62 all ensuite
Pricing: Sgl £59–62 Dbl £66–68
CC: Accepted
Room facilities:
Children: Welcome
Parking: Off-street and free
Directions: Junction of A507 and A1(M) Junction 10, on new service area.
Map ref: Baldock 5 D1

Steyning, West Sussex

The Old Tollgate Restaurant and Hotel

★★★

The Street, Bramber, Steyning, West Sussex, BN44 3WE
Tel: 01903 879494 Fax: 01903 813399
Email: info@oldtollgatehotel.com
Web: www.oldtollgatehotel.com
Rooms: 30 all ensuite
Pricing: Sgl £91.95–144.95 Dbl £101.90–154.90
Dinner available from £18.95–23.95
CC: Accepted
Room facilities:
Access:
Conference: 7 meeting rooms (Thtr 50 max), 24hr-delegate from £116.27, day-delegate from £35.19
Children: Welcome
Licenses:
Parking: Off-street and free
Directions: From A24 or A27, take A283 signposted to Steyning, then follow signposts to Bramber. Brown tourist signs advertise hotel.
Map ref: Bramber 4 C3

Penfold Gallery Guest House   Little Gem

30 High Street, Steyning, West Sussex, BN44 3GG
Tel: 01903 815595 Fax: 01903 816686
Email: johnturner57@aol.com
Web: www.artyguesthouse.co.uk
Rooms: 3 all ensuite
Pricing: Sgl £52–54 Dbl £84–86
Dinner available from £26–28
CC: Accepted
Room facilities:
Children: Welcome 12yrs min age
Licenses:
Directions: Leave A27 at junction with A283 and follow signs to Steyning. The Penfold Gallery Guest House is east of the mini-roundabout in the High Street.
Map ref: Steyning 4 C3

Southeast

Springwells Hotel

9 High Street, Steyning, West Sussex, BN44 3GG
Tel: 01903 812446 Fax: 01903 879823
Email: contact@springwells.co.uk
Web: www.springwells.co.uk
Seasonal closure: Christmas to New Year

A former Georgian Merchant House in a picturesque village. All rooms are individually furnished with TV and telephone; the bar and adjoining conservatory lead to a patio and outdoor heated swimming pool.
Rooms: 11 (9 ensuite) 🛏 🚭
Pricing: Sgl £38–55 Dbl £61–110
CC: Accepted
Room facilities: 📺 ☎ 🍵
Conference: 3 meeting rooms (Thtr 30 max)
Children: Welcome 🍼
Dogs: Welcome
Licenses: ⚭
Leisure: Outdoor pool
Parking: Off-street and free
Directions: From M25 take A24, at Washington turn onto A283 for 3 miles. Turn right into town, Springwells is on the right.
Map ref: Steyning 4 C3

Stockbridge, Hampshire

Carbery Guest House

◆◆◆

Salisbury Hill, Stockbridge, Hampshire, SO20 6EZ
Tel: 01264 810771 Fax: 01264 811022
Seasonal closure: 3 weeks around Christmas

Rooms: 11 (8 ensuite)
Pricing: Sgl £35–43 Dbl £57–61
Dinner available from £15
CC: Accepted
Room facilities: 📺 🍵
Children: Welcome
Licenses: ⚭
Leisure: Outdoor pool, Snooker/billiards
Parking: Off-street and free
Directions: Carbery Guest House is at Salisbury end of Stockbridge on A30.
Map ref: Stockbridge 4 B3

Streatley-on-Thames, Berkshire

The Swan at Streatley

★★★★ ⚭⚭

Streatley-on-Thames, Berkshire, RG8 9HR
Tel: 01491 878800 Fax: 01491 872554
Email: sales@swan-at-streatley.co.uk
Web: www.swanatstreatley.co.uk
Rooms: 46 all ensuite 🛏 🚭 ⌖
Pricing: Sgl £70–140 Dbl £85–175
Dinner available from £29.95
CC: Accepted
Room facilities: 📺 ☎ 🍵 🔌
Conference: 5 meeting rooms (Thtr 120 max), 24hr-delegate from £225, day-delegate from £70
Children: Welcome 🍴
Dogs: Welcome
Licenses: 🍾 ⚭
Leisure: Indoor pool, Gym, Beauty salon
Parking: Off-street and free
Directions: Leave M4 at Junction 12, take exit towards Theale, then take A340 to Pangbourne. Once there take A329 to Streatley.
Map ref: Streatley-on-Thames 4 B2

Surbiton, Surrey

Pembroke Lodge Guest House

◆◆◆ ⚭

35 Cranes Park, Surbiton, Surrey, KT5 8AB
Tel: 020 8390 0731 Fax: 020 8390 0731
Rooms: 6 🛏 ⌖
Pricing: Sgl £36 Dbl £52
Room facilities: 📺 🍵
Children: Welcome 🍴
Dogs: Welcome
Parking: Off-street and free
Map ref: Surbiton 4 C2

Are the bells ringing?

Getting married? Congratulations! Look for the wedding bells symbol which shows hotels licensed for civil ceremonies.

Sway, Hampshire

The Nurse's Cottage Little Gem

◆◆◆◆◆ 📶📶 ✂ ☕

Station Road, Sway, Lymington, Hampshire, SO41 6BA
Tel: 01590 683402 Fax: 01590 683402
Email: nurses.cottage@lineone.net
Web: www.nursescottage.co.uk
Seasonal closure: 3 weeks in March and November

One of the New Forest's most highly acclaimed guest accommodations, selected universally by the UK's leading hospitality guides. Three-course dinner and award-winning breakfast included in rates below. Reduced rates for 2+ nights. Open to non-residents: booking essential.
Rooms: 4 all ensuite ⊛
Pricing: Sgl £80 Dbl £150–160 CC: Accepted
Room facilities: 📺 ☎ 🖳 📞
Children: Welcome 10yrs min age Dogs: Welcome
Licenses: 👤👤👤 Parking: Off-street and free
Directions: Off B3055 in centre of village.
Map ref: Lymington 4 B4

Taplow, Berkshire

Cliveden House

★★★★★ 📶📶📶 Premier

Taplow, Berkshire, SL6 0JF
Tel: 01628 668561 Fax: 01628 661837
Email: reservations@clivedenhouse.co.uk
Web: www.clivedenhouse.co.uk

Set in spectacular surroundings on the banks of the River Thames. The unique combination of the House, the setting, hospitality, service and fine dining make Cliveden an unforgettable experience.
Rooms: 39 all ensuite 🍽 💺 ⊛
Pricing: Sgl £225–335 Dbl £335–950
Dinner available from £49.50
CC: Accepted
Room facilities: 📺 ☎ 📞 Access: 👤👤
Conference: 2 meeting rooms (Thtr 40 max),
24hr-delegate from £355, day-delegate from £95
Children: Welcome 🍴 ☕ Dogs: Welcome
Licenses: 🍷 👤👤👤
Leisure: Indoor pool, Outdoor pool, Gym, Health spa, Beauty salon, Tennis, Snooker/billiards
Parking: Off-street and free
Directions: From Junction 7 of M4, follow brown National Trust signs to Taplow. From M40 Junction 2, follow signs to Taplow.
Map ref: Taplow 4 C2

Thame, Oxfordshire

Spread Eagle Hotel

★★★ 📶📶

16 Cornmarket, Thame, Oxfordshire, OX9 2BR
Tel: 01844 213661 Fax: 01844 261380
Email: enquiries@spreadeaglehotelthame.co.uk
Web: www.spreadeaglehotelthame.co.uk

Carefully-modernised former coaching inn, set in town centre. Large car park. Good centre for visiting Oxford and the Vale of Aylesbury. Hospitality is the speciality.
Rooms: 33 all ensuite 🍽 💺
Pricing: Sgl £98–115 Dbl £115–140
Dinner available from £25 CC: Accepted
Room facilities: 📺 ☎ 📞 📞
Conference: 6 meeting rooms (Thtr 200 max),
24hr-delegate from £145, day-delegate from £42
Children: Welcome 🍴 ☕
Licenses: 🍷 👤👤👤
Parking: Off-street and free
Directions: In town centre of Thame, on A418 between Aylesbury and Oxford. Leave M40 at Junction 6 southbound, Junction 8 northbound. Car park at rear of hotel.
Map ref: Thame 4 B1

Southeast

Tring, Hertfordshire

Pendley Manor

★★★★ ㍿㍿

Cow Lane, Tring, Hertfordshire, HP23 5QY
Tel: 01442 891891 Fax: 01442 890687
Email: info@pendley-manor.co.uk
Web: www.pendley-manor.co.uk
Rooms: 74 all ensuite 🛏 📺 🚭
Pricing: Dinner available from £30
CC: Accepted
Room facilities: ☐ ☎ ☕ 🛎
Access: ⬆
Conference: 20 meeting rooms (Thtr 300 max),
24hr-delegate from £230, day-delegate from £68
Children: Welcome 🪑 🐴 🍼
Dogs: Welcome
Licenses: ⚓ 🍴
Leisure: Indoor pool, Gym, Health spa, Beauty salon,
Tennis, Snooker/billiards
Parking: Off-street
Directions: M25 J20, take A41 Aylesbury from Tring,
exit, join A4251 Berkhamsted (200m), first left, Cow
Lane, Pendley Manor on right-hand side.
Map ref: Tring 4 C1
See advert on this page

Uxbridge, Middlesex

"Here!"

Need a pet friendly property? Look
out for 'Dogs welcome' in our listings.

The big sleep

As part of our comprehensive
inspection process, RAC
Inspectors investigate the comfort
of the beds.

Ventnor, Isle of Wight
(see also Isle of Wight and Niton Undercliffe)

Melbury

Niton Road, Rookley, Ventnor, Isle of Wight, PO38 3NX
Tel: 01983 721931 Fax: 01983 721977
Web: www.melbury-iow.co.uk
Seasonal closure: 23 December to 2 January

Melbury B&B is ideally situated to explore the Island and its natural beauty. Only minutes away from local beaches and attractions. Wheelchair access.
Rooms: 3 (1 ensuite) ⊛
Pricing: Sgl £25–30 Dbl £30–35
Room facilities: ▯ ☺
Children: Welcome
Parking: Off-street and free
Directions: A3056 from Newport/Sandown/Blackwater. 1 mile south of Newport turn right for Shanklin/ Godshill/Rookley. Turn right for Blackgang, Niton Road. Approximately ¼ mile to Melbury.
Map ref: Rookley 4 B4

Wallingford, Oxfordshire

George Hotel
★★★☆
High Street, Wallingford, Oxfordshire, OX10 0BS
Tel: 01491 836665 Fax: 01491 825359
Email: info@george-hotel-wallingford.com
Web: www.george-hotel-wallingford.com
Rooms: 39 all ensuite ✥ ⊛
Pricing: Sgl £116.50–136.50 Dbl £128
Dinner available from £17.50
CC: Accepted

Room facilities: ▯ ☎ ☺
Conference: 3 meeting rooms (Thtr 120 max), 24hr-delegate from £139, day-delegate from £44
Children: Welcome ᚼ ᛰ
Dogs: Assistance dogs only
Licenses: ⟁ ᛁᛁᛁ
Parking: Off-street and free
Directions: M4 (junction 12) – 13 miles, follow A34 then A4130. M40 (junction 6) – 8 miles, follow A329. Cholsey rail station – 1¼ miles, Didcot rail station – 6 miles.
Map ref: Wallingford 4 B2

Springs Hotel & Golf Club
★★★★ ⌂⌂
Wallingford Road, North Stoke, Wallingford, Oxfordshire, OX10 6BE
Tel: 01491 836687 Fax: 01491 836877
Email: info@thespringshotel.com
Web: www.thespringshotel.com

The Springs is a fine example of a 3-star country house hotel. Most of our 32 individually furnished bedrooms have lakeside views overlooking our spring fed lake and our 18-hole par 72 golf course.
Rooms: 32 all ensuite ✥ ⊘ ⊛
Pricing: Sgl £95–120 Dbl £115–155
Dinner available from £32.50
CC: Accepted
Room facilities: ▯ ☎ ☺ ☏
Conference: 4 meeting rooms (Thtr 100 max), 24hr-delegate from £155, day-delegate from £40
Children: Welcome ᚼ ᛰ
Dogs: Welcome
Licenses: ⟁ ᛁᛁᛁ
Leisure: Outdoor pool, Golf, Fishing
Parking: Off-street and free
Directions: M40 join the A423 towards Reading and after the Wallingford roundabout rejoin to B4009 towards Goring. Hotel is on right-hand side.
Map ref: North Stoke 4 B2

Watford, Hertfordshire

White House Hotel

★★★★

Upton Road, Watford, Hertfordshire, WD18 0JF
Tel: 01923 237316 Fax: 01923 233109
Email: info@whitehousehotel.co.uk
Web: www.whitehousehotel.co.uk
Rooms: 57 all ensuite
Pricing: Sgl £59–129 Dbl £79–144
Dinner available from £22.95–30
CC: Accepted
Room facilities:
Access:
Conference: 5 meeting rooms (Thtr 200 max),
24hr-delegate from £135, day-delegate from £45
Children: Welcome
Licenses:
Leisure: Link with local gym
Parking: Off-street and free
Directions: Follow signs to town centre ring road. Take
centre lane past lights at Market Street. Upton Road is
on left.
Map ref: Watford 4 C2

Welwyn, Hertfordshire

Quality Hotel Welwyn

★★★

A1(M) Junction 6, The Link, Welwyn,
Hertfordshire, AL6 9XA
Tel: 01438 716911 Fax: 01438 714065
Email: enquiries@hotels-welwyn.com
Web: www.choicehotelseurope.com
Rooms: 96 all ensuite
Pricing: Sgl £34.50–113 Dbl £39–135
Dinner available from £10.95–20.95
CC: Accepted
Room facilities:
Conference: 5 meeting rooms (Thtr 250 max),
24hr-delegate from £120, day-delegate from £36
Children: Welcome
Licenses:
Parking: Off-street and free
Directions: Located off J6 A1(M), follow signs to
Welwyn (not Welwyn Garden City). Nearest railway
station is Welwyn Garden City.
Map ref: Welwyn Garden City 5 D1

Ice & slice?

RAC's comprehensive
inspection means we
even check drinks are
served the way you want.

Wembley, Middlesex

Adelphi Hotel

◆◆◆

4 Forty Lane, Wembley, Middlesex, HA9 9EB
Tel: 020 8904 5629 Fax: 020 8908 5314
Email: hoteladelphi@btconnect.com
Web: www.hoteladelphi.co.uk

All rooms are well-equipped and furnished to a high
standard; ensuite rooms with tea and coffee making
facilities and direct-dial telephones. Easy access to
Wembley Stadium complex and main north London
routes.
Rooms: 13 (9 ensuite)
Pricing: Sgl £35–45 Dbl £45–55
CC: Accepted
Room facilities:
Conference: 1 meeting room (Thtr 15 max),
24hr-delegate from £150, day-delegate from £100
Children: Welcome
Parking: Off-street and free
Directions: M1 last exit onto A406, about 2 miles take
exit to Kingsbury, about 5 minutes only.
Map ref: Wembley 4 C2

Westcliff-on-Sea, Essex

Rose House Hotel

◆◆◆

21–23 Manor Road, Westcliff-on-Sea, Essex, SS0 7SR
Tel: 01702 341959 Fax: 01702 390918
Rooms: 21 (15 ensuite)
Pricing: Sgl £25–30 Dbl £50–60
CC: Accepted
Room facilities:
Children: Welcome
Dogs: Welcome
Licenses:
Leisure: Snooker/billiards
Parking: Off-street and free
Map ref: Westcliff-on-Sea 5 E2

Southeast

Weybridge, Surrey

Oatlands Park Hotel

★★★★ ®

146 Oatlands Drive, Weybridge, Surrey, KT13 9HB
Tel: 01932 847242 Fax: 01932 842252
Email: info@oatlandsparkhotel.com
Web: www.oatlandsparkhotel.com

Oatlands Park Hotel is a four-star country house hotel
set in ten acres of picturesque parkland overlooking
the Broadwater Lake. Enriched in history, Oatlands
Park Hotel is the perfect location for all occasions.
Rooms: 144 all ensuite 🐕 🗄 🚫
Pricing: Sgl £108–176 Dbl £125–210 Dinner available
CC: Accepted
Room facilities: 🖵 ☎ 🗄 🌡 ❄ Access: ⬆
Conference: 12 meeting rooms (Thtr 300 max),
24hr-delegate from £225, day-delegate from £75
Children: Welcome ⫪
Licenses: ♨ ⁙ Leisure: Gym, Tennis, Golf
Parking: Off-street and free
Directions: From Weybridge town centre, follow road
up Monument Hill to mini roundabout. Turn left into
Oatlands Drive. Hotel 500 yards on left.
Map ref: Weybridge 4 C2

Winchester, Hampshire

The Winchester Royal

★★★ ®

St Peter Street, Winchester, Hampshire, SO23 8BS
Tel: 01962 840840 Fax: 01962 841582
Email: reservationswr@forestdale.com
Web: www.forestdale.com/winchester-royal-hotel.htm
Rooms: 75 all ensuite 🐕 🚫
Dinner available CC: Accepted
Room facilities: 🖵 ☎ 🗄 🌡
Conference: 6 meeting rooms (Thtr 120 max)
Children: Welcome ⫪ Dogs: Welcome
Licenses: ♨ ⁙
Parking: Off-street and free
Directions: Leave M3 at junction 9 towards town
centre, bottom of hill, first right one-way system, take
second right.
Map ref: Winchester 4 B3

Norton Manor

 New for 2006

Sutton Scotney, Winchester, Hampshire, SO21 3NE
Tel: 0845 074 0055 Fax: 01962 760860
Email: nortonreservations@qhotels.co.uk
Web: www.qhotels.co.uk
Rooms: 97 (96 ensuite) 🗄 🚫
Pricing: Sgl £85–165 Dbl £117–195
Dinner available from £25–35
CC: Accepted
Room facilities: 🖵 ☎ 🗄 🌡
Access: ⬆
Conference: 24 meeting rooms (Thtr 120 max),
24hr-delegate from £180, day-delegate from £58
Children: Welcome ⫪ Dogs: Assistance dogs only
Licenses: ♨ ⁙
Leisure: Indoor pool, Gym, Health spa, Beauty salon,
Tennis, Games room
Parking: Off-street and free
Directions: Exit M3 J8 then A303 towards Micheldever
station. From M4, exit A34 Bullington Cross. For full
directions please visit website.
Map ref: Sutton Scotney 4 B3

Twyford House

◆◆◆◆ ⟨

Twyford, Winchester, Hampshire, SO21 1NU
Tel: 01962 713114 Fax: 01962 712719
Email: crchtwyho@aol.com
Rooms: 3 all ensuite 🐕 🚫
Pricing: Sgl £35–40 Dbl £60–70
Room facilities: 🖵 🗄 🌡
Children: Welcome ⫪ 🐾
Leisure: Outdoor pool
Parking: Off-street and free
Directions: Follow signs Marwell Zoo from Junction 11
on M3. Turn right into gap in high brick wall after
Church Lane.
Map ref: Twyford 4 B3

"I do!"

Want a honeymoon hotel? Look
for our Gold, Blue, and White
Ribbon Award winning hotels.

Windsor, Berkshire

Clarence Hotel

◆◆◆

9 Clarence Road, Windsor, Berkshire, SL4 5AE
Tel: 01753 864436 Fax: 01753 857060
Email: enquiries@clarence-hotel.co.uk
Web: www.clarence-hotel.co.uk

Town centre hotel, close to Windsor Castle, river and
Eton. All ensuite, TV, radio, tea-maker, radio alarm and
hairdryer. Bar and steam-sauna. Free internet and Wi-
Fi. Convenient for Legoland and Heathrow Airport.
Rooms: 20 all ensuite
Pricing: Sgl £49–65 Dbl £55–76
CC: Accepted
Room facilities:
Children: Welcome
Dogs: Welcome
Licenses:
Leisure: Steam-sauna
Parking: Off-street and free
Directions: Leave M4 at Junction 6 and follow dual
carriageway towards Windsor. Turn left at roundabout
onto Clarence Road.
Map ref: Windsor 4 C2

Witney, Oxfordshire

Witney Four Pillars Hotel

★★★

Ducklington Lane, Witney, Oxfordshire, OX8 7TJ
Tel: 01993 779777 Fax: 01993 703467
Email: witney@four-pillars.co.uk
Web: www.four-pillars.co.uk
Rooms: 83 all ensuite
Dinner available CC: Accepted
Room facilities:
Conference: 15 meeting rooms (Thtr 160 max)
Children: Welcome Licenses:
Leisure: Indoor pool, Gym, Health spa
Parking: Off-street and free
Directions: A40 towards Cheltenham; 2nd exit for
Witney A415; hotel is on the left.
Map ref: Witney 4 B1

Woburn, Bedfordshire

The Inn at Woburn

★★★★

George Street, Woburn,
Milton Keynes, Bedfordshire, MK17 9PX
Tel: 01525 290441 Fax: 01525 290432
Email: enquiries@theinnatwoburn.com
Web: www.theinnatwoburn.com
Rooms: 58 all ensuite
Pricing: Sgl £110–148 Dbl £125–195
Dinner available from £20–35 CC: Accepted
Room facilities:
Conference: 3 meeting rooms (Thtr 60 max),
24hr-delegate from £135, day-delegate from £38
Children: Welcome
Dogs: Welcome
Licenses:
Parking: Off-street and free
Directions: M1 Junction 13 Northbound turn left,
Southbound turn right. Pass petrol station and come
to Husborne Crawley village. Go through the village to
T-junction, turn right, follow road straight to Woburn.
Map ref: Woburn 4 C1
See advert on this page

Woodstock, Oxfordshire

The Feathers

★★★

Excellent

Market Street, Woodstock, Oxfordshire, OX20 1SX
Tel: 01993 812291 Fax: 01993 813158
Email: enquiries@feathers.co.uk
Web: www.feathers.co.uk

17th-century country town house. Situated in the heart
of Woodstock, nestled by the gates of Blenheim
Palace. A comfortable friendly atmosphere pervades
throughout with charm and character.
Rooms: 20 all ensuite
Pricing: Sgl £99–199 Dbl £135–275
Dinner available from £35
CC: Accepted
Room facilities:
Conference: 2 meeting rooms (Thtr 25 max),
24hr-delegate from £176.25, day-delegate from £58.75
Children: Welcome Dogs: Welcome Licenses:
Directions: Exit J8 M40. Take A40 towards Oxford; A44
towards Woodstock. Take 2nd left into town centre,
first hotel on left.
Map ref: Woodstock 4 B1

Gorselands Hall

Boddington Lane, North Leigh, Witney,
Oxfordshire, OX29 6PU
Tel: 01993 882292 Fax: 01993 883629
Email: hamilton@gorselandshall.com
Web: www.gorselandshall.com
Rooms: 6 all ensuite
Pricing: Sgl £36–45 Dbl £50–60 CC: Accepted
Room facilities:
Children: Welcome Dogs: Welcome
Leisure: Tennis, Snooker/billiards
Parking: Off-street and free
Directions: From Oxford take A4 to Woodstock. Left onto
A4075 towards Witney. After 4 miles turn right at sign for
Roman Villa. Gorselands Hall is 150 yards on left.
Map ref: North Leigh 4 B1

Sturdy's Castle

Country Inn/Restaurant, Banbury Road, Tackley,
Oxford, Oxfordshire, OX5 3EP
Tel: 01869 331328 Fax: 01869 331686
Email: enquiries@sturdyscastle.com
Web: www.sturdyscastle.com

Refurbished to a high standard, Sturdy's boasts a
traditional bar, 80 seater restaurant, function room and
separate accommodation block offering ensuite
bedrooms — the perfect setting for the business
traveller or those seeking somewhere to stay whilst
enjoying the many delights of Oxfordshire.
Rooms: 20 all ensuite
Pricing: Dbl £65–100
Dinner available from £7.50 CC: Accepted
Room facilities: Access:
Conference: 1 meeting room (Thtr 50 max)
Children: Welcome
Licenses:
Parking: Off-street and free
Directions: Situated on the main A4260 Oxford to
Banbury road. Approx. 2 miles from Woodstock and 9
1/2 miles from Oxford.
Map ref: Tackley 4 B1

Worthing, West Sussex

Best Western Berkeley Hotel

★★★

86-95 Marine Parade,
Worthing, West Sussex, BN11 3QD
Tel: 01903 820000 Fax: 01903 821333
Email: reservations@berkeleyhotel-worthing.co.uk
Web: www.bw-berkeleyhotel.co.uk
Rooms: 80 all ensuite
Pricing: Dinner available from £21.95
CC: Accepted
Room facilities:
Access:
Conference: 5 meeting rooms (Thtr 50 max),
24hr-delegate from £145, day-delegate from £40
Children: Welcome
Licenses:
Parking: Off-street and free
Directions: Follow the signs to Worthing seafront.
Travel west from the pier for 1/2 mile.
Map ref: Worthing 4 C4

Southeast

Cavendish

115/116 Marine Parade,
Worthing, West Sussex, BN11 3QG
Tel: 01903 236767 Fax: 01903 823840
Email: reservations@cavendishworthing.co.uk
Web: www.cavendishworthing.co.uk
Rooms: 17 all ensuite ⊛
Pricing: Sgl £45–50 Dbl £69.50–85
Dinner available from £15 CC: Accepted
Room facilities: ☐ ☎ ☕
Children: Welcome ⌘ Dogs: Welcome
Licenses: ⚎ Parking: Off-street
Directions: From the A27 or A24, follow signs to seafront.
Hotel 600 yards from Pier in a westerly direction.
Map ref: Worthing 4 C4

The Beacons Hotel

18 Shelley Road, Worthing, West Sussex, BN11 1TU
Tel: 01903 230948
Email: beaconshotel@amserve.net
Rooms: 8 all ensuite
Pricing: Sgl £36–42 Dbl £60–68 CC: Accepted
Room facilities: ☐ ☕ Children: Welcome
Dogs: Welcome Licenses: ⚎
Parking: Off-street and free
Map ref: Worthing 4 C4

Avalon Guest House

8 Windsor Road, Worthing, West Sussex, BN11 2LX
Tel: 01903 233808
Email: avalon-worthing@ntlworld.com
Web: www.avalon-worthing.co.uk
Rooms: 7 (2 ensuite)
Pricing: Sgl £20 Dbl £40–50
Room facilities: ☐ ☕ Children: Welcome 5yrs min age ⽊
Parking: Off-street and free
Directions: Worthing is on the main east-west A27 and
the A24 with its direct link to the M25 and the north.
Worthing is well signposted from the A27.
Map ref: Worthing 4 C4

St Michael's Manor, St Albans

Southwest

Glasgow • • Edinburgh

• Newcastle

Belfast •

Dublin • • Manchester

Birmingham •

Cardiff • London

BRISTOL CHANNEL

Lundy

ISLES OF SCILLY

Tresco • St Martin's
Bryher • H Tresco
Hugh Town • • St Mary's
St Agnes • St Mary's

ISLES OF SCILLY

Ilfracombe
Morthoe
Woolacombe
Combe Martin
Lynton Lynmouth
Porlock Minehead
Watc
EXMOOR Dunster Willit

Barnstaple
or
Bideford Bay
Croyde
Saunton
Braunton
Northam
Westward Ho!
Instow
Barnstaple
Exford Winsford
Raleigh's Cross
Dulverton
Wiveliscombe

Hartland Point
Clovelly
Hartland
Bideford
South Molton
Bampton

Great Torrington
Umberleigh
Burrington
Chittlehamholt
Chulmleigh
Tiverton
Cullompton

Bude
Stratton
R Torridge
Hatherleigh
DEVON
Cheriton Fitzpaine
Crediton
Exeter

Crackington Haven
Holsworthy
Okehampton
Virginstow
Topsham

Boscastle
Tintagel
Launceston
Lewdown
Chagford
Moretonhampstead
Matfo
Exe

Trebarwith Strand
Port Isaac
Landrake
Camelford
Lifton
Lydford
Milton Abbot
Chillaton
DARTMOOR
Postbridge
North Bovey
Bovey Tracey
Lowerdown
Chudleigh
Dawlish Wa

Padstow
Rock
CORNWALL
Rilla Mill
St Cleer
Tavistock
Two Bridges
Dartmeet
Ashburton
Isington
Newton Abbot
Teignmouth
Babbaco
Maidencombe

Constantine Bay
Bedruthan Steps
Mawgan Porth
Trevarrian
Wadebridge
St Breock
Bodmin
Callington
R Tavy
Buckfastleigh
Torquay
TORBAY

Newquay
St Columb Major
Downs
Liskeard
Tamar
Plymouth
Totnes
Paignton
Goodrington

Pentire
Crantock
Lower Polscoe
Hornicotts
Widegates
Saltash
Torpoint
Plymouth
Ivybridge
Brixham
Kingswear

Perranporth
St Agnes
Bugcovey
Waldreath
Fowey
Polperro
Looe
Whitsand Bay
Pomicknockle
Plymouth
Modbury
Dartmouth

Redruth
Camborne
Scorrier
St Carlyon Bay
Austell
Mevagissey
Polkirt
Bigbury-on-Sea
Thurlestone
Hope Cove
Kingsbridge
Start Bay

St Ives
Carbis Bay
Lelant
Illogan
Highway
Truro
Portloe
Warne Beach
Rosevine
Bigbury Bay
Soar Mill Cove
Salcombe
Start Point
Torcross

St Just
Chrysauster
Penzance
Hayle
Penryn
Mawnan
Smith
St Mawes
Trewennack

Land's End
Mayon
Sennen
Penzance
Marazion
Mount's Bay
Helston
Gweek
Falmouth
Falmouth Bay
Mullion
St Keverne

Lizard Point
Lizard

Southwest

Award winners

To help you choose somewhere really special for your stay, we've listed here all RAC Award-winning properties in this region.

Gold Ribbon Award

Premier

		pg
Castle Hotel, Taunton	★★★	236
Combe House Hotel & Restaurant, Exeter	★★★	176
Hell Bay, Isles of Scilly	★★★	189
Island Hotel, Isles of Scilly	★★★	190
Little Barwick House, Yeovil	★	259
Lucknam Park Hotel, Bath	★★★★	151
Northcote Manor Hotel, Umberleigh	★★★	248
Percy's Country Hotel & Restaurant, Okehampton	★★	205
Priory Hotel, Wareham	★★★	248
Queensberry Hotel & Olive Tree Restaurant, Bath	★★★	153
St Martin's on the Isle, Isles of Scilly	★★★	190
Stock Hill Country House & Restaurant, Gillingham	★★★	185
Ston Easton Park, Bath	★★★★	152
Summer Lodge, Evershot	★★★★	176
The Bath Priory, Bath	★★★★	152
Thornbury Castle, Thornbury	★★★	238
Whatley Manor, Malmesbury	★★★★	196

Combe House Hotel & Restaurant, Exeter

Hell Bay, Isles of Scilly

Lucknam Park Hotel, Bath

Northcote Manor Hotel, Umberleigh

Blue Ribbon Award

Excellent

		pg
Arundell Arms Hotel, Lifton	★★★	192
Budock Vean – The Hotel On The River, Falmouth	★★★★	180
Howards House Hotel, Salisbury	★★	217
Hunstrete House Hotel, Bath	★★★	153
Lewtrenchard Manor, Lewdown	★★★	191
Meudon Hotel, Falmouth	★★★	182
Nare Hotel, Truro	★★★★	246
Oaks Hotel, Porlock	★★	214
Orestone Manor Hotel & Restaurant, Torquay	★★★	241
Riviera, Sidmouth	★★★★	222
Rosevine Hotel, St Maws	★★★	232
Royal Crescent Hotel, Bath	★★★★★	150
The Lugger Hotel, Truro	★★★	247
The Pear Tree at Purton, Swindon	★★★	235
Thurlestone Hotel, Salcombe	★★★★	216
Tides Reach Hotel, Salcombe	★★★	216

White Ribbon Award

Commended

		pg
Soar Mill Cove Hotel, Salcombe	★★★★	216
The Garrack Hotel & Restaurant, St Ives	★★★	229
The Mansion House, Poole	★★★	214
Victoria Hotel, Sidmouth	★★★★	223
Whitsand Bay Hotel, Looe	★★★	192

Howards House Hotel, Salisbury

Meudon Hotel, Falmouth

The Mansion House, Poole

The Garrack Hotel & Restaurant, St Ives

Little Gem Award

Croyde Bay House Hotel, Croyde

Lydgate House, Postbridge

Moor View House, Lydford

Woodlands Country House, Padstow

Barnstaple, Devon

The Imperial Hotel

★★★★

Taw Vale Parade, Barnstaple,
Devon, EX32 8NB
Tel: 01271 345861 Fax: 01271 324448
Email: info@brend-imperial.co.uk
Web: www.brend-imperial.co.uk

Hotel Group of the Year

With luxury refurbishment now completed The Imperial is Barnstaple's premier hotel and the only 4-star. The

hotel overlooks the River Taw and Barnstaple.
Rooms: 63 all ensuite
Pricing: Sgl £92.50–112.50 Dbl £115–155
Dinner available from £25
CC: Accepted
Room facilities: 🖥 ☎ ☕ 📞
Access: ||↑
Children: Welcome ♯ ☕
Dogs: Assistance dogs only
Licenses: 🍴
Leisure: Snooker/billiards
Parking: Off-street and free
Directions: A361 Barnstaple, signs for town centre passing Tesco. Straight over next two roundabouts, road forks right. Hotel on right.
Map ref: Barnstaple 2 C2
See advert on this page

Barnstaple Hotel

★★★★

Braunton Road, Barnstaple,
Devon, EX31 1LE
Tel: 01271 376221 Fax: 01271 324101
Email: info@barnstaplehotel.co.uk
Web: www.barnstaplehotel.co.uk

Hotel Group of the Year

On the coastal side of Barnstaple, offering easy access to North Devon's beaches and Exmoor. The hotel has a superb health and leisure complex.
Rooms: 60 all ensuite
Pricing: Sgl £70–95 Dbl £90–115
Dinner available from £22
CC: Accepted
Room facilities: 🖥 ☎ ☕ 📞
Children: Welcome ♯ ☕
Dogs: Welcome
Licenses: 🍷 🍴
Leisure: Indoor pool, Outdoor pool, Gym, Health spa, Games room, Snooker/billiards
Parking: Off-street and free
Directions: Take A361 Braunton/Ilfracombe road from Barnstaple. Hotel is located on left approximately 1 mile from town centre.
Map ref: Barnstaple 2 C2

Southwest

Park Hotel

★★★

New Road, Taw Vale,
Barnstaple, Devon, EX32 9AE
Tel: 01271 372166 Fax: 01271 323157
Email: info@parkhotel.co.uk
Web: www.parkhotel.co.uk

With the whole of North Devon on your doorstep, the Park Hotel combines luxury with excellent value. Overlooking a park and the River Taw, and an easy walk to the town centre.
Rooms: 42 all ensuite
Pricing: Sgl £70–80 Dbl £90–100
Dinner available from £22
CC: Accepted
Room facilities:
Children: Welcome   Dogs: Welcome
Licenses:
Parking: Off-street and free
Directions: A361 Barnstaple. Follow signs to town centre, passing 'Tesco' straight ahead at next two roundabouts. Hotel located on right.
Map ref: Barnstaple 2 C2

Relax & smell the coffee

Fresh coffee, chilled juices for breakfast. RAC's team of qualified Inspectors check them both.

Royal and Fortescue Hotel

★★★★

Boutport Street,
Barnstaple, Devon, EX31 1HG
Tel: 01271 342289 Fax: 01271 340102
Email: info@royalfortescue.co.uk
Web: www.royalfortescue.co.uk

A former coaching inn, recent refurbishment has retained this historic charm whilst adding fine modern facilities. Lord Fortescue's restaurant, beautiful bedrooms and the adjacent bar and brasserie "62 the Bank" are all at your disposal.
Rooms: 50 all ensuite
Pricing: Sgl £65–75 Dbl £85–95
Dinner available from £21
CC: Accepted
Room facilities:
Access:
Children: Welcome
Dogs: Welcome
Licenses:
Parking: Off-street and free
Directions: Located in the town centre at the junction of High Street and Boutport Street.
Map ref: Barnstaple 2 C2

Bath, Bath & NE Somerset

Royal Crescent Hotel

★★★★★  Excellent

16 Royal Crescent, Bath,
Bath & NE Somerset, BA1 2LS
Tel: 01225 823333 Fax: 01225 339401
Email: info@royalcrescent.co.uk
Web: www.royalcrescent.co.uk
Rooms: 45 all ensuite
Pricing: Sgl £280–840 Dbl £290–850
Dinner available from £55
CC: Accepted
Room facilities:
Access:
Conference: 5 meeting rooms (Thtr 60 max), 24hr-delegate from £225, day-delegate from £85
Children: Welcome

Southwest

Dogs: Welcome
Licenses: ⚫ 👭
Leisure: Indoor pool, Gym, Health spa, Beauty salon
Parking: Off-street and free
Directions: Guests are provided with precise directions when making reservations.
Map ref: Bath 3 F1

The Bath Spa Hotel
★★★★★ 👹👹👹
Sydney Road, Bath, Bath & NE Somerset, BA2 6JF
Tel: 0870 4008222 Fax: 01225 444006
Email: sales@bathspahotel.com
Web: www.bathspahotel.com
Rooms: 104 all ensuite 📺 ⊗
Pricing: Sgl £175–275 Dbl £250–360
Dinner available from £37.50
CC: Accepted
Room facilities: 📺 ☎ 🍵 📠
Access: |↕
Conference: 6 meeting rooms (Thtr 130 max), 24hr-delegate from £229, day-delegate from £65
Children: Welcome 🍴
Dogs: Welcome
Licenses: ⚫ 👭
Leisure: Indoor pool, Gym, Health spa, Beauty salon, Treatment rooms
Parking: Off-street and free
Directions: M4 at J18, A46 to Bath. At first major roundabout turn right onto A4. Follow signs for city centre. Turn left onto A36 at lights. Past fire station on left, turn right at traffic lights after pedestrian crossing, next left into Sydney Place. Hotel 200 yards on right.
Map ref: Bath 3 F1

Luckham Park Hotel
★★★★ 👹👹👹   *Premier*
Colerne, Chippenham, Wiltshire, SN14 8AZ
Tel: 01225 742777 Fax: 01225 743536
Email: reservations@lucknampark.co.uk
Web: www.lucknampark.co.uk
Rooms: 41 all ensuite 📺
Pricing: Sgl £235–800 Dbl £235–800
Dinner available from £55
CC: Accepted
Room facilities: 📺 ☎ 📠
Conference: 4 meeting rooms (Thtr 50 max), 24hr-delegate from £260, day-delegate from £80
Children: Welcome 🍴
Licenses: ⚫ 👭
Leisure: Indoor pool, Gym, Health spa, Beauty salon, Tennis, Riding, Games room, Snooker/billiards
Parking: Off-street and free
Directions: From west exit M4 J18 onto A46 for 3 miles. Take A420 towards Chippenham. At Ford turn left to Colerne and right at the crossroads. From London exit M4 J17.
Map ref: Colerne 3 F1
See advert on this page

Ston Easton Park

★★★★ ♔♔♔ Premier

Ston Easton, Bath, Bath & NE Somerset, BA3 4DF
Tel: 01761 241631 Fax: 01761 241377
Email: info@stoneaston.co.uk
Web: www.stoneaston.co.uk
Rooms: 23 all ensuite ♨ 🖥 ⊛
Dinner available
CC: Accepted
Room facilities: ▭ ☎ 📠
Conference: 7 meeting rooms (Thtr 65 max)
Children: Welcome ♬ ≋ℂ
Dogs: Welcome
Licenses: ⟁ ⚏
Leisure: Tennis, Snooker/billiards
Parking: Off-street and free
Directions: On the A37 10 minutes north of Shepton Mallet in the village of Ston Easton, 11 miles south from Bath and Bristol.
Map ref: Ston Easton 3 E2

The Bath Priory

★★★★ ♔♔♔ Premier

Weston Road, Bath, Bath & NE Somerset, BA1 2XT
Tel: 01225 331922 Fax: 01225 448276
Email: mail@thebathpriory.co.uk
Web: www.thebathpriory.co.uk
Rooms: 31 all ensuite ♨ 🖥
Pricing: Sgl £200–245 Dbl £245–425
Dinner available from £49.50
CC: Accepted
Room facilities: ▭ ☎ 📠
Conference: 3 meeting rooms (Thtr 60 max), 24hr-delegate from £223, day-delegate from £88
Children: Welcome ♬ ≋ℂ
Licenses: ⟁ ⚏
Leisure: Indoor pool, Outdoor pool, Gym, Health spa, Beauty salon
Parking: Off-street and free
Directions: Situated in the north-west corner of the city, the Bath Priory Hotel is a 15-minute walk from the city centre.
Map ref: Bath 3 F1
See advert on this page

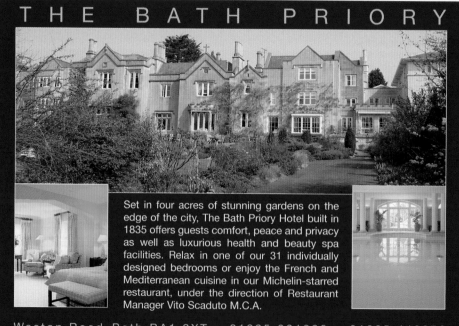

THE BATH PRIORY

Set in four acres of stunning gardens on the edge of the city, The Bath Priory Hotel built in 1835 offers guests comfort, peace and privacy as well as luxurious health and beauty spa facilities. Relax in one of our 31 individually designed bedrooms or enjoy the French and Mediterranean cuisine in our Michelin-starred restaurant, under the direction of Restaurant Manager Vito Scaduto M.C.A.

Weston Road, Bath BA1 2XT TEL 01225 331922 FAX 01225 448276
mail@thebathpriory.co.uk   www.thebathpriory.co.uk

Hunstrete House Hotel

★★★★ ⓡⓡ Excellent

Pensford, Hunstrete, Somerset, BS31 4NS
Tel: 01761 490490 Fax: 01761 490732
Email: reception@hunstretehouse.co.uk
Web: www.hunstretehouse.co.uk
Rooms: 25 all ensuite 🖨 ⓢ
Pricing: Sgl £135–145 Dbl £185–205
Dinner available from £47.75–55 CC: Accepted
Room facilities: 🖵 ☎
Conference: 3 meeting rooms (Thtr 80 max),
24hr-delegate from £175, day-delegate from £49
Children: Welcome 🅷 🐾 Dogs: Welcome
Licenses: 🜹 👯
Leisure: Outdoor pool, Tennis
Directions: From Bath A4 to A39 and A368. From
Bristol A37 to A368.
Map ref: Hunstrete 3 E1

Queensberry Hotel & Olive Tree Restaurant

★★★★ ⓡⓡⓡ Premier

Russell Street, Bath,
Bath & NE Somerset, BA1 2QF
Tel: 01225 447928 Fax: 01225 446065
Email: reservations@thequeensberry.co.uk
Web: www.thequeensberry.co.uk
Rooms: 29 all ensuite 🖨 ⓢ
Pricing: Sgl £114–154 Dbl £123–163
Dinner available from £32
CC: Accepted
Room facilities: 🖵 ☎ 🔌 Access: ⬆
Conference: 1 meeting room (Thtr 30 max),
24hr-delegate from £170, day-delegate from £50
Children: Welcome 🐾
Licenses: 👯
Parking: Off-street and free
Directions: A4 London Road turn right into Landsdown
Hill. Take second left into Bennet Street, first right into
Russell Street.
Map ref: Bath 3 F1
See advert on this page

The Lansdown Grove

★★★★ ⓡⓡ

Lansdown Road, Bath, Bath & NE Somerset, BA1 5EH
Tel: 01225 483888 Fax: 01225 483838
Email: lansdown@marstonhotels.com
Web: www.marstonhotels.com
Rooms: 60 all ensuite ♨ 🖨 ⓢ
Dinner available CC: Accepted
Room facilities: 🖵 ☎ ☕ 🔌
Access: ⬆
Conference: 6 meeting rooms (Thtr 100 max)
Children: Welcome 🅷 🐾
Licenses: 🜹 👯
Parking: Off-street and free
Directions: Leave M4 at Junction 18. Follow A46
towards Bath city centre. Take Broad Street. Follow
signs for Lansdown and Bath Races.
Map ref: Bath 3 F1

Southwest

Compass Inn

★★

Tormarton, near Badminton,
South Gloucestershire, GL9 1JB
Tel: 01454 218242 Fax: 01454 218741
Email: info@compass-inn.co.uk
Web: www.compass-inn.co.uk
Seasonal closure: Christmas Day
Rooms: 26 all ensuite
Pricing: Sgl £98–108 Dbl £117.50–127.50
Dinner available from £8–30
CC: Accepted
Room facilities:
Conference: 7 meeting rooms (Thtr 100 max),
24hr-delegate from £114.95, day-delegate from £42.95
Children: Welcome
Dogs: Welcome
Licenses:
Leisure: Games room, Boules
Parking: Off-street and free
Directions: Situated in the Cotswolds, the Compass
Inn has easy access to both Bath and Bristol, located
on Junction 18 of M4.
Map ref: Tormarton 3 F1

George's Hotel

★★

2-3 South Parade, Bath,
Bath & NE Somerset, BA2 4AA
Tel: 01225 464923 Fax: 01225 425471
Email: info@georgeshotel.co.uk
Web: www.georgeshotel.co.uk
Rooms: 19 all ensuite
Dinner available CC: Accepted
Room facilities:
Children: Welcome
Licenses:
Directions: In city centre between Abbey and stations,
next to public car park.
Map ref: Bath 3 F1

Athole Guest House

◆◆◆◆◆

33 Upper Oldfield Park, Bath,
Bath & NE Somerset, BA2 3JX
Tel: 01225 334307 Fax: 01225 320009
Email: bookings@atholehouse.co.uk
Web: www.atholehouse.co.uk

No Laura Ashley or dusty four-posters at Athole
House. Instead, a large Victorian home restored to give
bright, inviting, quiet bedrooms, sleek furniture,
sparkling bathrooms. 12 minutes walk to centre.
Secure parking, electronic gates.
Rooms: 3 all ensuite
Pricing: Sgl £48–58 Dbl £68–78 CC: Accepted
Room facilities:
Children: Welcome
Parking: Off-street and free
Directions: From M4 follow signs for Through
traffic/Radstock/Wells into Wells Road. Take first
turning on right.
Map ref: Bath 3 F1

Dorian House

◆◆◆◆◆

1 Upper Oldfield Park, Bath,
Bath & NE Somerset, BA2 3JX
Tel: 01225 426336 Fax: 01225 444699
Email: info@dorianhouse.co.uk
Web: www.dorianhouse.co.uk
Rooms: 8 all ensuite
Pricing: Sgl £47–78 Dbl £59–150
CC: Accepted
Room facilities:
Children: Welcome
Licenses: Parking: Off-street
Directions: Exit M4 J18, A46, A4 to Bath. Follow A36
signposted Bristol. Left on A367. First right is Upper
Oldfield Park.
Map ref: Bath 3 F1
See advert on opposite page

Oldfields

◆◆◆◆◆

102 Wells Road, Bath, Bath & NE Somerset, BA2 3AL
Tel: 01225 317984 Fax: 01225 444471
Email: info@oldfields.co.uk
Web: www.oldfields.co.uk

Elegant and traditional bed & breakfast with panoramic views of Bath and only 8 minutes walk to Bath city centre. A delicious choice of breakfast to include full English, fresh seasonal fruits and smoked salmon with scrambled eggs are served in the magnificent dining room. Car park and residents' garden.
Rooms: 16 all ensuite ⊗
Pricing: Sgl £45–95 Dbl £59–160
CC: Accepted
Room facilities: ▢ ☎ ⊚

Children: Welcome
Parking: Off-street and free
Directions: Oldfields is situated ½ mile from the city centre on the A367, Wells Road at the corner of Upper Oldfield park
Map ref: Bath 3 F1

Tasburgh House Hotel Little Gem

◆◆◆◆◆ ✕ ⌇

Warminster Road, Bath,
Bath & NE Somerset, BA2 6SH
Tel: 01225 425096 Fax: 01225 463842
Email: hotel@bathtasburgh.co.uk
Web: www.bathtasburgh.co.uk
Seasonal closure: 22 December to 9 January

Charming, award-winning Victorian mansion in seven acres of landscaped gardens and meadow park bordering the Kennet and Avon Canal. Spectacular views and convenient for the city centre. Personal, caring service with country house comforts and a gourmet breakfast. Perfect place to mix relaxation with sight-seeing.
Rooms: 12 all ensuite 🐾 ⊗
Pricing: Sgl £60–75 Dbl £110–140
CC: Accepted
Room facilities: ▢ ☎ ⊚ 🔌
Conference: 2 meeting rooms (Thtr 15 max), day-delegate from £28
Children: Welcome
Licenses: ⚏
Parking: Off-street and free
Directions: Follow signs A36 to Warminster from city centre. From Bathwick Street continue to traffic lights. Take left exit, hotel is at top of hill on left.
Map ref: Bath 3 F1

Southwest

Oakleigh House

19 Upper Oldfield Park, Bath,
Bath & NE Somerset, BA2 3JX
Tel: 01225 315698 Fax: 01225 448223
Email: oakleigh@which.net
Web: www.oakleigh-house.co.uk
Rooms: 3 all ensuite ⊗
Pricing: Sgl £55–65 Dbl £70–90
CC: Accepted
Room facilities: ▢ ◱
Parking: Off-street and free
Directions: Take A367 from centre of Bath, then first
turning on right. Oakleigh is 100m on right.
Map ref: Bath 3 F1

The Talbot 15th Century Coaching Inn

Selwood Street, Mells, near Bath,
Bath & NE Somerset, BA11 3PN
Tel: 01373 812254 Fax: 01373 813599
Email: roger@talbotinn.com
Web: www.talbotinn.com

Medieval village housing this "treasure of a place" just
south of Bath. Lovely bedrooms (including four-
posters) within an enchanting coach house setting.
Cosy restaurant serving excellent fresh food.
Rooms: 8 (7 ensuite) ♥ ▨ ⊗
Pricing: Sgl £75 Dbl £85–135
Dinner available from £10–30
CC: Accepted
Room facilities: ▢ ☎ ◱
Conference: 1 meeting room (Thtr 12 max)
Children: Welcome ⅄
Dogs: Welcome
Licenses: ▟▟▟
Leisure: Nearby golf course
Parking: Off-street and free
Directions: From Bath in Somerset, take the Wells road
south to Radstock, then east towards Frome. Turning
right signposted Mells.
Map ref: Mells 3 F2

Lamp Post Villa

3 Crescent Gardens, Bath,
Bath & NE Somerset, BA1 2NA
Tel: 01225 331221 Fax: 01225 426783
Seasonal closure: Christmas

A lovely Edwardian house situated ten minutes walk
from the city centre attractions. Rooms are comfortable
with ensuite bathrooms. Full choice of breakfast menu
including vegetarian option. Private car park available.
Rooms: 4 all ensuite ⊗
Pricing: Sgl £40–45 Dbl £55–65 CC: Accepted
Room facilities: ▢ ☎ ◱
Children: Welcome ⅄ Dogs: Welcome
Parking: Off-street
Directions: On A4 Bristol road, in western side of city
centre close to Victoria Park.
Map ref: Bath 3 F1

Are the bells ringing?

Getting married? Congratulations!
Look for the wedding bells symbol
which shows hotels licensed for
civil ceremonies.

The big sleep

As part of our
comprehensive
inspection process,
RAC Inspectors
investigate the
comfort of the beds.

Bideford, Devon

Royal Hotel

★★★

Barnstaple Street, Bideford,
Devon, EX39 4AE
Tel: 01237 472005 Fax: 01237 478957
Email: info@royalbideford.co.uk
Web: www.royalbideford.co.uk

Hotel Group of the Year

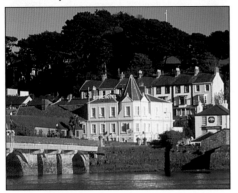

The Royal Hotel overlooks ancient Bideford Bridge and
the River Torridge and is a good base for exploring the
countryside and coastline of North Devon.
Rooms: 32 all ensuite 🍽
Pricing: Sgl £70–90 Dbl £90–110
Dinner available from £21
CC: Accepted
Room facilities: 🖵 ☎ 🍵 📞 Access: ⬆
Children: Welcome ⫟ 🐾 Dogs: Welcome
Licenses: ⬧ ♟
Parking: Off-street and free
Directions: At the eastern end of old Bideford bridge.
Map ref: Bideford 2 C2

Riversford Hotel

★★ ⓡ

Limers Lane, Bideford, Devon, EX39 2RG
Tel: 01237 474239 Fax: 01237 421661
Email: riversford@aol.com
Web: www.riversford.co.uk
Rooms: 15 all ensuite 🏧 ⓢ
Pricing: Sgl £50–60 Dbl £75–110
Dinner available from £15 CC: Accepted
Room facilities: 🖵 ☎ 🍵
Conference: 1 meeting room (Thtr 30 max),
24hr-delegate from £75, day-delegate from £50
Children: Welcome ⫟ Dogs: Welcome
Licenses: ♟ Parking: Off-street
Directions: From the M5 turn off at junction 27 onto the
north Devon Link road. Stay on until you cross the
Torridge bridge, turn right at the roundabout, take first
right into Limers Lane.
Map ref: Bideford 2 C2

THE ANVIL INN

The Anvil is a charming privately owned
16th century thatched hotel, restaurant and
bar. Located in the pretty village of
Pimperne, the hotel offers a fine and
relaxing setting for holiday breaks, and also
for business travellers.

Salisbury Road, Pimperne,
Blandford Forum, Dorset, DTII 8UQ

Tel: 01258 453431 Fax: 01258 480182

Email: info@anvilhotel.co.uk
Web: www.anvilhotel.co.uk

Blandford Forum, Dorset

The Anvil Inn

◆◆◆◆ ✕

Salisbury Road, Pimperne, Blandford Forum,
Dorset, DT11 8UQ
Tel: 01258 453431 Fax: 01258 480182
Email: info@anvilhotel.co.uk
Web: www.anvilhotel.co.uk
Rooms: 13 all ensuite 🏧 ⓢ
Pricing: Sgl £60–65 Dbl £80–100
Dinner available from £8.50–25
CC: Accepted
Room facilities: 🖵 ☎ 🍵
Children: Welcome ⫟
Dogs: Welcome
Licenses: ♟
Parking: Off-street and free
Directions: One mile from Blandford Forum on the
main Salisbury Road A354.
Map ref: Pimperne 3 F2
See advert on this page

Be more mobile **Dial 1740 from any
mobile phone to get up-to-the-
minute RAC traffic information.**

Calls cost up to 59p per minute. Please check with your network operator.

Boscastle, Cornwall

The Wellington Hotel

★★

The Harbour, Old Road, Boscastle,
Cornwall, PL35 0AQ
Tel: 01840 250202 Fax: 01840 250621
Email: info@boscastle-wellington.com
Web: www.boscastle-wellington.com

Listed 16th century coaching inn in Elizabethan
harbour of Boscastle. Fantastic fine dining restaurant,
traditional pub with Cornish real ales and log fires. Ten
acres of private woodland walks. Recently refurbished.
Rooms: 15 all ensuite
Pricing: Sgl £40–45 Dbl £80–130
Dinner available from £20
CC: Accepted
Room facilities: 🖵 ☎ 🍵
Conference: 2 meeting rooms (Thtr 30 max),
24hr-delegate from £75, day-delegate from £25
Children: Welcome
Licenses: ††† Parking: Off-street and free
Directions: From Exeter A30 to Launceston, at
Kennards House A395 to Camelford, at Davidstow
B3262 to A39, left then right on to B3266, follow signs
to Boscastle.
Map ref: Boscastle 2 B3

Bournemouth, Dorset

Norfolk Royale Hotel

★★★★

Richmond Hill, Bournemouth, Dorset, BH2 6EN
Tel: 01202 551521 Fax: 01202 299729
Email: norfolkroyale@englishrosehotels.co.uk
Web: www.englishrosehotels.co.uk

Rooms: 95 all ensuite
Pricing: Sgl £60–115 Dbl £90
Dinner available from £22.50
CC: Accepted
Room facilities: 🖵 ☎ 🍵 Access: ⏫
Conference: 9 meeting rooms,
24hr-delegate from £130, day-delegate from £37.50
Children: Welcome

Licenses: †††
Leisure: Indoor pool, Health spa
Parking: Off-street
Directions: M3 from London area then A27 via A33.
Take A31 to Wessex Way and at A34 junction left into
Richmond Hill.
Map ref: Bournemouth 4 A4
See advert on this page

Bay View Court Hotel

★★★

35 East Overcliff Drive, East Cliff,
Bournemouth, Dorset, BH1 3AH
Tel: 01202 294449 Fax: 01202 292883
Email: enquiry@bayviewcourt.co.uk
Web: www.bayviewcourt.co.uk
Rooms: 64 all ensuite
Pricing: Sgl £39–52 Dbl £78–104
Dinner available from £20 CC: Accepted
Room facilities: 🖵 ☎ 🍵 Access: ⏫
Conference: 2 meeting rooms (Thtr 170 max),
24hr-delegate from £70, day-delegate from £22
Children: Welcome Dogs: Welcome
Licenses: †††
Leisure: Indoor pool, Health spa, Games room,
Snooker/billiards
Parking: Off-street and free
Directions: Turn off A338 at St Paul's roundabout.
Head for clifftop. Go over two roundabouts, head for
clifftop.
Map ref: Bournemouth 4 A4

Best Western East Anglia Hotel

6 Poole Road, Bournemouth, Dorset, BH2 5QX
Tel: 01202 765163 Fax: 01202 752949
Email: info@eastangliahotel.com
Web: www.eastangliahotel.com
Rooms: 70 all ensuite ♨ ⊛
Pricing: Sgl £59 Dbl £118
Dinner available from £21
CC: Accepted
Room facilities: ▢ ☎ ⌨ ☏
Access: |↓↑
Conference: 4 meeting rooms (Thtr 150 max),
24hr-delegate from £90, day-delegate from £30
Children: Welcome ♿ ≋
Dogs: Assistance dogs only
Licenses: ⋔⋔⋔
Leisure: Outdoor pool, Games room, Sauna, Spa pool,
Pool room
Parking: Off-street and free
Directions: From A338, take exit signposted BIC &
West Cliff. Take 3rd exit at next roundabout into Poole
Road. Hotel is located on your right.
Map ref: Bournemouth 4 A4

Burley Court Hotel

Bath Road, Bournemouth, Dorset, BH1 2NP
Tel: 01202 552824 Fax: 01202 298514
Email: info@burleycourthotel.co.uk
Web: www.burleycourthotel.co.uk
Seasonal closure: early January
Rooms: 38 all ensuite ♨ ⊞ ⊛
Pricing: Sgl £35–49 Dbl £70–98
Dinner available from £18.50
CC: Accepted
Room facilities: ▢ ☎ ⌨
Access: |↓↑
Children: Welcome ♿
Dogs: Welcome
Licenses: ⋔⋔⋔
Leisure: Outdoor pool, Games room
Parking: Off-street and free
Directions: Leave A338 at St Paul's roundabout. Take
third exit at next two roundabouts. Burley Court is the
first hotel after the crossing.
Map ref: Bournemouth 4 A4

"Here!"

Need a pet friendly property?
Look out for 'Dogs welcome' in
our listings.

Chine

25 Boscombe Spa Road, Bournemouth,
Dorset, BH5 1AX
Tel: 01202 396234 Fax: 01202 391737
Email: enquiries@chinehotel.co.uk
Web: www.chinehotel.co.uk

Attractive Victorian Hotel with award-winning cuisine,
located in three acres of mature gardens with direct
access to the beach. Indoor and outdoor pools,
Jacuzzi, outdoor hot tub, sauna, gymnasium and
games room.
Rooms: 87 all ensuite ♨ ⊞ ⊛
Pricing: Sgl £70–95 Dbl £140–180
Dinner available from £24.95 CC: Accepted
Room facilities: ▢ ☎ ⌨ Access: |↓↑
Conference: 9 meeting rooms (Thtr 140 max),
24hr-delegate from £135, day-delegate from £42
Children: Welcome ♿ ♘ ≋ Licenses: ⟁ ⋔⋔⋔
Leisure: Indoor pool, Outdoor pool, Gym, Health spa,
Games room
Parking: Off-street and free
Directions: At first roundabout follow signs for
Boscombe into Christchurch Road. Turn right after
second traffic lights into Boscombe Spa Road.
Map ref: Bournemouth 4 A4

Durley Hall Hotel

Durley Chine Road, Bournemouth, Dorset, BH2 5JS
Tel: 01202 751000 Fax: 01202 757585
Email: sales@durleyhall.co.uk
Web: www.durleyhall.co.uk
Rooms: 77 all ensuite ♨ ⊛
Pricing: Sgl £35–65 Dbl £70–130
Dinner available from £20 CC: Accepted
Room facilities: ▢ ☎ ⌨ ☏ Access: |↓↑
Conference: 11 meeting rooms (Thtr 200 max),
24hr-delegate from £95, day-delegate from £35
Children: Welcome ♿ ≋ Licenses: ⟁ ⋔⋔⋔
Leisure: Indoor pool, Gym, Health spa, Beauty salon
Parking: Off-street and free
Directions: Approaching on the A338 Wessex Way,
follow signs to the West Cliff and Bournemouth
International Centre.
Map ref: Bournemouth 4 A4

Elstead Classic Hotel

★★★

Knyveton Road, Bournemouth, Dorset, BH1 3QP
Tel: 01202 293071 Fax: 01202 293827
Email: info@the-elstead.co.uk
Web: www.the-elstead.co.uk
Rooms: 50 all ensuite
Pricing: Sgl £62.45–80 Dbl £101.85–130
Dinner available from £18.50 CC: Accepted
Room facilities: Access:
Conference: 5 meeting rooms (Thtr 90 max),
24hr-delegate from £95, day-delegate from £25
Children: Welcome Dogs: Welcome
Licenses: Leisure: Indoor pool, Gym, Games room,
Snooker/billiards Parking: Off-street and free
Directions: From A338 follow signs to Bournemouth.
Turn into St Paul's Road off the main Wessex Way.
Turn first left into Knyveton Road.
Map ref: Bournemouth 4 A4
See advert on this page

Heathlands

★★★

12 Grove Road, East Cliff, Bournemouth,
Dorset, BH1 3AY
Tel: 01202 553336 Fax: 01202 555937
Email: info@heathlandshotel.com
Web: www.heathlandshotel.com

115-bedroom hotel located on the East Cliff within
easy walking distance to sandy beaches, cosmopolitan
town centre and award-winning gardens. The hotel is
justly proud of its reputation for fine cuisine and
friendly efficient staff.
Rooms: 115 all ensuite
Pricing: Sgl £49–98 Dbl £98–196
Dinner available from £16.50 CC: Accepted
Room facilities:
Access:
Conference: 7 meeting rooms (Thtr 270 max),
24hr-delegate from £80, day-delegate from £30
Children: Welcome
Dogs: Welcome
Licenses:
Leisure: Outdoor pool, Gym, Health spa
Parking: Off-street and free
Directions: Follow signs to East Cliff. At roundabout,
turn into Gervis Road.
Map ref: Bournemouth 4 A4

Mayfair Hotel

★★★

27 Bath Road, Bournemouth, Dorset, BH1 2NW
Tel: 01202 551983 Fax: 01202 551002
Email: info@themayfair.com
Web: www.themayfair.com
Rooms: 40 all ensuite
Pricing: Sgl £30–50 Dbl £60–100
Dinner available from £14.95
CC: Accepted
Room facilities:
Access:
Conference: 3 meeting rooms (Thtr 70 max)
Children: Welcome
Dogs: Assistance dogs only
Licenses:
Leisure: Games room
Parking: Off-street and free
Directions: Leave A338 at St Paul's roundabout, take
third exit at next two roundabouts. The Mayfair is the
second hotel in Bath Road.
Map ref: Bournemouth 4 A4

Ocean View Hotel

★★★

East Overcliff Drive, East Cliff, Bournemouth,
Dorset, BH1 3AR
Tel: 01202 558057 Fax: 01202 556285
Email: enquiry@oceanview.uk.com
Web: www.oceanview.uk.com

Rooms: 52 all ensuite
Pricing: Sgl £39–52 Dbl £78–104
Dinner available from £20 CC: Accepted
Room facilities: Access:
Conference: 4 meeting rooms (Thtr 170 max), 24hr-delegate from £70, day-delegate from £22
Children: Welcome Dogs: Welcome
Licenses: Leisure: Outdoor pool, Games room
Parking: Off-street and free
Directions: Go along A338 in to Bournemouth. Follow signs for East Cliff. Situated on clifftop between the two piers.
Map ref: Bournemouth 4 A4

Arlington Hotel

★★

Exeter Park Road, Lower Gardens, Bournemouth, Dorset, BH2 5BD
Tel: 01202 552879/553012 Fax: 01202 298317
Email: enquiries@arlingtonbournemouth.co.uk
Web: www.arlingtonbournemouth.co.uk
Rooms: 28 all ensuite
Pricing: Sgl £36.50–43.50 Dbl £73–87
Dinner available from £12.50 CC: Accepted
Room facilities: Access:
Children: Welcome 2yrs min age
Licenses:
Parking: Off-street and free
Directions: Follow all signs to Bournemouth International Centre, Town Centre, Pier, Beach. Exeter Park Road runs behind Royal Exeter Hotel.
Map ref: Bournemouth 4 A4

Chequers Hotel

★★

17 West Cliff Road, Bournemouth, Dorset, BH2 5EX
Tel: 01202 553900 Fax: 01202 551015
Email: bookings@chequershotel.net
Web: www.chequershotel.net
Seasonal closure: First 2 weeks January
Rooms: 23 (22 ensuite)
Pricing: Sgl £24–38 Dbl £48–76 CC: Accepted
Room facilities: Children: Welcome
Dogs: Welcome Licenses:
Parking: Off-street and free
Directions: Follow signs to BIC, Chequers Hotel is then up the hill from mini roundabout and on right after next roundabout.
Map ref: Bournemouth 4 A4

Grange Hotel

★★

Overcliff Drive, Southbourne, Bournemouth, Dorset, BH6 3NL
Tel: 01202 433093 Fax: 01202 424228
Web: www.bournemouthgrangehotel.co.uk
Rooms: 31 all ensuite
Dinner available CC: Accepted
Room facilities: Access:
Children: Welcome
Licenses:
Leisure: Games room
Parking: Off-street and free
Directions: Follow Overcliff Drive to clifftop.
Map ref: Bournemouth 4 A4

Liston Hotel — Gilbeys Restaurant

★★

Wollstonecraft Road, Boscombe, on corner of Boscombe Cliff Road, Bournemouth, Dorset, BH5 1JQ
Tel: 01202 394588 Fax: 01202 394588
Email: diane@gilbeysrestaurant.co.uk
Web: www.gilbeysrestaurant.co.uk

Independently owned occupying a quiet secluded position but very close to beach & shops. Fully licensed. Lovely south facing garden and al fresco area. Fine dining restaurant. Comfortable bedrooms.
Rooms: 25 all ensuite
Pricing: Sgl £28–40 Dbl £56–80
Dinner available from £12.50–30 CC: Accepted
Room facilities: Access:
Conference: 1 meeting room (Thtr 30 max)
Children: Welcome
Dogs: Welcome
Licenses:
Parking: Off-street and free
Directions: From Boscombe Pier take first right into The Marina. First right Boscombe Cliff Road opposite Ocean Heights Flats.
Map ref: Bournemouth 4 A4

Tower House Hotel

★★

West Cliff Gardens, Bournemouth, Dorset, BH2 5HP
Tel: 01202 290742 Fax: 01202 299311
Email: towerhouse.hotel@btconnect.com
Web: www.towerhousehotelbournemouth.com
Rooms: 32 all ensuite
Pricing: Sgl £30–38 Dbl £60–78
Dinner available from £11 CC: Accepted
Room facilities: Access:
Conference: 1 meeting room (Thtr 20 max)
Children: Welcome Dogs: Welcome
Licenses:
Parking: Off-street and free
Directions: A338 for Bournemouth, take town centre west exit for BIC and seafront parking. Second exit off Durley roundabout towards the sea.
Map ref: Bournemouth 4 A4

Southwest

Ullswater Hotel

West Cliff Gardens, Bournemouth, Dorset, BH2 5HW
Tel: 01202 555181 Fax: 01202 317896
Email: enquiries@ullswater.uk.com
Web: www.ullswater.uk.com
Rooms: 42 all ensuite
Pricing: Sgl £32–40 Dbl £64–80
Dinner available from £12.50 CC: Accepted
Room facilities: Access:
Conference: 2 meeting rooms (Thtr 40 max),
24hr-delegate from £55, day-delegate from £25
Children: Welcome Dogs: Welcome
Licenses:
Leisure: Games room, Snooker/billiards
Parking: Off-street and free
Directions: From any major route into Bournemouth,
follow the signs for the West Cliff. The Ullswater Hotel
is situated in West Cliff Gardens, just off the main West
Cliff Road.
Map ref: Bournemouth 4 A4

Whitehall Hotel

Exeter Park Road, Bournemouth, Dorset, BH2 5AX
Tel: 01202 554682 Fax: 01202 292637
Email: reservations@thewhitehallhotel.co.uk
Web: wwww.thewhitehallhotel.co.uk
Rooms: 46 all ensuite
Pricing: Sgl £34–50 Dbl £68–100
Dinner available from £12–20 CC: Accepted
Room facilities: Access:
Conference: 2 meeting rooms (Thtr 70 max),
24hr-delegate from £39, day-delegate from £5
Children: Welcome Dogs: Welcome Licenses:
Directions: Follow all signs to Bournemouth
International Centre (BIC). Exeter Park Road is situated
off small roundabout off Exeter Road.
Map ref: Bournemouth 4 A4

Balincourt Hotel

◆◆◆◆◆

58 Christchurch Road, Bournemouth, Dorset, BH1 3PF
Tel: 01202 552962 Fax: 01202 552962
Email: rooms@balincourt.co.uk
Web: www.balincourt.co.uk

A warm welcome awaits you at this non-smoking
family run hotel, a comfortable and elegant Victorian
residence, specialising in traditional English cooking.
The hotel is conveniently situated on the East Cliff, set
back from the main road. Bournemouth's seven miles
of sandy beach is only a short stroll away.
Rooms: 10 all ensuite
Pricing: Sgl £38–50 Dbl £74–80
Dinner available from £15 CC: Accepted
Room facilities:
Licenses:
Parking: Off-street and free
Directions: On A338 at roundabout (for Station) turn
onto St Paul's Road. Straight over into St Paul's Road.
2nd roundabout straight over into St Swithuns Road.
3rd roundabout left into Christchurch Road. A35
towards Boscombe & Southbourne. Hotel is on left
opposite Lynton Court Pub.
Map ref: Bournemouth 4 A4

Boltons Hotel

◆◆◆◆

9 Durley Chine Road South, Westcliff, Bournemouth,
Dorset, BH2 5JT
Tel: 01202 751517 Fax: 01202 751629
Email: info@boltonshotel.co.uk
Web: www.boltonshotel.co.uk
Rooms: 13 all ensuite
Pricing: Sgl £28–45 Dbl £28–45
CC: Accepted
Room facilities:
Children: Welcome
Licenses:
Leisure: Outdoor pool
Parking: Off-street and free
Directions: From A338 take turn off for BIC and
Westcliff, at second roundabout turn right, hotel's road
is second right.
Map ref: Bournemouth 4 A4

Carisbrooke Hotel

◆◆◆◆

42 Tregonwell Road, Westcliff,
Bournemouth, Dorset, BH2 5NT
Tel: 01202 290432 Fax: 01202 310499
Email: info@carisbrooke.co.uk
Web: www.carisbrooke.co.uk
Rooms: 22 (20 ensuite)
Pricing: Sgl £20–33 Dbl £50–70
Dinner available from £9.75 CC: Accepted
Room facilities:
Children: Welcome Dogs: Welcome
Licenses: Parking: Off-street and free
Directions: A338 Bournemouth. Follow signs for BIC
and West Cliff. First exit pass roundabout, third left,
second hotel on right.
Map ref: Bournemouth 4 A4

Durley Court Hotel

◆◆◆◆

5 Durley Road, West Cliff, Bournemouth, Dorset, BH2 5JQ
Tel: 01202 556857 Fax: 01202 552455
Email: durleycourthotel@lineone.net
Web: www.tiscover.co.uk/durleycourthotel
Rooms: 16 (14 ensuite) 🍴 🚭
Pricing: Sgl £30–40 Dbl £54–70
Dinner available from £12
CC: Accepted
Room facilities: 🖵 🍵
Children: Welcome 5yrs min age 🍴
Licenses: ⅲ
Parking: Off-street and free
Directions: Leave A338 at Bournemouth west roundabout, at next roundabout take second exit, take first left then first right into Durley Road.
Map ref: Bournemouth 4 A4

The Fairmount Hotel

◆◆◆◆

15 Priory Road, Bournemouth, Dorset, BH2 5DF
Tel: 01202 551105 Fax: 01202 553210
Email: stay@fairmounthotel.co.uk
Web: www.fairmounthotel.co.uk

The Fairmount is a family run hotel which prides itself on its cleanliness, comfort and cuisine, situated in a prime position on the West Cliff. Just a few minutes walk away is the main shopping centre, golden beaches, delightful chines, famous gardens, pubs, bars and the Bournemouth International Centre.
Rooms: 20 all ensuite 🍴 🚭
Pricing: Sgl £28.50–40 Dbl £57–80
CC: Accepted
Room facilities: 🖵 ☎ 🍵
Conference: 1 meeting room (Thtr 30 max), 24hr-delegate from £28, day-delegate from £15
Children: Welcome 🍴 ☕
Licenses: ⅲ
Parking: Off-street and free
Directions: On town bypass follow signs for West Cliff/Bournemouth International Centre (BIC). Hotel is 150 yards from BIC.
Map ref: Bournemouth 4 A4

The Lodge At Meyrick Park

◆◆◆◆

Central Drive, Bournemouth, Dorset, BH2 6LH
Tel: 01202 786000 Fax: 01202 786020
Email: meyrickpark.lodge@theclubcompany.com
Web: www.theclubcompany.com
Rooms: 17 all ensuite 🚭
Pricing: Sgl £75–95 Dbl £75–95
Dinner available from £17
CC: Accepted
Room facilities: 🖵 ☎ 🍵
Licenses: ⅲ
Leisure: Indoor pool, Gym, Health spa, Beauty salon, Golf
Parking: Off-street and free
Directions: Follow A338 to Bournemouth to Wessex Way roundabout, straight over to Richmond Hill, third exit to Wimborne Road, first left to Braidley Road. Turn right at T-junction.
Map ref: Bournemouth 4 A4

Tudor Grange Hotel

◆◆◆◆

31 Gervis Road, Bournemouth, Dorset, BH1 3EE
Tel: 01202 291472 Fax: 01202 311503
Email: info@tudorgrangehotel.co.uk
Web: www.tudorgrangehotel.co.uk
Seasonal closure: 24 December to 2 January

Rooms: 11 (10 ensuite) 🛏
Pricing: Sgl £30–37 Dbl £60–75
CC: Accepted
Room facilities: 🖵 ☎ 🍵
Children: Welcome
Licenses: ⅲ
Parking: Off-street and free
Directions: Five minutes from A338 follow signs for East Cliff, at roundabout turn into Gervis Road.
Map ref: Bournemouth 4 A4

Winter Dene Hotel

◆◆◆◆

11 Durley Road South, West Cliff, Bournemouth,
Dorset, BH2 5JH
Tel: 01202 554150
Email: info@winterdenehotel.com
Web: www.winterdenehotel.com
Seasonal closure: January, February, March

Elegant Victorian residence standing in its own lovely
gardens, close to beach and town centre attractions.
Comfortable, spacious ensuite bedrooms. Excellent
home cooking a speciality of this friendly family-run
hotel which holds the Warm Welcome award.
Rooms: 13 all ensuite
Pricing: Sgl £30–40 Dbl £60–80
Dinner available from £15
CC: Accepted
Room facilities: 🖵 ☕
Children: Welcome 8yrs min age
Licenses:
Parking: Off-street and free
Directions: A338 to Cambridge Roundabout. Follow
Westcliff signs straight over Poole Hill Roundabout for
400m. Hotel is right of Durley roundabout.
Map ref: Bournemouth 4 A4

Brooklands Hotel

◆◆◆

1 Kerley Road, West Cliff, Bournemouth,
Dorset, BH2 5DW
Tel: 01202 552887 Fax: 01202 315393
Email: info@brooklands.co.uk
Web: www.brooklands.co.uk
Rooms: 21 (19 ensuite) 🍴 ⊗
CC: Accepted
Room facilities: 🖵 ☕ ☎
Children: Welcome
Licenses: ▮▮▮
Parking: Off-street and free
Directions: Bournemouth, Ring Road West, A338
Wessex Way, B3066 head towards pier, top of Priory
Road Hill.
Map ref: Bournemouth 4 A4

Denewood Hotel

◆◆◆

40 Sea Road, Bournemouth, Dorset, BH5 1BQ
Tel: 01202 394493 Fax: 01202 391155
Email: info@denewood.co.uk
Web: www.denewood.co.uk

Friendly hotel, locally situated to take advantage of the
famous Bournemouth beaches, on-site parking, varied
breakfasts served, on-site health and beauty salon.
Shops nearby. Internet access points available.
Rooms: 11 all ensuite ⊗
Pricing: Sgl £25–30 Dbl £50–60
CC: Accepted
Room facilities: 🖵 ☕
Conference: 1 meeting room (Thtr 20 max)
Children: Welcome
Dogs: Welcome
Leisure: Beauty salon
Parking: Off-street and free
Directions: On entering Bournemouth, follow the signs
for Boscombe Pier. Hotel is only 500 metres away from
the pier.
Map ref: Bournemouth 4 A4

Ravenstone Hotel

 ◆◆◆

36 Burnaby Road, Alum Chine, Westbourne,
Bournemouth, Dorset, BH4 8JG
Tel: 01202 761047 Fax: 01202 761047
Email: holidays@ravenstonehotel.co.uk
Web: www.ravenstonehotel.co.uk
Seasonal closure: November to March

Situated in quiet road, yet close to wooded chine and
safe sandy beach. Easy access to Bournemouth and
Poole town centres. Same owner since 1986.
Rooms: 9 all ensuite
Pricing: Sgl £28–35 Dbl £56–60
Dinner available from £12
CC: Accepted
Room facilities: ☐ ☕
Children: Welcome
Leisure: Games room
Parking: Off-street and free
Directions: Follow A338 to Westbourne, then signs for
Alum Chine. From Alumhurst Road, turn left into
Beaulieu Road. Then turn right into Burnaby Road.
Map ref: Bournemouth 4 A4

The Roselyn Hotel

 ◆◆◆

55 West Cliff Road, Alum Chine,
Bournemouth, Dorset, BH4 8BA
Tel: 01202 761037 Fax: 01202 767554
Email: theroselynhotel@yahoo.co.uk
Web: www.roselynhotel.co.uk
Rooms: 9 (7 ensuite) 🐾 ⊗
Pricing: Sgl £25–50 Dbl £45–70
CC: Accepted
Room facilities: ☐ ☕ 📞
Children: Welcome
Licenses: ▮▮▮
Parking: Off-street and free
Directions: From A338 or A35 follow signs to
Westbourne. Hotel is off Alum Chine Road.
Map ref: Bournemouth 4 A4

Ilsington Country House Hotel

 ★★★ ☕☕

Ilsington Village, near Newton Abbot, Devon, TQ13 9RR
Tel: 01364 661452 Fax: 01364 661307
Email: hotel@ilsington.co.uk
Web: www.ilsington.co.uk
Rooms: 25 all ensuite 🐾 ⊗
Pricing: Sgl £85–92 Dbl £128–135
Dinner available from £28.95
CC: Accepted
Room facilities: ☐ ☎ ☕
Access: ⏷
Conference: 3 meeting rooms (Thtr 40 max),
24hr-delegate from £140, day-delegate from £40
Children: Welcome ⏷ ☕
Dogs: Welcome
Licenses: ▮▮▮
Leisure: Indoor pool, Gym, Health spa
Parking: Off-street and free
Directions: Follow A38 towards Plymouth. Take exit to
Bovey Tracey, then third exit from roundabout, first
right to Ilsington. Hotel 5 miles on, on right.
Map ref: Ilsington 3 D3

The Edgemoor Country House Hotel & Restaurant

★★★ ☕☕

Lowerdown Cross, Haytor Road,
Bovey Tracey, Devon, TQ13 9LE
Tel: 01626 832466 Fax: 01626 834760
Email: reservations@edgemoor.co.uk
Web: www.edgemoor.co.uk
Seasonal closure: New Year
Rooms: 16 all ensuite 📺 ⊗
Pricing: Sgl £85–90 Dbl £130–135
Dinner available from £32.50
CC: Accepted
Room facilities: ☐ ☎ ☕
Conference: 3 meeting rooms (Thtr 60 max),
24hr-delegate from £135, day-delegate from £37.50
Children: Welcome 14yrs min age
Dogs: Welcome
Licenses: ▮▮▮
Leisure: Walking on Dartmoor
Parking: Off-street and free
Directions: From A38, take A382 towards Bovey
Tracey. Then take B3387 towards Haytor and
Widecombe. Fork left after 1/4 mile. Hotel is then 1/2
mile on right.
Map ref: Lowerdown Cross 3 D3

Relax & smell the coffee

Fresh coffee, chilled juices for breakfast.
RAC's team of qualified Inspectors
check them both.

Southwest

Bradford-on-Avon, Wiltshire

Widbrook Grange `Little Gem`

♦♦♦♦♦ ☆☆ ✕🗡 ☕

Trowbridge Road, Bradford-on-Avon, Wiltshire, BA15 1UH
Tel: 01225 863173 Fax: 01225 862890
Email: stay@widbrookgrange.com
Web: www.widbrookgrange.com
Seasonal closure: 24-31 December

An elegant yet homely Georgian country house,
peacefully located in 11 acres of gardens and grounds
near the ancient Saxon town of Bradford-on-Avon,
only 17 minutes from Bath.
Rooms: 20 all ensuite 🛏 🖥 ⊘
Pricing: Sgl £95–110 Dbl £110–130
Dinner available from £27.50–34.50
CC: Accepted
Room facilities: ☐ ☎ ☕
Conference: 3 meeting rooms (Thtr 50 max),
24hr-delegate from £134.50, day-delegate from £35
Children: Welcome 🍴 ☾
Licenses: ⚓ ⱴⱴ
Leisure: Indoor pool, Gym, Games room
Parking: Off-street and free
Directions: Located 1 mile ouside Bradford-on-Avon
on A363 Trowbridge road. 250 metres south of Kennet
and Avon canal.
Map ref: Bradford-on-Avon 3 F1

Bridgwater, Somerset

The Boat & Anchor Inn

♦♦♦

Mead Crossing, Huntworth,
Bridgwater, Somerset, TA7 0AQ
Tel: 01278 662473 Fax: 01278 662542
Email: boatand.anchorinn@virgin.net
Web: www.boatandanchorinn.co.uk

Canal side location, less than a mile from motorway
junction, excellent cuisine, full à la carte menu, family
run, ideal for cycling, walking and fishing. We cater for
large parties and have a function suite.
Rooms: 11 all ensuite 🛏 ⊘
Pricing: Sgl £49.50 Dbl £65
Dinner available from £6.95
CC: Accepted
Room facilities: ☐ ☕
Conference: 1 meeting room (Thtr 100 max)
Children: Welcome 🍴
Dogs: Assistance dogs only
Licenses: ⱴⱴ
Parking: Off-street and free
Directions: M5 turn off at Junction 24 take Huntworth
turning. Travel 1½ miles through village. Pub visible
from road.
Map ref: Huntworth 3 E2

Bridport, Dorset

Haddon House Hotel

★★★

West Bay, Bridport, Dorset, DT6 4EL
Tel: 01308 423626 Fax: 01308 427348
Web: www.haddonhousehotel.co.uk
Rooms: 12 all ensuite 🛏 ⊘
Dinner available
CC: Accepted
Room facilities: ☐ ☎ ☕ 🗝
Conference: 1 meeting room (Thtr 40 max)
Children: Welcome 🍴 ☾
Licenses: ⱴⱴ
Parking: Off-street and free
Directions: At the Crown Inn roundabout take the
B3157 West Bay road, travel ½ mile to mini
roundabout. Hotel on right-hand side of road.
Map ref: West Bay 3 E3

The Marquis of Lorne Inn

Nettlecombe, near Bridport, Dorset, DT6 3SY
Tel: 01308 485236 Fax: 01308 485666
Email: enquiries@marquisoflorne.com
Web: www.marquisoflorne.com
Rooms: 7 all ensuite
Pricing: Sgl £50–65 Dbl £75–95
Dinner available from £8.95–22.95
CC: Accepted
Room facilities:
Children: Welcome 10yrs min age
Dogs: Assistance dogs only
Licenses:
Parking: Off-street and free
Directions: North from Bridport on B3066 after 1½ miles, after mini roundabout turn right (signposted West Milton, Powerstock) follow for 3 miles, at Powerstock junction, straight over junction, Inn 500 yards up hill on left.
Map ref: Nettlecombe 3 E3

Bristol

Aztec Hotel & Spa

★★★★

Aztec West Business Park,
Almondsbury, Bristol, BS32 4TS
Tel: 01454 201090 Fax: 01454 201593
Email: aztec@shirehotels.com
Web: www.shirehotels.com

SHIRE
HOTELS

Stunning timber beams blend with contemporary artwork and stone flagged floors adorned by feature rugs purvey a mix of old and new at the Aztec. All hotel bedrooms are bright and airy. The Spa challenges you to a workout in the gym and a swim in the 13m pool. Meeting rooms and wireless internet access invite business and pleasure.
Rooms: 128 all ensuite
Pricing: Sgl £92–164 Dbl £134–184
Dinner available from £25
CC: Accepted
Room facilities:
Access:
Conference: 22 meeting rooms (Thtr 200 max), 24hr-delegate from £179, day-delegate from £64
Children: Welcome
Licenses:
Leisure: Indoor pool, Gym, Beauty salon
Parking: Off-street and free
Directions: Close to M4/M5 intersection. Leave M5 at Junction 16. Follow signs for Aztec West.
Map ref: Almondsbury 3 E1

Jurys Bristol Hotel

★★★★

Prince Street, Bristol, BS1 4QF
Tel: 0117 923 0333 Fax: 0117 923 0300
Email: bookings@jurysdoyle.com
Web: www.jurysdoyle.com

JURYS DOYLE
HOTELS

Rooms: 191 all ensuite
Pricing: Sgl £76–171 Dbl £89–185
Dinner available from £25.20
CC: Accepted
Room facilities:
Access:
Conference: 10 meeting rooms (Thtr 400 max), 24hr-delegate from £182, day-delegate from £61
Children: Welcome
Licenses:
Parking: Off-street
Directions: Situated along River Quayside in the centre of city. Only five minutes' drive from Templemeads train station.
Map ref: Bristol 3 E1

Tortworth Court Four Pillars Hotel

★★★★

Wotton-under-Edge, South Gloucestershire, GL12 8HH
Tel: 01454 263000 Fax: 01454 263753
Email: tortworth@four-pillars.co.uk
Web: www.four-pillars.co.uk
Rooms: 189 all ensuite
Pricing: Sgl £69–149 Dbl £89–174
Dinner available from £25.95
CC: Accepted
Room facilities:
Access:
Conference: 20 meeting rooms (Thtr 400 max), 24hr-delegate from £159, day-delegate from £52
Children: Welcome
Dogs: Assistance dogs only
Licenses:
Leisure: Indoor pool, Gym, Health spa, Beauty salon, 30 acre arboretum
Parking: Off-street and free
Directions: Exit M5 J14, head towards Yates/Wotton on B4509. Pass Tortworth visitors' centre, take next right. Hotel is situated approximately ½ mile on right.
Map ref: Tortworth 3 F1

Alveston House Hotel

★★★★

Alveston, Thornbury, Bristol, BS35 2LA
Tel: 01454 415050 Fax: 01454 415425
Email: info@alvestonhousehotel.co.uk
Web: www.alvestonhousehotel.co.uk
Rooms: 30 all ensuite 🚭
Pricing: Sgl £75–99.50 Dbl £95–114.50
Dinner available from £19.75–27.5
CC: Accepted
Room facilities: 🖵 ☎ 🍵 ⬍
Conference: 8 meeting rooms (Thtr 85 max),
24hr-delegate from £145, day-delegate from £40
Children: Welcome ⍭ ⍥
Dogs: Welcome
Licenses: ⬧ ♙♙♙
Parking: Off-street and free
Directions: 3¹/₂ miles north of M4/M5 junction on main
A38 at Alveston.
Map ref: Alveston 3 E1

Avon Gorge Hotel

★★★

Sion Hill, Bristol, BS8 4LD
Tel: 0117 973 8955 Fax: 0117 923 8125
Email: info@avongorge-hotel-bristol.com
Web: www.peelhotel.com
Rooms: 76 all ensuite ⍩ ⍰ 🚭
Pricing: Sgl £85–120 Dbl £95–130
Dinner available from £16.50
CC: Accepted
Room facilities: 🖵 ☎ 🍵
Access: |↕|
Conference: 6 meeting rooms (Thtr 100 max),
24hr-delegate from £150, day-delegate from £45
Children: Welcome ⍭
Dogs: Assistance dogs only
Licenses: ⬧ ♙♙♙
Directions: From M5, use Junction 19, signposted
Clifton; go over suspension bridge, turn right. From
M4, use Junction 19 and take M32 to city; follow signs
to Clifton and Bridge.
Map ref: Bristol 3 E1

Berkeley Square Hotel

★★★ ⍟

15 Berkeley Square, Clifton, Bristol, BS8 1HB
Tel: 0117 925 4000 Fax: 0117 925 2970
Email: berkeley@cliftonhotels.com
Web: www.cliftonhotels.com
Rooms: 42 all ensuite 🚭
Dinner available Room facilities: 🖵 ☎ 🍵 ⬍
Access: |↕|
Children: Welcome ⍭
Dogs: Welcome
Licenses: ♙♙♙
Parking: Off-street
Map ref: Clifton 3 E1

HENBURY LODGE HOTEL

Established in 1987, Henbury Lodge combines traditional warmth with modern facilities. The founding vision was one of gracious living in a country house surrounded by history, yet only a short distance from the centre of Bristol. Today the lodge's informality and flexibility enables families, couples or single guests to feel equally at home. Traditional English dishes are served with a touch of continental flair, using fresh local produce.

RAC Dining Award

STATION ROAD, HENBURY, BRISTOL BS10 7QQ
Tel: 0117 950 2615   Fax: 0117 950 9532
Email: contactus@henburylodgehotel.com
Web: www.henburylodgehotel.com

Henbury Lodge Hotel

★★★ ⍟

Station Road, Henbury, Bristol, BS10 7QQ
Tel: 0117 950 2615 Fax: 0117 950 9532
Email: contactus@henburylodgehotel.com
Web: www.henburylodgehotel.com
Rooms: 21 all ensuite ⍩ 🚭
Pricing: Sgl £57–96 Dbl £102–125
Dinner available from £19.75
CC: Accepted
Room facilities: 🖵 ☎ 🍵
Conference: 1 meeting room (Thtr 32 max),
day-delegate from £25
Children: Welcome ⍭
Dogs: Welcome
Licenses: ♙♙♙
Leisure: Gym, Sunbed
Parking: Off-street and free
Directions: From M5 Junction 17, follow A4018 to third
roundabout. Turn right. At T-junction, turn right. Hotel
is 200m up on corner. For more detailed directions,
see hotel website.
Map ref: Henbury 3 E1

See advert on this page

Best Western Victoria Square Hotel

★★

Victoria Square, Clifton, Bristol, BS8 4EW
Tel: 0117 973 9058 Fax: 0117 970 6929
Email: victoriasquare@btopenworld.com
Web: www.vicsquare.com
Seasonal closure: Christmas
Rooms: 40 all ensuite ⊗
Pricing: Sgl £59–89 Dbl £79–99
Dinner available from £15
CC: Accepted
Room facilities: ▢ ☎ ⌂ ☍
Conference: 2 meeting rooms (Thtr 30 max)
Children: Welcome ⅏ Dogs: Welcome
Licenses: ⅏⅏⅏
Parking: Off-street and free
Directions: From M5 Junction 19, follow signs for
Clifton. Proceed over bridge and turn right into Clifton
Down, turn left into Merchants Road.
Map ref: Clifton 3 E1

Clifton Hotel

★★★

St Paul's Road, Clifton, Bristol, BS8 1LX
Tel: 0117 973 6882 Fax: 0117 974 1082
Email: clifton@cliftonhotels.com
Web: www.cliftonhotels.com
Rooms: 59 all ensuite ⊛ ⊗
Dinner available
CC: Accepted
Room facilities: ▢ ☎ ⌂ ☍
Access: ⅃⅃
Children: Welcome ⅏ Dogs: Welcome
Licenses: ⅏⅏⅏
Parking: Off-street
Directions: From M4: leave M4 junction 19 onto M32,
follow Clifton signs to Whiteladies Road, left at first set
traffic lights.
Map ref: Clifton 3 E1

Rodney Hotel

★★

4 Rodney Place, Clifton, Bristol, BS8 4HY
Tel: 0117 973 5422 Fax: 0117 946 7092
Email: rodney@cliftonhotels.com
Web: www.cliftonhotels.com
Rooms: 31 all ensuite ⊛ ⊗
Dinner available
CC: Accepted
Room facilities: ▢ ☎ ⌂ ☍
Conference: 1 meeting room (Thtr 30 max)
Children: Welcome
Dogs: Welcome
Licenses: ⅏⅏⅏
Parking: Off-street
Directions: Junction 19 off M5. Follow signs to toll
bridge. Turn right at mini roundabout. The Rodney is
on the right.
Map ref: Clifton 3 E1

Westbourne Hotel

★★

40-44 St Paul's Road, Clifton, Bristol, BS8 1LR
Tel: 0117 973 4214 Fax: 0117 974 3552
Email: westbournehotel@bristol8.fsworld.co.uk
Web: www.westbournehotel-bristol.co.uk
Rooms: 31 (27 ensuite) ⊛
Pricing: Sgl £55–69 Dbl £75–83
Dinner available from £12
CC: Accepted
Room facilities: ▢ ☎ ⌂
Children: Welcome ⌖
Licenses: ⅏⅏⅏
Parking: Off-street and free
Directions: City centre, up Park Street, at top take
right-hand lane to Whiteladies Road, turn left at first
traffic lights opposite BBC into St Paul's Road.
Map ref: Clifton 3 E1

Downs View Hotel

◆◆◆

38 Upper Belgrave Road, Clifton, Bristol, BS8 2XN
Tel: 0117 973 7046 Fax: 0117 973 8169
Email: bookings@downsview.co.uk
Web: www.downsview.co.uk
Seasonal closure: Christmas and New Year
Rooms: 15 (9 ensuite) ⊗
Pricing: Sgl £40–50 Dbl £55–65
CC: Accepted
Room facilities: ▢ ⌂
Children: Welcome 2yrs min age
Directions: Exit J17 M5, follow signs to Zoo; on left
after 5 miles. From centre, top of Whiteladies Road,
turn left.
Map ref: Clifton 3 E1

Washington Hotel

◆◆◆

St Paul's Road, Clifton, Bristol, BS8 1LX
Tel: 0117 973 3980 Fax: 0117 973 4740
Email: washington@cliftonhotels.com
Web: www.cliftonhotels.com
Seasonal closure: Christmas
Rooms: 46 (40 ensuite) ⊗
CC: Accepted
Room facilities: ▢ ☎ ⌂ ☍
Conference: 1 meeting room (Thtr 150 max)
Children: Welcome
Dogs: Welcome
Parking: Off-street
Directions: Leave M4 at junction 19 onto M32. Follow
Clifton signs to Whiteladies Road. Left at first traffic lights.
Map ref: Clifton 3 E1

Southwest

"Stay!"

Need a pet friendly property? Look
out for 'Dogs welcome' in our listings.

Brixham, Devon

Harbour View Hotel

◆◆◆ ✕

65 King Street, Brixham, Devon, TQ5 9TH
Tel: 01803 853052 Fax: 01803 853052
Rooms: 8 all ensuite ✪ ⊛
Pricing: Sgl £28–37 Dbl £44–58 CC: Accepted
Room facilities: ▢ ⊛ Children: Welcome
Parking: Off-street and free
Directions: A3022 Brixham road to town
centre/harbour, left at lights, right at T-junction. Hotel is
on right of inner harbour.
Map ref: Brixham 3 D4

Bude, Cornwall

Camelot Hotel

★★★★ ☖☖

Downs View, Bude, Cornwall, EX23 8RE
Tel: 01288 352361 Fax: 01288 355470
Email: stay@camelot-hotel.co.uk
Web: www.camelot-hotel.co.uk
Seasonal closure: Christmas and New Year

Overlooking Bude golf course. A short walk from
beaches and town centre. Elegantly refurbished to a
high standard with first class, friendly service and
superb freshly-prepared food.
Rooms: 24 all ensuite ✪ ⊛
Pricing: Sgl £69 Dbl £98
Dinner available from £25 CC: Accepted
Room facilities: ▢ ☎ ⊛ ☏
Children: Welcome ♀ ☕ Licenses: ♦♦♦
Leisure: Games room Parking: Off-street and free
Directions: Follow one-way system past Post Office.
Stay in left lane; Camelot is at bottom of hill on left.
Map ref: Bude 2 B3

Hartland Hotel

★★★

Hartland Terrace, Bude, Cornwall, EX23 8JY
Tel: 01288 355661 Fax: 01288 355664
Web: www.thehartlandhotel.co.uk
Seasonal closure: December to February
Rooms: 28 all ensuite ✪ ⊟ ⊛
Pricing: Sgl £50–62 Dbl £88–104

Dinner available from £24
Room facilities: ▢ ☎ ⊛ Access: ♿
Conference: 1 meeting room (Thtr 50 max)
Children: Welcome ♀ ☕ Dogs: Welcome
Licenses: ♦♦♦ Leisure: Outdoor pool
Parking: Off-street and free
Directions: Turn left into Hartland Terrace from main
street (opposite Boots). Hotel signposted in main street.
Map ref: Bude 2 B3

Coombe Barton Inn

◆◆◆

Crackington Haven, near Bude, Cornwall, EX23 0JG
Tel: 01840 230345 Fax: 01840 230788
Email: info@coombebarton.co.uk
Web: www.coombebarton.co.uk

Fully licensed freehouse next to beach in a beautiful
Cornish bay serving fresh Cornish-landed fish,
chargrilled steaks etc. Cornish real ales and a large
selection of lagers and wines.
Rooms: 6 (4 ensuite) ✪ ⊛
Pricing: Sgl £30–58 Dbl £50–96
Dinner available from £8.50–15.50 CC: Accepted
Room facilities: ⊛
Conference: 1 meeting room (Thtr 50 max)
Children: Welcome ♀ Dogs: Welcome
Licenses: ♦♦♦ Leisure: Games room
Parking: Off-street and free
Directions: From Bude head south on A39, turn right at
Wainhouse Corner junction and follow lane down to
the beach.
Map ref: Crackington Haven 2 B3

Budleigh Salterton, Devon

Long Range Hotel

◆◆◆◆ ☖ ✕

5 Vales Road, Budleigh Salterton, Devon, EX9 6HS
Tel: 01395 443321 Fax: 01395 442132
Email: info@thelongrangehotel.co.uk
Web: www.thelongrangehotel.co.uk
Rooms: 7 (6 ensuite) ⊛
Pricing: Sgl £40–44 Dbl £70–88
Dinner available from £20.95–22.95 CC: Accepted
Room facilities: ▢ ⊛
Conference: 2 meeting rooms (Thtr 25 max)
Children: Welcome 10yrs min age

Licenses:
Parking: Off-street and free
Directions: From Exeter approach Budleigh Salterton.
Turn left at traffic lights. Continue to T-junction, turn
left. Take first right and first right again. Hotel on left.
Map ref: Budleigh Salterton 3 D3

Burnham-on-Sea, Somerset

Battleborough Grange Country Hotel

★★

Bristol Road, A38, Brent Knoll, near Highbridge,
Somerset, TA9 4HJ
Tel: 01278 760208 Fax: 01278 761950
Email: info@battleboroughgrangehotel.co.uk
Web: www.battleboroughgrangehotel.co.uk
Seasonal closure: 26 December to 2 January
Rooms: 21 all ensuite
Pricing: Sgl £60–100 Dbl £80–150
Dinner available from £19 CC: Accepted
Room facilities:
Conference: 3 meeting rooms (Thtr 100 max),
24hr-delegate from £95, day-delegate from £30
Children: Welcome
Licenses: Parking: Off-street and free
Directions: M5 Junction 22, turn right at roundabout
onto A38, past Garden World on right. Hotel is on left
300 yards.
Map ref: Brent Knoll 3 E2
See advert on this page

BATTLEBOROUGH GRANGE COUNTRY HOTEL

Nestling at the foot of the historic Iron Age Fort
at Brent Knoll, the Battleborough Grange is one
mile from Junction 22, M5, surrounded by
landscaped gardens and the beautiful Somerset
Levels.
Civil Marriage Licence, Wedding Receptions,
Conferences etc. A friendly atmosphere for any
occasion or no occasion at all.
Bristol Road, A38, Brent Knoll, near
Highbridge, Somerset, TA9 4HJ
Tel: 01278 760208 Fax: 01278 761950
Email: info@battleboroughgrangehotel.co.uk
Web: www.battleboroughgrangehotel.co.uk

Callington, Cornwall

Woodpeckers

◆◆◆◆

Rilla Mill, Callington, Cornwall, PL17 7NT
Tel: 01579 363717
Email: alison.merchant@virgin.net
Rooms: 3 all ensuite
Pricing: Sgl £32 Dbl £50–60
Dinner available from £18
Room facilities: Children: Welcome
Parking: Off-street and free
Directions: M5, A30 past Oakhampton towards Bodmin.
At Launceston follow the B3254 towards Liskeard, left at
roundabout through Daws House South Petherwin
straight over crossroads, at Congdons shop, North Hill,
left at crossroads. In Upton Cross for Rilla Mill, first turn
left after sign. Guest House on right.
Map ref: Rilla Mill 2 C3

Camelford, Cornwall

Bowood Park Hotel & Golf Course

★★★

Lanteglos, Camelford, Cornwall, PL32 9RF
Tel: 01840 213017 Fax: 01840 212622
Email: golf@bowoodpark.com
Web: www.bowoodpark.com
Rooms: 31 all ensuite
Dinner available CC: Accepted
Room facilities:
Conference: 1 meeting room (Thtr 150 max)
Children: Welcome
Licenses: Leisure: Golf
Parking: Off-street and free
Directions: Take A39 south-west through Camelford.
Then turn right to Tintagel just before BP Garage. Then
follow brown signs.
Map ref: Lanteglos 2 B3

Are the bells ringing?

Getting married? Congratulations!
Look for the wedding bells symbol
which shows hotels licensed for
civil ceremonies.

Southwest

Chagford, Devon

Three Crowns Hotel

★★

High Street, Chagford, Devon, TQ13 8AJ
Tel: 01647 433444 Fax: 01647 433117
Email: threecrowns@msn.com
Web: www.chagford-accom.co.uk

A warm and friendly 13th-century inn situated in a picturesque village within Dartmoor. Oak beams, four-poster beds. Noted for good food and ale.
Rooms: 17 all ensuite
Pricing: Sgl £55–75 Dbl £60–75
Dinner available from £19.50
CC: Accepted
Room facilities: 💻 ☎ ☕
Conference: 1 meeting room (Thtr 100 max)
Children: Welcome
Dogs: Welcome
Licenses:
Leisure: Games room
Parking: Off-street and free
Directions: M5 towards Exeter. A30 from Exeter towards Okehampton. Leave at Merrymeet roundabout, follow signs for Chagford. Right at Easton Cross.
Map ref: Chagford 2 C3

Chideock, Dorset

Betchworth House

◆◆◆◆

Main Street, Chideock, Dorset, DT6 6JW
Tel: 01297 489478 Fax: 01297 489932
Email: info@betchworthhouse.co.uk
Web: www.betchworthhouse.co.uk
Seasonal closure: Christmas
Rooms: 5 all ensuite
Pricing: Sgl £35–37 Dbl £50–55
CC: Accepted
Room facilities: 💻 ☕
Children: Welcome 8yrs min age
Parking: Off-street and free
Directions: Located on A35, 2 miles from Bridport and 6 miles from Lyme Regis.
Map ref: Chideock 3 E3

Warren House

◆◆◆◆

Chideock, Bridport, Dorset, DT6 6JW
Tel: 01297 489996
Email: kathy@warren-house.com
Web: www.warren-house.com

A thatched Dorset long house, situated in the centre of this picturesque village. The Jurassic coast with its fossils and the Dorset coast path are less than a mile away.
Rooms: 4 all ensuite
Pricing: Sgl £30 Dbl £50 CC: Accepted
Room facilities: 💻 ☕
Children: Welcome
Parking: Off-street and free
Directions: From Bridport on A35, turn right by Chideock Church (signed North Chideock). After 40m turn left. Signed parking area.
Map ref: Chideock 3 E3

Christchurch, Dorset

Marshwalk

◆◆◆◆

28 Asquith Close, Riverslea, Mudeford, Christchurch, Dorset, BH23 3DX
Tel: 07702 352027
Email: enq@marshwalkaccommodation.co.uk
Web: www.marshwalkaccommodation.co.uk
Rooms: 1 ensuite
Pricing: Dbl £50–60
Room facilities: 💻 ☕
Children: Welcome
Parking: Off-street and free
Directions: One mile from Mudeford Quay and Christchurch, adjacent to Stanpit Marsh and a short drive to the New Forest. Telephone for directions.
Map ref: Riverslea 4 A4

Combe Martin, Devon

Acorns Guest House

◆◆◆◆

2 Woodlands, Combe Martin, Devon, EX34 0AT
Tel: 01271 882769 Fax: 01271 882769
Email: info@acorns-guesthouse.co.uk

Southwest

Web: www.acorns-guesthouse.co.uk
Rooms: 8 all ensuite
Pricing: Sgl £29–31 Dbl £45–55
Dinner available from £11 CC: Accepted
Room facilities: ▢ ⌚
Children: Welcome ♁
Licenses: ♦♦♦
Parking: Off-street and free
Directions: M5 then A361 towards Barnstaple, A399 to Combe Martin, 300 yards past bay on left, private parking at rear.
Map ref: Combe Martin 2 C2

Corsham, Wiltshire

Methuen Arms Hotel

★★

High Street, Corsham, Wiltshire, SN13 0HB
Tel: 01249 714867 Fax: 01249 712004
Rooms: 23 all ensuite ⌚ ⊗
Pricing: Sgl £55 Dbl £75
Dinner available from £17.95–30 CC: Accepted
Room facilities: ▢ ☎ ⌚
Conference: 2 meeting rooms (Thtr 80 max), 24hr-delegate from £85, day-delegate from £25
Children: Welcome
Licenses: ♦ ♦♦♦ Parking: Off-street and free
Directions: Exit 17 A429 south towards Chippenham. Follow A4 to Bath. After 3 miles, at traffic lights turn left to Corsham.
Map ref: Corsham 3 F1

Crantock, Cornwall

Fairbank Hotel

★★

West Pentire Road, Crantock,
near Newquay, Cornwall, TR8 5SA
Tel: 01637 830424 Fax: 01637 830424
Email: enquiries@fairbankhotel.co.uk
Web: www.fairbankhotel.co.uk

Totally refurbished for March 2005, situated in a perfect tranquil location with stylish ambience, superb sea views and a very relaxing atmosphere. From the moment you arrive, sit back... relax... enjoy the view.
Rooms: 14 all ensuite
Pricing: Sgl £32–35 Dbl £64–80
Dinner available from £10–20
CC: Accepted
Room facilities: ▢ ⌚
Children: Welcome ♁
Dogs: Welcome
Licenses: ♦♦♦
Parking: Off-street and free
Directions: From A30 Indian Queens, A392 towards Newquay. Roundabout with A3075, first exit towards Redruth. Approx 500m, turn right signposted Crantock. At T-junction turn right, follow road through Crantock. Hotel on right.
Map ref: Crantock 2 B3

Crediton, Devon

Lower Burrow Coombe

♦♦♦

Cheriton Fitzpaine, Crediton, Devon, EX17 4JS
Tel: 01363 866220
Seasonal closure: December to February
Rooms: 3 (1 ensuite) ⌚ ⊗
Pricing: Sgl £20–35 Dbl £40–60
Room facilities: ▢ ⌚
Children: Welcome ♁ ⌖
Parking: Off-street and free
Directions: M5 to Tiverton; follow signs to Exeter. At Bickleigh take the A3072 towards Crediton; 3 miles on the right, sign for the farm.
Map ref: Cheriton Fitzpaine 3 D3

Croyde, Devon

Croyde Bay House Hotel   Little Gem

♦♦♦♦♦

Moor Lane, Croyde, Devon, EX33 1PA
Tel: 01271 890270
Seasonal closure: December to February
Rooms: 7 all ensuite ⌚
Pricing: Sgl £37–64 Dbl £74–97
Dinner available from £10
CC: Accepted
Room facilities: ▢ ⌚
Children: Welcome ♁
Dogs: Welcome
Licenses: ♦♦♦
Parking: Off-street and free
Directions: M5 Junction 27, follow A361 to Barnstaple, then signs for Braunton. Left in Braunton to Croyde village. Left in centre of Croyde, left again into Moor Lane. Follow road to slipway ³/₄ mile.
Map ref: Croyde 2 C2

Cullompton, Devon

Padbrook Park

★★★

Cullompton, Devon, EX15 1RU
Tel: 01884 836100 Fax: 01884 836101
Email: info@padbrookpark.co.uk
Web: www.padbrookpark.co.uk

Ideally located, just one mile from J28 M5, Padbrook Park offers all ensuite accommodation together with 6 conference/function suites, golf course and driving range, beauty salon and fitness studio.
Rooms: 40 all ensuite
Pricing: Sgl £50–65 Dbl £70–130
Dinner available from £15 CC: Accepted
Room facilities: Access:
Conference: 6 meeting rooms (Thtr 250 max)
Children: Welcome Dogs: Assistance dogs only
Licenses:
Leisure: Gym, Health spa, Beauty salon, Golf, Fishing, Riding, Games room, Snooker/billiards, Indoor bowls
Parking: Off-street and free
Directions: M5 J28. Go through town centre. When reaching roundabout, Padbrook can be seen on right-hand side (1 mile from J28).
Map ref: Cullompton 3 D3

The big sleep

As part of our comprehensive inspection process, RAC Inspectors investigate the comfort of the beds.

Dartmouth, Devon

Royal Castle Hotel

★★★★

11 The Quay, Dartmouth, Devon, TQ6 9PS
Tel: 01803 833033 Fax: 01803 835445
Email: enquiry@royalcastle.co.uk
Web: www.royalcastle.co.uk

Award-winning hotel situated in the heart of Dartmouth overlooking the River Dart. 25 luxurious ensuite rooms. Four-poster rooms and spa baths. River view restaurant, two bars and guest parking.
Rooms: 25 all ensuite
Pricing: Sgl £75–95 Dbl £125–195
Dinner available from £25 CC: Accepted
Room facilities:
Conference: 2 meeting rooms (Thtr 25 max), 24hr-delegate from £75, day-delegate from £25
Children: Welcome Dogs: Welcome
Licenses: Parking: Off-street and free
Directions: Leave M5 and take A38 to Totnes. Once in Totnes, turn right towards Dartmouth at first lights. Follow road to Dartmouth for approximately 12 miles. Royal Castle is in town centre opposite inner harbour.
Map ref: Dartmouth 3 D4

Dawlish, Devon

Langstone Cliff Hotel

★★★

Dawlish Warren, Dawlish, Devon, EX7 0NA
Tel: 01626 868000 Fax: 01626 868006
Email: rac@langstone-hotel.co.uk
Web: www.langstone-hotel.co.uk
Rooms: 66 all ensuite
Pricing: Sgl £64–76 Dbl £108–120
Dinner available from £17.50 CC: Accepted
Room facilities: Access:
Conference: 6 meeting rooms (Thtr 400 max), 24hr-delegate from £95, day-delegate from £32
Children: Welcome
Dogs: Welcome
Licenses:
Leisure: Indoor pool, Outdoor pool, Gym, Beauty

salon, Tennis, Games room, Snooker/billiards,
Childrens play areas
Parking: Off-street and free
Directions: From M5 Junction 30, follow A379 for
Dawlish. Turn left at Harbour for Dawlish Warren. At
beach turn right up hill. Hotel 500 metres.
Map ref: Dawlish Warren 3 D3

Lammas Park House

3 Priory Road, Dawlish, Devon, EX7 9JF
Tel: 01626 888064 Fax: 01626 888064
Email: lammaspark@hotmail.com
Web: www.lammasparkhouse.co.uk
Rooms: 2 all ensuite ⊗
Pricing: Dbl £60–75
Dinner available from £12.95–15.95
Room facilities: ☐ ☕ Children: Welcome ⛨ ☼
Parking: Off-street and free
Map ref: Dawlish 3 D3

Dorchester, Dorset

The Wessex Royale Hotel

★★★

High West Street, Dorchester, Dorset, DT1 1UP
Tel: 01305 262660 Fax: 01305 251941
Email: info@wessex-royale-hotel.com
Web: www.wessex-royale-hotel.com
Rooms: 27 all ensuite 🍽 🖥 ⊗
Pricing: Sgl £80–120 Dbl £100–160
Dinner available from £15 CC: Accepted
Room facilities: ☐ ☎ ☕
Conference: 1 meeting room (Thtr 80 max)
Children: Welcome ⛨
Licenses: ⛨⛨⛨
Parking: Off-street and free
Directions: Follow A35 town centre up main high
street. Hotel 50 yards before roundabout on left.
Map ref: Dorchester (Dorset) 3 F3
See advert on this page

The Acorn Inn

◆◆◆◆ 🍴

28 Fore Street, Evershot, Dorchester, Dorset, DT2 0JW
Tel: 01935 83228 Fax: 01935 83707
Email: stay@acorn-inn.co.uk
Web: www.acorn-inn.co.uk
Rooms: 10 all ensuite 🖥 ⊗
Pricing: Sgl £75–140 Dbl £100–235
Dinner available from £13.25–18.95 CC: Accepted
Room facilities: ☐ ☎ ☕ 🍴
Conference: 1 meeting room
Children: Welcome Dogs: Welcome
Licenses: ⛨⛨⛨ Leisure: Games room
Parking: Off-street and free
Directions: Halfway between Yeovil and Dorchester on
A37 turning to Evershot. Continue for 1 mile. Hotel is
located on right-hand side.
Map ref: Evershot 3 E3

THE WESSEX ROYALE HOTEL

RAC
★★★
Hotel

The Wessex Royale Hotel is a delightful
Georgian Hotel built in 1756. Over the last 10
years the hotel has been substantially and
sympathetically refurbished although retaining
a lot of its original character. The hotel has a
superb lounge where guests relax with a drink
and listen to the piano.

High West Street, Dorchester,
Dorset DT1 1UP

Tel: 01305 262660 Fax: 01305 251941

Email: info@wessex-royale-hotel.com
Web: www.wessex-royale-hotel.com

Evercreech, Somerset

Pecking Mill Inn

◆◆

A371, Evercreech, Shepton Mallett,
Somerset, BA4 6PG
Tel: 01749 830336 Fax: 01749 831316
Email: info@peckingmillinn.co.uk
Web: www.peckingmillinn.co.uk
Rooms: 7 all ensuite 🍽
Pricing: Sgl £35–50 Dbl £55–65
Dinner available from £10
CC: Accepted
Room facilities: ☐ ☎ ☕
Children: Welcome ⛨
Licenses: ⛨⛨⛨
Parking: Off-street and free
Directions: 4 miles south-east of Shepton Mallett on
A371, 1 mile from Bath & West Showground. 9 miles
north of Wincanton.
Map ref: Evercreech 3 E2

"Here!"

Need a pet friendly property? Look
out for 'Dogs welcome' in our listings.

Evershot, Dorset

Summer Lodge

★★★★★ ℝℝℝ Premier

9 Fore Street, Evershot, Dorset, DT2 0JR
Tel: 01935 482000 Fax: 01935 482040
Email: summer@relaischateaux.com
Web: www.summerlodgehotel.com
Rooms: 24 all ensuite 🛏 🖨 🚭
Pricing: Sgl £152.50–305 Dbl £185–510
Dinner available from £35–48 CC: Accepted
Room facilities: 🖵 ☎ 🗗 🗮 ❄
Conference: 1 meeting room (Thtr 22 max),
24hr-delegate from £195, day-delegate from £60
Children: Welcome ⱶ ːℂ Dogs: Welcome
Licenses: ⬠ ⛊
Leisure: Indoor pool, Gym, Health spa, Beauty salon,
Tennis, Croquet Parking: Off-street and free
Directions: Exit J8 M3, A303, then A37 towards
Dorchester, then Evershot, Summer Lane.
Map ref: Evershot 3 E3

Exeter, Devon

Woodbury Park Hotel Golf & Country Club

★★★★ ℝ

Woodbury Castle, Woodbury, Exeter, Devon, EX5 1JJ
Tel: 01395 233382 Fax: 01395 234701
Email: reservations@woodburypark.co.uk
Web: www.woodburypark.co.uk

One of the UK's top sporting retreats. This luxurious
hotel, set in idyllic Devonshire countryside, offers the
best of everything with the renowned warmth and
hospitality of the West Country.
Rooms: 56 all ensuite 🚭
Pricing: Dinner available from £21 CC: Accepted
Room facilities: 🖵 ☎ 🗗 🗮 Access: ⸾ᵢ
Conference: 6 meeting rooms (Thtr 250 max),
24hr-delegate from £145, day-delegate from £35
Children: Welcome ⱶ
Licenses: ⬠ ⛊
Leisure: Indoor pool, Gym, Health spa, Beauty salon,
Tennis, Golf, Fishing, Riding, Snooker/billiards, Squash
Parking: Off-street and free
Directions: Exit M5 J30. Follow A376, then A3052
towards Sidmouth; join B3180 where hotel is signed.
Map ref: Woodbury 3 D3

Combe House Hotel & Restaurant

★★★ ℝℝℝ Premier

Gittisham, Honiton, Exeter, Devon, EX14 3AD
Tel: 01404 540400 Fax: 01404 46004
Email: stay@thishotel.com
Web: www.thishotel.com
Rooms: 15 all ensuite 🛏 🖨
Pricing: Dinner available from £38 CC: Accepted
Room facilities: 🖵 ☎ 🗗
Conference: 3 meeting rooms (Thtr 50 max),
24hr-delegate from £215, day-delegate from £45
Children: Welcome ⱶ ːℂ Dogs: Welcome
Licenses: ⬠ ⛊ Leisure: Fishing
Parking: Off-street and free
Directions: M5 exits 28 or 29 and A303/30. Head to
Honiton, follow signs for Sidmouth and Combe House
Hotel. Combe House is at the end of mile-long private
drive.
Map ref: Gittisham 3 D3

Devon Hotel

★★★

Exeter Bypass, Matford, Exeter,
Devon, EX2 8XU
Tel: 01392 259268 Fax: 01392 413142
Email: info@devonhotel.co.uk
Web: www.devonhotel.co.uk

Hotel Group of the Year

Brend Hotels

Luxurious standards of comfort, personal service and
fine wine in the hotel's bar and brasserie 'Carriages'.
The Devon Hotel is conveniently located within easy
reach of the M5 and Exeter city centre.
Rooms: 41 all ensuite 🚭
Pricing: Sgl £70–95 Dbl £95–105
Dinner available from £21 CC: Accepted
Room facilities: 🖵 ☎ 🗗 🗮
Children: Welcome ⱶ ːℂ
Dogs: Welcome
Licenses: ⬠ ⛊
Parking: Off-street and free
Directions: Leave M5 at Junction 30. Take third exit,
signposted Torquay. On old Exeter bypass at Matford.
Map ref: Matford 3 D3

Great Western Hotel

St David's Station Approach, Exeter, Devon, EX4 4NU
Tel: 01392 274039 Fax: 01392 425529
Email: reception@greatwesternhotel.co.uk
Web: www.greatwesternhotel.co.uk
Rooms: 35 all ensuite ✇
Dinner available CC: Accepted
Room facilities: ▢ ☎ ⬒
Conference: 2 meeting rooms (Thtr 80 max)
Children: Welcome Ħ Dogs: Welcome
Licenses: ♦♦♦
Parking: Off-street and free
Directions: M5 exit at junction 29. Head towards city centre and follow directions to St David's railway station.
Map ref: Exeter 3 D3

Red House Hotel

2 Whipton Village Road, Whipton, Exeter,
Devon, EX4 8AR
Tel: 01392 256104 Fax: 01392 666145
Email: info@redhousehotelexeter.co.uk
Web: www.redhousehotelexeter.co.uk
Rooms: 12 all ensuite ✇ ⊗
Pricing: Sgl £45–48 Dbl £58–62
Dinner available from £5.95–25
CC: Accepted
Room facilities: ▢ ☎ ⬒ ☏

Conference: 1 meeting room (Thtr 40 max),
day-delegate from £17.50
Children: Welcome Ħ
Dogs: Assistance dogs only
Licenses: ♦♦♦
Parking: Off-street
Directions: On the B3212 Pinhoe to Exeter road.
Map ref: Exeter 3 D3

The Galley Restaurant & spa with cabins `Little Gem`

◆◆◆◆◆ ☏☏☏ ✖ ☟

41 Fore Street, Topsham, Exeter, Devon, EX3 0HU
Tel: 0845 602 6862 Fax: 01392 876078
Email: fish@galleyrestaurant.co.uk
Web: www.galleyrestaurant.co.uk
Rooms: 4 all ensuite ⊗
Pricing: Sgl £62.50–95 Dbl £125–200
Dinner available from £35
CC: Accepted
Room facilities: ▢ ☎ ⬒ ☏
Children: Welcome 12yrs min age
Licenses: ♦♦♦
Parking: Off-street and free
Directions: M5 J30 follow signs to Topsham. Then follow signs to Quay. The Galley Restaurant is behind Lighter Inn overlooking the river.
Map ref: Topsham 3 D3
See advert on this page

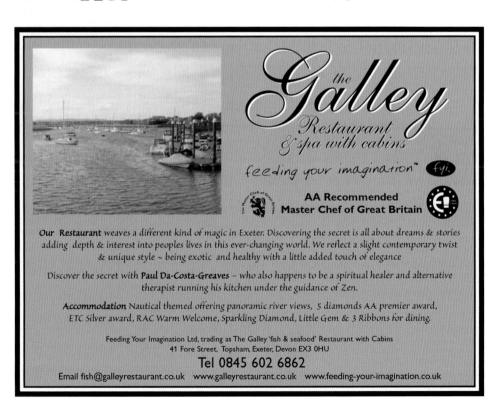

Heath Gardens

◆◆◆◆

Broadclyst, Exeter, Devon, EX5 3HL
Tel: 01392 462311 Fax: 01392 462311
Email: info@heathgardens.co.uk
Web: www.heathgardens.co.uk

Heath Gardens is a listed Artisan's Thatched Cottage
on the outskirts of Broadclyst 5 miles from the centre
of Exeter. All rooms have a southern aspect
overlooking open countryside.
Rooms: 3 all ensuite ⊛
Pricing: Sgl £30 Dbl £45–50
Room facilities: ☐ ⊘ Children: Welcome
Dogs: Welcome Parking: Off-street and free
Directions: From B3181 at Broadclyst take the road
signed for Whimple. Heath Gardens is ¼ mile on the left.
Map ref: Broadclyst 3 D3

St Andrews Hotel

◆◆◆◆

28 Alphington Road, Exeter, Devon, EX2 8HN
Tel: 01392 276784 Fax: 01392 250249
Email: standrewsexeter@aol.com
Seasonal closure: Christmas to New Year
Rooms: 17 all ensuite ⊛ ⊛
Pricing: Sgl £45–60 Dbl £65–80
Dinner available from £16 CC: Accepted
Room facilities: ☐ ☎ ⊘
Conference: 1 meeting room (Thtr 10 max)
Children: Welcome ⼍
Licenses: ⫴ Parking: Off-street and free
Directions: Leave M5 at Junction 31, signposted Exeter.
Follow signs to city centre and Marsh Barton along
Alphington Road (A377). St Andrews is on the left.
Map ref: Exeter 3 D3
See advert on this page

Telstar Hotel

◆◆◆◆

75-77 St David's Hill, Exeter, Devon, EX4 4DW
Tel: 01392 272466 Fax: 01392 272466
Email: reception@telstar-hotel.co.uk
Web: www.telstar-hotel.co.uk
Seasonal closure: Christmas

Situated in the heart of the beautiful city of Exeter, the
Telstar is a charming late-Victorian hotel that is within
walking distance of the university and the city centre.
Rooms: 20 (15 ensuite) ⊛ ⊛
Pricing: Sgl £25–35 Dbl £50–65 CC: Accepted
Room facilities: ☐ ☎ ⊘ ⼍
Children: Welcome Dogs: Welcome
Parking: Off-street and free
Directions: Drive through city centre from Junction 29 of
M5 or A30. Follow signs for railway station. Hotel is
between city centre and St David's station, follow signs
for station.
Map ref: Exeter 3 D3

Braeside

21 New North Road, Exeter, Devon, EX4 4HF
Tel: 01392 256875 Fax: 01392 256875
Rooms: 7 (3 ensuite)
Room facilities: 🖵 🍺
Children: Welcome Dogs: Welcome
Directions: From M5 J29 follow all signs to town centre, straight through to New North Road. Braeside is between the clock tower and the prison.
Map ref: Exeter 3 D3

Exford, Somerset

Stockleigh Lodge

Exmoor, Somerset, TA24 7PZ
Tel: 01643 831500 Fax: 01643 831595
Email: myra@stockleighexford.freeserve.co.uk
Web: www.stockleighexford.freeserve.co.uk
Rooms: 9 all ensuite 🍴 🚭
Pricing: Dinner available from £20 CC: Accepted
Room facilities: 🍺 Children: Welcome 🍴 ☕
Licenses: 👥 Parking: Off-street and free
Directions: Exit M5 at Junction 25, Taunton. Follow signs to Minehead on A358. At Bishops Lydeard turn left onto B3224. Follow signs to Exford. Take Simons Bath Road out of Exford. Lodge on right.
Map ref: Exmoor 3 D2

Exmouth, Devon

Royal Beacon Hotel

The Beacon, Exmouth, Devon, EX8 2AF
Tel: 01395 264886 Fax: 01395 268890
Email: reception@royalbeaconhotel.co.uk
Web: www.royalbeaconhotel.co.uk

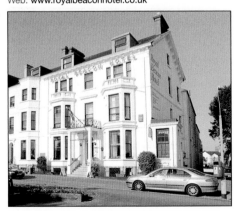

Former Georgian posting house overlooking the sea, with 55 guest rooms, spacious lounge and bar, and a charming restaurant featuring superbly prepared fresh local cuisine.
Rooms: 55 all ensuite 🍴 🍽 🚭
Pricing: Sgl £55–78 Dbl £75–110
Dinner available from £20 CC: Accepted
Room facilities: 🖵 ☎ 🍺 🔌 Access: 👥
Conference: 3 meeting rooms (Thtr 160 max), 24hr-delegate from £105, day-delegate from £28
Children: Welcome 🍴 ☕ Dogs: Welcome
Licenses: 🔷 👥 Parking: Off-street and free
Directions: Only 10 miles from the M5 and clearly visible from Exmouth's lovely sandy beach.
Map ref: Exmouth 3 D3

Manor Hotel

The Beacon, Exmouth, Devon, EX8 2AG
Tel: 01395 272549 Fax: 01395 225519
Email: post@manorexmouth.co.uk
Web: www.manorexmouth.co.uk
Rooms: 40 all ensuite 🍴 🚭
Pricing: Sgl £35–40 Dbl £70-80
Dinner available from £13.95
CC: Accepted
Room facilities: 🖵 ☎ 🍺 Access: 👥
Conference: 2 meeting rooms (Thtr 100 max), 24hr-delegate from £20
Children: Welcome 🍴 ☕ Dogs: Assistance dogs only
Licenses: 👥
Parking: Off-street and free
Directions: From M5 Junction 30 take A376 to Exmouth: signs for seafront, then left at T-junction at end of Imperial Road.
Map ref: Exmouth 3 D3

Devoncourt Hotel

16 Douglas Avenue, Exmouth, Devon, EX8 2EX
Tel: 01395 272277 Fax: 01395 269315
Email: enquiries@devoncourt.com
Web: www.devoncourt.com
Rooms: 10 all ensuite 🍴
Dinner available CC: Accepted
Room facilities: 🖵 ☎ 🍺 🔌 Access: 👥
Children: Welcome
Dogs: Welcome
Licenses: 👥
Leisure: Indoor pool, Outdoor pool, Gym, Health spa, Beauty salon, Tennis, Fishing, Games room, Snooker/billiards, Putting course
Parking: Off-street and free
Directions: M5 junction 30. A376 to Exmouth seafront. Turn left to Maer Road. At T-junction turn right. Hotel on right.
Map ref: Exmouth 3 D3

Falfield, South Gloucestershire

The Bristol Inn

Bristol Road, Falfield,
South Gloucestershire, GL12 8DL
Tel: 01454 260502 Fax: 01454 261821
Map ref: Falfield 3 E1

Falmouth, Cornwall

Budock Vean — The Hotel On The River

★★★★ **Excellent**

Mawnan Smith, near Falmouth, Cornwall, TR11 5LG
Tel: 01326 252100 Fax: 01326 250892
Email: relax@budockvean.co.uk
Web: www.budockvean.co.uk
Seasonal closure: 2-27 January
Rooms: 57 all ensuite
Pricing: Sgl £58–103 Dbl £116–206
Dinner available from £29.50–30.5 CC: Accepted
Room facilities: Access:
Conference: 3 meeting rooms (Thtr 50 max),
day-delegate from £29
Children: Welcome 7yrs min age Dogs: Welcome
Licenses:
Leisure: Indoor pool, Health spa, Beauty salon, Tennis,
Golf, Fishing, Snooker/billiards
Parking: Off-street and free
Directions: From A39 Truro to Falmouth road, follow
brown tourist signs to Trebah Garden. Continue for half
a mile past Trebah to the hotel.
Map ref: Mawnan Smith 2 B4
See advert on this page

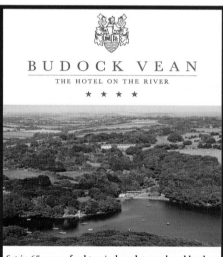

BUDOCK VEAN
THE HOTEL ON THE RIVER
★ ★ ★ ★

Set in 65 acres of subtropical gardens and parkland on
the banks of the Helford River. This family run 4-star
hotel includes golf course, large indoor pool, private
foreshore, health spa and award-winning restaurant.

Cornwall Tourist Board Hotel of the Year 2002, 2003 & 2004
South West Tourism Large Hotel of the Year 2003

Mawnan Smith, near Falmouth, Cornwall, TR11 5LG
Tel: 01326 252100 Fax: 01326 250892
Email: relax@budockvean.co.uk
Web: www.budockvean.co.uk

Royal Duchy Hotel

★★★★

Cliff Road, Falmouth, Cornwall, TR11 4NX
Tel: 01326 313042 Fax: 01326 319420
Email: info@royalduchy.com
Web: www.royalduchy.com

Brend Hotels

On the seafront, Falmouth's only four star hotel is
renowned for award-winning cuisine, warm attentive
service and luxurious accommodation.
Rooms: 43 all ensuite
Pricing: Sgl £70–100 Dbl £130–230
Dinner available from £28 CC: Accepted
Room facilities: Access:
Children: Welcome Dogs: Assistance dogs only
Licenses: Leisure: Indoor pool, Games room,
Snooker/billiards Parking: Off-street and free
Directions: Situated at the castle end of the seafront
on the left-hand side.
Map ref: Falmouth 2 B4
See advert on opposite page

Falmouth Beach Resort Hotel & Apartments

★★★

Gyllyngvase Beach, Seafront,
Falmouth, Cornwall, TR11 4NA
Tel: 01326 310500 Fax: 01326 319147
Email: info@falmouthbeachhotel.co.uk
Web: www.falmouthbeachhotel.co.uk
Rooms: 121 all ensuite
Pricing: Sgl £58–80 Dbl £116–160
Dinner available from £18 CC: Accepted
Room facilities: Access:
Conference: 6 meeting rooms (Thtr 300 max),
24hr-delegate from £90, day-delegate from £25
Children: Welcome Dogs: Welcome
Licenses: Leisure: Indoor pool, Gym, Health
spa, Beauty salon, Tennis, Games room
Parking: Off-street and free
Directions: From Truro take A39 to Falmouth. Follow
signs to seafront and beaches. The hotel is right
opposite Gyllyngvase beach.
Map ref: Falmouth 2 B4
See advert on opposite page

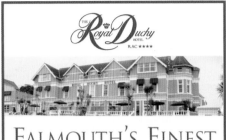

Southwest

Falmouth Hotel

★★★

Castle Beach, Falmouth, Cornwall, TR11 4NZ
Tel: 0800 0193121 Fax: 01326 319533
Email: info@falmouthhotel.com
Web: www.falmouthhotel.com
Seasonal closure: Christmas
Rooms: 129 all ensuite 🛏 🛋 ⊛
Pricing: Sgl £60–69 Dbl £82–131
Dinner available from £18
CC: Accepted
Room facilities: ⬚ ☎ ☕ ⌨
Access: |↕|
Conference: 9 meeting rooms (Thtr 300 max),
24hr-delegate from £79, day-delegate from £25
Children: Welcome ⋔ ⫶©
Dogs: Welcome
Licenses: ⬥ ⦀
Leisure: Indoor pool, Gym, Health spa, Beauty salon,
Games room, Snooker/billiards
Parking: Off-street and free
Directions: Upon entering Falmouth from any direction,
follow signs for the seafront. Located at the castle end
overlooking the beach.
Map ref: Falmouth 2 B4
See advert on this page

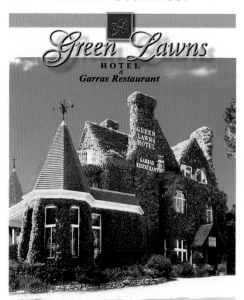
Green Lawns Hotel

★★★★ ⓇⓇ

Western Terrace, Falmouth, Cornwall, TR11 4QJ
Tel: 01326 312734 Fax: 01326 211427
Email: info@greenlawnshotel.com
Web: www.greenlawnshotel.com
Rooms: 39 all ensuite 🐕 📺 ⊗
Pricing: Sgl £55–110 Dbl £100–170
Dinner available from £25
CC: Accepted
Room facilities: 🖵 ☎ 🍵 📞
Conference: 3 meeting rooms (Thtr 200 max),
24hr-delegate from £110, day-delegate from £26
Children: Welcome 🍴 🍼
Dogs: Welcome
Licenses: ⚖ 🍸
Leisure: Indoor pool, Gym, Health spa
Parking: Off-street and free
Directions: Follow A39 to Falmouth. Continue to main
beaches; hotel is on right by mini-roundabout.
Map ref: Falmouth 2 B4
See advert on this page

Greenbank Hotel

★★★★ ⓇⓇ

Harbourside, Falmouth, Cornwall, TR11 2SR
Tel: 01326 312440 Fax: 01326 211362
Email: sales@greenbank-hotel.com
Web: www.greenbank-hotel.com

On the water's edge overlooking Falmouth Harbour.
Once the base of the Packet Ship Captains, sense the
atmosphere of history and tradition, comfort and
hospitality.
Rooms: 58 all ensuite 📺 ⊗
Pricing: Sgl £65–75 Dbl £105–185
Dinner available from £24.50–29.50 CC: Accepted
Room facilities: 🖵 ☎ 🍵 📞 Access: ⬆
Conference: 2 meeting rooms (Thtr 60 max),
24hr-delegate from £120, day-delegate from £22.50
Children: Welcome 🍼 Dogs: Welcome
Licenses: ⚖ 🍸 Parking: Off-street and free
Directions: Approach Falmouth from Penryn. Follow
the Greenbank sign from roundabout along North
Parade. Hotel is ¹/₂ mile past Marina on left.
Map ref: Falmouth 2 B4

Meudon Hotel

★★★★ Ⓡ   *Excellent*

Maenporth Road, Mawnan Smith,
Falmouth, Cornwall, TR11 5HT
Tel: 01326 250541 Fax: 01326 250543
Email: wecare@meudon.co.uk
Web: www.meudon.co.uk
Seasonal closure: 1-31 January

A place of peace and beauty where sub-tropical
gardens sweep down to the sea. Family run country
house hotel, specialists in local seafood, traditional

service, cosseted comforts, antiques and fresh
flowers.
Rooms: 29 all ensuite
Pricing: Sgl £60–89 Dbl £120–178
Dinner available from £27.50–33 CC: Accepted
Room facilities: 📺 ☎ ☕ ✆
Access: ♿
Conference: 1 meeting room (Thtr 30 max),
24hr-delegate from £130, day-delegate from £35
Children: Welcome 🏇 🎠 Dogs: Welcome
Licenses: 🍴
Leisure: Beauty salon, Golf, Fishing, Hotel yacht, 8.5
acres of sub-tropical gardens, Cliff walks
Parking: Off-street and free
Directions: From Truro A39 towards Falmouth at
Hillhead roundabout follow signs to Maenporth beach.
Hotel on left one mile after beach.
Map ref: Mawnan Smith 2 B4

St Michaels Hotel
★★★☆
Gyllyngvase Beach, Seafront, Falmouth,
Cornwall, TR11 4NB
Tel: 01326 312707 Fax: 01326 211772
Email: info@stmichaelshotel.co.uk
Web: www.stmichaelshotel.com
Rooms: 62 all ensuite
Pricing: Sgl £36–84 Dbl £72–168
Dinner available from £15 CC: Accepted
Room facilities: 📺 ☎ ☕
Conference: 5 meeting rooms (Thtr 200 max),
24hr-delegate from £74, day-delegate from £17.50
Children: Welcome 🏇
Licenses: ⚜ 🍴
Leisure: Indoor pool, Gym, Health spa, Beauty salon,
Sauna, Steam room, Jacuzzi
Parking: Off-street and free
Directions: Follow A39 into Falmouth. Take signs for
beaches. At third roundabout turn right into Penance
Road. Left at end, then second left into Stracey Road.
Map ref: Falmouth 2 B4
See advert on this page

Bosanneth Hotel
◆◆◆◆
Gyllyngvase Hill, Falmouth, Cornwall, TR11 4DW
Tel: 01326 314649 Fax: 01326 314649
Email: bosanneth@fsbdial.co.uk
Web: www.bosannethhotel.com
Seasonal closure: October to March
Rooms: 8 all ensuite
Pricing: Sgl £30 Dbl £60
Dinner available from £15
Room facilities: 📺 ☕
Children: Welcome 12yrs min age
Licenses: 🍴 Parking: Off-street and free
Directions: Enter Falmouth on A39, follow signs for
beaches. Take Dracaena Avenue, Western Terrace,
Melvill Road. Turn right after rail bridge into
Gyllyngvase Hill.
Map ref: Falmouth 2 B4

Relax at St Michael's

Chellowdene
◆◆◆◆
Gyllyngvase Hill, Falmouth, Cornwall, TR11 4DN
Tel: 01326 314950
Seasonal closure: October to February
Rooms: 6 all ensuite
Pricing: Dbl £54–60 Dinner available from £13.50
Room facilities: 📺 ☕
Parking: Off-street and free
Directions: Take A39 into Falmouth. Follow road signed
Beaches, Gyllyngvase Beach. Chellowdene 60 metres
from main beach.
Map ref: Falmouth 2 B4

Gyllyngvase House Hotel
◆◆◆◆
Gyllyngvase Road, Falmouth, Cornwall, TR11 4GH
Tel: 01326 312956 Fax: 01326 316166
Email: info@gyllyngvase.co.uk
Web: www.gyllyngvase.co.uk
Seasonal closure: Christmas
Rooms: 14 (12 ensuite)
Pricing: Sgl £30–50 Dbl £60–75 CC: Accepted
Room facilities: 📺 ☎ ☕ Children: Welcome
Licenses: ⚜ 🍴 Leisure: Beauty salon
Parking: Off-street and free
Directions: From A30, follow signs to Truro, then from
Truro to Falmouth. Follow sign to beaches and dock.
Hotel is on the corner of Gyllyngvase and Melvill roads.
Map ref: Falmouth 2 B4

Southwest

Hawthorne Dene Hotel

◆◆◆◆

12 Pennance Road, Falmouth, Cornwall, TR11 4EA
Tel: 01326 311427 Fax: 01326 311994
Email: enquiries@hawthornedenehotel.co.uk
Web: www.hawthornedenehotel.com
Rooms: 10 all ensuite
Pricing: Sgl £35–45 Dbl £70–80
Dinner available from £15 CC: Accepted
Room facilities:
Children: Welcome
Licenses:
Parking: Off-street and free
Directions: Approach Falmouth on A39 following signs
for town centre and beaches. Go straight across at
traffic lights, at first mini roundabout take right-hand
exit, Pennance Road. Hotel is on right.
Map ref: Falmouth 2 B4

Highcliffe

◆◆◆◆

22 Melvill Road, Falmouth, Cornwall, TR11 4AR
Tel: 01326 314466 Fax: 01326 212779
Email: info@highcliffe-falmouth.co.uk
Web: www.stayinfalmouth.co.uk
Rooms: 6 all ensuite
Pricing: Sgl £26–30 Dbl £52–60
Room facilities:
Children: Welcome
Parking: Off-street and free
Directions: Follow signs for beaches/docks. At mini-
roundabout turn left into Melvill Road. Highcliffe is
approximately 1/2 mile on left.
Map ref: Falmouth 2 B4

Rathgowry Hotel

◆◆◆◆

Gyllyngvase Hill, Gyllyngvase Beach, Falmouth,
Cornwall, TR11 4DN
Tel: 01326 313482
Email: rathgowry@yahoo.co.uk
Seasonal closure: October to April
Rooms: 10 all ensuite
Pricing: Sgl £26–29 Dbl £52–58
Dinner available from £14–16
Room facilities:
Children: Welcome
Licenses:
Parking: Off-street and free
Directions: Enter Falmouth on A39. Follow signs for
beaches along Dracaena Avenue, Western Terrace,
Melvill Road; turn right into Gyllyngvase Hill.
Map ref: Falmouth 2 B4

"I do!" Want a honeymoon hotel?
Look for our Gold, Blue, and White
Ribbon Award winning hotels.

Seaward Guest House

◆◆◆◆

44 Melvill Road, Falmouth, Cornwall, TR11 4DQ
Tel: 01326 318100
Seasonal closure: 23 December to 3 January
Rooms: 3 all ensuite
Pricing: Sgl £28 Dbl £55
Room facilities:
Leisure: Free use of videos Parking: Off-street and free
Directions: Arriving Falmouth on A39 follow brown
signs to docks and castle. Seaward is on left, 1/2 mile
past Green Lawns Hotel.
Map ref: Falmouth 2 B4

Trevaylor Hotel

◆◆◆◆

8 Pennance Road, Falmouth, Cornwall, TR11 4EA
Tel: 01326 313041
Email: trevaylorhotel@aol.com
Web: www.trevaylorhotel.com
Rooms: 9 all ensuite
Pricing: Sgl £24–29 Dbl £46–54
Room facilities:
Children: Welcome
Licenses: Parking: Off-street and free
Directions: Take signs for the beaches. Go along
Western Terrace, Green Lawns Hotel on right, turn
right at mini-roundabout.
Map ref: Falmouth 2 B4

Tudor Court Hotel

◆◆◆◆

55 Melvill Road, Falmouth, Cornwall, TR11 4DF
Tel: 01326 312807 Fax: 01326 312807
Email: enquiries@tudor-court-hotel.freeserve.co.uk
Web: www.cornwall-online.co.uk/tudor-court-hotel
Seasonal closure: Christmas and New Year.
Rooms: 9 (8 ensuite)
Pricing: Sgl £26–30 Dbl £50–60 CC: Accepted
Room facilities:
Children: Welcome
Licenses: Parking: Off-street and free
Directions: From Truro, continue on main road and
head for docks. Hotel on right side of Melvill Road.
Map ref: Falmouth 2 B4

Wellington House

◆◆◆◆

26 Melvill Road, Falmouth, Cornwall, TR11 4AR
Tel: 01326 319947 Fax: 01326 211533
Email: wellingtonhouse@msn.com
Rooms: 3 all ensuite
Pricing: Sgl £30–35 Dbl £50–60 CC: Accepted
Room facilities:
Children: Welcome 14yrs min age Dogs: Welcome
Parking: Off-street and free
Directions: Follow A39 from Truro. Pick up signs for
'docks' on entering Falmouth. On left-hand side just
past Princess Pavilion.
Map ref: Falmouth 2 B4

The Oasis Guest House

13 Dracaena Avenue, Falmouth, Cornwall, TR11 2EG
Tel: 01326 311457
Email: enquiries@oasis-falmouth.co.uk
Web: www.oasis-falmouth.co.uk
Rooms: 5 (3 ensuite)
Pricing: Sgl £20–24 Dbl £42-54 CC: Accepted
Room facilities:
Children: Welcome
Dogs: Welcome
Parking: Off-street and free
Map ref: Falmouth 2 B4

The Palms Guest House

11 Castle Drive, Falmouth, Cornwall, TR11 4NF
Tel: 01326 314007 Fax: 01326 314007
Email: j_miller99@hotmail.com
Web: www.thepalmsguesthouse.co.uk
Rooms: 3 all ensuite
Pricing: Sgl £15–25 Dbl £35–60
Room facilities:
Parking: Off-street and free
Directions: Follow brown signs 'beaches and castle'.
Continue to end of Melvill Road, right at roundabout,
up hill, white house in front on bend.
Map ref: Falmouth 2 B4

Fowey, Cornwall

Trenython Manor Hotel and Spa

★★★

Castledore Road, Tywardreath,
near Fowey, Cornwall, PL24 2TS
Tel: 01726 814797 Fax: 01726 817030
Email: enquiries@trenython.co.uk
Web: www.trenython.co.uk
Rooms: 24 all ensuite
Pricing: Sgl £105–195 Dbl £125–225
Dinner available from £16–39 CC: Accepted
Room facilities:
Conference: 4 meeting rooms (Thtr 80 max),
24hr-delegate from £125, day-delegate from £35
Children: Welcome
Dogs: Assistance dogs only
Licenses:
Leisure: Indoor pool, Gym, Health spa, Beauty salon
Parking: Off-street and free
Directions: From A30 follow signs for Lostwithiel then
Fowey. At Castledore crossroads turn right. Trenython
is 200 yards in on the left.
Map ref: Tywardreath 2 B4

Be more mobile **Dial 1740 from any
mobile phone to get up-to-the-
minute RAC traffic information.**

Calls cost up to 59p per minute. Please check with your network operator.

Fowey Marine Guest House

21 Station Road, Fowey, Cornwall, PL23 1DF
Tel: 01726 833920 Fax: 01726 833920
Email: enquiries@foweymarine.com
Web: www.foweymarine.com
Rooms: 4 all ensuite
Pricing: Sgl £30–45 Dbl £50–60 CC: Accepted
Room facilities:
Children: Welcome
Dogs: Welcome
Leisure: Television/sitting room
Parking: Off-street
Directions: From mini roundabout on outskirts of
Fowey, follow B3269 to Fowey, signed Caffa Mill. Car
park on left, guesthouse opposite.
Map ref: Fowey 2 B4

Gillingham, Dorset

Stock Hill Country House & Restaurant

Premier

Stock Hill, Gillingham, Dorset, SP8 5NR
Tel: 01747 823626 Fax: 01747 825628
Email: reception@stockhillhouse.co.uk
Web: www.stockhillhouse.co.uk
Rooms: 8 all ensuite
Pricing: Sgl £125–165 Dbl £240–300
Dinner available from £38
CC: Accepted
Room facilities:
Conference: 1 meeting room
Children: Welcome 7yrs min age
Licenses:
Leisure: Tennis
Directions: 3 miles off the A303 sign Gillingham/
Shaftesbury on B3081, right-hand side.
Map ref: Stock Hill 3 F2

Glastonbury, Somerset

Lower Farm

Kingweston, Somerton, Somerset, TA11 6BA
Tel: 01458 223237 Fax: 01458 223276
Email: lowerfarm@btconnect.com
Web: www.lowerfarm.net
Seasonal closure: Christmas and New Year
Rooms: 3 (2 ensuite)
Pricing: Sgl £45–55 Dbl £60–65
CC: Accepted
Room facilities:
Conference: 1 meeting room (Thtr 35 max)
Children: Welcome
Parking: Off-street and free
Directions: Exit A303 at Podimore roundabout on A37
north to Lydford-on-Fosse. At traffic light intersection
with B3153 proceed through Keinton to Kingweston,
farmhouse on right.
Map ref: Kingweston 3 E2

Southwest

Helston, Cornwall

Treloquithack Farmhouse

♦♦♦♦

Gweek, Helston, Cornwall, TR13 0NH
Tel: 01326 564359
Email: post@treloquithack.co.uk
Web: www.treloquithack.co.uk
Rooms: 3 (2 ensuite) 🐾 🖥 ⊗
Pricing: Sgl £40–50 Dbl £60–70
Dinner available from £22.45–25
Room facilities: 🖵 ☕. Children: Welcome
Parking: Off-street and free
Directions: 2 miles from Helston on A349, turn left at
Manhay. Signposted to Gweek. In about ½ mile is
Treloquithack Farmhouse.
Map ref: Gweek 2 A4

Roslyn Cottage

♦♦♦

Trewennack, Helston, Cornwall, TR13 0PQ
Tel: 01326 573581
Email: roslyncottage@hotmail.com
Web: www.cornwall-online.co.uk/roslyn-cottage
Rooms: 3 (1 ensuite) ⊗
Pricing: Sgl £26–30 Dbl £46–52
Room facilities: 🖵 ☕. Children: Welcome 🕇
Dogs: Welcome Parking: Off-street and free
Directions: Truro/Falmouth past Trewennack sign. Stop
in bus laybay and Roslyn Cottage is behind where the
kerb is raised.
Map ref: Trewennack 2 A4

Highcliffe, Dorset

Rothesay Hotel

♦♦♦♦

175 Lymington Road, Highcliffe, Christchurch,
Dorset, BH23 4JS
Tel: 01425 274172
Email: rothesayhotel.1@tiscali.co.uk
Web: www.rothesayhotel.net

Set in the original grounds of Highcliffe Castle, offering
a high standard of accommodation. All rooms ensuite
with tea and coffee facilities and colour TV. Large
heated indoor pool and sauna. Private parking.

Rooms: 13 all ensuite 🖥 ⊗
Pricing: Sgl £30–40 Dbl £60–90 CC: Accepted
Room facilities: 🖵 ☕
Children: Welcome 12yrs min age
Licenses: ♦♦♦
Leisure: Indoor pool
Parking: Off-street and free
Directions: Take A35 from Lyndhurst. Turn left after Cat
and Fiddle pub past railway station. Rothesay is at the
end of the road.
Map ref: Highcliffe 4 B4

Honiton, Devon

The Deer Park Country Hotel

★★★

Weston, Honiton, Devon, EX14 3PG
Tel: 01404 41266 Fax: 01404 46598
Email: admin@deerparkcountryhotel.com
Web: www.deerparkcountryhotel.com
Rooms: 25 all ensuite 🐾 🖥
Pricing: Sgl £60–95 Dbl £100–200
Dinner available from £26–32
CC: Accepted
Room facilities: 🖵 ☎ ☕ 📞
Conference: 3 meeting rooms (Thtr 60 max),
24hr-delegate from £95, day-delegate from £30
Children: Welcome 🕇 🔆
Dogs: Welcome
Licenses: ♦ ♦♦♦
Leisure: Outdoor pool, Tennis, Fishing, Games room,
Snooker/billiards
Parking: Off-street and free
Directions: Follow brown signs from A30 Honiton turn-
off. Approximately 4 miles from Honiton town between
villages of Weston and Buckerell.
Map ref: Buckerell Village 3 D3

Ilfracombe, Devon

Arlington Hotel

★★

Sommers Crescent, Ilfracombe, Devon, EX34 9DT
Tel: 01271 862002 Fax: 01271 862803
Email: bookings@devoniahotels.co.uk
Web: www.devoniahotels.co.uk
Rooms: 33 all ensuite 🐾
Pricing: Sgl £26–36 Dbl £52–72
Dinner available from £15.50
CC: Accepted
Room facilities: 🖵 ☎ ☕
Access: ♿
Children: Welcome 🕇 🔆
Dogs: Welcome
Licenses: ♦♦♦
Leisure: Outdoor pool, Sauna, Solarium
Parking: Off-street and free
Directions: Leave M5 at Junction 27. Take A361 to
Barnstaple, then to Ilfracombe. Straight across two
sets of traffic lights, then left-hand fork and first left.
Map ref: Ilfracombe 2 C2

Darnley Hotel

3 Belmont Road, Ilfracombe, Devon, EX34 8DR
Tel: 01271 863955 Fax: 01271 864076
Email: darnleyhotel@yahoo.co.uk
Web: www.darnleyhotel.co.uk

A small, privately run quality hotel. Four-poster rooms, spa bath room available. Car park, some under cover. Licensed bar/restaurant. Close to town and seafront. Open all year including Christmas.
Rooms: 10 (7 ensuite) ♨ 🛏 🚫
Pricing: Sgl £33.50–48.50 Dbl £48–80
Dinner available from £12.50
CC: Accepted
Room facilities: 🖵 🕾
Conference: 1 meeting room (Thtr 20 max)
Children: Welcome 🍽
Dogs: Welcome
Licenses: ♦♦♦
Leisure: Games room
Parking: Off-street and free
Directions: J27 M5: follow A361 Barnstaple to Ilfracombe. First left on entering Ilfracombe Church Hill, first left Belmont Road.
Map ref: Ilfracombe 2 C2

Elmfield Hotel

Stands in an acre of gardens, with a heated indoor swimming pool, jacuzzi, sauna, solarium and car park. For that special occasion two rooms have four-poster beds. The Hotel has an excellent reputation for its English and Continental cuisine and has received an RAC Dining Award.

Torrs Park, Ilfracombe,
North Devon EX34 8AZ
Tel: 01271 863377   Fax: 01271 866828
Website: www.elmfieldhotelilfracombe.co.uk
Email: ann@elmfieldhotelilfracombe.co.uk

Elmfield Hotel

Torrs Park, Ilfracombe, Devon, EX34 8AZ
Tel: 01271 863377 Fax: 01271 866828
Email: ann@elmfieldhotelilfracombe.co.uk
Web: www.elmfieldhotelilfracombe.co.uk
Seasonal closure: November to March
Rooms: 13 all ensuite 🛏 🚫
Pricing: Sgl £42–45 Dbl £84–90
Dinner available from £16
CC: Accepted
Room facilities: 🖵 🕾
Licenses: ♦♦♦
Leisure: Indoor pool, Gym, Games room, Sauna, Jacuzzi, Solarium
Parking: Off-street and free
Directions: Take A361 from Barnstaple, at first lights in Ilfracombe turn left, at second lights turn left, 10 metres left again, hotel at top of hill on the left.
Map ref: Ilfracombe 2 C2
See advert on this page

Ilfracombe Carlton Hotel

Runnacleave Road, Ilfracombe, Devon, EX34 8AR
Tel: 01271 862446 Fax: 01271 865379
Email: ilfracombe-hotel@btconnect.com
Web: www.ilfracombecarlton.co.uk

Lovely Victorian-style hotel. Central location adjacent to coastal walks, beach, gardens and theatre. We aim to please — somewhere special for you!
Rooms: 48 all ensuite
Pricing: Sgl £32.50–40 Dbl £65–80
Dinner available from £15.50
CC: Accepted
Room facilities:
Access: |↓↑
Children: Welcome
Licenses:
Parking: Off-street and free
Directions: From M5 J27, take A361 to Barnstaple, then A361 to Ilfracombe. Turn left at lights (seafront) then left again.
Map ref: Ilfracombe 2 C2

St Brannock's House

61 St Brannock's Road, Ilfracombe, Devon, EX34 8EQ
Tel: 01271 863873 Fax: 01271 863873
Email: stbrannocks@aol.com
Web: www.stbrannockshotel.co.uk
Rooms: 6 all ensuite
Pricing: Sgl £29–31 Dbl £58–62
Dinner available from £12.50–14
CC: Accepted
Room facilities:
Children: Welcome
Dogs: Welcome
Licenses:
Parking: Off-street and free
Directions: Leave M5 at Junction 27. Take A361 through Barnstaple to Ilfracombe. The hotel is on A361 on left as you approach town.
Map ref: Ilfracombe 2 C2

The Palm Court Hotel

Wilder Road, Ilfracombe, Devon, EX34 9AS
Tel: 01271 866644 Fax: 01271 863581
Email: holiday@palmcourt-hotel.co.uk
Web: www.palmcourt-hotel.co.uk
Rooms: 50 all ensuite
Dinner available
CC: Accepted
Room facilities:
Access: |↓↑
Conference: 2 meeting rooms (Thtr 100 max)
Children: Welcome
Licenses:
Leisure: Games room
Parking: Off-street
Directions: Come off A39 link road follow Sien Barn-Ilfracombe. Take sign to seafront on entering Ilfracombe, hotel on left-hand side.
Map ref: Ilfracombe 2 C2

Westwell Hall Hotel

Torrs Park, Ilfracombe, Devon, EX34 8AZ
Tel: 01271 862792 Fax: 01271 862792
Email: westwell@hotel.co.uk.
Web: www.westwellhall.co.uk
Seasonal closure: November to March
Rooms: 10 all ensuite
Dinner available CC: Accepted
Room facilities:
Children: Welcome
Dogs: Welcome
Licenses:
Parking: Off-street
Directions: Take A361 from Barnstaple. Turn left at both first and second traffic lights, then immediately left. Take second on right into Upper Torrs.
Map ref: Ilfracombe 2 C2

Torrs Hotel

Torrs Park, Ilfracombe, Devon, EX34 8AY
Tel: 01271 862334
Email: torrshotel@aol.com
Web: www.thetorrshotel.co.uk
Rooms: 11 all ensuite
Pricing: Sgl £25–30 Dbl £50–60
Dinner available from £10
CC: Accepted
Room facilities:
Children: Welcome
Dogs: Welcome
Licenses:
Parking: Off-street and free
Directions: From Barnstaple (A361), turn left at first set of traffic lights in Ilfracombe. At second set turn left and then left again.
Map ref: Ilfracombe 2 C2

Ilminster, Somerset

The Old Rectory

◆◆◆◆◆ ◻ ✕

Cricket Malherbie, Ilminster, Somerset, TA19 0PW
Tel: 01460 54364 Fax: 01460 57374
Email: info@malherbie.co.uk
Web: www.malherbie.co.uk
Seasonal closure: Christmas

Award-winning small country hotel. Idyllic 16th century thatched house, flagstone floors, oak beams. Luxury bedrooms overlooking glorious gardens. Superb food featuring local produce, excellent wine list. Best B&B south-west 2003.
Rooms: 5 all ensuite ⊗
Pricing: Sgl £60–65 Dbl £90–105
Dinner available from £30 CC: Accepted
Room facilities: ◻ ☕
Children: Welcome 16yrs min age
Licenses: ⚖ ⅲ Parking: Off-street and free
Directions: From junction A303/A358 south towards Chard on A358. After Donyatt, left towards Ilminster. After one mile right to Cricket Malherbie.
Map ref: Cricket Malherbie 3 E2

Instow, Devon

The Commodore Hotel

★★★★ ▥▥

Marine Parade, Instow, Bideford, Devon, EX39 4JN
Tel: 01271 860347 Fax: 01271 861233
Email: admin@commodore-instow.co.uk
Web: www.commodore-instow.co.uk

Privately owned and managed The Commodore Hotel is set in the waterside village of Instow. The Hotel's five suites and twenty bedrooms are all individually designed to a high standard.

Rooms: 25 all ensuite ⊗
Pricing: Sgl £60–80 Dbl £110–180
Dinner available from £26
CC: Accepted
Room facilities: ◻ ☎ ☕
Children: Welcome ⱨ
Licenses: ⅲ
Parking: Off-street and free
Directions: Leave M5 at Junction 27, onto North Devon Link Road. The turn-off for Instow is signposted just before the Torridge Bridge. Follow the signs for Instow to bring you to Marine Parade.
Map ref: Bideford 2 C2

Isles of Scilly

Hell Bay

★★★ ▥▥▥   *Premier*

Bryher, Isles of Scilly, Cornwall, TR23 0PR
Tel: 01720 422947 Fax: 01720 423004
Email: contactus@hellbay.co.uk
Web: www.hellbay.co.uk
Seasonal closure: January & February

Unique hotel in a stunning location. Next stop New York. All suite accommodation most with stunning views. Art led interiors dominate public areas. Relax and chillout on the edge of England. All room rates include breakfast and dinner.
Rooms: 25 all ensuite ⊛ ▤ ⊗
Pricing: Sgl £137.50–275 Dbl £220–440
Dinner available from £35
CC: Accepted
Room facilities: ◻ ☎ ☕ ☏
Access: ⇞
Children: Welcome ⱨ ⌖
Dogs: Welcome
Licenses: ⚖ ⅲ
Leisure: Outdoor pool, Gym, Golf, Games room
Directions: Flights from Penzance, Exeter, Bristol, Newquay, Southampton, Land's End, direct to islands. Boat from Penzance. Hell Bay makes all arrangements.
Map ref: Bryher 2 A3

Island Hotel

★★★ ₰₰₰
Tresco, Isles of Scilly, Cornwall, TR24 0PU
Tel: 01720 422883 Fax: 01720 423008
Email: islandhotel@tresco.co.uk
Web: www.tresco.co.uk
Seasonal closure: November to February
Rooms: 48 all ensuite 🥢 🚭
Pricing: Dinner available from £37.50 CC: Accepted
Room facilities: ▢ ☎ ☕
Conference: 3 meeting rooms (Thtr 60 max)
Children: Welcome 🏕 ❆
Licenses: ♦♦♦
Leisure: Outdoor pool, Tennis, Games room,
Snooker/billiards
Directions: Departure from Penzance via British
International Helicopters. Direct to Tresco Heliport for
collection. Departure St Mary's via boat to Tresco for
collection. Flights by skybus from Exeter, Bristol,
Newquay or Lands End to St Mary's via boat to
Tresco.
Map ref: Isles of Scilly 2 A3

St Martin's on the Isle

★★★ ₰₰₰₰
St Martin's, Isles of Scilly, Cornwall, TR25 0QW
Tel: 01720 422090 Fax: 01720 422298
Email: stay@stmartinshotel.co.uk
Web: www.stmartinshotel.co.uk
Seasonal closure: November to February
Rooms: 30 all ensuite 🥢
Pricing: Sgl £130–155 Dbl £260–310
Dinner available from £44.50
CC: Accepted
Room facilities: ▢ ☎ ☕
Conference: 3 meeting rooms (Thtr 60 max)
Children: Welcome 🏕 ❆
Dogs: Welcome
Licenses: ⬙ ♦♦♦
Leisure: Indoor pool, Tennis, Snooker/billiards
Directions: 20-minute helicopter journey from
Penzance, and then 20-minute boat trip to St Martin's
from St Mary's.
Map ref: Isles of Scilly 2 A3

St Mary's Hall Hotel

★★★ ₰₰₰
Church Street, Hugh Town, St Mary's, Isles of Scilly,
Cornwall, TR21 0JR
Tel: 01720 422316 Fax: 01720 422252
Email: recept@stmaryshallhotel.demon.co.uk
Web: www.stmaryshallhotel.demon.co.uk
Seasonal closure: November to March
Rooms: 19 all ensuite
Pricing: Sgl £75–137.50 Dbl £150–240
Dinner available from £29.95
CC: Accepted
Room facilities: ▢ ☎ ☕ 📞
Children: Welcome 5yrs min age 🏕
Licenses: ♦♦♦
Map ref: Hugh Town 2 A3

Star Castle Hotel

★★★ ₰₰₰
The Garrison, St Mary's, Isles of Scilly, TR21 0JA
Tel: 01720 422317 Fax: 01720 422343
Web: www.star-castle.co.uk
Rooms: 34 all ensuite 🥢
Pricing: Dinner available from £23 CC: Accepted
Room facilities: ▢ ☎ ☕
Conference: 2 meeting rooms (Thtr 30 max)
Children: Welcome 🏕 ❆ Dogs: Welcome
Licenses: ♦♦♦ Leisure: Indoor pool, Tennis
Parking: Off-street and free
Directions: A five-minute walk from the quay. A
courtesy car will collect all guests from the airport.
Map ref: The Garrison 2 A3

Tregarthen's Hotel

★★★★ ₰₰
Hughtown, St Mary's, Isles of Scilly, TR21 0PP
Tel: 01720 422540 Fax: 01720 422089
Email: reception@tregarthens-hotel.co.uk
Web: www.tregarthens-hotel.co.uk
Seasonal closure: October to March
Rooms: 32 all ensuite 🥢 🚭
Pricing: Sgl £93–120 Dbl £196–240
Dinner available from £20–25 CC: Accepted
Room facilities: ▢ ☎ ☕
Children: Welcome 🏕
Licenses: ♦♦♦ Parking: Off-street
Map ref: Isles of Scilly 2 A3

Amaryllis   Little Gem

◆◆◆◆◆ ✗ ☕
Buzza Hill, St Mary's, Isles of Scilly, TR21 0NQ
Tel: 01720 423387
Email: earlsamaryllis@aol.com
Web: www.scillyonline.co.uk
Rooms: 3 all ensuite 🚭
Pricing: Sgl £60–65 Dbl £120–130
Room facilities: ▢ ☕
Licenses: ♦♦♦ Parking: Off-street and free
Directions: Situated 5 minutes from St Mary's town on
secluded hillside overlooking sea. Transport available
from airport or boat quay.
Map ref: Isles of Scilly 2 A3

Seaview Moorings   Little Gem

◆◆◆◆◆ ✗ ☕
The Strand, St Mary's, Isles of Scilly, TR21 0PT
Tel: 01720 422327 Fax: 01720 422211
Seasonal closure: November to February
Rooms: 4 all ensuite
Pricing: Dbl £90
Room facilities: ▢ ☎ ☕
Children: Welcome 14yrs min age Dogs: Welcome
Licenses: ♦♦♦
Directions: Situated alongside (and all rooms
overlooking) St Mary's Harbour and quay whilst only a
few minutes walk from the town.
Map ref: Isles of Scilly 2 A3

Ivybridge, Devon

Sportsmans Inn

★★

Exeter Road, Ivybridge, Devon, PL21 0BQ
Tel: 01752 892280 Fax: 01752 690714
Rooms: 14 (13 ensuite)
Dinner available
CC: Accepted
Room facilities: 🖵 ☎ 📺 📞
Children: Welcome 🍴
Licenses: 🚻
Leisure: Games room
Parking: Off-street
Directions: Just off A38, 10 miles from Plymouth,
centre of Ivybridge town.
Map ref: Ivybridge 2 C4

Keynsham, Bath & NE Somerset

Grasmere Court

◆◆◆◆ ✵🏠

22 Bath Road, Keynsham, near Bristol,
Bath & NE Somerset, BS31 1SN
Tel: 01179 862662 Fax: 01179 862762
Email: grasmerecourt@aol.com
Web: www.grasmerecourthotel.co.uk

Superior family-run hotel conveniently situated
between Bristol and Bath. The hotel has been recently
refurbished to a high standard. All rooms are well-
appointed with private facilities. Free parking for all.
Rooms: 16 all ensuite 📠 📺
Pricing: Dinner available from £17
CC: Accepted
Room facilities: 🖵 ☎ 📺 📞
Conference: 1 meeting room
Children: Welcome
Licenses: 🍷 🚻
Parking: Off-street and free
Directions: Situated on main A4 road, midway between
the cities of Bristol and Bath.
Map ref: Keynsham 3 E1

Kingsbridge, Devon

Cottage Hotel, Hope Cove

★★ 📶 📶

Near Kingsbridge, Devon, TQ7 3HJ
Tel: 01548 561555 Fax: 01548 561455
Email: info@hopecove.com
Web: www.hopecove.com
Seasonal closure: January
Rooms: 35 (26 ensuite) 🏊
Pricing: Dinner available from £17.25–21.85
CC: Accepted
Room facilities: ☎ 📺 📞
Conference: 1 meeting room (Thtr 50 max),
24hr-delegate from £55, day-delegate from £11.95
Children: Welcome 🍴 ℃
Dogs: Welcome
Licenses: 🚻
Leisure: Games room
Directions: From Kingsbridge take A381 towards
Salcombe; Hope Cove signposted. Continue towards
Hope Cove, turn left for Inner Hope. Hotel is on right.
Map ref: Hope Cove 2 C4

Lewdown, Devon

Lewtrenchard Manor

★★★★ 📶 📶 📶  Excellent

Lewdown, Okehampton, Devon, EX20 4PN
Tel: 01566 783 222 Fax: 01566 783 332
Email: info@lewtrenchard.co.uk
Web: www.lewtrenchard.co.uk
Rooms: 14 all ensuite 🏊 📠 📺
Pricing: Sgl £95–130 Dbl £155–250
Dinner available from £39.50
CC: Accepted
Room facilities: 🖵 ☎ 📞
Access: ⬆
Conference: 3 meeting rooms (Thtr 50 max),
24hr-delegate from £185, day-delegate from £45
Children: Welcome 8yrs min age
Dogs: Welcome
Licenses: 🍷 🚻
Leisure: Fishing
Parking: Off-street and free
Directions: A30 from Exeter turn onto A386. T-junction
right and immediately left onto old A30. Lewdown 6
miles. Turn left signposted Lewtrenchard.
Map ref: Lewdown 2 C3

Southwest

Lifton, Devon

Arundell Arms Hotel

★★★ Excellent

Lifton, Devon, PL16 0AA
Tel: 01566 784666 Fax: 01566 784494
Email: reservations@arundellarms.com
Web: www.arundellarms.com
Seasonal closure: 3 days over Christmas

Former coaching inn on Devon Cornish border offering log fire comfort, caring service and outstanding gourmet food, internationally famed for its Salmon and Trout fishing and shooting. Excellent conference facilities.
Rooms: 21 all ensuite
Pricing: Sgl £95 Dbl £150–180
Dinner available from £35–40
CC: Accepted
Room facilities:
Conference: 2 meeting rooms (Thtr 100 max), 24hr-delegate from £143, day-delegate from £30
Children: Welcome
Dogs: Welcome
Licenses:
Leisure: Fishing, Games room
Parking: Off-street and free
Directions: Leave M5 at Junction 31. Take A30 towards Launceston. Hotel is 2 miles east of Launceston in Lifton village.
Map ref: Lifton 2 C3

Liskeard, Cornwall

Great Trethew Manor

◆◆◆◆

Horningtops, Liskeard, Cornwall, PL14 3PY
Tel: 01503 240663 Fax: 01503 240695
Web: www.great-trethew-manor.co.uk
Rooms: 12 all ensuite
Pricing: Sgl £37.50–45 Dbl £60–70
Dinner available from £10–15
CC: Accepted
Room facilities:
Children: Welcome
Licenses:
Leisure: Tennis, Fishing, Riding
Parking: Off-street and free
Directions: From A38 take B3251. Hotel is 500m on the left.
Map ref: Horningtops 2 C3

Lizard, Cornwall

Housel Bay Hotel & Restaurant

★★★

Housel Bay, The Lizard, Helston, Cornwall, TR12 7PG
Tel: 01326 290417/917 Fax: 01326 290359
Email: info@houselbay.com
Web: www.houselbay.com
Rooms: 20 all ensuite
Pricing: Sgl £30–40 Dbl £60–130
Dinner available from £21.50 CC: Accepted
Room facilities: Access:
Children: Welcome
Licenses: Parking: Off-street and free
Directions: At the Lizard signpost, take the left fork. Follow hotel signs.
Map ref: Lizard 2 A4

Looe, Cornwall

Whitsand Bay Hotel

★★★★ Commended

Portwrinkle, near Looe, Cornwall, PL11 3BU
Tel: 01503 230276 Fax: 01503 230329
Email: whitsandbayhotel@btconnect.com
Web: www.whitsandbayhotel.co.uk
Rooms: 32 all ensuite
Pricing: Sgl £85–95 Dbl £85–95
Dinner available from £26.95 CC: Accepted
Room facilities:
Conference: 2 meeting rooms
Children: Welcome Dogs: Welcome
Licenses:
Leisure: Indoor pool, Gym, Health spa, Beauty salon, Golf, Games room, Snooker/billiards
Parking: Off-street and free
Directions: A38 past Plymouth. At Trerulefoot roundabout, take A374 towards Torpoint and follow signs after approximately 3 miles.
Map ref: Portwrinkle 2 C4
See advert on opposite page

Klymiarven

★★

Barbican Hill, Looe, Cornwall, PL13 1BH
Tel: 01503 262333 Fax: 01503 262333
Email: reception@klymiarven.co.uk
Web: www.klymiarven.co.uk
Seasonal closure: January
Rooms: 14 all ensuite
Pricing: Sgl £44–65 Dbl £78–110
Dinner available from £19.95 CC: Accepted
Room facilities:
Children: Welcome Dogs: Welcome
Licenses: Leisure: Outdoor pool
Parking: Off-street and free
Directions: From M5 South take A38 Plymouth-Liskeard road. After 50 miles take A374 towards Looe, then B3253. Turn left after Looe Garden Centre onto Barbican. Take tourist bed sign Barbican Hill to Klymiarven.
Map ref: Looe 2 C4

Whitsand Bay Hotel

GOLF & COUNTRY CLUB

Recently refurbished hotel, set upon the Cornish coastline in the old fishing village of Portwrinkle.

Our 18-hole cliff top golf course along with the hotel boasts rolling views of Whitsand Bay and the local countryside.

Facilities include à la carte restaurant, bar, swimming pool, beauty salon, steam room and sauna. Hotel is situated between the city of Plymouth and Looe.

Tel: 01503 230276

www.whitsandbayhotel.co.uk

Coombe Farm

Widegates, Looe, Cornwall, PL13 1QN
Tel: 01503 240223 Fax: 01503 240895
Email: coombe_farm@hotmail.com
Web: www.coombefarmhotel.co.uk
Seasonal closure: Christmas through to New Year

Guests relax in three spacious ensuite cottage rooms within Coombe Farm's 12 acres of grounds. Outdoor pool, ponies, peacocks, nearby beaches, Eden, Heligan, National Trust properties plus golf and watersports.
Rooms: 3 all ensuite ⛱ Ⓢ
Pricing: Sgl £50–60 Dbl £68–80 CC: Accepted
Room facilities: ▢ ☎ ⛁ ⌁
Children: Welcome Dogs: Welcome
Licenses: ♦♦♦ Leisure: Outdoor pool

Parking: Off-street and free
Directions: A38 to Plymouth, continue on A38 then turn left at Trerulefoot roundabout, 6 miles after Tamar Bridge follow A387 to Looe. Hotel 1 mile after Hessenford on A387 on left.
Map ref: Looe 2 C4

Deganwy Hotel

Station Road, Looe, Cornwall, PL13 1HL
Tel: 01503 262984
Email: enquiries@deganwyhotel.co.uk
Web: www.deganwyhotel.co.uk
Rooms: 8 (6 ensuite) ⛱ Ⓢ
Pricing: Sgl £35–36 Dbl £50–60 CC: Accepted
Room facilities: ▢ ⛁
Children: Welcome 🛏
Licenses: ♦♦♦ Parking: Off-street and free
Directions: From the Plymouth direction, on approaching Looe the hotel is directly after the Texaco Garage on the left.
Map ref: Looe 2 C4

Meneglaze

♦♦♦

Shutta, Looe, Cornwall, PL13 1LY
Tel: 01503 269227
Email: meneglaze@tiscali.co.uk
Web: www.looebedandbreakfast.com
Rooms: 4 all ensuite Ⓢ
Pricing: Dbl £23.50–27.50
Room facilities: ▢ ⛁ Children: Welcome
Parking: Off-street and free
Directions: A38 into Cornwall. Take A374 then A387 towards Looe. Entering Looe, turn left opposite the railway station beside The Globe.
Map ref: Looe 2 C4

Lostwithiel, Cornwall

Lostwithiel Hotel Golf & Country Club

★★★

Lower Polscoe, Lostwithiel, Cornwall, PL22 0HQ
Tel: 01208 873550 Fax: 01208 873479
Email: reception@golf-hotel.co.uk
Web: www.golf-hotel.co.uk
Rooms: 27 all ensuite ⛱ Ⓢ
Pricing: Sgl £33–50 Dbl £66–100
Dinner available from £17.95–19.95 CC: Accepted
Room facilities: ▢ ☎ ⛁
Conference: 3 meeting rooms (Thtr 100 max), 24hr-delegate from £75, day-delegate from £23
Children: Welcome 🛏 ⌁ Dogs: Welcome
Licenses: ⚓ ♦♦♦
Leisure: Indoor pool, Gym, Tennis, Golf, Games room, Snooker/billiards
Parking: Off-street and free
Directions: Off A390 eastern side of Lostwithiel. Tourist signposted.
Map ref: Lower Polscoe 2 B3

Tremont House

◆◆◆◆

2 The Terrace, Lostwithiel, Cornwall, PL22 0DT
Tel: 01208 873055
Email: tremonthouse@aol.com
Rooms: 3 (2 ensuite)
Pricing: Sgl £30–35 Dbl £52–70
Room facilities: ☐ ☕
Children: Welcome ħ
Parking: Off-street and free
Directions: Parking at rear of property. Second on right in
Scrations Lane off A390, on the west side of Lostwithiel.
Map ref: Lostwithiel 2 B3

Lulworth Cove, Dorset

Cromwell House Hotel

★★

Lulworth Cove, near Wareham, Dorset, BH20 5RJ
Tel: 01929 400253 Fax: 01929 400566
Email: catriona@lulworthcove.co.uk
Web: www.lulworthcove.co.uk
Seasonal closure: Christmas and New Year

Lulworth Cove 200 yards, spectacular sea views.
Direct access Dorset coastal footpath. Swimming pool
(May-October), home cooking, fish specialities, bar,
wine list. Group bookings welcome. Special breaks.
Open all year.
Rooms: 17 all ensuite 🍴 🖼 ⊗
Pricing: Sgl £35–61 Dbl £70–89
Dinner available from £18–35
CC: Accepted
Room facilities: ☐ ☎ ☕ 🌿
Conference: 1 meeting room (Thtr 15 max),
24hr-delegate from £80, day-delegate from £30
Children: Welcome ħ ⅲ
Dogs: Welcome
Licenses: ⅲ
Leisure: Outdoor pool
Parking: Off-street and free
Directions: London M3 to Winchester, M27 to
Ringwood, A31 to Bere Regis, B3501 south to West
Lulworth, 200 yards after end of West Lulworth on left
high above main road before you reach Lulworth Cove.
Map ref: Lulworth Cove 3 F3

Lydford, Devon

Moor View House
Little Gem

◆◆◆◆◆ 🛏🛏 ⅗

Vale Down, Lydford, Okehampton, Devon, EX20 4BB
Tel: 01822 820220 Fax: 01822 820220

Licensed Victorian country house in moorland.
Gardens, log fires, peace and quiet, lovely views,
"ideal touring centre for NT property." Reputation for
good English food, sound wines.
Rooms: 4 all ensuite ⊛
Pricing: Sgl £50–60 Dbl £65–80
Dinner available from £25 Room facilities: ☐ ☕
Licenses: ⅲ Parking: Off-street and free
Directions: From M5 at Exeter A30 to Sourton Cross,
A386 Tavistock, Moor View House drive 4 miles on
right, 8 miles before Tavistock.
Map ref: Okehampton 2 C3

Lyme Regis, Dorset

Hotel Alexandra

★★★

Pound Street, Lyme Regis, Dorset, DT7 3HZ
Tel: 01297 442010 Fax: 01297 443229
Email: enquiries@hotelalexandra.co.uk
Web: www.hotelalexandra.co.uk
Seasonal closure: January and Christmas

The Alexandra combines the spirit of times past with
friendly and efficient service. With stunning sea views,
the elegant restaurant offers an award-winning menu
and first class wine list.

Rooms: 26 (25 ensuite)
Pricing: Sgl £60 Dbl £106–150
Dinner available from £29.50
CC: Accepted
Room facilities: 🖵 ☎ 🍵
Children: Welcome Ḧ ⅍
Dogs: Welcome
Licenses: ▮▮▮
Parking: Off-street and free
Directions: Turn off M5 at Junction 25. Take A358 to Axminster. Take B3261 to B3165 Lyme Regis. From M5, take A303 to reach A358.
Map ref: Lyme Regis 3 E3

Kersbrook Hotel

◆◆◆

Pound Road, Lyme Regis, Dorset, DT7 3HX
Tel: 01297 442596 Fax: 01297 442596
Web: www.lymeregis.com/kersbrook-hotel
Rooms: 10 all ensuite
Pricing: Sgl £45–50 Dbl £60–80
CC: Accepted
Room facilities: 🖵 🍵
Children: Welcome
Dogs: Welcome
Licenses: ▮▮▮
Parking: Off-street and free
Directions: The road that leads to the harbour is Cobb Road. Pound Road is at the top of Cobb Road crossroads.
Map ref: Lyme Regis 3 E3

Lympsham, Somerset

Batch Country Hotel

★★

Batch Lane, Lympsham, near Weston-Super-Mare, Somerset, BS24 0EX
Tel: 01934 750371 Fax: 01934 750501
Web: www.batchcountryhotel.co.uk

A short distance from Weston-Super-Mare and Burnham-on-Sea, this attractive hotel offers a relaxed and friendly environment. The bedrooms are comfortable and well equipped, and have views of the Mendip Hills. The spacious lounges overlook the gardens, and an extensive range of dishes is served in the attractive restaurant. Easy access from junction 22 of the M5.

Rooms: 11 all ensuite 📔
Pricing: Sgl £56 Dbl £78
Dinner available from £12–22
CC: Accepted
Room facilities: 🖵 ☎ 🍵 🔌
Conference: 3 meeting rooms (Thtr 100 max), 24hr-delegate from £75, day-delegate from £19.50
Children: Welcome Ḧ
Licenses: ⚓ ▮▮▮
Parking: Off-street and free
Directions: Leave M5 motorway at junction 22, take last exit on roundabout, signposted A370 to Weston-Super-Mare. Keep on A370 for approx 3½ miles then turn left into Lympsham village, follow tourist board signs to hotel.
Map ref: Lympsham 3 E2

Lynmouth, Devon

Tors Hotel

★★★★ ♙♙

Lynmouth, Devon, EX35 6NA
Tel: 01598 753236 Fax: 01598 752544
Email: torshotel@torslynmouth.co.uk
Web: www.torslynmouth.co.uk
Seasonal closure: January to February
Rooms: 31 all ensuite ♨ ⊘
Pricing: Sgl £70–180 Dbl £100–220
Dinner available from £25–30 CC: Accepted
Room facilities: 🖵 ☎ 🍵 Access: |↕|
Children: Welcome Ḧ ⅍
Dogs: Welcome
Licenses: ▮▮▮
Leisure: Outdoor pool, Games room
Parking: Off-street and free
Directions: Leave M5 at Junction 23. Take A39 for Bridgwater. Travel west for 40 miles through Minehead and Porlock. Down Countisbury Hill, the hotel is on left as you enter Lynmouth.
Map ref: Lynmouth 3 D2

Bath Hotel

★★

Seafront, Lynmouth, Devon, EX35 6EL
Tel: 01598 752238 Fax: 01598 753894
Email: bathhotel@torslynmouth.co.uk
Web: www.torslynmouth.co.uk
Seasonal closure: December to January
Rooms: 22 all ensuite ♨ ⊘
Pricing: Sgl £39–55 Dbl £64–130
Dinner available from £19 CC: Accepted
Room facilities: 🖵 ☎ 🍵
Children: Welcome Ḧ ⅍
Dogs: Welcome
Licenses: ▮▮▮
Leisure: Games room, Snooker/billiards
Parking: Off-street and free
Directions: On A39 from Minehead, on entering Lynmouth turn right towards the sea. Hotel on left by harbour.
Map ref: Lynmouth 3 D2

Lynton, Devon

Valley House

◆◆◆◆

Lynbridge Road, Lynton, Devon, EX35 6BD
Tel: 01598 752285
Email: info@valley-house.co.uk
Web: www.valley-house.co.uk
Rooms: 6 all ensuite 🍵 ⊗
Pricing: Sgl £27.50–48.75 Dbl £55–65
Dinner available from £13.25–17 CC: Accepted
Room facilities: 🖵 🎨 Children: Welcome 8yrs min age ☷
Dogs: Welcome Licenses: ♦♦♦
Parking: Off-street and free
Directions: Within Exmoor National Park. Between
Lynton and Lynmouth off the B3234 (Lynbridge Road).
Map ref: Lynton 3 D2

Malmesbury, Wiltshire

Whatley Manor

★★★★ 🍵🍵🍵 Premier

Easton Grey, Malmesbury, Wiltshire, SN16 0RB
Tel: 01666 822888 Fax: 01666 826120
Email: reservations@whatleymanor.com
Web: www.whatleymanor.com

Guests staying at this breathtakingly stylish and
sophisticated retreat, set amidst 12 acres of superb
English country gardens, will find a relaxing yet luxurious
atmosphere of understated elegance, reminiscent of a
friendly, welcoming private stylish country home.
Rooms: 23 all ensuite 🎨 ⊗
Pricing: Sgl £275–850 Dbl £275–850
Dinner available from £25–75 CC: Accepted
Room facilities: 🖵 🎨 🧹 Access: ⌊↥
Conference: 4 meeting rooms (Thtr 40 max),
24hr-delegate from £265, day-delegate from £65
Children: Welcome 12yrs min age Dogs: Welcome
Licenses: ⬙ ♦♦♦
Leisure: Indoor pool, Outdoor pool, Gym, Health spa,
Cinema Parking: Off-street and free
Directions: Leave M4 J17. Following signs to
Malmesbury town centre, take B4040. Continue for 2
miles, turn left into Whatley Manor.
Map ref: Easton Grey 3 F1

Mayfield House Hotel

★★★ 🍵🍵

Crudwell, Malmesbury, Wiltshire, SN16 9EW
Tel: 01666 577409 Fax: 01666 577977
Email: reception@mayfieldhousehotel.co.uk
Web: www.mayfieldhousehotel.co.uk
Rooms: 24 all ensuite 🍵 ⊗
Pricing: Sgl £65–75 Dbl £85–95
Dinner available from £19.50–25
CC: Accepted
Room facilities: 🖵 🎨 🧹 🧹
Conference: 1 meeting room (Thtr 20 max),
24hr-delegate from £114, day-delegate from £32
Children: Welcome ☷ ⎇
Dogs: Welcome
Licenses: ♦♦♦
Parking: Off-street and free
Directions: On the A429 between Malmesbury and
Cirencester. 7 miles north of Junction 17 on the M4.
Map ref: Crudwell 3 F1

Mawgan Porth, Cornwall

Bedruthan Steps Hotel

★★★★ 🍵🍵

Mawgan Porth, Cornwall, TR8 4BU
Tel: 01637 860555 Fax: 01637 860714
Email: office@bedruthan.com
Web: www.bedruthan.com
Rooms: 99 all ensuite 🍵 ⊗
Pricing: Sgl £67–112 Dbl £134–224
Dinner available from £25.50
CC: Accepted
Room facilities: 🖵 🎨 🧹
Access: ⌊↥
Conference: 8 meeting rooms (Thtr 200 max),
day-delegate from £30
Children: Welcome ☷ 🧸 ⎇
Dogs: Assistance dogs only
Licenses: ⬙ ♦♦♦
Leisure: Indoor pool, Outdoor pool, Gym, Health spa,
Beauty salon, Tennis, Snooker/billiards
Parking: Off-street and free
Directions: A30 to A39 onto A3059 signed Newquay
Airport. Past airport. Next right to Mawgan Porth. Up
hill, hotel on left at top.
Map ref: Mawgan Porth 2 B3
See advert on opposite page

"Stay!"

Need a pet friendly property?
Look out for 'Dogs welcome' in
our listings.

At Bedruthan, the glorious views, delicious food and a friendly welcome combine to give you the perfect break. Situated on the North Cornwall Coast, overlooking the golden sands of Mawgan Porth beach, this stylish contemporary hotel is the ideal place to relax and revive. Superb for business or pleasure, Bedruthan is five minutes drive from Newquay Airport.

Facilities include indoor and outdoor pools, Ocean Spa, Ofsted inspected childcare, Conference centre.

Bedruthan Steps Hotel
Mawgan Porth Cornwall
www.bedruthan.com
Tel 01637 860555
email:office@bedruthan.com

Southwest

Blue Bay Hotel, Restaurant & Lodges
◆◆◆ ℞☕

Trenance, Mawgan Porth, Newquay, Cornwall, TR8 4DA
Tel: 01637 860324
Email: hotel@bluebaycornwall.co.uk
Web: www.bluebaycornwall.co.uk
Seasonal closure: Christmas

Superb views of the Atlantic, pristine beach and easy access to coastal path; Blue Bay Hotel offers you the very best Cornwall has to offer. Award-winning hospitality and restaurant.
Rooms: 8 all ensuite 🛁 🚭
Pricing: Sgl £31–37 Dbl £62–74
Dinner available from £14 CC: Accepted

Room facilities: 📺 ☕
Conference: 1 meeting room (Thtr 15 max)
Children: Welcome 🍴 ☕
Dogs: Welcome
Licenses: 👪
Leisure: Books, Games, Beach
Parking: Off-street and free
Directions: Turn off A30 after Iron Bridge, follow signs to airport. At T-junction follow signs to Mawgan Porth then Trenance. At Bedruthan Steps Hotel turn past front door onto unmade road, Blue Bay fourth building on right.
Map ref: Mawgan Porth 2 B3

Are the bells ringing?

Getting married? Congratulations! Look for the wedding bells symbol which shows hotels licensed for civil ceremonies.

Moretonhampstead, Devon

Bovey Castle

★★★★★

North Bovey, Moretonhampstead,
Dartmoor National Park, Devon, TQ13 8RE
Tel: 01647 445000 Fax: 01647 445020
Email: enquiries@boveycastle.com
Web: www.boveycastle.com
Rooms: 65 all ensuite 🛏 🚭
Pricing: Sgl £195 Dbl £250
Dinner available from £52.50 CC: Accepted
Room facilities: 💻 ☎ ☕ Access: ♿
Conference: 3 meeting rooms (Thtr 120 max),
24hr-delegate from £340, day-delegate from £95
Children: Welcome 🍴 🎠 ☕ Dogs: Welcome
Licenses: ⚓ ⛲ Leisure: Indoor pool, Outdoor pool,
Gym, Health spa, Beauty salon, Tennis, Golf, Fishing,
Riding, Snooker/billiards, Falconry, Archery, Childrens
club Parking: Off-street and free
Directions: From M5 take J31, take first exit on A30 to
Moretonhampstead on A382. B3212 to Postbridge for
2 miles.
Map ref: North Bovey 3 D3

The White Hart Hotel

★★★

The Square, Moretonhampstead, Devon, TQ13 8NF
Tel: 01647 441340 Fax: 01647 441341
Email: whitehart1600@aol.com
Web: www.whitehartdartmoor.co.uk
Rooms: 20 all ensuite 🚭
Pricing: Sgl £45–55 Dbl £70–90
Dinner available from £18
CC: Accepted
Room facilities: 💻 ☕
Conference: 1 meeting room (Thtr 60 max)
Children: Welcome 🍴
Dogs: Welcome
Licenses: ⚓ ⛲
Parking: Off-street and free
Directions: M5 south to Devon, becomes A38 just
before Exeter. Exit at J31 and follow A30 towards
Oakhampton. At Widdon Down take A382 for
Moretonhampstead.
Map ref: Moretonhampstead 3 D3

Newquay, Cornwall

Headland Hotel

★★★★

Headland Road, Newquay, Cornwall, TR7 1EW
Tel: 01637 872211 Fax: 01637 872212
Email: reception@headlandhotel.co.uk
Web: www.headlandhotel.co.uk
Seasonal closure: 24-27 December
Rooms: 104 all ensuite 🛏 🚭
Pricing: Dinner available from £30
CC: Accepted
Room facilities: 💻 ☎ ☕ 📞 Access: ♿
Conference: 5 meeting rooms (Thtr 175 max),

24hr-delegate from £135, day-delegate from £32.50
Children: Welcome 🍴
Dogs: Welcome
Licenses: ⚓ ⛲
Leisure: Indoor pool, Outdoor pool, Tennis, Golf,
Snooker/billiards, In-house surf school
Parking: Off-street and free
Directions: Off A30 onto A392 at Indian Queens and
when approaching Newquay follow signs for Fistral
Beach.
Map ref: Newquay 2 B3
See advert on opposite page

Barrowfield Hotel

★★★

Hilgrove Road, Newquay, Cornwall, TR7 2QY
Tel: 01637 878878 Fax: 01637 879490
Email: booking@barrowfield.prestel.co.uk
Web: www.cranstar.co.uk

The Barrowfield Hotel includes suites with spas, four-
poster bedrooms, honeymoon suite and family suite.
There is a superb heated indoor pool with jacuzzi and
sauna, outdoor heated pool and snooker room. The
Hilgrove restaurant offers delicious cuisine.
Rooms: 81 all ensuite 🛏 🚮
Pricing: Sgl £49–60 Dbl £52–75
Dinner available from £16
CC: Accepted
Room facilities: 💻 ☎ ☕
Access: ♿
Conference: 2 meeting rooms (Thtr 350 max),
24hr-delegate from £95, day-delegate from £95
Children: Welcome 🍴
Dogs: Welcome
Licenses: ⚓ ⛲
Leisure: Indoor pool, Outdoor pool, Games room,
Snooker/billiards, Jacuzzi
Parking: Off-street and free
Directions: Enter Newquay via seafront. Turn left onto
Hilgrove Road. Situated on right-hand side.
Map ref: Newquay 2 B3

H E A D L A N D   H O T E L

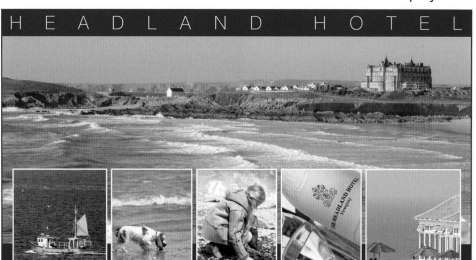

In 1900 when we opened our doors, service was our top priority. It still is. The view hasn't changed much either, a breathtaking sweep of Britain's most charismatic coastline. But in the twenty-first century our guests can also delight in our two heated pools, mouthwatering cuisine, a chilled out sundowner at the Sand Brasserie, a sauna, a brisk cliff top walk with the dog, learning to surf on the best waves in the country, a round of golf...

N O R T H   C O R N W A L L ' S   F I R S T   F O U R   S T A R   H O T E L
Headland Hotel, Fistral Beach, Newquay, Cornwall, TR7 1EW TEL 01637 872211 FAX 01637 872212
EMAIL reception@headlandhotel.co.uk   WEBSITE www.headlandhotel.co.uk

Hotel Bristol

★★★★ ☆

Narrowcliff, Newquay, Cornwall, TR7 2PQ
Tel: 01637 875181 Fax: 01637 879347
Email: info@hotelbristol.co.uk
Web: www.hotelbristol.co.uk
Rooms: 74 all ensuite ✥ ⊗
Pricing: Dinner available from £21.50
CC: Accepted
Room facilities: ▢ ☎ ▢ ✎
Access: |↕↑
Conference: 6 meeting rooms (Thtr 250 max),
24hr-delegate from £110, day-delegate from £35
Children: Welcome ℍ ⁓℮
Dogs: Welcome
Licenses: ♦♦♦
Leisure: Indoor pool, Beauty salon, Games room,
Snooker/billiards
Parking: Off-street and free
Directions: At Highgate Hill (A30), turn off to A39 then
A392. At Quintrell Downs take A3058, keep straight on
for 2.5 miles.
Map ref: Newquay 2 B3
See advert on this page

AA
★ ★ ★
RAC

The
BEST WESTERN
HOTEL BRISTOL

Narrowcliff, Newquay, Cornwall, TR7 2PQ
Fax: 01637 879347
Website: www.hotelbristol.co.uk
E-mail: info@hotelbristol.co.uk

For reservations call:

01637 875181

Hotel California

★★★

Pentire Crescent, Newquay, Cornwall, TR7 1PU
Tel: 01637 879292 Fax: 01637 875611
Email: info@hotel-california.co.uk
Web: www.hotel-california.co.uk
Rooms: 70 all ensuite 🐾 📠 🚭
Pricing: Sgl £30–45 Dbl £60–90
Dinner available from £14.95
CC: Accepted
Room facilities: 🖳 ☎ ☕
Access: |↓↑
Conference: 3 meeting rooms (Thtr 150 max),
24hr-delegate from £45, day-delegate from £15
Children: Welcome ╞ 🐴 ₰℃
Dogs: Welcome
Licenses: ⟁ ⅲ
Leisure: Indoor pool, Outdoor pool, Beauty salon,
Games room, Snooker/billiards, Four lane bowling
alley, Squash court, Table tennis
Parking: Off-street and free
Directions: From A30 take A392 Newquay through
Quintrell Downs. Pass Safeway, right 1st roundabout,
left on 2nd roundabout, left on 1st roundabout, onto
Pentire Crescent.
Map ref: Newquay 2 B3
See advert on opposite page

Hotel Riviera

★★★

1 Lusty Glaze Road, Newquay, Cornwall, TR7 3AA
Tel: 01637 874251 Fax: 01637 850823
Email: hotelriviera@btconnect.com
Web: www.hotelrivieranewquay.com
Rooms: 48 all ensuite 🐾 📠
Pricing: Dinner available from £18
CC: Accepted
Room facilities: 🖳 ☎ ☕
Access: |↓↑
Conference: 5 meeting rooms (Thtr 150 max),
24hr-delegate from £76.95, day-delegate from £21.95
Children: Welcome ╞ ₰℃
Licenses: ⟁ ⅲ
Leisure: Outdoor pool, Beauty salon
Parking: Off-street and free
Map ref: Newquay 2 B3
See advert on opposite page

Kilbirnie Hotel

★★★

Narrowcliffe, Newquay, Cornwall, TR7 2RS
Tel: 01637 875155 Fax: 01637 850769
Email: enquirykilbirnie@aol.com
Web: www.kilbirniehotel.co.uk
Rooms: 65 all ensuite 🐾 🚭
Pricing: Sgl £40–55 Dbl £80–110
Dinner available from £15.50
CC: Accepted
Room facilities: 🖳 ☎ ☕ 📠
Access: |↓↑
Conference: 2 meeting rooms (Thtr 100 max),

24hr-delegate from £70, day-delegate from £30
Children: Welcome ╞ ₰℃
Licenses: ⅲ
Leisure: Indoor pool, Outdoor pool, Gym, Health spa,
Games room, Snooker/billiards
Parking: Off-street and free
Directions: When entering Quintrell Downs, turn right
and take the seafront road for approximately 3 miles.
Hotel is on left overlooking seafront.
Map ref: Newquay 2 B3
See advert on following page

The Watermark at Porth Beach

★★★★ 🏮🏮

Lusty Glaze Road, Newquay, Cornwall, TR7 3AB
Tel: 01637 874937 Fax: 01637 851341
Email: info@watermarkporthbeach.com
Web: www.watermarkporthbeach.com
Rooms: 25 all ensuite 🚭
Pricing: Sgl £53–85 Dbl £80–140 Dinner available
CC: Accepted
Room facilities: 🖳 ☎ ☕ 📠
Conference: 1 meeting room (Thtr 50 max),
24hr-delegate from £90, day-delegate from £35
Children: Welcome ╞ Dogs: Welcome
Licenses: ⟁ ⅲ Leisure: Indoor pool, Gym, Health
spa, Beauty salon, Tennis
Parking: Off-street and free
Directions: A392 to Newquay from A30. Turn right at
Quintrell Downs roundabout. Look for signs to Lusty
Glaze Beach.
Map ref: Porth 2 B3

Trebarwith Hotel

★★★

Trebarwith Crescent, Newquay, Cornwall, TR7 1BZ
Tel: 01637 872288 Fax: 01637 875431
Email: enquiry@trebarwith-hotel.co.uk
Web: www.trebarwith-hotel.co.uk
Seasonal closure: November to April
Rooms: 41 all ensuite 🐾 📠 🚭
Pricing: Sgl £29–69 Dbl £58–116
Dinner available from £18–28 CC: Accepted
Room facilities: 🖳 ☎ ☕ 📠
Conference: 2 meeting rooms (Thtr 40 max),
24hr-delegate from £50, day-delegate from £50
Children: Welcome ╞ ₰℃ Licenses: ⅲ
Leisure: Indoor pool, Fishing, Games room,
Snooker/billiards, Cinema
Parking: Off-street and free
Directions: Follow signs to town centre and turn right
off East Street into Trebarwith Crescent. The hotel is
situated at the end of the crescent.
Map ref: Newquay 2 B3
See advert on following page

Southwest

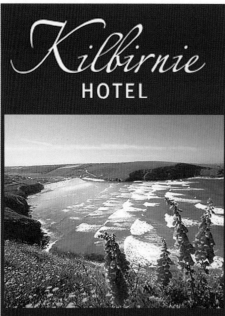

Great Western Hotel
★★
Cliff Road, Newquay, Cornwall, TR7 2PT
Tel: 01637 872010 Fax: 01637 874435
Email: bookings@great-western.fsnet.co.uk
Web: www.chycor.co.uk/greatwestern
Rooms: 70 all ensuite
Pricing: Sgl £40–45 Dbl £80–90
Dinner available from £17 CC: Accepted
Room facilities: ☐ ☎ ⬚ Access: ||↑
Children: Welcome ⼉ Dogs: Welcome
Licenses: ⅲ Leisure: Indoor pool
Parking: Off-street and free
Directions: Take A30 'Indian Queens' to Quintrell Downs roundabout. Turn right, over level crossing, to seafront in Newquay. Hotel is on right.
Map ref: Newquay 2 B3

Philema Hotel
★★
1 Esplanade Road, Pentire, Newquay, Cornwall, TR7 1PY
Tel: 01637 872571 Fax: 01637 873188
Email: info@philema.co.uk
Web: www.philema.co.uk
Seasonal closure: January
Rooms: 32 all ensuite ⬚ ⬚
Dinner available
CC: Accepted

Room facilities:
Children: Welcome
Dogs: Welcome
Licenses:
Leisure: Indoor pool, Health spa, Games room, Snooker/billiards
Parking: Off-street and free
Directions: Follow A392 to roundabout; turn left for Pentire Hotels. Continue down Pentire Road. Hotel situated on corner.
Map ref: Pentire 2 B3

Carlton Hotel

♦♦♦♦
6 Dane Road, Newquay, Cornwall, TR7 1HL
Tel: 01637 872658
Email: enquiries@carltonhotelnewquay.co.uk
Web: www.carltonhotelnewquay.co.uk
Rooms: 11 (9 ensuite)
Room facilities:
Children: Welcome
Licenses:
Parking: Off-street and free
Directions: A392 to Newquay. Follow signs for Fistral Beach by Red Lion Pub, turn left, Carlton Hotel at top of hill.
Map ref: Newquay 2 B3

Chynoweth Lodge

♦♦♦♦
1 Eliot Gardens, Newquay, Cornwall, TR7 2QE
Tel: 01637 876684 Fax: 01637 876684
Email: chynowethlodge@btconnect.com
Web: www.chynowethlodge.co.uk
Rooms: 9 all ensuite
Pricing: Sgl £22.50–29 Dbl £45–58
Dinner available from £8.50
Room facilities:
Children: Welcome
Parking: Off-street and free
Directions: Approach Newquay, past Narrowcliffe, turn left into Edgcumbe Avenue, then second left into Eliot Gardens. Third house on the left.
Map ref: Newquay 2 B3

Pine Lodge Hotel

♦♦♦♦
91 Henver Road, Newquay, Cornwall, TR7 3DJ
Tel: 01637 850891 Fax: 01637 877804
Email: enquiries@pinelodgehotel.co.uk
Web: www.pinelodgehotel.co.uk
Rooms: 12 all ensuite
Pricing: Sgl £27–40 Dbl £54–80
Dinner available from £8.95–12.95 CC: Accepted
Room facilities:
Conference: 1 meeting room (Thtr 12 max)
Children: Welcome
Licenses:
Leisure: Outdoor pool, Games room, Snooker/billiards, Golf offers 2 for 1 green fees

Parking: Off-street and free
Directions: A30, take a right exit sign-posted RAF St Mawgan and airport, take the 3059 from Newquay. T-Junction, turn right. Over double roundabout and Pine Lodge is immediately on right.
Map ref: Newquay 2 B3

Priory Lodge Hotel

♦♦♦♦
30 Mount Wise, Newquay, Cornwall, TR7 2BN
Tel: 01637 874111 Fax: 01637 851803
Email: fiona@priorylodgehotel.fsnet.co.uk
Seasonal closure: January to February
Rooms: 28 (26 ensuite)
Pricing: Sgl £25–35 Dbl £50–70
Dinner available from £10
CC: Accepted
Room facilities:
Children: Welcome
Licenses:
Leisure: Outdoor pool, Health spa, Games room, Snooker/billiards
Parking: Off-street and free
Directions: Enter Newquay via seafront, left onto B3282; 500 metres on right, black-and-white telephone box in grounds.
Map ref: Newquay 2 B3

St Andrews Hotel

♦♦♦♦
Island Crescent, Newquay, Cornwall, TR7 1DZ
Tel: 01637 873556
Email: enquiries@standrewsnewquay.co.uk
Web: www.standrewsnewquay.co.uk
Rooms: 8 all ensuite
Pricing: Dbl £60–80 CC: Accepted
Room facilities:
Children: Welcome
Licenses: Leisure: Games room
Directions: From Tourist Information Centre on Marcus Hill, travel down hill to junction. Straight over to Trebarwith Crescent, first on left into Island Crescent.
Map ref: Newquay 2 B3

The Metro Hotel

♦♦♦♦
142 Henver Road, Newquay, Cornwall, TR7 3EQ
Tel: 01637 871638 Fax: 01637 871638
Email: themetrohotel@btconnect.com
Web: www.metrohotelnewquay.co.uk
Rooms: 15 all ensuite
Pricing: Sgl £35–75 Dbl £50–80 CC: Accepted
Room facilities: Children: Welcome
Leisure: Outdoor pool Parking: Off-street and free
Directions: M5 to Exeter, then A30 to Newquay sign. Take A392 to Quintrell Downs, turn right over level crossing. Follow A3058 for 1 mile. Hotel is on the left.
Map ref: Newquay 2 B3

The Philadelphia

◆◆◆◆

19 Eliot Gardens, Newquay, Cornwall, TR7 2QE
Tel: 01637 877 747
Email: stay@thephiladelphia.co.uk
Web: www.thephiladelphia.co.uk

You will be made to feel very welcome at The Philadelphia, a former gentleman's residence boasting seven luxury themed ensuite rooms with the emphasis on comfort, good food and great hospitality.
Rooms: 7 all ensuite
Pricing: Sgl £25–33 Dbl £50–66 CC: Accepted
Room facilities:
Children: Welcome
Leisure: Health spa
Parking: Off-street and free
Directions: A30, A3058 to Newquay. Left at seafront, left at Bristol Hotel into Ula Road, then Eliot Gardens.
Map ref: Newquay 2 B3

The Windward Hotel

◆◆◆◆

Alexandra Road, Porth Bay, Newquay, Cornwall, TR7 3NB
Tel: 01637 873185 Fax: 01637 851400
Email: enquiries@windwardhotel.co.uk
Web: www.windwardhotel.co.uk
Seasonal closure: November to February
Rooms: 12 all ensuite
Pricing: Sgl £54–78 Dbl £74–98 CC: Accepted
Room facilities:
Conference: 1 meeting room (Thtr 20 max)
Children: Welcome
Licenses:
Parking: Off-street and free
Directions: Join the A392 at Indian Queens for 7 miles. At the roundabout at Quintell Downs, take the A3058 to Newquay, then B3276 to Padstow at the double roundabout. Hotel is on right after 1 mile.
Map ref: Porth Bay 2 B3

Dewolf Guest House

◆◆◆

100 Henver Road, Newquay, Cornwall, TR7 3BL
Tel: 01637 874746
Email: holidays@dewolfguesthouse.com

Web: www.dewolfguesthouse.com
Rooms: 6 all ensuite
Pricing: Sgl £25–40 Dbl £50–80
Dinner available from £10 CC: Accepted
Room facilities:
Children: Welcome Dogs: Welcome
Licenses: Parking: Off-street and free
Directions: Take A30 "Indian Queens" to Quintrell Downs roundabout. Turn right onto A3058, over double roundabout and Dewolf Guest House is on the left.
Map ref: Newquay 2 B3

Kenton Hotel

◆◆◆

Watergate Road, Porth, Newquay, Cornwall, TR7 3LX
Tel: 01637 872736 Fax: 01637 851596
Email: info@hotelsinnewquay.co.uk
Web: www.hotelsinnewquay.co.uk
Rooms: 17 all ensuite
Pricing: Sgl £27–35 Dbl £54–70
Dinner available from £10 CC: Accepted
Room facilities:
Children: Welcome Dogs: Welcome
Licenses: Leisure: Games room
Parking: Off-street and free
Directions: Located on B3276 at Porth towards Watergate Bay. Kenton Hotel on right (private parking). Full directions from A30 provided.
Map ref: Porth 2 B3

Rolling Waves Hotel

◆◆◆

Alexandra Road, Porth, Newquay, Cornwall, TR7 3NB
Tel: 01637 873236 Fax: 01637 873236
Email: enquiries@rollingwaves.co.uk
Web: www.rollingwaves.co.uk
Rooms: 9 (8 ensuite)
Pricing: Sgl £20–28 Dbl £44–60
Dinner available from £10 CC: Accepted
Room facilities:
Children: Welcome
Licenses:
Parking: Off-street and free
Directions: From A30 turn into A3059 Newquay Road. On entering Newquay at first roundabout turn right into B3276 to Padstow. Hotel is on right past Porth beach.
Map ref: Porth 2 B3

North Petherton, Somerset

The Walnut Tree Hotel

★★★

Fore Street, North Petherton, near Bridgwater, Somerset, TA6 6QA
Tel: 01278 662255 Fax: 01278 663946
Email: info@walnuttreehotel.com
Web: www.walnuttreehotel.com
Rooms: 33 all ensuite
Pricing: Sgl £65–100 Dbl £90–140
Dinner available from £19.95

Southwest

CC: Accepted
Room facilities:
Conference: 6 meeting rooms (Thtr 100 max),
24hr-delegate from £149, day-delegate from £35
Children: Welcome 卄
Licenses:
Parking: Off-street and free
Directions: Exit J24 M5; follow signs for North
Petherton, hotel is opposite the Church.
Map ref: North Petherton 3 E2

Okehampton, Devon

Percy's Country Hotel & Restaurant

★★★ R R R R

Coombeshead Estate, Virginstow, Devon, EX21 5EA
Tel: 01409 211236 Fax: 01409 211460
Email: info@percys.co.uk
Web: www.percys.co.uk
Rooms: 11 all ensuite Pricing: Sgl £90 Dbl £150
Dinner available from £40 CC: Accepted
Room facilities:
Conference: 1 meeting room (Thtr 10 max)
Dogs: Welcome Licenses:
Leisure: Fishing, Riding, 130 acre estate to explore
Parking: Off-street and free
Directions: From Launceston A388, right at St Giles on
the Heath, then 2.2 miles on the right. See website for
full directions.
Map ref: Virginstow 2 C3

Padstow, Cornwall

Treglos Hotel

★★★★★ R R

Constantine Bay, Padstow, Cornwall, PL28 8JH
Tel: 01841 520727 Fax: 01841 521163
Email: stay@tregloshotel.com
Web: www.tregloshotel.com
Seasonal closure: December to February

Overlooking the spectacular North Cornish coastline,
Treglos is situated in "Betjeman country", generally
acknowledged to be one of the most beautiful parts of
Cornwall and immortalised in the former Poet Laureate's
verses. Cuisine has earned wide recognition, young fresh
local produce, combined with traditional standards of
service and hospitality. Safes available in rooms.

Rooms: 42 all ensuite
Pricing: Sgl £51.75–78.50 Dbl £103.80–157
Dinner available from £26
CC: Accepted
Room facilities: Access:
Conference: 1 meeting room (Thtr 20 max)
Children: Welcome 卄
Dogs: Welcome
Licenses:
Leisure: Indoor pool, Health spa, Games room,
Snooker/billiards
Parking: Off-street and free
Directions: From Padstow follow signs to St Merryn,
then Constantine Bay (from St Merryn brown signs).
Map ref: Constantine Bay 2 B3

St Ervan Manor   Little Gem

◆◆◆◆◆ R R R

The Old Rectory, St Ervan,
Near Padstow, Cornwall, PL27 7TA
Tel: 01841 540255 Fax: 01841 540255
Email: info@stervanmanor.co.uk
Web: www.stervanmanor.co.uk
Seasonal closure: 20-27 December and
8 January to 1 February
Rooms: 6 (5 ensuite)
Pricing: Sgl £80–195 Dbl £120–225
Dinner available from £35–60 CC: Accepted
Room facilities:
Children: Welcome 14yrs min age
Licenses:
Parking: Off-street and free
Directions: From Wadebridge on A39 to roundabout,
take B3274 to Padstow. Next left, follow brown signs
to St Ervan Manor.
Map ref: St Ervan 2 B3

Treravel House

◆◆◆◆◆

Padstow, Cornwall, PL28 8LB
Tel: 01841 532931
Map ref: Padstow 2 B3

Woodlands Country House   Little Gem

◆◆◆◆◆

Treator, Padstow, Cornwall, PL28 8RU
Tel: 01841 532426 Fax: 01841 533353
Email: info@woodlands-padstow.co.uk
Web: www.woodlands-padstow.co.uk
Seasonal closure: December to February
Rooms: 9 all ensuite
Pricing: Sgl £51–65 Dbl £78–132 CC: Accepted
Room facilities: Children: Welcome
Dogs: Welcome
Licenses:
Leisure: Croquet
Parking: Off-street and free
Directions: Hotel is on B3276 between Padstow and
Trevone, half a mile from Padstow.
Map ref: Treator 2 B3

Bedruthan House Hotel

Bedruthan Steps, St Eval, Cornwall, PL27 7UW
Tel: 01637 860346 Fax: 01637 860763
Email: reception@bedruthanhousehotel.co.uk
Web: www.bedruthanhousehotel.co.uk
Rooms: 8 (7 ensuite)
Pricing: Sgl £30–35 Dbl £58–64
Dinner available from £10 CC: Accepted
Room facilities: Children: Welcome
Licenses: Parking: Off-street and free
Directions: On B3276 coast road halfway between
Newquay and Padstow. Opposite Bedruthan Steps
and National Trust beauty spot Carnewas.
Map ref: Bedruthan Steps 2 B3

Paignton, Devon

The Redcliffe Hotel

Marine Drive, Paignton, Devon, TQ3 2NL
Tel: 01803 526397 Fax: 01803 528030
Email: redclfe@aol.com
Web: www.redcliffehotel.co.uk
Rooms: 68 all ensuite
Pricing: Sgl £56–62 Dbl £112–124
Dinner available from £17.50 CC: Accepted
Room facilities: Access:
Conference: 2 meeting rooms (Thtr 160 max),
24hr-delegate from £72, day-delegate from £22
Children: Welcome Licenses:
Leisure: Indoor pool, Outdoor pool, Gym, Health spa,
Beauty salon, Games room
Parking: Off-street and free
Directions: Follow the signs to Paignton seafront, the
Redcliffe Hotel is at the Torquay end of Paignton
Green.
Map ref: Paignton 3 D3

Sea Verge Hotel

Marine Drive, Preston, Paignton, Devon, TQ3 2NJ
Tel: 01803 557795
Seasonal closure: November to March
Rooms: 12 all ensuite
Pricing: Dbl £40–50
Dinner available from £9.50
Room facilities:
Children: Welcome 9yrs min age
Licenses: Parking: Off-street and free
Directions: On the seafront overlooking Preston Beach
and Green.
Map ref: Preston 3 D3

The big sleep

As part of our comprehensive inspection
process, RAC Inspectors investigate the
comfort of the beds.

Torbay Holiday Motel

Purpose-built motel on the A385
Totnes/Paignton road,
2 miles from Paignton.

Totnes Road, Paignton, TQ4 7PP

Tel: 01803 558226
Fax: 01803 663375
Email: enquiries@thm.co.uk
Website: www.thm.co.uk

Torbay Holiday Motel

Totnes Road, Paignton, Devon, TQ4 7PP
Tel: 01803 558226 Fax: 01803 663375
Email: enquiries@thm.co.uk
Web: www.thm.co.uk
Rooms: 16 all ensuite
Pricing: Sgl £36.50–41.50 Dbl £55–65
Dinner available from £9
CC: Accepted
Room facilities: Access:
Conference: 1 meeting room
Children: Welcome
Dogs: Welcome
Licenses:
Leisure: Indoor pool, Outdoor pool, Gym,
Games room, Adventure playground, Crazy golf,
Sauna, Sun beds
Parking: Off-street and free
Directions: Situated on the A385 Totnes road 2½ miles
from Paignton.
Map ref: Paignton 3 D3
See advert on this page

Roundham Lodge

16 Roundham Road, Paignton, Devon, TQ4 6DN
Tel: 01803 558485 Fax: 01803 553090
Email: enquiries@roundhamlodge.co.uk
Web: www.roundham-lodge.co.uk

Seasonal closure: 2 weeks Christmas/New Year
Rooms: 5 all ensuite ⊛
Pricing: Sgl £42.50–65 Dbl £57.50–95 CC: Accepted
Room facilities: ▯ ☎ ☕
Conference: 1 meeting room (Thtr 16 max)
Children: Welcome ⍩
Parking: Off-street and free
Directions: Just off Eastern Esplanade at mini-
roundabout Sands Road. Turn left. Follow road round
then second turning on right. Hotel on left-hand side.
Map ref: Paignton 3 D3

Redcliffe Lodge

◆◆◆

1 Marine Drive, Paignton, Devon, TQ3 2NJ
Tel: 01803 551394 Fax: 01803 551394
Email: holiday@redcliffelodgehotel.fsnet.co.uk
Web: www.redcliffelodge.co.uk

The family-run hotel that offers a great friendly
atmosphere with excellent cuisine and breathtaking
sea views. If it is a fun-packed holiday you want, or
just to unwind and relax, Paignton's the place to be.
Rooms: 17 all ensuite ⊛⊛ ⊛
Pricing: Sgl £18–35 Dbl £36–60
Dinner available from £15
CC: Accepted
Room facilities: ▯ ☕
Children: Welcome 1yrs min age ⍩ ⍩
Licenses: ⍩⍩⍩
Parking: Off-street and free
Directions: At northern end of Paignton seafront,
opposite Paignton Green and close to the beach.
Map ref: Paignton 3 D3

Par, Cornwall

Elmswood House Hotel

◆◆◆◆ ⍩

73 Tehidy Road, Tywardreath, Par, Cornwall, PL24 2QD
Tel: 01726 814221 Fax: 01726 814399
Rooms: 7 (6 ensuite) ⊛
Pricing: Sgl £25–40 Dbl £56–60
Dinner available from £10
Room facilities: ▯ ☕
Children: Welcome ⍩
Licenses: ⍩⍩⍩

Parking: Off-street
Directions: Turn off A390 at junction for Fowey. Follow
road for 3 miles B3269, turn right at junction for
Tywardreath & Par. Hotel opposite St Andrew's Church.
Map ref: Tywardreath 2 B4

Penzance, Cornwall

Queens Hotel

★★★ ⍩

The Promenade, Penzance, Cornwall, TR18 4HG
Tel: 01736 362371 Fax: 01736 350033
Email: enquiries@queens-hotel.com
Web: www.queens-hotel.com
Rooms: 70 all ensuite ⊛⊛ ⊠ ⊛
Pricing: Sgl £61–79
Dinner available from £14–18
CC: Accepted
Room facilities: ▯ ☎ ☕
Access: ⍩⍩
Conference: 5 meeting rooms (Thtr 200 max)
Children: Welcome ⍩
Dogs: Welcome
Licenses: ⍩ ⍩⍩⍩
Leisure: Yoga
Parking: Off-street and free
Directions: Follow signs for harbour and Promenade.
Follow to Promenade on seafront.
Map ref: Penzance 2 A4
See advert on this page

Camilla House

12 Regent Terrace, Penzance, Cornwall, TR18 4DW
Tel: 01736 363771 Fax: 01736 363771
Email: enquiries@camillahouse-hotel.co.uk
Web: www.camillahouse-hotel.co.uk

Award-winning regency townhouse overlooking
Mount's Bay, offering comfortable non-smoking
accommodation with quality of service for both
business and tourist visitors alike to west Cornwall.
Rooms: 8 (7 ensuite)
Pricing: Sgl £28–35 Dbl £56–79
Dinner available from £3.50–10
CC: Accepted
Room facilities:
Children: Welcome
Licenses:
Parking: Off-street and free
Directions: A30 to Penzance follow signs to Newlyn.
Pass through harbour until Jubilee Pool. Turn 2nd right
by Stanley Hotel.
Map ref: Penzance 2 A4

Chy Bowjy

Chysauster, Penzance, Cornwall, TR20 8XA
Tel: 01736 368815 Fax: 01736 363440
Web: www.chy-bowjy.co.uk
Rooms: 2
Pricing: Sgl £36 Dbl £50
Dinner available from £25
Room facilities:
Parking: Off-street and free
Directions: A30 turn right after Crowlas, follow signs
Chysauster ancient village, 200 yards before village
house sign on right Chy Bowjy.
Map ref: Chysauster 2 A4

Glendower

5 Mennaye Road, Penzance, Cornwall, TR18 4NG
Tel: 01736 365991 Fax: 01736 365991
Email: glendowerpz@aol.com
Web: www.glendowerguesthouse.co.uk
Seasonal closure: Christmas

Rooms: 5 (3 ensuite)
Pricing: Sgl £18–23 Dbl £36–56
Room facilities:
Children: Welcome 8yrs min age
Directions: Follow around harbour and prom to
roundabout, Beachfield Hotel in front, turn right
Alexandra Road, second turning right, second
guesthouse.
Map ref: Penzance 2 A4

Pendennis Hotel

Alexandra Road, Penzance, Cornwall, TR18 4LZ
Tel: 01736 363823 Fax: 01736 363823
Email: pendennis@fsmail.net
Rooms: 10 (8 ensuite)
Pricing: Sgl £20–25 Dbl £50–60
CC: Accepted
Room facilities:
Children: Welcome
Directions: A30 into Penzance. Follow coastal road to
end of promenade. Turn right into Alexandra Road.
Map ref: Penzance 2 A4

The Old Barn Bosulval

New Mill, Penzance, Cornwall, TR20 8XA
Tel: 01736 367742
Email: info@laidback-trails.co.uk
Web: www.laidback-trails.co.uk
Rooms: 3 (1 ensuite)
Pricing: Dinner available from £22 CC: Accepted
Room facilities:
Children: Welcome
Dogs: Assistance dogs only
Leisure: Walking
Parking: Off-street and free
Directions: A30 to Crowlas, turn right to Ludgvan onto
Castle Gate A3311. Turn left at brown sign 'Chysauster
English Heritage' for two miles. Old Barn is first house
in hamlet.
Map ref: Penzance 2 A4

The Stanley Hotel

23 Regent Terrace, Penzance, Cornwall, TR18 4DW
Tel: 01736 362146 Fax: 01736 362146
Email: info@stanley-hotel.co.uk
Web: www.stanley-hotel.co.uk
Rooms: 10 all ensuite
Pricing: Sgl £25–32 Dbl £50–64
CC: Accepted
Room facilities:
Children: Welcome
Parking: Off-street and free
Directions: Coming into Penzance, follow signs for
Newlyn and Ferry. Pass Dolphin and Yacht pubs. The
Stanley Hotel is on the right-hand side, facing seafront.
Map ref: Penzance 2 A4

Carlton Hotel

Promenade, Penzance, Cornwall, TR18 4NW
Tel: 01736 362081 Fax: 01736 362081
Email: carltonhotelpenzance@talk21.com
Rooms: 12 (9 ensuite)
Pricing: Sgl £22–30 Dbl £50–60 CC: Accepted
Room facilities: ☐ ☕ Children: Welcome
Directions: From Penzance railway/bus station follow
signs for seafront and harbour. Carlton is 1 mile on the
right.
Map ref: Penzance 2 A4

Mount Royal Hotel

Chyandour Cliff, Penzance, Cornwall, TR18 3LQ
Tel: 01736 362233 Fax: 01736 362233
Email: mountroyal@btconnect.com
Web: www.s-h-systems.co.uk/hotels/mountroyal.html
Seasonal closure: November to February
Rooms: 7 all ensuite ♨ ⊗
Pricing: Sgl £60 Dbl £65–70
Room facilities: ☐ ☕ Children: Welcome
Leisure: Snooker/billiards
Parking: Off-street and free
Directions: Situated on the main road entering
Penzance on the old A30.
Map ref: Penzance 2 A4

Torwood House Hotel

Alexandra Road, Penzance, Cornwall, TR18 4LZ
Tel: 01736 360063 Fax: 01736 360063
Email: lyndasowerby@aol.com
Web: www.torwoodhousehotel.co.uk
Rooms: 8 (6 ensuite) ♨ 🛏 ⊗
Pricing: Sgl £22–28 Dbl £44–56
Dinner available from £15–16 CC: Accepted
Room facilities: ☐ ☕ 🌊
Children: Welcome ⍾ 🐾 Dogs: Welcome
Licenses: ⵊⵊⵊ
Directions: As you come into Penzance take seafront
road until roundabout, turn right into Alexandra Road.
Map ref: Penzance 2 A4

Woodstock Guest House, Penzance

29 Morrab Road, Penzance, Cornwall, TR18 4EZ
Tel: 01736 369049 Fax: 01736 369049
Email: info@woodstockguesthouse.co.uk
Web: www.woodstockguesthouse.co.uk
Rooms: 8 (5 ensuite) 🛏 ⊗
Pricing: Sgl £22–32 Dbl £44–64 CC: Accepted
Room facilities: ☐ ☕
Children: Welcome 5yrs min age Dogs: Welcome
Directions: Enter Penzance, past railway station and
drive along sea front. Turn right after The Lugger Inn.
Woodstock 200 metres on right.
Map ref: Penzance 2 A4

Plymouth, Devon

Copthorne Hotel Plymouth

★★★★ ☕

Armada Way, Plymouth, Devon, PL1 1AR
Tel: 01752 224161 Fax: 01752 670688
Email: sales.plymouth@mill-cop.com
Web: www.copthornehotels.com

MILLENNIUM
HOTELS AND RESORTS

MILLENNIUM HOTELS
COPTHORNE HOTELS

Located in the city centre, with sweeping views down
Armada Way towards the famous Hoe. The hotel is
easily accessible by road, rail and air. Weekend rates
are also available.
Rooms: 135 all ensuite ⊗
Pricing: Sgl £78.75–175.75 Dbl £94.50–201.50
Dinner available from £18.50 CC: Accepted
Room facilities: ☐ ☎ ☕ 🌊 Access: ⊥↑
Conference: 9 meeting rooms (Thtr 140 max),
24hr-delegate from £155, day-delegate from £45
Children: Welcome ⍾
Licenses: ⬦ ⵊⵊⵊ Parking: Off-street
Directions: Follow signs for Plymouth and then
Continental Ferry port. At the forth roundabout the
hotel is on the first left. Close to the railway station.
Map ref: Plymouth 2 C4

Browns Hotel
Townhouse

★★★★ ☕☕

80 West Street, Tavistock, Plymouth, Devon, PL19 8AQ
Tel: 01822 618686 Fax: 01822 618646
Email: enquiries@brownsdevon.co.uk
Web: www.brownsdevon.co.uk
Rooms: 20 all ensuite ♨ 🛏 ⊗
Pricing: Sgl £65 Dbl £90–140
Dinner available from £17.95 CC: Accepted
Room facilities: ☐ ☎ ☕ 🌊 Access: ⊥↑
Children: Welcome ⍾
Licenses: ⵊⵊⵊ Leisure: Gym
Parking: Off-street and free
Directions: In town centre, on right-hand side of West
Street, which is one-way, follow brown tourist sign.
Map ref: Tavistock 2 C3

Invicta Hotel

★★★★ ℛ

11 Osborne Place, Lockyer Street, The Hoe,
Plymouth, Devon, PL1 2PU
Tel: 01752 664997 Fax: 01752 664994
Email: info@invictahotel.co.uk
Web: www.invictahotel.co.uk

Invicta has 23 well-appointed bedrooms. It is very
close to the city centre, historic Barbican and Brittany
ferries. Friendly and personal service, lock-up car park
with CCTV.
Rooms: 23 all ensuite ⊗
Pricing: Sgl £55–60 Dbl £65–80
Dinner available from £20
CC: Accepted
Room facilities: 🖵 ☎ ⬛ ⬛
Conference: 2 meeting rooms (Thtr 40 max),
24hr-delegate from £101, day-delegate from £34
Children: Welcome ⼙ ⬛
Dogs: Welcome
Licenses: ⬛
Parking: Off-street and free
Directions: M5, A38 to Plymouth. Follow signs to City
Centre A374. At first major roundabout, filter left and
follow Hoe & Barbican signs. After second lights filter
left, left at mini roundabout. Follow road into Notte
Street. At fourth lights left into Lockyer Street. Follow
to crossroads, Invicta on right corner.
Map ref: Plymouth 2 C4

The Duke of Cornwall Hotel

★★★★ ℛ ℛ

Millbay Road, Plymouth, Devon, PL1 3LG
Tel: 01752 275850 Fax: 01752 275854
Email: bookings@thedukeofcornwallhotel.com
Web: www.thedukeofcornwallhotel.com
Seasonal closure: 26–30 December
Rooms: 72 all ensuite ⬛ ⬛ ⊗
Pricing: Sgl £94–150 Dbl £110–180
Dinner available from £20–40
CC: Accepted
Room facilities: 🖵 ☎ ⬛ ⬛
Access: |⬛|
Conference: 7 meeting rooms (Thtr 300 max),
24hr-delegate from £135, day-delegate from £35
Children: Welcome ⼙ ⬛

Dogs: Welcome
Licenses: ⬛ ⬛
Parking: Off-street and free
Directions: Plymouth is signposted from A38, then
follow signs for Plymouth Pavilions. Hotel is opposite
with car park at rear.
Map ref: Plymouth 2 C4

Camelot Hotel

★★

5 Elliot Street, The Hoe, Plymouth, Devon, PL1 2PP
Tel: 01752 221255 Fax: 01752 603660
Email: info@camelotplymouth.co.uk
Web: www.camelotplymouth.co.uk
Rooms: 18 all ensuite ⊗
Pricing: Sgl £30–44 Dbl £56
Dinner available from £5.95–15
CC: Accepted
Room facilities: 🖵 ☎ ⬛
Children: Welcome ⼙ ⬛
Dogs: Welcome
Licenses: ⬛
Directions: Leaving A38 at Plymouth, follow signs for
city centre, the Hoe, Citadel Road, then onto Elliot
Street.
Map ref: Plymouth 2 C4

Drake Hotel

★★

1 Windsor Villas, Lockyer Street,
The Hoe, Plymouth, Devon, PL1 2QD
Tel: 01752 229730 Fax: 01752 255092
Email: reception@drakehotel.net
Web: www.drakehotel.net
Seasonal closure: Christmas to New Year

Our recently refurbished hotel offers a warm and friendly
welcome, offering good quality accommodation and
food. Within easy walking distance to shops and
seafront. Ample off-street parking.
Rooms: 35 all ensuite ⬛ ⊗
Pricing: Sgl £52–56 Dbl £65–70
Dinner available from £9.50–15.250 CC: Accepted
Room facilities: 🖵 ☎ ⬛
Conference: 1 meeting room (Thtr 35 max)
Children: Welcome ⼙ ⬛ Dogs: Assistance dogs only
Licenses: ⬛ Parking: Off-street and free
Directions: Follow signs to city centre. Turn left at
Theatre Royal. Take last left and first right.
Map ref: Plymouth 2 C4

Imperial Hotel

Lockyer Street, The Hoe, Plymouth, Devon, PL1 2QD
Tel: 01752 227311 Fax: 01752 674986
Email: info@imperialplymouth.co.uk
Web: www.imperialplymouth.co.uk
Seasonal closure: 23 December to 2 January

A warm welcome awaits you from Carol and Kevin
Neil, resident proprietors of this ideally situated and
elegant licensed Victorian hotel. It stands between the
famous Hoe and modern city centre, and is within easy
walking distance of the historic Barbican with its
Mayflower Steps and picturesque harbour front.
Rooms: 20 all ensuite
Pricing: Sgl £46–58 Dbl £58
Dinner available from £7.95 CC: Accepted
Room facilities:
Children: Welcome
Licenses: Parking: Off-street and free
Directions: Head for city centre, at Theatre Royal turn
left up hill, turn left at traffic lights then first right.
Map ref: Plymouth 2 C4

Victoria Court Hotel

62-64 North Road East, Plymouth, Devon, PL4 6AL
Tel: 01752 668133 Fax: 01752 668133
Email: victoria.court@btinternet.com
Web: www.victoriacourthotel.co.uk
Rooms: 13 all ensuite
Pricing: Sgl £42–48 Dbl £62–68
Dinner available from £16.50 CC: Accepted
Room facilities: Children: Welcome
Licenses: Parking: Off-street and free
Directions: Follow signs for city centre Northcross
roundabout, turn for railway station follow North Road
East for 200 yards, hotel on left.
Map ref: Plymouth 2 C4

"Here!"

Need a pet friendly property? Look
out for 'Dogs welcome' in our listings.

Ashgrove Hotel

218 Citadel Road, The Hoe, Plymouth, Devon, PL1 3BB
Tel: 01752 664046 Fax: 01752 252112
Email: ashgroveho@aol.com
Web: www.ashgrovehotel-plymouth.co.uk
Seasonal closure: Christmas and New Year

Small, no-smoking, friendly, family-run hotel that caters
for children of all ages. A wide choice of breakfast is
served from the menu. The hotel is conveniently
situated near the historic Hoe and Barbican and a
short walk from the town centre. Bus and train stations
and ferry port are close by.
Rooms: 10 all ensuite
Pricing: Sgl £35.25 Dbl £47
CC: Accepted
Room facilities:
Children: Welcome
Directions: Leave A38 head for city centre, continue
down Royal Parade, turn left at Theatre Royal. Right
into Notte Street, left into Athenaeum Street, then right
into Citadel Road.
Map ref: Plymouth 2 C4

Cranbourne Hotel

Citadel Road, The Hoe, Plymouth, Devon, PL1 2PZ
Tel: 01752 263858/661400/224646 Fax: 01752 263858
Email: cran.hotel@virgin.net
Web: www.cranbournehotel.co.uk
Rooms: 40 (28 ensuite)
Pricing: Sgl £30–45 Dbl £42–54
CC: Accepted
Room facilities:
Children: Welcome
Dogs: Welcome
Licenses:
Parking: Off-street and free
Map ref: Plymouth 2 C4

Chester House

54 Stuart Road, Pennycomequick, Plymouth,
Devon, PL3 4EE
Tel: 01752 663706 Fax: 01752 269235
Web: www.chesterplymouth.co.uk
Rooms: 10 (4 ensuite) 🍴 🚭
Pricing: Sgl £22–30 Dbl £42–50
Room facilities: 📺 🍵
Children: Welcome
Parking: Off-street and free
Directions: From A38 take A386 and follow signs for
city centre. At Pennycomequick roundabout turn right.
Chester House is 100 yards on right.
Map ref: Plymouth 2 C4

Edgcumbe Guest House

50 Pier Street, West Hoe, Plymouth, Devon, PL1 3BT
Tel: 01752 660675 Fax: 01752 666510
Email: enquiries@edgcumbeguesthouse.co.uk
Web: www.edgcumbeguesthouse.co.uk
Rooms: 6 all ensuite 📺 🚭
Pricing: Sgl £20–35 Dbl £45–60
CC: Accepted
Room facilities: 📺 🍵
Children: Welcome
Dogs: Welcome
Parking: Off-street and free
Directions: Follow signs for 'city centre' then 'Hoe and
Seafront'. After passing 'Dome Visitor Centre' turn next
right into Pier Street.
Map ref: Plymouth 2 C4

Kynance Hotel

107-113 Citadel Road, The Hoe, Plymouth,
Devon, PL1 2RN
Tel: 01752 662284 or 266821 Fax: 01752 254076
Email: info@kynancehotel.co.uk
Web: www.kynancehotel.co.uk
Rooms: 26 all ensuite 🍴
CC: Accepted
Room facilities: 📺 ☎ 🍵
Children: Welcome
Licenses: 👥
Parking: Off-street and free
Directions: Follow Continental Ferry signs. At ferry
entrance, mini roundabout, first exit left, next mini
roundabout second left. Citadel Road, very last hotel
on left.
Map ref: Plymouth 2 C4

Rainbow Lodge Guest House

29 Athenaeum Street, The Hoe, Plymouth,
Devon, PL1 2RQ
Tel: 01752 229699 Fax: 01752 229357
Web: www.rainbow-lodge-plymouth.co.uk
Seasonal closure: 20 December to 2 January

Rooms: 11 (7 ensuite) 🍴
Pricing: Sgl £20–30 Dbl £34–40
CC: Accepted
Room facilities: 📺 🍵
Children: Welcome 1yrs min age
Dogs: Welcome
Parking: Off-street and free
Directions: From A38 follow A374 for 3 miles left lane.
Take second left, mini-roundabout, turn left, 6 traffic
lights, turn left.
Map ref: Plymouth 2 C4

Riviera Hotel

8 Elliott Street, The Hoe, Plymouth, Devon, PL1 2PP
Tel: 01752 667379 Fax: 01752 667379
Email: riviera.hotel@btconnect.com
Web: www.rivieraplymouth.co.uk
Seasonal closure: Christmas/New Year
Rooms: 11 (8 ensuite) 🍴 🚭
Pricing: Sgl £33–38 Dbl £58
CC: Accepted
Room facilities: 📺 ☎ 🍵
Children: Welcome
Licenses: 👥
Directions: Head towards city centre, then to
Hoe/Barbican, at "The Walrus" turn left. Riviera Hotel
on right 300 metres.
Map ref: Plymouth 2 C4

The Firs Guest House

13 Pier Street, West Hoe, Plymouth,
South Devon, PL1 3BS
Tel: 01752 262870 Fax: 01752 294003
Email: TheFirsinPlymouthUK@hotmail.com
Web: www.TheFirsinPlymouthUK.co.uk

The Firs is a friendly, family run guest house suitable for a holiday or business trip to Plymouth and its surrounding areas. It's just 150 yards from the famous Hoe seafront, while a wealth of attractions are within a mile radius.

Rooms: 9 (2 ensuite)
Pricing: Sgl £20–25 Dbl £40–50
CC: Accepted
Room facilities: 🖥 🍵
Children: Welcome 🍴
Dogs: Welcome
Directions: A38, A374; city centre; follow signs "To The Sea & The Hoe", Seafront (sea on your left) first right into Pier Street 100 yards, inland on right.
Map ref: Plymouth 2 C4

Tudor House

◆◆◆

105 Citadel Road, Plymouth, Devon, PL1 2RN
Tel: 01752 661557 Fax: 01752 661557
Web: www.smoothhound.co.uk/hotels/tudor-house.html
Seasonal closure: Christmas and New Year
Rooms: 8 (5 ensuite) 🍴 🚭
Pricing: Sgl £18–30 Dbl £32–45 CC: Accepted
Room facilities: 🖥 🍵
Children: Welcome 🍴
Parking: Off-street and free
Directions: A38 Plymouth turnoff, signs to city centre. Hoe signs. Onto Citadel Road, halfway along.
Map ref: Plymouth 2 C4

Poole, Dorset

Harbour Heights

★★★★ ®

Haven Road, Sandbanks, Poole, Dorset, BH13 7LW
Tel: 01202 707272 Fax: 01202 708594
Email: enquiries@harbourheights.net
Web: www.fjbhotels.co.uk

Luxury boutique hotel with stunning views over Poole Harbour. Individually designed rooms, highly acclaimed restaurant, landscaped/terraced garden, unobtrusive charm and hospitality you will cherish — the perfect coastal retreat.

Rooms: 38 all ensuite 🚭
Pricing: Sgl £155–170 Dbl £240–270
Dinner available from £25–39.75
CC: Accepted
Room facilities: 🖥 ☎ 🍵 📠 ❄
Access: ♿
Conference: 1 meeting room (Thtr 50 max), 24hr-delegate from £195, day-delegate from £55
Children: Welcome 🍴
Licenses: ⬥ 🛏
Directions: Leave Poole, follow signs for Sandbanks. When in Sandbanks Road (B3369), approximately 2½ miles from Poole turn into Haven Road for Harbour Heights.
Map ref: Sandbanks 3 F3

Haven

★★★★ ®®

Sandbanks, Poole, Dorset, BH13 7QL
Tel: 01202 707333 Fax: 01202 708796
Email: enquiries@havenhotel.co.uk
Web: www.havenhotel.co.uk

An exclusive hotel located on the tip of Sandbanks peninsula. Stunning sea views, award-winning cuisine, first class service, fabulous leisure and beauty spa facilities.

Rooms: 78 all ensuite 🍴
Pricing: Sgl £90–280 Dbl £180–345
Dinner available from £27
CC: Accepted
Room facilities: 🖥 ☎ 🍵 📠
Access: ♿
Conference: 9 meeting rooms (Thtr 160 max), 24hr-delegate from £170, day-delegate from £45
Children: Welcome 🍴 ☕
Licenses: ⬥ 🛏
Leisure: Indoor pool, Outdoor pool, Gym, Health spa, Beauty salon, Tennis, Sauna, Hot tub, Dance studio
Parking: Off-street and free
Directions: Take A31 towards Bournemouth, A338 Wessex Way, onto B3065. At Sandbanks Bay turn left, follow road to end of peninsula, hotel on left by Ferry Point.
Map ref: Sandbanks 3 F3

Sandbanks Hotel

★★★★

Banks Road, Sandbanks, Poole, Dorset, BH13 7PS
Tel: 01202 707377 Fax: 01202 708885
Email: enquiries@sandbankshotel.co.uk
Web: www.sandbankshotel.co.uk

On Blue Flag Award golden sands, the Sandbanks is perfect for holidays and short breaks. Special children's restaurant and play facilities, waterside brasserie and leisure centre.
Rooms: 110 all ensuite 🛏 🚭
Pricing: Sgl £60–120 Dbl £120–240
Dinner available from £24.95 CC: Accepted
Room facilities: 📺 ☎ 🍵 🥃
Access: ♿
Conference: 12 meeting rooms (Thtr 120 max), 24hr-delegate from £105, day-delegate from £39
Children: Welcome 🍴 🐴 🎠
Licenses: ⚓ ♣
Leisure: Indoor pool, Gym, Health spa, Games room
Parking: Off-street and free
Directions: Take A31 towards Bournemouth. Turn onto A338. At Liverpool Victoria roundabout, keep far left and take B3065 to Sandbanks Beach. At T-junction, turn left. Hotel 500 metres on left.
Map ref: Sandbanks 3 F3

The Mansion House

★★★★

Thames Street, Poole, Dorset, BH15 1JN
Tel: 01202 685666 Fax: 01202 665709
Email: enquiries@themansionhouse.co.uk
Web: www.themansionhouse.co.uk

Elegant Georgian townhouse set on the edge of the vibrant quayside. Individual and stylish guestrooms. Highly acclaimed restaurant with an outstanding reputation for some of the finest cuisine in the south. Ideally located for the Channel ferries.
Rooms: 32 all ensuite 📠 🚭
Pricing: Sgl £75–95 Dbl £125–145
Dinner available from £26.50 CC: Accepted
Room facilities: 📺 ☎ 🍵
Conference: 2 meeting rooms (Thtr 25 max), 24hr-delegate from £145, day-delegate from £32
Children: Welcome 🍴 🎠
Licenses: ⚓ ♣ Parking: Off-street and free
Directions: On entering Poole follow signs to Channel Ferry. At lifting bridge turn left into Quayside, take first road on the left (Thames Street).
Map ref: Poole 3 F3

Porlock, Somerset

Oaks Hotel

★★★

Porlock, Somerset, TA24 8ES
Tel: 01643 862265 Fax: 01643 863131
Email: info@oakshotel.co.uk
Web: www.oakshotel.co.uk
Rooms: 8 all ensuite 🚭
Pricing: Sgl £77.50 Dbl £115
Dinner available from £30
CC: Accepted
Room facilities: 📺 ☎ 🍵
Children: Welcome 8yrs min age Dogs: Welcome
Licenses: ♣
Parking: Off-street and free
Directions: The hotel is on the A39 just as you enter the village from the west.
Map ref: Porlock 3 D2

Ship Inn

 ◆◆◆ ✕〉

High Street, Porlock, Somerset, TA24 8QD
Tel: 01643 862507 Fax: 01643 863244
Email: mail@shipinnporlock.co.uk
Web: www.shipinnporlock.co.uk/www.shipsmews.co.uk

The Ship Inn is one of the oldest inns in the locality,
with roaring log fires in the winter and a sunny, decked
beer garden in the summer months. Accommodation
consists of ten centrally heated ensuite bedrooms, all
with colour television and tea making facilities. Home
made food using local produce is served daily in the
bar and restaurant. CAMRA recommended real ales
are served in a genuine Exmoor bar. Pets are most
welcome and ample car parking is available. Four
Ships Mews four star (English Tourist Board)
apartments created from our stables with mini-kitchen
and sea views.
Rooms: 14 all ensuite ♨ ㉐
Pricing: Sgl £27–35 Dbl £54–60
Dinner available from £5.95–10.95
CC: Accepted
Room facilities: ▢ ☕
Conference: 2 meeting rooms (Thtr 50 max)
Children: Welcome ♜ Dogs: Welcome
Licenses: ♦♦♦
Leisure: Games room, Snooker/billiards, Gardens,
Play area, Boules pitch
Parking: Off-street and free
Directions: Follow the A39 to Porlock, the Ship Inn is
on the High Street at the bottom of Porlock Hill.
Map ref: Porlock 3 D2

Portland, Dorset

Alessandria Hotel

71 Wakeham, Easton, Portland,
Weymouth, Dorset, DT5 1HW
Tel: 01305 822270 Fax: 01305 820561
Web: www.smoothhound.co.uk/hotels/alessand.html
Rooms: 14 (10 ensuite) ♨ ㉐
CC: Accepted
Room facilities: ▢ ☕
Children: Welcome
Licenses: ♦♦♦
Parking: Off-street and free
Map ref: Easton 3 F3

Postbridge, Devon

Lydgate House

◆◆◆◆◆ ♖♖ ✕〉 ♜

Postbridge, Dartmoor, Devon, PL20 6TJ
Tel: 01822 880209 Fax: 01822 880202
Email: lydgatehouse@email.com
Web: www.lydgatehouse.co.uk
Rooms: 7 all ensuite ㉐
Pricing: Sgl £50–60 Dbl £110–130
Dinner available from £24
CC: Accepted
Room facilities: ▢ ☕
Children: Welcome 12yrs min age
Dogs: Welcome
Licenses:
Leisure: Fishing
Parking: Off-street and free
Directions: Between Morton Hampstead and
Princetown on B3212. Turn south just by bridge over
East Dart. 400 yards down lane.
Map ref: Postbridge 2 C3

Redruth, Cornwall

Lyndhurst Guest House

◆◆◆

80 Agar Road, Illogan Highway, Redruth,
Cornwall, TR15 3NB
Tel: 01209 215146 Fax: 01209 217643
Email: sales@lyndhurst-guesthouse.net
Web: www.lyndhurst-guesthouse.net
Rooms: 6 (4 ensuite) ♨
CC: Accepted
Room facilities: ▢ ☕
Children: Welcome
Parking: Off-street
Directions: On the A3047, between Redruth and Pool
by traffic lights at Railway Inn.
Map ref: Redruth 2 A4

Rock, Cornwall

Tzitzikama Lodge

◆◆◆◆ ✕〉

Rock Road, Rock, Cornwall, PL27 6NP
Tel: 01208 862839
Email: tzitzikama.lodge@btinternet.com
Web: www.cornwall-online.co.uk/tzitzikama-lodge
Rooms: 8 all ensuite ♨ ㉐
Pricing: Sgl £46–51 Dbl £62–72
CC: Accepted
Room facilities: ▢ ☕
Children: Welcome ♜
Dogs: Welcome
Parking: Off-street and free
Directions: Follow the signs to Rock where we are in
the centre of the village.
Map ref: Rock 2 B3

Southwest

Salcombe, Devon

Soar Mill Cove Hotel

★★★★ 🍷🍷🍷 Commended

Soar Mill Cove,
Salcombe, Devon, TQ7 3DS
Tel: 01548 561566 Fax: 01548 561223
Email: info@soarmillcove.co.uk
Web: www.soarmillcove.co.uk

Wake up late and enjoy lemon presse and scrambled eggs with smoked salmon, on your private patio facing the Eddystone lighthouse... Relax with Ingrid Bergman or chill with Quincy Jones from our free CD/video/DVD library.
Rooms: 22 all ensuite 🛏 📺 ⊗
Pricing: Sgl £100–200 Dbl £150–250
Dinner available from £38
CC: Accepted
Room facilities: 🖥 ☎ 🖇 🍵
Conference: 2 meeting rooms (Thtr 50 max),
24hr-delegate from £150, day-delegate from £50
Children: Welcome 🍴 🌙
Dogs: Welcome
Licenses: 👫
Leisure: Indoor pool, Outdoor pool, Beauty salon, Tennis, Games room, Snooker/billiards, Sauna
Parking: Off-street and free
Directions: From Totnes, follow A381 to Kingsbridge. Turn right towards Salcombe (on A381). Four miles at Malborough, turn right to Soar. After church, bear left.
Map ref: Soar Mill Cove 2 C4

"I do!"

Want a honeymoon hotel? Look for our Gold, Blue, and White Ribbon Award winning hotels.

Thurlestone Hotel

★★★★★ 🍷🍷 Excellent

Thurlestone, Devon, TQ7 3NN
Tel: 01548 560382 Fax: 01548 561069
Email: enquiries@thurlestone.co.uk
Web: www.thurlestone.co.uk

This privately owned award-winning family hotel boasts magnificent views over Bigbury Bay from its newly refurbished glass fronted restaurant and many of its elegant bedrooms, some with balcony.
Rooms: 64 all ensuite 🛏 ⊗
Pricing: Sgl £60–160 Dbl £120–320
Dinner available from £32 CC: Accepted
Room facilities: 🖥 ☎ 🖇 🍵 Access: ♿
Conference: 3 meeting rooms (Thtr 120 max),
24hr-delegate from £180, day-delegate from £50
Children: Welcome 🍴 🌙 Dogs: Welcome
Licenses: 👫
Leisure: Indoor pool, Outdoor pool, Gym, Health spa, Beauty salon, Tennis, Golf, Riding, Games room, Snooker/billiards, Toddler room, Badminton, Squash
Parking: Off-street and free
Directions: At Buckfastleigh (A38), A384 to Totnes then A381 to Kingsbridge. At roundabout, A379 to Churchstow. At second roundabout, left onto B3197, then right into lane to Thurlestone.
Map ref: Thurlestone 2 C4

Tides Reach Hotel

★★★★ 🍷🍷 Excellent

South Sands, Salcombe, Devon, TQ8 8LJ
Tel: 01548 843466 Fax: 01548 843954
Email: enquire@tidesreach.com
Web: www.tidesreach.com
Seasonal closure: December to January
Rooms: 35 all ensuite 🛏 ⊗
Pricing: Sgl £60–115 Dbl £110–250
Dinner available from £35 CC: Accepted
Room facilities: 🖥 ☎ 🖇 🍵 Access: ♿
Children: Welcome 8yrs min age Dogs: Welcome
Licenses: 👫 Leisure: Indoor pool, Gym, Beauty salon, Games room, Snooker/billiards
Parking: Off-street and free
Directions: Leave A38 at Buckfastleigh. Follow A384 to Totnes, then A381 to Salcombe. Follow sandcastle symbol signs to South Sands.
Map ref: Salcombe 3 D4
See advert on opposite page

Salisbury, Wiltshire

The Best Western Red Lion
★★★
Milford Street, Salisbury, Wiltshire, SP1 2AN
Tel: 01722 323334 Fax: 01722 325756
Email: reception@the-redlion.co.uk and
conference@the-redlion.co.uk
Web: www.the-redlion.co.uk

A traditional 13th century coaching inn in the heart of Salisbury's beautiful city centre. A warm welcome, tastefully styled bedrooms and rosette awarded Vine Restaurant await you.
Rooms: 51 all ensuite 🛏 🚭 ⊗
Pricing: Sgl £97–114 Dbl £126–146
Dinner available from £25 CC: Accepted
Room facilities: 🖥 ☎ 🍵 🎣 Access: ♿
Conference: 7 meeting rooms (Thtr 100 max),

24hr-delegate from £132, day-delegate from £38.50
Children: Welcome
Licenses: 🎭
Directions: From A303 take A30 10 miles south, located in central city off market square in Milford Street.
Map ref: Salisbury 4 A3

Howards House Hotel

★★ 🔵🔵🔵 *Excellent*
Teffont Evias, Salisbury, Wiltshire, SP3 5RJ
Tel: 01722 716392 Fax: 01722 716820
Email: enq@howardshousehotel.com
Web: www.howardshousehotel.com
Rooms: 9 all ensuite 🛏 🚭 ⊗
Pricing: Sgl £95 Dbl £145–165
Dinner available from £25.95–40
CC: Accepted
Room facilities: 🖥 ☎ 🍵 🎣
Conference: 1 meeting room (Thtr 12 max), day-delegate from £40
Children: Welcome 🍴 Dogs: Welcome
Licenses: 🎭
Leisure: Croquet
Parking: Off-street and free
Directions: From London turn left off A303 after Wyle. Head for B3089, turn right ⅓ mile, hotel on right 400 yards.
Map ref: Teffont Evias 3 F2
See advert on this page

Southwest

Cricket Field House Hotel

◆◆◆◆ ⬢ ✕🔲

Wilton Road, Salisbury, Wiltshire, SP2 9NS
Tel: 01722 322595 Fax: 01722 322595
Email: cricketfieldcottage@btinternet.com
Web: www.cricketfieldhousehotel.co.uk

Each of the 14 bedrooms, both in the main house and
The Pavilion Annex, are all individually decorated.
Situated in its own large garden with views of the village
church. 'Best Conference Facility in Salisbury Award.'
Rooms: 14 all ensuite 🛏 🚭
Pricing: Sgl £50–65 Dbl £65–85 Dinner available
CC: Accepted
Room facilities: 🔲 🍵
Conference: 1 meeting room (Thtr 25 max)
Children: Welcome 14yrs min age Licenses: ♦♦♦
Parking: Off-street and free
Directions: On A36 from Salisbury over railway bridge
on left hand side. ³/₄ mile from city centre.
Map ref: Salisbury 4 A3

Stratford Lodge

◆◆◆◆ ⬢ ✕🔲

4 Park Lane, Salisbury, Wiltshire, SP1 3NP
Tel: 01722 325177 Fax: 01722 325177
Email: enquiries@stratfordlodge.co.uk
Web: www.stratfordlodge.co.uk
Rooms: 8 all ensuite 🛏 🔳
Pricing: Sgl £62–65 Dbl £80–82
Dinner available from £15–20 CC: Accepted
Room facilities: 🔲 🍵 Children: Welcome 5yrs min age
Dogs: Assistance dogs only Licenses: ♦♦♦
Parking: Off-street and free
Directions: A345 signposted Stratford Lodge at top of
Victoria Park.
Map ref: Salisbury 4 A3

The Junipers

◆◆◆◆ 🍸

3 Juniper Road, Firsdown,
near Salisbury, Wiltshire, SP5 1SS
Tel: 01980 862330 Fax: 01980 862071
Email: junipers.bb@tesco.net
Web: www.thejunipers.co.uk
Rooms: 2 all ensuite 🚭

Pricing: Sgl £38 Dbl £55–60
Room facilities: 🔲 🍵 Parking: Off-street and free
Directions: A30 to London 5 miles north-east of
Salisbury, follow brown signs to The Junipers.
Map ref: Firsdown 4 A3

Websters   Little Gem

◆◆◆◆ ✕🔲 🍸

11 Hartington Road, Salisbury, Wiltshire, SP2 7LG
Tel: 01722 339779 Fax: 01722 421903
Email: enquiries@websters-bed-breakfast.com
Web: www.websters-bed-breakfast.com

Our guests say "wonderful B&B", "the best",
"comfortable", "friendly", "helpful", "fantastic". Find
out why so many guests return time and time again, to
experience excellent hospitality delivered with good
humour.
Rooms: 5 all ensuite 🚭
Pricing: Sgl £40 Dbl £50 CC: Accepted
Room facilities: 🔲 🍵 🔌 Children: Welcome 12yrs min age
Parking: Off-street and free
Directions: From city centre head west towards Wilton.
At St Paul's roundabout take A360 Devizes Road. 400
metres on left is Hartington Road.
Map ref: Salisbury 4 A3

Byways House

◆◆◆

31 Fowler's Road, City Centre, Salisbury,
Wiltshire, SP1 2QP
Tel: 01722 328364 Fax: 01722 322146
Email: byways@bed-breakfast-salisbury.co.uk
Web: www.stonehenge-uk.com
Seasonal closure: Christmas and New Year

Attractive family-run Victorian house close to cathedral in quiet area of city centre. Large car park. Traditional English or vegetarian breakfasts. Ideal for Stonehenge and Wilton House.
Rooms: 23 (19 ensuite) 🍵 🚭
Pricing: Sgl £35–65 Dbl £60–85 CC: Accepted
Room facilities: 🖥 📠
Conference: 1 meeting room (Thtr 43 max),
24hr-delegate from £60, day-delegate from £60
Children: Welcome Dogs: Welcome
Licenses: ⛉ Leisure: Garden
Parking: Off-street and free
Directions: Arriving in Salisbury, follow A36, then follow Youth Hostel signs until outside hostel. Fowler's Road is opposite: Byways is a large Victorian house on the left.
Map ref: Salisbury 4 A3

Hayburn Wyke Guest House

◆◆◆ 🐾

72 Castle Road, Salisbury, Wiltshire, SP1 3RL
Tel: 01722 412627 Fax: 01722 412627
Email: hayburn.wyke@tinyonline.co.uk
Web: www.hayburnwykeguesthouse.co.uk
Rooms: 7 (4 ensuite) 🚭
Pricing: Sgl £35–66 Dbl £45–68 CC: Accepted
Room facilities: 🖥 📠
Children: Welcome ⛉ ☕
Parking: Off-street and free
Directions: Situated on Castle Road (A345), half a mile north of city centre at the junction with Stratford Road, by Victoria Park.
Map ref: Salisbury 4 A3

Saunton, Devon

Saunton Sands Hotel

★★★★ 🍴🍴🍴

Saunton, Devon, EX33 1LQ
Tel: 01271 890212 Fax: 01271 890145
Email: info@sauntonsands.com
Web: www.sauntonsands.com

Hotel Group of the Year

North Devon's premier 4-star hotel commands spectacular views, and provides a wealth of facilities.
Rooms: 92 all ensuite 🍵
Pricing: Sgl £77–114 Dbl £154–242
Dinner available from £30 CC: Accepted
Room facilities: 🖥 ☎ 📠 🔌 Access: ⛉
Children: Welcome ⛉ 🐕 ☕ Licenses: ⚟ ⛉
Leisure: Indoor pool, Outdoor pool, Gym, Health spa, Beauty salon, Tennis, Games room, Snooker/billiards, Sauna, Sun shower Parking: Off-street and free
Directions: From Barnstaple town centre take A361 Braunton road. From Braunton follow the Saunton sign.
Map ref: Saunton 2 C2
See advert on this page

Scorrier, Cornwall

The Crossroads Lodge

★★

Scorrier, Redruth, Cornwall, TR16 5BP
Tel: 01209 820551 Fax: 01209 820392
Email: crossroads@hotelstruro.com
Web: www.hotelstruro.com
Rooms: 36 all ensuite 🍵 🚭
Pricing: Sgl £51–62 Dbl £69.50–77
Dinner available from £12.50 CC: Accepted
Room facilities: 🖥 ☎ 📠 🔌 Access: ⛉
Conference: 3 meeting rooms (Thtr 120 max)
Children: Welcome ⛉ ☕ Dogs: Welcome
Licenses: ⛉ Leisure: Games room
Parking: Off-street and free
Directions: Follow the A30 for Redruth, take the first exit left for Scorrier after the Chiverton roundabout.
Map ref: Redruth 2 A4
See advert on following page

Southwest

The Crossroads Lodge

A family owned establishment extending a warm welcome, offering friendly service and fine cuisine.
The Crossroads Lodge is set in the heart of the county, giving convenient access to all major resorts and attractions. Its accessibility makes it an ideal location for that executive conference, family function, or a welcome stop-over.
Lift to most bedrooms

Scorrier, Redruth, Cornwall TR16 5BP
Tel: 01209 820551 Fax: 01209 820392

Shaftesbury, Dorset

Royal Chase

★★★★

Salisbury Road, Shaftesbury, Dorset, SP7 8DB
Tel: 01747 853355 Fax: 01747 851969
Email: royalchasehotel@btinternet.com
Web: www.theroyalchasehotel.co.uk
Rooms: 33 all ensuite
Dinner available CC: Accepted
Room facilities:
Conference: 6 meeting rooms (Thtr 150 max),
24hr-delegate from £107.50, day-delegate from £34.50
Children: Welcome Dogs: Welcome
Licenses:
Leisure: Indoor pool
Parking: Off-street and free
Directions: On the outskirts of Shaftesbury on the roundabout joining the A30 and A350 Salisbury and Blandford roads.
Map ref: Shaftesbury 3 F2

Be more mobile **Dial 1740 from any mobile phone to get up-to-the-minute RAC traffic information.**

Calls cost up to 59p per minute. Please check with your network operator.

The Crown Inn

◆◆◆

Fontmell Magna, Shaftesbury, Dorset, SP7 0PA
Tel: 01747 811441 Fax: 01747 811145
Web: www.crowninn.me.uk

In an original Georgian building, furnished in the classic style of the north Dorset farming gentry, great care is taken to make guests feel comfortable and welcome. The head chef, Robin Davies, presides over a brigade that has won many awards. Fresh fish is delivered daily from Poole and Lyme Bay and all meat is locally sourced. Fresh milk, cream and cheese come from the Blackmore Vale. Real ale, with the Casque Mark award for excellence, is served in the bar.
Rooms: 3 all ensuite
Pricing: Sgl £35–50 Dbl £65–100
Dinner available from £8.95–21.5
CC: Accepted
Room facilities:
Dogs: Welcome
Licenses:
Parking: Off-street and free
Directions: A350 Shaftesbury to Blandford at crossroads in Fontmell by the Brook in the centre of the village.
Map ref: Fontmell Magna 3 F2

Ice & slice?

RAC's comprehensive inspection means we even check drinks are served the way you want.

Shepton Mallet, Somerset

Belfield House

34 Charlton Road, Shepton Mallet, Somerset, BA4 5PA
Tel: 01749 344353 Fax: 01749 344353
Email: belfieldhouse@aol.com
Web: www.belfieldguesthouse.co.uk
Rooms: 7 (4 ensuite)
Pricing: Sgl £30–40 Dbl £50–75
CC: Accepted
Room facilities:
Children: Welcome
Parking: Off-street and free
Directions: On main A361 Wells/Frome Road. Just 200 yards from main A37 junction, opposite leisure centre.
Map ref: Shepton Mallet 3 E2

43 Maesdown Road

Evercreech, Shepton Mallet, Somerset, BA4 6LE
Tel: 01749 830721
Rooms: 3 (1 ensuite)
Pricing: Sgl £23–25 Dbl £42–45
Room facilities:
Children: Welcome 5yrs min age Dogs: Welcome
Parking: Off-street and free
Directions: From Bath & West Showground on A37, turn left, then first right for village, 1 mile. First left after village name sign.
Map ref: Evercreech 3 E2

Sherborne, Dorset

The Grange at Oborne

★★★ ♔♔♔

Oborne, Sherborne, Dorset, DT9 4LA
Tel: 01935 813463 Fax: 01935 817464
Email: reception@thegrange.co.uk
Web: www.thegrangeatoborne.co.uk

The Grange is a glorious mellow stone country house hotel. It is situated within its own beautiful, formal gardens and lies just one mile from the historic town of Sherborne.
Rooms: 18 all ensuite
Pricing: Sgl £85 Dbl £100–140
Dinner available from £23.50–29.50 CC: Accepted

Room facilities:
Conference: 1 meeting room (Thtr 25 max)
Children: Welcome Dogs: Assistance dogs only
Licenses: Leisure: Access to golf with special rates
Parking: Off-street and free
Directions: Oborne will be found on the A30 one mile east of Sherborne. Follow the signs to 'The Grange At Oborne'.
Map ref: Oborne 3 E2

Sidmouth, Devon

Belmont Hotel

★★★★ ♔♔

The Esplanade, Sidmouth, Devon, EX10 8RX
Tel: 01395 512555 Fax: 01395 579101
Email: reservations@belmont-hotel.co.uk
Web: www.belmont-hotel.co.uk

Hotel Group of the Year

Located on Sidmouth's famous Esplanade, the Belmont offers all the amenities you would expect from a four-star hotel, while retaining the charm and character of its origin.
Rooms: 50 all ensuite
Pricing: Sgl £83–123 Dbl £126–206
Dinner available from £30
CC: Accepted
Room facilities:
Access:
Children: Welcome
Licenses:
Parking: Off-street and free
Directions: On Sidmouth seafront.
Map ref: Sidmouth 3 D3
See advert on following page

Southwest

Room facilities:
Access: |↥|
Conference: 1 meeting room (Thtr 85 max)
Children: Welcome ⋔ ⅀ℂ
Dogs: Welcome
Licenses: ⅏⅏⅏
Parking: Off-street
Directions: M5 from London, Exit 30, follow A3052. Hotel Riviera is situated in centre of the Esplanade.
Map ref: Sidmouth 3 D3
See advert on following page

Victoria Hotel

★★★★

Commended

The Esplanade, Sidmouth,
Devon, EX10 8RY
Tel: 01395 512651 Fax: 01395 579154
Email: info@victoriahotel.co.uk
Web: www.victoriahotel.co.uk

Overlooking the Esplanade and the sea, magnificent rooms, renowned cuisine and superb leisure facilities make the Victoria one of England's finest hotels.
Rooms: 61 all ensuite ✍
Pricing: Sgl £95–125 Dbl £150–250
Dinner available from £32
CC: Accepted
Room facilities: ▢ ☎ ⅀ ⍨
Access: |↥|
Children: Welcome ⋔ ⅀ℂ
Licenses: ⅏⅏⅏
Leisure: Indoor pool, Outdoor pool, Beauty salon, Tennis, Games room, Snooker/billiards
Parking: Off-street and free
Directions: Located on Sidmouth seafront.
Map ref: Sidmouth 3 D3
See advert on opposite page

Sleep easy Rest assured. Our comprehensive inspection process includes checking beds are comfortable.

Bedford Hotel

★★★★

The Esplanade, Sidmouth, Devon, EX10 8NR
Tel: 01395 513047 Fax: 01395 578563
Rooms: 36 all ensuite ⊞ ⊛
Pricing: Sgl £48–85 Dbl £96–170
Dinner available from £21.95
CC: Accepted
Room facilities: ▢ ☎ ⅀
Access: |↥|
Children: Welcome ⋔ ⅀ℂ
Dogs: Welcome
Licenses: ⅏⅏⅏
Parking: Off-street and free
Directions: Centrally situated on Sidmouth seafront.
Map ref: Sidmouth 3 D3
See advert on opposite page

Royal Glen Hotel

★★★

Glen Road, Sidmouth, Devon, EX10 8RW
Tel: 01395 513221 Fax: 01395 514922
Email: info@royalglenhotel.co.uk
Web: www.royalglenhotel.co.uk

In a secluded position close to the seafront, this one-time royal residence will appeal to those seeking old-world charm, comfort, good catering and personal service.
Rooms: 32 all ensuite ✍
Pricing: Sgl £37–50
Dinner available from £22.50
CC: Accepted
Room facilities: ▢ ☎ ⅀
Children: Welcome ⋔
Dogs: Welcome
Licenses: ⅏⅏⅏
Leisure: Indoor pool
Parking: Off-street and free
Directions: Follow signs to seafront. Turn right onto Esplanade. Turn right into Glen Road at the end of the Promenade.
Map ref: Sidmouth 3 D3

Westcliff Hotel
★★★

Manor Road, Sidmouth, Devon, EX10 8RU
Tel: 01395 513252 Fax: 01395 578203
Email: stay@westcliffhotel.co.uk
Web: www.westcliffhotel.co.uk
Seasonal closure: November to March
Rooms: 40 all ensuite
Pricing: Sgl £58–120 Dbl £103–256
Dinner available from £27.50
CC: Accepted
Room facilities:
Access:
Children: Welcome 6yrs min age
Licenses:
Leisure: Outdoor pool, Gym, Games room,
Snooker/billiards, Putting green, Croquet
Parking: Off-street and free
Directions: Turn right at Sidmouth seafront, then right
into Manor Road; first right into hotel.
Map ref: Sidmouth 3 D3

Royal York & Faulkner Hotel
★★

Esplanade, Sidmouth, Devon, EX10 8AZ
Tel: 0800 220714 Fax: 01395 577472
Email: stay@royalyorkhotel.net
Web: www.royalyorkhotel.net
Seasonal closure: January
Rooms: 70 (68 ensuite)
Pricing: Sgl £35–62.50 Dbl £70–125
Dinner available from £18.50
CC: Accepted
Room facilities:
Access:
Children: Welcome
Dogs: Welcome
Licenses:
Leisure: Indoor pool, Health spa, Beauty salon,
Snooker/billiards, Steam sauna
Parking: Off-street and free
Directions: Exit M5 at junction 30. A3052 following
signs to Sidmouth. Hotel on centre of Esplanade.
Map ref: Sidmouth 3 D3

Avalon – A Haven For Non Smokers
◆◆◆◆

Vicarage Road, Sidmouth, Devon, EX10 8UQ
Tel: 01395 513443
Email: owneravalon@aol.com
Web: www.avalonsidmouth.co.uk
Rooms: 4 all ensuite
Pricing: Dbl £50–60
Room facilities:
Parking: Off-street and free
Directions: At Sidford take the Sidmouth turning
opposite the car dealership. Avalon is 1.3 miles away
on your left.
Map ref: Sidmouth 3 D3

Groveside
◆◆◆◆

Vicarage Road, Sidmouth, Devon, EX10 8UQ
Tel: 01395 513406
Email: groveside.sidmouth@virgin.net
Web: www.eastdevon.net/groveside
Seasonal closure: December to January
Rooms: 9 (7 ensuite)
Room facilities:
Children: Welcome 8yrs min age
Parking: Off-street and free
Directions: From M5 or A303 follow signs to Honiton,
then signs to Sidmouth. Hotel is just on the edge of
town, to left on the main road.
Map ref: Sidmouth 3 D3

Bramley Lodge Guest House
◆◆◆

Vicarage Road, Sidmouth, Devon, EX10 8UQ
Tel: 01395 515710
Email: haslam@bramleylodge.fsnet.co.uk

Owned and run by David and Linda Haslam. Only half a
mile level walk via shops or park to Esplanade. Garden
by River Sid and Byes Parkland. Victorian town house.
Rooms: 6 (5 ensuite)
Pricing: Sgl £25–30 Dbl £50–58
Dinner available from £11.50–12.50
Room facilities: Children: Welcome
Dogs: Welcome Leisure: Garden
Parking: Off-street and free
Directions: From Sidford traffic lights follow Sidmouth
signs towards town centre. 150 metres past police
station on left-hand side, before cinema.
Map ref: Sidmouth 3 D3

South Molton, Devon

Highbullen Hotel

★★★

Chittlehamholt, Umberleigh, Devon, EX37 9HD
Tel: 01769 540561 Fax: 01769 540492
Email: info@highbullen.co.uk
Web: www.highbullen.co.uk
Rooms: 40 all ensuite
Pricing: Sgl £78–150 Dbl £156–210
Dinner available from £25 CC: Accepted
Room facilities: ☐ ☎ ⌕   Licenses: ♦♦♦
Leisure: Indoor pool, Outdoor pool, Gym, Health spa,
Beauty salon, Tennis, Golf, Fishing, Snooker/billiards,
Indoor tennis Parking: Off-street
Directions: Leave M5 at Junction 27. Take A361 to South
Molton. Take B3226. After 5 miles turn right up hill to
Chittlehamholt. Highbullen is ½ mile beyond village, on left.
Map ref: Chittlehamholt 2 C2

Stumbles Hotel & Restaurant

◆◆◆

134 East Street, South Molton, Devon, EX36 3BU
Tel: 01769 574145 Fax: 01769 572558
Email: cp@stumbles.co.uk
Web: www.stumbles.co.uk
Rooms: 10 all ensuite
Pricing: Sgl £40–50 Dbl £50–80
Dinner available from £12–25 CC: Accepted
Room facilities: ☐ ☎ ⌕
Conference: 1 meeting room (Thtr 50 max),
24hr-delegate from £60, day-delegate from £15
Children: Welcome ♭ Dogs: Welcome
Licenses: ♦♦♦ Parking: Off-street and free
Directions: Leave M5 at junction 27 Tiverton, follow
A361 to South Molton, on left in main street. Just
before square, parking behind.
Map ref: South Molton 3 D2

St Agnes, Cornwall

Rose-in-Vale Country House Hotel

★★★⌖⌖

Mithian, St Agnes, Cornwall, TR5 0QD
Tel: 01872 552202 Fax: 01872 552700
Email: reception@rose-in-vale-hotel.co.uk
Web: www.rose-in-vale-hotel.co.uk
Seasonal closure: January to February
Rooms: 18 all ensuite ⌕ ⌨ ⊛
Pricing: Sgl £68 Dbl £120–180
Dinner available from £32 CC: Accepted
Room facilities: ☐ ☎ ⌕
Conference: 3 meeting rooms (Thtr 50 max),
24hr-delegate from £90, day-delegate from £30
Children: Welcome ♭ ⌖ Dogs: Welcome
Licenses: ⌕ ♦♦♦ Leisure: Outdoor pool, Games room
Parking: Off-street and free
Directions: A30 through Cornwall, turn right onto
B3277 signed St. Agnes, pick up Rose-In-Vale
directions within 500 yards.
Map ref: Mithian 2 B4

Rosemundy House Hotel

★★★★

Rosemundy, St Agnes, Cornwall, TR5 0UF
Tel: 01872 552101 Fax: 01872 554000
Email: info@rosemundy.co.uk
Web: www.rosemundy.co.uk
Rooms: 44 all ensuite ⌕ ⌨ ⊛
Pricing: Sgl £27–52 Dbl £54–104
Dinner available from £33
CC: Accepted
Room facilities: ☐ ☎ ⌕
Children: Welcome 5yrs min age
Licenses: ♦♦♦
Leisure: Outdoor pool, Games room
Parking: Off-street and free
Directions: A30 until Chiverton Cross roundabout,
fourth exit signposted St Agnes, second right, second
left, Rosemundy House Hotel on left.
Map ref: St Agnes 2 A4

Little Trevellas farm

◆◆◆

St Agnes, Cornwall, TR5 0XX
Tel: 01872 552945 Fax: 01872 552945
Email: velvetcrystal@ukonline.co.uk
Web: www.stagnesbandb.co.uk

Come to stay on a traditional farm. Enjoy a Cornish
breakfast with eggs from our chickens and home-made
bread. Special diets available by prior arrangement.
Well behaved dogs welcome.
Rooms: 3 all ensuite ⊛
Pricing: Sgl £25 Dbl £50
Room facilities: ☐ ⌕
Children: Welcome
Dogs: Welcome
Parking: Off-street and free
Directions: Take B3285 from Perranporth to St Agnes
past airfield on right. Go around the right-hand bend,
then straight on to lane to Crossacombe. Parking area
is approximately 50 yards on left.
Map ref: St Agnes 2 A4

"Stay!"

**Need a pet friendly property? Look
out for 'Dogs welcome' in our listings.**

Penkerris

Penwinnick Road, St Agnes, Cornwall, TR5 0PA
Tel: 01872 552262 Fax: 01872 552262
Email: info@penkerris.co.uk
Web: www.penkerris.co.uk

Creeper-clad Edwardian residence with garden in unspoilt Cornish village. A home-from-home with real food and comfortable rooms. Licensed. Ample parking. Only 1km from beach & dramatic cliff walks.
Rooms: 6 (3 ensuite)
Pricing: Sgl £20–30
Dinner available from £12.50 CC: Accepted
Room facilities: ▯ ▤
Children: Welcome ⯅ ⯈ Dogs: Welcome
Licenses: ⯅⯅⯅ Parking: Off-street and free
Directions: From roundabout at Chiverton Cross on A30, take B3277 to St Agnes. Penkerris is first on right after village sign and 30mph limit sign.
Map ref: St Agnes 2 A4

St Austell, Cornwall

Carlyon Bay Hotel

★★★★★ ⯗⯗

Sea Road, Carlyon Bay, St Austell,
Cornwall, PL25 3RD
Tel: 01726 812304 Fax: 01726 814938
Email: reservations@carlyonbay.com
Web: www.carlyonbay.com

Hotel Group of the Year

A superb hotel in a clifftop location offering spectacular views. The hotel's 18-hole golf course runs along the clifftop adjacent to the hotel.
Rooms: 87 all ensuite ⯗ ⯗
Pricing: Sgl £90–115 Dbl £170–270
Dinner available from £30
CC: Accepted
Room facilities: ▯ ☎ ▤ ⯗
Access: ⯗⯗
Children: Welcome ⯅ ⯈
Licenses: ⯗ ⯅⯅⯅
Leisure: Indoor pool, Outdoor pool, Health spa, Beauty salon, Tennis, Golf, Games room, Snooker/billiards
Parking: Off-street and free
Directions: From St Austell follow signs for Charlestown. Carlyon Bay is signposted on left. Hotel at end of sea road.
Map ref: Carlyon Bay 2 B4
See advert on this page

Are the bells ringing?

Getting married? Congratulations! Look for the wedding bells symbol which shows hotels licensed for civil ceremonies.

Southwest

Cliff Head Hotel

★★★ ☆

Sea Road, Carlyon Bay, St Austell, Cornwall, PL25 3RB
Tel: 01726 812345 Fax: 01726 815511
Email: cliffheadhotel@btconnect.com
Web: www.cliffheadhotel.com
Rooms: 60 all ensuite 🛏 🗄 🚭
Dinner available
CC: Accepted
Room facilities: 📺 ☎ ☕
Conference: 1 meeting room (Thtr 180 max)
Children: Welcome ♬ ☕
Licenses: ◁ 👬
Leisure: Indoor pool, Gym, Health spa, Games room
Parking: Off-street and free
Directions: From Plymouth, take A390 to Dobwalls,
then to St Austell. Just before entering St Austell,
follow signs to Carlyon Bay.
Map ref: Carlyon Bay 2 B4

Our spectacular clifftop location and 180° sea
views over St Austell Bay make us the ideal place
to stay and explore Cornwall's attractions
including Eden and Heligan. Award-winning
cuisine uses the best local produce. Well
appointed bedrooms and public rooms are
luxurious and comfortable.
"THE BEST KEPT SECRET IN CORNWALL"
Sea Road, Carlyon Bay, St Austell,
Cornwall, PL25 3SG
Tel: 01726 812802 Fax: 01726 817097
Email: info@porthavallen.co.uk
Web: www.porthavallen.co.uk

The Porth Avallen Hotel

★★★ ☆ ☆

Sea Road, Carlyon Bay, St Austell, Cornwall, PL25 3SG
Tel: 01726 812802 Fax: 01726 817097
Email: info@porthavallen.co.uk
Web: www.porthavallen.co.uk
Rooms: 27 all ensuite 🗄 🚭
Pricing: Sgl £68–85 Dbl £110–150
Dinner available from £28.50–500 CC: Accepted
Room facilities: 📺 ☎ ☕ 🔌

Conference: 1 meeting room (Thtr 100 max),
24hr-delegate from £125, day-delegate from £19.50
Children: Welcome ♬
Licenses: ◁ 👬 Parking: Off-street and free
Directions: A30 onto A391, follow signs to St Austell,
Charlestown and Carlyon Bay. Turn right into Sea Road.
Map ref: Carlyon Bay 2 B4
See advert on this page

Spa Hotel

★★

Polkirt, Mevagissey, St Austell, Cornwall, PL26 6UY
Tel: 01726 842244 Fax: 01726 842244
Email: enquiries@spahotel-cornwall.co.uk
Web: www.spahotel-cornwall.co.uk
Seasonal closure: 31 October to 1 February

Family hotel with all ensuite bedrooms close to the
Eden Project, Lost Gardens of Heligan, beaches and
coastal path. Fine food and wines. Children welcome.
Most rooms non-smoking.
Rooms: 10 all ensuite 🛏 🚭
Pricing: Sgl £35–45 Dbl £64–74
Dinner available from £16 CC: Accepted
Room facilities: 📺 ☕
Children: Welcome ♬ Dogs: Welcome
Licenses: 👬 Leisure: Putting green
Parking: Off-street and free
Directions: Follow signs to St Austell, Mevagissey, then
Port Mellon. Private drive with sign on right after 1/2 mile.
Map ref: Polkirk 2 B4

Highland Court Lodge

◆◆◆◆◆

Biscovey Road, Biscovey, St Austell, Cornwall, PL24 2HW
Tel: 01726 813320 Fax: 01726 813320
Email: enquiries@highlandcourt.co.uk
Web: www.highlandcourt.co.uk
Rooms: 5 all ensuite 🗄 🚭
Pricing: Sgl £75–95 Dbl £110–170
Dinner available from £35 CC: Accepted
Room facilities: 📺 ☎ ☕ 🔌
Conference: 1 meeting room (Thtr 12 max)
Children: Welcome ♬ ☕
Licenses: 👬 Parking: Off-street and free
Directions: A390 to St Blazey Gate, left into Biscovey
Road. Lodge is 400 yards down on right.
Map ref: Biscovey 2 B4

Auraville B & B

◆◆◆◆

Auraville, The Drive, Trevarth, Mevagissey,
St Austell, Cornwall, PL26 6RX
Tel: 01726 843293
Web: www.auraville.co.uk
Seasonal closure: November to January
Rooms: 3 all ensuite 🍴 🅢
Pricing: Sgl £35 Dbl £50
Room facilities: 💻 🕮
Children: Welcome Dogs: Assistance dogs only
Parking: Off-street and free
Directions: Turn right into Trevarth opposite main car park, keeping left follow private road to top, bear right, at top Auraville is on left.
Map ref: Trevarth 2 B4

Arches

◆◆◆ 🦪

78 Bodmin Road, St Austell, Cornwall, PL25 5AG
Tel: 01726 64644
Email: nikki@archesbedandbreakfast.co.uk
Web: www.archesbedandbreakfast.co.uk
Rooms: 3 all ensuite 🗄 🅢
Pricing: Sgl £25–30 Dbl £50–60
Dinner available from £16
Room facilities: 💻 🕮
Children: Welcome 🖰 Dogs: Welcome
Parking: Off-street and free
Map ref: St Austell 2 B4

Cornerways Guest House

◆◆◆

Penwinnick Road, St Austell, Cornwall, PL25 5DS
Tel: 01726 61579 Fax: 01726 66871
Email: nwsurveys@aol.com
Seasonal closure: Christmas
Rooms: 5 (3 ensuite) 🅢
Pricing: Sgl £19–26 Dbl £40–46
Room facilities: 🕮
Children: Welcome
Parking: Off-street and free
Map ref: St Austell 2 B4

St Ives, Cornwall

Porthminster

★★★

The Terrace, St Ives, Cornwall, TR26 2BN
Tel: 01736 795221 Fax: 01736 797043
Email: reception@porthminster-hotel.co.uk
Web: www.porthminster-hotel.co.uk
Seasonal closure: early January
Rooms: 43 all ensuite 🍴 🅢
Pricing: Sgl £54–100 Dbl £108–200
Dinner available from £19.50
CC: Accepted
Room facilities: 💻 ☎ 🕮 Access: ⌷
Children: Welcome 🖰
Dogs: Welcome

Licenses: 🜲 👯
Leisure: Indoor pool, Outdoor pool, Gym, Health spa
Parking: Off-street
Directions: Porthminster Hotel is on A3074.
Map ref: St Ives (Cornwall) 2 A4

The Garrack Hotel & Restaurant

★★★ 🮲🮲🮲
Commended

Burthallan Lane, St. Ives,
Cornwall, TR26 3AA
Tel: 01736 796199 Fax: 01736 798955
Email: rac@garrack.com
Web: www.garrack.com

Small, family-run hotel & restaurant. Secluded position with 30 miles of coastal views overlooking St Ives. Four poster beds, sea view rooms, private car parking and indoor pool.
Rooms: 18 all ensuite 🍴 🗄
Pricing: Sgl £68–90 Dbl £121–176
Dinner available from £25.50
CC: Accepted
Room facilities: 💻 ☎ 🕮
Conference: 1 meeting room (Thtr 18 max)
Children: Welcome 🖰
Dogs: Welcome
Licenses: 👯
Leisure: Indoor pool, Gym
Parking: Off-street and free
Directions: B3311 to St Ives, into town first mini roundabout, first left Carnellis Road, ½km road bends right, first turning on left Burthallan Lane.
Map ref: St Ives (Cornwall) 2 A4

Nancherrow Cottage

◆◆◆◆◆ 🦪

7 Fish Street, St Ives, Cornwall, TR26 1LT
Tel: 01736 798496
Email: peterjean@nancherrowcottage.fsnet.co.uk
Web: www.nancherrow-cottage.co.uk
Seasonal closure: Christmas, New Year and January
Rooms: 3 all ensuite 🅢
Pricing: Sgl £50–60 Dbl £70–85
Room facilities: 💻 🕮
Children: Welcome 12yrs min age
Directions: Proceed through town along harbour to the Sloop Inn, turn left into Fish Street. Situated on right hand side of road.
Map ref: St Ives (Cornwall) 2 A4

Porthglaze

 ♦♦♦♦♦

Steeple Lane, St Ives, Cornwall, TR26 2AY
Tel: 01736 799409 or 07967 008327 Fax: 01736 791936
Email: info@porthglaze.co.uk
Web: www.porthglaze.co.uk
Rooms: 2 all ensuite ⊗ CC: Accepted
Room facilities: ▢ ⬆
Children: Welcome 14yrs min age
Parking: Off-street and free
Directions: Follow signs to St Ives, then left at Cornish
Arms, immediately left again into Steeple Lane.
Porthglaze is 500 yards on the left side of the lane.
Map ref: St Ives (Cornwall) 2 A4

The Light House Bed & Breakfast

♦♦♦♦♦

Pannier Lane, Carbis Bay, St Ives, Cornwall, TR26 2RA
Tel: 01736 793830 Fax: 01736 793830
Email: info@thelighthousebedandbreakfast.co.uk
Web: www.thelighthousebedandbreakfast.co.uk
Rooms: 3 (2 ensuite) ⊗
Pricing: Sgl £68 Dbl £80
Room facilities: ▢ ⬆
Leisure: Internet access Parking: Off-street and free
Directions: A3074 to St Ives. At Carbis Bay turn right
into Pannier Lane. Sharp right turn, Light House
second on the right.
Map ref: Carbis Bay 2 A4

The Nook Hotel

♦♦♦♦♦ ⌀

Ayr, St Ives, Cornwall, TR26 1EQ
Tel: 01736 795913 Fax: 01736 796536
Email: info@nookstives.co.uk
Web: www.nookstives.co.uk

Escape to the Nook Hotel, a family-run licensed hotel
in a peaceful location of St Ives. Relax and enjoy the
home comforts — the perfect base for exploring
beautiful St Ives and beyond.
Rooms: 10 all ensuite ⚲ ⊗
Pricing: Sgl £30–45 Dbl £60–75 CC: Accepted
Room facilities: ▢ ⬆
Children: Welcome Dogs: Assistance dogs only
Licenses: ♦♦♦ Parking: Off-street and free

Directions: A30 to St Ives, Porthminster Hotel right, left
Gabriel Street, roundabout right Bullans Lane, left Ayr
Terrace, second left private lane.
Map ref: St Ives (Cornwall) 2 A4

Bay View Guest House

♦♦♦♦

5 Pednolver Terrace, St Ives, Cornwall, TR26 2EL
Tel: 01736 796765
Email: bay-view@btconnect.com
Web: www.bayview-guesthouse.co.uk
Seasonal closure: November to Easter
Rooms: 5 (3 ensuite) ⚲ ⊗
Pricing: Sgl £26–30 Dbl £52–60
Room facilities: ▢ ⬆ Children: Welcome 4yrs min age
Parking: Off-street and free
Directions: Take the B3074 via Carbis Bay to St Ives.
At Porthminster Hotel take left towards leisure centre
for 100 yards to the Bay View.
Map ref: St Ives 2 A4

Dean Court Hotel

♦♦♦♦

Trelyon Avenue, St Ives, Cornwall, TR26 2AD
Tel: 01736 796023 Fax: 01736 796233
Email: deancourt@amserve.net
Web: www.deancourthotel.com
Seasonal closure: 31 October to 1 November
Rooms: 12 all ensuite ⊗
Pricing: Sgl £40–52 Dbl £80–114 CC: Accepted
Room facilities: ▢ ⬆
Children: Welcome 14yrs min age
Parking: Off-street and free
Directions: From A30 take A3074 through Carbis Bay
to St Ives. Dean Court is located on the right side of
Trelyon Avenue, overlooking St Ives Bay.
Map ref: St Ives (Cornwall) 2 A4

Halwell

♦♦♦♦

Fore Street, Lelant, St Ives, Cornwall, TR26 3EL
Tel: 01736 752003
Email: randsrook@aol.com
Rooms: 3 all ensuite ⊗
Pricing: Dbl £49–59
Room facilities: ▢ ⬆
Parking: Off-street and free
Directions: A30 Exeter to Lelant. Turn right onto A3074.
Straight over mini-roundabout. 100 yards, turn right.
After 1 mile turn left into Halwell
Map ref: Lelant 2 A4

Longships Hotel

♦♦♦♦

Talland Road, St Ives, Cornwall, TR26 2DF
Tel: 01736 798180 Fax: 01736 798180
Email: enquiries@longships-hotel.co.uk
Web: www.longships-hotel.co.uk
Rooms: 25 all ensuite ▱

Pricing: Sgl £35 Dbl £70
Dinner available from £13.50 CC: Accepted
Room facilities: ☐ ☕ Children: Welcome � 🌡
Licenses: 👥 Parking: Off-street and free
Directions: Take left fork at Portminster Hotel. Follow Talland Area Accommodation sign. Hotel is first in Talland Road.
Map ref: St Ives (Cornwall) 2 A4

Regent Hotel

Fern Lea Terrace, St Ives, Cornwall, TR26 2BH
Tel: 01736 796195 Fax: 01736 794641
Email: enquiries@regenthotel.com
Web: www.regenthotel.com
Rooms: 9 (7 ensuite) 🅰 CC: Accepted
Room facilities: ☐ ☕
Parking: Off-street
Directions: Follow A30, second exit at large roundabout at St Erth. Continue through Lelant and Carbis Bay. Pass Ford garage, continue to left and down hill, right at bottom of hill. Straight ahead, past Porthminster Hotel, down hill, sharp left.
Map ref: St Ives (Cornwall) 2 A4

Rivendell

7 Porthminster Terrace, St Ives, Cornwall, TR26 2DQ
Tel: 01736 794923 Fax: 01736 794923
Email: rivendellstives@aol.com
Web: www.rivendell-stives.co.uk
Rooms: 7 (5 ensuite) 🅰
Pricing: Sgl £21–28 Dbl £48-68
Dinner available from £14.95 CC: Accepted
Room facilities: ☐ ☕ Children: Welcome
Parking: Off-street and free
Directions: B3074 St Ives, bear left Albert Road, left uphill, directly ahead 200 yards on right, Porthminster Terrace, blue sign.
Map ref: St Ives (Cornwall) 2 A4

The Old Count House

Trenwith Square, St Ives, Cornwall, TR26 1DQ
Tel: 01736 795369 Fax: 01736 799109
Email: counthouse@btconnect.com
Web: www.connexions.co.uk/counthouse

Delightful guest house with unique history in quiet location close to town, Tate Gallery and beaches. Beautiful rooms with sea views. Four-poster with jacuzzi bath. Conservatory, sauna and garden.
Rooms: 9 (8 ensuite) 📺 🅰
Pricing: Sgl £35–38 Dbl £65–80 CC: Accepted
Room facilities: ☐ ☕
Licenses: 👥 Leisure: Sauna
Parking: Off-street and free
Directions: Exit A30, take B3311, approx 4 miles at T-Junction right onto B3306, right towards leisure centre, right turn after school.
Map ref: St Ives (Cornwall) 2 A4

Amie B&B

Spernen Close, Carbis Bay, St Ives, Cornwall, TR26 2QT
Tel: 01736 797643
Email: amie@stives.fsworld.co.uk
Web: www.accommodationstives.com
Rooms: 3 all ensuite 📺 🅰
Pricing: Sgl £30–32 Dbl £50–56
Room facilities: ☐ ☕
Children: Welcome 2yrs min age
Parking: Off-street and free
Directions: A30, follow signs St Ives for approximately 3 miles. Pass Howards Hotel, turn into Count House Lane and then Menhyr Drive. Right into Spernen Close, Amie is fifth bungalow on right.
Map ref: Carbis Bay 2 A4

Carlyon

18 The Terrace, St Ives, Cornwall, TR26 2BP
Tel: 01736 795317
Email: andrea.papworth@btinternet.com
Web: www.carlyon-stives.co.uk
Rooms: 6 all ensuite 🐾 🅰
Pricing: Sgl £30–40 Dbl £54–70
Room facilities: ☐ ☕
Children: Welcome
Parking: Off-street and free
Map ref: St Ives 2 A4

Wheal-E-Mine

9 Belmont Terrace, St Ives, Cornwall, TR26 1DZ
Tel: 01736 795051 Fax: 01736 795051
Email: whealemine@btinternet.com
Web: www.whealemine.co.uk
Seasonal closure: 1 November to 28 February
Rooms: 3 all ensuite 🐾 🅰
Pricing: Dbl £44–52
Room facilities: ☐ ☕
Children: Welcome 12yrs min age
Parking: Off-street and free
Directions: Head into town centre, take left into Gabriel Street then right at mini roundabout. Top of hill, 50 yards on the left.
Map ref: St Ives 2 A4

St Mawes, Cornwall

Rosevine Hotel

★★★★

Rosevine, Porthscatho,
St Mawes, Truro, Cornwall, TR2 5EW
Tel: 01872 580206 Fax: 01872 580230
Email: info@rosevine.co.uk
Web: www.rosevine.co.uk
Seasonal closure: December to January

Set in beautiful subtropical gardens facing directly over
the safe, sandy Porthcurnick beach. Ideally placed for
Eden and Heligan. Indoor pool, award-winning cuisine,
children welcome.
Rooms: 17 all ensuite
Pricing: Sgl £86–171 Dbl £172–256
Dinner available from £38 CC: Accepted
Room facilities:
Children: Welcome Dogs: Welcome
Licenses:
Leisure: Indoor pool, Games room
Parking: Off-street and free
Directions: Approaching St Mawes on A3078, turn
right at sign for Rosevine Hotel and Porthcurnick
beach.
Map ref: Truro 2 B4

Stanton Saint Quintin, Wiltshire

Stanton Manor Hotel

★★★

Stanton Saint Quintin, near Chippenham,
Wiltshire, SN14 6DQ
Tel: 0870 890 2880 Fax: 0870 890 2881
Email: reception@stantonmanor.co.uk
Web: www.stantonmanor.co.uk
Rooms: 24 all ensuite
Pricing: Sgl £100–155 Dbl £100–210
Dinner available from £28 CC: Accepted
Room facilities:
Conference: 4 meeting rooms (Thtr 60 max),
24hr-delegate from £135, day-delegate from £29.50
Children: Welcome Dogs: Welcome
Licenses: Leisure: Golf
Parking: Off-street and free
Directions: Junction 17 off M4 take exit A429
Cirencester roundabout. First left-hand turn Stanton
Saint Quintin. Into village on left-hand just past the
church.
Map ref: Stanton Saint Quintin 3 F1

Stoke Gabriel, Devon

Gabriel Court Hotel

★★★★

Stoke Hill, Stoke Gabriel, near Totnes, Devon, TQ9 6SF
Tel: 01803 782206 Fax: 01803 782333
Email: reservations@gabrielcourthotel.co.uk
Web: www.gabrielcourthotel.co.uk
Rooms: 19 all ensuite
Pricing: Sgl £67.50–73.50 Dbl £98–125
Dinner available from £30 CC: Accepted
Room facilities:
Conference: 1 meeting room (Thtr 20 max)
Children: Welcome Dogs: Welcome
Licenses:
Leisure: Outdoor pool, Snooker/billiards
Parking: Off-street and free
Directions: Turn off A385 (between Totnes and
Paignton) at Parkers Arms pub. Proceed towards
Stoke Gabriel. On entering village, stay left and you will
reach hotel.
Map ref: Stoke Gabriel 3 D4

Stourton, Warminster

Spread Eagle Inn

◆◆◆◆

Stourton, Warminster, Wiltshire, BA12 6QE
Tel: 01747 840587 Fax: 01747 840954
Email: spreadeagle@aol.com
Web: www.latonahotels.co.uk
Rooms: 5 all ensuite
Dinner available CC: Accepted
Room facilities:
Conference: 1 meeting room (Thtr 40 max)
Children: Welcome Dogs: Welcome
Licenses: Parking: Off-street and free
Directions: Situated at Stourhead Estates and
Gardens, 2 miles from Hotel off the B3092.
Map ref: Stourton 3 F2

Street, Somerset

Wessex Hotel

★★★

High Street, Street, Somerset, BA16 0EF
Tel: 01458 443383 Fax: 01458 446589
Email: info@wessexhotel.com
Web: www.wessexhotel.com
Rooms: 49 all ensuite
Dinner available CC: Accepted
Room facilities: Access:
Conference: 3 meeting rooms (Thtr 250 max),
24hr-delegate from £85, day-delegate from £17.95
Children: Welcome
Licenses:
Parking: Off-street and free
Directions: From M5, Junction 23 to Bridgwater,
Glastonbury and Street. From A303, follow B3151 to
Street. Nearest railway station Castle Cary.
Map ref: Street 3 E2

The Birches

13 Housman Road, Street, Somerset, BA16 0SD
Tel: 01458 442902 Fax: 01458 442902
Email: askins@ukonline.co.uk
Rooms: 2 all ensuite
Pricing: Sgl £35 Dbl £55
Room facilities:
Children: Welcome
Parking: Off-street and free
Directions: From A39: B3151, second right after
Millfield traffic lights. Then first right. From A303: first
left after 30mph sign, then first right.
Map ref: Street 3 E2

Swanage, Dorset

PINES HOTEL

Situated at the secluded end of Swanage Bay
with marvellous panoramic sea views and
private steps down to the beach. Long
established reputation for our service and
cuisine. Beautifully refurbished award-winning
restaurant. Undoubtedly one of the finest
views on the South Coast.

**Burlington Road, Swanage,
Dorset BH19 1LT**
Tel: 01929 425211
Fax: 01929 422075
reservations@pineshotel.co.uk
www.pineshotel.co.uk

Pines Hotel

★★★

Burlington Road, Swanage, Dorset, BH19 1LT
Tel: 01929 425211 Fax: 01929 422075
Email: reservations@pineshotel.co.uk
Web: www.pineshotel.co.uk
Rooms: 48 all ensuite
Pricing: Sgl £56.50–74.50 Dbl £113–161
Dinner available from £22.50–25.50 CC: Accepted
Room facilities: Access:
Conference: 4 meeting rooms (Thtr 80 max),
24hr-delegate from £88.30, day-delegate from £18.80

Children: Welcome Dogs: Welcome
Licenses: Parking: Off-street and free
Directions: At Swanage seafront, left then second right
to end of road.
Map ref: Swanage 3 F3
See advert on this page

The Castleton

1 Highcliffe Road, Swanage, Dorset, BH19 1LW
Tel: 01929 423972 Fax: 01929 425154
Email: stay@castletonhotel-swanage.co.uk
Web: www.castletonhotel-swanage.co.uk

Family run non-smoking hotel situated 150 yards from
Swanage's beach. All rooms ensuite and decorated to
high standard. Please telephone for brochure and tariff.
Rooms: 9 all ensuite
Pricing: Sgl £30–50 Dbl £60–80
Room facilities:
Children: Welcome 6yrs min age
Parking: Off-street and free
Directions: A351 via Wareham to Swanage, left at
seafront. Follow road up hill towards Studland. First
road on right off seafront.
Map ref: Swanage 3 F3

Swindon, Wiltshire

Blunsdon House Hotel

★★★★

Blunsdon, Swindon, Wiltshire, SN26 7AS
Tel: 01793 721701 Fax: 01793 720625
Email: info@blunsdonhouse.co.uk
Web: www.blunsdonhouse.co.uk
Rooms: 117 all ensuite
Pricing: Sgl £75–150 Dbl £95–160
Dinner available from £20 CC: Accepted
Room facilities: Access:
Conference: 10 meeting rooms (Thtr 300 max),
24hr-delegate from £145, day-delegate from £45
Children: Welcome Licenses:
Leisure: Indoor pool, Gym, Health spa, Beauty salon,
Tennis, Golf, Games room, Snooker/billiards
Parking: Off-street and free
Directions: Leave M4 at Junction 15. Take A419 to
Cirencester. After 7 miles you reach Broad Blunsdon.
200 yards past traffic lights, turn right into village.
Map ref: Blunsdon 4 A2

Southwest

Cricklade Hotel & Country Club

★★★★ ⓇⓇ

Common Hill, Cricklade, Swindon, Wiltshire, SN6 6HA
Tel: 01793 750751 Fax: 01793 751767
Email: reception@crickladehotel.co.uk
Web: www.cricklehotel.co.uk

Spectacular panoramic views over Wiltshire
countryside, this hotel is encompassed by a
challenging golf course. Good food and wines, well
appointed bedrooms, conference and banqueting
facilities and health suite.
Rooms: 46 all ensuite ⚄ ⊗
Pricing: Sgl £112–120 Dbl £152–158
Dinner available from £26.50 CC: Accepted
Room facilities: ▯ ☎ ☺
Conference: 6 meeting rooms (Thtr 80 max),
24hr-delegate from £165, day-delegate from £49
Children: Welcome 14yrs min age
Licenses: ◈ ♙
Leisure: Indoor pool, Gym, Health spa, Beauty salon,
Tennis, Golf, Games room, Snooker/billiards
Parking: Off-street and free
Directions: From M4 Junction 15, take A419 north to
Cricklade, exit B4040 (Malmesbury), ½ mile top of hill
on left.
Map ref: Common Hill 4 A2

Marsh Farm Hotel

★★★★ ⓇⓇ

Coped Hall, Wootton Bassett, Swindon, Wiltshire, SN4 8ER
Tel: 01793 848044 Fax: 01793 851528
Email: marshfarmhotel@btconnect.com
Web: www.marshfarmhotel.co.uk
Seasonal closure: 26–30 December

This beautiful grade 2 listed Victorian farm house has
been tastefully restored and converted into a luxury
country hotel. Reid's Conservatory Restaurant offers
excellent cuisine and fine wines.
Rooms: 50 all ensuite ⚄ ⊗
Pricing: Sgl £55–110 Dbl £70–150
Dinner available from £24.50 CC: Accepted
Room facilities: ▯ ☎ ☺ ☏
Conference: 8 meeting rooms (Thtr 120 max),
24hr-delegate from £135, day-delegate from £38
Children: Welcome
Licenses: ◈ ♙ Parking: Off-street and free
Directions: Leave M4 at Junction 16. Take A3102
towards Wootton Bassett, at second roundabout turn
right. Hotel is immediately on left.
Map ref: Wootton Bassett 4 A2

Stanton House Hotel

★★★

The Avenue, Stanton Fitzwarren,
Swindon, Wiltshire, SN6 7SD
Tel: 01793 861777 Fax: 01793 861857
Email: info@stantonhouse.co.uk
Web: www.stantonhouse.co.uk
Rooms: 84 all ensuite ⚄ ⚄ ⊗
Pricing: Sgl £65 Dbl £109
Dinner available from £15 CC: Accepted
Room facilities: ▯ ☎ ☺ ☏ Access: ♙
Conference: 3 meeting rooms (Thtr 110 max),
24hr-delegate from £117.50, day-delegate from £32.50

Children: Welcome
Licenses: Leisure: Tennis
Parking: Off-street and free
Directions: M4 J15 onto A419. Turn onto the A361 for Highworth. Stanton Fitzwarren is on left after second roundabout. Stanton House Hotel is approximately ¹/₂ mile on left.
Map ref: Stanton Fitzwarren 4 A2
See advert on opposite page

The Pear Tree at Purton

★★★★

Excellent

Church End, Purton, Swindon, Wiltshire, SN5 4ED
Tel: 01793 772100 Fax: 01793 772369
Email: relax@peartreepurton.co.uk
Web: www.peartreepurton.co.uk
Seasonal closure: 26-30 December

This personally run Cotswold stone former vicarage is set in 7¹/₂ acres and surrounded on all sides by rolling Wiltshire farmland. Ideal for visiting the Cotswolds, Bath, Oxford and Swindon.
Rooms: 17 all ensuite
Pricing: Sgl £120–160 Dbl £120–180
Dinner available from £32.50 CC: Accepted
Room facilities:
Conference: 4 meeting rooms (Thtr 50 max), 24hr-delegate from £160, day-delegate from £45
Children: Welcome
Dogs: Welcome
Licenses:
Parking: Off-street and free
Directions: From M4 J16 follow signs to Purton. At Spar grocers turn right. Hotel is half mile on left.
Map ref: Purton 4 A2

The Wiltshire Golf & Country Club

★★★

Wootton Bassett, Swindon, Wiltshire, SN4 7PB
Tel: 01793 849999 Fax: 01793 849988
Email: thelodge@the-wiltshire.co.uk
Web: www.the-wiltshire.co.uk
Seasonal closure: 24-25 December
Rooms: 58 all ensuite
Pricing: Sgl £80 Dbl £85–115
Dinner available from £18.50–22.5
CC: Accepted
Room facilities: Access:

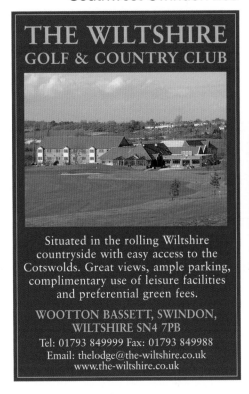

Conference: 3 meeting rooms (Thtr 220 max), 24hr-delegate from £120, day-delegate from £37
Children: Welcome
Licenses:
Leisure: Indoor pool, Gym, Beauty salon, Golf
Parking: Off-street and free
Directions: Exit M4 at J16. Follow A3103 through Wootton Bassett towards Lyneham. Club is situated 1 mile outside Wootton Bassett on the left-hand side.
Map ref: Wooton Bassett 3 F1
See advert on this page

Fir Tree Lodge

◆◆◆

17 Highworth Road, Stratton St Margaret, Swindon, Wiltshire, SN3 4QL
Tel: 01793 822372 Fax: 01793 822372
Email: info@firtreelodge.com
Web: www.firtreelodge.com
Rooms: 14 (12 ensuite)
Pricing: Sgl £32.32–35 Dbl £52.88–55
CC: Accepted
Room facilities:
Children: Welcome
Dogs: Welcome
Parking: Off-street and free
Directions: Opposite Rat Trap public house. Follow A419 until A361 Highworth/Burford turn. Right at roundabout, approximately 100 metres on right.
Map ref: Stratton St Margaret 4 A2

Taunton, Somerset

Castle Hotel

★★★☆☆☆☆ *Premier*

Castle Green, Taunton, Somerset, TA1 1NF
Tel: 01823 272671 Fax: 01823 336066
Email: reception@the-castle-hotel.com
Web: www.the-castle-hotel.com
Rooms: 44 all ensuite 🛏 🖥 ⊗
Pricing: Sgl £130 Dbl £310
Dinner available from £29
CC: Accepted
Room facilities: 🖳 ☎ ☕ ⬚
Access: |↑|
Conference: 4 meeting rooms (Thtr 100 max),
24hr-delegate from £155, day-delegate from £47
Children: Welcome
Dogs: Welcome
Licenses: 🚻
Parking: Off-street and free
Directions: From M5, take Junction 25 and follow signs
to town centre, then brown signs to Castle Hotel.
Map ref: Taunton 3 E2

The Mount Somerset Hotel

★★★☆☆☆

Lower Henlade, Taunton, Somerset, TA3 5NB
Tel: 01823 442500 Fax: 01823 442900
Email: info@mountsomersethotel.co.uk
Web: www.mountsomersethotel.co.uk
Rooms: 11 all ensuite 🛏 🖥 ⊗
Pricing: Sgl £105–120 Dbl £145–225
Dinner available from £27.50
CC: Accepted
Room facilities: 🖳 ☎
Access: |↑|
Conference: 2 meeting rooms (Thtr 50 max),
24hr-delegate from £175, day-delegate from £35
Children: Welcome 🍴 ☕
Dogs: Assistance dogs only
Licenses: ⬙ 🚻
Leisure: Beauty salon
Parking: Off-street and free
Directions: Junction 25, M5, take A358 for Chard, turn
right to Stoke St Mary, left at T-junction. Hotel on right.
Map ref: Lower Henlade 3 E2

Elm Villa

◆◆◆◆◆ ✗ ☕

Private Road, Staplegrove Road, Taunton,
Somerset, TA2 6AJ
Tel: 01823 336165
Email: ferguson@elmvilla10.freeserve.co.uk
Rooms: 2 all ensuite
Pricing: Sgl £35 Dbl £46–50
Room facilities: 🖳 ☕
Parking: Off-street and free
Directions: From Taunton centre, private road is off
A3027 near junction with A358 Minehead road.
Map ref: Taunton 3 E2

Salisbury House Hotel

◆◆◆◆◆ ✗

14 Billetfield, Taunton, Somerset, TA1 3NN
Tel: 01823 272083 Fax: 01823 365978
Email: res@salisburyhousehotel.co.uk
Web: www.salisburyhousehotel.co.uk

Victorian family-owned hotel in unrivalled town centre
location. Modern comforts combined with charm and
character will ensure a memorable stay. Four-poster
and ground floor rooms available. Car park.
Rooms: 17 all ensuite 🛏 🖥 ⊗
Pricing: Sgl £45–65 Dbl £60–85 Dinner available
CC: Accepted Room facilities: 🖳 ☎ ☕ ⬚
Conference: 1 meeting room (Thtr 15 max)
Children: Welcome ☕ Licenses: 🚻
Parking: Off-street and free
Directions: Follow signs to Taunton town centre. From
East Reach, bear left and go past Sainsbury's and BP
garage. Hotel is on left, past church.
Map ref: Taunton 3 E2

Meryan House Hotel

◆◆◆◆ ☆☆ ✗

Bishops Hull, Taunton, Somerset, TA1 5EG
Tel: 01823 337445 Fax: 01823 322355
Email: meryanhouse@yahoo.co.uk
Web: www.meryanhouse.co.uk

Delightful country house set in own gardens yet only 5
minutes from Taunton. The house is a wealth of beams
and inglenooks, and elegantly furnished with antiques.
All bedrooms are ensuite, with TV and video channel,
tea/coffee making facilities, telephone and radio. The
award-winning restaurant, set in a delightful room with
large inglenook fireplace, uses local produce wherever
possible.

Rooms: 12 all ensuite
Pricing: Sgl £53–60 Dbl £65–75
Dinner available from £16 CC: Accepted
Room facilities:
Conference: 2 meeting rooms (Thtr 20 max),
24hr-delegate from £95, day-delegate from £20
Children: Welcome Dogs: Welcome
Licenses:
Parking: Off-street and free
Directions: Take A38 out of Taunton for about 1 mile,
after crematorium turn right into Bishops Hull Road.
Hotel approximately 600 yards.
Map ref: Bishops Hull 3 E2

Ralegh's Cross Inn

Brendon Hill, Exmoor, Somerset, TA23 0LN
Tel: 01984 640343 Fax: 01984 641111
Email: enquiries@raleghscross.co.uk
Web: www.raleghscross.co.uk
Rooms: 17 all ensuite
Dinner available CC: Accepted
Room facilities:
Conference: 2 meeting rooms (Thtr 250 max)
Children: Welcome Dogs: Welcome
Licenses:
Leisure: Riding
Parking: Off-street and free
Directions: Take Minehead Road A358 from Taunton,
past Bishops Lideard, turn left onto B3224. After six
miles, hotel on left.
Map ref: Ralegh's Cross 3 D2

Tavistock, Devon

Tor Cottage   Little Gem

Chillaton, Devon, PL16 0JE
Tel: 01822 860248 Fax: 01822 860126
Email: info@torcottage.co.uk
Web: www.torcottage.co.uk
Seasonal closure: Mid December to mid January

National award-winning romantic retreat. Enjoy
complete peace and privacy in beautiful ensuite bed-
sitting rooms, each with log fire, garden and terrace.
Streamside setting in a hidden valley. Heated pool
(summer). Special breaks available.

Rooms: 5 all ensuite
Pricing: Sgl £94 Dbl £140–150
Dinner available from £22
CC: Accepted
Room facilities:
Leisure: Outdoor pool, Walking
Parking: Off-street and free
Directions: From A30 exit Lewdown through Chillaton
towards Tavistock. Right 300 yards after Post Office.
Signed 'bridle path, no public vehicular access to end.'
Map ref: Chillaton 2 C3

Beera Farmhouse

Beera Farm, Milton Abbot, Tavistock, Devon, PL19 8PL
Tel: 01822 870216 Fax: 01822 870216
Email: hilary.tucker@farming.co.uk
Web: www.beera-farm.co.uk
Seasonal closure: December

Enjoy a relaxing, peaceful break on a working farm in
the heart of the Tamar Valley, amidst wonderful
surroundings. Excellent food and hospitality. Ideal base
for touring the West Country.
Rooms: 3 all ensuite
Pricing: Sgl £50–65 Dbl £60–75
Dinner available from £16–19 CC: Accepted
Room facilities:
Children: Welcome
Leisure: Farm walks
Parking: Off-street and free
Directions: From Tavistock, take B3362 to Milton Abbot,
take first left (Endsleigh) for 2.2 miles. Farm on left.
Map ref: Milton Abbot 2 C3

The big sleep

As part of our comprehensive
inspection process, RAC
Inspectors investigate the comfort
of the beds.

THORNBURY CASTLE

Beautiful 16th century Castle-palace, once owned by Henry VIII, offering 25 carefully restored bedchambers. Renowned for its fine food, the castle has three dining rooms, each baronial in style with open fires.

CASTLE STREET, THORNBURY, SOUTH GLOUCESTERSHIRE BS35 1HH
Tel: 01454 281182 Fax: 01454 416188
Email: info@thornburycastle.co.uk
Web: www.thornburycastle.co.uk

Port William Inn
Trebarwith Strand

Probably the best located inn in Cornwall, romantically situated 50 yards from the sea, overlooking the sea, beach and cliffs at Trebarwith Strand.
The Inn is known for its food, offering homecooked dishes, local fish and seafood, and a good range of vegetarian fare, all at 'bar menu' prices. All rooms are newly refurbished, ensuite and have views across the bay.
Conference/function room.
We welcome well behaved children and dogs.

Trebarwith Strand, Tintagel, Cornwall PL34 0HB
Tel: 01840 770230 Fax: 01840 770936
Email: theportwilliam@btinternet.com
Web: www.theportwilliam.com

Thornbury, South Gloucestershire

Thornbury Castle

★★★★ 👥👥👥 Premier

Castle Street, Thornbury,
South Gloucestershire, BS35 1HH
Tel: 01454 281182 Fax: 01454 416188
Email: info@thornburycastle.co.uk
Web: www.thornburycastle.co.uk
Rooms: 25 all ensuite 🐾 🎴
Pricing: Sgl £90–150 Dbl £150–375
Dinner available from £42.50 CC: Accepted
Room facilities: ☐ ☎ ☺
Conference: 3 meeting rooms (Thtr 50 max), 24hr-delegate from £250, day-delegate from £65
Children: Welcome ⅄ ⅊ Dogs: Welcome
Licenses: 🍸 🍴 Leisure: Archery, Croquet
Parking: Off-street and free
Directions: To Thornbury on A38. At traffic lights turn to town centre. Through High Street and left into Castle Street. Castle behind St Mary's church (look for brown castle signage).
Map ref: Thornbury 3 E1
See advert on this page

Tintagel, Cornwall

Port William Inn

◆◆◆◆

Trebarwith Strand, Tintagel, Cornwall, PL34 0HB
Tel: 01840 770230 Fax: 01840 770936
Email: theportwilliam@btinternet.com
Web: www.theportwilliam.com
Rooms: 8 all ensuite 🎴 ⊛ CC: Accepted
Room facilities: ☐ ☎ ☺ 🐾
Conference: 1 meeting room (Thtr 85 max)
Children: Welcome ⅄ Dogs: Welcome
Licenses: 🍸 🍴
Parking: Off-street and free
Map ref: Trebarwith Strand 2 B3
See advert on this page

Tiverton, Devon

Bridge Guest House

◆◆◆

23 Angel Hill, Tiverton, Devon, EX16 6PE
Tel: 01884 252804 Fax: 01884 252804
Web: www.smoothhound.co.uk/hotels/bridgegh.html
Rooms: 10 (6 ensuite) ⊛
Pricing: Sgl £23–29 Dbl £46–58
Dinner available from £16
Room facilities: ☐ ☺
Children: Welcome ⅄ ⅊
Licenses: 🍴
Leisure: Fishing, Games room
Parking: Off-street and free
Directions: Leave M5 at Junction 27. Take A361 north for 7 miles. Leave A361 into Tiverton. Bridge Guest House situated in centre of town, by river.
Map ref: Tiverton 3 D2

Southwest

Torquay, Devon

Osborne Hotel

★★★★ ♨♨♨

Hesketh Crescent, Meadfoot, Torquay, Devon, TQ1 2LL
Tel: 01803 213311 Fax: 01803 296788
Email: enq@osborne-torquay.co.uk
Web: www.osborne-torquay.co.uk
Rooms: 33 all ensuite ♨ ⊚
Pricing: Sgl £57–82 Dbl £114–164
Dinner available from £23.95 CC: Accepted
Room facilities: ▢ ☎ ⊙ ⌇ Access: |↓↑
Conference: 2 meeting rooms (Thtr 60 max),
24hr-delegate from £99, day-delegate from £31
Children: Welcome ♬ ⌇℮
Licenses: ⟁ ♟♟
Leisure: Indoor pool, Outdoor pool, Gym, Tennis,
Putting green
Parking: Off-street and free
Directions: A380 via Newton Abbot, follow signs to
seafront, follow A3022 down and turn left, turn onto
B3199 and follow road up to hotel.
Map ref: Torquay 3 D3

Belgrave Hotel

★★★

Seafront, Torquay, Devon, TQ2 5HE
Tel: 01803 296666 Fax: 01803 211308
Email: info@belgrave-hotel.co.uk
Web: www.belgrave-hotel.co.uk

A stone's throw from the beach, this leading 3-star
hotel prides itself on its high standard of service and
cuisine. With 72 ensuite bedrooms, elegant restaurant,
pool and large car park, why look elsewhere!
Rooms: 72 all ensuite ♨ ⊚
Pricing: Sgl £58–77 Dbl £116–154
Dinner available from £25 CC: Accepted
Room facilities: ▢ ☎ ⊙ Access: |↓↑
Conference: 5 meeting rooms (Thtr 200 max),
24hr-delegate from £75, day-delegate from £20
Children: Welcome ♬ Dogs: Welcome
Licenses: ♟♟♟
Leisure: Outdoor pool
Parking: Off-street and free
Directions: M5 to Exeter. A380 to Torquay. Follow signs
to seafront. Hotel at seafront on left-hand side.
Map ref: Torquay 3 D3

Corbyn Head Hotel

★★★★ ♨

Seafront, Torquay, Devon, TQ2 6RH
Tel: 01803 213611 Fax: 01803 296152
Email: info@corbynhead.com
Web: www.corbynhead.com
Rooms: 50 all ensuite ♨ ⊚
Pricing: Sgl £55–75 Dbl £110–202
Dinner available from £24.95
CC: Accepted
Room facilities: ▢ ☎ ⊙ ⌇
Conference: 1 meeting room (Thtr 40 max),
24hr-delegate from £80, day-delegate from £45
Children: Welcome ♬
Dogs: Welcome
Licenses: ♟♟♟
Leisure: Outdoor pool
Parking: Off-street and free
Directions: At sea front, turn right towards Livermead
and Cockington. Hotel is situated just past Cockington
Lane on right opposite Livermead beach.
Map ref: Torquay 3 D3
See advert on following page

Hotel Gleneagles

★★★

Asheldon Road, Wellswood, Torquay, Devon, TQ1 2QS
Tel: 01803 293637 Fax: 01803 295106
Email: enquiries@hotel-gleneagles.com
Web: www.hotel-gleneagles.com
Rooms: 41 all ensuite
Room facilities: ▢ ☎ ⊙
Access: |↓↑
Children: Welcome 12yrs min age
Leisure: Jacuzzi, Solarium
Parking: Off-street and free
Directions: Detailed directions available on our website
Map ref: Torquay 3 D3

Livermead Cliff Hotel

★★★

Seafront, Torquay, Devon, TQ2 6RQ
Tel: 01803 299666 Fax: 01803 294496
Email: enquiries@livermeadcliff.co.uk
Web: www.livermeadcliff.co.uk
Rooms: 67 all ensuite ♨ ⊚
Dinner available
CC: Accepted
Room facilities: ▢ ☎ ⊙ ⌇
Access: |↓↑
Conference: 3 meeting rooms (Thtr 100 max),
24hr-delegate from £99, day-delegate from £29
Children: Welcome ♬ ⌇℮
Dogs: Welcome
Licenses: ♟♟♟
Leisure: Outdoor pool
Parking: Off-street and free
Directions: From M5, take A379 to Torquay. Follow
A3022 through town to seafront. Turn right, sign to
Paignton. Hotel 600 yards seaward side.
Map ref: Torquay 3 D3

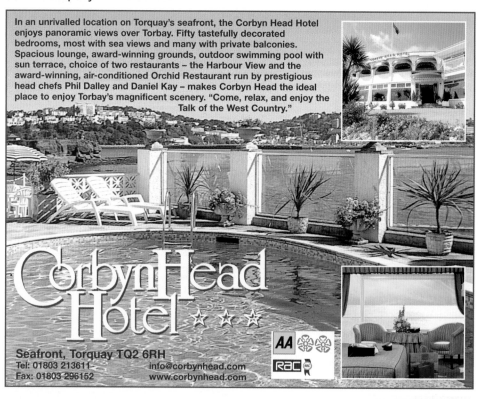

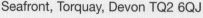

Southwest

Livermead House Hotel

Seafront, Torquay, Devon, TQ2 6QJ
Tel: 01803 294361 Fax: 01803 200758
Email: info@livermead.com
Web: www.livermead.com
Rooms: 67 all ensuite
Pricing: Sgl £60–85 Dbl £120–170
Dinner available from £24.95
CC: Accepted
Room facilities:
Access:
Conference: 5 meeting rooms (Thtr 300 max),
24hr-delegate from £51, day-delegate from £24.75
Children: Welcome
Dogs: Welcome
Licenses:
Leisure: Outdoor pool, Gym, Snooker/billiards, Squash,
Sauna, Solarium
Parking: Off-street and free
Directions: From Exeter, take A380 to Torquay then
follow the signs for seafront. Turn right towards
Livermead.
Map ref: Torquay 3 D3
See advert on opposite page

Orestone Manor Hotel & Restaurant

Excellent

Rockhouse Lane, Maidencombe,
Torquay, Devon, TQ1 4SX
Tel: 01803 328098 Fax: 01803 328336
Email: enquiries@orestone.co.uk
Web: www.orestone.co.uk
Rooms: 12 all ensuite
Pricing: Sgl £95–135 Dbl £135–225
Dinner available from £25–45
CC: Accepted
Room facilities:
Conference: 2 meeting rooms (Thtr 45 max),
24hr-delegate from £135, day-delegate from £45
Children: Welcome
Dogs: Welcome
Licenses:
Leisure: Outdoor pool
Directions: The hotel is located 200 yards down
Rockhouse Lane, off the A379 halfway between
Torquay and Teignmouth.
Map ref: Maidencombe 3 D3

Toorak Hotel

Chestnut Avenue, Torquay, Devon, TQ2 5JS
Tel: 01803 400500 Fax: 01803 400150
Email: rooms@tlh.co.uk
Web: www.tlh.co.uk
Rooms: 92 all ensuite
Dinner available
CC: Accepted
Room facilities:
Access:

Conference: 4 meeting rooms (Thtr 200 max)
Children: Welcome
Licenses:
Leisure: Indoor pool, Outdoor pool, Gym, Beauty
salon, Tennis, Games room, Snooker/billiards
Parking: Off-street and free
Directions: Immediately opposite the Riviera Centre,
which is clearly signed from major routes into the
town.
Map ref: Torquay 3 D3

Abbey Court Hotel

Falkland Road, Torquay, Devon, TQ2 5JR
Tel: 01803 297316 Fax: 01803 297316
Map ref: Torquay 3 D3

Allerdale Hotel

21 Croft Road, Torquay, Devon, TQ2 5UD
Tel: 01803 292667 Fax: 01803 292667
Email: info@allerdalehotel.co.uk
Web: www.allerdalehotel.co.uk
Seasonal closure: January

A Victorian villa nestling in its own spacious south-
facing garden with path to seafront. Friendly family-run
hotel which has been tastefully refurbished offering a
comfortable base to stay. All rooms are ensuite.
Excellent food with a wide choice of menu. Centrally
situated for all amenities. Parking available.
Rooms: 20 all ensuite
Pricing: Sgl £25–40 Dbl £50–100
Dinner available from £20
CC: Accepted
Room facilities:
Conference: 1 meeting room
Children: Welcome
Dogs: Welcome
Licenses:
Leisure: Games room, Snooker/billiards
Parking: Off-street and free
Directions: Follow A380 to sea front. Turn left, next
traffic lights take left fork (Sheddon Hill). First turning
on left is Croft Road.
Map ref: Torquay 3 D3

Anchorage Hotel

★★

Aveland Road, Babbacombe, Torquay, Devon, TQ1 3PT
Tel: 01803 326175 Fax: 01803 316439
Email: enquiries@anchoragehotel.co.uk
Web: www.anchorage.co.uk

This hotel is a family-run establishment and is situated on the flat in beautiful Cary Park, five minutes walk from Babbacombe Downs.
Rooms: 56 all ensuite
Pricing: Sgl £21.50–33.50
Dinner available from £11
CC: Accepted
Room facilities: 📺 ☎ 🍵 📞 ❄
Access: ↕↑
Children: Welcome
Licenses: ♙♙♙
Leisure: Outdoor pool
Parking: Off-street and free
Directions: Leave A380 and head towards Babbacombe. Straight over first roundabout to mini-roundabout leading to Warbro Road, second road left.
Map ref: Torquay 3 D3

Ashley Rise Hotel

★★

18 Babbacombe Road, Torquay, Devon, TQ1 3SJ
Tel: 01803 327282 Fax: 01803 327177
Email: ashleyrisehotel@ukonline.co.uk
Web: www.ashleyrisehotel.co.uk
Rooms: 26 all ensuite
Pricing: Sgl £20–32 Dbl £40–70
Dinner available from £8
CC: Accepted
Room facilities: 📺 🍵
Access: ↕↑
Children: Welcome
Dogs: Welcome
Licenses: ♙♙♙
Parking: Off-street and free
Directions: Follow signs to Babbacombe model village; at St Mary's church turn left towards Torquay town centre; on to Babbacombe Road, third left.
Map ref: Torquay 3 D3

Bute Court Hotel

★★

Belgrave Road, Torquay, Devon, TQ2 5HQ
Tel: 01803 293771 Fax: 01803 213429
Email: stay@butecourthotel.co.uk
Web: www.butecourthotel.co.uk
Rooms: 44 all ensuite
Dinner available
CC: Accepted
Room facilities: 📺 ☎ 🍵 Access: ↕↑
Children: Welcome
Licenses: ♙♙♙
Leisure: Outdoor pool, Games room, Snooker/billiards
Parking: Off-street
Directions: From A380 to Torquay follow seafront signs. At seafront turn left. Belgrave Road is first left at traffic lights.
Map ref: Torquay 3 D3

Coppice Hotel

★★

Babbacombe Road, Torquay, Devon, TQ1 2QJ
Tel: 01803 297786 Fax: 01803 211085
Email: peter@coppicehotel.demon.co.uk
Web: www.coppicehotel.co.uk
Seasonal closure: December to February
Rooms: 40 all ensuite
Dinner available
CC: Accepted
Room facilities: 📺 ☎ 🍵
Children: Welcome ♐
Dogs: Welcome
Licenses: ♙♙♙
Leisure: Indoor pool, Outdoor pool, Gym, Health spa, Games room, Snooker/billiards
Parking: Off-street and free
Directions: From Torquay Harbour turn left at clock tower onto Babbacombe Road. Continue for one mile, the hotel is on left.
Map ref: Torquay 3 D3

Crofton House Hotel

★★

Croft Road, Torquay, Devon, TQ2 5TZ
Tel: 01803 293761 Fax: 01803 211796
Email: stay@croftonhousetorquay.co.uk
Web: www.croftonhousetorquay.co.uk
Seasonal closure: January
Rooms: 35 all ensuite
Dinner available
CC: Accepted
Room facilities: 📺 🍵
Children: Welcome ♐
Licenses: ♙♙♙
Leisure: Indoor pool, Outdoor pool, Health spa, Games room, Snooker/billiards
Parking: Off-street
Directions: Follow signs for town centre into Belgrave Road, turn left into Lucius Street at lights, and take first right into Croft Road.
Map ref: Torquay 3 D3

Gresham Court Hotel

 ★★

Babbacombe Road, Torquay, Devon, TQ1 1HG
Tel: 01803 293007 Fax: 01803 215951
Email: via web-site
Web: www.gresham-court-hotel.co.uk
Seasonal closure: January
Rooms: 30 all ensuite
Pricing: Dinner available from £13
CC: Accepted
Room facilities: ▢ ⚙ Access: ♿
Children: Welcome 3yrs min age
Licenses: ⛟
Leisure: Games room
Parking: Off-street
Directions: Bear left at clocktower (harbour/strand), cross set of lights into Babbacombe Road, travel short distance, hotel on left near museum.
Map ref: Torquay 3 D3

Howden Court Hotel

 ★★

23 Croft Road, Torquay, Devon, TQ2 5UD
Tel: 01803 294844 Fax: 01803 211356
Email: info@howdencourthotel.co.uk
Web: www.howdencourthotel.co.uk
Rooms: 38 all ensuite ⚃
Pricing: Sgl £26–35 Dbl £52–70
Dinner available from £15
CC: Accepted
Room facilities: ▢ ⚙
Children: Welcome ⅄ Dogs: Welcome
Licenses: ⛟
Leisure: Games room, Access to Torbay Private Tennis Club
Parking: Off-street and free
Directions: Follow A380 to sea front. Turn left at lights, take second left (Sheddon Hill), then first left into Croft Road.
Map ref: Torquay 3 D3

Inglewood Hotel

 ★★

Belgrave Road, Torquay, Devon, TQ2 5HR
Tel: 01803 293800 Fax: 01803 297300
Email: enquiry@theinglewoodhotel.co.uk
Web: www.theinglewoodhotel.co.uk
Rooms: 52 all ensuite ⚃
Pricing: Sgl £25–45 Dbl £50–90
Dinner available from £8–10
CC: Accepted
Room facilities: ▢ ⚙
Access: ♿
Children: Welcome ⅄
Licenses: ⛟
Leisure: Outdoor pool, Games room, Snooker/billiards
Parking: Off-street and free
Directions: From M5 take A380 to Torquay; follow seafront signs; at seafront turn left, then first left; hotel is second on the left.
Map ref: Torquay 3 D3

Shedden Hall Hotel

 ★★

Shedden Hill, Torquay, Devon, TQ2 5TX
Tel: 01803 292964 Fax: 01803 295306
Email: sheddenhtl@aol.com
Web: www.sheddenhtl.co.uk
Seasonal closure: January
Rooms: 26 all ensuite ⚃ ▣ ⊗
Dinner available
CC: Accepted
Room facilities: ▢ ☎ ⚙
Conference: 1 meeting room (Thtr 60 max)
Children: Welcome ⅄ Dogs: Welcome
Licenses: ⛟
Leisure: Outdoor pool, Snooker/billiards
Parking: Off-street and free
Directions: From Newton Abbott follow signs for Torquay, till Torre station, then signs to seafront to traffic lights. Turn left till next set of traffic lights, inside lane up the hill. Hotel on left hand side.
Map ref: Torquay 3 D3

The Marstan Hotel

◆◆◆◆◆ ⏍✕ ✎

Meadfoot Sea Road, Torquay, Devon, TQ1 2LQ
Tel: 01803 292837 Fax: 01803 299202
Email: enquiries@marstanhotel.co.uk
Web: www.marstanhotel.co.uk
Rooms: 10 all ensuite ⚃ ▣ ⊗
Dinner available
CC: Accepted
Room facilities: ▢ ☎ ⚙ ⚬
Conference: 2 meeting rooms (Thtr 50 max)
Children: Welcome ⏍
Licenses: ⛟
Leisure: Outdoor pool
Parking: Off-street and free
Directions: Follow A380 towards Torquay seafront, at seafront turn left, follow coastal road to second roundabout. Turn left onto Babbacombe Road, right at next traffic lights onto Meadfoot Sea Road, 1½ miles on right.
Map ref: Torquay 3 D3

Haytor Hotel

◆◆◆◆ ✕ ✎

Meadfoot Road, Torquay, Devon, TQ1 2JP
Tel: 01803 294708 Fax: 01803 292511
Email: enquiries@haytorhotel.com
Web: www.haytorhotel.com
Rooms: 15 all ensuite ▣ ⊗
Pricing: Sgl £50–60 Dbl £80–100
CC: Accepted
Room facilities: ▢ ☎ ⚙
Children: Welcome 12yrs min age
Licenses: ⛟
Parking: Off-street and free
Directions: Turn left at seafront past Princess Theatre. Head for inner harbour to clocktower roundabout. Turn left, then right at lights.
Map ref: Torquay 3 D3

Hotel Patricia

◆◆◆◆

64 Belgrave Road, Torquay, Devon, TQ2 5HY
Tel: 01803 293339
Email: info@hotel-patricia.co.uk
Web: www.hotel-patricia.co.uk

All rooms ensuite and non-smoking. Ideally situated
close to the beach, conference centre, marina, theatre,
shops and restaurants. Regret no facilities for babies,
children, teenagers or single sex groups.
Rooms: 10 all ensuite
Pricing: Sgl £28–35 Dbl £56–80
Dinner available from £15–18
CC: Accepted
Room facilities:
Licenses:
Leisure: Discount off-site leisure facilities
Directions: Turn into Belgrave Road from seafront; 600
metres on left-hand side.
Map ref: Torquay 3 D3

Lawnswood

◆◆◆◆

6 Scarborough Road, Torquay, Devon, TQ2 5UJ
Tel: 01803 403593
Rooms: 5 all ensuite
Pricing: Sgl £22–25 Dbl £44–50
Room facilities:
Children: Welcome
Parking: Off-street and free
Directions: Follow A380 into Torquay. Follow signs for
seafront. When in Belgrave Road, turn left after traffic
lights into Scarborough Road.
Map ref: Torquay 3 D3

Mount Nessing Hotel

◆◆◆◆

St Lukes Road North, Torquay, Devon, TQ2 5PD
Tel: 01803 294259
Email: mntnessing@hotmail.com
Web: www.english-riviera.co.uk/hotels/mount-nessing
Seasonal closure: November

A former Victorian villa, built in 1872, enjoying beautiful
views across Torbay from its elevated position.
Centrally located on a quiet tree-lined road close to
restaurants, bars, clubs and attractions.
Rooms: 13 all ensuite
Pricing: Sgl £22–35 Dbl £44–70
Dinner available from £11
CC: Accepted
Room facilities:
Children: Welcome 12yrs min age
Dogs: Assistance dogs only
Licenses:
Parking: Off-street and free
Directions: Entering Torquay head for sea front. Turn
left at sea front. Pass Belgrave Hotel, up Sheddon Hill.
Second road on right.
Map ref: Torquay 3 D3

The Exton

◆◆◆◆

12 Bridge Road, Torquay, Devon, TQ2 5BA
Tel: 01803 293561
Email: enquiries@extonhotel.co.uk
Web: www.extonhotel.co.uk
Rooms: 5 (4 ensuite)
Pricing: Sgl £22–28 Dbl £44–56
Dinner available from £13
CC: Accepted
Room facilities:
Children: Welcome
Licenses:
Parking: Off-street and free
Directions: Bear right at Torre station (Avenue Road).
Through lights, then left into Bampfylde, then first left
into Rowdens.
Map ref: Torquay 3 D3

Briarfields Hotel

◆◆◆

84-86 Avenue Road, Torquay, Devon, TQ2 5LF
Tel: 01803 297844
Email: briarfieldshotel@aol.com
Web: www.briarfields.co.uk
Seasonal closure: December
Rooms: 10 all ensuite
Pricing: Dbl £35–45
CC: Accepted
Room facilities: 🖵 🍵
Children: Welcome
Dogs: Welcome
Parking: Off-street and free
Directions: Approaching Torquay from Newton Abbot, bear right at the junction of Torre station and Halfords down Avenue Road. Hotel is halfway down on right.
Map ref: Torquay 3 D3

Devon Court Hotel

◆◆◆

Croft Road, Torquay, Devon, TQ2 5UE
Tel: 01803 293603 Fax: 01803 213660
Email: info@devoncourt.co.uk
Web: www.devoncourt.co.uk
Rooms: 15 (13 ensuite) 🍵 📺
Pricing: Sgl £34–52 Dbl £48–84 CC: Accepted
Room facilities: 🖵 🍵
Children: Welcome �📍 ⌖
Licenses: ⚏
Leisure: Outdoor pool
Parking: Off-street and free
Directions: From A380 follow signs to seafront, left at seafront, cross lights up Shedden Hill, first left into Croft Road.
Map ref: Torquay 3 D3

Totnes, Devon

The Royal Seven Stars Hotel

★★

The Plains, Totnes, Devon, TQ9 5DD
Tel: 01803 862125 Fax: 01803 867925
Email: enquiry@royalsevenstars.co.uk
Web: www.royalsevenstars.co.uk

17th century historic inn with a contemporary twist. Situated in the heart of Totnes – voted one of the funkiest towns in Europe. Excellent food, vintage cellars, riverside walks, guest parking.

Rooms: 15 all ensuite 📺 ⊛
Pricing: Dbl £65–114 Dinner available
CC: Accepted
Room facilities: 🖵 ☎ 🍵
Conference: 2 meeting rooms (Thtr 100 max), day-delegate from £27
Children: Welcome �📍
Dogs: Welcome
Licenses: ⚐ ⚏
Parking: Off-street and free
Directions: Follow signs for Totnes from A38 for 6 miles, then signs for town centre.
Map ref: Totnes 3 D3

Trevarrian, Cornwall

Kernow Trek Lodge

◆◆◆

Trevarrian, near Mawgan Porth, Cornwall, TR8 4AQ
Tel: 01637 860437 Fax: 01637 860437
Email: info@activityholidayscornwall.co.uk
Web: www.activityholidayscornwall.co.uk
Seasonal closure: January & February
Rooms: 8 (3 ensuite) 🍵 ⊛
CC: Accepted
Room facilities: 🖵 🍵
Conference: 1 meeting room (Thtr 23 max)
Children: Welcome
Dogs: Welcome
Parking: Off-street and free
Directions: Follow signs to Newquay airport. Past airport turn right at T-junction and follow road to Trevarrian. Turn left into village.
Map ref: Trevarrian 2 B3

Trowbridge, Wiltshire

Hilbury Court

★★

Hilperton Road, Trowbridge, Wiltshire , BA14 7JW
Tel: 01225 752949 Fax: 01225 777990
Email: info@hilburycourt.co.uk
Web: www.hilburycourt.co.uk
Rooms: 14 all ensuite 📺 ⊛
Pricing: Sgl £45–50 Dbl £65–75
Dinner available from £8–16
CC: Accepted
Room facilities: 🖵 ☎ 🍵 🔌
Children: Welcome �📍
Dogs: Welcome
Licenses: ⚏
Parking: Off-street and free
Directions: Hilbury Court is on the A361 Trowbridge to Devizes Road.
Map ref: Trowbridge 3 F2

Bridge House Bed and Breakfast

Bridge House, Canal Bridge, Semington, Trowbridge,
Wiltshire, BA14 6JT
Tel: 01225 706101 Fax: 01225 790892
Email: jeanpaynedhps@aol.com
Rooms: 4 ⊗
Room facilities: ▢ ☕
Children: Welcome 5yrs min age
Parking: Off-street and free
Directions: Come off A361 at Semington Roundabout.
Proceed through village and over canal bridge. Bridge
House Bed and Breakfast is on right-hand side.
Map ref: Semington 3 F1

Truro, Cornwall

Nare Hotel

★★★★★ ♛♛♛

Excellent

Carne Beach, Veryan-In-Roseland,
Truro, Cornwall, TR2 5PF
Tel: 01872 501111 Fax: 01872 501856
Email: office@narehotel.co.uk
Web: www.narehotel.co.uk

Peace, tranquility and stunning seaviews are what
make The Nare such a find. It is considered by many
to be the most comfortable hotel in Cornwall,
attributable to the increasingly rare, unobtrusive,
traditional service and country house charm.
Rooms: 39 all ensuite ⊛
Pricing: Sgl £85–185 Dbl £180–570
Dinner available from £38
CC: Accepted
Room facilities: ▢ ☎ ☕
Access: ⓵
Children: Welcome ☂ ☕
Dogs: Welcome
Licenses: ♟
Leisure: Indoor pool, Outdoor pool, Gym, Health spa,
Beauty salon, Tennis, Snooker/billiards, Croquet
Parking: Off-street and free
Directions: From M5 and A30, 8 miles after Bodmin
B3275. Turn right 2 miles after Ladock for Truro, then
left towards St Mawes. Right onto A3078, over
Tregony bridge, left after 1½ miles for Veryan. Hotel 1
mile beyond village.
Map ref: Carne Beach 2 B4

Alverton Manor

★★★★ ♛♛

Tregolls Road, Truro, Cornwall, TR1 1ZQ
Tel: 01872 276633 Fax: 01872 222989
Email: reception@alvertonmanor.co.uk

A 10-minute walk from the city, the Alverton Manor
rises majestically within its immaculate surroundings.
Its 33 ensuite rooms have been individually designed
to provide style and luxury with the modern comforts
you would expect. The award-winning restaurant offers
a welcoming and relaxing ambience, serving English
cuisine using the finest Cornish produce.
Rooms: 33 all ensuite ⊛ ▨ ⊗
Pricing: Sgl £75 Dbl £125–140
Dinner available from £29.50 CC: Accepted
Room facilities: ▢ ☎ ☕ ☏ Access: ⓵
Conference: 8 meeting rooms (Thtr 100 max),
24hr-delegate from £120, day-delegate from £30
Children: Welcome ☂ Dogs: Welcome
Licenses: ⚒ ♟
Leisure: Golf, Fishing
Parking: Off-street and free
Directions: Take M5 south-west to Exeter, then A30 for
Oakhampton, leading to A39 into Truro, Alverton
Manor on the right.
Map ref: Truro 2 B4

The Brookdale Hotel

★★★

Tregolls Road, Truro, Cornwall, TR1 1JZ
Tel: 01872 273513 Fax: 01872 272400
Email: brookdale@hotelstruro.com
Web: www.hotelstruro.com
Rooms: 30 all ensuite ⊛ ⊗
Dinner available
CC: Accepted
Room facilities: ▢ ☎ ☕ ☏
Conference: 3 meeting rooms (Thtr 75 max)
Children: Welcome ☂ ☕
Dogs: Welcome
Licenses: ♟
Parking: Off-street and free
Directions: On A39 approach road into Truro, at lower
end of Tregolls Road, 250 metres to the east of the
roundabout.
Map ref: Truro 2 B4

The Lugger Hotel

★★★★
Excellent

Portloe, Truro, Cornwall, TR2 5RD
Tel: 01872 501322 Fax: 01872 501691
Email: office@luggerhotel.com
Web: www.luggerhotel.com
Rooms: 21 all ensuite
Pricing: Sgl £125–220 Dbl £150–340
Dinner available from £37.50 CC: Accepted
Room facilities: 🖵 ☎ ☕
Children: Welcome 12yrs min age
Licenses: ⚲
Leisure: Health spa, Beauty salon
Parking: Off-street and free
Directions: M5 A30 or A38 A390 left to Tregony B3287
A3078 Veryan left Portloe. Air: Gatwick/Stansted to
Newquay.
Map ref: Portloe 2 B4

Carlton Hotel

★★

Falmouth Road, Truro, Cornwall, TR1 2HL
Tel: 01872 272450 Fax: 01872 223938
Email: reception@carltonhotel.co.uk
Web: www.carltonhotel.co.uk
Seasonal closure: 16 December to 2 January
Rooms: 29 all ensuite ☕ ⊗
Pricing: Sgl £42.50–50 Dbl £60–70
Dinner available from £12.95
CC: Accepted
Room facilities: 🖵 ☎ ☕
Conference: 3 meeting rooms (Thtr 60 max)
Children: Welcome ⼁
Dogs: Welcome
Licenses: ⚲
Leisure: Health spa, Sauna
Parking: Off-street and free
Directions: Take A39 to Truro. Proceed across two
roundabouts onto bypass. At top of hill, turn right into
Falmouth Road. Hotel is 100 metres on right.
Map ref: Truro 2 B4

Townhouse Rooms & Breakfast

♦♦♦♦

20 Falmouth Road, Truro, Cornwall, TR1 2HX
Tel: 01872 277374 Fax: 01872 241666
Email: info@trurohotels.com
Web: www.trurohotels.com
Rooms: 14 all ensuite ☕ ⊿ ⊗
Pricing: Sgl £25–55 Dbl £65–75
CC: Accepted
Room facilities: 🖵 ☕
Children: Welcome
Dogs: Welcome
Licenses: ⚲
Parking: Off-street and free
Directions: Approach Truro A39. Turn right at traffic
lights onto Tregolls Road. Second roundabout take
second exit. Double roundabout turn right. Hotel is on
left down the hill.
Map ref: Truro 2 B4

The Donnington Guest House

♦♦♦

43 Treyew Road, Truro, Cornwall, TR1 2BY
Tel: 01872 222552
Email: eathorne-gibbons@donnington-
guesthouse.co.uk
Web: www.donnington-guesthouse.co.uk
Rooms: 5 (3 ensuite) ⊗
Pricing: Sgl £25–40 Dbl £50–65
Dinner available
Room facilities: 🖵 ☕
Access: |↓↑
Children: Welcome ⼁ 🐎 ⼁
Dogs: Welcome
Parking: Off-street and free
Directions: Opposite football club, near Sainsbury's.
From station, up hill to Sainsbury's, turn left and
proceed 300 yards.
Map ref: Truro 2 B4

The Bay Tree

♦♦

28 Ferris Town, Truro, Cornwall, TR1 3JH
Tel: 01872 240274
Web: www.baytree-guesthouse.co.uk
Rooms: 4 ☕ ⊗
Pricing: Sgl £25–30 Dbl £38–40
Room facilities: 🖵 ☕
Children: Welcome
Dogs: Welcome
Directions: 5 minutes from railway station, 6 minutes
from bus station. If driving, 5 minutes from M5
roundabout, turn right at second roundabout. Straight
over at end of Fairmantle Street, right at small
roundabout, guest house on left.
Map ref: Truro 2 B4

Ice & slice?

RAC's comprehensive
inspection means we
even check drinks are
served the way you want.

"I do!"

Want a honeymoon
hotel? Look for our
Gold, Blue, and
White Ribbon Award
winning hotels.

Southwest

Umberleigh, Devon

Northcote Manor Hotel

★★★★ ♖♖

Burrington, near Umberleigh, Devon, EX37 9LZ
Tel: 01769 560501 Fax: 01769 560770
Email: rest@northcotemanor.co.uk
Web: www.northcotemanor.co.uk

The 18th century Manor and the grounds located high above the Taw River Valley offer an atmosphere of timeless tranquility. Professional, attentive but unobtrusive service with excellent food is what Northcote Manor aims to provide. Awarded 3 AA red stars and 2 AA red rosettes.
Rooms: 11 all ensuite 🖨 ⊗
Pricing: Sgl £100–170 Dbl £150–250
Dinner available from £38 CC: Accepted
Room facilities: 📺 ☎
Children: Welcome 10yrs min age Dogs: Welcome
Licenses: ⟐ ♦♦♦
Leisure: Tennis, Croquet
Parking: Off-street and free
Directions: Do not enter Burrington village: Entrance to Northcote estate is on main A377 Barnstaple/Exeter road opposite Portsmouth Arms Pub and railway station.
Map ref: Burrington 2 C2

Rising Sun Inn

★★★ ♖♖

Umberleigh, near Barnstaple,
North Devon, EX37 9DU
Tel: 01769 560447 Fax: 01769 560764
Email: therisingsuninn@btopenworld.com
Web: www.risingsuninn.com
Rooms: 8 all ensuite 🐾 ⊗
Pricing: Sgl £46–49 Dbl £75–85 Dinner available
CC: Accepted
Room facilities: 📺 ☎ 🍵
Conference: 2 meeting rooms (Thtr 70 max),
24hr-delegate from £40, day-delegate from £25
Children: Welcome ♍ Dogs: Welcome
Licenses: ⟐ ♦♦♦
Leisure: Fishing
Parking: Off-street and free
Directions: Junction of A377 and B3227, opposite Umberleigh Bridge.
Map ref: Umberleigh 2 C2

Wadebridge, Cornwall

Roskarnon House Hotel

◆◆◆

Rock, near Wadebridge, Cornwall, PL27 6LD
Tel: 01208 862785
Seasonal closure: October to March
Rooms: 12 (10 ensuite)
Dinner available CC: Accepted
Room facilities: 📺 🍵
Children: Welcome ♍ Licenses: ♦♦♦
Parking: Off-street and free
Directions: From Wadebridge, follow road to Rock, Trebetherick, Polzeath and then to St Enodoc golf course. Hotel situated on road to golf course.
Map ref: Rock 2 B3

Wareham, Dorset

Priory Hotel

★★★★ ♖♖♖

Church Green, Wareham, Dorset, BH20 4ND
Tel: 01929 551666 Fax: 01929 554519
Email: reservations@theprioryhotel.co.uk
Web: www.theprioryhotel.co.uk

The Priory
country house hotel
and restaurant

Somewhere very special indeed

16th century former priory, nestled on the banks of the River Frome, where peace and tranquility prevail. Charming bedrooms and suites are complemented by fine food and wine, and superb, yet unobtrusive, standards of service.
Rooms: 18 all ensuite 🖨
Pricing: Sgl £110–125 Dbl £170–230
Dinner available from £35 CC: Accepted
Room facilities: 📺 ☎ 🍵 🔌
Conference: 1 meeting room (Thtr 24 max)
Children: Welcome 14yrs min age
Licenses: ♦♦♦
Parking: Off-street and free
Directions: Wareham is on the A351 to the west of Poole: hotel is at southern end of town between church and river.
Map ref: Wareham 3 F3

Springfield Country Hotel

★★★

Grange Road, Stoborough, Wareham, Dorset, BH20 5AL
Tel: 01929 552177 Fax: 01929 551862
Email: enquiries@springfield-country-hotel.co.uk
Web: www.springfield-country-hotel.co.uk
Rooms: 50 all ensuite
Pricing: Sgl £77–97 Dbl £120–160
Dinner available from £22.50
CC: Accepted
Room facilities: 📺 ☎ 🍵 📞
Access: ⬆
Conference: 12 meeting rooms (Thtr 200 max)
Children: Welcome ╥
Dogs: Welcome
Licenses: ⛟
Leisure: Indoor pool, Outdoor pool, Gym, Health spa, Beauty salon, Tennis, Games room, Snooker/billiards, Sauna, Spa bath
Parking: Off-street and free
Directions: A35 towards Wareham. At end of dual carriageway, 1st exit off roundabout (A351). At roundabout just outside Wareham, take 2nd exit. Straight over next roundabout. After ³/₄ mile turn right.
Map ref: Stoborough 3 F3

The Old Granary

◆◆◆◆ 🍴 🍷

West Holme Farm, Wareham, Dorset, BH20 6AQ
Tel: 01929 552972 Fax: 01929 551616
Email: venngoldsack@lineone.net
Web: www.theoldgranarybandb.co.uk

We particularly welcome those interested in birdwatching, walking and gardening to this interesting, comfortable barn conversion. Both rooms are twin-bedded and one is on the ground floor, suitable for less able guests.
Rooms: 2 all ensuite
Pricing: Dbl £60–70
Dinner available from £12.50
CC: Accepted
Room facilities: 📺 🍵
Parking: Off-street and free
Directions: A352 west from Wareham bypass, take B3070 for ¹/₂ mile. Turn left into 'Holme Nurseries'. House on right.
Map ref: Wareham 3 F3

Warminster, Wiltshire

Bishopstrow House & Spa

★★★★ 🍴🍴

Boreham Road, Warminster, Wiltshire, BA12 9HH
Tel: 01985 212312 Fax: 01985 216769
Email: info@bishopstrow.co.uk
Web: www.bishopstrow.co.uk
Rooms: 32 all ensuite
Dinner available
CC: Accepted
Room facilities: 📺 ☎ 📞
Conference: 4 meeting rooms (Thtr 80 max)
Children: Welcome ╥ 🍼
Dogs: Welcome
Licenses: ⚓ ⛟
Leisure: Indoor pool, Outdoor pool, Gym, Health spa, Beauty salon, Tennis, Fishing
Parking: Off-street and free
Directions: A303 A36 B3414, premises 2 miles on right.
Map ref: Warminster 3 F2

The George Inn

◆◆◆◆ 🍴🍷

Longbridge Deverill, Warminster, Wiltshire, BA12 7DG
Tel: 01985 840396 Fax: 01985 841333
Web: www.thegeorgeinnlongbridgedeverill.co.uk
Rooms: 11 all ensuite
Pricing: Sgl £55 Dbl £75
Dinner available from £7.95
CC: Accepted
Room facilities: 📺 ☎ 🍵
Conference: 1 meeting room (Thtr 100 max), 24hr-delegate from £70, day-delegate from £25
Children: Welcome ╥
Licenses: ⛟
Directions: Hotel is on the main A350 from Sailsbury, follow A36 then A350 Blandford. From London A303 then A350 to Warminister.
Map ref: Longbridge Deverill 3 F2

Southwest

Wells, Somerset

White Hart Hotel

★★

Sadler Street, Wells, Somerset, BA5 2RR
Tel: 01749 672056 Fax: 01749 671074
Email: info@whitehart-wells.co.uk
Web: www.whitehart-wells.co.uk

15th-century coaching hotel, situated directly opposite
Wells Cathedral, offering comfortable accommodation
and fine English food. Open fires and an ideal location
make this family-run hotel an excellent choice.
Rooms: 15 all ensuite 🛁 ⊗
Pricing: Sgl £78–83 Dbl £99–110
Dinner available from £19.50 CC: Accepted
Room facilities: 🖥 ☎ ☕ 🔌
Conference: 2 meeting rooms (Thtr 100 max),
24hr-delegate from £99, day-delegate from £20
Children: Welcome � ☕ Dogs: Welcome
Licenses: ◇ ♟
Parking: Off-street and free
Directions: Approaching Wells, follow signs for Hotels
and Deliveries. Hotel is the first one on the right as you
enter Wells.
Map ref: Wells 3 E2

Willow Bridge Farms Country Guest House

◆◆◆◆◆ ☙

Godney, Wells, Somerset, BA5 1RZ
Tel: 01458 835371 Fax: 01458 834885
Email: julie@willowbridgefarm.co.uk
Web: www.willowbridgefarm.co.uk
Seasonal closure: 2 weeks over Christmas

We are a working beef farm situated on the banks of
the River Sheppey enabling you to enjoy the peace
and tranquility of the Somerset Levels. AA 5 diamonds
and South West Tourism 5 diamonds and Silver
accolade.
Rooms: 5 all ensuite 🛁 ⊗
Pricing: Sgl £45 Dbl £65 CC: Accepted
Room facilities: 🖥 ☕ Children: Welcome � ☕
Parking: Off-street and free
Directions: From Glastonbury head for Godney. Follow
river, Guest House first bridge on left over river.
Map ref: Godney 3 E2

Double Gate Farm

◆◆◆◆ ✗☯ ☙

Godney, Wells, Somerset, BA5 1RX
Tel: 01458 832217 Fax: 01458 835612
Email: doublegatefarm@aol.com
Web: www.doublegatefarm.com
Seasonal closure: Christmas to New Year

Award-winning farmhouse accommodation — outdoor,
sunshine breakfasts in summertime — includes home-
made bread and local produce. Ideally situated for
sightseeing, walking and cycling. Two Golden
Retrievers and two mischievous moggies! M3 access
and facilities for the disabled.
Rooms: 6 all ensuite 🛁 ⊗
Pricing: Sgl £45–50 Dbl £60–65
CC: Accepted
Room facilities: 🖥 ☕
Children: Welcome
Leisure: Fishing, Games room, Snooker/billiards
Parking: Off-street and free
Directions: From Wells take A39 south. At Polsham
turn right. Continue approx 3 miles. Farmhouse on left.
Map ref: Godney 3 E2

Crossways Hotel

◆◆◆

Stocks Lane, North Wootton,
near Wells, Somerset, BA4 4EU
Tel: 01749 899000 Fax: 01749 890476
Email: enquiries@thecrossways.co.uk
Web: www.thecrossways.co.uk
Rooms: 21 all ensuite 🛁 📺
Pricing: Sgl £50–60 Dbl £70–110
Dinner available from £3.75–14.50
CC: Accepted

Room facilities:
Conference: 2 meeting rooms (Thtr 100 max)
Children: Welcome ⍾
Licenses: ⌂ ⁂
Leisure: Games room, Snooker/billiards
Parking: Off-street and free
Directions: From Bristol, take A37 to Shepton Mallet, then follow A361. Situated centrally between Glastonbury, Wells and Shepton Mallet.
Map ref: North Wootton 3 E2

West Tytherley, Wiltshire

The Black Horse Inn

◆◆◆

The Village, West Tytherley, Salisbury, Wiltshire, SP5 1NF
Tel: 01794 340308
Rooms: 2 ⊗
Pricing: Sgl £30–40 Dbl £40–50
Dinner available from £5
CC: Accepted
Room facilities: ☐ ⌧
Children: Welcome ⍾
Dogs: Welcome
Licenses: ⁂
Leisure: Snooker/billiards
Parking: Off-street and free
Directions: A30 from Salisbury towards Stockbridge. Turn right through the Winterslows. Left down into village of West Tytherley. Pub on right.
Map ref: West Tytherley 4 B3

Weston-Super-Mare, Somerset

Beachlands Hotel

★★★

17 Uphill Road North,
Weston-Super-Mare, Somerset, BS23 4NG
Tel: 01934 621401 Fax: 01934 621966
Email: info@beachlandshotel.com
Web: www.beachlandshotel.com
Seasonal closure: 23 December to 3 January

This delightful family-run hotel, situated overlooking the 18-hole golf course, only 300 yards from the sandy beach, benefits from ample parking and an indoor heated swimming pool and sauna.

Rooms: 23 all ensuite ⍾ ⊗
Pricing: Sgl £42.50–77.50 Dbl £85–107.50
Dinner available from £14.50–21
CC: Accepted
Room facilities: ☐ ☎ ⌧ ☏
Conference: 2 meeting rooms (Thtr 50 max), 24hr-delegate from £93.50, day-delegate from £20
Children: Welcome ⍾ ☽
Licenses: ⌂ ⁂
Leisure: Indoor pool, Sauna
Parking: Off-street and free
Directions: From Junction 21 on M5, follow signs for beach. Hotel is 6½ miles from exit, overlooking golf course 200 yards before beach.
Map ref: Weston-Super-Mare 3 E1

Arosfa

★★

Lower Church Road,
Weston-Super-Mare, Somerset, BS23 2AG
Tel: 01934 419523 Fax: 01934 636084
Email: reception@arosfahotel.co.uk
Web: www.arosfahotel.co.uk
Rooms: 46 all ensuite ⍾ ⊗
Pricing: Sgl £40–45 Dbl £70–75
Dinner available from £19
CC: Accepted
Room facilities: ☐ ☎ ⌧
Access: �|↕
Conference: 4 meeting rooms (Thtr 100 max), 24hr-delegate from £75, day-delegate from £25
Children: Welcome ⍾ ☽
Dogs: Welcome
Licenses: ⁂
Parking: Off-street and free
Directions: From seafront take first right past Winter Gardens; Hotel is 100m on left beyond the college.
Map ref: Weston-Super-Mare 3 E1

Dauncey's Hotel

★★

Claremont Crescent,
Weston-Super-Mare, Somerset, BS23 2ED
Tel: 01934 410180 Fax: 01934 410181
Email: reservations@daunceyshotel.fsnet.co.uk
Web: www.daunceyshotel.co.uk
Rooms: 74 all ensuite ⍾
Pricing: Sgl £41–45 Dbl £82–90
Dinner available from £16
CC: Accepted
Room facilities: ☐ ⌧
Access: ⁂↕
Conference: 5 meeting rooms (Thtr 50 max)
Children: Welcome ⍾
Dogs: Welcome
Licenses: ⁂
Leisure: Games room
Directions: Situated at the north end of the promenade, in a Victorian crescent.
Map ref: Weston-Super-Mare 3 E1

Queenswood

Victoria Park, Weston-Super-Mare,
Somerset, BS23 2HZ
Tel: 01934 416141 Fax: 01934 621759
Email: stay@queenswoodhotel.com
Web: www.queenswoodhotel.com
Seasonal closure: Christmas and New Year
Rooms: 19 all ensuite
Pricing: Sgl £55 Dbl £80
Dinner available from £19.50
CC: Accepted
Room facilities:
Conference: 2 meeting rooms (Thtr 25 max)
Children: Welcome
Dogs: Welcome
Licenses:
Parking: Off-street and free
Directions: From Grand Pier with sea on left. First right
at Cabot Bars. First left at College, second right after
church.
Map ref: Weston-Super-Mare 3 E1

Oakover Guest House

25 Clevedon Road, Weston-Super-Mare,
Somerset, BS23 1DA
Tel: 01934 620125
Email: info@oakover.co.uk
Web: www.oakover.co.uk

Recently refurbished, Oakover combines warm
hospitality, traditional features and modern facilities.
Perfect for both business and leisure visitors. Stylish
and elegantly furnished, large bedrooms designed for
ultimate comfort and relaxation.
Rooms: 6 all ensuite
Pricing: Sgl £23–42 Dbl £46–56
CC: Accepted
Room facilities:
Parking: Off-street and free
Directions: M5 J21, follow dual carriageway straight
across four roundabouts. Fifth roundabout (gasworks),
turn left, then second right (Brighton Road) follows into
Clevedon Road.
Map ref: Weston-Super-Mare 3 E1

The Grove

43 Grove Road, Milton, Weston-Super-Mare,
Somerset, BS22 8HF
Tel: 01934 612868 Fax: 01934 429737
Email: thegrove@weston-super-mare.net
Web: www.weston-super-mare.net
Rooms: 4 (3 ensuite)
Dinner available
Room facilities:
Children: Welcome
Parking: Off-street and free
Directions: M5 J21 onto A370 (WSM) immediately left
(B3440) 1½ miles right at roundabout, left at lights, first
right into Grove Road.
Map ref: Milton 3 E1

Wychwood Hotel

148 Milton Road, Weston-Super-Mare,
Somerset, BS23 2UZ
Tel: 01934 627793
Rooms: 9 all ensuite
Pricing: Sgl £30–32 Dbl £50–52
Dinner available from £14
CC: Accepted
Room facilities:
Children: Welcome 4yrs min age
Licenses:
Leisure: Outdoor pool
Parking: Off-street and free
Directions: From Junction 21 of M5, follow signs for
town centre. Take third exit at fifth roundabout and at
second traffic lights turn right into Milton Road — hotel
400 yards on right.
Map ref: Weston-Super-Mare 3 E1

Linden Lodge Guest House

27 Clevedon Road, Weston-Super-Mare,
Somerset, BS23 1DA
Tel: 01934 645797
Rooms: 5 all ensuite
Pricing: Sgl £25–35 Dbl £40–54
CC: Accepted
Room facilities:
Children: Welcome 8yrs min age
Parking: Off-street and free
Directions: Follow signs to seafront. Half mile south of
Grand Pier turn into Clevedon Road. Hotel on left just
before lights.
Map ref: Weston-Super-Mare 3 E1

Sunfold Hotel

39 Beach Road, Weston-Super-Mare,
Somerset, BS23 1BG
Tel: 01934 624700 Fax: 01934 624700
Email: enquiries@sunfold-hotel.co.uk
Web: www.sunfold-hotel-co.uk
Seasonal closure: 20 December to 5 January

Family run hotel. Comfortable and friendly service.
Seafront location. Well equipped rooms all ensuite.
Enjoy a meal and a drink in our restaurant and bar or
relax in our sea view lounge.
Rooms: 11 all ensuite
Pricing: Sgl £40–45 Dbl £48–65
Dinner available from £9
CC: Accepted
Room facilities:
Children: Welcome
Dogs: Welcome
Licenses:
Parking: Off-street and free
Directions: Weston-Super-Mare is located on junction
21 of the M5. Follow signs for seafront, Sunfold is
almost opposite the Sea Life Centre.
Map ref: Weston-Super-Mare 3 E1

Weymouth, Dorset

Best Western Hotel Prince Regent

139 The Esplanade, Weymouth, Dorset, DT4 7NR
Tel: 01305 771313 Fax: 01305 778100
Email: info@princeregentweymouth.co.uk
Web: www.princeregentweymouth.co.uk

Newly refurbished seafront hotel with magnificent views
of the bay and coastline. A short level stroll to the town
centre and attractions. A good base to explore Dorset.
Rooms: 70 all ensuite
Pricing: Sgl £49–79 Dbl £59–130
Dinner available from £16 CC: Accepted
Room facilities: Access:
Conference: 4 meeting rooms (Thtr 150 max),
24hr-delegate from £79, day-delegate from £21
Children: Welcome
Licenses:
Parking: Off-street
Directions: At Dorchester, take A354 for Weymouth.
Follow signs for town centre. Turn left at clock tower
and proceed along Esplanade.
Map ref: Weymouth 3 E3

Sleep easy

Rest assured. Our
comprehensive
inspection process
includes checking
beds are comfortable.

"Stay!"

Need a pet friendly property?
Look out for 'Dogs welcome' in
our listings.

Hotel Rembrandt

★★★

12-18 Dorchester Road, Weymouth, Dorset, DT4 7JU
Tel: 01305 764000 Fax: 01305 764022
Email: reception@hotelrembrandt.co.uk
Web: www.hotelrembrandt.co.uk
Rooms: 75 all ensuite 🛏 🖭 ⊗
Pricing: Sgl £62.50–83 Dbl £85
Dinner available from £15.95 CC: Accepted
Room facilities: 💻 ☎ ☕ Access: ⬇
Conference: 6 meeting rooms (Thtr 200 max),
24hr-delegate from £98, day-delegate from £22
Children: Welcome ⱦ 🌡
Dogs: Welcome
Licenses: ⬥ ⁂
Leisure: Indoor pool, Gym
Parking: Off-street and free
Directions: From Dorchester, along A354, straight on at
Manor roundabout (by Safeway). Hotel ¾ mile on left,
800 yards from seafront.
Map ref: Weymouth 3 E3

Hotel Rex

★★★

29 The Esplanade, Weymouth, Dorset, DT4 8DN
Tel: 01305 760400 Fax: 01305 760500
Email: rex@kingshotels.f9.co.uk
Web: www.kingshotel.co.uk
Rooms: 31 all ensuite 🛏 🖭
Pricing: Dinner available from £13.75 CC: Accepted
Room facilities: 💻 ☎ ☕
Access: ⬇
Conference: 1 meeting room (Thtr 35 max),
24hr-delegate from £68, day-delegate from £17
Children: Welcome ⱦ
Dogs: Welcome
Licenses: ⁂
Parking: Off-street
Directions: Take A354 to Weymouth. Head towards
seafront. Follow signs towards ferry and harbour. The
Rex overlooks beach and harbour.
Map ref: Weymouth 3 E3

Central Hotel

★★

15 Maiden Street, Weymouth, Dorset, DT4 8BB
Tel: 01305 760700 Fax: 01305 760300
Email: central@kingshotels.co.uk
Web: www.kingshotels.co.uk
Seasonal closure: 15 December to 2 March
Rooms: 29 all ensuite
Pricing: Sgl £46–48 Dbl £78–80
Dinner available from £9.50 CC: Accepted
Room facilities: 💻 ☕ Access: ⬇
Children: Welcome ⱦ
Licenses: ⁂
Parking: Off-street
Directions: Take A354 from Dorchester. Head for
seafront. At Marks & Spencer, take small road called
New Street to rear of hotel.
Map ref: Weymouth 3 E3

Crown Hotel

★★

51/52 St Thomas Street, Weymouth, Dorset, DT4 8EQ
Tel: 01305 760800 Fax: 01305 760300
Email: crown@kingshotels.co.uk
Web: www.kingshotels.co.uk
Rooms: 86 all ensuite 🛏
Pricing: Sgl £43–47 Dbl £80–88
Dinner available from £10
CC: Accepted
Room facilities: 💻 ☎ ☕
Access: ⬇
Children: Welcome ⱦ
Licenses: ⁂
Parking: Off-street
Directions: From Dorchester, take the A354 to
Weymouth. When you reach the back water on the left,
follow this. Take the second bridge over the water.
Crown Hotel is on left.
Map ref: Weymouth 3 E3

Fairhaven Hotel

★★

37 The Esplanade, Weymouth, Dorset, DT4 8DH
Tel: 01305 760200 Fax: 01305 760300
Email: fairhaven@kingshotels.co.uk
Web: www.kingshotels.co.uk
Seasonal closure: November to March
Rooms: 90 all ensuite 🛏
Pricing: Sgl £46–48 Dbl £78–80
Dinner available from £10
CC: Accepted
Room facilities: 💻 ☎ ☕
Access: ⬇
Children: Welcome ⱦ
Licenses: ⁂
Leisure: Games room
Parking: Off-street
Directions: Take A354 to Weymouth. Head towards
seafront. Follow signs towards Ferry. Fairhaven Hotel
is 200 yards before ferry terminal.
Map ref: Weymouth 3 E3

Russell Hotel

★★

135-138 The Esplanade, Weymouth, Dorset, DT4 7NG
Tel: 01305 786059 Fax: 01305 775723
Rooms: 93 all ensuite ⊗
Pricing: Sgl £31–45.50 Dbl £27–50.50
Dinner available from £9
CC: Accepted
Room facilities: 💻 ☎ ☕
Access: ⬇
Licenses: ⁂
Parking: Off-street
Directions: At Dorchester, take A354 for Weymouth.
Follow signs for town centre. Turn left at clock tower
and proceed along esplanade.
Map ref: Weymouth 3 E3

The Chandlers Hotel

4 Westerhall Road, Weymouth, Dorset, DT4 7SZ
Tel: 01305 771341 Fax: 01305 830122
Email: debbiesare@chandlershotel.com
Web: www.chandlershotel.com

The highest rated guest accommodation provider in
Weymouth, the hotel is a unique port of call where
great attention has been paid to the quality of the
furnishings. 100 yards from the seafront, parking for all
guests, free broadband internet connection in all
bedrooms, single occupancy welcomed.
Rooms: 9 all ensuite
Pricing: Sgl £50–65 Dbl £75–120
CC: Accepted
Room facilities:
Children: Welcome
Licenses:
Parking: Off-street and free
Directions: Follow A354 from Dorchester to the Manor
Roundabout. Then take first exit to Dorchester Road.
Follow to end into Westerhall Road. Take right-hand
lane and Chandlers is on right.
Map ref: Weymouth 3 E3

Are the bells ringing?

Getting married? Congratulations!
Look for the wedding bells symbol
which shows hotels licensed for
civil ceremonies.

Westwey Hotel

62 Abbotsbury Road, Weymouth, Dorset, DT4 0BJ
Tel: 01305 784564 Fax: 01305 770920
Email: stay@westweyhotel.co.uk
Web: www.westweyhotel.co.uk

Small family run hotel personally supervised by the
resident proprietors. Situated a short walking distance
from beach and town centre of Weymouth. Westwey
Hotel pride themselves on a relaxed atmosphere with
excellent services and surroundings.
Rooms: 7 all ensuite
Pricing: Sgl £30–45 Dbl £55–90
CC: Accepted
Room facilities:
Children: Welcome
Licenses:
Parking: Off-street and free
Directions: Take A354 into Weymouth. At Manor
roundabout take third exit, at Chafeys roundabout take
first exit. Third exit on Westham roundabout.
Map ref: Weymouth 3 E3

Sandcombe Hotel

8 The Esplanade, Weymouth, Dorset, DT4 8EB
Tel: 01305 786833
Email: ann.mcveigh@virgin.net
Web: www.resort-guide.co.uk/sandcombe or
www.sandcombehotel.co.uk
Rooms: 9 (5 ensuite)
Pricing: Sgl £27 Dbl £54
Room facilities:
Children: Welcome 5yrs min age
Licenses:
Directions: Located on Esplanade between beach and
harbour. Near to Pavilion Theatre and Condor ferry port.
Map ref: Weymouth 3 E3

The Concorde Hotel

131 The Esplanade, Weymouth, Dorset, DT4 7EY
Tel: 01035 776900 Fax: 01305 776900
Email: sunbeaml@gotadsl.co.uk
Web: www.theconcordehotel.co.uk
Seasonal closure: January
Rooms: 14 all ensuite
Pricing: Dbl £54–70
CC: Accepted
Room facilities:
Children: Welcome
Dogs: Assistance dogs only
Licenses:
Leisure: TV lounge, Bar
Parking: Off-street and free
Map ref: Weymouth 3 E3

Weymouth Sands Hotel

5 The Esplanade, Weymouth, Dorset, DT4 8EA
Tel: 01305 839022
Email: enquiries@weymouthsands.co.uk
Web: www.weymouthsands.co.uk
Rooms: 9 (6 ensuite)
Pricing: Sgl £26–28 Dbl £27–31
CC: Accepted
Room facilities:
Children: Welcome
Directions: Take A354 to Weymouth. Follow signs for
Channel Ferry. Weymouth Sands is opposite the
Pavilion Theatre and Ferry Terminal.
Map ref: Weymouth 3 E3

Williton, Somerset

Stilegate Bed & Breakfast

Staple Close, West Quantoxhead,
Williton, Taunton, Somerset, TA4 4DN
Tel: 01984 639119 Fax: 01984 639119
Email: stilegate@aol.com
Web: www.stilegate.co.uk
Seasonal closure: January
Rooms: 3 all ensuite
Pricing: Sgl £30–50 Dbl £50–70
CC: Accepted
Room facilities:
Children: Welcome 10yrs min age
Dogs: Welcome
Parking: Off-street and free
Directions: Take A39 from Bridgwater to Minehead.
First left past Windmill public house, through West
Quantoxhead. Second right into Staple Lane, first right
into Staple Close. Stilegate in far left corner down
short driveway.
Map ref: West Quantoxhead 3 D2

Wimborne, Dorset

Bless this Nest B&B

21 Moorside Road, Corfe Mullen, Wimborne,
Dorset, BH21 2NB
Tel: 01202 602534
Email: janetc@gotadsl.co.uk
Web: www.blessthisnest.co.uk
Rooms: 4 (1 ensuite)
Pricing: Sgl 25–35 Dbl 50–60
Room facilities:
Leisure: Outdoor pool, Putting Green
Parking: Off-street and free
Directions: Leaving Wimborne over Julian's Bridge,
straight over three roundabouts. Continue on Wareham
Road quarter of a mile further Moorside Road on right.
Map ref: Corfe Mullen 3 F3

Wincanton, Somerset

Holbrook House Hotel

Wincanton, Somerset, BA9 8BS
Tel: 01963 824466 Fax: 01963 32681
Email: enquiries@holbrookhouse.co.uk
Web: www.holbrookhouse.co.uk
Rooms: 21 all ensuite
Dinner available CC: Accepted
Room facilities:
Conference: 3 meeting rooms (Thtr 160 max)
Children: Welcome
Licenses:
Leisure: Indoor pool, Gym, Health spa,
Beauty salon, Tennis
Parking: Off-street and free
Directions: From A303 exit at Wincanton, Castle Cary
A371, follow signs to Holbrook House Hotel, nearest
railway station Castle Cary.
Map ref: Wincanton 3 F2

Winsford, Somerset

Royal Oak Inn

Exmoor National Park, Winsford, Somerset, TA24 7JE
Tel: 01643 851455 Fax: 01643 851009
Email: enquiries@royaloak-somerset.co.uk
Web: www.royaloak-somerset.co.uk
Rooms: 10 all ensuite
Pricing: Dinner available from £25 CC: Accepted
Room facilities:
Children: Welcome Dogs: Welcome
Licenses: Leisure: Fishing
Parking: Off-street and free
Directions: Take M5 south, exit at Junction 27. At
Tiverton roundabout take A396 north for 20 miles
through Exbridge and Bridgetown. Next left to
Winsford.
Map ref: Winsford (Somerset) 3 D2
See advert on opposite page

The big sleep

As part of our comprehensive inspection process, RAC Inspectors investigate the comfort of the beds.

"Here!"

Need a pet friendly property? Look out for 'Dogs welcome' in our listings.

Karslake House

Halse Lane, Winsford, Exmoor National Park, Somerset, TA24 7JE
Tel: 01643 851242 Fax: 01643 851242
Email: enquiries@karslakehouse.co.uk
Web: www.karslakehouse.co.uk
Seasonal closure: Limited opening from November to March

A 15th century malthouse nestling in the wooded hills of Exmoor. Ideal for walking or fishing. Suitable for seeing the coasts of Somerset and Devon.
Rooms: 6 (4 ensuite)
Pricing: Sgl £53–68 Dbl £74–108
Dinner available from £29.00
CC: Accepted
Room facilities:
Children: Welcome 12yrs min age
Dogs: Welcome
Licenses:
Parking: Off-street and free
Directions: Leave A396. In village turn left past village stores. Turn left again, hotel is 50 yards on the right.
Map ref: Winsford (Somerset) 3 D2

Winterborne Whitechurch, Dorset

The Mousehouse

Underacre Cottage, Chescombe Lane, Winterborne Whitechurch, near Blandford Forum, Dorset, DT11 0AR
Tel: 01258 880623
Email: graeme.lucas@btopenworld.com
Rooms: 2 (1 ensuite)
Pricing: Dbl £70–90
Room facilities:
Leisure: Riding
Parking: Off-street and free
Directions: Village on A354 between Dorchester and Blandford. Turn past Milton Arms pub, towards Milton Abbas. Property half mile on left.
Map ref: Winterborne Whitechurch 3 F3

Southwest

Woolacombe, Devon

Watersmeet Hotel

★★★★ ⓇⓇ

Mortehoe, Woolacombe, Devon, EX34 7EB
Tel: 01271 870333 Fax: 01271 870890
Email: info@watersmeethotel.co.uk
Web: www.watersmeethotel.co.uk

One of Devon's finest coastal hotels privately situated on Woolacombe's dramatic coastline. Panoramic sea views can be enjoyed from the reception rooms, restaurant and all bedrooms. Award-winning AA rosette cuisine in candlelit Pavilion restaurant; enjoy the delightful sunsets. Private steps lead directly to sandy beach. Licenced for civil weddings. Special 3 and 5 night breaks. Non-residents welcome.
Rooms: 25 all ensuite ♨ 🚭 ⊗
Pricing: Sgl £75–150 Dbl £92–264
Dinner available from £33.50
CC: Accepted
Room facilities: 🖥 ☎ 🍵
Children: Welcome 🍴 🐴 🍼
Licenses: 🜍 🍸
Leisure: Indoor pool, Outdoor pool, Health spa, Hot spa, Steam room
Parking: Off-street and free
Directions: Leave M5 at Junction 27. Take A361 to Barnstaple. Follow signs for Woolacombe. Take Esplanade along seafront. The hotel is on left.
Map ref: Mortehoe 2 C2

Woolacombe Bay Hotel

★★★★ ⓇⓇ

South Street, Woolacombe, Devon, EX34 7BN
Tel: 01271 870388 Fax: 01271 870613
Email: woolacombe.bayhotel@btinternet.com
Web: www.woolacombe-bay-hotel.co.uk
Seasonal closure: January

Set in 6 acres of own grounds running down to spectacular unbroken 3 miles of golden sands. A haven of good living, coupled with old world charm, courteous service & comfort with excellent food. Perfect for family holidays.
Rooms: 64 all ensuite ♨ 🚭 ⊗
Pricing: Sgl £65–92 Dbl £130–184
Dinner available from £29 CC: Accepted
Room facilities: 🖥 ☎ 🍵
Access: ⬆
Conference: 4 meeting rooms (Thtr 150 max), 24hr-delegate from £89, day-delegate from £17
Children: Welcome 🍴 🐴 🍼
Licenses: 🍸
Leisure: Indoor pool, Outdoor pool, Gym, Health spa, Beauty salon, Tennis, Golf, Games room, Snooker/billiards, Squash, Sauna, Short mat bowls
Parking: Off-street and free
Directions: Leave M5 at Junction 27. Follow A361 to Mullacott Cross. Take B3343 to Woolacombe. Hotel in centre of village.
Map ref: Woolacombe 2 C2

Cleeve House

♦♦♦♦ Ⓡ ✕ 🍷

North Morte Road, Mortehoe,
Woolacombe, Devon, EX34 7ED
Tel: 01271 870719 Fax: 01271 870719
Email: info@cleevehouse.co.uk
Web: www.cleevehouse.co.uk
Seasonal closure: November to March
Rooms: 6 all ensuite ⊗
Dinner available
CC: Accepted
Room facilities: 🖥 🍵
Children: Welcome 10yrs min age
Licenses: 🍸
Parking: Off-street and free
Directions: In the village of Mortehoe, 50 yards on the left side of the lighthouse road (North Morte Road).
Map ref: Mortehoe 2 C2

Yeovil, Somerset

Little Barwick House

★ ♔ ♔ ♔ ♔   *Premier*

Barwick Village, near Yeovil, Somerset, BA22 9TD
Tel: 01935 423902 Fax: 01935 420908
Email: reservations@barwick7.fsnet.co.uk
Web: www.littlebarwickhouse.co.uk
Rooms: 6 all ensuite ⊛
Pricing: Dinner available from £28.95
CC: Accepted
Room facilities: ☐ ☎ ⊙
Children: Welcome 5yrs min age
Dogs: Welcome
Licenses: ♦♦♦
Parking: Off-street
Directions: On A37 south from Yeovil, left at first
roundabout (by Red House pub) through village. House
signed left after 200 yards.
Map ref: Barwick 3 E2

Crown & Victoria

◆◆◆◆ ♖ ✕ ☙

Farm Street, Tintinhull, Yeovil, Somerset, BA22 8PZ
Tel: 01935 823341 Fax: 01935 825786
Email: info@crownandvictoriainn.co.uk
Web: www.crownandvictoriainn.co.uk

Set in the heart of the beautiful Somerset village of
Tintinhull, the inn has been completely and
sympathetically refurbished. Award-winning restaurant
and accommodation. Dine by the open fire in the
winter months, in the conservatory or in the beautiful
gardens.
Rooms: 5 all ensuite ⊛
Pricing: Sgl £65–75 Dbl £85
Dinner available from £7.25–14 CC: Accepted
Room facilities: ☐ ⊙
Licenses: ♦♦♦
Parking: Off-street and free
Directions: Tintinhull off A303. Follow signs to Tintinhull
National Trust gardens.
Map ref: Tintinhull 3 E2

Southwest

Headland Hotel, Newquay

East Anglia

Glasgow • •Edinburgh

•Newcastle

Belfast •

Dublin • •Manchester

Birmingham •

Cardiff • London •

Skegne

Wainfleet
All Saints

THE WASH

Hunstant

Swineshead   Boston

Kirton

Donington   Sutterton   Gedney
Drove End

Corby Glen   Holbeach   Long Sutton   King's
Lynn

North Witham   Bourne   Spalding   Clenchwarton

Cottesmore   Market   Crowland   Wisbech   Downham
Deeping   Market

Oakham   Stamford   Thorney   Outwell
                                   Guyhirn

Belton   Uppingham   Wansford   March

Corby   Haddon   Whittlesey
         Stilton   Peterborough

Oundle   Ramsey   Chatteris   Littlepo

Desborough   Ely

Kettering   Thrapston   Huntingdon   Stretham   Soham

Burton Latimer   Raunds   St Ives   Swavesey   Cottenham   Burwell

Finedon   Irthlingborough   Godmanchester   Buckden   Histon   Waterbeach

Higham
Ferrers   Boxworth   Cambourne

Rushden   St Neots   Cambridge

Bedford   Great Shelford

Sandy   Potton

Kempston   Melbourn   Great
            Biggleswade   Chesterford   Saffron Wal

Shefford   Astwick   Royston

Flitwick   Letchworth   Baldock   Buntingford

Hitchin   Redcoats Green   Stansted
                             Mountfitchet

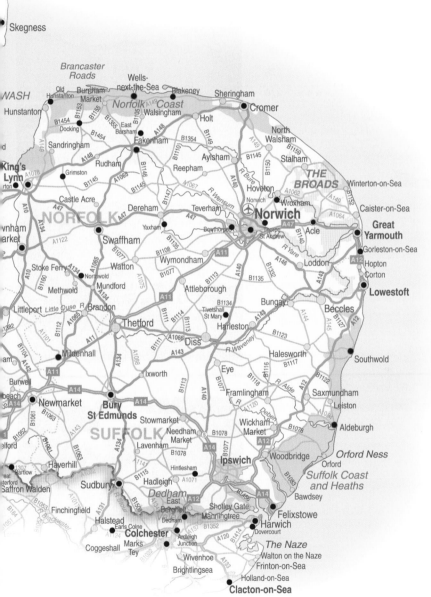

Skegness

WASH

Hunstanton

Brancaster Roads

Old Hunstanton
Burnham Market
Wells-next-the-Sea
Blakeney
Sheringham
Cromer

B1454
Docking
B1153
B1155
B1355
B1105
Walsingham
Norfolk Coast
East Barsham
A148
Holt
Fakenham
B1354
A148
North Walsham
B1159
Stalham

Sandringham
B1454
B1110
A148
Aylsham
B1145
B1150

King's Lynn
rton
A1078
Rudham
B1146
Reepham
R Bure
Hoveton
Wroxham
THE BROADS
Winterton-on-Sea

Grimston
B1145
A1065
B1145
A1067
R Wensum
Norwich
Caister-on-Sea

Castle Acre
B1147
Dereham
Teverham
A140
A47
Norwich
A149
A1064

NORFOLK
A47
Yaxham
Bawthorpe
Thorpe St Andrew
A47
Acle
Great Yarmouth

vnham arket
A1122
Swaffham
B1135
B1108
Wymondham
A11
A140
A146
Loddon
Gorleston-on-Sea
A12
Hopton
Corton

Stoke Ferry
A134
A1065
Watton
B1077
B1077
B1113
A140
B1135
B1332
Lowestoft

Methwold
Northwold
Mundford
A134
A1075
Attleborough
Bungay
A149
Beccles

Littleport
Little Ouse R
A1065
Brandon
A11
B1134
Tivetshall St Mary
A144
B1121
A12

am
A1112
A1101
Thetford
B1111
B1114
B1113
Harleston
B1123

beach
A1104
A142
A11
Mildenhall
A134
A1066
Diss
R Waveney
Halesworth
B1117
Southwold

Burwell
A11
A1068
Ixworth
B1113
Eye
B1077
B1116
B1118
R Alde
B1122

Newmarket
A14
A14
Bury St Edmunds
Stowmarket
B1140
Framlingham
A12
Saxmundham
Leiston

B1061
B1063
A14
Needham Market
B1078
A1077
Wickham Market
A12
Aldeburgh

lford
B1082
B1063
A143
A134
Lavenham
B1078
A14
Ipswich
Woodbridge
Orford Ness
Orford

1
Haverhill
1307
Bartlow
terford
A131
B1115
Hintlesham
A1071
Suffolk Coast and Heaths
Bawdsey

Saffron Walden
B1053
Finchingfield
Sudbury
Hadleigh
Dedham
East Dedham
A12
Shotley Gate
Manningtree
Felixstowe

B1184
Halstead
Earls Colne
Colchester
Ardleigh Junction
B1352
B1414
Harwich
Dovercourt

Coggeshall
Marks Tey
Wivenhoe
A120
The Naze
Walton on the Naze

Brightlingsea
Frinton-on-Sea

Holland-on-Sea
Clacton-on-Sea

SUFFOLK

East Anglia

Award winners

To help you choose somewhere really special for your stay, we've listed here all RAC Award-winning properties in this region.

Gold Ribbon Award

		pg
Congham Hall Hotel, King's Lynn	★★★	276
Hintlesham Hall, Ipswich	★★★★	276

Blue Ribbon Award

		pg
Maison Talbooth, Dedham	★★★	267

Hintlesham Hall, Ipswich

Congham Hall Hotel, King's Lynn

Maison Talbooth, Dedham

Acle, Norfolk

Kings Head Inn

The Street, Acle, Norfolk, NR13 3DY
Tel: 01493 750204 Fax: 01493 750713
Rooms: 6 all ensuite
Dinner available
CC: Accepted
Room facilities:
Conference: 1 meeting room (Thtr 30 max)
Children: Welcome 12yrs min age
Dogs: Welcome
Licenses:
Leisure: Games room
Parking: Off-street and free
Directions: From A11 or A140, join A47 to Yarmouth.
Continue to Acle, turn off into Acle, Kings Head in
centre.
Map ref: Acle 9 F2

Aldeburgh, Suffolk

The Oak

111 Saxmundham Road, Aldeburgh, Suffolk, IP15 5JF
Tel: 01728 453528/453503 Fax: 01728 452099
Email: info@ppaskletting.co.uk
Web: www.ppaskletting.co.uk
Rooms: 2 all ensuite
Pricing: Sgl £45–55 Dbl £50–65
Room facilities:
Dogs: Welcome
Parking: Off-street and free
Directions: Leave A12 at Aldeburgh sign. The Oak is ¼
mile past the 30mph sign on entering Aldeburgh on the
left-hand side.
Map ref: Aldeburgh 9 F4

Bartlow, Cambridgeshire

The Three Hills

Ashdon Road, Bartlow, Cambridgeshire, CB1 6PW
Tel: 01223 891259 Fax: 01223 890543
Map ref: Bartlow 9 D4

Blakeney, Norfolk

Blakeney Hotel

Quayside, Blakeney, Norfolk, NR25 7NE
Tel: 01263 740797 Fax: 01263 740795
Email: reception@blakeney-hotel.co.uk
Web: www.blakeney-hotel.co.uk
Rooms: 64 all ensuite
Pricing: Sgl £77–119 Dbl £154–238
Dinner available from £22.50
CC: Accepted
Room facilities:

Access:
Conference: 6 meeting rooms (Thtr 100 max),
24hr-delegate from £108, day-delegate from £28
Children: Welcome
Dogs: Welcome
Licenses:
Leisure: Indoor pool, Gym, Games room,
Snooker/billiards
Parking: Off-street and free
Directions: Situated on the quayside in Blakeney just
off the A149 coast road between Sheringham and
Wells.
Map ref: Blakeney (Norfolk) 9 E2

Blakeney Manor Hotel

The Quay, Blakeney, Holt, Norfolk, NR25 7ND
Tel: 01263 740376 Fax: 01263 741116
Email: reception@blakeneymanor.co.uk
Web: www.blakeneymanor.co.uk
Seasonal closure: 9-15 January
Rooms: 36 all ensuite
Pricing: Sgl £35–58 Dbl £70–116
Dinner available from £17
CC: Accepted
Room facilities:
Dogs: Welcome
Licenses:
Parking: Off-street and free
Directions: Blakeney Quay is located off the A149
coast road between Cromer and Wells.
Map ref: Holt 9 E2

Buckden, Cambridgeshire

The Lion

High Street, Buckden, Cambridgeshire, PE19 5XA
Tel: 01480 810313 Fax: 01480 811070
Email: reception.lionhotel@virgin.net
Web: www.lionhotel.co.uk
Rooms: 15 all ensuite
Pricing: Sgl £65–73.50 Dbl £80–90
Dinner available from £13.95
CC: Accepted
Room facilities:
Conference: 1 meeting room (Thtr 10 max),
24hr-delegate from £125, day-delegate from £60
Children: Welcome
Licenses:
Parking: Off-street and free
Directions: Situated between St Neots and Huntington
150 yards east of A1 in Buckden reached via the
roundabout on the A1.
Map ref: Buckden 8 C3

East Anglia

Bury St Edmunds, Suffolk

Ramada

★★★

Symonds Road, Moreton Hall Estate,
Bury St Edmunds, Suffolk, IP32 7DZ
Tel: 01284 760884 Fax: 01284 755476
Email: reception@ramadaburystedmunds.co.uk
Web: www.ramadainternational.com

 R A M A D A.

Rooms: 66 all ensuite ⊛
Pricing: Sgl £69.95–89.95 Dbl £79.90–99.90
Dinner available from £17.50
CC: Accepted
Room facilities: ☐ ☎ ☺ ✎
Conference: 5 meeting rooms (Thtr 40 max),
24hr-delegate from £97.50, day-delegate from £32.50
Children: Welcome ♄
Licenses: ▮▮▮ Parking: Off-street and free
Directions: Take A14 towards Bury St Edmunds (Bury
East exit).
Map ref: Bury St Edmunds 9 E3

Cambridge, Cambridgeshire

The Cambridge Belfry

★★★★ ⓡⓡ

Cambourne, Cambridge, Cambridgeshire, CB3 6BW
Tel: 01954 714995 Fax: 01954 714998
Email: cambridge@marstonhotels.com
Web: www.marstonhotels.com
Rooms: 120 all ensuite ⊛
Dinner available
CC: Accepted
Room facilities: ☐ ☎ ☺ ✎
Access: |↕|
Conference: 11 meeting rooms (Thtr 258 max)
Children: Welcome ♄
Licenses: ◈ ▮▮▮
Leisure: Indoor pool, Gym, Health spa,
Beauty salon, Tennis
Parking: Off-street and free
Directions: From M11 take junction 13. Follow A428 to
Bedford. Take turning to Cambourne at roundabout.
Take first left.
Map ref: Cambourne 9 D4

Best Western Gonville Hotel

★★★

Gonville Place, Cambridge, Cambridgeshire, CB1 1LY
Tel: 01223 221111 Fax: 01223 315470
Email: info@gonvillehotel.co.uk
Web: www.gonvillehotel.co.uk
Rooms: 73 all ensuite
Pricing: Sgl £99–140 Dbl £99–160
Dinner available from £13
CC: Accepted
Room facilities:
Access: |↓|
Conference: 6 meeting rooms (Thtr 200 max),
24hr-delegate from £145, day-delegate from £42
Children: Welcome
Dogs: Welcome
Licenses:
Leisure: Garden
Parking: Off-street and free
Directions: Exit M11 at junction 11. Take A1309 to city
centre. At second mini-roundabout turn right into
Lensfield Road. Straight on at main junction. Hotel 20
yards on right.
Map ref: Cambridge 9 D3

Arundel House Hotel

★★

Chesterton Road, Cambridge, Cambridgeshire, CB4 3AN
Tel: 01223 367701 Fax: 01223 367721
Email: info@arundelhousehotels.co.uk
Web: www.arundelhousehotels.co.uk
Seasonal closure: Christmas

Beautifully located overlooking the River Cam and
open parkland, this elegant Victorian terrace hotel
offers some of the best food in the area. Close to the
city centre and University colleges.
Rooms: 103 all ensuite
Pricing: Sgl £75–95 Dbl £95–120
Dinner available from £19.75
CC: Accepted
Room facilities:
Conference: 3 meeting rooms (Thtr 50 max),
24hr-delegate from £107.50, day-delegate from £25

Centennial Hotel

Modernised, recently refurbished, family-
run hotel, opposite the Botanical Gardens,
the Centennial Hotel offers a pleasing
combination of home comforts and full
conference facilities.
The hotel is conveniently situated within
walking distance of both the railway station
and historic Cambridge City.

63–71 Hills Road
Cambridge CB2 1PG

Tel: 01223 314652   Fax: 01223 315443

Children: Welcome
Licenses:
Parking: Off-street and free
Directions: In the north of the city, overlooking River
Cam. From M11 J13, follow signs to Cambridge until
mini-roundabout. Turn left then through traffic lights.
Hotel 400 yards on left.
Map ref: Cambridge 9 D3
See advert on opposite page

Centennial Hotel

★★

63–71 Hills Road, Cambridge, Cambridgeshire, CB2 1PG
Tel: 01223 314652 Fax: 01223 315443
Email: reception@centennialhotel.co.uk
Web: www.centennialhotel.co.uk
Seasonal closure: Christmas to New Year
Rooms: 39 all ensuite
Pricing: Sgl £70–80 Dbl £88–96
Dinner available from £13.50
CC: Accepted
Room facilities:
Conference: 1 meeting room (Thtr 20 max),
day-delegate from £100
Children: Welcome
Licenses: Parking: Off-street and free
Directions: Opposite Botanical Gardens, conveniently
near railway station and city centre.
Map ref: Cambridge 9 D3
See advert on this page

Cambridge Lodge Hotel

 ◆◆◆◆

139 Huntingdon Road, Cambridge,
Cambridgeshire, CB3 0DQ
Tel: 01223 352833 Fax: 01223 355166
Email: cambridge.lodge@btconnect.com

Only one mile from the historic city, this spacious
mock-Tudor house offers a warm welcome to all
guests. The oak-beamed restaurant has an excellent
reputation for high quality cuisine.
Rooms: 15 (12 ensuite) ⊗
Pricing: Sgl £75–77.50 Dbl £95–100
Dinner available from £24.45
CC: Accepted
Room facilities: ▯ ☎ ☕
Conference: 1 meeting room (Thtr 25 max)
Children: Welcome
Licenses: ♦♦♦
Parking: Off-street and free
Directions: J13 M11, turn right onto Madingley Road,
then left into Storeys Way. From A14 onto A1307, then
onto Huntingdon Road.
Map ref: Cambridge 9 D3

Hills Guesthouse Cambridge

 ◆◆◆◆

157 Hills Road, Cambridge,
Cambridgeshire, CB2 2RJ
Tel: 01223 214216 Fax: 01223 214216
Email: hillsguesthouse@msn.com
Seasonal closure: Christmas and New Year
Rooms: 4 all ensuite ⊗
Pricing: Sgl £36–45 Dbl £55–60
CC: Accepted
Room facilities: ▯ ☕
Children: Welcome 9yrs min age
Parking: Off-street and free
Directions: From railway station turn left. M11 go
through Trumpington, turn right into Longroad. At
crossroads turn left into Hills Road.
Map ref: Cambridge 9 D3

Lensfield Hotel

 ◆◆◆◆

53 Lensfield Road, Cambridge,
Cambridgeshire, CB2 1EN
Tel: 01223 355017 Fax: 01223 312022
Email: enquiries@lensfieldhotel.co.uk
Web: www.lensfieldhotel.co.uk
Seasonal closure: Christmas
Rooms: 30 (29 ensuite) ⊗ ⊗
Pricing: Sgl £65–90 Dbl £98–110
Dinner available from £14
CC: Accepted
Room facilities: ▯ ☎ ☕ ☏
Children: Welcome ♦
Licenses: ♦♦♦
Parking: Off-street and free
Directions: Take signposts to Cambridge centre and
join city ring road. Approach hotel via Silver Street or
Trumpington Street, turning into Lensfield Road.
Map ref: Cambridge 9 D3

The Golden Ball Hotel

◆◆◆◆

High Street, Boxworth, Cambridgeshire, CB3 8LY
Tel: 01954 267397 Fax: 01954 267497
Email: info@goldenballhotel.co.uk
Web: www.goldenballhotel.com
Rooms: 11 all ensuite ⊗ ⊗
Pricing: Dinner available from £12
CC: Accepted
Room facilities: ▯ ☎ ☕ ☏
Conference: 3 meeting rooms (Thtr 30 max)
Children: Welcome ♦
Licenses: ♦♦♦
Parking: Off-street and free
Directions: One mile A14 between Cambridge/St Ives
at turn for Cambridge Services.
Map ref: Boxworth 9 D3

Sleep Inn Cambridge
Travel Accommodation

Cambridge Services, A14 Boxworth Junction 28,
Cambridge, Cambridgeshire, CB3 8WU
Tel: 01954 268400 Fax: 01954 268419
Email: enquiries@hotels-cambridge.com
Web: www.choicehotelseurope.com
Rooms: 82 all ensuite ⊗ ⊗
CC: Accepted
Room facilities: ▯ ☎ ☕ ☏ ❄
Children: Welcome ♦
Parking: Off-street and free
Directions: 6 miles north of Cambridge at junction 28
of A14.
Map ref: Cambridge 9 D3

Dedham, Essex

Maison Talbooth

★★★★ ⓡⓡⓡ

Excellent

Stratford Road, Dedham,
Colchester, Essex, CO7 6HN
Tel: 01206 322367 Fax: 01206 322752
Email: maison@milsomhotels.com
Web: www.milsomhotels.com

In the heart of Constable country with ten superb suites, the two principal suites have recently been transformed and have hot tubs on their private terraces. Guests dine at the award-winning Le Talbooth – a minute away by courtesy car.
Rooms: 10 all ensuite 🦪 ⊗
Pricing: Sgl £120–180 Dbl £165–325
Dinner available from £46
CC: Accepted
Room facilities: ▢ ☎
Conference: 2 meeting rooms (Thtr 32 max),
24hr-delegate from £160, day-delegate from £50
Children: Welcome 🜂 ℃
Dogs: Assistance dogs only
Licenses: ◁ ⅲ
Leisure: Outdoor pool
Parking: Off-street and free
Directions: A12 towards Ipswich. Turn off Stratford St Mary/Dedham, second right over bridge, hotel is ¹/₂ mile on the right.
Map ref: Colchester 5 E1

milsoms

★★★★ ⓡ
Stratford Road, Dedham, Colchester, Essex, CO7 6HW
Tel: 01206 322795 Fax: 01206 323689
Email: milsoms@milsomhotels.com
Web: www.milsomhotels.com

Contemporary gastro bar with 15 stylish bedrooms in the Dedham Vale. Open throughout the day for breakfast, lunch or dinner or just for a relaxing glass of wine after a busy day.
Rooms: 15 all ensuite 🦪 ⊗
Pricing: Sgl £75–95 Dbl £95–135
Dinner available from £25
CC: Accepted
Room facilities: ▢ ☎ ⊙
Conference: 1 meeting room (Thtr 14 max),
24hr-delegate from £140, day-delegate from £45
Children: Welcome 🜂
Dogs: Welcome
Licenses: ⅲ
Parking: Off-street and free
Directions: North of Colchester A12, take slip road to Dedham/Stratford St Mary, turn right over bridge, hotel first left.
Map ref: Colchester 5 E1

Dereham, Norfolk

Yaxham Mill

◆◆◆
Norwich Road, Yaxham, Dereham, Norfolk, NR19 1RP
Tel: 01362 851182 Fax: 01362 691482
Email: traypooh1@aol.com
Web: www.yaxhammill.co.uk
Rooms: 9 all ensuite 🦪 ⊗
Pricing: Sgl £40–45 Dbl £55–70
Dinner available from £6.95–14.95
CC: Accepted
Room facilities: ▢ ⊙
Children: Welcome 🜂
Dogs: Assistance dogs only
Licenses: ⅲ
Parking: Off-street and free
Directions: From A47 Dereham follow signs for Wynmondham until you reach Yaxham, then continue on towards Mattishall, ¹/₂ mile on the right.
Map ref: Yaxham 9 E2

Docking, Norfolk

Jubilee Lodge

Station Road, Docking, King's Lynn, Norfolk, PE31 8LS
Tel: 01485 518473 Fax: 01485 518473
Email: eghoward62@hotmail.com
Web: www.jubilee-lodge.com
Rooms: 3 all ensuite ⊛
Pricing: Sgl £30 Dbl £50
Room facilities: ☐ ☕
Parking: Off-street and free
Directions: From King's Lynn take A148 to Cromer. At second roundabout, turn right onto A148 through Hillington. Turn left to Docking and take road between the church and school. Lodge is approximately 300 yards on left.
Map ref: Docking 9 E2

Downham Market, Norfolk

Castle Hotel

High Street, Downham Market, Norfolk, PE38 9HF
Tel: 01366 384311 Fax: 01366 384311
Email: castle@castle-hotel.com
Web: www.castle-hotel.com
Rooms: 12 all ensuite ⊛ 🖥
Dinner available
CC: Accepted
Room facilities: ☐ ☎ ☕
Conference: 2 meeting rooms (Thtr 20 max)
Children: Welcome ⋔ Dogs: Welcome
Licenses: ⅲ
Parking: Off-street and free
Directions: From M11 take A10 for Ely into Downham Market. At traffic lights straight over. Hotel on next corner.
Map ref: Downham Market 9 D3

Duxford, Cambridgeshire

Duxford Lodge Hotel

Ickleton Road, Duxford, Cambridgeshire, CB2 4RT
Tel: 01223 836444 Fax: 01223 832271
Email: admin@duxfordlodgehotel.co.uk
Web: www.duxfordlodgehotel.co.uk
Seasonal closure: 26–30 December
Rooms: 15 all ensuite ⊛ 🖥 ⊛
Pricing: Sgl £77.50–92.50 Dbl £107.50–127.50
Dinner available from £17.50–380 CC: Accepted
Room facilities: ☐ ☎ ☕
Conference: 1 meeting room (Thtr 30 max), 24hr-delegate from £130, day-delegate from £30
Children: Welcome ⋔ ☕ Dogs: Welcome
Licenses: ⟁ ⅲ Parking: Off-street and free
Directions: Leave M11 at Junction 10 and take A505 eastbound. Take right turn at roundabout into village. Hotel half a mile.
Map ref: Duxford 9 D4
See advert on this page

East Barsham, Norfolk

Fieldview

West Barsham Road, East Barsham, Fakenham, Norfolk, NR21 0AR
Tel: 01328 820083 Fax: 01328 820083
Email: info@fieldview.net
Web: www.fieldview.net
Rooms: 5 (2 ensuite) ⊛
Room facilities: ☐ ☕
Children: Welcome 7yrs min age
Parking: Off-street and free
Directions: Take B1105 from Fakenham, follow "Walsingham light vehicles only" until reaching East Barsham, take first left signposted West Barsham.
Map ref: Fakenham 9 E2

Fakenham, Norfolk

Wensum Lodge Hotel

★★★

Bridge Street, Fakenham, Norfolk, NR21 9AY
Tel: 01328 862100 Fax: 01328 863365
Email: enquiries@wensumlodge.fsnet.co.uk
Web: www.wensumlodge.co.uk
Rooms: 17 all ensuite
Pricing: Sgl £56 Dbl £82
Dinner available from £6–15 CC: Accepted
Room facilities:
Conference: 2 meeting rooms (Thtr 150 max)
Children: Welcome
Dogs: Assistance dogs only
Licenses: Leisure: Fishing
Parking: Off-street and free
Directions: Easily reached from Norwich on A1067, King's Lynn on A148 and Swaffham on A1065. Opposite Fakenham Bowl at the bottom of Bridge Street, Fakenham.
Map ref: Fakenham 9 E2

Felixstowe, Suffolk

Hotel Elizabeth Orwell

★★★★

Hamilton Road, Felixstowe, Suffolk, IP11 7DX
Tel: 01394 285511 Fax: 01394 670687
Email: elizabeth.orwell@elizabethhotels.co.uk
Web: www.elizabethhotels.co.uk
Rooms: 58 all ensuite
Dinner available CC: Accepted
Room facilities: Access:
Conference: 11 meeting rooms (Thtr 250 max)
Children: Welcome 13yrs min age
Dogs: Welcome
Licenses:
Parking: Off-street and free
Directions: A14 to Felixstowe. Straight at dock roundabout. Straight at second roundabout. Right at third roundabout into Beatrice Avenue. Hotel at end.
Map ref: Felixstowe 9 F4

Grafton Guest House

◆◆◆◆

The Grafton, 13 Sea Road, Felixstowe, Suffolk, IP11 2BB
Tel: 01394 284881 Fax: 01394 279101
Email: info@grafton-house.com
Web: www.grafton-house.com
Rooms: 8 (6 ensuite)
Pricing: Sgl £23.50–29.50 Dbl £40–48
Room facilities:
Conference: 1 meeting room
Children: Welcome
Directions: A14 to Felixstowe, straight at first roundabout, right at second. Straight over two traffic lights, left at first roundabout, right at second. Guest house 250 yards on right.
Map ref: Felixstowe 9 F4

Gorleston-on-Sea, Norfolk

The Pier Hotel

★★

Harbour Mouth, Gorleston-on-Sea, Norfolk, NR31 6PL
Tel: 01493 662631 Fax: 01493 440263
Email: bookings@pierhotelgorleston.co.uk
Web: www.pierhotelgorleston.co.uk
Rooms: 19 all ensuite
Pricing: Sgl £40–50 Dbl £60–70
Dinner available from £5.95–14.95 CC: Accepted
• Room facilities:
Conference: 3 meeting rooms (Thtr 125 max), 24hr-delegate from £75, day-delegate from £13.50
Children: Welcome
Licenses:
Parking: Off-street and free
Directions: A12 from Lowestoft or A47 from Norwich, head for Great Yarmouth; hotel 3 miles from Yarmouth. Ask for Harbour Mouth Gorleston-on-Sea.
Map ref: Gorleston-on-Sea 9 F3

Great Yarmouth, Norfolk

Imperial Hotel

★★★★

North Drive, Great Yarmouth, Norfolk, NR30 1EQ
Tel: 01493 842000 Fax: 01493 852229
Email: reception@imperialhotel.co.uk
Web: www.imperialhotel.co.uk
Rooms: 39 all ensuite
Pricing: Sgl £55–80 Dbl £70–95
Dinner available from £20.50–300 CC: Accepted
Room facilities: Access:
Conference: 6 meeting rooms (Thtr 140 max), 24hr-delegate from £95, day-delegate from £25
Children: Welcome Dogs: Welcome
Licenses:
Parking: Off-street and free
Directions: Follow signs to seafront. Turn left into North Drive. Hotel is 1/2 mile north of Britannia Pier.
Map ref: Great Yarmouth 9 F2

Star Hotel

★★★

Hall Quay, Great Yarmouth, Norfolk, NR30 1HG
Tel: 01493 842294 Fax: 01493 330215
Email: star.hotel@elizabethhotels.co.uk
Web: www.elizabethhotels.co.uk
Rooms: 40 all ensuite
Pricing: Sgl £65–95 Dbl £85–125
Dinner available from £5.95–16.95 CC: Accepted
Room facilities: Access:
Conference: 2 meeting rooms (Thtr 100 max)
Children: Welcome
Licenses:
Parking: Off-street and free
Directions: From A12 directly opposite Haven Bridge. On entering Yarmouth from A47 take the third exit on first roundabout on right.
Map ref: Great Yarmouth 9 F2

East Anglia

Burlington Palm Court Hotel

 ★★

North Drive, Great Yarmouth, Norfolk, NR30 1EG
Tel: 01493 844568 Fax: 01493 331848
Email: enquiries@burlington-hotel.co.uk
Web: www.burlington-hotel.co.uk
Seasonal closure: January

This family-run hotel has views of the sea and
recreation grounds. There is ample car parking and an
indoor swimming pool.
Rooms: 70 all ensuite 🛏 🅿
Pricing: Sgl £40–50 Dbl £72–88
Dinner available from £18
CC: Accepted
Room facilities: 📺 ☎ 🍵
Access:
Conference: 6 meeting rooms (Thtr 120 max),
24hr-delegate from £50, day-delegate from £30
Children: Welcome 🍴 🎠
Licenses: 👫
Leisure: Indoor pool, Health spa, Games room,
Snooker/billiards, Jacuzzi
Parking: Off-street and free
Directions: Follow signs for seafront, turn left. Hotel is
600 yards from Britannia Pier, overlooking sea and
golden sands.
Map ref: Great Yarmouth 9 F2

Admiral House Hotel

♦♦♦♦ ✗ 🍷

12a Nelson Road South,
Great Yarmouth, Norfolk, NR30 3JL
Tel: 01493 843712
Email: anne@admiralhouse.co.uk
Web: www.admiralhouse.co.uk
Rooms: 8 all ensuite 🛏 🅿
Pricing: Sgl £18–30 Dbl £36–60
Dinner available from £10.50
CC: Accepted
Room facilities: 📺 🍵
Children: Welcome 🍴 🎠
Licenses: 👫
Directions: From seafront turn right (Kings Road) at
Wellington Pier. Turn right into Nelson Road South,
Fifth hotel on left side.
Map ref: Great Yarmouth 9 F2

Beaumont House Hotel

♦♦♦♦ ✗ 🍷

52 Wellesley Road, Great Yarmouth,
Norfolk, NR30 1EX
Tel: 01493 843957 Fax: 01493 301241
Email: info@beaumonthousehotel.com
Web: www.beaumonthousehotel.com
Rooms: 14 (9 ensuite) 🛏 📠 🅿
Pricing: Sgl £33–45 Dbl £68–156 Dinner available
CC: Accepted
Room facilities: 📺 🍵
Children: Welcome 🍴 🎠
Licenses: 👫
Leisure: Jacuzzi
Parking: Off-street and free
Directions: Located in quiet area. Five minutes to
beach and all amenities. Town centre close by. Train
station approximately 15 minutes.
Map ref: Great Yarmouth 9 F2

Bonheur Hotel

♦♦♦♦ ✗

3 Norfolk Square, Great Yarmouth, Norfolk, NR30 1EE
Tel: 01493 843042 Fax: 01493 745235
Email: enq@bonheur-hotel.co.uk
Web: www.bonheur-hotel.co.uk
Rooms: 8 all ensuite 🛏 🅿
Pricing: Sgl £25–45 Dbl £35–55
Dinner available from £8
CC: Accepted
Room facilities: 📺 🍵
Children: Welcome 🍴
Licenses: 👫
Parking: Off-street and free
Directions: 200 yards north of Britannia Pier along
North Drive, turn left into Albemarle Road, Bonheur 50
yards on left.
Map ref: Great Yarmouth 9 F2

Corner House Hotel

♦♦♦♦ 🅡 ✗ 🍷

Albert Square, Great Yarmouth, Norfolk, NR30 3JH
Tel: 01493 842773
Email: stay@thecornerhousehotel.co.uk
Web: www.thecornerhousehotel.co.uk
Seasonal closure: October to March
Rooms: 8 all ensuite 🅿
Pricing: Sgl £28–38 Dbl £56–76
Dinner available from £12
Room facilities: 📺 🍵
Licenses: 👫
Parking: Off-street and free
Directions: From A37 and A12 locate seafront. Albert
Square to be found opposite Wellington Pier.
Map ref: Great Yarmouth 9 F2

Fjaerland Hotel

◆◆◆◆

24–25 Trafalgar Road, Great Yarmouth,
Norfolk, NR30 2LD
Tel: 01493 856339/0780 3859951 Fax: 01493 856339
Web: www.fjaerland.co.uk or
www.smoothhound.co.uk/hotels/fjaerland
Rooms: 12 all ensuite ♨ ⊗
Pricing: Sgl £30 Dbl £45–50
CC: Accepted
Room facilities: ▢ ☕
Children: Welcome �
Licenses: ♦♦♦
Directions: Follow signs for seafront onto Marine
Parade. Hotel is on Trafalgar Road overlooking two
grass squares across to beach and sea.
Map ref: Great Yarmouth 9 F2

Kensington Hotel

◆◆◆◆ ✕ ✎

29 North Drive, Great Yarmouth, Norfolk, NR30 4EW
Tel: 01493 844145 Fax: 01493 852364
Rooms: 26 all ensuite ♨
Pricing: Sgl £35–45 Dbl £55–80
Dinner available from £11.95
CC: Accepted
Room facilities: ▢ ☕
Access: ♿
Conference: 2 meeting rooms (Thtr 50 max),
24hr-delegate from £75, day-delegate from £10
Children: Welcome
Dogs: Welcome
Licenses: ♦♦♦
Parking: Off-street and free
Directions: Head towards the seafront, turn left at the
sea front and proceed north along North Drive.
Map ref: Great Yarmouth 9 F2

Maluth Lodge

◆◆◆◆ ✕ ✎

40 North Denes Road, Great Yarmouth,
Norfolk, NR30 4LU
Tel: 01493 304652 Fax: 01493 308112
Email: enquiries@maluthlodge.co.uk
Web: www.maluthlodge.co.uk
Rooms: 8 all ensuite ♨
Pricing: Sgl £23–30 Dbl £46–60
Dinner available from £8
Room facilities: ▢ ☕
Children: Welcome
Dogs: Assistance dogs only
Licenses: ♦♦♦
Directions: Left on seafront past waterways, left onto
Salisbury Road, right onto North Denes, Maluth Lodge
on your left.
Map ref: Great Yarmouth 9 F2

Marine Lodge

◆◆◆◆

19-20 Euston Road, Great Yarmouth,
Norfolk, NR30 1DY
Tel: 01493 331120
Email: reception@marinelodge.co.uk
Web: www.marinelodge.co.uk

Relax and enjoy a top English resort. See the history,
walk the beaches, wine, dine or dance, the choice is
yours. Overlooking the sea, private car park, all rooms
ensuite.
Rooms: 40 all ensuite ♨ ⊗
Pricing: Sgl £40–45 Dbl £59–65
CC: Accepted
Room facilities: ▢ ☕
Access: ♿
Conference: 2 meeting rooms (Thtr 60 max),
24hr-delegate from £50, day-delegate from £20
Children: Welcome ♔
Licenses: ⚗ ♦♦♦
Leisure: Private park
Parking: Off-street and free
Directions: Following signs to seafront the Marine
Lodge is situated 300 yards north of the Britannia Pier
on Great Yarmouth seafront.
Map ref: Great Yarmouth 9 F2

Southern Hotel

◆◆◆◆ ✕ ✎

46 Queens Road, Great Yarmouth, Norfolk, NR30 3JR
Tel: 01493 843313 Fax: 01493 843242
Email: sally@southernhotel.co.uk
Web: www.southernhotel.co.uk
Rooms: 18 all ensuite ♨ ⊗
Pricing: Sgl £30–35 Dbl £60–70
Dinner available from £15
CC: Accepted
Room facilities: ▢ ☕ ⚑
Children: Welcome ♔ ☃
Licenses: ♦♦♦
Parking: Off-street and free
Directions: Turn right along seafront to model village.
Turn right at 'all major routes' sign, Kings Road.
Second hotel on right.
Map ref: Great Yarmouth 9 F2

East Anglia

The Hamilton

◆◆◆◆

23/24 North Drive, Great Yarmouth,
Norfolk, NR30 4EW
Tel: 01493 844662 Fax: 01493 745772
Email: enquiries@hamilton-hotel.co.uk
Web: www.hamilton-hotel.co.uk
Rooms: 23 all ensuite
Dinner available
CC: Accepted
Room facilities:
Children: Welcome
Dogs: Welcome
Licenses:
Leisure: Games room
Parking: Off-street and free
Directions: Follow signs for seafront. Turn left at
Brittania Pier. Hotel 800 yards along the seafront.
Map ref: Great Yarmouth 9 F2

A'rona Hotel

◆◆◆

14-15 Sandown Road, Great Yarmouth,
Norfolk, NR30 1EY
Tel: 01493 843870 Fax: 01493 843870
Email: aronahotel@yahoo.co.uk
Web: www.aronahotel.co.uk
Rooms: 22 all ensuite
Pricing: Sgl £30–40 Dbl £50–70
Dinner available from £10
Room facilities:
Access:
Conference: 3 meeting rooms (Thtr 60 max),
day-delegate from £15
Children: Welcome 3yrs min age
Licenses:
Leisure: Games room
Parking: Off-street and free
Directions: Follow signs to seafront. On seafront turn
left. Sandown Road is second turn left opposite
entrance to Waterways Garden.
Map ref: Great Yarmouth 9 F2

Amber Lodge

◆◆◆

21 Princes Road, Great Yarmouth, Norfolk, NR30 2DG
Tel: 01493 843371
Email: paul@amberlodgehotel.co.uk
Web: www.amberlodgehotel.co.uk
Rooms: 10 (7 ensuite)
Pricing: Sgl £17–25 Dbl £34–50
Dinner available from £8
Room facilities:
Children: Welcome
Licenses:
Directions: Amber Lodge is off Marine Parade, just
opposite Britannia Pier.
Map ref: Great Yarmouth 9 F2

Anglia House Hotel

◆◆◆

56 Wellesley Road, Great Yarmouth,
Norfolk, NR30 1EX
Tel: 01493 844395
Email: angliahouse@talk21.com
Rooms: 9 (8 ensuite)
Pricing: Sgl £16–25 Dbl £32–50
Room facilities: Children: Welcome
Licenses:
Directions: Follow seafront signs. Left at lights,
keeping Sainsbury's on left. Through traffic lights, next
left opposite Wellesley Park.
Map ref: Great Yarmouth 9 F2

Belvedere

◆◆◆

90 North Denes Road, Great Yarmouth,
Norfolk, NR30 4LW
Tel: 01493 844200
Email: info@stayatbelvedere.co.uk
Web: www.stayatbelvedere.co.uk
Rooms: 9 (5 ensuite)
Pricing: Sgl £20–30 Dbl £40–60
Room facilities:
Children: Welcome Dogs: Welcome
Parking: Off-street and free
Directions: At seafront, proceed north to 'Waterways'
— turn left into Beaconsfield Road. Turn right at mini
roundabout. Hotel fifth property on right.
Map ref: Great Yarmouth 9 F2

Cavendish House

◆◆◆

19-20 Princes Road, Great Yarmouth,
Norfolk, NR30 2DG
Tel: 01493 844829 Fax: 01493 843148
Rooms: 19 all ensuite
Dinner available
Room facilities: Access:
Children: Welcome Licenses:
Directions: Follow A12 into Great Yarmouth, follow
signs to seafront and Britannia Pier, Princes Road is
immediately left before pier.
Map ref: Great Yarmouth 9 F2

Chateau Hotel

◆◆◆

1 North Drive, Great Yarmouth, Norfolk, NR30 1ED
Tel: 01493 859052
Web: www.chateau-gy.fsbusiness.co.uk
Seasonal closure: October to March
Rooms: 11 all ensuite
Pricing: Sgl £34.50–38.50 Dbl £53–61 CC: Accepted
Room facilities: Children: Welcome
Dogs: Welcome Licenses:
Parking: Off-street and free
Directions: Opposite bowling greens on seafront, just
north of Britannia Pier.
Map ref: Great Yarmouth 9 F2

Chequers Hotel

27 Nelson Road South, Great Yarmouth,
Norfolk, NR30 3JA
Tel: 01493 853091
Email: chequershotel@greatyarmouth.fsbusiness.co.uk
Rooms: 8 all ensuite
Pricing: Sgl £20–26 Dbl £40–80
Dinner available from £8
Room facilities:
Children: Welcome
Licenses:
Parking: Off-street and free
Directions: Drive to seafront. Turn opposite Wellington
Pier, then turn down Albert Square. At T-junction,
Chequers is on opposite corner.
Map ref: Great Yarmouth 9 F2

Cleasewood Private Hotel

55 Wellesley Road, Great Yarmouth,
Norfolk, NR30 1EX
Tel: 01493 843960 Fax: 01493 843960
Rooms: 9 (6 ensuite)
Pricing: Sgl £17–25 Dbl £34–50
Room facilities:
Children: Welcome 5yrs min age
Licenses:
Leisure: Games room
Directions: A12/A47 roundabout, follow signs for
seafront. At third set of lights turn left. Over next lights
then first left.
Map ref: Great Yarmouth 9 F2

Gable End Hotel

◆◆◆

30 North Drive, Great Yarmouth, Norfolk, NR30 4EW
Tel: 01493 842112
Web: www.thegableendhotel.fsnet.co.uk
Rooms: 17 all ensuite
Dinner available
CC: Accepted
Room facilities:
Children: Welcome
Dogs: Welcome
Licenses:
Parking: Off-street and free
Directions: Head towards the seafront, turn left and
head north along North Drive.
Map ref: Great Yarmouth 9 F2

Hotel Victoria

◆◆◆

2 Kings Road, Great Yarmouth, Norfolk, NR30 3JW
Tel: 01493 843872 Fax: 01493 843872
Seasonal closure: January to Easter
Rooms: 35 (30 ensuite)
Pricing: Sgl £25–30 Dbl £50–60 Dinner available
CC: Accepted
Room facilities:

Access:
Children: Welcome
Licenses:
Leisure: Outdoor pool, Games room
Parking: Off-street and free
Directions: Kings Road is opposite the model village,
close to Wellington Pier. Second building in from
seafront.
Map ref: Great Yarmouth 9 F2

Kentville Guest House

5 Kent Square, Great Yarmouth, Norfolk, NR30 2EX
Tel: 01493 844783
Email: rogernol@aol.com
Rooms: 9 (5 ensuite)
Pricing: Sgl £14–18 Dbl £28–36
Dinner available from £5
Room facilities:
Children: Welcome
Dogs: Welcome
Directions: Kent Square is just off the seafront. Take
Standard Road (opposite Marina leisure centre). Hotel
is in the right-hand corner.
Map ref: Great Yarmouth 9 F2

Kilbrannan

◆◆◆

14 Trafalgar Road, Great Yarmouth, Norfolk, NR30 2LD
Tel: 01493 850383
Rooms: 5 all ensuite
Pricing: Sgl £20–25 Dbl £40–50
Room facilities:
Children: Welcome
Parking: Off-street
Directions: Approach sea front past Britannia Pier.
Before the Marina Centre, turn right up Trafalgar Road.
Kilbrannan is halfway up.
Map ref: Great Yarmouth 9 F2

Kingsley House

68 King Street, Great Yarmouth, Norfolk, NR30 2PP
Tel: 01493 850948 Fax: 01493 850948
Email: Abkingsleyhouse@aol.com
Rooms: 7 all ensuite
Pricing: Sgl £15–20 Dbl £30–40
CC: Accepted
Room facilities:
Children: Welcome
Dogs: Welcome
Licenses:
Directions: Located at the southern end of King Street.
Kingsley House is a short walk from seafront and town
centre.
Map ref: Great Yarmouth 9 F2

East Anglia

Lea Hurst Guest House

◆◆◆

117 Wellesley Road, Great Yarmouth,
Norfolk, NR30 2AP
Tel: 01493 843063
Email: tsmillership@aol.com
Rooms: 8 (6 ensuite) ⬥⬥ ⊛
Pricing: Sgl £15–26 Dbl £30–52
Dinner available from £8–10
Room facilities: ▢ ☕
Children: Welcome
Licenses: ▥
Directions: Follow signs for sea front. Turn left at traffic
lights at Sainsbury's. Take second right into Wellesley
Road, guest house on left.
Map ref: Great Yarmouth 9 F2

Little Emily Hotel

◆◆◆

18 Princes Road, Great Yarmouth, Norfolk, NR30 2DG
Tel: 01493 842515
Rooms: 10 all ensuite
Pricing: Sgl £16–25 Dbl £32–50
Dinner available from £7.50
Room facilities: ▢ ☕
Children: Welcome ♑
Dogs: Assistance dogs only
Licenses: ▥
Leisure: Games room, Snooker/billiards
Parking: Off-street and free
Directions: Follow A12/A47 into Great Yarmouth.
Follow signs to seafront. Princes Road is opposite
Britannia Pier.
Map ref: Great Yarmouth 9 F2

Lyndhurst Hotel

◆◆◆

22 Princes Road, Great Yarmouth, Norfolk, NR30 2DG
Tel: 01493 332393 Fax: 01493 332393
Email: info@lyndhursthotel.co.uk
Web: www.lyndhursthotel.co.uk
Rooms: 10 (8 ensuite) ⬥⬥ ⊛
Pricing: Sgl £18–22.50 Dbl £40–60
Room facilities: ▢ ☕
Children: Welcome ⟁
Directions: Follow A47 from Norwich to Great
Yarmouth. Follow sign to seafront. Right into Wellesley
Road and left into Princes Road.
Map ref: Great Yarmouth 9 F2

Maryland

◆◆◆

53 Wellesley Road, Great Yarmouth,
Norfolk, NR30 1EX
Tel: 01493 844409
Rooms: 7 all ensuite ⊛
Pricing: Sgl £18–26 Dbl £35–52
Dinner available from £8.50
Room facilities: ▢ ☕
Children: Welcome 2yrs min age ♑

Licenses: ▥
Parking: Off-street and free
Directions: Overlooking Wellesley Park one minute from
seafront, two minutes from attractions and town centre.
Map ref: Great Yarmouth 9 F2

Raynscourt Hotel

◆◆◆

83 Marine Parade, Great Yarmouth, Norfolk, NR30 2DJ
Tel: 01493 856554 Fax: 01493 856554
Seasonal closure: January to March
Rooms: 55 (54 ensuite) ⬥⬥
Pricing: Sgl £30–35 Dbl £56–64
Dinner available from £8
CC: Accepted
Room facilities: ▢ ☕
Access: ♿
Children: Welcome
Licenses: ▥
Parking: Off-street and free
Directions: Follow signs for seafront. Approaching
seafront, hotel is on the right-hand corner.
Map ref: Great Yarmouth 9 F2

Russell Private Hotel

◆◆◆

26 Nelson Road South, Great Yarmouth,
Norfolk, NR30 3JL
Tel: 01493 843788
Web: www.russellhoteluk.com
Rooms: 10 all ensuite
Pricing: Sgl £15–30 Dbl £30–60
Dinner available from £8
CC: Accepted
Room facilities: ▢ ☕
Children: Welcome ♑
Licenses: ▥
Directions: Turn right past Wellington Pier, onto Kings
Road. Take next right onto Nelson Road South. Hotel
150 yards on left.
Map ref: Great Yarmouth 9 F2

Sandholme Hotel

◆◆◆

12 Sandown Road, Great Yarmouth, Norfolk, NR30 1EY
Tel: 01493 852498 Fax: 01493 308869
Email: sandholmehotel@ntlworld.com
Web: www.sandholmehotel.co.uk
Rooms: 9 (6 ensuite) ⬥⬥ ▱
Pricing: Dbl £35–50
Dinner available from £7 CC: Accepted
Room facilities: ▢ ☎ ☕
Children: Welcome ♑
Dogs: Assistance dogs only
Licenses: ⚓ ▥
Directions: Come down to seafront, turn left. Go along
past cinema to the water gardens on right. Imperial
Hotel on left. Turn left into Sandown Road. Fourth
hotel on right (No.12).
Map ref: Great Yarmouth 9 F2

Senglea Lodge

7 Euston Road, Great Yarmouth, Norfolk, NR30 1DX
Tel: 01493 859632
Email: info@senglealodge.freeserve.co.uk
Web: www.uk-bedandbreakfasts.com
Seasonal closure: Christmas and New Year
Rooms: 6 (4 ensuite)
Pricing: Sgl £17.50–20 Dbl £35–40 CC: Accepted
Room facilities: Children: Welcome
Licenses:
Directions: On entering Great Yarmouth on the A47 or A12, go straight over first and second roundabouts. Take a left turn to seafront. Go straight through traffic lights. Lodge on right-hand side.
Map ref: Great Yarmouth 9 F2

Shemara Guest House

11 Wellesley Road, Great Yarmouth, Norfolk, NR30 2AR
Tel: 01493 844054 Fax: 01493 844054
Seasonal closure: December
Rooms: 9 all ensuite
Room facilities:
Children: Welcome
Directions: Take A47 to Yarmouth, past rail station. Follow signs for seafront. Take fourth turning right. Wellesley Road is halfway down on right.
Map ref: Great Yarmouth 9 F2

Sienna Lodge

17-18 Camperdown, Great Yarmouth, Norfolk, NR30 3JB
Tel: 01493 843361
Rooms: 14 all ensuite
Pricing: Sgl £25–30 Dbl £50
Dinner available from £8.50
Room facilities:
Children: Welcome
Directions: Opposite Wellington Pier, two minutes walk to seafront.
Map ref: Great Yarmouth 9 F2

Swiss Cottage Hotel Bed & Breakfast

31 North Drive, Great Yarmouth, Norfolk, NR30 4EW
Tel: 01493 855742
Email: bookings@swisscottagehotel.com
Web: www.swisscottagehotel.com
Seasonal closure: November to February
Rooms: 9 all ensuite
Pricing: Sgl £23–29 Dbl £44–65 CC: Accepted
Room facilities:
Children: Welcome 8yrs min age
Dogs: Welcome
Parking: Off-street and free
Directions: A47 to A149 left roundabout, next lights right, first left to end. Right into North Drive, hotel 400 metres on right.
Map ref: Great Yarmouth 9 F2

Trevi Guest House

57 Wellesley Road, Great Yarmouth, Norfolk, NR30 1EX
Tel: 01493 842821
Web: www.treviguesthouse.co.uk
Rooms: 9 (5 ensuite)
Pricing: Sgl £18–25 Dbl £36–50
Dinner available from £7
Room facilities: Children: Welcome
Licenses:
Directions: Follow signs to seafront. Proceed through traffic lights past Sainsbury's. Take first turning on left. Trevi Guest House is opposite the recreation ground.
Map ref: Great Yarmouth 9 F2

Willow Tree Lodge

13 Sandown Road, Great Yarmouth, Norfolk, NR30 1EY
Tel: 01493 842161 Fax: 01493 843065
Email: tania.willowtreelodge@ntlworld.com
Web: www.willowtreelodge.co.uk
Rooms: 8 (6 ensuite)
Pricing: Sgl £20–25 Dbl £40–50
Dinner available from £8 CC: Accepted
Room facilities: Children: Welcome
Licenses: Parking: Off-street and free
Directions: Follow sea front signs. When sea is in front of you, turn left. At the Imperial Hotel & Waterways turn left. Willow Tree Lodge is 50 yards on right.
Map ref: Great Yarmouth 9 F2

Woods End

49 Wellesley Road, Great Yarmouth, Norfolk, NR30 1EX
Tel: 01493 842229 Fax: 01493 842229
Rooms: 8 all ensuite
Pricing: Sgl £17–26 Dbl £34–52
Room facilities: Children: Welcome
Licenses: Parking: Off-street
Directions: Off Norwich roundabout, follow seafront signs past Sainsbury's, first left into Wellesley Road, proceed approx 200 yards opposite recreation ground.
Map ref: Great Yarmouth 9 F2

Chatsworth Hotel

32 Wellesley Road, Great Yarmouth, Norfolk, NR30 1EU
Tel: 01493 842890 Fax: 01493 842890
Seasonal closure: 1 October to Easter
Rooms: 14 all ensuite
Pricing: Sgl £30–45 Dbl £40–56
Dinner available from £7
Room facilities: Access:
Conference: 2 meeting rooms (Thtr 45 max)
Children: Welcome   Licenses:
Leisure: Indoor pool, Games room, Snooker/billiards, Sun lounges Parking: Off-street and free
Directions: 100 yards north of Britannia Pier, 450 yards due east from railway station.
Map ref: Great Yarmouth 9 F2

East Anglia

The Collingwood Hotel

 ◆◆

25/26 Princes Road, Great Yarmouth, Norfolk, NR30 2DG
Tel: 01493 844398 Fax: 01493 844398
Web: www.the-collingwood-hotel.co.uk
Rooms: 19 (10 ensuite) 🛏 ⊘
Pricing: Sgl £20–25 Dbl £40–55
CC: Accepted
Room facilities: ▢ ♨
Children: Welcome ♀
Licenses: ⚏
Leisure: Snooker/billiards
Directions: Follow signs to the seafront. Turn right.
Princes Road is opposite the Britannia Pier.
Collingwood is the second hotel on the left.
Map ref: Great Yarmouth 9 F2

Hunstanton, Norfolk

Caley Hall Hotel

 ★★

Old Hunstanton Road, Old Hunstanton,
Norfolk, PE36 6HH
Tel: 01485 533486 Fax: 01485 533348
Email: mail@caleyhallhotel.co.uk
Web: www.caleyhallhotel.co.uk
Seasonal closure: 17 December to 20 January

Old farm buildings set around a 1648 manor house
have been converted, providing restaurant, bar and
spacious ensuite bedrooms. Mostly ground floor, some
feature four-poster bed, whirlpool bath or disabled
shower.
Rooms: 40 all ensuite 🛏 🖨 ⊘
Pricing: Sgl £45–69 Dbl £70–109
Dinner available from £23 CC: Accepted
Room facilities: ▢ ♨
Children: Welcome ♀
Dogs: Welcome
Licenses: ⚏
Parking: Off-street and free
Directions: Sign is on the left-hand side of the A149 in
the village of Old Hunstanton.
Map ref: Old Hunstanton 9 D2

Ipswich, Suffolk

Hintlesham Hall

 Premier

★★★★ 🔔🔔🔔

Hintlesham, near Ipswich, Suffolk, IP8 3NS
Tel: 01473 652334 Fax: 01473 652463
Email: reservations@hintleshamhall.com
Web: www.hintleshamhall.com

A warm and friendly welcome awaits you at this
magnificent 16th century hall which offers a glorious
hotel and award-winning restaurant. Also within the
estate a unique health club and associated top class
golf club.
Rooms: 33 all ensuite 🖨
Pricing: Dinner available from £30 CC: Accepted
Room facilities: ▢ ☎ ☏
Conference: 6 meeting rooms (Thtr 80 max),
24hr-delegate from £205, day-delegate from £45
Children: Welcome ⅍ Dogs: Welcome
Licenses: ⚐ ⚏
Leisure: Outdoor pool, Gym, Health spa, Beauty salon,
Tennis, Golf
Parking: Off-street and free
Directions: 4 miles west of Ipswich on the A1071.
Map ref: Hintlesham 9 E4

King's Lynn, Norfolk

Congham Hall Hotel

 Premier

★★★ 🔔🔔🔔

Grimston, King's Lynn, Norfolk, PE32 1AH
Tel: 01485 600250 Fax: 01485 601191
Email: info@conghamhallhotel.co.uk
Web: www.conghamhallhotel.co.uk
Rooms: 14 all ensuite 🛏 ⊘
Pricing: Sgl £99–210 Dbl £185–360
Dinner available from £35–55 CC: Accepted
Room facilities: ▢ ☎ ☏
Conference: 2 meeting rooms (Thtr 50 max),
24hr-delegate from £185, day-delegate from £29
Children: Welcome ♀ ⅍
Licenses: ⚐ ⚏
Leisure: Tennis, Croquet lawn, Putting green
Parking: Off-street and free
Directions: A148 towards Sandringham, right-hand
turn signposted Grimston and Congham Hall. Hotel is
2½ miles on left as you enter Grimston village.
Map ref: Grimston 9 E2

East Anglia

Ramada

★★★

Beveridge Way, Hardwick Narrows Estate,
King's Lynn, Norfolk, PE30 4NB
Tel: 01553 771707 Fax: 01553 768027
Email: reception@ramadakingslynn.co.uk
Web: www.ramadainternational.com

 R A M A D A.

Rooms: 50 all ensuite 🐾 🚳
Pricing: Sgl £69.95–89.95 Dbl £79.90–99.90
Dinner available from £17.50
CC: Accepted
Room facilities: 🖵 ☎ ☕ 🚰
Conference: 4 meeting rooms (Thtr 80 max),
24hr-delegate from £97.50, day-delegate from £32.50
Children: Welcome �
Licenses: ♦♦♦
Parking: Off-street and free
Directions: A10/A47 roundabout. Follow signs to
Hardwick Narrows.
Map ref: King's Lynn 9 D2

Kismet Lodge

◆◆◆◆ ✂ ☂

15 Willow Drive, Clenchwarton, King's Lynn,
Norfolk, PE34 4EN
Tel: 01553 761409
Email: kismetlodgebb@aol.com
Rooms: 2 all ensuite 🚳
Pricing: Sgl £35 Dbl £55
Room facilities: 🖵 ☕
Children: Welcome 15yrs min age
Parking: Off-street and free
Directions: Hardwick roundabout follow Wisbech. Next
roundabout third exit Clenchwarton, left Rookery
Road, left Linden Road, right Willow Drive. Property on
bottom left.
Map ref: Clenchwarton 9 D2

Beeches Guest House

◆◆◆ ✂ ☂

2 Guanock Terrace, King's Lynn, Norfolk, PE30 5QT
Tel: 01553 766577 Fax: 01553 776664
Email: kelvin.sellers@virgin.net
Web: www.beechesguesthouse.co.uk
Rooms: 7 (4 ensuite) 🐾 🚳
Pricing: Sgl £30–35 Dbl £45–52
Dinner available from £8.50
CC: Accepted
Room facilities: 🖵 ☎ ☕
Children: Welcome �
Dogs: Welcome
Licenses: ⚓ ♦♦♦
Parking: Off-street and free
Directions: From A10 and A47 to town centre, first left
through Southgates and first right before statue.
Map ref: King's Lynn 9 D2

Guanock Hotel

◆◆◆

South Gates, King's Lynn, Norfolk, PE30 5QJ
Tel: 01553 772959 Fax: 01553 772959
Rooms: 17 🚳
Pricing: Sgl £25–29 Dbl £46–48
Dinner available from £5
CC: Accepted
Room facilities: 🖵 ☕
Children: Welcome �
Licenses: ♦♦♦
Leisure: Games room
Parking: Off-street
Directions: From A47 A17 follow signs to town centre.
Hotel is on right immediately after passing through the
South Gates.
Map ref: King's Lynn 9 D2

Twinson Lee

◆◆◆

109 Tennyson Road, King's Lynn, Norfolk, PE30 5PA
Tel: 01553 762900 Fax: 01533 769944
Seasonal closure: Christmas
Rooms: 3 (1 ensuite) 🚳
Pricing: Sgl £22–25 Dbl £44–50
Dinner available from £6
Room facilities: 🖵 ☕
Children: Welcome ⽕
Dogs: Welcome
Parking: Off-street and free
Directions: Follow Town Centre signs, mini roundabout
third exit Vancouver Avenue, straight on. Twinson Lee
is on right hand side.
Map ref: King's Lynn 9 D2

Lowestoft, Suffolk

Albany Hotel

◆◆◆◆ ✂ ☂

400 London Road South, Lowestoft,
Suffolk, NR33 0BQ
Tel: 01502 574394 Fax: 01502 581198
Email: geoffrey.ward@btclick.com
Web: www.albanyhotel-lowestoft.co.uk
Rooms: 8 (6 ensuite) 🐾 🚳
Dinner available
CC: Accepted
Room facilities: 🖵 ☕
Children: Welcome ⽕ ☕
Dogs: Welcome
Licenses: ♦♦♦
Directions: Situated on A12 northbound, the hotel is
approx 350 yards on right once you have entered the
one-way system.
Map ref: Lowestoft 9 F3

Hazeldene

21 Marine Parade, Lowestoft, Suffolk, NR33 0QL
Tel: 01502 517 907
Email: thelma.davies@tesco.net
Rooms: 5 🐾 ⊗
Pricing: Sgl £22–25 Dbl £44–48
Room facilities: ▢ ⌇
Children: Welcome ⼁
Parking: Off-street and free
Directions: Seafront location at South Beach adjacent to Royal Green. Five minutes walk to town centre, railway station and local amenities.
Map ref: Lowestoft 9 F3

March, Cambridgeshire

The Olde Griffin Hotel

★★

High Street, March, Cambridgeshire, PE15 9JS
Tel: 01354 652517 Fax: 01354 650086
Email: griffhotel@aol.com
Web: www.smoothhound.co.uk/hotels/oldegrif.html

The Olde Griffin is a fine example of a 16th century coaching inn, steeped in history and tradition. The hotel has been owned by Dee Reeve since 1983, during which time it has undergone extensive modernisation and improvements. The hotel now caters for the most discerning patron, who enjoys comfortable ensuite accommodation together with good food.
Rooms: 21 (20 ensuite) 🐾 ⛁
Pricing: Sgl £45 Dbl £59.50
Dinner available from £6.95–16.95
CC: Accepted
Room facilities: ▢ ☎ ⌇ ⌕
Conference: 2 meeting rooms (Thtr 55 max)
Children: Welcome ⼁
Dogs: Welcome
Licenses: ⫙
Parking: Off-street and free
Directions: Entering March from any direction, the hotel is the biggest white building in the middle of the High Street.
Map ref: March 9 D3

Mildenhall, Suffolk

Riverside Hotel

★★★★ ⍥⍥

17 Mill Street, Mildenhall, Suffolk, IP28 7DP
Tel: 01638 717274 Fax: 01638 715997
Email: bookings@riverside-hotel.net
Web: www.riverside-hotel.net
Rooms: 22 all ensuite 🐾 ⛁ ⊗
Pricing: Sgl £69.50–125 Dbl £95–150
Dinner available from £22.50 CC: Accepted
Room facilities: ▢ ☎ ⌇
Access: ⼁⼁
Conference: 2 meeting rooms (Thtr 120 max), 24hr-delegate from £142, day-delegate from £31.50
Children: Welcome ⼁ ⍟
Dogs: Welcome
Licenses: ⌾ ⫙
Parking: Off-street and free
Directions: Follow A11 to 'Fiveways' roundabout, take A1101 into Mildenhall town. Turn left at mini roundabout into the High Street. Hotel is on the left.
Map ref: Mildenhall 9 E3

Smoke House

★★★

Beck Row, Mildenhall, Suffolk, IP28 8DH
Tel: 01638 713223 Fax: 01638 712202
Email: enquiries@smoke-house.co.uk
Web: www.smoke-house.co.uk

Oak beams, log fires and a warm welcome await you at the Smoke House. Facilities include modern bedrooms, two bars, two lounges and a restaurant. 96 bedrooms, all ensuite.
Rooms: 96 all ensuite ⛁ ⊗
Pricing: Sgl £97.50 Dbl £140
Dinner available from £16.95–19.95
CC: Accepted
Room facilities: ▢ ☎ ⌇
Conference: 6 meeting rooms (Thtr 120 max), 24hr-delegate from £100, day-delegate from £32
Children: Welcome ⼁ ⍟
Licenses: ⫙
Parking: Off-street
Directions: A14 to A11 (Mildenhall), left at roundabout, follow A1101 to RAF Mildenhall, through village of Beck Row. Hotel on right.
Map ref: Mildenhall 9 E3

East Anglia

Newmarket, Suffolk

Swynford Paddocks Hotel

★★★ ®

Six Mile Bottom, Newmarket, Suffolk, CB8 0UE
Tel: 01638 570234 Fax: 01638 570283
Email: sales@swynfordpaddocks.com
Web: www.swynfordpaddocks.com
Rooms: 15 all ensuite ◔ ☷
Pricing: Sgl £110–145 Dbl £135–175
Dinner available from £30 CC: Accepted
Room facilities: ▢ ☎ ◵ ✆
Conference: 2 meeting rooms (Thtr 100 max),
24hr-delegate from £145, day-delegate from £40
Children: Welcome ᚼ ℈℃ Dogs: Welcome
Licenses: ◬ ▟
Leisure: Tennis
Parking: Off-street and free
Directions: From Newmarket take A1304 southbound
past racecourse. Straight over at roundabout towards
London. Hotel is in Six Mile Bottom on right.
Map ref: Newmarket 9 D3

The Rutland Arms Hotel

★★★

High Street, Newmarket, Suffolk, CB8 8NB
Tel: 01638 664251 Fax: 01638 666298
Email: gapleisure@rutlandarmshotel.com
Web: www.rutlandarmshotel.com

One of the most distinctive and attractive buildings in
Newmarket, the 'Rutland' combines the very best in
old fashioned hospitality with modern facilities. Stylish
and elegantly furnished rooms are designed for
comfort and relaxation. Civil wedding ceremonies and
wedding events available in fabulous surroundings.
Rooms: 46 all ensuite ☷ ◔
Pricing: Sgl £90 Dbl £114
Dinner available from £19.95
CC: Accepted
Room facilities: ▢ ☎ ◵ ✆
Conference: 4 meeting rooms (Thtr 80 max),
24hr-delegate from £105, day-delegate from £35
Children: Welcome ᚼ
Licenses: ◬ ▟
Parking: Off-street and free
Directions: From M11 take A11 (Junction 9) and signs
to Newmarket town centre. Hotel is on the High Street.
Map ref: Newmarket 9 D3

Norwich, Norfolk

Annesley House Hotel

★★★ ®

6 Newmarket Road, Norwich, Norfolk, NR2 2LA
Tel: 01603 624553 Fax: 01603 621577
Email: annesleyhouse@bestwestern.co.uk
Web: www.bw-annesleyhouse.co.uk
Seasonal closure: Christmas and New Year
Rooms: 26 all ensuite ◔
Pricing: Dinner available from £7.50 CC: Accepted
Room facilities: ▢ ☎ ◵ ✆
Conference: 1 meeting room (Thtr 16 max)
Licenses: ▟
Parking: Off-street and free
Directions: On A11, 1/2 mile from city centre on
right-hand side.
Map ref: Norwich 9 F2

Oaklands Hotel

★★★

89 Yarmouth Road, Thorpe St Andrew, Norfolk, NR7 0HH
Tel: 01603 434471 Fax: 01603 700318
Email: reception@oaklands-hotel.co.uk
Web: www.oaklands-hotel.co.uk
Rooms: 38 all ensuite ◔
Pricing: Dinner available from £23.95
CC: Accepted
Room facilities: ▢ ☎ ◵ ✆
Conference: 4 meeting rooms (Thtr 60 max),
24hr-delegate from £79.50, day-delegate from £23.95
Children: Welcome ᚼ ℈℃
Licenses: ◬ ▟
Parking: Off-street and free
Directions: Turn off the A47 onto the A1042. Then join
the A1242 towards Norwich. The Oaklands is on the
right-hand side.
Map ref: Norwich 9 F2

Quality Hotel Norwich

★★★

2 Barnard Road, Bowthorpe, Norwich,
Norfolk, NR5 9JB
Tel: 01603 741161 Fax: 01603 741500
Email: enquiries@hotels-norwich.com
Web: www.choicehotelseurope.com
Rooms: 80 all ensuite ☷ ◔
Pricing: Sgl £112–125 Dbl £140–150
Dinner available from £17.95 CC: Accepted
Room facilities: ▢ ☎ ◵ ✆ ✳
Conference: 7 meeting rooms (Thtr 200 max),
24hr-delegate from £105, day-delegate from £35
Children: Welcome ᚼ
Licenses: ◬ ▟
Leisure: Indoor pool, Gym
Parking: Off-street and free
Directions: From A11, follow A47 towards Swaffham.
Situated on A1074 Norwich Road. Double roundabout,
follow signage A1074. Situated on next roundabout.
Map ref: Bowthorpe 9 E2

Hotel Wroxham

★★

The Bridge, Wroxham, Norwich, Norfolk, NR12 8AJ
Tel: 01603 782061 Fax: 01603 784279
Email: reservations@hotelwroxham.co.uk
Web: www.hotelwroxham.co.uk

Situated on the banks of the River Bure, in the capital of Broadland, only seven miles from Norwich on the A1151, the Hotel Wroxham is a riverside oasis catering for both the leisure and business visitor. Its unique "Waterside Terrace Bar and Restaurant" serves à la carte, carvery and bar snack meals. Excellent wedding and conference facilities, riverside suites with balconies, private boat moorings and car parking.
Rooms: 18 all ensuite
Pricing: Dinner available from £16
CC: Accepted
Room facilities: ▢ ☎ ☺ ☜
Conference: 3 meeting rooms (Thtr 250 max), 24hr-delegate from £99, day-delegate from £25
Children: Welcome ㅐ
Licenses: ◁ ⭢⭢⭢
Leisure: Fishing
Parking: Off-street and free
Directions: Take A1151 from Norwich at Wroxham, first right after the River Bridge, then hard right again. Car park is on the right.
Map ref: Wroxham 9 F2

Beaufort Lodge

◆◆◆◆ ⊠ ☟

62 Earlham Road, Norwich, Norfolk, NR2 3DF
Tel: 01603 627928 Fax: 01603 440712
Email: beaufortlodge@aol.com
Web: www.beaufortlodge.com
Rooms: 4 (3 ensuite) ☺
Pricing: Sgl £50–60 Dbl £60–65
Room facilities: ▢ ☺
Parking: Off-street and free
Directions: Follow A140 ring road towards airport. At B1108 roundabout take exit signed city centre Earlham Road, 1½ miles to Beaufort Lodge on right.
Map ref: Norwich 9 F2

Bristol House Hotel

◆◆◆◆ ⊠

80 Unthank Road, Norwich, Norfolk, NR2 2RW
Tel: 01603 625729 Fax: 01603 625794
Rooms: 9 all ensuite ☺
Pricing: Sgl £48–55 Dbl £65–75 CC: Accepted
Room facilities: ▢ ☺
Children: Welcome 12yrs min age
Licenses: ⭢⭢⭢
Parking: Off-street and free
Directions: 10 minutes to City Centre. 10 minutes to University of East Anglia.
Map ref: Norwich 9 F2

Edmar Lodge

◆◆◆

64 Earlham Road, Norwich, Norfolk, NR2 3DF
Tel: 01603 615599 Fax: 01603 495599
Email: mail@edmarlodge.co.uk
Web: www.edmarlodge.co.uk

Edmar Lodge is a family-run guest house where you will find a warm welcome. Digital TV in rooms. We are situated only 10 minutes walk from city centre. Non-smoking.
Rooms: 5 all ensuite ☺
Pricing: Sgl £35–40 Dbl £40–44 CC: Accepted
Room facilities: ▢ ☺
Children: Welcome ㅐ Dogs: Welcome
Parking: Off-street
Directions: Ring road or A47 take B1108 into city. Edmar Lodge on the right towards city, just past controlled zone signs.
Map ref: Norwich 9 F2

Wedgewood House

◆◆◆ ☟

42 St Stephen's Road, Norwich, Norfolk, NR1 3RE
Tel: 01603 625730 Fax: 01603 615035
Email: stay@wedgewoodhouse.co.uk
Web: www.wedgewoodhouse.co.uk
Rooms: 12 (9 ensuite) ☙ ☺
Pricing: Sgl £31–34 Dbl £50–60 CC: Accepted
Room facilities: ▢ ☺
Children: Welcome
Parking: Off-street and free
Directions: Follow A11 or A140 towards city centre, Wedgewood House is on right, opposite old hospital.
Map ref: Norwich 9 F2

Old Hunstanton, Norfolk

The Neptune Inn & Restaurant
Restaurant with Rooms

85 Old Hunstanton Road, Old Hunstanton,
Norfolk, PE36 6HZ
Tel: 01485 532122 Fax: 01485 535314
Email: reservations@theneptune.co.uk
Web: www.theneptune.co.uk

Charming 18th century coaching inn situated on north
Norfolk coast. Refurbished by new owners in New
England style. Located in area of outstanding natural
beauty near beach and golf course.
Rooms: 7 all ensuite
Pricing: Sgl £50–70 Dbl £90–100 Dinner available
CC: Accepted
Room facilities:
Children: Welcome 10yrs min age
Dogs: Welcome
Licenses:
Parking: Off-street and free
Directions: Follow A149 from King's Lynn to
Hunstanton. The Neptune is situated on the A149 in
the village of Old Hunstanton.
Map ref: Old Hunstanton 9 D2

Peterborough, Cambridgeshire

Bull Hotel
★★★

Westgate, Peterborough, Cambridgeshire, PE1 1RB
Tel: 01733 561364 Fax: 01733 557304
Email: info@bull-hotel-peterborough.com
Web: www.peelhotel.com
Rooms: 118 all ensuite
Pricing: Sgl £55–95 Dbl £65–105
Dinner available from £21.50 CC: Accepted
Room facilities:
Conference: 12 meeting rooms (Thtr 300 max),
24hr-delegate from £145, day-delegate from £39
Children: Welcome Dogs: Welcome
Licenses: Parking: Off-street
Directions: From A1, follow city centre signs. Boures
Boulevard, St John's Road. First left at roundabout,
New Road, right along Northminster, hotel on left.
Map ref: Peterborough 8 C3

Ramada
★★★

Thorpe Meadows, off Longthorpe Parkway,
Peterborough, Cambridgeshire, PE3 6GA
Tel: 01733 564240 Fax: 01733 565538
Email: reception@ramadapeterborough.co.uk
Web: www.ramadainternational.com

 R A M A D A.

Rooms: 70 all ensuite
Pricing: Sgl £69.95–89.95 Dbl £79.90–99.90
Dinner available from £17.50
CC: Accepted
Room facilities:
Conference: 5 meeting rooms (Thtr 80 max),
24hr-delegate from £97.50, day-delegate from £32.50
Children: Welcome
Licenses:
Parking: Off-street and free
Directions: A1(M) follow signs to city centre, then
Thorpe Meadows and rowing course.
Map ref: Peterborough 8 C3

Sleep Inn Peterborough
Travel Accommodation

Peterborough Services, Great North Road, Haddon,
Peterborough, Cambridgeshire, PE7 3UQ
Tel: 01733 396850 Fax: 01733 396869
Email: enquiries@hotels-peterborough.co.uk
Web: www.choicehotelseurope.com
Rooms: 82 all ensuite
Pricing: Sgl £55 Dbl £66
CC: Accepted
Room facilities:
Children: Welcome
Leisure: Games room
Parking: Off-street and free
Directions: On junction of A605 and Junction 17 A1(M)
2 miles west of Peterborough.
Map ref: Peterborough 8 C3

Southwold, Suffolk

28 Fieldstile Road
◆◆◆

28 Fieldstile Road, Southwold, Suffolk, IP18 6LD
Tel: 01502 723588 Fax: 01502 723588
Seasonal closure: November to February
Rooms: 3
Pricing: Dbl £60
Room facilities:
Children: Welcome
Dogs: Welcome
Directions: Southwold. Cross mini-roundabout, first
left. Past church & hospital towards seafront, No.28
left side with sign and red door.
Map ref: Southwold 9 F3

East Anglia

St Ives, Cambridgeshire

Dolphin Hotel

★★★

London Road, St Ives, Huntingdon,
Cambridgeshire, PE27 5EP
Tel: 01480 466966 Fax: 01480 495597
Email: enquiries@dolphinhotelcambs.co.uk
Web: www.dolphinhotelcambs.co.uk
Rooms: 67 all ensuite 🐾 📠 ⊗
Pricing: Sgl £80–100 Dbl £100–130
Dinner available from £14.50–350 CC: Accepted
Room facilities: 🖵 ☎ ⊗ 🌺
Conference: 1 meeting room (Thtr 150 max),
24hr-delegate from £100, day-delegate from £30
Children: Welcome Licenses: ⟁ ♟
Leisure: Gym, Fishing
Parking: Off-street and free
Directions: From A14, take A1096 towards St Ives.
Turn left at first roundabout, then immediately right.
The Dolphin is 800 yards further on.
Map ref: Huntingdon 9 D3

Slepe Hall Hotel

★★★

Ramsey Road, St Ives, Cambridgeshire, PE27 5RB
Tel: 01480 463122 Fax: 01480 300706
Email: mail@slepehall.co.uk
Web: www.slepehall.co.uk
Seasonal closure: 25 December and 1 January

A former private Victorian girls' school, Slepe Hall is an
excellent starting point for visiting Cambridgeshire and
boasts a popular restaurant offering high quality English
and continental cuisine and a modern bar menu.
Rooms: 16 all ensuite 📠
Pricing: Sgl £50–100 Dbl £75–120
Dinner available from £10 CC: Accepted
Room facilities: 🖵 ☎ ⊗ 🌺
Conference: 4 meeting rooms (Thtr 200 max),
24hr-delegate from £115, day-delegate from £25
Children: Welcome ⟡ Dogs: Welcome
Licenses: ⟁ ♟
Parking: Off-street and free
Directions: Leave A14 on A1096. At roundabout with
Manchester Arms pub, A1123 towards Huntingdon. At
traffic lights by Toyota garage turn left. Slepe Hall ⅓
mile on left.
Map ref: St Ives (Cambs) 9 D3

Stretham, Cambridgeshire

The Red Lion

◆◆◆

47 High Street, Stretham, near Ely,
Cambridgeshire, CB6 3JQ
Tel: 01353 648132 Fax: 01353 648327
Email: info@redlion-stretham.co.uk
Web: www.redlion-stretham.co.uk
Rooms: 10 all ensuite
Room facilities: 🖵 ☎ ⊗ 🌺
Children: Welcome ♟
Dogs: Welcome
Parking: Off-street and free
Map ref: Stretham 9 D3

Sudbury, Suffolk

Mill Hotel

★★★★ ⃝

Walnut Tree Lane, Sudbury, Suffolk, CO10 1BD
Tel: 01787 375544 Fax: 01787 373027
Email: reservations@millhotelsuffolk.co.uk
Web: www.millhotelsuffolk.co.uk
Rooms: 56 all ensuite 📠 ⊗
Pricing: Sgl £67–70.50 Dbl £105–154
Dinner available from £25 CC: Accepted
Room facilities: 🖵 ☎ ⊗ 🌺
Conference: 5 meeting rooms (Thtr 70 max),
24hr-delegate from £85, day-delegate from £25
Children: Welcome ♟ ⟡ Dogs: Welcome
Licenses: ♟
Parking: Off-street and free
Directions: From A12 Colchester take A134 to
Sudbury. Follow signs for A131. Pass main square,
third on right.
Map ref: Sudbury (Suffolk) 9 E4

Swaffham, Norfolk

Lydney House Hotel

★★

Norwich Road, Swaffham, Norfolk, PE37 7QS
Tel: 01760 723355 Fax: 01760 721410
Email: rooms@lydney-house.demon.co.uk
Web: www.lydney-house.demon.co.uk
Rooms: 12 all ensuite 📠
Pricing: Sgl £70–80 Dbl £90–100
Dinner available from £12
CC: Accepted
Room facilities: 🖵 ☎ ⊗ 🌺
Conference: 2 meeting rooms (Thtr 140 max),
24hr-delegate from £82.50, day-delegate from £27.50
Children: Welcome ♟ Dogs: Welcome
Licenses: ♟
Parking: Off-street and free
Directions: Lydney House can be found on Norwich
Road, ¼ mile from traffic lights in centre of town.
Map ref: Swaffham 9 E2

Thetford, Norfolk

Comfort Inn Thetford

★★

Thetford Road, Northwold, near Thetford,
Norfolk, IP26 5LQ
Tel: 01366 728888 Fax: 01366 727121
Email: enquiries@hotels-thetford.com
Web: www.choicehotelseurope.com
Rooms: 34 all ensuite
Pricing: Sgl £55–85 Dbl £65–130
Dinner available from £14.95 CC: Accepted
Room facilities:
Conference: 2 meeting rooms (Thtr 160 max),
24hr-delegate from £85, day-delegate from £30
Children: Welcome 🏌 Dogs: Welcome
Licenses: 🏵 🍴
Parking: Off-street and free
Directions: From Thetford roundabout (A11/A134 north)
follow A134 north for 12 miles, over a roundabout and
past Northwold. Hotel then on left.
Map ref: Northwold 9 E3

Tivetshall St Mary, Norfolk

Old Ram Coaching Inn

★★★🐾

Ipswich Road, Tivetshall St Mary, Norfolk, NR15 2DE
Tel: 01379 606000 Fax: 01379 608399
Email: theoldram@btinternet.com
Web: www.theoldram.com

Listed 17th century hotel, restaurant and free house.
Award-winning food. Big on fish. Over-sixties' and
children's menus. Superb accommodation, meeting
space. Ample car parking. Dining on terrace in
summer.
Rooms: 11 all ensuite 🛏
Pricing: Sgl £60.50–66.50 Dbl £83–94
Dinner available from £11.95
CC: Accepted
Room facilities:
Conference: 1 meeting room (Thtr 20 max),
24hr-delegate from £99.95, day-delegate from £24.95
Children: Welcome 🏌
Licenses: 🍴
Parking: Off-street and free
Directions: On the A140, 15 minutes south of Norwich
and the A47 bypass. Five miles from the market town
of Diss.
Map ref: Tivetshall St Mary 9 E3

Wells-next-the-Sea, Norfolk

Mill House

◆◆◆◆ ✍

Northfield Lane, Wells-next-the-Sea,
Norfolk, NR23 1JZ
Tel: 01328 710739
Map ref: Wells-next-the-sea 9 E2

Kilcoroon

◆◆◆

Chancery Lane, Wells-next-the-Sea,
Norfolk, NR23 1ER
Tel: 01328 710270
Email: guest@kilcoroon.co.uk
Web: www.smoothhound.co.uk/hotels/kilcoroon.html
Rooms: 3 (1 ensuite) 🚭
Room facilities: 📺 🍵
Children: Welcome 10yrs min age
Directions: At Wells town sign, turn towards town
centre. Third turning right onto Buttlands, Kilcoroon
situated left of Crown Hotel.
Map ref: Wells-next-the-Sea 9 E2

Oyster Cottage Bed & Breakfast

◆◆◆

Oyster Cottage, 20 High Street, Wells-next-the-Sea,
Norfolk, NR23 1EP
Tel: 01328 711997 Fax: 01328 711910
Email: bb@oyster-cottage.com
Web: www.oyster-cottage.com
Rooms: 4 all ensuite 🛏 🚭
Room facilities: 📺 🍵
Children: Welcome 🏌
Dogs: Welcome
Directions: From town sign take Mill Road to town
centre, at junction by Barclays Bank. High Street is on
the right.
Map ref: Wells-next-the-sea 9 E2

Are the bells ringing?

Getting married? Congratulations!
Look for the wedding bells symbol
which shows hotels licensed for
civil ceremonies.

Wisbech, Cambridgeshire

Crown Lodge Hotel

★★★

Downham Road, Outwell, Wisbech,
Cambridgeshire, PE14 8SE
Tel: 01945 773391 Fax: 01945 772668
Email: crownlodgehotel@hotmail.com
Web: www.thecrownlodgehotel.co.uk
Seasonal closure: 25-26 December and 31 December

Situated on the banks of Well Creek, in the village of
Outwell, this family-run hotel offers a warm, friendly
atmosphere with excellent standards of
accommodation and cuisine.
Rooms: 10 all ensuite ⊗
Pricing: Sgl £62 Dbl £84
Dinner available from £18.75
CC: Accepted
Room facilities: ☐ ☎ ☺ ⌐
Conference: 1 meeting room (Thtr 50 max)
Children: Welcome ⋔
Dogs: Welcome
Licenses: ▪▪▪
Leisure: Snooker/billiards, Squash courts
Parking: Off-street and free
Directions: Situated on the A1122/A1101 Downham
Market to Wisbech road. Approximately 5 miles to
Wisbech and 7 miles to Downham Market.
Map ref: Outwell 9 D3

The big sleep

As part of our comprehensive
inspection process, RAC
Inspectors investigate the comfort of the beds.

Arundel House Hotel, Cambridge

East Midlands

South
Cave
Hessle
New
Holland
Hedon
Withernsea
**Kingston
upon Hull**
Humber Br.
ton
Barton-upon-
Humber
Patrington
Easington
Immingham
Barnetby
le Wold
Grimsby
Spurn Head
cunthorpe
Broughton
Humberside
Cleethorpes
Brigg
THE LINCOLNSHIRE
Caistor
irton in
indsey
Lincolnshire
Wolds
North Somercotes
borough
Market
Rasen
Louth
Mablethorpe
Sutton on Sea
Sandilands
Wragby
Chapel St Leonards
North
Kelham
Lincoln
Branston
Horncastle
Alford
Woodhall Spa
Spilsby
Skegness
South
Hykeham
Metheringham
Wainfleet
All Saints
LINCOLNSHIRE
Tattershall
Cranwell
Brancaster
Roads
Sleaford
Boston
THE WASH
Old
Hunstanton
Burnham
Market
Swineshead
Kirton
Hunstanton
Grantham
Donington
Sutterton
Docking
Sandringham
Corby Glen
Gedney
Drove End
orth
North Witham
Holbeach
Long Sutton
**King's
Lynn**
Grimston
Bourne
Spalding
Clenchwarton
Market
Deeping
Crowland
Stamford
Wisbech
Downham
Market
Thorney
Outwell
Wansford
Guyhirn
March
Whittlesey
Peterborough
Haddon
Stilton
CAMBR
Oundle
Ramsey
Chatteris
Thrapston
Huntingdon
Raunds
rthlingborough
Higham
Ferrers
Godmanchester
Buckden
ushden
St Neots
pton
Bedford
Olney
Kempston
ewport
agnell
Ampthill
aspley
suise
Woburn
ighton
zzard

Glasgow • • Edinburgh
Belfast •
• Newcastle
Dublin •
• Manchester
Birmingham •
Cardiff •
London

Award winners

To help you choose somewhere really special for your stay, we've listed here all RAC Award-winning properties in this region.

Gold Ribbon Award

		pg
Stapleford Park Hotel, Melton Mowbray	★★★★	302

Blue Ribbon Award

Excellent

		pg
Cavendish Hotel, Baslow	★★★	290
George of Stamford, Stamford	★★★	307

White Ribbon Award

Commended

		pg
George Hotel, Hathersage	★★★	296
Kettering Park Hotel and Spa, Kettering	★★★★	297
Riber Hall, Matlock	★★★	301

Little Gem Award

Little Gem

		pg
Buckingham's Hotel and The Restaurant With One Table, Chesterfield	◆◆◆◆	293
Dannah Farm Country House, Belper	◆◆◆◆◆	290
Rock Lodge, Stamford	◆◆◆◆◆	307
The Grange Courtyard, Shepshed	◆◆◆◆◆	304

George of Stamford, Stamford

George Hotel, Hathersage

The Grange Courtyard, Shepshed

Dannah Farm Country House, Belper

Ashbourne, Derbyshire

Callow Hall Hotel

Mappleton, Ashbourne, Derbyshire, DE6 2AA
Tel: 01335 300900 Fax: 01335 300512
Email: reservations@callowhall.co.uk
Web: www.callowhall.co.uk
Seasonal closure: Christmas Day and Boxing Day

Situated at the Gateway to the Peak National Park.
Family run — providing utmost comfort and superb
food in a graceful country house setting. Close to
many stately homes and attractions.
Rooms: 16 all ensuite
Pricing: Sgl £95–120 Dbl £135–200
Dinner available from £39.50 CC: Accepted
Room facilities:
Conference: 3 meeting rooms (Thtr 30 max),
24hr-delegate from £155, day-delegate from £30
Children: Welcome Dogs: Welcome
Licenses:
Leisure: Fishing
Parking: Off-street and free
Directions: Follow A515 through Ashbourne (Buxton
direction). At top of hill turn left at Bowling Green pub.
Then first right for Mappleton Road, over bridge, Hall
on right.
Map ref: Mappleton 8 A2

Dog and Partridge Country Inn
★★

Swinscoe, Ashbourne, Derbyshire, DE6 2HS
Tel: 01335 343183 Fax: 01335 342742
Email: info@dogpartridge.co.uk
Web: www.dogandpartridge.co.uk
Rooms: 29 all ensuite
Pricing: Dinner available from £18.95 CC: Accepted
Room facilities:
Conference: 5 meeting rooms (Thtr 25 max),
24hr-delegate from £85, day-delegate from £25
Children: Welcome Dogs: Welcome
Licenses:
Leisure: Fishing
Parking: Off-street and free
Directions: Follow A52 from Ashbourne towards Leek.
Located on the left-hand side, 3 miles from
Ashbourne.
Map ref: Swinscoe 8 A2

Ashby-de-la-Zouch, Leicestershire

The Royal Hotel
★★★

Station Road, Ashby-de-la-Zouch,
Leicestershire, LE65 2GP
Tel: 01530 412833 Fax: 01530 564548
Email: theroyalhotel@email.com
Web: www.royalhotelashby.com
Rooms: 34 all ensuite
Pricing: Sgl £40–70 Dbl £65–95
Dinner available from £18–24
CC: Accepted
Room facilities:
Conference: 3 meeting rooms (Thtr 70 max),
24hr-delegate from £105, day-delegate from £25
Children: Welcome Dogs: Welcome
Licenses:
Parking: Off-street and free
Directions: J12 on the A42/M42, continue towards
Ashby-de-la-Zouch. The Royal Hotel is approximately
1 mile from J12 on the right hand side.
Map ref: Ashby-de-la-Zouch 8 B2

Fallen Knight Restaurant & Hotel
◆◆◆

Kilwardby Street, Ashby-de-la-Zouch,
Leicestershire, LE65 2FQ
Tel: 01530 412230 Fax: 01530 417596
Web: www.fallenknight.co.uk
Rooms: 24 all ensuite
Pricing: Sgl £45–65 Dbl £69–125
Dinner available from £21–30
CC: Accepted
Room facilities:
Access:
Conference: 1 meeting room (Thtr 80 max),
day-delegate from £170
Children: Welcome Dogs: Welcome
Licenses:
Parking: Off-street and free
Directions: Situated 150 yards from town centre.
Map ref: Ashby-de-la-Zouch 8 B2

Ashover, Derbyshire

Old School Farm
◆◆◆◆

Uppertown, Ashover, Derbyshire, S45 0JF
Tel: 01246 590813
Seasonal closure: November to March
Rooms: 4 (2 ensuite)
Pricing: Sgl £25–26 Dbl £50–54
Room facilities:
Children: Welcome
Parking: Off-street and free
Directions: Take A362 Chesterfield to Matlock road.
Turn onto the B5057 Darley Dale road. Turn left to
Uppertown.
Map ref: Ashover 8 B1

East Midlands

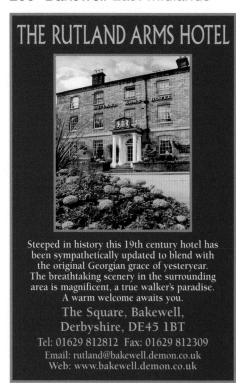

THE RUTLAND ARMS HOTEL

Steeped in history this 19th century hotel has been sympathetically updated to blend with the original Georgian grace of yesteryear. The breathtaking scenery in the surrounding area is magnificent, a true walker's paradise. A warm welcome awaits you.

The Square, Bakewell, Derbyshire, DE45 1BT

Tel: 01629 812812 Fax: 01629 812309
Email: rutland@bakewell.demon.co.uk
Web: www.bakewell.demon.co.uk

Bakewell, Derbyshire

Rutland Arms Hotel

★★★★ 🛏🛏

The Square, Bakewell, Derbyshire, DE45 1BT
Tel: 01629 812812 Fax: 01629 812309
Email: rutland@bakewell.demon.co.uk
Web: www.rutlandarmsbakewell.com
Rooms: 35 all ensuite 🛏 📺 ⊗
Pricing: Sgl £55–64 Dbl £94–104
Dinner available from £24.50–28.50
CC: Accepted
Room facilities: ▯ ☎ ☕
Conference: 2 meeting rooms (Thtr 100 max),
24hr-delegate from £119, day-delegate from £39
Children: Welcome ⼁ ⼎
Dogs: Welcome
Licenses: ⋔
Parking: Off-street and free
Directions: The hotel is in the centre of Bakewell.
Map ref: Bakewell 8 A1
See advert on this page

Barton-upon-Humber, Lincolnshire

Reeds Hotel

★★★★ 🛏

Westfield Lakes, Far-ings Road, Barton-upon-Humber,
Lincolnshire, DN18 5RG
Tel: 01652 632313 Fax: 01652 636361
Email: info@reedshotel.co.uk
Web: www.reedshotel.co.uk
Rooms: 31 all ensuite 🛏 📺 ⊗
Dinner available
CC: Accepted
Room facilities: ▯ ☎ ☕ ⼍
Access: ⊩⼁
Conference: 4 meeting rooms (Thtr 300 max)
Children: Welcome ⼁ ⼎
Licenses: ◈ ⋔
Parking: Off-street and free
Directions: Exit M180 onto A15 at Barton-upon-
Humber. Take first exit onto A1077. Take first right,
hotel is straight on.
Map ref: Barton-upon-Humber 11 E4

Baslow, Derbyshire

Cavendish Hotel

★★★★ 🛏🛏🛏

Excellent

Church Lane, Baslow, Derbyshire, DE45 1SP
Tel: 0845 4561753
Fax: 01246 582312
Email: info@cavendish-hotel.net
Web: www.cavendish-hotel.net
Rooms: 24 all ensuite 🛏 📺 ⊗
Pricing: Sgl £106–143 Dbl £139–178
Dinner available from £30–45
CC: Accepted
Room facilities: ▯ ☎ ☕ ⼍
Conference: 2 meeting rooms (Thtr 20 max),
24hr-delegate from £192, day-delegate from £38
Children: Welcome ⼁ ⼎
Licenses: ⋔
Leisure: Fishing
Parking: Off-street and free
Directions: From M1 exit 29 follow A617 to
Chesterfield. Take A619 to Baslow, Cavendish is on
left-hand side.
Map ref: Baslow 8 B1

Belper, Derbyshire

Dannah Farm Country House Little Gem

◆◆◆◆◆ 🛏 ⼐ ⼍

Bowmans Lane, Shottle, Belper, Derbyshire, DE56 2DR
Tel: 01773 550273 Fax: 01773 550590
Email: slack@dannah.demon.co.uk
Web: www.dannah.co.uk
Rooms: 8 all ensuite 🛏 📺 ⊗
Pricing: Sgl £65–85 Dbl £90–170
Dinner available from £23.95
CC: Accepted

Room facilities: ☐ ☎ ☕ 📞
Conference: 12 meeting rooms (Thtr 12 max),
24hr-delegate from £120, day-delegate from £32.50
Children: Welcome
Licenses: ♦♦♦
Parking: Off-street and free
Directions: From Belper A517 signposted Ashbourne.
Past Hanging Gate pub, next right signposted Shottle.
1½ miles, over crossroads, next right Bowmans Lane.
Map ref: Shottle 8 B2
See advert on this page

Buckminster, Leicestershire

The Tollemache Arms

 New for 2006

48 Main Street, Buckminster, Leicestershire, NG33 5SA
Tel: 01476 860007
Email: enquiries@thetollemachearms.com
Web: www.thetollemachearms.com
Rooms: 5 all ensuite ⊛
Pricing: Sgl £45 Dbl £60
Dinner available from £16–40
CC: Accepted
Room facilities: ☐ ☕
Children: Welcome ♒ ☕
Dogs: Welcome
Licenses: ♦♦♦
Parking: Off-street and free
Directions: Follow turn-off to Buckminster from M1.
Map ref: Buckminster 8 C2

Burbage, Leicestershire

Burbage Guest House

♦♦♦♦ ☆☌

2 Windsor Street, Burbage, Leicestershire, LE10 2EF
Tel: 01455 615990
Email: bobsuinman@aol.com
Web: www.burbageguesthouse.co.uk
Rooms: 7 all ensuite ☕ ⊛
Pricing: Sgl £55 Dbl £75
CC: Accepted
Room facilities: ☐ ☕ 📞
Conference: 1 meeting room (Thtr 30 max)
Children: Welcome
Dogs: Welcome
Parking: Off-street and free
Map ref: Burbage 8 B3

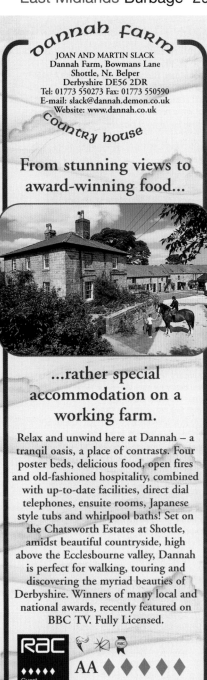

Buxton, Derbyshire

Palace Hotel

★★★★

Palace Road, Buxton, Derbyshire, SK17 6AG
Tel: 01298 22001 Fax: 01298 72131
Email: palacereservations@paramount-hotels.co.uk
Web: www.paramount-hotels.co.uk

PARAMOUNT
GROUP OF HOTELS

The Palace is an historic Victorian hotel situated within
5 acres of beautifully manicured gardens. The
magnificent features and friendly service combine to
ensure that your stay at Palace Hotel is truly memorable.
Rooms: 122 all ensuite
Pricing: Sgl £60–110 Dbl £120
Dinner available from £21.50 CC: Accepted
Room facilities: Access:
Conference: 7 meeting rooms (Thtr 300 max),
24hr-delegate from £148, day-delegate from £43
Children: Welcome Dogs: Welcome
Licenses:
Leisure: Indoor pool, Gym, Beauty salon
Parking: Off-street
Directions: From M6 north, exit at junction 20, follow
Stockport signs then A6 to Buxton, hotel is in Buxton
town centre, adjacent to railway station.
Map ref: Buxton 7 F1

Best Western Leewood Hotel

★★★★

The Park, Buxton, Derbyshire, SK17 6TQ
Tel: 01298 23002 Fax: 01298 23228
Email: leewoodhotel@btinternet.com
Web: www.leewoodhotel.co.uk
Rooms: 40 all ensuite
Pricing: Sgl £75–95 Dbl £115–140
Dinner available from £29.50 CC: Accepted
Room facilities: Access:
Conference: 10 meeting rooms (Thtr 120 max),
24hr-delegate from £130, day-delegate from £45
Children: Welcome Dogs: Welcome
Licenses:
Leisure: Games room, Snooker/billiards
Parking: Off-street and free

Directions: From North, leave M1 at Junction 29,
Chesterfield-Baslow-Buxton. From South, leave M1 at
Junction 23A/24: take A50 for approx 19 miles then
A515 to Buxton.
Map ref: Buxton 7 F1

Buckingham Hotel

★★★

1-2 Burlington Road, Buxton, Derbyshire, SK17 9AS
Tel: 01298 70481 Fax: 01298 72186
Email: frontdesk@buckinghamhotel.co.uk
Web: www.buckinghamhotel.co.uk
Seasonal closure: Christmas
Rooms: 37 all ensuite
Pricing: Sgl £45–70 Dbl £90–105
Dinner available from £20.50 CC: Accepted
Room facilities:
Access:
Conference: 3 meeting rooms (Thtr 75 max),
24hr-delegate from £90, day-delegate from £27.50
Children: Welcome
Dogs: Welcome
Licenses:
Parking: Off-street and free
Directions: Opposite Pavilion Gardens car park (brown
tourist signs). At junction of Burlington/St Johns Road
(A53), own car park (40).
Map ref: Buxton 7 F1

Grove Hotel

★★

Grove Parade, Buxton, Derbyshire, SK17 6AJ
Tel: 01298 23804 Fax: 01298 71229
Email: brewery@frederic-robinson.co.uk
Web: www.frederic-robinson.com
Rooms: 14 all ensuite
Pricing: Sgl £40–70 Dbl £50–95
Dinner available from £10.50 CC: Accepted
Room facilities:
Children: Welcome
Licenses:
Directions: Grove Hotel is situated in the town centre,
opposite Spa Baths.
Map ref: Buxton 7 F1

Netherdale Guest House

♦♦♦♦

16 Green Lane, Buxton, Derbyshire, SK17 9DP
Tel: 01298 23896 Fax: 01298 73771
Seasonal closure: November to January
Rooms: 10 (8 ensuite)
Pricing: Sgl £25–45 Dbl £50–75
Room facilities:
Children: Welcome 10yrs min age
Licenses:
Parking: Off-street and free
Directions: From London Road traffic lights, the hotel
is 600 metres up Green Lane towards Pooles Cavern
on the right-hand side.
Map ref: Buxton 7 F1

Hawthorn Farm Guest House

 ◆◆◆

Fairfield Road, Buxton, Derbyshire, SK17 7ED
Tel: 01298 23230 Fax: 01298 71322
Email: alan.pimblett@virgin.net
Web: www.hawthorn-farm.co.uk
Rooms: 10 (6 ensuite) 🛏 🚭
Pricing: Sgl £25–35 Dbl £55–65
CC: Accepted
Room facilities: 🖵 🍵
Children: Welcome ♁ 🍼
Dogs: Welcome
Parking: Off-street and free
Directions: Hawthorn Farm is situated on the A6
towards Manchester on leaving Buxton.
Map ref: Buxton 7 F1

Castle Donington, Leicestershire

Donington Park Farmhouse Hotel

 ◆◆◆◆ 🦌

Melbourne Road, Isley Walton, near Derby,
Leicestershire, DE74 2RN
Tel: 01332 862409 Fax: 01332 862364
Email: info@parkfarmhouse.co.uk
Web: www.parkfarmhouse.co.uk
Seasonal closure: Christmas
Rooms: 19 all ensuite 🛏 🚭
Pricing: Sgl £65–140 Dbl £95–140
Dinner available from £14
CC: Accepted
Room facilities: 🖵 ☎ 🍵 🎣
Conference: 4 meeting rooms (Thtr 100 max),
24hr-delegate from £105, day-delegate from £30
Children: Welcome ♁ 🍼
Dogs: Welcome
Licenses: ◇ ♟
Leisure: Deer stalking courses
Parking: Off-street and free
Directions: From exit 23A or 24 on M1, proceed past
East Midlands airport to Isley Walton. Turn right, hotel
is ¹/₂ mile on right.
Map ref: Isley Walton 8 B2

Chapel St Leonards, Lincolnshire

South Sands

 ◆◆◆

35 South Road, Chapel St Leonards, Skegness,
Lincolnshire, PE24 5TL
Tel: 01754 873066 Fax: 01754 873066
Rooms: 4 (2 ensuite) 🛏 🚭
Pricing: Dbl £44
Room facilities: 🖵 🍵
Children: Welcome ♁
Licenses: ♟
Leisure: Games room
Parking: Off-street and free
Map ref: Chapel St Leonards 9 D1

Chesterfield, Derbyshire

Abbeydale Hotel

 ★★★ 🛏🛏

Cross Street, Chesterfield, Derbyshire, S40 4TD
Tel: 01246 277849 Fax: 01246 558223
Email: abbeydale1ef@aol.com
Web: www.abbeydalehotel.co.uk
Seasonal closure: 24 December to 1 January
Rooms: 12 all ensuite 🛏 🚭
Pricing: Sgl £45 Dbl £60–70
Dinner available from £22 CC: Accepted
Room facilities: 🖵 ☎ 🍵 🎣
Children: Welcome
Licenses: ♟
Parking: Off-street and free
Directions: From M1 J29 to Chesterfield, A619 towards
Chatsworth/Buxton. At third roundabout, B&Q, third
exit to Foljambe Road, over traffic lights into West
Street. Right at T-junction into Cross Street.
Map ref: Chesterfield 8 B1

Buckingham's Hotel and The Restaurant With One Table `Little Gem`

◆◆◆◆ 🛏🛏 🗡 🦌

85 Newbold Road, Newbold,
Chesterfield, Derbyshire, S41 7PU
Tel: 01246 201041 Fax: 01246 550059
Email: info@buckinghams-table.com
Web: www.buckinghams-table.com
Rooms: 10 all ensuite 🛏 🚭
Pricing: Sgl £60–80 Dbl £80–100
Dinner available from £17.50–27.50 CC: Accepted
Room facilities: 🖵 ☎ 🍵 🎣
Conference: 2 meeting rooms (Thtr 8 max),
24hr-delegate from £120, day-delegate from £40
Children: Welcome ♁ 🍼 Dogs: Welcome
Licenses: ♟
Parking: Off-street and free
Directions: From M1 exit 29. Follow A617 to
Chesterfield town centre. Take B6051 (Barlow).
Buckingham's is 800 yards on the right.
Map ref: Newbold 8 B1

Twin Oaks Hotel
Travel Accommodation

M1 Junction 29, Church Lane, Palterton, Chesterfield,
Derbyshire, S44 6UZ
Tel: 01246 855455 Fax: 01246 851708
Email: rob@twinoakshotel.co.uk
Web: www.twinoakshotel.co.uk
Rooms: 22 (20 ensuite) 🛏 🚭
Pricing: Dinner available from £7.95 CC: Accepted
Room facilities: 🖵 ☎ 🍵 🎣
Conference: 2 meeting rooms (Thtr 60 max)
Children: Welcome ♁ Dogs: Welcome
Licenses: ♟ Leisure: Gym, Snooker/billiards
Parking: Off-street and free
Directions: From M1 junction 29 roundabout, take
Palterton exit, 100 yards turn left into hotel.
Map ref: Palterton 8 B1

East Midlands

Coalville, Leicestershire

Hermitage Park Hotel

★★★

Whitwick Road, Coalville, Leicestershire, LE67 3FA
Tel: 01530 814814 Fax: 01530 814202
Email: hotel@hermitageparkhotel.co.uk
Web: www.hermitageparkhotel.co.uk

This independently owned hotel overlooks a bowling green. The Lamp House restaurant has a varied seasonal menu. The hotel can be booked for weddings and other functions. Good access from motorways and close to commercial areas.
Rooms: 25 all ensuite ⊛
Pricing: Sgl £60–70 Dbl £65.50–75.50
Dinner available from £11.95
CC: Accepted
Room facilities: ▢ ☎ ⊙ ⟍
Conference: 5 meeting rooms (Thtr 60 max),
24hr-delegate from £98.50, day-delegate from £19.50
Children: Welcome ⟊ ⟩⟨
Dogs: Assistance dogs only
Licenses: ⟁ ⓲
Parking: Off-street and free
Directions: Exit Junction 13/A42 or Junction 22/M1 and take A511 to Coalville, then follow tourism signs from A511 to Hermitage Park Hotel.
Map ref: Coalville 8 B2

Daventry, Northamptonshire

Hellidon Lakes

★★★★ ⓡ

Hellidon, Daventry, Northamptonshire, NN11 6GG
Tel: 01327 262550 Fax: 01327 262559
Email: hellidon@marstonhotels.com
Web: www.marstonhotels.com
Rooms: 110 all ensuite ⟆ ⊛
Dinner available
CC: Accepted
Room facilities: ▢ ☎ ⊙ ⟍
Access: ⟦⟧
Conference: 22 meeting rooms (Thtr 300 max)
Children: Welcome ⟊ ⟩⟨
Licenses: ⟁ ⓲
Leisure: Indoor pool, Gym, Health spa, Beauty salon, Tennis, Golf, Fishing
Parking: Off-street and free
Directions: Leave M1 at junction 16, take A45 to Daventry, take A361 to Banbury, turn right towards Hellidon then second right.
Map ref: Hellidon 8 B3

The Daventry Hotel

★★★★

Sedgemoor Way, Daventry,
Northamptonshire, NN11 0SG
Tel: 01327 307000 Fax: 01327 706313
Email: daventry@paramount-hotels.co.uk
Web: www.paramount-hotels.co.uk

PARAMOUNT
GROUP OF HOTELS

Stylish and elegant, located in the Nene Valley close to Silverstone, with a superb fully equipped leisure club. The Waterside Restaurant overlooks Drayton Water.
Rooms: 138 all ensuite ⊛
Pricing: Sgl £36–94 Dbl £84–104
Dinner available from £20
CC: Accepted
Room facilities: ▢ ☎ ⊙ ⟍
Access: ⟦⟧
Conference: 20 meeting rooms (Thtr 600 max),
24hr-delegate from £175, day-delegate from £58
Children: Welcome ⟊
Licenses: ⟁ ⓲
Leisure: Indoor pool, Gym, Beauty salon, Games room
Parking: Off-street
Directions: M1 south junction 16, A45 to Daventry; M1 north junction 18, A361 to Daventry; M40 junction 11, A361 to Daventry.
Map ref: Daventry 8 B3

The big sleep

As part of our comprehensive inspection process, RAC Inspectors investigate the comfort of the beds.

Derby, Derbyshire

Hotel La Gondola

★★★★

220 Osmaston Road, Derby, Derbyshire, DE23 8JX
Tel: 01332 332895 Fax: 01332 384512
Email: service@la-gondola.co.uk
Web: www.la-gondola.co.uk

Privately owned La Gondola offers 20 luxurious ensuite bedrooms and highly accredited continental restaurant. Located 5 minutes from the city centre. On-site parking. Function rooms available for weddings, conferences and private parties.
Rooms: 20 all ensuite
Pricing: Sgl £64.50–69.50 Dbl £69.50–77.50
Dinner available from £16.50
CC: Accepted
Room facilities:
Conference: 4 meeting rooms (Thtr 120 max)
Children: Welcome
Licenses:
Parking: Off-street and free
Directions: Leave M1 at Junction 25. Take A514 towards Melbourne. Hotel is 5 minutes from city centre and 10 minutes from Derby station.
Map ref: Derby 8 B2

Rose & Thistle

◆◆◆

21 Charnwood Street, Derby, Derbyshire, DE1 2GU
Tel: 01332 344103 Fax: 01332 291006
Rooms: 8 (2 ensuite)
CC: Accepted
Room facilities:
Parking: Off-street
Directions: Leave M1 at Junction 24, take A6 to Derby. Follow inner ring road to Charnwood Street.
Map ref: Derby 8 B2

"Here!"

Need a pet friendly property? Look out for 'Dogs welcome' in our listings.

Dovedale, Derbyshire

Izaak Walton Hotel

★★★★

Dovedale, Derbyshire, DE6 2AY
Tel: 01335 350555 Fax: 01335 350539
Email: reception@izaakwaltonhotel.com
Web: www.izaakwaltonhotel.com

Situated just above the River Dove in the idyllic hills of Dovedale. Originally built as a farmhouse in the 17th century, the hotel retains much of its original charm. Dovedale bar offers various home-cooked dishes, whilst the Haddon Restaurant serves more traditional fayre, for Sunday lunches and evenings.
Rooms: 34 all ensuite
Pricing: Sgl £110 Dbl £135–175
Dinner available from £28
CC: Accepted
Room facilities:
Conference: 4 meeting rooms (Thtr 50 max), 24hr-delegate from £145, day-delegate from £50
Children: Welcome
Licenses:
Leisure: Fishing
Parking: Off-street
Directions: Hotel is 5 miles north-west of Ashbourne. Take A515 towards Buxton. After 2 miles turn left on the B5054 to Thorpe, Dovedale and Ilam. Izaak Walton Hotel after 4 miles.
Map ref: Dovedale 8 A2

Edale, Derbyshire

The Rambler Country House Hotel

◆◆◆

Edale, Hope Valley, Derbyshire, S33 7SA
Tel: 01433 670268 Fax: 01433 670106
Email: therambler@dorbiere.co.uk
Web: www.theramblerinn.co.uk
Rooms: 9 all ensuite
Dinner available CC: Accepted
Room facilities:
Children: Welcome
Licenses:
Parking: Off-street
Map ref: Edale 8 A1

Froggatt Edge, Derbyshire

The Chequers Inn

Froggatt Edge, Hope Valley, Derbyshire, S32 3ZJ
Tel: 01433 630231 Fax: 01433 631072
Email: info@chequers-froggatt.com
Web: www.chequers-froggatt.com
Rooms: 5 all ensuite
Pricing: Sgl £65–90 Dbl £65–90 Dinner available
CC: Accepted
Room facilities:
Children: Welcome
Licenses:
Parking: Off-street and free
Directions: Situated on the A625 in Froggatt, between
Sheffield & Bakewell.
Map ref: Froggatt Edge 8 B1

Glossop, Derbyshire

Wind in the Willows Hotel

Derbyshire Level, Glossop, Derbyshire, SK13 7PT
Tel: 01457 868001 Fax: 01457 853354
Email: info@windinthewillows.co.uk
Web: www.windinthewillows.co.uk
Rooms: 12 all ensuite
Pricing: Sgl £88–105 Dbl £120–145
Dinner available from £24
CC: Accepted
Room facilities:
Conference: 2 meeting rooms (Thtr 40 max),
24hr-delegate from £135, day-delegate from £35
Children: Welcome 8yrs min age
Licenses:
Leisure: Fishing
Parking: Off-street and free
Directions: 1 mile east of Glossop centre on A57 to
Sheffield. Turn right opposite Royal Oak pub. Hotel
400 yards on right.
Map ref: Glossop 10 C4

Grantham, Lincolnshire

Angel & Royal

High Street, Grantham, Lincolnshire, NG31 6PN
Tel: 01476 565817 Fax: 01476 567149
Email: enquiries@angelandroyal.co.uk
Web: www.angelandroyal.com
Rooms: 29 all ensuite
Pricing: Sgl £85 Dbl £110–140
Dinner available from £19.50
CC: Accepted
Room facilities:
Conference: 2 meeting rooms (Thtr 30 max),
24hr-delegate from £129, day-delegate from £35
Children: Welcome
Licenses:
Parking: Off-street and free

Directions: Just off A1 in Grantham town centre. Free
car parking at rear, taking 1st left after Marks and
Spencer's or first right turn before, then left again.
Parking 300 yards on right.
Map ref: Grantham 8 C2

Black Bull

Black Bull Farm, North Witham, Grantham,
Lincolnshire, NG33 5LL
Tel: 01476 860086 Fax: 01476 861611

Former coaching inn dating back to 1730. Ideal resting
place for Stamford and Grantham, situated next to A1.
Set in quiet gardens with lots of parking, home cooked
food. Visitors have excellent facilities near Rutland
Water, shooting, fishing and golf courses. Lots of
historical sites within easy reach. Also self-catering
stone cottages. Fully modernised, sleeps 4/6.
Rooms: 9 all ensuite
Pricing: Sgl £25–50 Dbl £50–75
Dinner available from £5 CC: Accepted
Room facilities:
Children: Welcome Dogs: Welcome
Directions: A1 Southbound turning Swayfield
Lobthorpe.
Map ref: North Witham 8 C2

Hathersage, Derbyshire

George Hotel

Main Road, Hathersage, Derbyshire, S32 1BB
Tel: 01433 650436 Fax: 01433 650099
Email: info@george-hotel.net
Web: www.george-hotel.net
Rooms: 21 all ensuite
Pricing: Sgl £82–126 Dbl £115–170
Dinner available from £20–35 CC: Accepted
Room facilities:
Conference: 2 meeting rooms (Thtr 80 max),
24hr-delegate from £135, day-delegate from £40
Children: Welcome Licenses:
Parking: Off-street and free
Directions: Leave M1 at Junction 29. Head west on
A619 to Baslow, then north onto B6001 to Hathersage.
Map ref: Hathersage 8 B1

Hinckley, Leicestershire

Hinckley Island Hotel

★★★★

A5 Watling Street, Hinckley, Leicestershire, LE10 3JA
Tel: 01455 631122 Fax: 01455 634536
Email: hinckleyisland@paramount-hotels.co.uk
Web: www.paramount-hotels.co.uk

PARAMOUNT
GROUP OF HOTELS

Unique, friendly modern hotel and extensive leisure club set in lovely countryside, with easy access to Midlands attractions, the NEC and motorway connections.
Rooms: 349 all ensuite
Pricing: Sgl £28–77 Dbl £56–70
Dinner available from £20 CC: Accepted
Room facilities: Access:
Conference: 20 meeting rooms (Thtr 300 max), 24hr-delegate from £189, day-delegate from £69
Children: Welcome
Licenses:
Leisure: Indoor pool, Gym, Health spa, Beauty salon
Parking: Off-street
Directions: Hinckley Island Hotel is just 300 yards from J1 of the M69 which links the M1 and M6.
Map ref: Hinckley 8 B3

Kings Hotel

★★

13–19 Mount Road, Hinckley, Leicestershire, LE10 1AD
Tel: 01455 637193 Fax: 01455 636201
Email: info@kings-hotel.net
Web: www.kings-hotel.net
Rooms: 7 all ensuite
Dinner available
CC: Accepted
Room facilities:
Conference: 2 meeting rooms (Thtr 30 max)
Children: Welcome 10yrs min age
Licenses:
Parking: Off-street
Directions: From Hinckley town centre follow signs for hospital. Hotel is at the bottom end of the same road (Mount Road).
Map ref: Hinckley 8 B3

Holbeach, Lincolnshire

Cackle Hill House

◆◆◆◆

Cackle Hill Lane, Holbeach, Lincolnshire, PE12 8BS
Tel: 01406 426721 Fax: 01406 426721/424659
Email: cacklehillhouse@farming.co.uk
Seasonal closure: 23 December to 2 January
Rooms: 3 (2 ensuite)
Pricing: Sgl £30 Dbl £48
Room facilities: Parking: Off-street and free
Directions: From A17 at Holbeach roundabout, take B1168 to Cackle Hill. Hotel 1/2 mile on right.
Map ref: Holbeach 9 D2

Kettering, Northamptonshire

Kettering Park Hotel and Spa

★★★★★ *Commended*

Kettering Parkway, Kettering,
Northamptonshire, NN15 6XT
Tel: 01536 416666 Fax: 01536 416171
Email: kpark@shirehotels.com
Web: www.shirehotels.com

SHIRE
HOTELS

Ideal location for exploring Northamptonshire and just 55 minutes from London by train. First-class spa with 13m pool and activity studios. Spacious lounges for relaxation. Good reputation for home-cooked food featuring local/regional produce.
Rooms: 119 all ensuite
Pricing: Sgl £90–179 Dbl £130–199
Dinner available from £25 CC: Accepted
Room facilities: Access:
Conference: 14 meeting rooms (Thtr 200 max), 24hr-delegate from £184, day-delegate from £65
Children: Welcome Licenses:
Leisure: Indoor pool, Gym, Activity studio
Parking: Off-street and free
Directions: Take Junction 9 on A14. Hotel is just off roundabout.
Map ref: Kettering 8 C3

East Midlands

Leicester, Leicestershire

Campanile Hotel & Restaurant
Travel Accommodation

Bedford Street North, St Mathews Way, Leicester,
Leicestershire, LE1 3JE
Tel: 0116 261 6600 Fax: 0116 261 6601
Email: leicester@campanile-hotels.com
Web: www.campanile.com

Campanile hotels offer comfortable and convenient
budget accommodation and a traditional French-style
Bistro providing freshly-cooked food for breakfast,
lunch and dinner. All rooms ensuite with tea/coffee-
making facilities, DDT and TV with Sky channels.
Rooms: 93 all ensuite ⊗
Pricing: Sgl £47.90–49.90 Dbl £53.85–55.85
Dinner available from £6.95–11.50 CC: Accepted
Room facilities: ▢ ☎ ⊿ ✆ Access: |↓↑
Conference: 3 meeting rooms (Thtr 40 max),
24hr-delegate from £75, day-delegate rate from £21.50
Children: Welcome ⼌ Dogs: Welcome
Licenses: ⍦
Parking: Off-street and free
Directions: From M1/M69, exit J21 and follow 'city
centre' signs along Narborough Road (A5460). At the
end of Narborough Road, turn left onto A594. Follow
inner ring road, hotel on left.
Map ref: Leicester 8 B3

Lincoln, Lincolnshire

Bentley Hotel & Leisure Club
★★★

Newark Road, South Hykeham, Lincoln,
Lincolnshire, LN6 9NH
Tel: 01522 878000 Fax: 01522 878001
Email: infothebentleyhotel@btconnect.com
Web: www.thebentleyhotel.uk.com
Rooms: 80 all ensuite ⍩ ▱ ⊗
Pricing: Sgl £83–93 Dbl £98–130
Dinner available from £20 CC: Accepted
Room facilities: ▢ ☎ ⊿ ✆ Access: |↓↑
Conference: 7 meeting rooms (Thtr 350 max),
24hr-delegate from £110, day-delegate from £28
Children: Welcome ⼌ ⍽
Licenses: ⍦ ⍦
Leisure: Indoor pool, Gym, Beauty salon

Parking: Off-street and free
Directions: From A1, take A46 towards Lincoln. After
10 miles, go straight over first roundabout on Lincoln
bypass. Hotel 50 yards on left.
Map ref: South Hykeham 8 C1
See advert on this page

Branston Hall Hotel
★★★ ⍩

Branston Park, Lincoln Road, Branston, Lincoln,
Lincolnshire, LN4 1PD
Tel: 01522 793305 Fax: 01522 790734
Email: reservations@branstonhall.com
Web: www.branstonhall.com
Rooms: 50 all ensuite ▱ ⊗
Pricing: Sgl £75–85 Dbl £105–175
Dinner available from £19.95–22.50
CC: Accepted
Room facilities: ▢ ☎ ⊿ Access: |↓↑
Conference: 5 meeting rooms (Thtr 200 max),
24hr-delegate from £100, day-delegate from £25.50
Children: Welcome
Licenses: ⍦ ⍦
Leisure: Indoor pool, Gym
Parking: Off-street and free
Directions: Branston Hall Hotel is on the B1188,
3 miles south of Lincoln in the village of Branston.
Map ref: Branston 8 C1

The Gables

546 Newark Road, North Hykeham, Lincoln,
Lincolnshire, LN6 9NG
Tel: 01522 829102 Fax: 01522 850497
Email: gablesguesthouse@ntlworld.com
Web: www.gablesguesthouse.co.uk
Rooms: 4 (2 ensuite) 🚫 CC: Accepted
Room facilities: ☐ 🍳 Children: Welcome
Dogs: Welcome Leisure: Games room
Parking: Off-street and free
Directions: A46 Newark to Lincoln bypass, follow
(A1434) Lincoln south. Guest house is 1½ miles on the
right after McDonalds.
Map ref: North Hykeham 8 C1

Admiral Guest House

16–18 Nelson Street, Lincoln, Lincolnshire, LN1 1PJ
Tel: 01522 544467 Fax: 01522 544467
Email: nicola.major1@ntlworld.com
Rooms: 9 (7 ensuite) 🚫 CC: Accepted
Room facilities: ☐ 🍳 Children: Welcome 🍴
Dogs: Welcome
Parking: Off-street and free
Directions: Follow A57 to Carlholme Road. Guest
house is situated on Nelson Street. Five minutes' walk
from University and town.
Map ref: Lincoln 8 C1

Hillside Guest House

34 Yarborough Road, Lincoln, Lincolnshire, LN1 1HS
Tel: 01522 888671 Fax: 01522 874744
Email: Jean.Bixley@ntlworld.com
Web: www.hillsideguesthouse.biz
Rooms: 3 (2 ensuite) 🚫
Pricing: Sgl £32 Dbl £42 CC: Accepted
Room facilities: ☐ 🍳
Children: Welcome 🍴 Dogs: Welcome
Parking: Off-street and free
Directions: Guest House is five minutes' walk from the
city centre and cathedral area, at the lower end of
Yarborough Road.
Map ref: Lincoln 8 C1

Tennyson Court

3 Tennyson Street, Lincoln, Lincolnshire, LN1 1LZ
Tel: 0800 980 5408 Fax: 01522 887997
Email: sales@tennyson-court.co.uk
Web: www.tennyson-court.co.uk
Rooms: 3 all ensuite 🚫 🚫
Pricing: Sgl £39.90–65 Dbl £39.90–65 CC: Accepted
Room facilities: ☐ ☎ 🍳 Children: Welcome
Parking: Off-street and free
Directions: Follow A57 into Lincoln, left onto Hewson
Road, right at top onto West Parade, then next left is
Tennyson Street.
Map ref: Lincoln 8 C1

The Quorn Country Hotel

★★★★★ 🔔🔔🔔

66 Leicester Road, Quorn, Leicestershire, LE12 8BB
Tel: 01509 415050 Fax: 01509 415557
Email: reservations@quorncountryhotel.co.uk
Web: www.quorncountryhotel.co.uk

www.primahotels.co.uk

Rooms: 30 all ensuite 🚫
Pricing: Sgl £95–146 Dbl £117–172
Dinner available from £25
CC: Accepted
Room facilities: ☐ ☎ 🍳 🔌 ❄
Access: ♿
Conference: 12 meeting rooms (Thtr 300 max),
24hr-delegate from £150, day-delegate from £45
Children: Welcome 🍴
Licenses: 🔞 🏛
Leisure: Fishing
Parking: Off-street and free
Directions: From A6 Loughborough to Leicester road,
take exit for Quorn (Quorndon) village. Hotel near
village hall and opposite police station.
Map ref: Loughborough 8 B2
See advert on this page

Quality Hotel & Suites Loughborough

★★★

Junction 23, M1, New Ashby Road, Loughborough,
Leicestershire, LE11 4EX
Tel: 01509 211800 Fax: 01509 211868
Email: enquiries@hotels-loughborough.com
Web: www.choicehotelseurope.com
Rooms: 94 all ensuite
Pricing: Sgl £105–160 Dbl £126–160
Dinner available from £18.95
CC: Accepted
Room facilities: 💻 ☎ 🍵 🔌
Conference: 9 meeting rooms (Thtr 250 max),
24hr-delegate from £160, day-delegate from £48
Children: Welcome ♀
Dogs: Welcome
Licenses: ◇ ♟
Leisure: Indoor pool, Gym, Health spa, Beauty salon,
Games room
Parking: Off-street and free
Directions: From Junction 23 M1, follow A512 towards
Loughborough town centre. Hotel is approx 800
metres on left-hand side.
Map ref: Loughborough 8 B2

Cedars Hotel

★★ ®

Cedar Road, Loughborough, Leicestershire, LE11 2AB
Tel: 01509 214459 Fax: 01509 233573
Email: info@thecedarshotel.com
Web: www.thecedarshotel.com
Rooms: 36 all ensuite 🕊 🚭
Dinner available
CC: Accepted
Room facilities: 💻 ☎ 🍵
Conference: 3 meeting rooms (Thtr 40 max)
Children: Welcome ♀ ☕ Dogs: Welcome
Licenses: ♟
Leisure: Outdoor pool
Parking: Off-street and free
Directions: Proceed along the A6 towards Leicester
turning left into Cedar Road opposite Loughborough
Crematorium. Situated along the A6 south of the town.
Map ref: Loughborough 8 B2

The Queens Head
Restaurant with Rooms

2 Long Street, Belton, Loughborough,
Leicestershire, LE12 9TP
Tel: 01530 222359 Fax: 01530 224860
Map ref: Belton 8 B2

De Montfort Hotel

◆◆◆

88 Leicester Road, Loughborough,
Leicestershire, LE11 2AQ
Tel: 01509 216061 Fax: 01509 233667
Email: thedemontforthotel@amserve.com
Web: www.smoothhound.co.uk/hotels/demont.html

Rooms: 10 (7 ensuite) 🕊
Pricing: Sgl £35–40 Dbl £50–55
Dinner available from £7
CC: Accepted
Room facilities: 💻 🍵
Children: Welcome ♀
Licenses: ♟
Parking: Off-street and free
Directions: Situated on A6 Leicester Road, 5 minutes
from the town centre, opposite Fairfield School and
Southfield Park.
Map ref: Loughborough 8 B2

Victoria Farm

◆◆◆

Highcross Road, Claybrooke Magna, Lutterworth,
Leicestershire, LE17 5AU
Tel: 01455 208270 Fax: 01455 208270
Email: eddypartridge2000@yahoo.co.uk
Web: www.vicfarm.co.uk
Seasonal closure: Christmas

A traditional old farmhouse which has large, inviting
rooms with outstanding rural views. It is situated at the
Roman centre of England where the Fosse Way and
Watling Street cross.
Rooms: 4 (2 ensuite) 🕊 🚭
Pricing: Sgl £25 Dbl £40
Room facilities: 💻 🍵
Children: Welcome ♀
Dogs: Welcome
Leisure: Fishing
Parking: Off-street and free
Directions: Between Hinckley and Lutterworth. 1
minute off A5 at Highcross. This is where the Fosse
Way crosses the A5 (Watling Street).
Map ref: Claybrooke Magna 8 B3

Relax & smell the coffee

Fresh coffee, chilled juices for breakfast.
RAC's team of qualified Inspectors
check them both.

Mablethorpe, Lincolnshire

Aura Lee Guest House

◆◆◆

22 The Boulevard, Mablethorpe,
Lincolnshire, LN12 2AD
Tel: 01507 477660 Fax: 01507 477660
Email: mccarthy@auralee.fsnet.co.uk
Web: www.mablethorpe.info/accommodation
Seasonal closure: January
Rooms: 7 all ensuite ⊗
Pricing: Sgl £30–35 Dbl £40–45
Dinner available from £6.50
CC: Accepted
Room facilities: ▢ ☐
Access: ⎮⎮⎮
Licenses: ⫻
Parking: Off-street and free
Directions: High Street to seafront, then right onto
Gibraltar Road. Bottom of Gibraltar Road T-junction.
Aura Lee Guest House across the road.
Map ref: Mablethorpe 9 D1

Colours Guest House

◆◆◆

Queens Park Close, Mablethorpe,
Lincolnshire, LN12 2AS
Tel: 01507 473427 Fax: 01507 473427
Email: info@coloursguesthouse.co.uk
Web: www.coloursguesthouse.co.uk
Rooms: 7 (2 ensuite) ⊗
Pricing: Sgl £20–25 Dbl £40–50
CC: Accepted
Room facilities: ▢ ☐
Children: Welcome
Parking: Off-street and free
Map ref: Mablethorpe 9 D1

Park View Guest House

◆◆

48 Gibraltar Road, Mablethorpe,
Lincolnshire, LN12 2AT
Tel: 01507 477267 Fax: 01507 477267
Email: malcolm@pvgh.freeserve.co.uk
Web: www.theparkview.co.uk
Rooms: 5 (2 ensuite) ⊌ ⊗
Pricing: Sgl £18–22 Dbl £36–40
Dinner available from £6
Room facilities: ▢ ☐
Children: Welcome ⫪
Dogs: Welcome
Licenses: ⫻
Leisure: Beach
Parking: Off-street and free
Directions: Proceed up High Street towards the beach.
At end turn right onto Gibraltar Road. Park View is
beside beach steps.
Map ref: Mablethorpe 9 D1

Market Harborough, Leicestershire

Sun Inn Hotel and Restaurant

★★⭐⭐

Main Street, Marston Trussell, Market Harborough,
Leicestershire, LE16 9TY
Tel: 01858 465531 Fax: 01858 433155
Email: manager@suninn.com
Web: www.suninn.com
Seasonal closure: Bank Holidays and 26 December
to 10 January
Rooms: 20 all ensuite ⊌ ⊠ ⊗
Pricing: Sgl £59 Dbl £69
Dinner available from £15.95 CC: Accepted
Room facilities: ▢ ☎ ☐
Conference: 2 meeting rooms (Thtr 70 max)
Children: Welcome ⫪ Licenses: ⫻
Parking: Off-street
Directions: Exit J20 M1, A4304. Marston Trussell is
between Husbands Bosworth and Lubenham. By rail,
Market Harborough is 3 miles away.
Map ref: Marston Trussell 8 B3

Matlock, Derbyshire

Riber Hall

★★★★⭐⭐

Matlock, Derbyshire, DE4 5JU
Tel: 01629 582795 Fax: 01629 580475
Email: info@riber-hall.co.uk
Web: www.riber-hall.co.uk
Seasonal closure: Christmas Day

Renowned historic and tranquil country manor house
set in peaceful rolling Derbyshire hills. Gourmet cuisine
— AA two rosettes, RAC two Dining Awards. Privately
owned and proprietor-run for over 30 years.
Rooms: 14 all ensuite ⊠ ⊗
Pricing: Sgl £97–112 Dbl £136–182
Dinner available from £32–37 CC: Accepted
Room facilities: ▢ ☎ ☐ ☍
Conference: 3 meeting rooms (Thtr 20 max),
24hr-delegate from £148, day-delegate from £36.75
Children: Welcome 10yrs min age Dogs: Welcome
Licenses: ⟁ ⫻ Leisure: Tennis
Parking: Off-street and free
Directions: One mile off A615 at Tansley, signed to Riber.
Map ref: Matlock 8 B1

Melbourne Arms
& Cuisine India

The historic Melbourne Arms, home to Cuisine India, where east meets west. Recommended by the AA & RAC with three diamonds, our comfortable accommodation is ideally situated for easy access to East Midlands International Airport, Donnington Park Race Track and the surrounding Derbyshire countryside.

92 Ashby Road, Melbourne DE73 1ES
Tel: 01332 864949 Fax: 01332 865525
Email: info@melbournearms.co.uk
Website: www.melbournearms.co.uk

The Temple Hotel
★★★

Temple Walk, Matlock Bath, Derbyshire, DE4 3PG
Tel: 01629 583911 Fax: 01629 580851
Email: templehotel@aol.com
Web: www.templehotel.co.uk
Rooms: 14 all ensuite
Pricing: Sgl £55–65 Dbl £89–105
Dinner available from £19.50 CC: Accepted
Room facilities:
Conference: 2 meeting rooms (Thtr 50 max)
Children: Welcome
Licenses:
Parking: Off-street and free
Directions: Entering Matlock Bath from the south along the A6 fork left at the Temple Hotel Obelisk, and follow the road for 300m.
Map ref: Matlock 8 B1

Hillview
◆◆◆

80 New Street, Matlock, Derbyshire, DE4 3FH
Tel: 01629 583662 Fax: 0870 127 7822
Email: enquiries@hillview.wyenet.co.uk
Seasonal closure: November to Easter
Rooms: 2 all ensuite
Room facilities:
Children: Welcome 5yrs min age
Parking: Off-street and free
Directions: From Matlock centre (A6, Crown Square),

proceed up the hill, take fourth right into New Street. Hillview is on the corner on the left. On street parking, but not on Henry Avenue.
Map ref: Matlock 8 B1

Melbourne, Derbyshire

Melbourne Arms & Cuisine India
◆◆◆

92 Ashby Road, Melbourne, Derbyshire, DE73 1ES
Tel: 01332 864949 Fax: 01332 865525
Email: info@melbournearms.co.uk
Web: www.melbournearms.co.uk
Rooms: 7 all ensuite
Pricing: Sgl £35–45 Dbl £55–60
Dinner available from £10 CC: Accepted
Room facilities:
Conference: 1 meeting room (Thtr 20 max)
Children: Welcome Licenses:
Parking: Off-street and free
Map ref: Melbourne 8 B2
See advert on this page

Melton Mowbray, Leicestershire

Stapleford Park Hotel
★★★★★

Stapleford, Melton Mowbray, Leicestershire, LE14 2EF
Tel: 01572 787000 Fax: 01572 787001
Email: reservations@stapleford.co.uk
Web: www.staplefordpark.com

Stapleford Park is a relaxed 17th century home set in 500 acres of parkland. The hotel offers 55 individually designed bedrooms, 18-hole golf course, Clarins spa and a TechnoGym.
Rooms: 55 all ensuite
Pricing: Sgl £195 Dbl £250–560
Dinner available from £44 CC: Accepted
Room facilities: Access:
Conference: 8 meeting rooms (Thtr 200 max), day-delegate from £85
Children: Welcome
Dogs: Welcome
Licenses:

Leisure: Indoor pool, Gym, Health spa, Beauty salon, Tennis, Golf, Fishing, Riding, Snooker/billiards, Archery, Falconry, Clay pigeon shooting, Off-road 4x4 driving
Parking: Off-street and free
Directions: From Melton Mowbray, follow ring road and signs for Grantham. Stay in left-hand lane until Grantham Road turns left: don't turn left, but drive through traffic lights. Follow signs for B676 Stapleford. After 4 miles, turn right at Stapleford signpost.
Map ref: Stapleford 8 C2

Northampton, Northamptonshire

Quality Hotel Northampton

★★★

Ashley Way, Weston Favell, Northampton, Northamptonshire, NN3 3EA
Tel: 01604 739955 Fax: 01604 415023
Email: enquiries@hotels-northampton.com
Web: www.hotels-northampton.com
Rooms: 71 all ensuite
Pricing: Sgl £35–125 Dbl £35–150
Dinner available from £20.95
CC: Accepted
Room facilities: 🖥 ☎ 🍵 🍴
Access: ♿
Conference: 6 meeting rooms (Thtr 140 max), 24hr-delegate from £135, day-delegate from £35
Children: Welcome ♀
Dogs: Welcome
Licenses: ◈ ♟♟♟
Parking: Off-street and free
Directions: M1, Junction 15, A508 Northampton, follow A45 Wellingborough, A43 Kettering, A4500 Weston Favell, left town centre, next right.
Map ref: Weston Favell 8 C3

Nottingham, Nottinghamshire

Bestwood Lodge Hotel

★★★

Bestwood Country Park, Arnold, Nottingham, Nottinghamshire, NG5 8NE
Tel: 0115 920 3011 Fax: 0115 967 0409
Email: bestwoodlodge@btconnect.com
Web: www.bw-bestwoodlodge.co.uk
Rooms: 39 all ensuite
Dinner available
CC: Accepted
Room facilities: 🖥 ☎ 🍵
Conference: 9 meeting rooms (Thtr 200 max)
Children: Welcome ♀ 🎨
Dogs: Welcome
Licenses: ♟♟♟
Leisure: Tennis, Riding
Parking: Off-street and free
Directions: 3¹/₂ miles north of city. Off A60 follow B6004. Turn right at lights, Queens Bower Road. First right Bestwood Lodge Drive.
Map ref: Bestwood 8 B2

Westminster Hotel

★★★

312 Mansfield Road, Nottingham, Nottinghamshire, NG5 2EF
Tel: 0115 955 5000 Fax: 0115 955 5005
Email: mail@westminster-hotel.co.uk
Web: www.westminster-hotel.co.uk
Seasonal closure: 25 December 2006 to 2 January 2007
Rooms: 73 all ensuite 🚭 🍸
Pricing: Sgl £40–95 Dbl £70–110
Dinner available from £17
CC: Accepted
Room facilities: 🖥 ☎ 🍵 🍴
Access: ♿
Conference: 5 meeting rooms (Thtr 60 max), 24hr-delegate from £107.50, day-delegate from £37.50
Children: Welcome
Licenses: ♟♟♟
Parking: Off-street and free
Directions: 1 mile from city centre on A60 north (Mansfield Road) leaving M1 at J26.
Map ref: Nottingham 8 B2
See advert on this page

East Midlands

Jurys Inn Nottingham

 New for 2006

Waterfront Plaza, Station Street, Nottingham,
Nottinghamshire, NG2 3BJ
Tel: 0115 901 6700 Fax: 0115 901 6777
Email: bookings@jurysdoyle.com
Web: www.jurysinns.com

JURYS DOYLE
HOTELS

Rooms: 264 all ensuite
Pricing: Sgl £98.50 Dbl £108 Dinner available
Room facilities: ☐ ☎ ☺ ☎ ✳ Access: |↕
Conference: 11 meeting rooms
Children: Welcome Dogs: Welcome
Licenses: ♟ Parking: Off-street
Directions: Jurys Inn Nottingham is centrally located
on Station Street close to the railway station and within
a two-minute walk from the new tramway station.
Map ref: Nottingham 8 B2

The Strathdon Hotel

 New for 2006

44 Derby Road, City Centre, Nottingham,
Nottinghamshire, NG1 5FT
Tel: 01159 418501 Fax: 01159 483725
Web: www.strathdon-hotel-nottingham.com
Rooms: 68 all ensuite ☺
Pricing: Sgl £75–95 Dbl £75–125
Dinner available from £10–20 CC: Accepted
Room facilities: ☐ ☎ ☺ ☎ Access: |↕
Conference: 6 meeting rooms (Thtr 150 max),
24hr-delegate from £145, day-delegate from £38
Children: Welcome ♟ ☕ Dogs: Welcome
Licenses: ♟
Directions: Situated in the centre of Nottingham. M1
northbound take J25, southbound take J26. Follow
city centre signs.
Map ref: Nottingham 8 B2

Oakham, Rutland

Old Wisteria Hotel
★★★ ☗

4 Catmose Street, Oakham, Rutland, LE15 6HW
Tel: 01572 722844 Fax: 01572 724473
Email: enquiries@wisteriahotel.co.uk
Web: www.wisteriahotel.co.uk
Rooms: 25 all ensuite ☗ ☺
Pricing: Sgl £70 Dbl £90
Dinner available from £20
CC: Accepted
Room facilities: ☐ ☎ ☺ ☎
Conference: 5 meeting rooms (Thtr 60 max),
24hr-delegate from £100, day-delegate from £25
Children: Welcome Licenses: ♟
Parking: Off-street and free
Directions: Hotel in Oakham town at junction
A606/A6003. From A1 North join B668. From A1 South
join A606. From Nottingham or Kettering join A6003.
Map ref: Oakham 8 C2

Scunthorpe, Lincolnshire

Forest Pines Hotel
★★★★ ☗

Ermine Street, Broughton, Brigg,
Lincolnshire, DN20 0AQ
Tel: 01652 650770 Fax: 01652 650495
Email: enquiries@forestpines.co.uk
Web: www.forestpines.co.uk
Rooms: 114 all ensuite ☜ ☗ ☺
Pricing: Sgl £79–99 Dbl £99–109
Dinner available from £9.95–39.95 CC: Accepted
Room facilities: ☐ ☎ ☺ ☎ Access: |↕
Conference: 6 meeting rooms (Thtr 220 max),
24hr-delegate from £149, day-delegate from £39
Children: Welcome ♟ Licenses: ◁ ♟
Leisure: Indoor pool, Gym, Health spa,
Beauty salon, Golf
Parking: Off-street and free
Directions: Exit J4 M180. Hotel is 200 metres to the
north at junction of A18 and A15.
Map ref: Broughton 11 E4

Shepshed, Leicestershire

The Grange Courtyard   `Little Gem`
◆◆◆◆◆ ✂ ☕

The Grange, Forest Street, Shepshed, Loughborough,
Leicestershire, LE12 9DA
Tel: 01509 600189 Fax: 01509 603834
Email: linda.lawrence@thegrangecourtyard.co.uk
Web: www.thegrangecourtyard.co.uk

Former farmhouse and outbuildings dating back to the
11th century. Beautifully restored with many original
features, providing luxury accommodation with the
benefit of full kitchen facilities, tranquil gardens and
free private parking.
Rooms: 20 all ensuite ☜ ☗ ☺
Pricing: Sgl £64.63 Dbl £76.38 CC: Accepted
Room facilities: ☐ ☎ ☺ ☎
Conference: 1 meeting room
Children: Welcome 8yrs min age Dogs: Welcome
Licenses: ♟ Parking: Off-street and free
Directions: Exit Junction 23 M1 A512 to Ashby. ³/₄ mile
turn right at traffic lights, over mini-roundabout by
petrol station into Forest Street.
Map ref: Loughborough 8 B2

Skegness, Lincolnshire

Crown Hotel

★★★

Drummond Road, Skegness, Lincolnshire, PE25 3AB
Tel: 01754 610760 Fax: 01754 610847
Email: reception@crownhotel.biz
Web: www.crownhotel.biz

3-star hotel offers the elegance of yesteryear
combined with the benefits of refurbishment to modern
standards, just 1¹/₂ miles from centre of Skegness, but
on the edge of the countryside.
Rooms: 29 all ensuite
Pricing: Sgl £50 Dbl £75 Dinner available
CC: Accepted Room facilities: Access:
Conference: 3 meeting rooms (Thtr 120 max)
Children: Welcome Licenses:
Leisure: Indoor pool Parking: Off-street
Directions: Turn right from Lumley Road into
Drummond Road. Crown Hotel 1¹/₂ miles down
Drummond Road (signposted nature reserve).
Map ref: Skegness 9 D1

The Best Western Vine Hotel

★★★

Vine Road, Skegness, Lincolnshire, PE25 3DB
Tel: 01754 763018 Fax: 01754 769845
Email: Info@thevinehotel.com
Web: www.thevinehotel.com and bw-vinehotel.co.uk

Beautiful tranquil hotel (1770) with famous gardens.
Completely refurbished ensuite rooms, five minutes
walk to the beach and nature reserve. Excellent bar
meals and fine dining restaurant. Families welcome.
Special breaks.
Rooms: 24 all ensuite
Pricing: Sgl £59–72 Dbl £84–92

Dinner available from £12 CC: Accepted
Room facilities:
Conference: 3 meeting rooms (Thtr 100 max),
24hr-delegate from £72, day-delegate from £24
Children: Welcome Dogs: Welcome
Licenses: Leisure: Golf
Parking: Off-street and free
Directions: Turn right from Lumley Road into
Drummond Road. Vine Hotel is ¹/₂ mile on the right at
the end of Vine Road.
Map ref: Skegness 9 D1

Amber Private Hotel

◆◆◆

19 Scarbrough Avenue, Skegness,
Lincolnshire, PE25 2SZ
Tel: 01754 766503 Fax: 01754 766503
Email: info@theamberhotel.co.uk
Web: www.theamberhotel.co.uk
Rooms: 8 all ensuite
Pricing: Sgl £21–24 Dbl £21–24
Dinner available from £7 CC: Accepted
Room facilities: Children: Welcome
Licenses: Parking: Off-street and free
Map ref: Skegness 9 D1

Fountaindale Hotel

◆◆◆

69 Sandbeck Avenue, Skegness,
Lincolnshire, PE25 3JS
Tel: 01754 762731
Email: info@fountaindale.co.uk
Web: www.fountaindale.co.uk

Refurbished small family-run hotel situated in a quiet
location minutes from the beach and town.
Fountaindale is a non-smoking hotel, big enough to
cope, small enough to care.
Rooms: 8 all ensuite
Pricing: Sgl £22–30 Dbl £44–60
Dinner available from £8–10 CC: Accepted
Room facilities:
Children: Welcome 5yrs min age Licenses:
Parking: Off-street and free
Directions: From Skegness pier turn right over clock
tower roundabout. First right over staggered junction
into Sandbeck Avenue. Fountaindale on right.
Map ref: Skegness 9 D1

East Midlands

Sun Hotel

♦♦♦ ✕

19 North Parade, Skegness, Lincolnshire, PE25 2UB
Tel: 01754 762364 Fax: 01754 762364
Web: www.sunhotel.co.uk
Rooms: 14 all ensuite ⊛
Pricing: Sgl £32.50–42.50 Dbl £55–75
Dinner available from £9.50 CC: Accepted
Room facilities: ▢ ☕
Licenses: ♦♦♦
Parking: Off-street and free
Directions: Situated on the northern promenade
opposite the rose gardens and bowling greens.
Map ref: Skegness 9 D1

Westdene Hotel

♦♦♦ ℰ

Trafalgar Avenue, Skegness, Lincolnshire, PE25 3EU
Tel: 01754 765168
Email: westdenehotel@aol.com
Web: www.skegness.net/hotels/westdene.htm
Seasonal closure: November to February
Rooms: 7 all ensuite ⅌
Pricing: Sgl £22–24 Dbl £44–48
Dinner available from £9.95
Room facilities: ▢ ☕
Children: Welcome 4yrs min age ♦
Licenses: ♦♦♦
Directions: In Skegness follow signs for Gibraltar Point.
Along Drummond Road, Trafalgar Avenue is fifth road
on the left. Telephone for brochure.
Map ref: Skegness 9 D1

Manderlay Guest House

♦♦ ✕ ℰ

49 Grosvenor Road, Skegness, Lincolnshire, PE25 2DD
Tel: 01754 899029 Fax: 01754 899029
Email: mikecaroline@fsmail.net
Web: www.smoothound.co.uk/hotels/manderlay.html

There is an in-house laundry service. Travel cot is
available for babies. Other room facilities include hair
dryers and irons.
Rooms: 3 all ensuite ⊛
Pricing: Dbl £40–45
Dinner available from £8
CC: Accepted
Room facilities: ▢ ☕
Children: Welcome ♦ ℃
Dogs: Welcome
Parking: Off-street and free
Directions: Manderlay House is five minutes from bus
and train stations and town centre.
Map ref: Skegness 9 D1

Sleaford, Lincolnshire

Carre Arms Hotel

★★★

1 Mareham Lane, Sleaford, Lincolnshire, NG34 7JP
Tel: 01529 303156 Fax: 01529 303139
Email: enquiries@carrearmshotel.co.uk
Web: www.carrearmshotel.co.uk

Day or night, you will be assured of a warm welcome
at the Carre Arms Hotel. We offer excellent
accommodation, a restaurant, brasserie, bar and a
newly opened Courtyard Suite Conference Centre that
has many facilities.
Rooms: 13 all ensuite ⅌
Pricing: Sgl £50–60 Dbl £70–80
Dinner available from £14.50
CC: Accepted
Room facilities: ▢ ☎ ☕ ⓛ
Conference: 2 meeting rooms (Thtr 120 max),
24hr-delegate from £65, day-delegate from £15.50
Children: Welcome ♦
Dogs: Assistance dogs only
Licenses: ♦♦♦
Parking: Off-street and free
Directions: 3 mins from Sleaford rail station, easy
access from Lincoln, Grantham (A1), Boston (A15) and
Newark (A1).
Map ref: Sleaford 8 C2

Spalding, Lincolnshire

Cley Hall Hotel

22 High Street, Spalding, Lincolnshire, PE11 1TX
Tel: 01775 725157 Fax: 01775 710785
Email: cleyhall@enterprise.net
Web: www.cleyhallhotel.com
Rooms: 15 all ensuite
Dinner available
CC: Accepted
Room facilities:
Conference: 2 meeting rooms (Thtr 30 max)
Children: Welcome
Dogs: Welcome
Licenses:
Parking: Off-street and free
Directions: The hotel is situated on a one-way system, not in the town centre. Phone, fax, e-mail for a map.
Map ref: Spalding 9 D2

Travel Stop Motel
◆◆
50 Cowbit Road, Spalding, Lincolnshire, PE11 2RJ
Tel: 01775 767290 Fax: 01775 767716
Email: Reception@TravelStopmotel.com
Rooms: 16 (14 ensuite)
Pricing: Sgl £35 Dbl £45
CC: Accepted
Room facilities:
Children: Welcome
Dogs: Welcome
Licenses:
Parking: Off-street and free
Directions: Located on B1173, ³/₄ mile from centre of Spalding, by the side of the River Welland.
Map ref: Spalding 9 D2

Stamford, Lincolnshire

George of Stamford
★★★★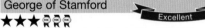
71 St Martin's, Stamford, Lincolnshire, PE9 2LB
Tel: 01780 750750 Fax: 01780 750701
Email: reservations@georgehotelofstamford.com
Web: www.georgehotelofstamford.com
Rooms: 47 all ensuite
Pricing: Sgl £78–110 Dbl £115–230
Dinner available from £7.95–28
CC: Accepted
Room facilities:
Conference: 9 meeting rooms (Thtr 50 max),
24hr-delegate from £145, day-delegate from £37.50
Children: Welcome
Dogs: Welcome
Licenses:
Parking: Off-street and free
Directions: North of Peterborough. From A1, B1081 to Stamford at roundabout. Hotel situated on left at first set of traffic lights.
Map ref: Stamford 8 C2

The Lady Anne's Hotel
★★
37–38 High Street, Saint Martins Without, Stamford, Lincolnshire, PE9 2LJ
Tel: 01780 481184 Fax: 01780 765422
Web: www.ladyannesstamford.co.uk
Rooms: 29 all ensuite
Pricing: Sgl £60–68 Dbl £80–130
Dinner available from £15.50
CC: Accepted
Room facilities:
Conference: 4 meeting rooms (Thtr 130 max),
24hr-delegate from £105, day-delegate from £28
Children: Welcome
Dogs: Welcome
Licenses:
Parking: Off-street
Directions: One mile from the A1.
Map ref: Stamford 8 C2

Rock Lodge   Little Gem
◆◆◆◆◆
1 Empingham Road, Stamford, Lincolnshire, PE9 2RH
Tel: 01780 481758 Fax: 01780 481757
Email: rocklodge@innpro.co.uk
Web: www.rock-lodge.co.uk

Imposing 1900 Edwardian Town House providing luxury ensuite accommodation. Set in an elevated position with gardens and bounded on all sides by high stone walls. Five minute walk from centre of historic Stamford.
Rooms: 6 all ensuite
Pricing: Sgl £58–99 Dbl £80–105
CC: Accepted
Room facilities:
Children: Welcome
Parking: Off-street and free
Directions: Leave A1 at A606, follow signs to Stamford 1¹/₄ miles. Entrance to Rock Lodge on left at junction of A606 and B1081.
Map ref: Stamford 8 C2

East Midlands

Candlesticks Hotel & Restaurant

◆◆◆

1 Church Lane, Stamford, Lincolnshire, PE9 2JU
Tel: 01780 764033 Fax: 01780 756071
Email: pinto@breathmail.net
Web: www.candlestickshotel.co.uk

A small family hotel run by Mr & Mrs Pinto for 25 years providing freshly cooked food and luxury bedrooms with a fridge and Sky TV. Dine in comfortable and elegant surroundings and enjoy excellent cuisine at a price you can afford.
Rooms: 8 all ensuite ⊗
Pricing: Sgl £45–60 Dbl £60
Dinner available from £17.90
CC: Accepted
Room facilities: ▯ ☎ ⊿
Children: Welcome ⅃ℂ
Licenses: ♦♦♦
Parking: Off-street
Directions: From A1 down St Martin's High Street. Turn left into Church Street by St Martin's Church.
Map ref: Stamford 8 C2

Stoney Middleton, Derbyshire

Lovers Leap

◆◆◆◆

Lovers Leap Cafe & Bistro, The Dale, Stoney Middleton, Hope Valley, Derbyshire, S32 4TF
Tel: 01433 630300 Fax: 01433 630618
Email: june@loversleap.biz
Web: www.loversleap.biz
Rooms: 2 all ensuite ⊗⊗
Pricing: Sgl £25–35 Dbl £45–50
Dinner available
CC: Accepted
Room facilities: ▯ ⊿ ⌇
Children: Welcome ⅃ ℂ
Dogs: Welcome
Licenses: ♦♦♦
Parking: Off-street and free
Directions: Take A619 to Baslow, follow A623 to Stoney Middleton (well signed). Building on right leaving village.
Map ref: Stoney Middleton 8 A1

Sutton Cheney, Leicestershire

The Royal Arms

◆◆◆◆

Main Street, Sutton Cheney, Leicestershire, CV13 0AG
Tel: 01455 290263 Fax: 01455 290124
Email: info@royalarms.co.uk
Web: www.royalarms.co.uk
Rooms: 15 all ensuite ⊗⊗ ⊿ ⊗
Pricing: Sgl £61.50–86.50 Dbl £136
Dinner available from £10–20
CC: Accepted
Room facilities: ▯ ⊿
Conference: 2 meeting rooms (Thtr 90 max), 24hr-delegate from £120, day-delegate from £25
Children: Welcome ⅃
Licenses: ♦♦♦
Parking: Off-street and free
Map ref: Sutton Cheney 8 B3

Sutton-on-Sea, Lincolnshire

Grange and Links Hotel

★★★★

Sea Lane, Sandilands, Sutton-on-Sea, Mablethorpe, Lincolnshire, LN12 2RA
Tel: 01507 441334 Fax: 01507 443033
Email: grangeandlinkshotel@btconnect.com
Web: www.thegrangeandlinkshotel.co.uk

This friendly, family-run hotel sits in 4 acres of beautiful grounds, close to the beach and its own 18-hole Links Golf Course. Bar meals and afternoon teas available.
Rooms: 23 all ensuite ⊗⊗ ⊿ ⊗
Pricing: Sgl £59.50 Dbl £78
Dinner available from £25
CC: Accepted
Room facilities: ▯ ☎ ⊿
Conference: 2 meeting rooms (Thtr 200 max), 24hr-delegate from £87, day-delegate from £30
Children: Welcome ⅃ ℂ Licenses: ◊ ♦♦♦
Leisure: Gym, Tennis, Golf, Snooker/billiards, Croquet
Parking: Off-street and free
Directions: From south, take A16 to Spilsby and Ulceby Cross. From north, take A16 to Louth and Ulceby Cross, then A1104 to Alford and A1111 to Sutton-on-Sea.
Map ref: Sandilands 9 D1

Towcester, Northamptonshire

Whittlebury Hall Hotel & Spa

★★★★

Whittlebury Hall, Whittlebury, near Towcester,
Northamptonshire, NN12 8QH
Tel: 01327 857857 Fax: 01327 857867
Email: sales@whittleburyhall.co.uk
Web: www.whittleburyhall.co.uk
Rooms: 211 all ensuite ⊛
Pricing: Sgl £99–130 Dbl £130–265
Dinner available from £32.50–450
CC: Accepted
Room facilities: ▢ ☎ ☺ ☎
Access: ♿
Conference: 55 meeting rooms (Thtr 400 max),
24hr-delegate from £185, day-delegate from £55
Children: Welcome ⋔ ⫶₡
Licenses: ⬧ ⅏
Leisure: Indoor pool, Gym, Health spa, Beauty salon,
Heat and ice experiences, Hydrotherapy pool, Rasul,
Hamman chamber
Parking: Off-street and free
Directions: M1 Junction 15a, A43 Silverstone, A413
Whittlebury/Buckingham. M40 Junction 10, A43
Silverstone, A413 Whittlebury/Buckingham. The hall is
situated at the end of the village on the right.
Map ref: Whittlebury 8 B4

Uppingham, Rutland

Old Rectory

◆◆◆

Belton-in-Rutland, Oakham, Rutland, LE15 9LE
Tel: 01572 717279 Fax: 01572 717343
Email: bb@iepuk.com
Web: www.theoldrectorybelton.co.uk
Rooms: 6 (4 ensuite) ⬧ ⊛
Pricing: Sgl £30–40 Dbl £48–60
CC: Accepted
Room facilities: ▢ ☺
Children: Welcome
Dogs: Welcome
Parking: Off-street and free
Directions: From Uppingham A47. Towards Leicester
take second turn right to Belton Village. Old Rectory is
on left after 400 yards.
Map ref: Belton 8 C3

Upton, Leicestershire

Upton Barn Restaurant and Accommodation

◆◆◆

Manor Farm, Upton, Near Nuneaton,
Leicestershire, CV13 6JX
Tel: 01455 212374 Fax: 01455 212328
Email: info@uptonbarn.co.uk
Web: www.uptonbarn.co.uk
Rooms: 5 all ensuite ⬧ ⊛
Pricing: Sgl £25–30 Dbl £40–50
Dinner available

CC: Accepted
Room facilities: ▢ ☺ ☎
Children: Welcome ⋔
Licenses: ⅏
Leisure: Indoor pool, Fishing, Games room
Parking: Off-street and free
Directions: Turn off A5 onto A444 towards Burton/
Twycross. Follow for 2 miles. Upton is signed 1 mile on
the right.
Map ref: Upton 8 B3

Woodhall Spa, Lincolnshire

Petwood Hotel

★★★

Stixwould Road, Woodhall Spa, Lincolnshire, LN10 6QF
Tel: 01526 352411 Fax: 01526 353473
Email: reception@petwood.co.uk
Web: www.petwood.co.uk

Delightful Edwardian Country House hotel set in 30
acres of secluded gardens and woodland. Home of the
Dambusters during the war. Extensive conference and
special event facilities, 53 bedrooms individually
designed.
Rooms: 53 all ensuite ⬧ ⊟ ⊛
Pricing: Sgl £90 Dbl £136
Dinner available from £22.50
CC: Accepted
Room facilities: ▢ ☎ ☺
Access: ♿
Conference: 6 meeting rooms (Thtr 250 max),
24hr-delegate from £95, day-delegate from £27.50
Children: Welcome ⋔ ⫶₡
Dogs: Welcome
Licenses: ⬧ ⅏
Leisure: Beauty salon, Snooker/billiards
Parking: Off-street and free
Directions: From Sleaford, take A153 to Tattershall.
Turn left onto B1192 to Woodhall Spa. From Lincoln,
south on B1188 and B1191.
Map ref: Woodhall Spa 8 C1

East Midlands

Worksop, Nottinghamshire

Charnwood Hotel

★★★

Sheffield Road, Blyth, Worksop,
Nottinghamshire, S81 8HF
Tel: 01909 591610 Fax: 01909 591429
Email: charnwood@bestwestern.co.uk
Web: www.bw-charnwoodhotel.co.uk

Situated amidst the peace and tranquility of rolling
Nottinghamshire countryside, the Charnwood Hotel is
an ideal base for discovering Robin Hood Country.
Independently owned and managed, the hotel's
relaxing ambience makes the Charnwood perfect for
business and pleasure.
Rooms: 33 all ensuite 🛏 ⊗
Pricing: Sgl £80–95 Dbl £90–160
Dinner available from £23.95
CC: Accepted
Room facilities: 🖵 ☎ 🗇 ✎
Conference: 3 meeting rooms (Thtr 126 max),
24hr-delegate from £110.95, day-delegate from £29.95
Children: Welcome ⼎
Licenses: 🔔 ⑂
Leisure: Gym
Directions: Just off the A1 outside the village of Blyth
on the A634 Sheffield road.
Map ref: Blyth 8 B1

Lion Hotel

★★★

112 Bridge Street, Worksop,
Nottinghamshire, S80 1HT
Tel: 01909 477925 Fax: 01909 479038
Email: enquiries@the-lionhotel.co.uk
Web: www.bw-lionhotel.co.uk
Rooms: 45 all ensuite 🛏 ⊗
Pricing: Sgl £75–95 Dbl £95–115
Dinner available from £15.95–26.95 CC: Accepted
Room facilities: 🖵 ☎ 🗇 ✎ Access: ⼧
Conference: 5 meeting rooms (Thtr 200 max),
24hr-delegate from £115, day-delegate from £35
Children: Welcome ⼎
Dogs: Welcome
Licenses: 🔔 ⑂
Parking: Off-street
Directions: A57 towards town centre.
Map ref: Worksop 8 B1

Stapleford Park Hotel, Melton Mowbray

West Midlands

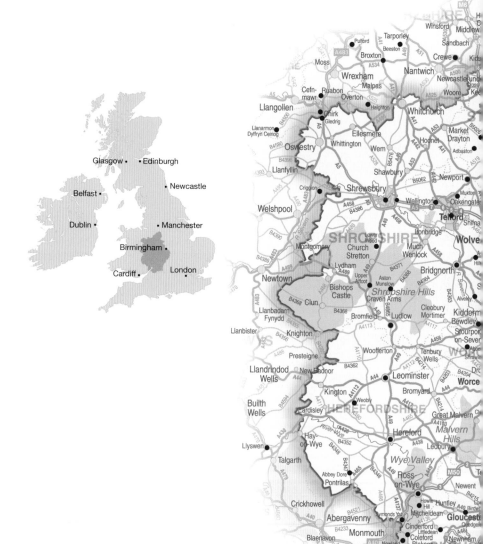

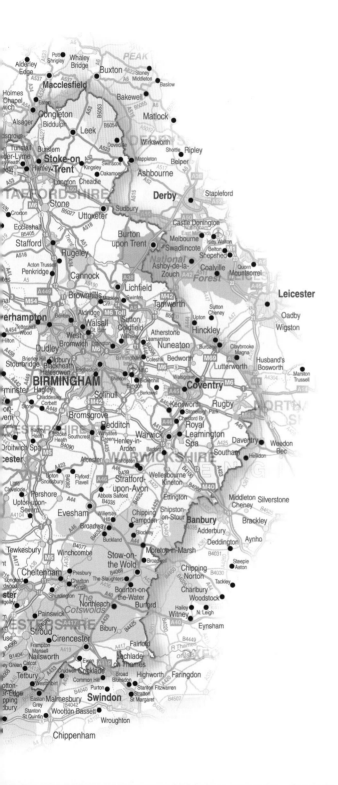

Award winners

To help you choose somewhere really special for your stay, we've listed here all RAC Award-winning properties in this region.

Gold Ribbon Award

Premier

		pg
Buckland Manor, Broadway	★★★	320
Calcot Manor Hotel & Spa, Tetbury	★★★	346
Castle House, Hereford	★★★	330
Cotswold House, Chipping Camden	★★★	325
Hotel on The Park, Cheltenham	★★★	323
Lords Of The Manor, Upper Slaughter	★★★	346

Blue Ribbon Award

Excellent

		pg
Best Western Peacock Hotel, Kenilworth	★★★	331
Brockencote Hall, Chaddesley Corbett	★★★	321
Greenway, Cheltenham	★★★	322
Lower Slaughter Manor, Lower Slaughter	★★★	334
New Hall Hotel, Sutton Coldfield	★★★★	345

White Ribbon Award

Commended

		pg
The Elms Hotel, Abberley	★★★	315

Little Gem Award

Little Gem

		pg
Bromley Court B&B, Ludlow	♦♦♦♦♦	336

Calcot Manor Hotel & Spa, Tetbury

Lords of the Manor, Upper Slaughter

Greenway, Cheltenham

The Elms Hotel, Abberley

Abberley, Worcestershire

THE ELMS HOTEL

Set in the beautiful Teme Valley between Worcester and Tenbury Wells, this Queen Anne mansion was built in 1710 by Gilbert White, a pupil of Christopher Wren. The Brooke Restaurant has a reputation for excellence, featuring ingredients from the hotel's garden.

STOCKTON ROAD, ABBERLEY, WORCESTER WR6 6AT

Tel: 01299 896666 Fax: 01299 896804

Email: info@theelmshotel.co.uk

Web: www.theelmshotel.co.uk

The Elms Hotel

Stockton Road, Abberley,
Worcester, Worcestershire, WR6 6AT
Tel: 01299 896666 Fax: 01299 896804
Email: info@theelmshotel.co.uk
Web: www.theelmshotel.co.uk
Rooms: 21 all ensuite
Pricing: Sgl £70–90 Dbl £130–160
Dinner available from £29.50–450
CC: Accepted
Room facilities:
Conference: 3 meeting rooms (Thtr 80 max),
24hr-delegate from £50, day-delegate from £150
Children: Welcome
Dogs: Welcome
Licenses:
Leisure: Tennis
Parking: Off-street and free
Directions: Join A4133 towards Tenbury Wells. Hotel is on the right about two miles after Great Witley.
Map ref: Abberley 7 E3
See advert on this page

Abbey Dore, Herefordshire

The Neville Arms
♦♦♦
Abbey Dore, Herefordshire, HR2 0AA
Tel: 01981 240319 Fax: 01432 356645
Rooms: 3 (1 ensuite)
Pricing: Dbl £40–60
Dinner available CC: Accepted
Room facilities:
Children: Welcome
Dogs: Welcome
Licenses:
Leisure: Games room
Parking: Off-street and free
Directions: Follow A465 Hereford to Abergavenny road to Wormbridge. Follow signs for Dore Abbey. The Neville Arms is 50 yards further on the right.
Map ref: Abbey Dore 7 D4

Berkswell, Warwickshire

Nailcote Hall Hotel
★★★★
Nailcote Lane, Berkswell, Warwickshire, CV7 7DE
Tel: 024 7646 6174 Fax: 024 7647 0720
Email: info@nailcotehall.co.uk
Web: www.nailcotehall.co.uk

Charming Elizabethan house in 15 acres of grounds. Relax in the Piano Bar Lounge, dine in the award-winning Oak Room Restaurant or Mediterranean Rick's. Swimming pool, gym, steam room, solarium, tennis, 9-hole golf course.
Rooms: 40 all ensuite
Pricing: Sgl £90–175 Dbl £100–190
Dinner available from £31.50
CC: Accepted
Room facilities:
Access:
Conference: 6 meeting rooms (Thtr 140 max),
24hr-delegate from £165, day-delegate from £47.50
Children: Welcome
Licenses:
Leisure: Indoor pool, Gym, Tennis, Golf, Snooker/billiards, Steam room, Solarium
Parking: Off-street and free
Map ref: Berkswell 8 B3

Bewdley, Worcestershire

George Hotel

★★ 🛆

Load Street, Bewdley, Worcestershire, DY12 2AW
Tel: 01299 402117 Fax: 01299 401269
Email: enquiries@georgehotelbewdley.co.uk
Web: www.georgehotelbewdley.co.uk
Rooms: 11 all ensuite 🛏
Pricing: Sgl £55–70 Dbl £78–110
Dinner available from £15 CC: Accepted
Room facilities: 🖵 ☎ 🗐
Conference: 1 meeting room (Thtr 80 max),
24hr-delegate from £74, day-delegate from £25
Children: Welcome ⱨ ⱦ
Dogs: Assistance dogs only
Licenses: ⱨⱨⱨ
Parking: Off-street and free
Directions: From M5 Junction 3, A456 to Bewdley.
From M5 Junction 6, A449 to Kidderminster, A456 to
Bewdley. From M42 Junction 1, A448 to Kidderminster,
A456 to Bewdley.
Map ref: Bewdley 7 E3

Birmingham, West Midlands

Copthorne Hotel Birmingham

★★★★ 🛆🛆

Paradise Circus, Birmingham, West Midlands, B3 3HJ
Tel: 0121 200 2727 Fax: 0121 200 1197
Email: reservations.birmingham@mill-cop.com
Web: www.copthornehotels.com

MILLENNIUM
HOTELS AND RESORTS

MILLENNIUM HOTELS
COPTHORNE HOTELS

Located in the heart of the city centre, this hotel is
ideally located for the NEC, National Indoor Arena and
International Convention Centre. Weekend rates are
also available.
Rooms: 212 all ensuite 🛇
Pricing: Sgl £87–210 Dbl £87–210
Dinner available from £17
CC: Accepted
Room facilities: 🖵 ☎ 🗐 ✆
Access: |ↂ

Conference: 13 meeting rooms (Thtr 200 max),
24hr-delegate from £170, day-delegate from £65
Children: Welcome ⱨ
Licenses: ⱨⱨⱨ
Leisure: Indoor pool, Gym, Steam room, Solarium,
Spa bath, Sauna
Parking: Off-street
Directions: Situated by Centenary Square,
approximately 10 minutes from M6 Junction 6, follow
city centre route (A38).
Map ref: Birmingham 7 F3

MacDonald Burlington Hotel

★★★★ 🛆

Burlington Arcade, 126 New Street,
Birmingham, West Midlands, B2 4JQ
Tel: 0121 643 9191 Fax: 0121 643 5075
Email: mail@burlingtonhotel.com
Web: www.burlingtonhotel.com
Seasonal closure: 24-29 December
Rooms: 112 all ensuite 🛆 🛏 🛇
Pricing: Sgl £105–145 Dbl £135–165
Dinner available from £24.95–40
CC: Accepted
Room facilities: 🖵 ☎ 🗐 ✆ ❄ Access: |ↂ
Conference: 14 meeting rooms (Thtr 450 max),
24hr-delegate from £170, day-delegate from £60
Children: Welcome ⱨ Dogs: Welcome
Licenses: 🛆 ⱨⱨⱨ
Leisure: Gym, Sauna
Directions: M6 J6. Follow signs for city centre then
onto A38.
Map ref: Birmingham 7 F3

Birmingham Great Barr Hotel

★★★

Pear Tree Drive, Newton Road, Great Barr,
Birmingham, West Midlands, B43 6HS
Tel: 0800 373 853 Fax: 0121 357 7557
Email: sales@thegreatbarrhotel.com
Web: www.thegreatbarrhotel.com

Situated in the leafy suburb of north Birmingham
offering tastefully furnished bedrooms of contemporary
design. Restaurant with a fine range of international
cuisine complemented by a "country pub" style bar
with real open fire.

Rooms: 105 all ensuite
Pricing: Dinner available from £17.95
CC: Accepted
Room facilities: 🖥 ☎ ☕ 📞
Conference: 10 meeting rooms (Thtr 200 max),
24hr-delegate from £135, day-delegate from £30
Children: Welcome ⼐ 🍼
Licenses: ◇ ⅲ
Parking: Off-street and free
Directions: Take M6 Exit 7, follow A34 to Birmingham.
Turn right at Scott Arms traffic lights onto Newton
Road. After 1¼ miles, turn right into Pear Tree Drive.
Map ref: Great Barr 7 F3

Jurys Inn Birmingham

★★★

245 Broad Street, Birmingham, West Midlands, B1 2HQ
Tel: 0121 606 9000 Fax: 0121 606 9001
Email: bookings@jurysdoyle.com
Web: www.jurysinns.com
Seasonal closure: 24–26 December

JURYS DOYLE
HOTELS

Rooms: 445 all ensuite
Pricing: Sgl £175
Dinner available from £16
CC: Accepted
Room facilities: 🖥 ☎ ☕ 📞 ❄
Access: ♿
Conference: 20 meeting rooms (Thtr 275 max),
24hr-delegate from £135, day-delegate from £45
Children: Welcome ⼐
Licenses: ⅲ
Parking: Off-street
Directions: Jurys Inn Birmingham is situated approx. 8
miles from Birmingham International Airport, or 1 mile
from New Street train station.
Map ref: Birmingham 7 F3

Portland Hotel

★★★

313 Hagley Road, Edgbaston,
Birmingham, West Midlands, B16 9LQ
Tel: 0121 455 0535 Fax: 0121 456 1841
Email: reception@theportlandhotel.com
Web: www.theportlandhotel.com
Rooms: 63 all ensuite ⊗
Pricing: Sgl £54.95–74.95 Dbl £64.95–89.95
Dinner available from £14.95
CC: Accepted
Room facilities: 🖥 ☎ ☕ 📞
Access: ♿
Conference: 4 meeting rooms (Thtr 80 max),
24hr-delegate from £81.95, day-delegate from £26.95
Children: Welcome
Licenses: ⅲ
Parking: Off-street and free
Directions: Hotel is situated on A456, Hagley Road into
Birmingham city centre from M5 Junction 3.
Map ref: Edgbaston 7 F3

Quality Hotel

★★★

166 Hagley Road, Edgbaston,
Birmingham, West Midlands, B16 9NZ
Tel: 0121 454 6621 Fax: 0121 456 2935
Email: enquiries@quality-hotels-birmingham.com
Web: www.choicehotelseurope.com
Rooms: 215 all ensuite ▱ ⊗
Pricing: Sgl £35–95 Dbl £59–120
Dinner available from £17.95
CC: Accepted
Room facilities: 🖥 ☎ ☕ 📞
Access: ♿
Conference: 8 meeting rooms (Thtr 100 max),
24hr-delegate from £131, day-delegate from £34
Children: Welcome ⼐ 🍼
Licenses: ◇ ⅲ
Leisure: Indoor pool, Gym, Health spa
Parking: Off-street and free
Directions: From M5 J3 turn onto A456 signposted to
Birmingham. Hotel is 3 miles down this dual track road
on the left, just past TGI Fridays.
Map ref: Edgbaston 7 F3

Woodlands Hotel & Restaurant

★★

379–381 Hagley Road, Edgbaston, Birmingham,
West Midlands, B17 8DL
Tel: 0121 420 2341 Fax: 0121 429 3935
Email: hotel@woodlands2000.freeserve.co.uk
Web: www.thewoodlandshotel.co.uk
Rooms: 20 all ensuite ▱ ⊗
Pricing: Sgl £45–50 Dbl £56–64
Dinner available from £12.50–17.50
CC: Accepted
Room facilities: 🖥 ☎ ☕ 📞
Conference: 1 meeting room (Thtr 40 max)
Children: Welcome
Licenses: ◇ ⅲ
Leisure: Snooker/billiards
Parking: Off-street and free
Map ref: Edgbaston 7 F3

La Caverna Restaurant and Hotel

◆◆◆

23-27 Coventry Road, Sheldon, Birmingham,
West Midlands, B26 3PG
Tel: 0121 743 7917/722 2725 Fax: 0121 722 3307
Email: hotel@lacaverna.uk.com
Web: www.lacaverna.uk.com
Rooms: 19 all ensuite
Pricing: Sgl £35–42 Dbl £50–59
Dinner available
CC: Accepted
Room facilities: 🖥 ☎ ☕
Conference: 1 meeting room
Children: Welcome
Parking: Off-street and free
Directions: 3 miles from NEC and Airport, close to
junction of Coventry Road and Wells Road.
Map ref: Sheldon 7 F3

Lyndhurst Hotel

♦♦♦

135 Kingsbury Road, Erdington,
Birmingham, West Midlands, B24 8QT
Tel: 0121 373 5695 Fax: 0121 373 5697
Email: info@lyndhurst-hotel.co.uk
Web: www.lyndhurst-hotel.co.uk
Seasonal closure: Christmas
Rooms: 14 all ensuite 🐾 🚭
Dinner available
CC: Accepted
Room facilities: 🖵 ☕
Children: Welcome
Licenses: 🍾
Parking: Off-street and free
Directions: Exit J6 M6; A5127 to roundabout. Second left up Gravelly Hill. Right-hand fork along Kingsbury Road. Hotel on the right.
Map ref: Erdington 7 F3

Tri-Star Hotel

♦♦♦

Coventry Road, Elmdon, Birmingham,
West Midlands, B26 3QR
Tel: 0121 782 1010 Fax: 0121 782 6131
Rooms: 15 all ensuite 🐾 🚭
Dinner available CC: Accepted
Room facilities: 🖵 ☕
Children: Welcome 🍴
Licenses: 🍾
Leisure: Games room, Snooker/billiards
Parking: Off-street
Directions: 2 miles from Junction 6 of M42, 1½ miles from Birmingham International Airport, train station and National Exhibition Centre.
Map ref: Elmdon 7 F3

Rollason Wood Hotel

♦♦

Wood End Road, Erdington, Birmingham,
West Midlands, B24 8BJ
Tel: 0121 373 1230 Fax: 0121 382 2578
Email: rollwood@globalnet.co.uk

Friendly family-run hotel with 35 bedrooms. Choose from economy, with shower, or fully ensuite. Licensed bar and à la carte restaurant. Weekend and weekly reductions.

Rooms: 35 (17 ensuite) 🐾 🚭
Pricing: Sgl £23–39.75 Dbl £39.25–49.75
Dinner available from £6
CC: Accepted
Room facilities: 🖵 ☕
Children: Welcome
Dogs: Welcome
Licenses: 🍾
Leisure: Games room
Parking: Off-street
Directions: Exit M6 at Junction 6 and take A5127 to Erdington. At island turn right onto A4040. Hotel 1/4 of a mile on left.
Map ref: Erdington 7 F3

Campanile Hotel
Travel Accommodation

Chester Street, Aston Locks, Birmingham,
West Midlands, B6 4BE
Tel: 0121 359 3330 Fax: 0121 359 1223
Email: birmingham@campanile-hotels.com
Web: www.activehotels.com

Campanile hotels offer comfortable and convenient budget accommodation and a traditional French-style Bistro providing freshly-cooked food for breakfast, lunch and dinner. All rooms ensuite with tea/coffee-making facilities, DDT and TV with pay satellite channels.
Rooms: 111 all ensuite 🚭
Pricing: Sgl £45.45–75.95 Dbl £51.40–81.90
Dinner available from £8
CC: Accepted
Room facilities: 🖵 ☎ ☕ 📞
Access: ♿
Conference: 5 meeting rooms (Thtr 200 max), 24hr-delegate from £75, day-delegate from £21.50
Children: Welcome 🍴
Dogs: Welcome
Licenses: 🍾
Parking: Off-street and free
Directions: Junction 6 of M6, then A38. Take second exit (ring road), go left at roundabout, then first left into Richard Street. From city centre, take M6 direction then ring road/NEC.
Map ref: Birmingham 7 F3

Blakeney, Gloucestershire

The Cock Inn

◆◆◆

Nibley Hill, Blakeney, Gloucestershire, GL15 4DB
Tel: 01594 510239
Email: cockinnenquiries@btinternet.com
Web: www.cockinnblakeney.co.uk
Rooms: 6 all ensuite
Pricing: Sgl £29.50 Dbl £50–90
Dinner available from £6.50–130
CC: Accepted
Room facilities:
Children: Welcome
Dogs: Assistance dogs only
Licenses:
Leisure: Games room
Parking: Off-street and free
Directions: From west and Wales take M4 J2
Chepstow – A466. A48 13 miles to Blakeney, Cock Inn
on left. From north and east exit M5 J11 onto A40 and
follow signs for Forest of Dean. A48 follow signs for
Chepstow 13 miles. Cock Inn on right.
Map ref: Blakeney 7 E4

Bourton-on-the-Water, Gloucestershire

The Old New Inn

★★

High Street, Bourton-on-the-Water,
Gloucestershire, GL54 2AF
Tel: 01451 820467 Fax: 01451 810236
Email: reception@theoldnewinn.co.uk
Web: www.theoldnewinn.co.uk

Rooms: 9 all ensuite
Pricing: Sgl £38 Dbl £38
Dinner available from £18
CC: Accepted
Room facilities:
Children: Welcome
Licenses:
Parking: Off-street and free
Directions: Situated on the left-hand side of the road at
the junction of the High Street and Rissington Road.
Map ref: Bourton-on-the-Water 4 A1

Bridgnorth, Shropshire

Mill Hotel

★★★★

Alveley, near Bridgnorth, Shropshire, WV15 6HL
Tel: 01746 780437 Fax: 01746 780850
Email: info@themill-hotel.co.uk
Web: www.themill-hotel.co.uk
Rooms: 41 all ensuite
Pricing: Sgl £80–150 Dbl £90–190
Dinner available from £19.95–25
CC: Accepted
Room facilities:
Access:
Conference: 6 meeting rooms (Thtr 250 max),
24hr-delegate from £135, day-delegate from £40
Children: Welcome
Licenses:
Leisure: Gym
Parking: Off-street and free
Directions: Situated just off main A442, midway
between Kidderminster and Bridgnorth.
Map ref: Alveley 7 E3

Parlor's Hall Hotel

★★

Mill Street, Bridgnorth, Shropshire, WV15 5AL
Tel: 01746 761931 Fax: 01746 767058
Email: info@parlorshallhotel.co.uk
Web: www.parlorshallhotel.co.uk
Rooms: 13 all ensuite
Pricing: Sgl £46–50 Dbl £66–75
Dinner available from £15
CC: Accepted
Room facilities:
Children: Welcome
Licenses:
Parking: Off-street and free
Map ref: Bridgnorth 7 E3
See advert on following page

The Old House

◆◆◆◆

Hilton, Bridgnorth, Shropshire, WV15 5PJ
Tel: 01746 716560 Fax: 01746 716560
Email: enquiries@oldhousehilton.co.uk
Web: www.oldhousehilton.co.uk
Rooms: 3 (1 ensuite)
Pricing: Sgl £38–45 Dbl £48–55
Room facilities:
Children: Welcome
Dogs: Welcome
Parking: Off-street and free
Directions: A454, 5 miles from Bridgnorth, off the layby
in Hilton.
Map ref: Hilton 7 E3

West Midlands

Parlor's Hall Hotel & Restaurant

The original 15th-century Parlor Family Home

13 Luxury ensuite bedrooms, singles, twins, doubles. Carvery and à la carte restaurant. Business meeting and conference facilities. Private functions catered for.

Mill Street, Bridgnorth WV15 5AL
Tel: 01746 761931/2   Fax: 01746 767058

Broadway, Worcestershire

Buckland Manor

★★★ ⌇⌇⌇ Premier

Buckland, near Broadway, Worcestershire, WR12 7LY
Tel: 01386 852626 Fax: 01386 853557
Email: enquire@bucklandmanor.com
Web: www.bucklandmanor.com

13th-century manor situated in the heart of the Cotswolds, in glorious grounds. Superb food and wines in award-winning restaurant. Luxury bedrooms with antiques and four-poster beds.
Rooms: 13 all ensuite
Pricing: Sgl £240–450 Dbl £250–460

Dinner available from £50 CC: Accepted
Room facilities: ▢ ☎
Children: Welcome 12yrs min age Licenses: ♦♦♦
Leisure: Outdoor pool, Tennis
Parking: Off-street and free
Directions: 2 miles south of Broadway, on B4632.
Map ref: Buckland 8 A4

Dormy House

★★★★ ⌇⌇⌇

Willersey Hill, Broadway, Worcestershire, WR12 7LF
Tel: 01386 852711 Fax: 01386 858636
Email: reservations@dormyhouse.co.uk
Web: www.dormyhouse.co.uk
Seasonal closure: Christmas

Meticulously converted 17th-century Cotswold farmhouse combining traditional charm with all the modern comforts. Leisure facilities include: games room, gym, sauna/steam room, putting green and croquet lawn.
Rooms: 47 all ensuite
Pricing: Sgl £115–120 Dbl £155–210
Dinner available from £35 CC: Accepted
Room facilities: ▢ ☎ ▢ ⌁
Conference: 8 meeting rooms (Thtr 170 max),
24hr-delegate from £185, day-delegate from £60
Children: Welcome ♩ ☽ Dogs: Welcome
Licenses: ⌂ ♦♦♦
Leisure: Gym, Games room, Snooker/billiards, Sauna, Croquet, Putting green
Parking: Off-street and free
Directions: Off A44 at top of Fish Hill. 1½ miles from Broadway, take turn signposted Saintbury/picnic area. After ½ mile fork left. Dormy House on left.
Map ref: Willersey Hill 8 A4

Russells
Restaurant with Rooms

⌇⌇⌇

The Green, 20 High Street, Broadway, Worcestershire, WR12 7AD
Tel: 01386 853555
Email: barry@russellsof broadway.com
Web: www.russellsofbroadway.com
Rooms: 4 all ensuite
Dinner available CC: Accepted
Room facilities: ▢ ☎ ▢ ⌁

Conference: 1 meeting room (Thtr 25 max)
Children: Welcome ⁑ Licenses: ♦♦♦
Parking: Off-street and free
Directions: In the middle of Broadway overlooking the village green on the High Street.
Map ref: Broadway 8 A4

Bromsgrove, Worcestershire

Avoncroft Guest House

77 Redditch Road, Stoke Heath, Bromsgrove, Worcestershire, B60 4JP
Tel: 01527 832819
Web: www.smoothhound.co.uk/avoncroft.html
Rooms: 4 all ensuite ⊗
Pricing: Sgl £35 Dbl £55 Room facilities: ☐ ⊚
Children: Welcome ♠ Parking: Off-street and free
Directions: Exit J1 M42, A38 south 3 miles. J5 M5 A38 north 2 miles, 300 yards from Hanbury turn crossroads.
Map ref: Stoke Heath 7 F3

Burton upon Trent, Staffordshire

Three Queens Hotel

★★★

One Bridge Street, Burton upon Trent, Staffordshire, DE14 1SY
Tel: 0845 230 1332 Fax: 01283 523823
Email: hotel@threequeenshotel.co.uk
Web: www.threequeenshotel.co.uk
Rooms: 38 all ensuite ⊞ ⊗
Pricing: Sgl £50–95 Dbl £60–105
Dinner available from £17.95–25 CC: Accepted
Room facilities: ☐ ☎ ⊚ ✆ ❄ Access: ⌊↑
Conference: 5 meeting rooms (Thtr 40 max),
24hr-delegate from £99.50, day-delegate from £22.50
Children: Welcome
Licenses: ⟁ ♦♦♦ Parking: Off-street and free
Directions: Town centre on corner of Bridge Street and High Street. From M42 Junction 11 take A444. From A38 follow town centre.
Map ref: Burton upon Trent 8 B2
See advert on this page

Delter Hotel

5 Derby Road, Burton upon Trent, Staffordshire, DE14 1RU
Tel: 01283 535115 Fax: 01283 845261
Email: delterhotel@burtonontrenthotels.co.uk
Web: www.burtonontrenthotels.co.uk
Rooms: 7 all ensuite ⊗
Pricing: Sgl £46–56 Dbl £66–76 CC: Accepted
Room facilities: ☐ ⊚ ✆ Children: Welcome
Licenses: ♦♦♦ Parking: Off-street and free
Directions: From A511 turn into Derby Road at roundabout. Hotel 50 yards on left. Or, from A38 join A5121 Burton north, straight over two roundabouts.
Hotel 1/2 mile on right. Map ref: Burton upon Trent 8 B2

Chaddesley Corbett, Worcestershire

Brockencote Hall

★★★ ⏚⏚⏚⏚   Excellent

Chaddesley Corbett,
Kidderminster, Worcestershire, DY10 4PY
Tel: 01562 777876 Fax: 01562 777872
Email: info@brockencotehall.com
Web: www.brockencotehall.com
Seasonal closure: 1-15 January
Rooms: 17 all ensuite ⊗ ⊞
Pricing: Sgl £89–140 Dbl £116–180
Dinner available from £32.50–450
CC: Accepted
Room facilities: ☐ ☎ ⊚ ✆
Access: ⌊↑
Conference: 1 meeting room (Thtr 20 max),
24hr-delegate from £160, day-delegate from £42
Children: Welcome ♠ ⁑
Licenses: ⟁ ♦♦♦
Leisure: Tennis
Parking: Off-street and free
Directions: Opposite the village of Chaddesley Corbett (A448) between Kidderminster and Bromsgrove.
Map ref: Chaddesley Corbett 7 E3

Three Queens Hotel

Welcome to our hotel and restaurant where you will enjoy friendly service and those extra touches associated with private ownership. Ideal for touring Derbyshire and Staffordshire - Call 0845 230 1332 or visit www.threequeenshotel.co.uk and book on-line.

West Midlands

Cheltenham, Gloucestershire

Cheltenham Park Hotel

★★★★ ®

Cirencester Road, Charlton Kings, Cheltenham,
Gloucestershire, GL53 8EA
Tel: 01242 222021 Fax: 01242 226935
Email: cheltenhamparkreservations@paramount-hotels.co.uk
Web: www.paramount-hotels.co.uk

PARAMOUNT
GROUP OF HOTELS

Luxurious country house set in the heart of the
Cotswolds yet only two miles from the beautiful spa
town of Cheltenham.
Rooms: 144 all ensuite 🛏 🚭
Pricing: Sgl £59–118 Dbl £118
Dinner available from £22.50
CC: Accepted
Room facilities: 📺 ☎ ☕ 🧺
Conference: 13 meeting rooms (Thtr 320 max),
24hr-delegate from £165, day-delegate from £52
Children: Welcome 🪑
Dogs: Welcome
Licenses: 🜷 ∭
Leisure: Indoor pool, Gym, Health spa, Beauty salon
Parking: Off-street and free
Directions: From M40, follow A40 to Cheltenham, on
approach to town follow A436 (A417) to Gloucester,
after 4½ miles turn right onto A435, hotel is on right.
Map ref: Charlton Kings 7 F4

Ice & slice?

RAC's comprehensive
inspection means we
even check drinks are
served the way
you want.

Charlton Kings Hotel

★★★ ®

London Road, Charlton Kings, Cheltenham,
Gloucestershire, GL52 6UU
Tel: 01242 231061 Fax: 01242 241900
Email: enquiries@charltonkingshotel.co.uk
Web: www.charltonkingshotel.co.uk

Privately owned hotel in an acre of grounds. Most
rooms have views of the Cotswolds. All areas
beautifully presented, few minutes from town centre,
ample parking.
Rooms: 13 all ensuite 🛏 🚭
Pricing: Sgl £65–85 Dbl £95–125
Dinner available from £20–25
CC: Accepted
Room facilities: 📺 ☎ ☕
Children: Welcome 🪑 Dogs: Welcome
Licenses: ∭
Parking: Off-street and free
Directions: First property on left as you enter
Cheltenham from Oxford on A40, or M5 junction 11
then A40 to Oxford.
Map ref: Charlton Kings 7 F4

Greenway

★★★ ®®® — Excellent

Shurdington, Cheltenham, Gloucestershire, GL51 4UG
Tel: 01242 862352 Fax: 01242 862780
Email: info@thegreenway.co.uk
Web: www.thegreenway.co.uk
Rooms: 21 all ensuite 📠 🚭
Pricing: Sgl £79–99 Dbl £130–260
Dinner available from £32–45
CC: Accepted
Room facilities: 📺 ☎
Conference: 2 meeting rooms (Thtr 45 max),
24hr-delegate from £205, day-delegate from £55
Children: Welcome ☕
Dogs: Welcome
Licenses: 🜷 ∭
Parking: Off-street
Directions: Located on the A46 Cheltenham to Stroud
road, approx 1½ miles from city centre.
Map ref: Shurdington 7 E4

Hotel on The Park

★★★★ 🛏🛏🛏

Evesham Road, Cheltenham,
Gloucestershire, GL52 2AH
Tel: 01242 518898 Fax: 01242 511526
Email: stay@hotelonthepark.co.uk
Web: www.hotelonthepark.com
Rooms: 12 all ensuite 🎴 ⊗
Pricing: Sgl £93.75–178.50 Dbl £128.50–203
Dinner available from £14.50–340
CC: Accepted Room facilities: ▢ ☎ 🖴 📞
Conference: 1 meeting room (Thtr 18 max)
Children: Welcome 8yrs min age
Licenses: ⓲ Parking: Off-street and free
Directions: Follow the signs for the A435 to Evesham
Race course. The hotel is opposite the start of Pittville
Park on the Evesham Road, Wellington Road
crossroads.
Map ref: Cheltenham 7 E4

The Carlton Hotel

★★★

Parabola Road, Cheltenham, Gloucestershire, GL50 3AQ
Tel: 01242 514453 Fax: 01242 226487
Email: enquiries@thecarltonhotel.co.uk
Web: www.thecarltonhotel.co.uk
Rooms: 76 all ensuite 🍴 🎴 ⊗
Dinner available CC: Accepted
Room facilities: ▢ ☎ 🖴 📞 Access: 👢
Conference: 3 meeting rooms (Thtr 200 max)
Children: Welcome 🍴 🐾 Dogs: Welcome
Licenses: ♿ ⓲
Parking: Off-street and free
Directions: Follow signs to Town Hall. At Town Hall,
take middle lane, across traffic lights, past Ladies'
College, left at lights and first right into Parabola Road.
Map ref: Cheltenham 7 E4

The Prestbury House Hotel & Oaks Restaurant

★★★ 🛏

The Burgage, Prestbury, Cheltenham,
Gloucestershire, GL52 3DN
Tel: 01242 529533 Fax: 01242 227076
Email: reservation@prestburyhouse.co.uk
Web: www.prestburyhouse.co.uk

300-year-old manor house hotel and restaurant (open
to non-residents), set in five acres of secluded
grounds. Cheltenham centre is 1½ miles away. Full
conference and wedding reception facilities.
Rooms: 16 (15 ensuite) 🍴 🎴 ⊗
Pricing: Sgl £50–65 Dbl £68–120
Dinner available from £22–25
CC: Accepted
Room facilities: ▢ ☎ 🖴 📞
Conference: 3 meeting rooms (Thtr 70 max),
24hr-delegate from £98, day-delegate from £32
Children: Welcome 🍴
Licenses: ♿ ⓲
Leisure: Gym, Golf, Riding, Mountain bike hire,
Trim trail, Boules
Parking: Off-street and free
Directions: Follow any sign for Cheltenham
Racecourse on entering Cheltenham. Hotel is ½ mile
from racecourse entrance, signposted from Prestbury
village.
Map ref: Prestbury 7 F4

Wyastone Hotel

★★★

Parabola Road, Montpellier, Cheltenham Spa,
Gloucestershire, GL50 3BG
Tel: 01242 245549 Fax: 01242 522659
Email: reservations@wyastonehotel.co.uk
Web: www.wyastonehotel.co.uk
Rooms: 13 all ensuite 🎴 ⊗
Pricing: Sgl £61–75 Dbl £75–95
Dinner available
CC: Accepted
Room facilities: ▢ ☎ 🖴 📞
Children: Welcome
Licenses: ⓲
Parking: Off-street
Directions: Exit M5 J11 and follow A40 to town centre.
Turn right, second roundabout at third exit. Take
second exit to Bayshill Road; Parabola Road bears off
to the left.
Map ref: Cheltenham 7 E4

Lypiatt House Hotel

Lypiatt Road, Cheltenham, Gloucestershire, GL50 2QW
Tel: 01242 224994 Fax: 01242 224996
Email: stay@lypiatt.co.uk
Web: www.lypiatt.co.uk

This lovely Victorian house, with its spacious accommodation, is located a short walk from the town centre. A gravelled drive with parking, elegant drawing room and conservatory but above all a very warm welcome is assured.
Rooms: 10 all ensuite
Pricing: Sgl £70–80 Dbl £80–90 CC: Accepted
Room facilities: ▢ ☎ ▣ ▙
Licenses: ♦♦♦
Parking: Off-street and free
Directions: From M5 J11, A40 to Montpellier from Oxford A40, Town Centre, Montpellier from M4 J15, A419/417, A46. See website map.
Map ref: Cheltenham 7 E4

Milton House Hotel

12 Bayshill Road, Cheltenham,
Gloucestershire, GL50 3AY
Tel: 01242 582601 Fax: 01242 222326
Email: info@miltonhousehotel.co.uk
Web: www.miltonhousehotel.co.uk
Seasonal closure: 18 December to 20 February
Rooms: 8 all ensuite ▨ ⊗
Pricing: Sgl £75–80 Dbl £95–115
CC: Accepted
Room facilities: ▢ ☎ ▣ ▙
Children: Welcome 6yrs min age
Parking: Off-street and free
Directions: M5 junction 11, A40 from Oxford, A65 from Bath/Stroud, at Cheltenham follow Town Centre route, Montpellier, then Bayshill Road.
Map ref: Cheltenham 7 E4

Beaumont House Hotel

56 Shurdington Road, Cheltenham,
Gloucestershire, GL53 0JE
Tel: 01242 245986 Fax: 01242 520044
Email: res@bhhotel.co.uk
Web: www.beaumonthousehotel.co.uk

Rooms: 16 all ensuite ❦ ▨ ⊗
Pricing: Sgl £55–69 Dbl £69–119
CC: Accepted
Room facilities: ▢ ☎ ▣ ▙
Children: Welcome 10yrs min age
Licenses: ♦♦♦
Leisure: Free membership LA Fitness
Parking: Off-street and free
Directions: From A40 follow A46 to Stroud. From M4 follow A419/417 then A46. From M5 Exit 11 A40 then A46. See website for directions.
Map ref: Cheltenham 7 E4

Moorend Park Hotel

Moorend Park Road, Cheltenham,
Gloucestershire, GL53 0LA
Tel: 01242 224441 Fax: 01242 572413
Email: moorendpark@freeuk.com
Web: www.moorendpark.freeuk.com
Seasonal closure: Christmas
Rooms: 9 all ensuite ⊗
Pricing: Sgl £56–60 Dbl £66–90 CC: Accepted
Room facilities: ▢ ☎ ▣
Conference: 1 meeting room (Thtr 30 max)
Children: Welcome
Licenses: ♦♦♦
Parking: Off-street and free
Directions: Located on the A46 off M5 Junction 11A.
Map ref: Cheltenham 7 E4

Chipping Campden, Gloucestershire

Charingworth Manor

★★★ ♛♛♛

Chipping Campden, Gloucestershire, GL55 6NS
Tel: 01386 593555 Fax: 01386 593353
Email: charingworthmanor@englishrosehotels.co.uk
Web: www.englishrosehotels.co.uk

Rooms: 26 all ensuite ▨
Pricing: Sgl £75–125 Dbl £125
Dinner available from £37.50
CC: Accepted
Room facilities: ▢ ☎
Conference: 3 meeting rooms (Thtr 50 max),
24hr-delegate from £175, day-delegate from £49.50
Children: Welcome ♯ ℃
Licenses: ⟁ ♦♦♦
Leisure: Indoor pool, Gym, Health spa, Tennis
Parking: Off-street and free
Directions: From M40 leave at Junction 15. Take A429 towards Stow, then B4035 toward Chipping Campden. Charingworth Manor is on the right.
Map ref: Chipping Campden 8 A4
See advert on opposite page

Cotswold House

★★★★♖♖♖

The Square, Chipping Campden,
Gloucestershire, GL55 6AN
Tel: 01386 840330 Fax: 01386 840310
Email: reception@cotswoldhouse.com
Web: www.cotswoldhouse.com
Rooms: 20 all ensuite 🍴 🖥 🚭
Pricing: Sgl £70–200 Dbl £125–250
Dinner available from £50
CC: Accepted
Room facilities: 🖥 ☎ ☕ 🚬
Conference: 3 meeting rooms (Thtr 40 max),
24hr-delegate from £225, day-delegate from £60
Children: Welcome ♿
Dogs: Welcome
Licenses: ⚖ ♟
Leisure: Gym
Parking: Off-street and free
Directions: Leave M40 at Junction 15, taking the A429
south towards Cirencester. After 16 miles turn right
onto B4035, signposted Campden.
Map ref: Chipping Campden 8 A4

Church Stretton, Shropshire

Malt House Farm

◆◆◆♋

Lower Wood, Church Stretton, Shropshire, SY6 6LF
Tel: 01694 751379 Fax: 01694 751379
Seasonal closure: November to January

Working farm peacefully situated on the lower slopes
of the Long Mynd Hills AONB. Stunning scenery.
Ironbridge, Ludlow and Shrewsbury within half an hour.
Oak beams. Comfortable rooms. Traditional home
cooking.
Rooms: 3 all ensuite 🚭
Pricing: Dbl £25–26 Dinner available
Room facilities: 🖥 ☕
Licenses: ♟
Parking: Off-street and free
Directions: Three miles north of Church Stretton, half a
mile off the A49 Shrewsbury to Ludlow Road.
Signposted Lower Wood.
Map ref: Lower Wood 7 E3

Charingworth Manor

Just 25 minutes from Stratford-upon-Avon,
this 14th-century Manor House hotel with
individually decorated bedrooms has a
reputation for excellent cuisine and attractive
accommodation. The hotel's romanesque
leisure spa with pool and gym is the place to
unwind. Splendid views and exciting
surprises for the avid explorer.

Chipping Campden,
Gloucestershire GL55 6NS

RAC Dining Award ♖♖♖

Tel: 01386 593555   Fax: 01386 593353
charingworthmanor@englishrosehotels.co.uk
www.englishrosehotels.co.uk

Travellers Rest Inn

◆◆◆

Upper Affcot, Church Stretton, Shropshire, SY6 6RL
Tel: 01694 781275 Fax: 01694 781555
Email: reception@travellersrestinn.co.uk
Web: www.travellersrestinn.co.uk
Rooms: 12 all ensuite
Pricing: Sgl £40 Dbl £60
Dinner available from £7
CC: Accepted
Room facilities: 🖥 ☕
Children: Welcome ♿
Dogs: Welcome
Licenses: ♟
Leisure: Games room
Parking: Off-street and free
Directions: Situated on west side of A49, 5 miles south
of Church Stretton, near the villages of Bushmore and
Wistanstow.
Map ref: Upper Affcot 7 D3

The big sleep

As part of our comprehensive inspection
process, RAC Inspectors investigate the
comfort of the beds.

West Midlands

Cinderford, Gloucestershire

The Belfry Hotel

♦♦♦

Broad Street, Littledean, Cinderford,
Gloucestershire, GL14 3JS
Tel: 01594 827858 Fax: 01594 825766
Email: info@thebelfryhotel.co.uk
Web: www.thebelfryhotel.co.uk
Rooms: 21 all ensuite
Pricing: Sgl £45 Dbl £60
Dinner available from £6.75
CC: Accepted
Room facilities:
Conference: 1 meeting room (Thtr 80 max)
Children: Welcome
Licenses:
Leisure: Games room, Snooker/billiards
Parking: Off-street and free
Directions: From south: M4, A48 Gloucester. A4157
Cinderford. Littledean, turn right on roundabout. From
north: M5, A48 Chepstow. Turn right onto A4151.
Map ref: Littledean 7 E4

Cirencester, Gloucestershire

Fleece Hotel

★★★

Market Place, Cirencester, Gloucestershire, GL7 2NZ
Tel: 01285 658507 Fax: 01285 651017
Email: relax@fleecehotel.co.uk
Web: www.fleecehotel.co.uk

Rooms: 28 all ensuite
Pricing: Sgl £59–115 Dbl £79–125
Dinner available from £14–25
CC: Accepted
Room facilities:
Conference: 1 meeting room (Thtr 60 max),
day-delegate from £50
Children: Welcome
Dogs: Welcome
Licenses:
Parking: Off-street and free
Directions: Follow town centre signs to the market
square, same side as Parish Church, Fleece has black
and white Tudor front.
Map ref: Cirencester 3 F1

Corinium Hotel

★★★

12 Gloucester Street, Cirencester,
Gloucestershire, GL7 2DG
Tel: 01285 659711 Fax: 01285 885807
Email: info@coriniumhotel.co.uk
Web: www.coriniumhotel.co.uk
Rooms: 15 all ensuite
Pricing: Sgl £55–75 Dbl £79–105
Dinner available from £6.95
CC: Accepted
Room facilities:
Children: Welcome
Dogs: Welcome
Licenses:
Parking: Off-street and free
Directions: On A435 towards Gloucester, turn left at
traffic lights into Spitalgate Lane, then first right
Trafalgar Road. Car park on left.
Map ref: Cirencester 3 F1

Wild Duck Inn

★★★

Drakes Island, Ewen, near Cirencester,
Gloucestershire, GL7 6BY
Tel: 01285 770310 Fax: 01285 770924
Email: wduckinn@aol.com
Web: www.thewildduckinn.co.uk
Rooms: 12 all ensuite
Pricing: Sgl £60–70 Dbl £95–150
Dinner available from £7.95–16.95
CC: Accepted
Room facilities:
Children: Welcome
Dogs: Welcome
Licenses:
Parking: Off-street
Directions: From Cirencester take A429 towards
Malmesbury and M4. At Kemble turn left to Ewen. The
Wild Duck is in the centre of the village.
Map ref: Ewen 3 F1
See advert on opposite page

Coleford, Gloucestershire

The Speech House

★★★

Forest of Dean, near Coleford,
Gloucestershire, GL16 7EL
Tel: 01594 822607 Fax: 01594 823658
Email: relax@thespeechhouse.co.uk
Web: www.thespeechhouse.co.uk

Charles II's hunting lodge, located in the heart of the Forest of Dean. Ideal for dog owners and walkers. Family cycle trail nearby. Christmas and new packages available.

Rooms: 37 all ensuite
Pricing: Sgl £60 Dbl £90–140
Dinner available from £26.85 CC: Accepted
Room facilities:
Conference: 6 meeting rooms (Thtr 60 max), 24hr-delegate from £120, day-delegate from £30
Children: Welcome Dogs: Welcome
Licenses:
Leisure: Gym, Health spa, Beauty salon, Golf
Parking: Off-street and free
Directions: Located on B4226 between Coleford and Cinderford. Nearest motorway junctions: M4 junction 21, M5 junction 11.
Map ref: Coleford 7 E4

Coleshill, Warwickshire

Old Barn Guest House

♦♦♦

Birmingham Road, Coleshill, Warwickshire, B46 1DP
Tel: 01675 463692 Fax: 01675 466275
Rooms: 11 all ensuite
Pricing: Sgl £40 Dbl £68.50 CC: Accepted
Room facilities:
Children: Welcome Dogs: Assistance dogs only
Licenses: Leisure: Indoor pool, Games room
Parking: Off-street and free
Directions: From M6 J4, turn onto A446 towards Coleshill. At first island carry straight on, turn left at next island onto B4114. Old Barn 1/4 mile on the left.
Map ref: Coleshill 8 A3

The Wild Duck Inn

An attractive 15th-century inn of great character

The Wild Duck is a mellow Cotswold stone Elizabethan Inn. A typical local English inn with a warm and welcoming ambience, rich in colours and hung with old oil portraits of English ancestors. Large open log fires burn in the bar and the oak-panelled residents' lounge in winter time.

The garden is secluded, delightful and perfect for 'alfresco' dining in the summer. The bar offers six real ales and the wine list is extensive and innovative.

The country-style dining room offers fresh seasonal food; game in winter and fresh fish delivered overnight from Brixham in Devon, which can include such exotic fare as parrot fish and tilapia.

There are twelve bedrooms, three of which have four-poster beds and overlook the garden. All rooms have direct dial telephone, colour TV and tea/coffee-making facilities.

Within one mile, The Wild Duck is surrounded by the Cotswold Water Park, with over 80 lakes providing fishing, swimming, sailing, water and jet skiing. Polo at Cirencester Park is a regular event and every March Cheltenham holds the Gold Cup Race Meeting. Horse trials at Gatcombe Park and Badminton are also held annually.

Location: From M4 take Junction 17 and follow Cirencester, turn right at Kemble and follow signs to Ewen

Drakes Island, Ewen, Near Cirencester GL7 6BY
Tel: 01285 770310 Fax: 01285 770924 Email: wduckinn@aol.com
Website: www.thewildduckinn.co.uk

Coventry, West Midlands

Brooklands Grange Hotel and Restaurant

★★★★ ℞℞

Holyhead Road, Coventry, West Midlands, CV5 8HX
Tel: 024 7660 1601 Fax: 024 7660 1277
Email: info@brooklands-grange.co.uk
Web: www.brooklands-grange.co.uk
Seasonal closure: Christmas to 2 January 2006

A 16th century Jacobean farmhouse, Brooklands has been sympathetically restored and refurbished to combine original character with modern facilities. We are just 5 minutes from the City and only 10 minutes from NEC, with easy access to all Midlands motorway networks.
Rooms: 31 all ensuite 🛏 ⊗
Pricing: Sgl £105 Dbl £120–135
Dinner available from £16.95–24.95 CC: Accepted
Room facilities: ▢ ☎ ☕
Conference: 1 meeting room (Thtr 16 max),
24hr-delegate from £130, day-delegate from £30
Children: Welcome ⊦ Licenses: ♦♦♦
Leisure: Games room
Parking: Off-street and free
Directions: Situated on the A4114, just off the A45, five minutes from Coventry Cathedral and 10 minutes drive from the NEC and Birmingham International Airport.
Map ref: Coventry 8 B3

Stoneleigh Park Lodge

◆◆◆◆ ⌖ ℘

Stoneleigh Park, near Coventry, Warwickshire, CV8 2LZ
Tel: 024 7669 0123 Fax: 024 7669 0789
Email: info@stoneleighparklodge.com
Web: www.stoneleighparklodge.com
Rooms: 58 all ensuite ⊗
Pricing: Sgl £68.50–78 Dbl £68.50–90
Dinner available from £9.75
CC: Accepted
Room facilities: ▢ ☎ ☕ ☍
Conference: 1 meeting room (Thtr 15 max)
Children: Welcome
Licenses: ♦♦♦
Parking: Off-street and free
Directions: From M40 J15, follow A46 towards Coventry, second exit A452, turn right towards Leamington, follow signs NAC Stoneleigh Park.
Map ref: Stoneleigh Park 7 F3

Campanile Hotel Restaurant
Travel Accommodation

4 Wigston Road, Walsgrave, Coventry,
West Midlands, CV2 2SD
Tel: 024 7662 2311 Fax: 024 7660 2362
Email: coventry@envergure.co.uk
Web: www.campanile.com

Campanile hotels offer comfortable and convenient budget accommodation and a traditional French-style Bistro providing freshly-cooked food for breakfast, lunch and dinner. All rooms ensuite with tea/coffee-making facilities, DDT and TV with Sky channels.
Rooms: 47 all ensuite ⊗
Dinner available
CC: Accepted
Room facilities: ▢ ☎ ☕ ☍
Conference: 1 meeting room (Thtr 30 max),
24hr-delegate from £70, day-delegate from £21.50
Children: Welcome ⊦
Dogs: Welcome
Licenses: ⟐ ♦♦♦
Parking: Off-street and free
Directions: The hotel is off M6 Junction 2. Take the A4600 for ³/₄ mile and turn right on second roundabout.
Map ref: Walsgrave 8 B3

Droitwich, Worcestershire

The Old Farmhouse

◆◆◆◆◆ ⌖ ℘

Hadley Heath, Ombersley, near Droitwich,
Worcestershire, WR9 0AR
Tel: 01905 620837 Fax: 01905 621722
Email: judylambe@ombersley.demon.co.uk
Web: www.the-old-farmhouse.com
Rooms: 5 all ensuite ⊗
Pricing: Sgl £40 Dbl £70
Room facilities: ▢ ☕
Children: Welcome ⊦
Leisure: Tennis
Parking: Off-street and free
Directions: Exit J6 M5, A449 towards Kidderminster; turn right to Hadley; third house 1 mile on right. From J5, take A38, A4133 for 1 mile, then left to end of lane.
Map ref: Hadley Heath 7 E3

Dudley, West Midlands

Copthorne Hotel Merry Hill Dudley

★★★★

The Waterfront, Level Street,
Brierley Hill, Dudley, West Midlands, DY5 1UR
Tel: 01384 482882 Fax: 01384 263282
Email: reservations.merryhill@mill-cop.com
Web: www.copthornehotels.com

MILLENNIUM
HOTELS AND RESORTS

MILLENNIUM HOTELS
COPTHORNE HOTELS

Modern 138-bedroom hotel in an attractive waterfront
setting in the heart of the Midlands. Faradays bar &
restaurant offers a wide range of Mediterranean dishes.
Rooms: 138 all ensuite
Pricing: Sgl £70–95 Dbl £80–105
Dinner available from £18.95 CC: Accepted
Room facilities: □ ☎ ☺ ☏ Access: ♿
Conference: 8 meeting rooms (Thtr 570 max),
24hr-delegate from £170, day-delegate from £55
Children: Welcome ♫ Licenses: ♠ ♦
Leisure: Indoor pool, Gym, Beauty salon, Spa, Sauna,
Steam room
Parking: Off-street and free
Directions: Leave M5 at Junction 2. Follow A4123 for
Dudley. After 2½ miles follow signs for A461 to
Stourbridge/Merry Hill Centre.
Map ref: Brierley Hill 7 E3

Eccleshall, Staffordshire

Glenwood

♦♦♦

Croxton, Stafford, Staffordshire, ST21 6PF
Tel: 01630 620238
Rooms: 3 (1 ensuite)
Pricing: Sgl £25 Dbl £40–50
Room facilities: ☺ Children: Welcome ♫
Dogs: Welcome Parking: Off-street
Directions: Leave M6 at Junction 14. Travel to
Eccleshall. Take B5026 to Loggerheads. After 3 miles,
enter the village of Croxton. Glenwood is on right.
Map ref: Croxton 7 E2

Evesham, Worcestershire

Evesham Hotel

★★★★ ⬭⬭

Cooper's Lane, off Waterside, Evesham,
Worcestershire, WR11 1DA
Tel: 01386 765566 Fax: 01386 765443
Email: reception@eveshamhotel.com
Web: www.eveshamhotel.com
Seasonal closure: 25-26 December
Rooms: 40 all ensuite ☜ ☒
Pricing: Sgl £78–92 Dbl £124
Dinner available from £24
CC: Accepted
Room facilities: □ ☎ ☺
Conference: 1 meeting room (Thtr 12 max)
Children: Welcome ♫ ☼ Dogs: Welcome
Licenses: ♦ Leisure: Indoor pool, Games room
Parking: Off-street and free
Directions: Cooper's Lane runs off Waterside, the road
that runs along the River Avon.
Map ref: Evesham 7 F4

Northwick Hotel

★★★

Waterside, Evesham, Worcestershire, WR11 1BT
Tel: 01386 40322 Fax: 01386 41070
Email: enquiries@northwickhotel.co.uk
Web: www.northwickhotel.co.uk
Rooms: 31 all ensuite ☜ ⬭ ☒
Dinner available
CC: Accepted
Room facilities: □ ☎ ☺ ☏
Conference: 3 meeting rooms (Thtr 160 max)
Children: Welcome ♫ Dogs: Welcome
Licenses: ♠ ♦ Leisure: Games room
Parking: Off-street and free
Directions: M5 J9, follow signposts to Evesham town
centre. Turn right at river bridge traffic lights. Hotel is
¼ mile on right.
Map ref: Evesham 7 F4

Flyford Flavell, Worcestershire

The Boot Inn

♦♦♦♦ ⬭⬯

Radford Road, Flyford Flavell, Worcester,
Worcestershire, WR7 4BS
Tel: 01386 462658 Fax: 01386 462547
Email: enquiries@thebootinn.com
Web: www.thebootinn.com
Rooms: 5 all ensuite
Pricing: Sgl £50 Dbl £60–80
Dinner available from £15
CC: Accepted
Room facilities: □ ☎ ☺ ☏
Children: Welcome ♫
Licenses: ♦
Leisure: Games room
Parking: Off-street and free
Map ref: Flyford Flavell 7 F4

West Midlands

Gloucester, Gloucestershire

Kings Head Inn

Birdwood, Huntley, Gloucestershire, GL19 3EF
Tel: 01452 750348 Fax: 01452 750348
Rooms: 6 all ensuite
Pricing: Sgl £30 Dbl £46
Dinner available from £4.50–120 CC: Accepted
Room facilities:
Conference: 2 meeting rooms (Thtr 50 max)
Children: Welcome Licenses:
Leisure: Beauty salon, Games room, Snooker/billiards
Parking: Off-street and free
Directions: From Gloucester bypass follow signs A40 towards Ross-on-Wye. Kings Head is 6 miles out on the left hand side with 8 flagpoles on front of property.
Map ref: Birdwood 7 E4

Longford Lodge

68 Tewkesbury Road, Longford, Gloucester, Gloucestershire, GL2 9EH
Tel: 01452 526380 Fax: 01452 536762
Email: jens_eberhardt_uk@hotmail.com
Web: www.longfordlodge.tk
Rooms: 10 all ensuite
Pricing: Sgl £25–35 Dbl £39–49
CC: Accepted
Room facilities:
Children: Welcome Dogs: Welcome
Parking: Off-street and free
Directions: M5 J11 to Gloucester. A40 anticlockwise to next roundabout. A38 towards Tewkesbury. 100 yards to right.
Map ref: Longford 7 E4

The Little Thatch

141 Bristol Road, Quedgeley, Gloucester, Gloucestershire, GL2 4PQ
Tel: 01452 720687 Fax: 01452 724141
Email: jackymcdougall@thelittlethatch.co.uk
Web: www.thelittlethatch.co.uk

Excellent, friendly, family-run hotel and restaurant offering comfortable ensuite rooms with colour television and tea/coffee making facilities. Restaurant and bar serves good quality food at reasonable prices.
Rooms: 22 all ensuite
Pricing: Sgl £30–50 Dbl £50–65
Dinner available from £5–20 CC: Accepted
Room facilities:
Conference: 2 meeting rooms (Thtr 50 max)
Children: Welcome
Licenses:
Parking: Off-street and free
Directions: Exit M5 junction 12, follow directions to Severn Vale shopping centre, B4008 to Quedgeley. Just past Tesco roundabout on the right.
Map ref: Quedgeley 7 E4

Hereford, Herefordshire

Castle House

★★★ Premier

Castle Street, Hereford, Herefordshire, HR1 2NW
Tel: 01432 356321 Fax: 01432 365909
Email: info@castlehse.co.uk
Web: www.castlehse.co.uk
Rooms: 15 all ensuite
Pricing: Sgl £113.50 Dbl £200–245
Dinner available from £36.95–42.95 CC: Accepted
Room facilities: Access:
Children: Welcome Dogs: Welcome
Licenses:
Parking: Off-street and free
Directions: Follow signs for city centre, then city centre east. At the end of St Owen Street, right into Ethelbert Street. Castle Street ahead. Car parking just before hotel on left-hand side.
Map ref: Hereford 7 E4
See advert on second page following

Three Counties Hotel

★★★

Belmont Road, Hereford, Herefordshire, HR2 7BP
Tel: 01432 299955 Fax: 01432 275114
Email: enquiries@threecountieshotel.co.uk
Web: www.threecountieshotel.co.uk

Modern hotel with a relaxing atmosphere set in
landscaped gardens on the outskirts of the city.
Bedrooms set by a quiet garden.
Rooms: 60 all ensuite 🐾 ⊗
Pricing: Sgl £56–72.50 Dbl £74–90
Dinner available from £19.50–26 CC: Accepted
Room facilities: ☐ ☎ ☺ ✆
Conference: 5 meeting rooms (Thtr 350 max),
24hr-delegate from £93, day-delegate from £29
Children: Welcome ⊁ Dogs: Welcome
Licenses: ⬥ ⅲ Parking: Off-street and free
Directions: 1½ miles outside Hereford city on A465 —
the main road to Abergavenny.
Map ref: Hereford 7 E4

Best Western Peacock Hotel

Excellent

★★★★ 🍴🍴

149 Warwick Road, Kenilworth,
Warwickshire, CV8 1HY
Tel: 01926 851156 Fax: 01926 864644
Email: reservations@peacockhotel.com
Web: www.peacockhotel.com

Award-winning Hotel including the RAC Blue Ribbon
Award, providing outstanding quality with first class

service. Luxurious accommodation. A choice of three
elegant restaurants. Ranked Best Restaurant Group in
the UK 2005.
Rooms: 29 all ensuite 🐾 🖊 ⊗
Pricing: Sgl £39–80 Dbl £59–160
Dinner available from £9.75
CC: Accepted
Room facilities: ☐ ☎ ☺ ✆ ✱
Conference: 6 meeting rooms (Thtr 90 max),
24hr-delegate from £90, day-delegate from £35
Children: Welcome ⊁ ⅈℂ
Licenses: ⬥ ⅲ Parking: Off-street and free
Directions: M40 junction 15, A46 north towards Coventry.
Left at A452 signposted Kenilworth and Leamington,
turn at first roundabout to Kenilworth town centre. Hotel
200 yards ahead on Warwick Road.
Map ref: Kenilworth 8 B3

Stone Manor Hotel

★★★★ 🍴

Near Kidderminster, Stone, Worcestershire, DY10 4PJ
Tel: 01562 777555 Fax: 01562 777834
Email: enquiries@stonemanorhotel.co.uk
Web: www.stonemanorhotel.co.uk
Rooms: 57 all ensuite 🖊 ⊗
Pricing: Sgl £101.50–159.50 Dbl £108–169
Dinner available from £27.50 CC: Accepted
Room facilities: ☐ ☎ ☺
Conference: 6 meeting rooms (Thtr 150 max),
24hr-delegate from £150, day-delegate from £50
Children: Welcome ⅈℂ
Licenses: ⬥ ⅲ
Leisure: Outdoor pool, Tennis, Games room
Parking: Off-street and free
Directions: From south M40/M42 J1 to A38 and A448
to Kidderminster. From south M5 J6 onto A449, A450
and A448. From north M5 J3, A456 to A450 and A448.
Map ref: Stone 7 E3

Abbacourt Hotel

★★ 🍴🍴

40 Kenilworth Road, Leamington Spa,
Warwickshire, CV32 6JF
Tel: 01926 451755 Fax: 01926 886339
Email: abbacourt@maganto.freeserve.co.uk
Web: www.abbacourthotel.com
Rooms: 23 all ensuite 🐾 🖊
Dinner available CC: Accepted
Room facilities: ☐ ☎ ☺ ✆
Conference: 2 meeting rooms (Thtr 60 max)
Children: Welcome ⊁ Dogs: Welcome
Licenses: ⬥ ⅲ
Parking: Off-street and free
Directions: Heading into Leamington Spa on the A452,
500 metres after the residential homes begin, hotel is
on left.
Map ref: Leamington Spa 8 B3

West Midlands

Ledbury, Herefordshire

Wall Hills Country House

◆◆◆◆ 🍽️🍽️ ✕ 🍷

Hereford Road, Ledbury, Herefordshire, HR8 2PR
Tel: 01531 632833 Fax: 01531 632833
Web: www.wallhills.com
Seasonal closure: Christmas & New Year

This Georgian house overlooking Ledbury offers outstanding views, peace and quiet. Excellent wine list. Short breaks available. "Jennifer's warm welcome ushers in David's stupendous dinners" (Country Living magazine).
Rooms: 3 all ensuite 🐾
Pricing: Sgl £55–70 Dbl £70–80
Dinner available from £17.50
CC: Accepted
Room facilities: 📺
Children: Welcome 🍴
Licenses: 👖
Parking: Off-street and free
Directions: Leave Ledbury on A438, Hereford Road entrance to drive is within 200 yards on left after roundabout.
Map ref: Ledbury 7 E4

Relax & smell the coffee

Fresh coffee, chilled juices for breakfast. RAC's team of qualified Inspectors check them both.

Leek, Staffordshire

Cottage Delight At Number 64
Restaurant with Rooms

🍽️🍽️

64 St Edward Street, Leek, Staffordshire, ST13 5DL
Tel: 01538 381900 Fax: 01538 370918
Email: enquiries@number64.com
Web: www.number64.com

Number 64 is a unique speciality food emporium. This impressive Grade II listed building has been sympathetically restored to incorporate a variety of facilities in a friendly and relaxed atmosphere.
Rooms: 3 all ensuite 📺 🐾
Pricing: Dbl £75–95
Dinner available from £20–30 CC: Accepted
Room facilities: 📺 ☎️ ☕ 📞 ❄️
Conference: 1 meeting room (Thtr 14 max), day-delegate from £125
Children: Welcome Licenses: 🍷 👖
Directions: Follow A53 from Stoke into Leek, turn left at the first lights, Number 64 is 30m on the left.
Map ref: Leek 7 F2

Sleep easy Rest assured. Our comprehensive inspection process includes checking beds are comfortable.

West Midlands

Leominster, Herefordshire

Talbot Hotel

★★★

West Street, Leominster, Herefordshire, HR6 8EP
Tel: 01568 616347 Fax: 01568 614880
Email: talbot@bestwestern.co.uk
Web: www.smoothhound.co.uk/hotels/talbot2.html
Rooms: 20 all ensuite 🚭
Pricing: Sgl £57.50–75.50 Dbl £78–98
Dinner available from £19–30 CC: Accepted
Room facilities: 🖵 ☎ 🍵 📠
Conference: 2 meeting rooms (Thtr 100 max),
24hr-delegate from £95, day-delegate from £40
Children: Welcome ♯ 🍼
Dogs: Welcome
Licenses: 🍶
Parking: Off-street and free
Directions: The Talbot Hotel is in the centre of
Leominster, found when following the one-way traffic
system.
Map ref: Leominster 7 E3

Lichfield, Staffordshire

Swinfen Hall Hotel

★★★★★ 🎗🎗

Swinfen, near Lichfield, Staffordshire, WS14 9RE
Tel: 01543 481494 Fax: 01543 480341
Email: info@swinfenhallhotel.co.uk
Web: www.swinfenhallhotel.co.uk

Set in picturesque gardens amid rolling historic
parkland, this 18th century manor house, lovingly
restored is now an independent hotel, offering
contemporary facilities in a relaxed yet professional
atmosphere.
Rooms: 17 all ensuite
Pricing: Sgl £120–215 Dbl £135–240
Dinner available from £35
CC: Accepted
Room facilities: 🖵 ☎ 🍵 📠
Conference: 5 meeting rooms (Thtr 180 max),
24hr-delegate from £160, day-delegate from £55
Children: Welcome 🍼
Licenses: ⟁ 🍶
Leisure: Tennis, 100 acres of parkland with private deer
park

Parking: Off-street and free
Directions: Exit M6 toll road at junction T4. Take A38
North to Lichfield. Hotel is half a mile on the right.
Map ref: Swinfen 8 A3

Angel Croft Hotel

★★

Beacon Street, Lichfield, Staffordshire, WS13 1AA
Tel: 01543 258737 Fax: 01543 415605
Map ref: Lichfield 8 A2

Coppers End Guest House

◆◆◆◆

Walsall Road, Muckley Corner,
Lichfield, Staffordshire, WS14 0BG
Tel: 01543 372910 Fax: 01543 360423
Email: info@coppersendguesthouse.co.uk
Web: www.coppersendguesthouse.co.uk
Seasonal closure: Christmas and New Year

Coppers End is a quiet, friendly guest house. All rooms
are centrally heated. Two ground floor bedrooms,
lovely conservatory, dining room, residents' lounge,
large attractive garden with patio. Motorcycle friendly.
Rooms: 6 (4 ensuite) 🚭
Pricing: Sgl £33–41 Dbl £47–57
CC: Accepted
Room facilities: 🖵 🍵
Children: Welcome ♯
Licenses: 🍶
Parking: Off-street and free
Directions: On the A461 100 yards from Muckley
Corner roundabout off the A5. 3 miles south of
Lichfield. Ordnance Survey SK083067.
Map ref: Lichfield 8 A2

Lower Slaughter, Gloucestershire

Lower Slaughter Manor

★★★★ 🎗🎗🎗
Excellent

Lower Slaughter, Gloucestershire, GL54 2HP
Tel: 01451 820456 Fax: 01451 822150
Email: info@lowerslaughter.co.uk
Web: www.lowerslaughter.co.uk
Rooms: 16 all ensuite 📠
Pricing: Sgl £155–175 Dbl £235–345
Dinner available from £45 CC: Accepted

Room facilities: 🖥 ☎
Conference: 1 meeting room (Thtr 20 max),
24hr-delegate from £225, day-delegate from £85
Children: Welcome 12yrs min age
Dogs: Welcome
Licenses: ◇ ♔
Leisure: Tennis
Parking: Off-street and free
Directions: From A429 Cirencester to Stow-on-the-Wold road, just 2 miles from Stow, follow signs to The Slaughters just past a Texaco garage. Entering the village, the Manor is on the right.
Map ref: Lower Slaughter 4 A1

Washbourne Court

★★★★ ☕☕

Lower Slaughter, Gloucestershire, GL54 2HS
Tel: 01451 822143 Fax: 01451 821045
Email: info@washbournecourt.co.uk
Web: www.washbournecourt.co.uk
Rooms: 28 all ensuite ♨ ⊗
Pricing: Sgl £90–110 Dbl £130–180
Dinner available from £30
CC: Accepted
Room facilities: 🖥 ☎ 🗗
Conference: 6 meeting rooms (Thtr 60 max),
24hr-delegate from £135, day-delegate from £45
Children: Welcome ♔
Dogs: Welcome
Licenses: ◇ ♔
Parking: Off-street and free
Directions: From Burford drive 8 miles on A424, turn left at traffic lights onto A429 signposted Cirencester. After 1 mile, turn right into the Slaughters. Washbourne Court is in centre of village on left.
Map ref: Lower Slaughter 4 A1

Ludlow, Shropshire

Dinham Hall

Dinham, Ludlow, Shropshire, SY8 1EJ
Tel: 01584 876464 Fax: 01584 876019
Email: info@dinhamhall.co.uk
Web: www.dinhamhall.co.uk
Rooms: 13 all ensuite 🗗
Pricing: Dinner available from £30.50
CC: Accepted
Room facilities: 🖥 ☎ 🗗
Conference: 2 meeting rooms (Thtr 43 max),
24hr-delegate from £125, day-delegate from £25
Children: Welcome
Dogs: Welcome
Licenses: ◇ ♔
Parking: Off-street
Directions: Turn left at Ludlow Castle: Dinham Hall is 50 metres on left.
Map ref: Ludlow 7 E3

The Feathers Hotel

★★★★ ☕☕

The Bull Ring, Ludlow, Shropshire, SY8 1AA
Tel: 01584 875261 Fax: 01584 876030
Email: feathers.ludlow@btconnect.com
Web: www.feathersatludlow.co.uk

Situated at the heart of the ancient market town of Ludlow The Feathers Hotel is internationally recognised for its beautiful Jacobean architecture and Medieval Heritage.
Rooms: 40 all ensuite ♨ 🗗 ⊗
Pricing: Sgl £70–75 Dbl £85–105
Dinner available from £27.50
CC: Accepted
Room facilities: 🖥 ☎ 🗗 ☏
Access: ♿
Conference: 3 meeting rooms (Thtr 108 max),
24hr-delegate from £130, day-delegate from £45
Children: Welcome ♔
Dogs: Welcome
Licenses: ◇ ♔
Parking: Off-street and free
Directions: Birmingham to Ludlow M6 M54 then A49 from Shrewsbury. From London M40 M5, A49 from Hereford.
Map ref: Ludlow 7 E3

West Midlands

Bromley Court B&B Little Gem

♦♦♦♦♦ ✶ ♐

73/74 Lower Broad Street,
Ludlow, Shropshire, SY8 1PH
Tel: 01584 876996/0845 0656 192 Fax: 01584 876860
Email: "please telephone – it's better to talk"
Web: www.ludlowhotels.com

Delightful, award winning B & B accommodation in
three Tudor suites (with own private sitting room) and
courtyard garden. Every comfort provided and full
traditional breakfast. Centrally situated in conservation
area, close to Michelin restaurants.
Rooms: 3 all ensuite ⊛
Pricing: Sgl £75–105 Dbl £95–115
CC: Accepted
Room facilities: ▢ ☎ ⊜
Children: Welcome
Dogs: Welcome
Directions: From South: A49 fork left on B4361,
through lights 100m on left. From North: A49 fork left
B4361 through town to lights; turn right, 100m on left.
Map ref: Ludlow 7 E3

Chadstone Guest House

♦♦♦♦♦ ⚲ ✶ ♐

Aston Munslow, Craven Arms, Shropshire, SY7 9ER
Tel: 01584 841675 Fax: 01584 841620
Email: chadstone.lee@btinternet.com
Web: www.chadstonebandb.co.uk
Rooms: 3 all ensuite ⊛
Pricing: Sgl £26–32 Dbl £52–64
Dinner available from £18–20
Room facilities: ▢ ⊜
Children: Welcome 12yrs min age
Licenses: ▟▟▟
Parking: Off-street and free
Directions: Turn east off A49 onto B4368 in Craven
Arms. In Aston Munslow, pass the Swan Inn;
Chadstone is 100 metres on right.
Map ref: Aston Munslow 7 E3

The Church Inn

♦♦♦♦ ✶

Buttercross, Ludlow, Shropshire, SY8 1AW
Tel: 01584 872174 Fax: 01584 877146
Email: reception@thechurchinn.com
Web: www.thechurchinn.com
Rooms: 9 all ensuite ⊛
Pricing: Sgl £35–70 Dbl £60–80
Dinner available from £5.95
CC: Accepted
Room facilities: ▢ ☎ ⊜ ⚲
Conference: 1 meeting room (Thtr 20 max)
Children: Welcome ♁
Dogs: Welcome
Licenses: ▟▟▟
Directions: From A49 Shrewsbury-Hereford road, signs
for town centre. Inn is behind the Buttercross in the
town centre.
Map ref: Ludlow 7 E3
See advert on this page

"Stay!"

Need a pet friendly property? Look
out for 'Dogs welcome' in our listings.

Lydney, Gloucestershire

George Inn

◆◆◆

High Street, St Briavels, Lydney,
Gloucestershire, GL15 6TA
Tel: 01594 530228 Fax: 01594 530260
Email: mail@ithegeorge.fsnet.co.uk
Web: www.thegeorgeinn.info
Rooms: 4 all ensuite
Pricing: Sgl £35 Dbl £50–60 Dinner available
CC: Accepted
Room facilities: 🖥 🛏
Children: Welcome 🍴
Licenses: 🍺
Parking: Off-street and free
Directions: 6 miles from Chepstow on the Lydney
Road.
Map ref: St Briavels 3 E1

Malvern, Worcestershire

Portocks End House

◆◆◆

Little Clevelode, Malvern, Worcestershire, WR13 6PE
Tel: 01684 310276
Email: mpa-cameron@countryside-inter.net
Web: www.portocksendbandb.co.uk
Rooms: 2 🛏
Pricing: Sgl £22.50 Dbl £45
Room facilities: 🛏
Children: Welcome
Dogs: Welcome
Parking: Off-street and free
Directions: On B4424 between Powick and Upton-
upon-Severn, ³/₄ mile north of B4211 junction to Great
Malvern. Opposite Riverside Caravan Park.
Map ref: Little Clevelode 7 E4

Moreton-in-Marsh, Gloucestershire

Crown Inn & Hotel

★★★★ 🕮🕮

High Street, Blockley, Gloucestershire, GL56 9EX
Tel: 01386 700245 Fax: 01386 700247
Email: info@crown-inn-blockley.co.uk
Web: www.crown-inn-blockley.co.uk
Rooms: 24 all ensuite 🍴 📺
Pricing: Sgl £59.95–79.95 Dbl £90–130
Dinner available from £25
CC: Accepted
Room facilities: 🖥 ☎ 🛏
Conference: 1 meeting room (Thtr 25 max),
24hr-delegate from £115, day-delegate from £35
Children: Welcome 🍴
Dogs: Welcome
Licenses: 🍺
Parking: Off-street and free
Directions: Follow tourist board signs after
Bourton-on-the-Hill.
Map ref: Blockley 4 A1

Redesdale Arms Hotel

★★★

High Street, Moreton-In-Marsh,
Gloucestershire, GL56 0AW
Tel: 01608 650308 Fax: 01608 651843
Email: info@redesdalearms.com
Web: www.redesdalearms.com

Dating back to the 17th century the Redesdale Arms is
a haven for anyone looking for traditional delights
fused with a fresh new atmosphere of contemporary
comfort. The old stable inn is now a fully refurbished
restaurant, bar and hotel with 18 ensuite rooms.
Rooms: 18 all ensuite 🍴 🛏
Pricing: Sgl £60–85 Dbl £65–120
Dinner available from £12–25 CC: Accepted
Room facilities: 🖥 ☎ 🛏
Children: Welcome 🍴
Licenses: 🍺 Parking: Off-street and free
Directions: On A429 Junction 17 of M4 or Junction 15
of M40, main line train station to London Paddington.
Map ref: Moreton-in-Marsh 8 A4

Newcastle-under-Lyme, Staffordshire

Stop Inn Newcastle-under-Lyme

★★

Liverpool Road, Cross Heath, Newcastle-under-Lyme,
Staffordshire, ST5 9DX
Tel: 01782 717000 Fax: 01782 713669
Email: enquiries@hotels-newcastle-under-lyme.com
Web: www.stop-inns.com
Rooms: 67 all ensuite 🍴 📺 🛏
Pricing: Sgl £50–76.95 Dbl £55–85.90
Dinner available from £17.95 CC: Accepted
Room facilities: 🖥 ☎ 🛏 🍴
Conference: 3 meeting rooms (Thtr 200 max),
24hr-delegate from £87, day-delegate from £29
Children: Welcome 🍴 Dogs: Welcome
Licenses: 🍺
Leisure: Snooker/billiards
Parking: Off-street and free
Directions: From the M6, take Junction 16 and pick up
A500 for Newcastle-under-Lyme, then the A34.
Map ref: Cross Heath 7 E2

Newland, Gloucestershire

Cherry Orchard Farm

Newland, Coleford, Gloucestershire, GL16 8NP
Tel: 01594 832212 Fax: 01594 832212
Rooms: 3
Pricing: Sgl £25–30 Dbl £50–60
Room facilities:
Children: Welcome
Parking: Off-street and free
Directions: 1¹/₂ miles east of Redbrook, 3 miles south of Monmouth off A466, ¹/₄ mile north of Newland on the B4231.
Map ref: Coleford 7 E4

Newport, Shropshire

Norwood House Hotel & Restaurant

Pave Lane, Newport, Shropshire, TF10 9LQ
Tel: 01952 825896 Fax: 01952 825896
Email: tonybaker55@aol.com
Web: www.norwoodhouse.org.uk
Rooms: 5 all ensuite
Pricing: Sgl £42 Dbl £55
Dinner available from £12.50
CC: Accepted
Room facilities:
Children: Welcome
Dogs: Welcome
Licenses:
Parking: Off-street and free
Directions: Junction 3 from M54, follow A41 Wolverhampton to Whitchurch. Follow signs, Lilleshall National Sports Centre and Pave Lane.
Map ref: Newport 7 E2

Northleach, Gloucestershire

Northfield Bed & Breakfast

Cirencester Road, Northleach, Cheltenham, Gloucestershire, GL54 3JL
Tel: 01451 860427 Fax: 01451 860427
Email: nrthfield0@aol.com
Web: www.northfieldbandb.co.uk
Seasonal closure: 21-31 December

Located south of the historic town, this Cotswold stone house offers homely and tastefully furnished bedrooms, two of which have direct access to the immaculate gardens. Tasty eggs from the resident hens feature at breakfast and imaginative dinners are also available, served in the elegant dining room. A comfortable guest lounge is provided for relaxation.
Rooms: 3 all ensuite
Pricing: Dbl £60–70
Dinner available from £16–22 CC: Accepted
Room facilities:
Children: Welcome
Licenses:
Parking: Off-street and free
Directions: Northfield just off A429 Northleach to Cirencester road. 1 mile, Northleach traffic lights. Well signed from main road.
Map ref: Northleach 4 A1

Oakamoor, Staffordshire

Ribden Farm

Oakamoor, Stoke-on-Trent, Staffordshire, ST10 3BW
Tel: 01538 702830 Fax: 01538 702830
Email: ribdenfarm@aol.com
Web: www.ribdenfarm.co.uk
Rooms: 5 all ensuite
Pricing: Dbl £56–60
CC: Accepted
Room facilities:
Children: Welcome
Parking: Off-street and free
Directions: Situated on the B5417 Cheadle to Wardlow Road, on the right, ¹/₂ mile before junction with A52. Ribden Farm is second farm down drive.
Map ref: Oakamoor 7 F2

Painswick, Gloucestershire

Painswick Hotel and Restaurant

★★★

Kemps Lane, Painswick, Gloucestershire, GL6 6YB
Tel: 01452 812160 Fax: 01452 814059
Email: reservations@painswickhotel.com
Web: www.painswickhotel.com
Rooms: 19 all ensuite
Pricing: Sgl £90–95 Dbl £145–150
Dinner available from £35–90
CC: Accepted
Room facilities:
Conference: 2 meeting rooms (Thtr 50 max), 24hr-delegate from £150, day-delegate from £45
Children: Welcome Dogs: Welcome
Licenses:
Parking: Off-street and free
Directions: Follow A46 to Painswick, turning into St Mary's Street next to the church. Follow the road around and turn right at The March Hare. Hotel 200 yards on right.
Map ref: Painswick 7 E4

Hambutts Mynd

Edge Road, Painswick, Gloucestershire, GL6 6UP
Tel: 01452 812352 Fax: 01452 813862
Email: ewarland@aol.com
Web: www.accommodation.uk.net/painswick.htm
Seasonal closure: January Rooms: 3 all ensuite ⊛
Pricing: Sgl £30–36 Dbl £55–60
CC: Accepted Room facilities: ⬛ ⬛
Children: Welcome 10yrs min age Dogs: Welcome
Parking: Off-street and free
Directions: Entering Painswick from Cheltenham, turn
right at end of church wall. From Stroud, take first left
after car park.
Map ref: Painswick 7 E4

Redditch, Worcestershire

Quality Hotel Redditch

Pool Bank, Southcrest, Redditch, Worcestershire, B97 4JS
Tel: 01527 541511 Fax: 01527 402600
Email: enquiries@hotels-redditch.com
Web: www.choicehotelseurope.com
Rooms: 73 all ensuite ⬛ ⬛ ⊛
Pricing: Sgl £70–96 Dbl £75–105
Dinner available from £18.95 CC: Accepted
Room facilities: ⬛ ☎ ⬛ ⬛
Conference: 5 meeting rooms (Thtr 100 max),
24hr-delegate from £126, day-delegate from £36
Children: Welcome ⍧ ⍝ Dogs: Welcome
Licenses: ⬥ ⍭ Parking: Off-street and free
Directions: From M42 take Junction 2 onto A411
following Redditch and all other districts. Pick up
Southcrest. Located on Pool Bank.
Map ref: Southcrest 7 F3

Campanile Hotel and Restaurant
Travel Accommodation

Far Moor Lane, Winyates Green, Redditch,
Worcestershire, B98 0SD
Tel: 01527 510710 Fax: 01527 517269
Email: redditch@campanile-hotels.com
Web: www.campanile.com

Campanile hotels offer comfortable and convenient
budget accommodation and a traditional French-style

Bistro providing freshly-cooked food for breakfast,
lunch and dinner. All rooms ensuite with tea/coffee
making facilities, DDT and TV with pay-per-view
channels.
Rooms: 45 all ensuite ⊛
Pricing: Sgl £50.90–60.90 Dbl £56.85–66.85
Dinner available CC: Accepted
Room facilities: ⬛ ☎ ⬛ ⬛
Conference: 1 meeting room (Thtr 30 max),
24hr-delegate from £91.50, day-delegate from £21.50
Children: Welcome ⍧ Dogs: Welcome
Licenses: ⬥ ⍭
Parking: Off-street and free
Directions: Leave the M42 at junction 3 and head for
Redditch A435. Take first exit for Redditch.
Map ref: Winyates Green 7 F3

Ross-on-Wye, Herefordshire

Chase Hotel

Gloucester Road, Ross-on-Wye,
Herefordshire, HR9 5LH
Tel: 01989 763161/760644 Fax: 01989 768330
Email: res@chasehotel.co.uk
Web: www.chasehotel.co.uk
Seasonal closure: 24-29 December

Georgian country house set in 11 acres of grounds.
Award-winning cuisine, relaxed and informal surroundings.
Conference and events for up to 300 guests.
Rooms: 36 all ensuite ⬛ ⬛ ⊛
Pricing: Sgl £79–135 Dbl £95–155
Dinner available from £25–35 CC: Accepted
Room facilities: ⬛ ☎ ⬛ ⬛
Conference: 7 meeting rooms (Thtr 300 max),
24hr-delegate from £135, day-delegate from £35
Children: Welcome ⍧ Licenses: ⬥ ⍭
Parking: Off-street and free
Directions: From M50 Junction 4, turn left for Ross-on-
Wye. Take A40 Gloucester at second roundabout and
right for town centre at third roundabout. Hotel on left.
Map ref: Ross-on-Wye 7 E4

Chasedale Hotel

★★

Walford Road, Ross-on-Wye, Herefordshire, HR9 5PQ
Tel: 01989 562423 Fax: 01989 567900
Email: chasedale@supanet.com
Web: www.chasedale.co.uk
Rooms: 10 all ensuite
Pricing: Sgl £35.50–38.50 Dbl £71–77
Dinner available from £17–24 CC: Accepted
Room facilities:
Conference: 2 meeting rooms (Thtr 50 max)
Children: Welcome Dogs: Welcome
Licenses:
Parking: Off-street and free
Directions: Half a mile south of Ross-on-Wye, on
B4234 Ross-to-Coleford road on left.
Map ref: Ross-on-Wye 7 E4

Shrewsbury, Shropshire

Albright Hussey Manor Hotel

★★★

Ellesmere Road, Shrewsbury, Shropshire, SY4 3AF
Tel: 01939 290571/290523 Fax: 01939 291143
Email: info@albrighthussey.co.uk
Web: www.albrighthussey.co.uk
Rooms: 26 all ensuite
Pricing: Sgl £79–160 Dbl £110–175
Dinner available from £25–35 CC: Accepted
Room facilities:
Conference: 4 meeting rooms (Thtr 220 max),
24hr-delegate from £120, day-delegate from £35
Children: Welcome 1yrs min age
Dogs: Welcome Licenses:
Leisure: Croquet
Parking: Off-street and free
Directions: On main A528, 4 miles from end of main
M54/A5, 2 miles from Shrewsbury town centre.
Map ref: Shrewsbury 7 E2

Prince Rupert Hotel

★★★★

Butcher Row, Shrewsbury, Shropshire, SY1 1UQ
Tel: 01743 499955 Fax: 01743 357306
Email: post@prince-rupert-hotel.co.uk
Web: www.prince-rupert-hotel.co.uk
Rooms: 70 all ensuite
Pricing: Sgl £95 Dbl £125–195
Dinner available from £25–35
CC: Accepted
Room facilities: Access:
Conference: 3 meeting rooms (Thtr 120 max),
24hr-delegate from £120, day-delegate from £40
Children: Welcome Dogs: Welcome
Licenses:
Leisure: Gym, Health spa, Beauty salon,
Snooker/billiards Parking: Off-street
Directions: From the M54, follow signs for town centre.
Travel over English Bridge and up the Wyle Cop. Turn
sharp right into Fish Street. Hotel is 200m ahead.
Map ref: Shrewsbury 7 E2

Solihull, West Midlands

The Arden Hotel & Leisure Club

★★★

Coventry Road, Bickenhill, Solihull,
West Midlands, B92 0EH
Tel: 01675 443221 Fax: 01675 445604
Web: www.ardenhotel.co.uk
Rooms: 216 all ensuite
Dinner available CC: Accepted
Room facilities: Access:
Conference: 16 meeting rooms (Thtr 180 max)
Children: Welcome Dogs: Welcome
Licenses:
Leisure: Indoor pool, Gym, Health spa, Games room,
Snooker/billiards Parking: Off-street
Directions: M42 junction 6, A4 to Birmingham, stay left
and at roundabout 180 degrees to A45 Coventry, slip-
road after petrol station.
Map ref: Bickenhill 8 A3

Stafford, Staffordshire

Moat House Classic Hotel

★★★★★

Lower Penkridge Road, Acton Trussell, Stafford,
Staffordshire, ST17 0RJ
Tel: 01785 712217 Fax: 01785 715344
Email: info@moathouse.co.uk
Web: www.moathouse.co.uk
Seasonal closure: 24-26 December, 1-2 January
Rooms: 32 all ensuite
Pricing: Sgl £125 Dbl £135
Dinner available from £29.50–39.50 CC: Accepted
Room facilities:
Conference: 7 meeting rooms (Thtr 200 max),
24hr-delegate from £150, day-delegate from £50
Children: Welcome
Licenses:
Parking: Off-street and free
Directions: Exit M6 J13, take A449 towards Stafford, at
first island turn right, signed Acton Trussell, for 1¹/₂
miles. Follow brown signs Moat House is on the right.
Map ref: Acton Trussell 7 E2

Quality Hotel Stafford

★★★

Pinfold Lane, Penkridge, Stafford,
Staffordshire, ST19 5QP
Tel: 01785 712459 Fax: 01785 715532
Email: enquiries@hotels-stafford.com
Web: www.choicehotelseurope.com
Rooms: 47 all ensuite
Pricing: Dinner available from £18.95 CC: Accepted
Room facilities:
Conference: 7 meeting rooms (Thtr 300 max),
24hr-delegate from £130, day-delegate from £35
Children: Welcome Dogs: Welcome
Licenses:
Leisure: Indoor pool, Gym, Sauna, Steam room
Parking: Off-street and free

Directions: Exit either J12 or J13 of the M6 motorway (toll road off J12). After approximately 2 miles, at George and Fox pub turn into Pinfold Lane. Hotel on left-hand side. Map ref: Penkridge 7 E2

Abbey Hotel

65–68 Lichfield Road, Stafford, Staffordshire, ST17 4LW
Tel: 01785 258531 Fax: 01785 246875
Web: www.abbeyhotelstafford.co.uk
Seasonal closure: Christmas and New Year
Rooms: 17 all ensuite
Pricing: Sgl £45–60 Dbl £60–75
Dinner available from £14 CC: Accepted
Room facilities:
Children: Welcome Licenses:
Parking: Off-street and free
Directions: Leave M6 at Junction 13, head towards Stafford. Turn right at Esso garage to roundabout, follow Silkmore Lane. At second roundabout take second exit. Hotel ¼ mile on right.
Map ref: Stafford 7 E2

Albridge Hotel

72 Wolverhampton Road, Stafford,
Staffordshire, ST17 4AW
Tel: 01785 254100 Fax: 01785 223895
Seasonal closure: 25-26 December
Rooms: 9 (7 ensuite)
Pricing: Sgl £38–45 Dbl £45–50 CC: Accepted
Room facilities:
Children: Welcome Dogs: Welcome
Licenses: Leisure: Games room
Parking: Off-street and free
Directions: Leave M6 at Junction 13. Follow signs for Stafford, the town is 2¾ miles on A449. Hotel is on left after Telegraph Inn, opposite local wine shop.
Map ref: Stafford 7 E2

Offley Grove Farm

Adbaston, near Eccleshall, Stafford,
Staffordshire, ST20 0QB
Tel: 01785 280205 Fax: 01785 280205
Email: accom@offleygrovefarm.freeserve.co.uk
Web: www.offleygrovefarm.co.uk

You'll consider this a good find! Traditional farm surrounded by beautiful countryside. Spacious comfortable accommodation, and excellent breakfasts. Many guests return. Established 20 years. Self catering cottages available. Brochure on request.
Rooms: 2 all ensuite
Pricing: Sgl £30–35 Dbl £50–52
Room facilities:
Children: Welcome Parking: Off-street and free
Directions: From North; exit J15 M6 onto A519; follow signs for Eccleshall, then Woodseaves, Shebdon and Adbaston. From South; J10A M6, M54, A41, A519 and first left, travel a further 3½ miles.
Map ref: Adbaston 7 E2

Stoke-on-Trent, Staffordshire

Corrie Guest House

13-15 Newton Street, Basford, Stoke-on-Trent,
Staffordshire, ST4 6JN
Tel: 01782 614838 Fax: 01782 614838
Email: info@thecorrie.co.uk
Web: www.thecorrie.co.uk
Rooms: 7 all ensuite
Pricing: Sgl £25–38 Dbl £40–50 CC: Accepted
Room facilities:
Children: Welcome 5yrs min age
Parking: Off-street and free
Directions: From M6 take Junction 15 or 16 onto A500 towards Stoke. Take the A53 exit towards Newcastle-under-Lyme. Take the third left turn.
Map ref: Stoke-on-Trent 7 E2

The Church Farm

Holt Lane, Kingsley, Stoke-on-Trent,
Staffordshire, ST10 2BA
Tel: 01538 754759 Fax: 01538 754759
Seasonal closure: Christmas and New Year
Rooms: 3 all ensuite
Pricing: Sgl £25–30 Dbl £44–50
Room facilities: Children: Welcome
Parking: Off-street and free
Directions: Turn off A52 in Kingsley on sharp bend, signed for Cheadle and Kingsley. Holt Farm is 200m on right.
Map ref: Kingsley 7 F2

L.Beez Guest House

46 Leek Road, Stoke-on-Trent, Staffordshire, ST4 2AR
Tel: 01782 846727 Fax: 01782 846727
Rooms: 5 (1 ensuite)
Pricing: Sgl £20 Dbl £35–42 CC: Accepted
Room facilities: Children: Welcome
Dogs: Welcome Parking: Off-street and free
Directions: On A52 Stoke to Ashbourne, 10 minutes from M6/J15, 250 yards Stoke Railway Station. Opposite Royal Mail enquiry office.
Map ref: Stoke-on-Trent 7 E2

West Midlands

Stow-on-the-Wold, Gloucestershire

Fosse Manor Hotel

★★★★

Fosse Way, Stow-on-the-Wold, Cheltenham,
Gloucestershire, GL54 1JX
Tel: 01451 830354 Fax: 01451 832486
Email: enquiries@fossemanor.co.uk
Web: www.fossemanor.co.uk

A Cotswold stone house that's country-contemporary
design creates a relaxed and simple environment.
Each room is furnished using natural tones and fabrics.
The restaurant offers award winning cuisine and a
comprehensive wine list.
Rooms: 20 all ensuite
Pricing: Sgl £85–95 Dbl £130–225
Dinner available from £20–35 CC: Accepted
Room facilities:
Conference: 1 meeting room (Thtr 60 max),
24hr-delegate from £150, day-delegate from £45
Children: Welcome Dogs: Welcome
Licenses: Parking: Off-street and free
Directions: 1 mile south of Stow-on-the-Wold on the
A429 Warwick to Cirencester road.
Map ref: Cheltenham 7 E4

Grapevine Hotel

★★★

Sheep Street, Stow-on-the-Wold,
Gloucestershire, GL54 1AU
Tel: 01451 830344 Fax: 01451 832278
Email: enquiries@vines.co.uk
Web: www.vines.co.uk

An award-winning 17th century hotel set in the pretty
market town of Stow-on-the-Wold, the Grapevine
mixes urban sophistication with rural charm and
intimacy, offering 22 beautifully furnished bedrooms
and fine dining in the Conservatory Restaurant.
Rooms: 22 all ensuite
Pricing: Sgl £85–95 Dbl £140–160
Dinner available from £23–28 CC: Accepted
Room facilities:
Conference: 1 meeting room (Thtr 30 max),
24hr-delegate from £140, day-delegate from £40
Children: Welcome Dogs: Welcome
Licenses:
Parking: Off-street and free
Directions: Off Fosse Way (A429) take A439 to
Chipping Norton, 150 yards on right facing the Green.
Map ref: Stow-on-the-Wold 4 A1

Aston House

◆◆◆◆

Broadwell, Moreton-in-Marsh,
Gloucestershire, GL56 0TJ
Tel: 01451 830475
Email: fja@netcomuk.co.uk
Web: www.astonhouse.net
Seasonal closure: November to February inclusive

We welcome guests to our home in the quiet village of
Broadwell. Comfortable accommodation includes
armchairs, bedtime drinks and electric blankets for
those colder nights. Pub within walking distance.
Rooms: 3 (2 ensuite)
Pricing: Dbl £56–58
Room facilities:
Children: Welcome 10yrs min age
Leisure: PC/Internet available.
Parking: Off-street and free
Directions: A429 from Stow-on-the-Wold towards
Moreton. After 1 mile turn right at Broadwell/
Donnington crossroads. First house on left after ¹/₂ mile.
Map ref: Broadwell 4 A1

Limes

◆◆◆

Tewkesbury Road, Stow-on-the-Wold,
Gloucestershire, GL54 1EN
Tel: 01451 830034 Fax: 01451 830034
Email: thelimes@zoom.co.uk

Seasonal closure: Christmas
Rooms: 5 all ensuite
Pricing: Sgl £35–48 Dbl £47–52
Room facilities:
Children: Welcome
Dogs: Welcome
Parking: Off-street and free
Directions: Off A429 towards Evesham & Broadway Road (A424). 300 yards on left.
Map ref: Stow-on-the-Wold 4 A1

Stratford-upon-Avon, Warwickshire

Stratford Manor

★★★★

Warwick Road, Stratford-upon-Avon,
Warwickshire, CV37 0PY
Tel: 01789 731173 Fax: 01789 731131
Email: stratfordmanor@marstonhotels.com
Web: www.marstonhotels.com
Rooms: 104 all ensuite
Dinner available
CC: Accepted
Room facilities:
Access:
Conference: 16 meeting rooms (Thtr 350 max)
Children: Welcome
Licenses:
Leisure: Indoor pool, Gym, Health spa,
Beauty salon, Tennis
Parking: Off-street and free
Directions: Leave M40 at Junction 15, follow A46 towards Stratford. Take A439 signposted Stratford town centre. Hotel 1 mile on left.
Map ref: Stratford-upon-Avon 8 A4

Stratford Victoria

★★★★

Arden Street, Stratford-upon-Avon,
Warwickshire, CV37 6QQ
Tel: 01789 271000 Fax: 01789 271001
Email: stratfordvictoria@marstonhotels.com
Web: www.marstonhotels.com
Rooms: 102 all ensuite
Dinner available
CC: Accepted
Room facilities:
Access:
Conference: 7 meeting rooms (Thtr 140 max)
Children: Welcome
Dogs: Welcome
Licenses:
Leisure: Gym
Parking: Off-street and free
Directions: Exit M40 Junction 15, take A46 then A3400. Turn right at traffic lights into Arden Street; hotel is 150 yards on right.
Map ref: Stratford-upon-Avon 8 A4

Salford Hall

★★★

Abbots Salford, Warwickshire, WR11 8UT
Tel: 01386 871300 Fax: 01386 871301
Email: reception@salfordhall.co.uk
Web: www.salfordhall.co.uk
Seasonal closure: Christmas

Ideally situated for exploring the Cotswolds or Shakespeare country, Salford Hall is a fine Tudor manor offering very friendly, professional service and food that merits a dining award.
Rooms: 33 all ensuite
Pricing: Sgl £60–120 Dbl £100–150
Dinner available from £20–30
CC: Accepted
Room facilities:
Conference: 5 meeting rooms (Thtr 50 max),
24hr-delegate from £140, day-delegate from £45
Children: Welcome
Licenses:
Leisure: Tennis, Snooker/billiards
Parking: Off-street
Directions: From M40 Junction 15, take A46 towards Stratford. After 12 miles, take road signposted "Salford Priors, Abbots Salford." Follow for 1 1/2 miles and Salford Hall is on left.
Map ref: Abbots Salford 8 A4

Ambleside Guest House

♦♦♦♦

41 Grove Road, Stratford-upon-Avon,
Warwickshire, CV37 6PB
Tel: 01789 297239 Fax: 01789 295670
Email: ruth@amblesideguesthouse.com
Web: www.amblesideguesthouse.com
Rooms: 8 (7 ensuite)
Pricing: Sgl £20–33 Dbl £40–72
CC: Accepted
Room facilities:
Children: Welcome
Parking: Off-street and free
Directions: Opposite Firs Park, five minutes' walk from railway station and town centre, ten minutes' walk from theatres and coach station.
Map ref: Stratford-upon-Avon 8 A4

West Midlands

Eastnor House Hotel

33 Shipston Road, Stratford-upon-Avon,
Warwickshire, CV37 7LN
Tel: 01789 268115 Fax: 01789 551133
Email: eastnorhouse@ntlworld.com
Web: www.eastnorhouse.com

Award-winning hotel, ideally located within a five
minute walk of RST. Well appointed, attractive rooms,
friendly service, lavish breakfast buffet, free parking,
BBQ, coffee/beer/wine terrace, residents' bar.
Rooms: 10 all ensuite
Pricing: Sgl £59–70 Dbl £79–90 CC: Accepted
Room facilities:
Children: Welcome Licenses:
Parking: Off-street and free
Directions: Located just south of the river on the
Shipston road (A3400) close to the centre of Stratford.
Map ref: Stratford-upon-Avon 8 A4

Moonraker House

40 Alcester Road, Stratford-upon-Avon,
Warwickshire, CU37 9DB
Tel: 01789 267115 Fax: 01789 295504
Email: moonrakerleonard@aol.com
Web: www.moonrakerhouse.com
Rooms: 10 all ensuite
Pricing: Sgl £40 Dbl £60–89 CC: Accepted
Room facilities:
Children: Welcome
Parking: Off-street and free
Directions: Located on the right-hand side on A422
north west, 900 yards from Stratford-upon-Avon
centre.
Map ref: Stratford-upon-Avon 8 A4

Twelfth Night

Evesham Place, Stratford-upon-Avon,
Warwickshire, CV37 6HT
Tel: 01789 414595 Fax: 01789 414595
Email: reservations@twelfthnight.co.uk
Web: www.twelfthnight.co.uk
Rooms: 6 all ensuite
Pricing: Sgl £35–45 Dbl £57–67 CC: Accepted
Room facilities:
Children: Welcome 12yrs min age
Parking: Off-street and free
Directions: M40 junction 15, A46, A439. Guild Street.
Left at traffic lights into Arden Street, Grove Road and
into Evesham Place.
Map ref: Stratford-upon-Avon 8 A4

Victoria Spa Lodge

Bishopton Lane, Bishopton, Stratford-upon-Avon,
Warwickshire, CV37 9QY
Tel: 01789 267985 Fax: 01789 204728
Email: ptozer@victoriaspalodge.demon.co.uk
Web: www.stratford-upon-avon.co.uk/victoriaspa.htm

Paul and Dreen Tozer welcome you to their Grade II
Listed Building, opened in 1837 by Princess Victoria.
Pleasant walks along the tow path to town and other
villages. Family rooms by quotation. Small Hotel of the
Midlands 1995 Award.
Rooms: 7 all ensuite
Pricing: Sgl £50 Dbl £65 CC: Accepted
Room facilities: Children: Welcome
Parking: Off-street and free
Directions: Take A3400 north from Stratford town
about 1½ miles where it intersects with A46. First exit,
Bishopton Lane, first house on right-hand side
Map ref: Bishopton 8 A4

Cymbeline House

24 Evesham Place, Stratford-upon-Avon,
Warwickshire, CV37 6HT
Tel: 01789 292958 Fax: 01789 292958
Email: cymbelinebb@btopenworld.com
Web: www.cymbelinehouse.co.uk
Seasonal closure: Christmas
Rooms: 6 all ensuite

Room facilities:
Children: Welcome Dogs: Welcome
Parking: Off-street and free
Map ref: Stratford-upon-Avon 8 A4

Hampton Lodge Guest House

◆◆◆ ✕ ✑

38 Shipston Road, Stratford-upon-Avon,
Warwickshire, CV37 7LP
Tel: 01789 299374 Fax: 01789 299374
Email: hamptonlodge.info@btopenworld.com
Web: www.hamptonlodge.co.uk
Rooms: 6 all ensuite ✆
Pricing: Sgl £25–40 Dbl £50–65 CC: Accepted
Room facilities:
Children: Welcome 5yrs min age
Parking: Off-street and free
Directions: M40 J15, take A46 then A439 to Stratford.
Follow A3400 over River Avon. Turn right into Shipston
Road; Hampton Lodge on left.
Map ref: Stratford-upon-Avon 8 A4

The Hunters Moon Guest House

◆◆◆ ✑

150 Alcester Road, Stratford-upon-Avon,
Warwickshire, CV37 9DR
Tel: 01789 292 888 Fax: 01789 204 101
Email: thehuntersmoon@ntlworld.com
Web: www.huntersmoonguesthouse.com
Rooms: 7 all ensuite ✆ ✆
Pricing: Sgl £28–35 Dbl £56–64
CC: Accepted
Room facilities:
Children: Welcome 5yrs min age
Parking: Off-street and free
Directions: On A442 6 miles from Junction 15 M40,
midway between Anne Hathaway's Cottage and
Stratford town centre.
Map ref: Stratford-upon-Avon 8 A4

The Crown Inn

◆◆◆◆

Frampton Mansell, Stroud, Gloucestershire, GL6 8JG
Tel: 01285 760601 Fax: 01285 760681
Web: www.english-inns.co.uk
Rooms: 12 all ensuite ✆ ✆
Pricing: Sgl £50–79 Dbl £90–99
Dinner available from £9.95 CC: Accepted
Room facilities: ▢ ☎ ✑ ✆
Conference: 1 meeting room (Thtr 40 max),
24hr-delegate from £99, day-delegate from £65
Children: Welcome ⅂ Dogs: Assistance dogs only
Licenses: ▦▦▦
Parking: Off-street and free
Directions: Take the A419 from Stroud or Cirencester.
From Stroud take left turn after roadside cafe. From
Cirencester right turn after petrol station.
Map ref: Frampton Mansell 3 F1

New Hall Hotel

★★★★ ⚑⚑⚑   Excellent

Walmley Road, Sutton Coldfield,
West Midlands, B76 1QX
Tel: 0121 378 2442 Fax: 0121 378 4637
Email: info@newhalluk.com
Web: www.newhalluk.com

Imagine staying in the oldest moated manor house in
England. If the walls could talk, after 900 years of
history, you'd hear spellbinding tales of royal intrigue,
forbidden passions and unrequited love.
Rooms: 60 all ensuite ⬚ ✆
Pricing: Sgl £146–150 Dbl £160–161
Dinner available from £25
CC: Accepted
Room facilities: ▢ ☎ ✑ ✆
Conference: 4 meeting rooms (Thtr 60 max),
24hr-delegate from £170, day-delegate from £60
Children: Welcome ⅂
Dogs: Welcome
Licenses: ⬙ ▦▦▦
Leisure: Indoor pool, Gym, Health spa, Beauty salon,
Tennis, Golf, Fishing
Parking: Off-street and free
Map ref: Walmley 8 A3

Reindeer Park Lodge

◆◆◆◆ ✕

Kingsbury Road, Leamarston, Sutton Coldfield,
West Midlands, B76 0DE
Tel: 01675 470811 Fax: 01675 470710
Email: beck@reindeerpark.co.uk
Web: www.reindeerpark.co.uk
Rooms: 6 all ensuite ✆ ✆
Pricing: Sgl £39.50–59.50 Dbl £59.50–79.50
Dinner available
CC: Accepted
Room facilities: ▢ ✑ ✆
Conference: 2 meeting rooms (Thtr 20 max),
24hr-delegate from £39.50
Children: Welcome ⅂ ✑
Dogs: Welcome
Parking: Off-street and free
Directions: Junction 9 M42 onto A4097, Lodge is ¼
mile on the right.
Map ref: Leamarston 7 F3

West Midlands

Symonds Yat, Herefordshire

Garth Cottage Hotel

Symonds Yat East, Herefordshire, HR9 6JL
Tel: 01600 890364 Fax: 01600 890364
Email: garthcot@yateast.fsnet.co.uk
Web: www.garthcottage-symondsyat.com
Seasonal closure: November to March
Rooms: 4 all ensuite
Pricing: Dbl £71
Dinner available from £22
Room facilities:
Children: Welcome 12yrs min age
Licenses: Leisure: Fishing
Parking: Off-street and free
Directions: From A40, leave at Little Chef Whitchurch.
Follow signs for Symonds Yat East on B4229.
Map ref: Symonds Yat 7 E4

Telford, Shropshire

Clarion, Madeley Court

Castlefields Way, Madeley Court, Telford,
Shropshire, TF7 5DW
Tel: 01952 680068 Fax: 01952 684275
Email: enquiries@hotels-telford.com
Web: www.choicehotelseurope.com
Rooms: 47 all ensuite
Pricing: Sgl £61.75–122.75 Dbl £80.50–149.50
Dinner available from £9–34 CC: Accepted
Room facilities:
Conference: 6 meeting rooms (Thtr 175 max),
24hr-delegate from £149.50, day-delegate from £45
Children: Welcome
Licenses: Leisure: Beauty salon
Parking: Off-street and free
Directions: Leave M54 at Exit 4. Take A442 towards
Kidderminster to Castlefields roundabout. Hotel is
situated as you exit first left.
Map ref: Telford 7 E2

Charlton Arms Hotel

Church Street, Wellington, Shropshire, TF1 1DG
Tel: 01952 251351 Fax: 01952 222077
Web: www.charltonarms.com
Rooms: 22 all ensuite
Pricing: Sgl £45.50 Dbl £55.50
Dinner available from £6.95 CC: Accepted
Room facilities:
Conference: 1 meeting room (Thtr 150 max),
24hr-delegate from £75, day-delegate from £15
Children: Welcome
Licenses:
Parking: Off-street and free
Directions: M54 J7. Head into Wellington town centre.
Follow one-way system to Vineyard Road and turn into
Church Street.
Map ref: Wellington 7 E2

White House Hotel

Wellington Road, Muxton, Telford, Shropshire, TF2 8NG
Tel: 01952 604276 Fax: 01952 670336
Email: james@whhotel.co.uk
Web: www.whhotel.co.uk
Rooms: 31 all ensuite
Pricing: Sgl £50–62.50 Dbl £65–82.50
Dinner available from £15.95 CC: Accepted
Room facilities:
Children: Welcome Dogs: Welcome
Licenses: Parking: Off-street and free
Directions: Leave M54 junction 4, follow B5060
towards Newport, then follow signs for Muxton. Hotel
is 1/4 mile on the right.
Map ref: Muxton 7 E2

Tetbury, Gloucestershire

Calcot Manor Hotel & Spa

Near Tetbury, Gloucestershire, GL8 8YJ
Tel: 01666 890391 Fax: 01666 890394
Email: reception@calcotmanor.co.uk
Web: www.calcotmanor.co.uk
Rooms: 30 all ensuite
Pricing: Sgl £160–185 Dbl £185–225
Dinner available from £35 CC: Accepted
Room facilities:
Conference: 3 meeting rooms (Thtr 100 max),
24hr-delegate from £215, day-delegate from £65
Children: Welcome Licenses:
Leisure: Indoor pool, Outdoor pool, Gym, Health spa,
Beauty salon, Tennis
Parking: Off-street and free
Directions: 3 miles outside Tetbury, on the crossroads
of the A4135 and A46.
Map ref: Calcot 3 F1

Upper Slaughter, Gloucestershire

Lords Of The Manor

Upper Slaughter, Gloucestershire, GL54 2JD
Tel: 01451 820243 Fax: 01451 820696
Email: enquiries@lordsofthemanor.com
Web: www.lordsofthemanor.com
Rooms: 27 all ensuite
Pricing: Sgl £100 Dbl £160–310
Dinner available from £40–59 CC: Accepted
Room facilities:
Conference: 2 meeting rooms (Thtr 20 max),
24hr-delegate from £170, day-delegate from £55
Children: Welcome Dogs: Welcome
Licenses: Leisure: Fishing Parking: Off-street
Directions: From M5, A40 heading for Oxford, left on
A429, "The Slaughters" turning on left. From M25, M40
heading for Oxford, A40 at junction 8, right onto A429,
take "The Slaughters" turning on left.
Map ref: Upper Slaughter 4 A1

Upton-upon-Severn, Worcestershire

White Lion Hotel

★★★★

High Street, Upton-upon-Severn, near Malvern,
Worcestershire, WR8 0HJ
Tel: 01684 592551 Fax: 01684 593333
Email: info@whitelionhotel.biz
Web: www.whitelionhotel.biz

A hostel since 1510, exposed timbers in many of the
rooms and a philosophy that is quite simple, "old-
fashioned hospitality, good food, fine wines, quality
beers and value for money".
Rooms: 13 all ensuite ⬥ 🖳 ⊗
Pricing: Sgl £67.50–90 Dbl £92.50–135
Dinner available from £12
CC: Accepted
Room facilities: ▢ ☎ 🕭 📞
Conference: 1 meeting room (Thtr 30 max)
Children: Welcome ⱦ
Dogs: Welcome
Licenses: ⅲ
Parking: Off-street and free
Directions: From Worcester, junction 7 and
Tewkesbury, junction 8 off M5. Take A38 for B4104
signposted Upton, over the bridge and turn left.
Map ref: Upton-upon-Severn 7 E4

Uttoxeter, Staffordshire

Loxley Bank Farm

◆◆◆◆

Loxley Lane, Uttoxeter, Staffordshire, ST14 8QB
Tel: 01889 562467 Fax: 01889 562467
Rooms: 2 all ensuite ⊗
Pricing: Sgl £35–45 Dbl £65–75
Room facilities: ▢ 🕭
Conference: 1 meeting room (Thtr 8 max)
Leisure: Walks
Parking: Off-street and free
Directions: 2 miles from Uttoxeter. On the A518 to
Stafford take left turn into Loxley Lane immediately
after layby. Farm first left after ½ mile.
Map ref: Uttoxeter 7 F2

Walsall, West Midlands

Quality Hotel and Suites Walsall

★★★

20 Wolverhampton Road West, Bentley, Walsall,
West Midlands, WS2 0BS
Tel: 01922 724444 Fax: 01922 723148
Email: enquiries@hotels-walsall.com
Web: www.choicehotelseurope.com
Rooms: 154 all ensuite ⬥ 🖳 ⊗
Pricing: Sgl £39.99–107.75 Dbl £49.99–135.50
Dinner available from £17.95–32 CC: Accepted
Room facilities: ▢ ☎ 🕭 📞
Conference: 13 meeting rooms (Thtr 180 max),
24hr-delegate from £140, day-delegate from £38
Children: Welcome ⱦ Licenses: ⬧ ⅲ
Leisure: Indoor pool, Gym, Sauna, Jacuzzi, Solarium
Parking: Off-street and free
Directions: Located at Junction 10 of M6.
Map ref: Bentley 7 F3

Quality Hotel M6 J7

★★★

Birmingham Road, Walsall, West Midlands, WS5 3AB
Tel: 01922 633609 Fax: 01922 635727
Email: info@boundaryhotel.com
Web: www.qualityhotelM6J7.co.uk
Rooms: 96 all ensuite ⬥ ⊗
Dinner available CC: Accepted
Room facilities: ▢ ☎ 🕭 📞
Access: ⌊↿
Conference: 9 meeting rooms (Thtr 50 max)
Children: Welcome ⱦ ⌬ Dogs: Welcome
Licenses: ⬧ ⅲ Leisure: Tennis
Parking: Off-street and free
Directions: Exit J7 M6; follow A34 for Walsall. Just over
1 mile on left.
Map ref: Walsall 7 F3

Warwick, Warwickshire

Chesford Grange Hotel

★★★★

Chesford Bridge, Kenilworth, Warwickshire, CV8 2LD
Tel: 01926 859331 Fax: 01926 859075
Email: chesfordgrangereservations@qhotels.co.uk
Web: www.qhotels.co.uk
Rooms: 209 all ensuite ⬥
Pricing: Sgl £95–170 Dbl £115–186
Dinner available from £23.50 CC: Accepted
Room facilities: ▢ ☎ 🕭 📞 Access: ⌊↿
Conference: 12 meeting rooms (Thtr 710 max),
24hr-delegate from £195, day-delegate from £65
Children: Welcome ⱦ Dogs: Welcome
Licenses: ⬧ ⅲ
Leisure: Indoor pool, Gym, Health spa, Beauty salon
Parking: Off-street and free
Directions: Exit M40 at Junction 15. Take A46 toward
Coventry and A452 slip road to Leamington. Right at
roundabout to Leamington; hotel is 250 yards on right.
Map ref: Chesford Bridge 8 B3

West Midlands

Glebe Hotel

★★★

Church Street, Barford, Warwick,
Warwickshire, CV35 8BS
Tel: 01926 624218 Fax: 01926 624625
Web: www.glebehotel.co.uk
Rooms: 39 all ensuite
Pricing: Sgl £105 Dbl £125
Dinner available from £25.95
CC: Accepted
Room facilities: 🖵 ☎ ☕
Access: ♿
Conference: 6 meeting rooms (Thtr 120 max),
24hr-delegate from £159, day-delegate from £49
Children: Welcome ♀
Dogs: Welcome
Licenses: ⟁ ♨
Leisure: Indoor pool, Gym, Health spa, Beauty salon,
Beauty room
Parking: Off-street and free
Directions: From junction 15 of the M40 follow A429
Stow over bridge and at small roundabout turn left.
Hotel ¹/₂ mile on right.
Map ref: Barford 8 B3

Chesterfields Guest House

◆◆◆

Chesterfields, 84 Emscote Road, Warwick,
Warwickshire, CV34 5QJ
Tel: 01926 774864
Email: jchapman@chesterfields.freeserve.co.uk
Web: www.smoothhound.co.uk/hotels/chesterfields
Seasonal closure: 24–27 December
Rooms: 7 (1 ensuite) ⊗
Pricing: Sgl £24–35 Dbl £46–54
Room facilities: 🖵 ☕
Children: Welcome ♀
Parking: Off-street and free
Directions: M40 J15 A429 Warwick, through town centre,
A445 Leamington Coten End leading to Emscote Road,
under railway bridge, 150 yards on right.
Map ref: Warwick 8 B3

King's Head Inn

◆◆◆ ☙

39 Saltisford, Warwick, Warwickshire, CV34 4TD
Tel: 08707 606363 Fax: 01926 775166
Email: info@thekingsheadwarwick.co.uk
Web: www.thekingsheadwarwick.co.uk
Rooms: 9 all ensuite ☕ 🖵 ⊗
Pricing: Sgl £65–85 Dbl £65–95
Dinner available from £11
CC: Accepted
Room facilities: 🖵 ☕
Children: Welcome ♀ ☙
Licenses: ♨
Parking: Off-street and free
Directions: M40 Junction 15 A429 Warwick, left at
Bowling Green Street, left at roundabout. King's Head
is on the left.
Map ref: Warwick 8 B3

The Rose and Crown

◆◆◆

30 Marketplace, Warwick, Warwickshire, CV34 4SH
Tel: 01926 411117 Fax: 01926 492117
Email: roseandcrown@peachpubs.com
Web: www.peachpubs.com

The 'people, food and fun' philosophy shows
throughout this 'Boutique food pub with rooms'
creating the most relaxed and stylish place to 'eat,
drink and sleep' in the Midlands.
Rooms: 5 all ensuite ⊗
Pricing: Sgl £65 Dbl £65
Dinner available from £12
CC: Accepted
Room facilities: 🖵 ☎ ☕ ☎
Conference: 1 meeting room (Thtr 22 max)
Children: Welcome
Licenses: ♨
Directions: M40 to Warwick Castle to town centre, in
the market square by the museum.
Map ref: Warwick 8 B3

The big sleep

As part of our comprehensive
inspection process, RAC
Inspectors investigate the comfort of the beds.

Weobley, Herefordshire

Ye Olde Salutation Inn

 ◆◆◆◆

Market Pitch, Weobley, Herefordshire, HR4 8SJ
Tel: 01544 318443 Fax: 01544 318405
Email: salutationinn@btinternet.com
Web: www.thesalutationinn.co.uk

Nestled in the centre of medieval Weobley. Black and white building dating back over 500 years. Run personally by the owner, it is a perfect base for the Welsh Marches.
Rooms: 4 all ensuite
Pricing: Sgl £52–57 Dbl £78–84
Dinner available from £25 CC: Accepted
Room facilities:
Conference: 1 meeting room (Thtr 30 max)
Children: Welcome
Licenses:
Parking: Off-street and free
Directions: A49 to Leominster, then A4112 to Weobley for 8 miles
Map ref: Weobly 7 D4

Westonbirt, Gloucestershire

Hare and Hounds

 ★★★

Westonbirt, Tetbury, Gloucestershire, GL8 8QL
Tel: 01666 881000 Fax: 01666 880241
Email: enquiries@hareandhoundshotel.com
Web: www.hareandhoundshotel.com

Spacious, comfortable hotel in extensive gardens next to Westonbirt Arboretum, within easy reach of M4 and M5. Quality dining in the restaurant or bar. Conference and banquetting suite. Tennis and squash.
Rooms: 31 all ensuite
Pricing: Sgl £88–98 Dbl £112–125
Dinner available from £23–25 CC: Accepted
Room facilities:
Conference: 4 meeting rooms (Thtr 150 max), 24hr-delegate from £130, day-delegate from £38
Children: Welcome Dogs: Welcome
Licenses:
Leisure: Tennis, Games room, Snooker/billiards
Parking: Off-street and free
Directions: Exit J17 M4 to Tetbury via Malmesbury; A433 for 2 miles to Westonbirt. Exit J13 M5, Stroud and A46 to Westonbirt turning.
Map ref: Tetbury 3 F1

Whitchurch, Shropshire

The Dukes

 ◆◆◆◆

Halghton, Whitchurch, Shropshire, SY13 3DU
Tel: 01948 830269
Email: gilberts@thedukes.fsbusiness.co.uk
Web: www.smoothhound.co.uk/hotels/dukes.html
Seasonal closure: Christmas
Rooms: 3 all ensuite
Pricing: Sgl £35 Dbl £60
Dinner available from £12.50–15.00
Room facilities: Children: Welcome
Leisure: Tennis Parking: Off-street and free
Directions: At Whitchurch, A525 for Wrexham. After 6 miles, turn left for Horseman's Green. Past houses, turn right for Halghton. The Dukes is on right after ½ mile.
Map ref: Halghton 7 D2

Wolverhampton, West Midlands

Quality Hotel Wolverhampton

 ★★★★

Penn Road, Wolverhampton, West Midlands, WV3 0ER
Tel: 01902 429216 Fax: 01902 710419
Email: enquiries@hotels-wolverhampton.com
Web: www.choicehotelseurope.com
Rooms: 92 all ensuite
Pricing: Sgl £39.32–94.42 Dbl £58–126.72
Dinner available from £19.95–32.50
CC: Accepted
Room facilities:
Conference: 6 meeting rooms (Thtr 140 max), 24hr-delegate from £128, day-delegate from £35
Children: Welcome Dogs: Welcome
Licenses:
Leisure: Indoor pool, Gym, Games room, Sauna, Steam room Parking: Off-street
Directions: M6 Junction 10, take A454 to Wolverhampton. From ring road follow A449 to Kidderminster. Hotel is ¼ mile on right.
Map ref: Wolverhampton 7 E3

West Midlands

Fox Hotel

118 School Street, Wolverhampton,
West Midlands, WV3 0NR
Tel: 01902 421680 Fax: 01902 711654
Email: sales@foxhotel.co.uk
Web: www.foxhotel.co.uk

A warm welcome awaits you at the Fox Hotel.
Business or pleasure, our aim is to make your visit to
Wolverhampton relaxing and memorable. Centrally
located, secure parking available.
Rooms: 33 all ensuite
Pricing: Sgl £44–49 Dbl £59–65
Dinner available from £10–19.50
CC: Accepted
Room facilities: □ ☎ ☺
Conference: 1 meeting room (Thtr 80 max),
24hr-delegate from £69, day-delegate from £25
Children: Welcome ♫ ☯ ☼
Licenses: ▮▮▮
Leisure: Games room
Parking: Off-street and free
Directions: Situated on city centre ring road, clockwise
on the right, anticlockwise on your left.
Map ref: Wolverhampton 7 E3

Worcester, Worcestershire

Bants

♦♦♦♦ ✂ ☕
Worcester Road, Upton Snodsbury, Worcester,
Worcestershire, WR7 4NN
Tel: 01905 381282 Fax: 01905 381173
Email: info@bants.co.uk
Web: www.bants.co.uk
Rooms: 9 (7 ensuite) ☺

Pricing: Sgl £45–95 Dbl £75–150
Dinner available from £15–25
CC: Accepted
Room facilities: □ ☺
Conference: 2 meeting rooms,
24hr-delegate from £125, day-delegate from £25
Children: Welcome ♫
Licenses: ▮▮▮
Parking: Off-street and free
Directions: M5 J6. Take turning for Evesham. Over mini
island, left next island. Take A422 Stratford. Two miles
on left side.
Map ref: Upton Snodsbury 7 F4

Manor Arms Country Inn & Hotel

♦♦♦

Abberley Village, Worcestershire, WR6 6BN
Tel: 01299 896507 Fax: 01299 896723
Email: info@themanorarms.co.uk
Web: www.themanorarms.co.uk
Rooms: 11 (9 ensuite)
Dinner available
CC: Accepted
Room facilities: □ ☎ ☺
Children: Welcome ♫
Dogs: Welcome
Licenses: ▮▮▮
Parking: Off-street and free
Directions: Leave A443 at Abberley, follow brown
tourist signs "Manor Arms Inn & Hotel".
Map ref: Abberley 7 E3

The Lenchford Inn

♦♦♦
Shrawley, Worcester, Worcestershire, WR6 6TB
Tel: 01905 562229 Fax: 01905 621125
Map ref: Shrawley 7 E3

Wotton-under-Edge, Gloucestershire

Burrows Court

♦♦♦
Nibley Green, North Nibley, Gloucestershire, GL11 6AZ
Tel: 01453 546230 Fax: 01453 546230
Email: p.f.rackley@tesco.net
Web: www.burrowscourt.co.uk
Seasonal closure: January to February
Rooms: 6 all ensuite
Pricing: Sgl £35–44 Dbl £52–66
CC: Accepted
Room facilities: □ ☺
Children: Welcome
Dogs: Welcome
Licenses: ▮▮▮
Parking: Off-street and free
Directions: From the A38 Bristol to Gloucester road,
turn off at sign to Blanchworth, North Nibley,
Stinchcombe. Hotel opposite North Nibley village sign.
Map ref: Nibley Green 3 F1

The Feathers Hotel, Ludlow

Northeast

Glasgow •   • Edinburgh

• Newcastle

Belfast •

Dublin •   • Manchester

Birmingham •

Cardiff •   London •

rtlepool

SIDE Redcar
      Saltburn-by-the-Sea
dlesbrough Loftus
on   A171
      Guisborough   A174
Newton under   Castle Park   Whitby
  Roseberry   A171
ockesley

R Esk   A169

NORTH YORK   Robin Hood's
                    Bay

  MOORS   A171
      Hartoft Levisham   Hackness   Gloughton
      End   Scalby
  Kirkbymoorside   Scarborough
msley   A170   East Ayton
      Harome Pickering   A170
                                Filey

Northeast

© Crown Copyright. All rights reserved.
Licence number 100022382

Award winners

To help you choose somewhere really special for your stay, we've listed here all RAC Award-winning properties in this region.

Gold Ribbon Award

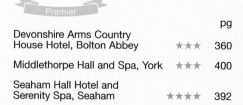

Premier

		pg
Devonshire Arms Country House Hotel, Bolton Abbey	★★★	360
Middlethorpe Hall and Spa, York	★★★	400
Seaham Hall Hotel and Serenity Spa, Seaham	★★★★	392

Blue Ribbon Award

Excellent

		pg
Aldwark Manor, York	★★★★	398
Grange Hotel, York	★★★	399
Judges Country House Hotel, Yarm	★★★	398
Rose & Crown, Romaldkirk	★★	382

White Ribbon Award

Commended

		pg
Boar's Head Hotel, Harrogate	★★★	367
Langley Castle Hotel, Hexham	★★★★	370
Thorpe Park Hotel & Spa, Leeds	★★★★	374

Little Gem Award

Little Gem

		pg
Clow Beck House, Darlington	◆◆◆◆◆	362
Moorlands Country House Hotel, Levisham	◆◆◆◆◆	375

Devonshire Arms Country House Hotel, Bolton Abbey

Seaham Hall Hotel and Serenity Spa, Seaham

Grange Hotel, York

Austwick, North Yorkshire

The Austwick Traddock

Austwick, near Settle, Via Lancaster,
North Yorkshire, LA2 8BY
Tel: 01524 251224 Fax: 01524 251796
Email: info@austwicktraddock.co.uk
Web: www.austwicktraddock.co.uk
Rooms: 10 all ensuite
Pricing: Sgl £60–80 Dbl £120–160
Dinner available from £20–30
CC: Accepted
Room facilities:
Conference: 2 meeting rooms
Children: Welcome
Dogs: Welcome
Licenses:
Parking: Off-street and free
Directions: Follow A65 from Skipton to Kendal. Three miles past Settle turn right marked Austwick. ³/₄ mile over bridge, hotel on left.
Map ref: Austwick 10 C3

Bamburgh, Northumberland

Waren House Hotel

Waren Mill, Belford, Northumberland, NE70 7EE
Tel: 01668 214581 Fax: 01668 214484
Email: enquiries@warenhousehotel.co.uk
Web: www.warenhousehotel.co.uk

Traditional Country House Hotel in 6 acres of grounds on the edge of Budle Bay and 2 miles from Bamburgh Castle. Superb accommodation, excellent food and extensive reasonably priced wine list.
Rooms: 13 all ensuite
Pricing: Sgl £79–115 Dbl £97.50–175
Dinner available from £22.50–28.50 CC: Accepted
Room facilities:
Conference: 1 meeting room (Thtr 20 max),
24hr-delegate from £120, day-delegate from £30
Children: Welcome 14yrs min age
Dogs: Welcome
Licenses:
Parking: Off-street and free
Directions: 14 miles south of Berwick-upon-Tweed. Take B1342, off the A1, to Waren Mill. Hotel on southwest corner of Budle Bay.
Map ref: Waren Mill 13 F3

The Lord Crewe, Bamburgh

Front Street, Bamburgh,
Northumberland, NE69 7BL
Tel: 01668 214243 Fax: 01668 214273
Email: lordcrewebamburgh@tiscali.co.uk
Web: www.lordcrewe.co.uk
Seasonal closure: 6 January to 1 February
Rooms: 18 (17 ensuite)
Pricing: Sgl £50–74 Dbl £98
Dinner available from £18
CC: Accepted
Room facilities:
Children: Welcome 5yrs min age
Dogs: Welcome
Licenses:
Parking: Off-street and free
Map ref: Bamburgh 13 F3

Barnard Castle, Co. Durham

Number 34

34 The Bank, Barnard Castle, Durham, DL12 8PN
Tel: 01833 631304 Fax: 01833 631304
Web: www.number34.com
Rooms: 3 all ensuite
Pricing: Sgl £35–45 Dbl £50–70
Room facilities:
Conference: 2 meeting rooms (Thtr 12 max)
Children: Welcome 12yrs min age
Directions: Situated in the centre of Barnard Castle in the antique quarter beyond the Market Cross and next to Blagraves Restaurant.
Map ref: Barnard Castle 10 C2

Barnetby le Wold, North Lincolnshire

Whistle & Flute

Railway Street, Barnetby le Wold,
North Lincolnshire, DN38 6DG
Tel: 01652 688238 Fax: 01652 688238
Rooms: 11 all ensuite
Pricing: Sgl £40 Dbl £50–60
Dinner available from £5.95–14.95
CC: Accepted
Room facilities:
Children: Welcome
Licenses:
Parking: Off-street and free
Directions: From J5 M180 head towards Humberside airport. Turn right to Brigg then left to Barnetby, heading directly for train station.
Map ref: Barnetby le Wold 11 E4

Northeast

Barnsley, South Yorkshire

Tankersley Manor

★★★★

Church Lane, Tankersley, Barnsley,
South Yorkshire, S75 3DQ
Tel: 01226 744700 Fax: 01226 745405
Email: tankersley@marstonhotels.com
Web: www.marstonhotels.com
Rooms: 100 all ensuite
Dinner available CC: Accepted
Room facilities:
Conference: 11 meeting rooms (Thtr 400 max)
Children: Welcome
Licenses:
Leisure: Indoor pool, Gym, Health spa, Beauty salon
Parking: Off-street and free
Directions: Leave M1 at junction 36, follow A61
towards Sheffield, hotel is half a mile on the left.
Map ref: Tankersley 11 D4

Bedale, North Yorkshire

Elmfield Country House

◆◆◆◆◆

Arrathorne, Bedale, North Yorkshire, DL8 1NE
Tel: 01677 450558 Fax: 01677 450557
Email: stay@elmfieldhouse.freeserve.co.uk
Web: www.elmfieldhouse.co.uk
Rooms: 9 all ensuite
Dinner available CC: Accepted
Room facilities:
Children: Welcome
Licenses:
Leisure: Fishing, Games room, Snooker/billiards
Parking: Off-street and free
Directions: From A1, take A684 into Bedale. Follow A684
towards Leyburn after village of Patrick Brompton. Turn
right at crossroads towards Richmond. Elmfield is 1½
miles on right.
Map ref: Arrathorne 11 D2

Belford, Northumberland

Blue Bell Hotel

★★★

Market Square, Belford, Northumberland, NE70 7NE
Tel: 01668 213543 Fax: 01668 213787
Email: bluebel@globalnet.co.uk
Web: www.bluebellhotel.com
Rooms: 17 all ensuite
Pricing: Dinner available from £25
CC: Accepted
Room facilities:
Conference: 2 meeting rooms (Thtr 80 max)
Children: Welcome
Dogs: Welcome
Licenses:
Leisure: Games room
Parking: Off-street and free
Map ref: Belford 13 F3

Bellingham, Northumberland

Riverdale Hall Hotel

★★★

Bellingham, Northumberland, NE48 2JT
Tel: 01434 220254 Fax: 01434 220457
Email: iben@riverdalehall.demon.co.uk
Web: www.riverdalehall.demon.co.uk
Rooms: 20 all ensuite
Pricing: Sgl £52–59 Dbl £96–150
Dinner available from £19.95
CC: Accepted
Room facilities:
Conference: 2 meeting rooms (Thtr 40 max),
24hr-delegate from £69, day-delegate from £25
Children: Welcome
Dogs: Welcome
Licenses:
Leisure: Indoor pool, Fishing, Sauna
Parking: Off-street and free
Directions: Turn off B6320 after bridge onto C200.
Hotel is 150 yards on left.
Map ref: Bellingham 13 E4
See advert on opposite page

Bentley, Yorkshire

Eastfarm B&B

◆◆◆◆

Eastfarm Owston Lane, Owston, Bentley,
Doncaster, Yorkshire, DN5 0LP
Tel: 01302 338300 Fax: 01302 726224
Web: www.eastfarm.co.uk
Rooms: 15 all ensuite
Pricing: Sgl £32–35 Dbl £47–55
CC: Accepted
Room facilities:
Children: Welcome Dogs: Welcome
Directions: From Doncaster take the A19 towards
Selby. Reach B1220, turn left onto this road. Take first
right, Eastfarm is 200 yards on right.
Map ref: Owston 11 D4

Berwick-upon-Tweed, Northumberland

Queen's Head Hotel

★★★

Sandgate, Berwick-upon-Tweed,
Northumberland, TD15 1EP
Tel: 01289 307852 Fax: 01289 307858
Email: queensheadhotel@berwickontweed.fsbusiness.co.uk
Web: www.thequeensheadhotel.com
Rooms: 6 all ensuite
Pricing: Sgl £55 Dbl £77.50
Dinner available from £18 CC: Accepted
Room facilities:
Children: Welcome
Licenses: Parking: Off-street
Directions: Into town centre, pass by town hall and
turn right into Hide Hill. Hotel at bottom of hill.
Map ref: Berwick-upon-Tweed 13 F2

RIVERDALE HALL HOTEL

A stone-built 19th-century mansion with a modern wing set in five acres of grounds alongside the North Tyne River.

BELLINGHAM,
NORTHUMBERLAND, NE48 2JT

Tel: 01434 220254 Fax: 01434 220457
Email: iben@riverdalehall.demon.co.uk
Web: www.riverdalehall.demon.co.uk

Beverley, East Riding of Yorkshire

Tickton Grange

★★★★ ⬤⬤

Tickton, Beverley, East Riding of Yorkshire, HU17 9SH
Tel: 01964 543666 Fax: 01964 542556
Email: info@ticktongrange.co.uk
Web: www.ticktongrange.co.uk
Rooms: 17 all ensuite ⬤ ⬤ ⬤
Pricing: Sgl £90 Dbl £120
Dinner available from £25–35
CC: Accepted
Room facilities: ⬤ ⬤ ⬤
Conference: 3 meeting rooms (Thtr 200 max)
Children: Welcome ⬤
Licenses: ⬤ ⬤ Parking: Off-street and free
Directions: 3 miles from Beverley on the A1035.
Map ref: Tickton 11 E3

Eastgate Guest House

◆◆◆◆ ⬤

7 Eastgate, Beverley, East Riding of Yorkshire, HU17 0DR
Tel: 01482 868464 Fax: 01482 871899
Rooms: 16 (7 ensuite) ⬤ ⬤
Pricing: Sgl £25–38 Dbl £40–65
Room facilities: ⬤ ⬤
Children: Welcome Dogs: Welcome
Directions: Very close to train and bus stations, within sight of Beverley Minster.
Map ref: Beverley 11 E3

Bingley, West Yorkshire

Five Rise Locks Hotel & Restaurant

◆◆◆◆ ⬤

Beck Lane, off Park Road, Bingley,
West Yorkshire, BD16 4DD
Tel: 01274 565296 Fax: 01274 568828
Email: info@five-rise-locks.co.uk
Web: www.five-rise-locks.co.uk
Rooms: 9 all ensuite ⬤
Pricing: Sgl £40–50 Dbl £70
Dinner available from £10
CC: Accepted
Room facilities: ⬤ ⬤ ⬤ ⬤
Conference: 1 meeting room (Thtr 20 max)
Children: Welcome
Dogs: Welcome
Licenses: ⬤
Parking: Off-street and free
Directions: At traffic lights in centre of Bingley, turn into Park Road. After ½ mile at crossroads turn left into Beck Lane.
Map ref: Bingley 10 C3

Bishop Auckland, Co. Durham

Greenhead Country House Hotel

◆◆◆◆ ⬤ ⬤

Fir Tree, Crook, Bishop Auckland,
Co. Durham, DL15 8BL
Tel: 01388 763143 Fax: 01388 763143
Email: info@thegreenheadhotel.co.uk
Web: www.thegreenheadhotel.co.uk

The Birbecks offer clean, comfortable accommodation set in acres of open countryside. Great hospitality ensuring guests' comfort. "Richly deserves the Warm Welcome and Sparkling Diamond awards" RAC report 2005.
Rooms: 7 all ensuite ⬤ ⬤
Pricing: Sgl £60–65 Dbl £70–75 Dinner available
CC: Accepted
Room facilities: ⬤ ⬤
Licenses: ⬤
Parking: Off-street and free
Directions: A1 to A68 into Fir Tree. Turn right at pub. Hotel 500 yards on the left.
Map ref: Fir Tree 11 D1

Northeast

Bolton Abbey, North Yorkshire

Devonshire Arms Country House Hotel

★★★★ ♔♔♔ *Premier*

Bolton Abbey, near Skipton, North Yorkshire, BD23 6AJ
Tel: 01756 718111 Fax: 01756 710564
Email: reservations@thedevonshirearms.co.uk
Web: www.devonshirehotels.co.uk
Rooms: 40 all ensuite 🛏 📺 ⊗
Pricing: Sgl £165–380 Dbl £195–380
Dinner available from £58–78 CC: Accepted
Room facilities: 🖵 ☎ ☕
Conference: 4 meeting rooms (Thtr 100 max),
24hr-delegate from £217.35, day-delegate from £64.65
Children: Welcome 🚼 ♨
Dogs: Welcome
Licenses: ♦ ♦♦♦
Leisure: Indoor pool, Gym, Health spa, Beauty salon,
Tennis, Fishing
Parking: Off-street and free
Directions: The Devonshire Arms is situated 5 miles
east of Skipton on the B6160, just 250 yards north of
the junction with the A59.
Map ref: Bolton Abbey 10 C3

Boroughbridge, North Yorkshire

Crown Hotel

★★★

Horsefair, Boroughbridge, North Yorkshire, YO51 9LB
Tel: 01423 322328 Fax: 01423 324512
Email: sales@crownboroughbridge.co.uk
Web: www.crownboroughbridge.co.uk
Rooms: 37 all ensuite 🛏 📺 ⊗
Pricing: Sgl £75–99 Dbl £99–120 Dinner available
CC: Accepted
Room facilities: 🖵 ☎ ☕
Access: ♿
Conference: 3 meeting rooms (Thtr 150 max)
Children: Welcome 🚼 ♨
Licenses: ♦ ♦♦♦
Leisure: Indoor pool, Gym
Parking: Off-street
Directions: Leave A1(M) at Junction 48 and take road
into Boroughbridge. Follow signs into town; hotel is
located on the T-junction. Car park is at rear.
Map ref: Boroughbridge 11 D3

Bradford, West Yorkshire

Cedar Court Hotel

★★★

Mayo Avenue, off Rooley Lane, Bradford,
West Yorkshire, BD5 8HZ
Tel: 01274 406601 Fax: 01274 406600
Email: sales@cedarcourtbradford.co.uk
Web: www.cedarcourthotels.co.uk
Rooms: 131 all ensuite 📺 ⊗
Pricing: Dinner available from £15.95–21.95
CC: Accepted

Room facilities: 🖵 ☎ ☕ 📞
Access: ♿
Conference: 14 meeting rooms (Thtr 800 max),
24hr-delegate from £145, day-delegate from £45
Children: Welcome 🚼 ♨
Dogs: Welcome
Licenses: ♦ ♦♦♦
Leisure: Indoor pool, Gym, Health spa, Beauty salon,
Games room
Parking: Off-street and free
Directions: Leave M62 at Junction 26. Take M606 to
Bradford. Take third exit A6177 Mayo Avenue off
roundabout at end of M606. Take first sharp right.
Map ref: Bradford 11 D3

Midland Hotel

★★★

Forster Square, Bradford, West Yorkshire, BD1 4HU
Tel: 01274 735735 Fax: 01274 720003
Email: info@midland-hotel-bradford.com
Web: www.midland-hotel-bradford.com
Rooms: 90 all ensuite 🛏 📺 ⊗
Pricing: Sgl £75–115 Dbl £85–125
Dinner available from £16.95
CC: Accepted

Room facilities: 🖵 ☎ ☕ 📞
Access: ♿
Conference: 11 meeting rooms (Thtr 450 max),
24hr-delegate from £130, day-delegate from £39
Children: Welcome 🚼 ♨
Dogs: Welcome
Licenses: ♦ ♦♦♦
Parking: Off-street and free
Directions: Hotel is located in city centre next to
Forster Square railway station. Follow City North and
Haworth signs.
Map ref: Bradford 11 D3

Bridlington, East Riding of Yorkshire

Expanse Hotel

★★★

North Marine Drive, Bridlington,
East Riding of Yorkshire, YO15 2LS
Tel: 01262 675347 Fax: 01262 604928
Email: guest@expanse.co.uk
Web: www.expanse.co.uk
Rooms: 48 all ensuite 🛏 ⊗
Dinner available
CC: Accepted
Room facilities: 🖵 ☎ ☕
Access: ♿
Conference: 4 meeting rooms (Thtr 200 max)
Children: Welcome 🚼 ♨
Licenses: ♦ ♦♦♦
Parking: Off-street
Directions: At A165 A614 roundabout take Bridlington
North, at mini roundabout take sign to Sewerby, follow
North Beach parking signs.
Map ref: Bridlington 11 F3

Revelstoke Hotel

1–3 Flamborough Road, Bridlington,
East Riding of Yorkshire, YO15 2HU
Tel: 01262 672362 Fax: 01262 672362
Email: info@revelstokehotel.co.uk
Web: www.revelstokehotel.co.uk
Rooms: 26 all ensuite
Dinner available CC: Accepted
Room facilities:
Conference: 1 meeting room (Thtr 250 max)
Children: Welcome
Licenses:
Leisure: Games room
Parking: Off-street and free
Directions: From town centre head north to
Flamborough, the Revelstoke is approx 400m from the
centre on the left of Flamborough Road.
Map ref: Bridlington 11 F3

Sunflower Lodge

24 Flamborough Road, Bridlington,
East Riding of Yorkshire, YO15 2HX
Tel: 01262 400447 Fax: 01262 400447
Email: rosie4info@sunlodge.wanadoo.co.uk
Web: www.sunflower-lodge.co.uk
Rooms: 4 all ensuite
Pricing: Sgl £35–45 Dbl £50–79
CC: Accepted
Room facilities:
Children: Welcome
Leisure: Children's play-room
Directions: From Howden A164 Bridlington signs to
Leisure World. Sunflower Lodge 500 yards past Trinity
Church on right-hand side.
Map ref: Bridlington 11 F3

The Marina

8 Summerfield Road, South Marine Drive, Bridlington,
East Riding of Yorkshire, YO15 3LF
Tel: 01262 677138
Email: themarina8@hotmail.com
Web: www.bridlingtonhotelsandguesthouses.co.uk/marina
Rooms: 8 (6 ensuite)
Pricing: Sgl £26–30 Dbl £42–50
Dinner available from £9
Room facilities:
Children: Welcome
Dogs: Welcome
Licenses:
Directions: From the Spa Theatre complex heading
south along South Marine Drive, Summerfield Road is
the second turning on the right.
Map ref: Bridlington 11 F3

Blacksmiths Country Cottage Guest House

Driffield Road, Kilham, near Bridlington,
East Riding of Yorkshire, YO25 4SN
Tel: 01262 420624
Email: maxatblacksmiths@ukonline.co.uk
Web: www.smoothhound.co.uk/hotels/blacksmithscottage.html
Seasonal closure: Christmas and New Year
Rooms: 4 all ensuite
Pricing: Sgl £35 Dbl £44–58
Room facilities:
Children: Welcome Dogs: Welcome
Parking: Off-street and free
Directions: A164 from Driffield next right after
Burton Agnes from Driffield, first left after Nafferton
roundabout. Hotel is in the middle of Kilham.
Map ref: Kilham 11 E3

Charleston Guest House

12 Vernon Road, Bridlington,
East Riding of Yorkshire, YO15 2HQ
Tel: 01262 676228 Fax: 01262 676228
Email: charlestonguesthouse@hotmail.com
Rooms: 4 all ensuite
Pricing: Dbl £48 CC: Accepted
Room facilities:
Children: Welcome 4yrs min age
Parking: Off-street and free
Map ref: Bridlington 11 F3

Oakwell Hotel

31-33 Horsforth Avenue, Bridlington,
East Riding of Yorkshire, YO15 3DG
Tel: 01262 401402
Email: oakwellholidays@aol.com
Rooms: 10 all ensuite
Dinner available Room facilities:
Children: Welcome
Licenses: Leisure: Games room
Directions: Follow signs for the Spa Theatre, take the
turning for Horsforth Avenue, off roundabout. Hotel is
situated 200 yards on the left.
Map ref: Bridlington 11 F3

Park View Hotel

9/11 Tennyson Avenue, Bridlington,
East Riding of Yorkshire, YO15 2EU
Tel: 01262 672140
Rooms: 16 (8 ensuite)
Pricing: Sgl £20–22 Dbl £40–48
Dinner available from £8
Room facilities: Children: Welcome
Licenses: Parking: Off-street and free
Directions: From town centre head north. Pass Leisure
World on right side of promenade. Take second left
turning onto Tennyson Avenue.
Map ref: Bridlington 11 F3

Northeast

The Ivanhoe Hotel

 ◆◆◆

63 Cardigan Road, Bridlington,
East Riding of Yorkshire, YO15 3JS
Tel: 01262 675983
Email: ivanhoe-hotel@yahoo.co.uk
Web: www.bridlington-hotel.co.uk
Rooms: 8 all ensuite
Dinner available CC: Accepted
Room facilities:
Children: Welcome
Licenses:
Parking: Off-street and free
Directions: 200 metres from Spa Theatre at junction of
Cardigan Road and Horsforth Avenue opposite church.
Map ref: Bridlington 11 F3

Cleethorpes, Lincolnshire

Kingsway Hotel

 ★★★

Kingsway, Cleethorpes, Lincolnshire, DN35 0AE
Tel: 01472 601122 Fax: 01472 601381
Email: reception@kingsway-hotel.com
Web: www.kingsway-hotel.com
Seasonal closure: 25–26 December
Rooms: 49 all ensuite
Pricing: Sgl £53–82 Dbl £88–97
Dinner available from £18.95 CC: Accepted
Room facilities: Access:
Conference: 1 meeting room (Thtr 22 max),
24hr-delegate from £94, day-delegate from £25
Children: Welcome 5yrs min age
Licenses: Parking: Off-street and free
Directions: From A180 follow signs for Cleethorpes.
Kingsway Hotel is on the seafront near the leisure
centre.
Map ref: Cleethorpes 11 F4

Mallow View

◆◆◆

9/11 Albert Road, Cleethorpes,
Lincolnshire, DN35 8LX
Tel: 01472 691297
Email: info@mallowviewhotel.co.uk
Web: www.cleethorpestourism.co.uk
Rooms: 13 (3 ensuite)
Pricing: Sgl £20 Dbl £45–55
CC: Accepted
Room facilities:
Children: Welcome
Licenses:
Directions: Just off sea front, centre.
Map ref: Cleethorpes 11 F4

Cornhill-on-Tweed, Northumberland

Collingwood Arms Hotel

 ★★

Cornhill-on-Tweed, Northumberland, TD12 4UH
Tel: 01890 882424 Fax: 01890 883644
Web: www.thecollingwoodarmshotel.co.uk
Rooms: 10 all ensuite
Pricing: Sgl £42.50 Dbl £70
Dinner available from £7.95–14.95 CC: Accepted
Room facilities:
Dogs: Welcome Licenses:
Parking: Off-street and free
Map ref: Cornhill-on-Tweed 13 E3

Darlington, Co. Durham

Walworth Castle Hotel

★★★★

Walworth, Darlington, Co. Durham, DL2 2LY
Tel: 01325 485470 Fax: 01325 462257
Email: enquiries@walworthcastle.co.uk
Web: www.walworthcastle.co.uk
Rooms: 34 all ensuite
Pricing: Sgl £75–95 Dbl £95–195
Dinner available from £18.50
CC: Accepted
Room facilities:
Conference: 9 meeting rooms (Thtr 120 max),
24hr-delegate from £92, day-delegate from £32
Children: Welcome Dogs: Welcome
Licenses: Parking: Off-street and free
Directions: Junction 58 off A1(M). Follow A68 towards
Cambridge. For 2 miles, turn left at Dog Pub.
Map ref: Walworth 11 D2

Coachman Hotel

★★

Victoria Road, Darlington, Co. Durham, DL1 5JJ
Tel: 01325 286116 Fax: 01325 382796
Email: enquiries@coachmanhotel.co.uk
Web: www.coachmanhotel.co.uk
Rooms: 29 all ensuite
Dinner available CC: Accepted
Room facilities:
Conference: 2 meeting rooms (Thtr 150 max)
Children: Welcome Dogs: Welcome
Licenses: Parking: Off-street and free
Directions: Follow Victoria Road signs from Darlington
Centre. Hotel is situated on left-hand side at top of
road close to railway station.
Map ref: Darlington 11 D2

Clow Beck House   Little Gem

 ◆◆◆◆◆

Monk End Farm, Croft-on-Tees, Darlington,
Co. Durham, DL2 2SW
Tel: 01325 721075 Fax: 01325 720419
Email: david@clowbeckhouse.co.uk
Web: www.clowbeckhouse.co.uk

Seasonal closure: Christmas to New Year
Rooms: 13 all ensuite
Pricing: Sgl £75 Dbl £110
Dinner available from £15
CC: Accepted
Room facilities: 🖥 ☎ ☕ 🎧
Conference: 1 meeting room (Thtr 20 max),
24hr-delegate from £110, day-delegate from £35
Children: Welcome ⱦ
Licenses: ♦♦♦
Leisure: Fishing
Parking: Off-street and free
Directions: Follow brown tourist signs that are on all roads leading to Croft-on-Tees.
Map ref: Croft-on-Tees 11 D2

Doncaster, South Yorkshire

Regent Hotel

★★★

Regent Square, Doncaster, South Yorkshire, DN1 2DS
Tel: 01302 364180 Fax: 01302 322331
Email: reservations@theregenthotel.co.uk
Web: www.theregenthotel.co.uk

A charming Victorian building overlooking a secluded Regency park. The hotel is ideally situated within easy reach of Doncaster's vibrant town centre and only minutes away from the historic racecourse.
Rooms: 52 all ensuite 🛏 🎧 🚭
Pricing: Sgl £60–95 Dbl £75–100
Dinner available from £12.50–260
CC: Accepted
Room facilities: 🖥 ☎ ☕ 🎧
Access: ♿
Conference: 3 meeting rooms (Thtr 150 max),
24hr-delegate from £125, day-delegate from £25
Children: Welcome ⱦ 🌟
Dogs: Welcome
Licenses: ♦ ♦♦♦
Parking: Off-street and free
Directions: Follow brown signs to racecourse. Turn into Bennetthorpe Road. After ½ mile, hotel is on right.
Map ref: Doncaster 11 D4

Wentbridge House Hotel

★★★★ 🏵🏵

Wentbridge, near Pontefract,
West Yorkshire, WF8 3JJ
Tel: 01977 620444 Fax: 01977 620148
Email: info@wentbridgehouse.co.uk
Web: www.wentbridgehouse.co.uk

Wentbridge House dates from 1700 and is set in 20 acres of the beautiful Went Valley. Individually furnished bedrooms, award winning Fleur de Lys Restaurant, delicious wines and less formal Brasserie.
Rooms: 18 all ensuite 🎧
Pricing: Sgl £80–120 Dbl £105–150
Dinner available from £26–35
CC: Accepted
Room facilities: 🖥 ☎ ☕ 🎧
Conference: 5 meeting rooms (Thtr 130 max),
24hr-delegate from £125, day-delegate from £35
Children: Welcome 🐴 🌟
Licenses: ♦ ♦♦♦
Parking: Off-street and free
Directions: Wentbridge House is ½ mile off the A1 and 4 miles south of the A1/M62 interchange.
Map ref: Wentbridge 11 D4

Canda Lodge

♦♦♦♦

Hampole Balk Lane, Skellow, Doncaster,
South Yorkshire, DN6 8LF
Tel: 01302 724028 Fax: 01302 727999
Web: www.candalodge.co.uk
Rooms: 4 all ensuite 🛏 🎧 🚭
Pricing: Sgl £36 Dbl £45
CC: Accepted
Room facilities: 🖥 ☎ ☕ 🎧
Parking: Off-street and free
Directions: On A1 south take Skellow exit, or northbound take Pontefract exit (A639), then take A1 south.
Map ref: Skellow 11 D4

Northeast

Wesley Guest House

◆◆◆◆

Wesley House, 16 Queen Street, Epworth,
near Doncaster, South Yorkshire, DN9 1HG
Tel: 01427 874512 Fax: 01427 875361
Email: bookings@wesleyguesthouse.co.uk
Web: www.wesleyguesthouse.co.uk
Rooms: 4 all ensuite 🚭
Dinner available
CC: Accepted
Room facilities: ▢ ☕
Children: Welcome 🍴
Leisure: Snooker/billiards
Parking: Off-street and free
Directions: Junction 2 M180 towards Epworth on
A161, at traffic lights in Epworth turn left into market
square, and turn right into Queen Street. Guest house
100 yards on left.
Map ref: Epworth 11 E4

Campanile Hotel
Travel Accommodation

Bawtry Road, Leisure Park, Doncaster,
South Yorkshire, DN4 7PD
Tel: 01302 370770 Fax: 01302 370813
Email: doncaster@envergure.co.uk
Web: www.campanile.com

A lodge-style hotel situated close to the town centre.
Ideal for all people, from business and leisure to
conferences. Restaurant open to non-residents.
Rooms: 50 all ensuite 🚭
Pricing: Sgl £36.50–43.95 Dbl £36.50–43.95
Dinner available from £12.95
CC: Accepted
Room facilities: ▢ ☎ ☕ 🍷
Conference: 1 meeting room (Thtr 25 max),
24hr-delegate from £70, day-delegate from £21.50
Children: Welcome 🍴
Dogs: Welcome
Licenses: ♟
Parking: Off-street and free
Directions: Exit M18 junction 3, follow brown signs for
Racecourse and Leisure Park towards Bawtry Road. At
the next roundabout for Easide, Campanile is behind
the Dome Leisure Centre.
Map ref: Doncaster 11 D4

Durham, Co. Durham
Helme Park Hall Hotel

★★★

Near Fir Tree, Bishop Auckland, Co. Durham, DL13 4NW
Tel: 01388 730970 Fax: 01388 731799
Email: post@helmeparkhotel.co.uk
Web: www.helmeparkhotel.co.uk
Rooms: 13 all ensuite 🐾 🖥 🚭
Pricing: Sgl £54 Dbl £90
Dinner available from £19.95–31.95
CC: Accepted
Room facilities: ▢ ☎ ☕
Conference: 3 meeting rooms (Thtr 220 max),
24hr-delegate from £84.95, day-delegate from £24.95
Children: Welcome 🍴
Dogs: Welcome
Licenses: ⚜ ♟
Parking: Off-street and free
Directions: Located on the A68 1½ miles north of the
intersection with the A689.
Map ref: Helme Park 11 D1
See advert on opposite page

The Old Manse Guest House

◆◆◆

Station Lane, Birtley, Chester-le-Street,
Co. Durham, DH3 1DG
Tel: 0191 410 2486 Fax: 0191 410 2486
Email: marianneporter@supanet.com
Web: www.oldmanseguesthouse.co.uk
Rooms: 8 (4 ensuite) 🐾 🚭
Pricing: Sgl £25 Dbl £40
Room facilities: ▢ ☕
Conference: 1 meeting room
Children: Welcome
Dogs: Welcome
Parking: Off-street and free
Directions: North on A1(M), exit at Angel of The North
(A167). First exit off roundabout, 1 mile to lights then
turn right into Station Lane. Guest house is on the
right.
Map ref: Birtley 11 D1

Gateshead, Tyne & Wear
Rowers Hotel & Restaurant

★★★

St Omers Road, Gateshead, Tyne & Wear, NE11 9EJ
Tel: 0191 460 6481 Fax: 0191 460 9106
Email: enquiries@rowershotel.com
Web: www.rowershotel.com
Seasonal closure: 26 December to 4 January
Rooms: 10 all ensuite
Pricing: Sgl £51.95–53.95 Dbl £61.90–64.90
Dinner available from £7.95–15 CC: Accepted
Room facilities: ▢ ☎ ☕ 🍷
Conference: 1 meeting room (Thtr 20 max)
Children: Welcome Dogs: Welcome
Licenses: ♟
Parking: Off-street and free

Directions: A1 motorway northbound. Take Dunston exit half mile after A184 Newcastle road. Top of sliproad, turn right, straight ahead, turn right into St Omers Road.
Map ref: Gateshead 13 F4

The Bowes Incline Hotel

★★★

Northside, Eighton Banks, Birtley, Co. Durham, DH1 1RF
Tel: 0191 410 2233 Fax: 0191 410 4756
Web: www.bowesinclinehotel.co.uk
Rooms: 15 all ensuite
Pricing: Dinner available from £10 CC: Accepted
Room facilities:
Conference: 2 meeting rooms (Thtr 200 max)
Children: Welcome Ħ Dogs: Assistance dogs only
Licenses: ᵼᵼᵼ Parking: Off-street and free
Directions: From A1(M) travelling north take Tyne Tunnel Road. Past Washington services exit at first junction (A182). First left at roundabout, third exit at next roundabout, first left after 1/2 mile, down country lane.
Map ref: Eighton Banks 11 D1
See advert on this page

The Ravensdene Lodge Hotel

★★

55 Consett Road, Lobley Hill, Gateshead,
Tyne & Wear, NE11 0AN
Tel: 0191 460 4312 Fax: 0191 460 1587
Email: ravensdenehotel@btconnect.com
Web: www.ravensdenelodge.com
Rooms: 37 all ensuite
Pricing: Sgl £40–57 Dbl £55–70
Dinner available from £3–18 CC: Accepted
Room facilities:
Conference: 2 meeting rooms (Thtr 200 max),
24hr-delegate from £75, day-delegate from £12.95
Children: Welcome Ħ
Licenses: ᵼᵼᵼ Leisure: Snooker/billiards
Directions: By road: from A1, take A692, signposted Consett and Whickham. Go left at the mini roundabout. By rail: Newcastle Central Station. By air: Newcastle International.
Map ref: Lobley Hill 11 D1

Hedley Hall

◆◆◆◆◆

Hedley Lane, near Sunniside, Gateshead,
Tyne & Wear, NE16 5EH
Tel: 01207 231835 Fax: 01207 231835
Map ref: Sunniside 11 D1

The Stables

◆◆◆◆◆

South Farm, Lamesley, Gateshead,
Tyne & Wear, NE11 0ET
Tel: 0191 492 1756 Fax: 0191 492 1756
Map ref: Lamesley 11 D1

A1 Summerville Guest House

◆◆◆

33 Orchard Road, Whickham, Newcastle upon Tyne, Tyne & Wear, NE16 4TG
Tel: 0191 488 3388
Web: www.visittyneandwear.com
Rooms: 4 (2 ensuite)
Room facilities:
Children: Welcome
Directions: Take the Metrocentre slip road from A1. Turn left to Market Lane then right up Lambton Avenue, then left on Orchard Road.
Map ref: Whickham 11 D1

Alexandra Guest House

◆◆◆

377 Alexandra Road, Gateshead, Tyne & Wear, NE8 4HY
Tel: 0191 478 1105 Fax: 0191 478 1105
Rooms: 4 (1 ensuite)
Pricing: Sgl £25 Dbl £40
Dinner available from £5
Room facilities:
Children: Welcome
Parking: Off-street and free
Directions: Please contact Alexandra Guest House who will forward directions depending on which direction driving from.
Map ref: Gateshead 13 F4

Gilsland, Cumbria

Bush Nook

◆◆◆◆

Upper Denton, Gilsland, Brampton, Cumbria, CA8 7AF
Tel: 01697 747194 Fax: 01697 747790
Email: info@bushnook.co.uk
Web: www.bushnook.co.uk
Seasonal closure: December to January

Overlooking Hadrian's Wall, Bush Nook provides superb views and accommodation in a comfortable, restful environment where you can relax and enjoy award-winning home fayre and hospitality.
Rooms: 6 all ensuite
Pricing: Sgl £28–35 Dbl £28–35
Dinner available from £15–21
CC: Accepted
Room facilities:
Licenses:
Parking: Off-street and free
Directions: Easy access from A1 or M6. ½ mile off A69 between Brampton and Haltwhistle, signposted Birdoswald Roman Fort, Spadeadam and Bush Nook.
Map ref: Upper Denton 10 B1

Halifax, West Yorkshire

The White Swan Hotel

★★★

Princess Street, Halifax, West Yorkshire, HX1 1TS
Tel: 01422 355541 Fax: 01422 357311
Email: info@white-swan.demon.co.uk
Web: www.whiteswanhalifax.com
Rooms: 42 all ensuite
Pricing: Sgl £60 Dbl £85–105
Dinner available from £15
CC: Accepted
Room facilities:
Access:
Conference: 3 meeting rooms (Thtr 80 max)
Children: Welcome
Licenses:
Leisure: Gym, Sauna
Parking: Off-street and free
Directions: In the town centre underneath the Town Hall. Head for town centre from all motorways. Look for Town Hall clock.
Map ref: Halifax 10 C4

Harrogate, North Yorkshire

Cedar Court Hotel

★★★★

Queen Building, Park Parade, Harrogate, North Yorkshire, HG1 5AH
Tel: 01423 858585 Fax: 01423 504950
Email: cedarcourt@bestwestern.co.uk
Web: www.cedarcourthotels.co.uk
Rooms: 100 all ensuite
Pricing: Sgl £68–145 Dbl £86–170
Dinner available from £20
CC: Accepted
Room facilities:
Access:
Conference: 10 meeting rooms (Thtr 323 max), 24hr-delegate from £145, day-delegate from £44
Children: Welcome
Licenses:
Leisure: Gym
Parking: Off-street and free
Directions: A1 to Wetherby, A661 to Harrogate. M1 or M62 to Leeds, then A61 to Harrogate or via M1/A1 Link.
Map ref: Harrogate 11 D3

The Majestic Hotel

★★★★

Ripon Road, Harrogate, North Yorkshire, HG1 2HU
Tel: 01423 700300 Fax: 01423 502283
Email: majesticreservations@paramount-hotels.co.uk
Web: www.paramount-hotels.co.uk

PARAMOUNT
GROUP OF HOTELS

Set in stunning grounds with a palatial presence, the Majestic Hotel is an ideal base from which to explore the Yorkshire Dales.
Rooms: 156 all ensuite ♨ ⊛
Pricing: Sgl £85–120 Dbl £120
Dinner available from £21
CC: Accepted
Room facilities: ☐ ☎ ☒ ☖
Access: ⏆
Conference: 9 meeting rooms (Thtr 500 max),
24hr-delegate from £180, day-delegate from £60
Children: Welcome ⼉
Dogs: Welcome
Licenses: ⬥ ⚶
Leisure: Indoor pool, Gym, Health spa, Beauty salon, Tennis, Snooker/billiards
Parking: Off-street
Directions: From A1/M1 follow signs for Harrogate or take A61 from Leeds. The hotel is on Ripon Road in Harrogate town centre.
Map ref: Harrogate 11 D3

Boar's Head Hotel

Commended

★★★⊛⊛⊛

Ripley, Harrogate, North Yorkshire, HG3 3AY
Tel: 01423 771888 Fax: 01423 771509
Email: reservations@boarsheadripley.co.uk
Web: www.boarsheadripley.co.uk

Elegantly restored coaching inn provides outstanding food, fine wines, friendly attentive service with comfortable and relaxing surroundings. In historic village location and beautiful Dales countryside.
Rooms: 25 all ensuite ⊛
Pricing: Sgl £105–125 Dbl £125–150
Dinner available from £21.50
CC: Accepted
Room facilities: ☐ ☎ ☒
Conference: 7 meeting rooms,
24hr-delegate from £155, day-delegate from £50
Children: Welcome ⼉ ⻌
Dogs: Welcome
Licenses: ⬥ ⚶
Leisure: Tennis, Fishing
Parking: Off-street and free
Directions: The Boar's Head is 3 miles north of Harrogate on the A61, 10 minutes from the A1.
Map ref: Ripley 11 D3

Grants Hotel & Chimney Pots Bistro

★★★⊛

3–13 Swan Road, Harrogate,
North Yorkshire, HG1 2SS
Tel: 0800 371 343 Fax: 01423 502550
Email: enquiries@grantshotel-harrogate.com
Web: www.grantshotel-harrogate.com
Rooms: 42 all ensuite ♨ ⊠
Pricing: Sgl £75–125 Dbl £100–174
Dinner available from £19.50
CC: Accepted
Room facilities: ☐ ☎ ☒ ☖
Access: ⏆
Conference: 3 meeting rooms (Thtr 70 max),
24hr-delegate from £110, day-delegate from £32
Children: Welcome ⼉ ⻌
Dogs: Welcome
Licenses: ⚶
Parking: Off-street and free
Directions: From south, take A61 past Betty's tea room on left, down hill to traffic lights, and straight across then first left into Swan Road.
Map ref: Harrogate 11 D3

Northeast

HOB GREEN HOTEL

Set in 800 acres of beautiful rolling countryside, a charming and elegant hotel known locally for its excellent restaurant. The main rooms, furnished with antiques, enjoy a stunning view of the valley below.

MARKINGTON, HARROGATE, NORTH YORKSHIRE, HG3 3PJ

Tel: 01423 770031 Fax: 01423 771589
Email: info@hobgreen.com
Web: www.hobgreen.com

Hob Green Hotel

★★★★ ☺☺

Markington, Harrogate, North Yorkshire, HG3 3PJ
Tel: 01423 770031 Fax: 01423 771589
Email: info@hobgreen.com
Web: www.hobgreen.com
Rooms: 12 all ensuite ♨ 🛏 ⊗
Pricing: Dinner available from £26
CC: Accepted
Room facilities: ▢ ☎ ☕ ☏
Conference: 1 meeting room (Thtr 10 max),
24hr-delegate from £115, day-delegate from £35
Children: Welcome ♁ ☕
Dogs: Welcome
Licenses: ⟁ ⅲ
Leisure: Large garden, Croquet lawn
Parking: Off-street and free
Directions: Between Harrogate and Ripon on A61 turn towards Markington at Wormald Green, following brown information road signs.
Map ref: Markington 11 D3
See advert on this page

The Cairn Hotel

★★★

13 Ripon Road, Harrogate, North Yorkshire, HG1 2JD
Tel: 01423 504005 Fax: 01423 500056
Email: cairnmanager@strathmorehotels.com
Web: www.strathmorehotels.com
Rooms: 135 all ensuite ♨ 🛏 ⊗

Pricing: Sgl £75–105 Dbl £85–150
Dinner available from £17.95–29
CC: Accepted
Room facilities: ▢ ☎ ☕ ☏
Access: ⅲ
Conference: 7 meeting rooms (Thtr 450 max),
24hr-delegate from £135, day-delegate from £35
Children: Welcome ♁
Dogs: Assistance dogs only
Licenses: ⟁ ⅲ
Parking: Off-street and free
Directions: Cairn Hotel is on A61 heading out of Harrogate town centre towards Ripon. On top of hill on left-hand side.
Map ref: Harrogate 11 D3

Ascot House Hotel

★★★ ☺

53 Kings Road, Harrogate, North Yorkshire, HG1 5HJ
Tel: 01423 531005 Fax: 01423 503523
Email: admin@ascothouse.com
Web: www.ascothouse.com
Seasonal closure: 28 December to 8 January and 29 January to 12 February
Rooms: 19 all ensuite ♨ 🛏 ⊗
Pricing: Sgl £62–72 Dbl £91–111
Dinner available from £18.95
CC: Accepted
Room facilities: ▢ ☎ ☕ ☏
Conference: 3 meeting rooms (Thtr 80 max),
24hr-delegate from £120, day-delegate from £33.50
Children: Welcome ♁ ☕
Dogs: Welcome
Licenses: ⟁ ⅲ
Parking: Off-street and free
Directions: Follow signs for town centre and conference/exhibition centre. Ascot House Hotel is on left as you drive up Kings Road, about 500 yards from conference centre.
Map ref: Harrogate 11 D3

Ashley House Hotel

♦♦♦♦ ✕

36–40 Franklin Road, Harrogate, North Yorkshire, HG1 5EE
Tel: 01423 507474 Fax: 01423 560858
Email: ron@ashleyhousehotel.com
Web: www.ashleyhousehotel.com
Rooms: 18 all ensuite ⊗
Pricing: Sgl £47.50–75 Dbl £75–89.50
CC: Accepted
Room facilities: ▢ ☎ ☕
Children: Welcome ☕
Licenses: ⅲ
Parking: Off-street and free
Directions: Opposite Harrogate International Centre, turn into Strawberry Dale Avenue, left into Franklin Road; hotel 200 yards up on the right.
Map ref: Harrogate 11 D3

Shannon Court Hotel

◆◆◆◆

65 Dragon Avenue, Harrogate,
North Yorkshire, HG1 5DS
Tel: 01423 509858 Fax: 01423 530606
Email: shannon@courthotel.freeserve.co.uk
Web: www.shannon-court.com
Rooms: 8 all ensuite 🐾 🚭
Pricing: Sgl £41–54 Dbl £64–70
CC: Accepted
Room facilities: 🖳 🗊
Children: Welcome 5yrs min age
Licenses: ⛶⛶⛶
Parking: Off-street and free
Directions: Five minutes from town centre in High
Harrogate, off the Skipton Road (A59).
Map ref: Harrogate 11 D3

Azalea Court Hotel

◆◆◆

56/58 Kings Road, Harrogate,
North Yorkshire, HG1 5JR
Tel: 01423 560424 Fax: 01423 505542
Rooms: 10 all ensuite 🚭
Dinner available
CC: Accepted
Room facilities: 🖳 🗊
Children: Welcome 🐾
Licenses: ⛶⛶⛶
Parking: Off-street and free
Directions: Follow the signs for Harrogate Town
Centre. Turn into Kings Road, the Azalea Court Hotel is
opposite the conference centre.
Map ref: Harrogate 11 D3

Hartlepool, Teeside

Grand Hotel

★★★

Swainson Street, Hartlepool, Teeside, TS24 8AA
Tel: 01429 266345 Fax: 01429 265217
Rooms: 47 all ensuite 🚭
Dinner available
CC: Accepted
Room facilities: 🖳 ☎ 🗊
Access: ⏐↑
Conference: 6 meeting rooms (Thtr 250 max)
Children: Welcome ⛩
Licenses: ⟁ ⛶⛶⛶
Leisure: Indoor pool, Gym
Parking: Off-street and free
Directions: The Grand Hotel is situated in the town
centre opposite the Middleton Grange Shopping
Centre in Victoria Road.
Map ref: Hartlepool 11 D1

Haworth, West Yorkshire

Woodlands Grange

◆◆◆

Belle Isle, Haworth, West Yorkshire, BD22 8PB
Tel: 01535 646814 Fax: 01535 648282
Email: woodlandsgrange@hotmail.com
Web: www.woodlandsgrange.com

Secluded detatched residence in Haworth village,
overlooking Worth Valley Preserved Steam Railway. All
rooms ensuite and large car park. Owners Caron and
Paul invite you to come and enjoy Yorkshire hospitality.
Rooms: 6 all ensuite 🐾 🚭
Pricing: Sgl £30 Dbl £50 CC: Accepted
Room facilities: 🖳 🗊
Children: Welcome
Dogs: Welcome
Licenses: ⛶⛶⛶
Parking: Off-street and free
Directions: 500 yards past railway station, drive over
bridge and turn sharp left. Woodlands Grange 100
yards along the private tarmac road.
Map ref: Haworth 10 C3

Helmsley, North Yorkshire

Feversham Arms Hotel

★★★★ 🏆🏆

1-8 High Street, Helmsley, North Yorkshire, YO62 5AG
Tel: 01439 770766 Fax: 01439 770346
Email: info@fevershamarmshotel.com
Web: www.fevershamarmshotel.com
Rooms: 19 all ensuite 🐾 🎽 🚭
Pricing: Sgl £130–200 Dbl £140–210
Dinner available from £40
CC: Accepted
Room facilities: 🖳 ☎
Conference: 1 meeting room (Thtr 30 max),
24hr-delegate from £170, day-delegate from £45
Children: Welcome ⛩ 🐾
Dogs: Welcome
Licenses: ⟁ ⛶⛶⛶
Leisure: Outdoor pool, Tennis
Parking: Off-street and free
Directions: From A1, take A168 dual carriageway to
Thirsk, then A170. Or, at A1 junction with A64, take
A64 to York North bypass, then B1363.
Map ref: York 11 D3
See advert on following page

Northeast

FEVERSHAM ARMS HOTEL

Luxury 19-bedroomed hideaway hotel with an excellent conservatory restaurant, chic design, outdoor swimming pool, tennis court, open fires and welcoming service. Nestling on the edge of the North Yorkshire Moors and close to York. Each bedroom has its own character and décor, B & O TV with integral DVD/CD. Bathrooms pamper you with Molton Brown toiletries and big, soft bathrobes.

1 HIGH STREET, HELMSLEY,
NORTH YORKSHIRE YO62 5AG

Tel: 01439 770766   Fax: 01439 770346
Email: info@fevershamarmshotel.com
Web: www.fevershamarmshotel.com

Pheasant Hotel

★★★

Harome, Helmsley, North Yorkshire, YO62 5JG
Tel: 01439 771241 Fax: 01439 771744
Seasonal closure: December to February
Rooms: 12 all ensuite
Pricing: Sgl £50–55 Dbl £100–110
Dinner available from £23 CC: Accepted
Room facilities: 🖥 ☎ 🍵
Children: Welcome 5yrs min age Dogs: Welcome
Licenses: 👬 Leisure: Indoor pool
Parking: Off-street and free
Directions: Leave Helmsley on A170 in direction of Scarborough, after ¼ mile, turn right for Harome, hotel opposite church.
Map ref: Harome 11 E2

The big sleep

As part of our comprehensive inspection process, RAC Inspectors investigate the comfort of the beds.

Hexham, Northumberland

Langley Castle Hotel

★★★★ ♜♜♜

Langley-on-Tyne, Hexham, Northumberland, NE47 5LU
Tel: 01434 688888 Fax: 01434 684019
Email: manager@langleycastle.co.uk
Web: www.langleycastle.co.uk

Genuine 14th century castle, set in woodland estate. All rooms with private facilities, four-poster beds, window seats set into 7ft thick walls. Magnificent drawing room and intimate restaurant.
Rooms: 18 all ensuite 🛏 🖼
Pricing: Sgl £109–175 Dbl £125–239
Dinner available from £32.50 CC: Accepted
Room facilities: 🖥 ☎ 🍵 🕯
Access: 👖
Conference: 2 meeting rooms (Thtr 100 max), 24hr-delegate from £175, day-delegate from £45
Children: Welcome 🚻 🌡
Licenses: ⚓ 👬
Parking: Off-street and free
Directions: By car, follow A69 to Haydon Bridge, then 2 miles south on A686 to Langley Castle.
Map ref: Langley-on-Tyne 10 C1

Huddersfield, West Yorkshire

Cedar Court Hotel

★★★★

Ainley Top, Huddersfield, West Yorkshire, HD3 3RH
Tel: 01422 314000 Fax: 01422 314050
Email: reservations@cedar-court-huddersfield.co.uk
Web: www.cedarcourthotels.co.uk
Rooms: 114 all ensuite 🖼 🛁
Pricing: Sgl £69–99 Dbl £79-109
Dinner available from £19.95–22.95 CC: Accepted
Room facilities: 🖥 ☎ 🍵 🕯 Access: 👖
Conference: 16 meeting rooms (Thtr 450 max)
Children: Welcome 🚻 Dogs: Welcome
Licenses: ⚓ 👬
Leisure: Indoor pool, Gym, Health spa
Parking: Off-street and free
Directions: M62 motorway to junction 24 Huddersfield Halifax then 280 metres to the roundabout, then first left.
Map ref: Ainley Top 11 D4

Huddersfield Central Lodge

◆◆◆◆

Beast Market, Off Load Street, Huddersfield,
West Yorkshire, HD1 1QF
Tel: 01484 515551 Fax: 01484 432349
Email: enquiries@centrallodge.com
Web: www.centrallodge.com

Family owned, free Sky channels, free secure parking.
Bar in refurbished lounge area. Large, newly
constructed conservatory. Within five minutes of
Kingsgate shopping centre, theatre, university, bus and
train stations.
Rooms: 23 all ensuite ♨ ⊛
Pricing: Sgl £45 Dbl £62
Dinner available from £11
CC: Accepted
Room facilities: ⬚ ☎ ⊡ ☍

Children: Welcome
Dogs: Welcome
Licenses: ♟♟♟
Parking: Off-street and free
Directions: On ring road follow signs for Beast Market.
Situated off Lord Street below new Methodist Mission.
Map ref: Huddersfield 11 D4

Hull, East Riding of Yorkshire

Portland Hotel

★★★

Paragon Street, Hull, East Riding of Yorkshire, HU1 3JP
Tel: 01482 326462 Fax: 01482 213460
Email: info@portland-hotel.co.uk
Web: www.portland-hull.com
Rooms: 126 all ensuite ♨ ⊛
Pricing: Sgl £79.50–162 Dbl £159–324
Dinner available from £18.90 CC: Accepted
Room facilities: ⬚ ☎ ⊡ ☍ Access: ♿
Conference: 6 meeting rooms (Thtr 220 max),
24hr-delegate from £135, day-delegate from £34.50
Children: Welcome ♨ ⊛ Dogs: Welcome
Licenses: ♟♟♟
Parking: Off-street and free
Directions: M62 leading to City Centre, signposted
Paragon Street Area. Two minutes walk from railway
station and next to City Hall.
Map ref: Hull 11 E3
See advert on this page

Northeast

Quality Hotel Royal Hull

★★★

170 Ferensway, Hull, East Riding of Yorkshire, HU1 3UF
Tel: 01482 325087 Fax: 01482 323172
Email: gm@hotels-hull.co.uk
Web: www.choicehotelseurope.com
Rooms: 155 all ensuite 🐾 ⊗
Pricing: Dinner available from £16.95
CC: Accepted
Room facilities: 🖥 ☎ ☕ 📞
Access:
Conference: 7 meeting rooms (Thtr 400 max),
24hr-delegate from £120, day-delegate from £31
Children: Welcome ﬁ Dogs: Welcome
Licenses: 🍷 🎽
Leisure: Indoor pool, Gym, Health spa
Parking: Off-street and free
Directions: M62 onto A63 into Hull. Turn left at lights,
after the flyover follow signs for station. Hotel is
adjacent.
Map ref: Hull 11 E3

Stop Inn Hull

★★

11 Anlaby Road, Hull, East Riding of Yorkshire, HU1 2PJ
Tel: 01482 323299 Fax: 01482 214730
Email: hull@stop-inns.com
Web: www.stop-inns.com
Rooms: 59 all ensuite 🐾 📠 ⊗
Pricing: Sgl £45.95–58.50 Dbl £51.95–64.50
Dinner available from £12 CC: Accepted
Room facilities: 🖥 ☎ ☕ 📞 Access:
Conference: 3 meeting rooms (Thtr 140 max),
24hr-delegate from £79.50, day-delegate from £24
Children: Welcome ﬁ
Dogs: Welcome
Licenses: 🎽
Leisure: Indoor pool, Gym, Games room
Parking: Off-street and free
Directions: Follow the signs to Hull railway station, hotel
is on the left, 250 yards before the station.
Map ref: Hull 11 E3

Redcliffe House

◆◆◆◆

Redcliff Road, Hessle,
East Riding of Yorkshire, HU13 0HA
Tel: 01482 648655
Web: www.redcliffehouse.co.uk
Rooms: 7 all ensuite 🐾 📠 ⊗
Pricing: Sgl £40–50 Dbl £60–70 CC: Accepted
Room facilities: 🖥 ☕
Children: Welcome 🍦
Dogs: Welcome
Licenses: 🎽
Leisure: Snooker/billiards
Parking: Off-street and free
Directions: A63 Humber Bridge. Exit signposted Hessle,
straight over slip road. First left Livingstone Road. First
house left-hand side past Rugby Club.
Map ref: Hessle 11 E4

Campanile Hotel
Travel Accommodation

Beverley Road, Freetown Way, Hull,
East Riding of Yorkshire, HU2 9AN
Tel: 01482 325530 Fax: 01482 587538
Email: hull@campanile-hotels.com
Web: www.campanile.com

The hotel is situated in the city centre of Hull. Facilities
include a French bistro restaurant and conference
facilities. Good access for the disabled.
Rooms: 47 all ensuite 📠 ⊗
Pricing: Sgl £39.95–43.95 Dbl £39.95–43.95
Dinner available from £4.95–11.95
CC: Accepted
Room facilities: 🖥 ☎ ☕ 📞
Conference: 1 meeting room (Thtr 40 max),
24hr-delegate from £68, day-delegate from £21.50
Children: Welcome ﬁ
Dogs: Welcome
Licenses: 🎽
Parking: Off-street and free
Directions: From M62, A63 into Hull, passing Humber
Bridge. Pass on a flyover, follow signs for city centre
and train station. At junction of Freetown Way and
Beverley Road, straight across lights and turn right.
Map ref: Hull 11 E3

Rombalds Hotel & Restaurant

★★★★ ℞℞

West View, Wells Road, Ilkley, West Yorkshire, LS29 9JG
Tel: 01943 603201 Fax: 01943 816586
Email: reception@rombalds.demon.co.uk
Web: www.rombalds.co.uk
Rooms: 15 all ensuite 🐾 📠 ⊗
Dinner available
CC: Accepted
Room facilities: 🖥 ☎ ☕ 📞
Conference: 2 meeting rooms (Thtr 70 max)
Children: Welcome ﬁ 🍦 Dogs: Welcome
Licenses: 🍷 🎽
Parking: Off-street and free
Directions: On Leeds/Skipton A65, left at third main
lights, follow signs for Ilkley Moor. Hotel 600 yards on
left.
Map ref: Ilkley 10 C3

Ingleton, North Yorkshire

Springfield Country House Hotel

◆◆◆

Main Street, Ingleton, North Yorkshire, LA6 3HJ
Tel: 01524 241280 Fax: 01524 241280
Web: www.yorkshire.dales.accommodation.co.uk
Seasonal closure: Christmas

Detached Victorian villa, large garden. Patio down to River Greta, with home-grown vegetables in season. Home cooking. Private fishing, car park. Pets welcome.
Rooms: 5 all ensuite
Pricing: Sgl £31–34 Dbl £48–52
Dinner available from £14
CC: Accepted
Room facilities: ☐ ☐
Children: Welcome
Dogs: Welcome
Leisure: Fishing
Parking: Off-street and free
Directions: On A65(T), 11 miles north-west of Settle. Springfield is 100 yards from A65(T).
Map ref: Ingleton 10 B3

Keighley, West Yorkshire

Dalesgate Hotel

★★

406 Skipton Road, Utley, Keighley,
West Yorkshire, BD20 6HP
Tel: 01535 664930 Fax: 01535 611253
Email: stephen.e.atha@btinternet.com
Web: www.dalesgate.co.uk
Rooms: 20 all ensuite
Pricing: Sgl £40–45 Dbl £55–65
Dinner available from £13.95
CC: Accepted
Room facilities: ☐ ☎ ☐
Children: Welcome
Dogs: Welcome
Licenses: ♦♦♦
Parking: Off-street and free
Directions: From Keighley town centre follow the signs for Skipton. At roundabout go straight across. The hotel is in the village of Utley, 1½ miles on right on Skipton Road.
Map ref: Utley 10 C3

Kielder Water, Northumberland

The Blackcock Inn

◆◆◆

Falstone, Kielder Water, Northumberland, NE48 1AA
Tel: 01434 240200 Fax: 01434 240200
Email: blackcock@falstone.fsbusiness.co.uk
Web: www.theblackcockinn.com
Rooms: 4 all ensuite
Dinner available CC: Accepted
Room facilities: ☐ ☐
Conference: 1 meeting room
Children: Welcome Dogs: Welcome
Licenses: ♦♦♦
Leisure: Games room
Parking: Off-street
Directions: Falstone can be accessed off the C200 road from Bellingham which can be accessed off the A68 or the B6320.
Map ref: Falstone 13 E4

Knaresborough, North Yorkshire

Abbey Garth

◆◆◆◆

28 Abbey Road, Knaresborough,
North Yorkshire, HG5 8HX
Tel: 01423 862043/07976 274458
Email: ianandcarolyn@abbeygarth.com
Web: www.geocities.com/abbey_garth
Rooms: 2 (1 ensuite)
Pricing: Sgl £40–45 Dbl £55–60
Room facilities: ☐ ☐ Children: Welcome
Leisure: Fishing
Parking: Off-street and free
Directions: A1(M) follow A59 to Knaresborough. Third traffic lights, turn left to river, left at Half Moon, Riverside House on left-hand side.
Map ref: Knaresborough 11 D3

Leeds, West Yorkshire

Queens Hotel

★★★★

City Square, Leeds, West Yorkshire, LS1 1PL
Tel: 0113 243 1323 Fax: 0113 242 5154
Email: queensreservations@qhotels.co.uk
Web: www.qhotels.co.uk
Rooms: 217 all ensuite
Pricing: Sgl £45–262.75 Dbl £70–262.75
Dinner available from £19.50 CC: Accepted
Room facilities: ☐ ☎ ☐ ☼ Access: ♿
Conference: 16 meeting rooms (Thtr 600 max), 24hr-delegate from £165, day-delegate from £65
Children: Welcome Dogs: Welcome
Licenses: ♦♦♦
Leisure: Off site leisure club free to residents
Parking: Off-street
Directions: Exit M621 J3 and follow signs for city centre. Hotel adjacent to railway station in city centre.
Map ref: Leeds 11 D3

Thorpe Park Hotel & Spa

★★★★★ ♖♖   *Commended*

1150 Century Way, Thorpe Park, Leeds,
West Yorkshire, LS15 8ZB
Tel: 0113 264 1000 Fax: 0113 264 1010
Email: thorpepark@shirehotels.com
Web: www.shirehotels.com

SHIRE
HOTELS

Great location for Leeds, York and the Yorkshire Dales,
a modern hotel with stunning design features. First-
class spa with treatments and activity studios.
Spacious lounges for relaxation. Good reputation for
home-cooked food featuring local/regional produce.
Rooms: 123 all ensuite 🛏 Ⓢ
Pricing: Sgl £92–155 Dbl £134–175
Dinner available CC: Accepted
Room facilities: 🖵 ☎ 🍵 ✳ Access: ⌊↑⌋
Conference: 14 meeting rooms (Thtr 200 max),
24hr-delegate from £180, day-delegate from £65
Children: Welcome ♁ Licenses: ◈ ♟
Leisure: Indoor pool, Gym, Health spa, Beauty salon
Parking: Off-street and free
Directions: At J46 of M1, 6 miles east of Leeds city
centre. Map ref: Leeds 11 D3

Chevin Country Park Hotel

★★★ ♖

Yorkgate, Otley, Leeds, West Yorkshire, LS21 3NU
Tel: 01943 467818 Fax: 01943 850335
Email: reception@chevinhotel.com
Web: www.chevinhotel.com
Rooms: 49 all ensuite ⌘ 🛏 Ⓢ
Pricing: Sgl £99–135 Dbl £110–210

Dinner available from £22.50 CC: Accepted
Room facilities: 🖵 ☎ 🍵 ⌇
Conference: 4 meeting rooms (Thtr 150 max)
Children: Welcome ♁ Dogs: Welcome Licenses: ◈ ♟
Leisure: Indoor pool, Gym, Beauty salon,
Tennis, Fishing Parking: Off-street and free
Directions: On a quiet rural road just off the A658 Leeds/
Bradford airport to Harrogate road, 2 miles north of airport.
Map ref: Yorkgate 11 D3
See advert on this page

Golden Lion Hotel

★★★

2 Lower Briggate, Leeds, West Yorkshire, LS1 4AE
Tel: 01132 436454 Fax: 01132 434241
Email: info@goldenlion-hotel-leeds.com
Web: www.thegoldenlion-leeds.co.uk
Rooms: 89 all ensuite Ⓢ
Pricing: Sgl £60.50–109.50 Dbl £72–143
Dinner available from £7.50–28 CC: Accepted
Room facilities: 🖵 ☎ 🍵 ⌇ Access: ⌊↑⌋
Conference: 3 meeting rooms (Thtr 120 max),
24hr-delegate from £140, day-delegate from £39
Children: Welcome ♁ ⌯ Dogs: Welcome
Licenses:
Parking: Off-street
Directions: Half mile from Junction 3 of M621, towards
city centre. On loop road Junction 16. Five minutes
walk from station.
Map ref: Leeds 11 D3

Jurys Inn Leeds

★★★

Kendell Street, Brewery Place, Brewery Wharf, Leeds,
West Yorkshire, LS10 1NE
Tel: 0113 283 8800 Fax: 0113 283 8888
Email: bookings@jurysdoyle.com
Web: www.jurysinns.com
Seasonal closure: 24-26 December

JURYS DOYLE
HOTELS

Rooms: 248 all ensuite 🛁 ♨
Pricing: Sgl £108.50 Dbl £108.50
Dinner available from £17 CC: Accepted
Room facilities: 📺 ☎ ☕ 📞 ❄ Access: ♿
Conference: 4 meeting rooms (Thtr 60 max),
24hr-delegate from £135, day-delegate from £37
Children: Welcome 🍴 Licenses: ⛺
Directions: Exit M1 onto M621. Left onto A61 Hunslet
Road. Follow signs to Tetleys Brewery Wharf. Hotel is
opposite brewery.
Map ref: Leeds 11 D3

Milford Hotel

★★★

Great North Road, Peckfield, Leeds,
West Yorkshire, LS25 5LQ
Tel: 01977 681800 Fax: 01977 681245
Email: enquiries@mlh.co.uk
Web: www.mlh.co.uk
Rooms: 47 all ensuite 🛁 ♨
Pricing: Sgl £75 Dbl £75
Dinner available from £16.50 CC: Accepted
Room facilities: 📺 ☎ ☕ 📞 ❄
Conference: 3 meeting rooms (Thtr 70 max),
24hr-delegate from £125, day-delegate from £35
Children: Welcome 🍴 Dogs: Welcome
Licenses: ⛺ Parking: Off-street and free
Directions: Situated on the A63 1½ miles west of the
A1(M) J42, 5 miles east of J46 of M1.
Map ref: Peckfield 11 D3

Sleep Inn
Travel Accommodation

97 Vicar Lane, Leeds, West Yorkshire, LS1 6PJ
Tel: 0113 243 6810 Fax: 0113 243 1229
Email: enquiries@hotels-leeds.com
Web: www.hotels-leeds.com
Rooms: 132 all ensuite ♨
Pricing: Sgl £55–60 Dbl £70–75
Dinner available from £7.50 CC: Accepted
Room facilities: 📺 ☎ ☕ 📞 ❄
Access: ♿
Conference: 1 meeting room (Thtr 20 max),
24hr-delegate from £85, day-delegate from £20
Children: Welcome
Licenses: ⛺
Directions: Follow signs for cityloop until junction 8,
leave at junction 8 and bear right onto Merrion Street.
Take next right and Sleep Inn is 100 yards on the right.
Map ref: Leeds 11 D3

Leeming Bar, North Yorkshire

The Lodge at Leeming Bar
Travel Accommodation

The Great North Road, Leeming Bar, Bedale,
North Yorkshire, DL8 1DT
Tel: 01677 422122 Fax: 01677 424507
Email: thelodgeatleemingbar@btinternet.com
Web: www.leemingbar.com
Rooms: 39 all ensuite 🛁 ♨
Pricing: Sgl £65–80 Dbl £75–95
Dinner available from £20 CC: Accepted
Room facilities: 📺 ☎ ☕
Conference: 4 meeting rooms (Thtr 150 max),
24hr-delegate from £23, day-delegate from £22
Children: Welcome 🍴 🎠 Dogs: Welcome
Licenses: ⛺
Parking: Off-street and free
Directions: Just off the A1 at the Bedale/Northallerton
junction, 10 miles south of Scotch Corner.
Map ref: Bedale 11 D2

Levisham, North Yorkshire

Moorlands Country House Hotel   `Little Gem`

◆◆◆◆◆ ⓡ✕☒ ♺

Pickering, Levisham, North Yorkshire, YO18 7NL
Tel: 01751 460229 Fax: 01751 460470
Email: ronaldoleonardo@aol.com
Web: www.moorlandslevisham.co.uk
Seasonal closure: December to March

A beautifully-restored Victorian country house in four
acres of wooded gardens with stunning views across
the valley. Ideal base for walking, cycling or touring the
beautiful North York Moors.
Rooms: 7 all ensuite 🚿 ♨
Pricing: Sgl £50–65 Dbl £100–130
Dinner available from £25–30
CC: Accepted
Room facilities: 📺 ☕
Children: Welcome 15yrs min age
Licenses: ⛺
Parking: Off-street and free
Directions: A169 from Pickering, turn left. Go through
Lockton into Levisham. First house on the right.
Map ref: Levisham 11 E2
See advert on following page

Moorlands Country House Hotel

A beautifully-restored Victorian country house in four acres of wooded gardens with stunning views across the valley. Ideal base for walking, cycling or touring the beautiful North York Moors, York, Scarborough, Whitby, or just relaxing. All rooms individually designed for your comfort.
A warm welcome awaits.

Pickering, Levisham, North Yorkshire, YO18 7NL
Tel: 01751 460229 Fax: 01751 460470
Email: ronaldoleonardo@aol.com
Web: www.moorlandslevisham.co.uk

Leyburn, North Yorkshire

Golden Lion Hotel
★

Market Square, Leyburn, North Yorkshire, DL8 5AS
Tel: 01969 622161 Fax: 01969 623836
Email: annegoldenlion@aol.com
Web: www.thegoldenlion.co.uk
Seasonal closure: 25–26 December
Rooms: 15 all ensuite
Pricing: Sgl £28–36 Dbl £56–72
Dinner available from £6.95–16 CC: Accepted
Room facilities: 🖵 ☎ 🍵 Access: |↓↑
Children: Welcome ⅄ ⅍ Dogs: Welcome
Licenses: ⅍⅍ Parking: Off-street
Directions: 8 miles from either Leeming or Scotch Corner exits from A1, centrally located in town centre. A684 main road through the Dales.
Map ref: Leyburn 10 C2

Malham, North Yorkshire

Buck Inn
★★

Malham, Skipton, North Yorkshire, BD23 4DA
Tel: 01729 830317 Fax: 01729 830670
Email: thebuckinn@uk.online.co.uk
Web: www.buckinnmalham.co.uk
Rooms: 10 all ensuite
Pricing: Sgl £37.50–50 Dbl £65–90

Dinner available CC: Accepted
Room facilities: 🖵 ☎ 🍵
Conference: 1 meeting room (Thtr 40 max)
Children: Welcome ⅄ ⅍ Licenses: ◇ ⅍⅍
Leisure: Games room Parking: Off-street and free
Directions: Take A65 Skipton–Settle. Turn right in Gargrove, signposted Malham. Follow this main road for seven miles to Malham. The Buck Inn is in the village centre.
Map ref: Skipton 10 C3

Malton, North Yorkshire

Green Man Hotel
★★

15 Market Street, Malton, North Yorkshire, YO17 7LY
Tel: 01653 600370 Fax: 01653 696006
Email: greenman@englishrosehotels.co.uk
Web: www.englishrosehotels.co.uk

Rooms: 24 all ensuite
Pricing: Sgl £40–65 Dbl £70
Dinner available from £16.95 CC: Accepted
Room facilities: 🖵 ☎
Conference: 2 meeting rooms (Thtr 150 max), 24hr-delegate from £85, day-delegate from £25
Children: Welcome ⅄ ⅍ Licenses: ⅍⅍
Leisure: Games room Parking: Off-street
Directions: Follow A64 from A1/M1. Leave at exit for Malton at start of bypass. Turn first left after passing Talbot Hotel. Map ref: Malton 11 E3

Talbot Hotel
★★

Yorkersgate, Malton, North Yorkshire, YO17 7AJ
Tel: 01653 694031 Fax: 01653 693355
Email: talbothotel@englishrosehotels.co.uk
Web: www.englishrosehotels.co.uk

A classic and comfortable inn, close to local attractions, which include Castle Howard and Eden

Camp. A warm welcome awaits at this hotel with its ample free parking.

Rooms: 31 all ensuite
Pricing: Sgl £35–55 Dbl £75
Dinner available from £16.95 CC: Accepted
Room facilities: □ ☎ ⌂
Conference: 5 meeting rooms (Thtr 70 max), 24hr-delegate from £85, day-delegate from £25
Children: Welcome 🕇 🌡
Dogs: Assistance dogs only
Licenses: ♦♦♦
Parking: Off-street and free
Directions: From A64 follow road into Malton: the hotel is on the right. Map ref: Malton 11 E3

Morpeth, Northumberland

The Cook and Barker Inn
♦♦♦♦🍷

Newton-on-the-Moor, Felton, Morpeth, Northumberland, NE65 9JY
Tel: 01665 575234 Fax: 01665 575234
Web: www.cookandbarkerinn.co.uk
Rooms: 19 all ensuite
Pricing: Sgl £47 Dbl £70
Dinner available from £25–32
CC: Accepted
Room facilities: □ ⌂
Conference: 1 meeting room (Thtr 25 max), 24hr-delegate from £100, day-delegate from £50
Children: Welcome 🕇
Licenses: ♦♦♦
Parking: Off-street and free
Directions: Heading north on the A1 from Morpeth, travel about 9 miles. The A1 merges back into dual carriageway; look for signs for Newton-on-the-Moor. Map ref: Newton-on-the-Moor 13 F3

Muker, North Yorkshire

Muker Tea Shop
♦♦♦♦🍷

The Village Store and Tea Shop, Muker, Richmond, North Yorkshire, DL11 6QG
Tel: 01748 886409
Email: teashop@mukervillage.co.uk
Web: www.mukervillage.co.uk
Seasonal closure: November
Rooms: 2 (1 ensuite) ⊗
Pricing: Sgl £20–35 Dbl £50
Dinner available from £7.50
CC: Accepted
Room facilities: □ ⌂ ⌂
Children: Welcome 🕇
Licenses: ♦♦♦
Parking: Off-street and free
Directions: Muker Tea Shop is situated on the B6270, 20 miles west of Richmond or 20 miles east of the M6, Sedburgh junction.
Map ref: Muker 10 C2

Newcastle upon Tyne, Tyne & Wear

Copthorne Hotel Newcastle
★★★★

The Close, Quayside, Newcastle upon Tyne, Tyne & Wear, NE1 3RT
Tel: 0191 222 0333 Fax: 0191 230 1111
Email: sales.newcastle@mill-cop.com
Web: www.copthornehotels.com

MILLENNIUM
HOTELS and RESORTS

MILLENNIUM HOTELS
COPTHORNE HOTELS

Situated on the Quayside, the hotel has clear views across the River Tyne where you can take a walk down to the Gateshead Millennium Bridge. Weekend rates are also available.
Rooms: 156 all ensuite ⊗
Pricing: Sgl £124–221.90 Dbl £124–221.90
Dinner available from £21
CC: Accepted
Room facilities: □ ☎ ⌂ ⌂
Access: ⌂⌂
Conference: 9 meeting rooms (Thtr 200 max), 24hr-delegate from £185, day-delegate from £50
Children: Welcome 🕇
Dogs: Welcome
Licenses: ⌂ ♦♦♦
Leisure: Indoor pool, Gym, Beauty salon, Sauna, Spa bath, Steam room
Parking: Off-street and free
Directions: From A1, follow signs for city centre (A184 and A189). Over the bridge, sharp left, left at mini roundabout, then B1600.
Map ref: Newcastle upon Tyne 13 F4

Are the bells ringing?

Getting married? Congratulations! Look for the wedding bells symbol which shows hotels licensed for civil ceremonies.

THE VERMONT HOTEL

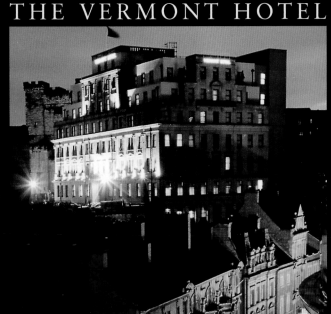

"An independently owned, glamorous Manhattan-style 1930s tower with traditional and contemporary plush interiors" is how Conde Nast Traveller describes The Vermont in Newcastle.

In an unrivalled setting next to the Castle, overlooking the Tyne and Millennium Bridges and walking distance to the Station, Universities, Courts, St James Park, Eldon Square and Galleries.

It has direct access to the Quayside and on-site complimentary parking.

Restaurant reservations are always recommended but are essential for Friday and Saturday.

CASTLE GARTH, NEWCASTLE, NE1 1RQ
Email: info@vermont-hotel.co.uk Web: www.vermont-hotel.com
Tel: 0191 233 1010
Fax: 0191 233 1234

The Vermont

★★★★ 🦐🦐

Castle Garth, Newcastle upon Tyne,
Tyne & Wear, NE1 1RQ
Tel: 0191 233 1010 Fax: 0191 233 1234
Email: info@vermont-hotel.co.uk
Web: www.vermont-hotel.com
Rooms: 101 all ensuite 🖨 ⊛
Pricing: Sgl £135–200 Dbl £135–200
Dinner available from £22–25
CC: Accepted
Room facilities: ▢ ☎ ☕ ⤶
Access: |↥↧
Conference: 12 meeting rooms (Thtr 200 max),
24hr-delegate from £165, day-delegate from £40
Children: Welcome �🍴
Dogs: Welcome
Licenses: ⬥ 🍾🍾🍾
Leisure: Gym
Parking: Off-street and free
Directions: Next to the castle, walking distance to rail station, quayside, universities, courts, St James Park, the main shopping centre and galleries.
Map ref: Newcastle upon Tyne 13 F4
See advert on this page

Jurys Inn Newcastle

★★★

St James Gate, Scotswood Road,
Newcastle upon Tyne, Tyne & Wear, NE4 7JH
Tel: 0191 201 4300 Fax: 0191 201 4411
Email: bookings@jurysdoyle.com
Web: www.jurysinns.com
Seasonal closure: 24-26 December

🖋JURYSDOYLE
HOTELS

Rooms: 274 all ensuite 🦐 ⊛
Pricing: Sgl £141 Dbl £151
Dinner available from £17
CC: Accepted
Room facilities: ▢ ☎ ☕ ⤶ ❄
Access: |↥↧
Conference: 9 meeting rooms (Thtr 100 max),
24hr-delegate from £121, day-delegate from £41
Children: Welcome �🍴
Licenses: 🍾🍾🍾
Parking: Off-street
Directions: Follow signs to Central Station Neville Street, take left and first right to Scotswood Road, then left into Hotel Plaza.
Map ref: Newcastle upon Tyne 13 F4

The Caledonian Hotel

★★★

Osborne Road, Jesmond, Newcastle upon Tyne,
Tyne & Wear, NE2 2AT
Tel: 0191 281 7881 Fax: 0191 281 6241
Email: caledonian.hotel@lineone.net
Web: www.peelhotel.com
Rooms: 89 all ensuite 🍴 🎘 🚭
Pricing: Sgl £85–100 Dbl £99–140
Dinner available from £15
CC: Accepted
Room facilities: 🖵 ☎ 🛆
Access: ♿
Conference: 5 meeting rooms (Thtr 100 max),
24hr-delegate from £130, day-delegate from £40
Children: Welcome 🍴
Dogs: Assistance dogs only
Licenses: ◈ ♦♦♦
Parking: Off-street and free
Directions: From A1 follow Jesmond signs. Turn left
into Osborne Road. Or from Tyne Tunnel follow
Newcastle signs, A1058. Turn right into Osborne Road.
Map ref: Newcastle upon Tyne 13 F4

Cairn Hotel

★★

97-103 Osborne Road, Jesmond,
Newcastle upon Tyne, Tyne & Wear, NE2 2TA
Tel: 0191 281 1358 Fax: 0191 281 9031
Email: info@cairnnewcastle.com
Web: www.cairnhotelgroup.com
Rooms: 50 all ensuite 🍴 🎘 🚭
Pricing: Dinner available from £12.50
CC: Accepted
Room facilities: 🖵 ☎ 🛆 ☎
Conference: 1 meeting room (Thtr 240 max),
24hr-delegate from £90, day-delegate from £25
Children: Welcome
Dogs: Welcome
Licenses: ♦♦♦
Parking: Off-street
Directions: Situated ¹/₂ mile from the city centre, in the
area of Jesmond, 2 minutes walk from West Jesmond
metro.
Map ref: Newcastle upon Tyne 13 F4
See advert on this page

Greenholme

♦♦♦

40 South View, East Denton, Newcastle upon Tyne,
Tyne & Wear, NE5 2BP
Tel: 0191 267 4828
Email: dansop@blueyonder.co.uk
Rooms: 2 (1 ensuite)
Pricing: Sgl £35–38 Dbl £46–48
Dinner available from £12.50
Room facilities: 🖵 🛆 ☎
Children: Welcome
Directions: A1 North/South – A69 Hexham. Slip Road
B6528. Fifth exit A69 Newcastle. Left slip at parking
sign. Immediate right. South View.
Map ref: East Denton 13 F4

The Adelphi Hotel

♦♦♦

63 Fern Avenue, Jesmond, Newcastle upon Tyne,
Tyne & Wear, NE2 2QU
Tel: 0191 281 3109
Seasonal closure: Christmas and New Year
Rooms: 7 (5 ensuite) 🚭
Pricing: Sgl £30–40 Dbl £50–60
CC: Accepted
Room facilities: 🖵 🛆
Children: Welcome
Directions: 1 mile from Newcastle City Centre.
Map ref: Newcastle upon Tyne 13 F4

Northeast

Newton under Roseberry, Cleveland

The Kings Head Hotel & Restaurant

The Green, Newton under Roseberry, near Great
Ayton, Middlesborough, Cleveland, TS9 6QR
Tel: 01642 722318 Fax: 01642 724750
Email: info@kingsheadhotel.co.uk
Web: www.kingsheadhotel.co.uk
Seasonal closure: 25-26 December, 1 January

Beautiful family owned hotel and restaurant situated at
the base of Roseberry Topping – the Matterhorn of
Cleveland. Oozing character and charm, bedrooms are
developed from converted 17th century country
cottages.
Rooms: 8 all ensuite
Pricing: Sgl £50–95 Dbl £60–95
Dinner available from £12.95–45
CC: Accepted
Room facilities:
Conference: 1 meeting room (Thtr 20 max)
Children: Welcome
Licenses:
Leisure: Walking, Mountain biking
Parking: Off-street and free
Directions: On A174 travel towards Guisborough. On
A171 follow directions to Newton-Under-Roseberry.
Situated underneath Roseberry Topping landmark on
A173.
Map ref: Newton under Roseberry

Pateley Bridge, North Yorkshire

Roslyn House (Guest House)

King Street, Pateley Bridge, North Yorkshire, HG3 5AT
Tel: 01423 711374
Email: enquiries@roslynhouse.co.uk
Web: www.roslynhouse.co.uk
Rooms: 6 all ensuite
Pricing: Sgl £32–40 Dbl £43–53
Room facilities:
Children: Welcome
Parking: Off-street and free
Directions: Turn right off Main Street. Hotel 250 yards
on left-hand side of King Street.
Map ref: Pateley Bridge 11 D3

Pickering, North Yorkshire

Blacksmith's Country Inn

Hartoft End, Rosedale Abbey, Pickering,
North Yorkshire, YO18 8EN
Tel: 01751 417331 Fax: 01571 417167
Email: office@blacksmithsinn-rosedale.co.uk
Web: www.blacksmithsinn-rosedale.co.uk
Rooms: 19 all ensuite
Pricing: Sgl £40–60 Dbl £80–120
Dinner available from £15
CC: Accepted
Room facilities:
Children: Welcome
Dogs: Welcome
Licenses:
Leisure: Fishing
Parking: Off-street and free
Directions: From Pickering A170 for Helmsley, right at
Wrelton. Hartoft signposted.
Map ref: Hartoft End 11 E2
See advert on this page

Redworth, Co. Durham

Redworth Hall Hotel

★★★★ 🍴🍴

Redworth, Newton Aycliffe, County Durham, DL5 6NL
Tel: 01388 770600 Fax: 01388 770654
Email:
redworthhallreservations@paramount-hotels.co.uk
Web: www.paramount-hotels.co.uk

PARAMOUNT
GROUP OF HOTELS

Redworth Hall is a beautiful Georgian manor house set
in 26 acres of private grounds with 100 bedrooms, two
restaurants and a superb leisure club with beauty and
hair salons.
Rooms: 100 all ensuite 🛏 💾 🚭
Pricing: Sgl £85–120 Dbl £120
Dinner available from £18
CC: Accepted
Room facilities: 🖥 ☎ 🍵 🔔
Access: ♿
Conference: 14 meeting rooms (Thtr 300 max),
24hr-delegate from £175, day-delegate from £55
Children: Welcome 🪑
Dogs: Welcome
Licenses: ⚖ 🍸
Leisure: Indoor pool, Gym, Health spa,
Beauty salon, Tennis
Parking: Off-street and free
Directions: Leave A1M at Junction 58. Take A68
towards Corbridge. Second exit at two roundabouts.
Hotel is on the left.
Map ref: Newton Aycliffe 11 D2

Richmond, North Yorkshire

The Kings Head Hotel

★★★ 🍴

Market Place, Richmond, North Yorkshire, DL10 4HS
Tel: 01748 850220 Fax: 01748 850635
Email: res@kingsheadrichmond.co.uk
Web: www.kingsheadrichmond.com

Attractive 18th Century hotel in the centre of historic
Richmond. Excellent food and service. Individually
furnished ensuite rooms. Charming restaurant
overlooking Norman Castle. Good walking and touring
base. Unique Georgian Theatre adjacent.
Rooms: 30 all ensuite 💾 🚭
Pricing: Sgl £78 Dbl £95–135
Dinner available from £18.95
CC: Accepted
Room facilities: 🖥 ☎ 🍵
Conference: 2 meeting rooms (Thtr 160 max),
24hr-delegate from £110, day-delegate from £32
Children: Welcome 🪑 🍼
Dogs: Welcome
Licenses: ⚖ 🍸
Parking: Off-street and free
Directions: Leave the A1 or A66 at Scotch Corner, take
A6108 to Richmond, follow signs to town centre. Hotel
located in the town centre in Market Square.
Map ref: Richmond (Yorkshire) 11 D2

Northeast

The Scotch Corner Hotel

★★★

Junction A1/A66, Scotch Corner, Richmond,
North Yorkshire, DL10 6NR
Tel: 01748 850900 Fax: 01748 825417
Email: enquiries@hotels-scotch-corner.com
Web: www.stop-inns.com
Rooms: 90 all ensuite
Pricing: Sgl £39.95 Dbl £79
Dinner available from £17.95
CC: Accepted
Room facilities:
Access:
Conference: 8 meeting rooms (Thtr 300 max),
24hr-delegate from £100, day-delegate from £35
Children: Welcome
Dogs: Welcome
Licenses:
Leisure: Indoor pool, Gym, Health spa, Beauty salon,
Games room
Parking: Off-street and free
Directions: Situated off Scotch Corner roundabout on
the A1/A66 junction on the northbound side of the A1.
Map ref: Scotch Corner 11 D2

Ripon, North Yorkshire

Unicorn Hotel

★★

Market Place, Ripon, North Yorkshire, HG4 1BP
Tel: 01765 602202 Fax: 01765 690734
Email: reservations@unicorn-hotel.co.uk
Web: www.unicorn-hotel.co.uk
Seasonal closure: Christmas
Rooms: 33 all ensuite
Pricing: Sgl £53–58 Dbl £75–82
Dinner available from £16.75 CC: Accepted
Room facilities:
Conference: 1 meeting room (Thtr 50 max),
24hr-delegate from £93.50, day-delegate from £30.50
Children: Welcome
Dogs: Welcome
Licenses:
Parking: Off-street and free
Directions: 4 miles from A1 on A61. Located in market
place, city centre.
Map ref: Ripon 11 D3

Relax & smell the coffee

Fresh coffee, chilled juices for breakfast. RAC's team of qualified Inspectors check them both.

Romaldkirk, Co. Durham

Rose & Crown

★★ Excellent

Romaldkirk, Barnard Castle,
County Durham, DL12 9EB
Tel: 01833 650213 Fax: 01833 650828
Email: hotel@rose-and-crown.co.uk
Web: www.rose-and-crown.co.uk
Seasonal closure: Christmas

An award winning 18th century coaching inn offering
very comfortable accommodation, the best of English
food and friendly, attentive service.
Rooms: 12 all ensuite
Pricing: Sgl £75–90 Dbl £126–140
Dinner available from £26
CC: Accepted
Room facilities:
Children: Welcome
Dogs: Welcome
Licenses:
Parking: Off-street and free
Directions: Six miles north-west from Barnard Castle
on B6277.
Map ref: Barnard Castle 10 C2

Rotherham, South Yorkshire

Hellaby Hall

★★★★

Old Hellaby Lane, Hellaby, Rotherham,
South Yorkshire, S66 8SN
Tel: 01709 702701 Fax: 01709 700979
Email: reservations@hellabyhallhotel.co.uk
Web: www.hellabyhallhotel.co.uk

www.primahotels.co.uk

Rooms: 90 all ensuite
Pricing: Sgl £50–111.50 Dbl £79–140
Dinner available from £29.95 CC: Accepted
Room facilities: Access:
Conference: 8 meeting rooms (Thtr 500 max),
24hr-delegate from £140, day-delegate from £45

Children: Welcome 🛉
Licenses: ⟁ 👬
Leisure: Indoor pool, Gym, Health spa, Beauty salon
Parking: Off-street and free
Directions: Exit J32 M1, then J1 M18. Follow signs for A631 to Bawtry. On the left after traffic lights. Go over roundabout, hotel is on the left.
Map ref: Hellaby 11 D4
See advert on this page

HELLABY HALL

RƎC ★★★★

Behind the original Dutch Colonial frontage, many features have been retained or restored and Hellaby is a fine example of the marriage between period charm and modern convenience. Our comfortable and tastefully decorated bedrooms reflect our basic philosophy of no compromise on quality and are equipped to the highest standard. Enjoy full use of Bodyscene Health & Leisure Club, including: swimming pool, gymnasium and beauty salon. From arrival and throughout your visit, our caring friendly staff will do all they can to make your stay as comfortable and as pleasurable as possible

Old Hellaby Lane, Hellaby,
Rotherham, South Yorkshire S66 8SN
Tel: 01709 702701 Fax: 01709 700979
reservations@hellabyhallhotel.co.uk
www.hellabyhallhotel.co.uk

Best Western Consort Hotel

★★★

Brampton Road, Thurcroft, Rotherham,
South Yorkshire, S66 9JA
Tel: 01709 530022 Fax: 01709 531529
Email: info@consorthotel.com
Web: www.consorthotel.com
Rooms: 27 all ensuite 🍴 📶 ⊗
Pricing: Sgl £51–90 Dbl £71–91
Dinner available from £18.95 CC: Accepted
Room facilities: ▢ ☎ ☕ ☏ ❄
Conference: 3 meeting rooms (Thtr 300 max),
24hr-delegate from £105, day-delegate from £28
Children: Welcome 🛉
Licenses: ⟁ 👬
Parking: Off-street
Directions: M18 junction 1 turn right, 200 yards right (double back) roundabout, 150 yards left after garage, 1½ miles T-junction, hotel on right.
Map ref: Thurcroft 11 D4

Best Western Elton Hotel

★★★★ ®

Main Street, Bramley, Rotherham,
South Yorkshire, S66 2SF
Tel: 01709 545681 Fax: 01709 549100
Email: res@eltonhotel.eclipse.co.uk
Web: www.bw-eltonhotel.co.uk
Rooms: 29 all ensuite ⊗
Pricing: Sgl £68–86 Dbl £75–95
Dinner available from £22–27.5
CC: Accepted
Room facilities: ▢ ☎ ☕ ☏
Conference: 3 meeting rooms (Thtr 55 max),
24hr-delegate from £115, day-delegate from £36
Children: Welcome 🛉
Dogs: Welcome
Licenses: ⟁ 👬
Parking: Off-street and free
Directions: ¼ mile from M18 Junction 1. Follow A631 Rotherham. Turn right into Ravenfield. Hotel at end of Bramley village. Follow the brown signs.
Map ref: Bramley 11 D4

Brecon Hotel

★★

Moorgate Road, Rotherham, South Yorkshire, S60 2AY
Tel: 01709 828811 Fax: 01709 513030
Web: www.breconhotel.co.uk

The Brecon's excellent reputation has been built up since 1963, giving a friendly atmosphere where all our staff care for your well-being.
Rooms: 21 all ensuite ⊗
Pricing: Sgl £45–55 Dbl £55–63
Dinner available from £18.50
CC: Accepted
Room facilities: ▢ ☎ ☕ ☕
Children: Welcome 🛉
Dogs: Welcome
Licenses: 👬
Parking: Off-street
Directions: Junction 33 of M1, follow signs to Bawtry (A631). After ½ mile turn left at traffic lights for A618. Hotel 1 mile on right.
Map ref: Rotherham 8 B1

Northeast

Restover Lodge Hotel
Travel Accommodation

Denby Way, Lowton Way, Hellaby Industrial Estate,
Rotherham, South Yorkshire, S66 8RY
Tel: 01709 700255 Fax: 01709 545169
Email: michelle.toms@btopenworld.com
Web: www.restoverlodge.co.uk
Rooms: 50 all ensuite
Pricing: Sgl £46–51.50 Dbl £50.50–60
Dinner available from £11.95–15.95 CC: Accepted
Room facilities: ▢ ☎ ⎙ ✆
Conference: 1 meeting room,
24hr-delegate from £95, day-delegate from £25
Children: Welcome ☍ Dogs: Welcome
Licenses: ⍟ Parking: Off-street and free
Directions: M18 J1. Take turning for Hellaby and
Maltby at roundabout. At next roundabout turn left.
Second left into Lowton Way, follow road to right.
Map ref: Hellaby 11 D4

Rowlands Gill, Tyne & Wear

Wensley Guest House
◆◆◆

Wensley House, Lockhaugh Road, Rowlands Gill,
Tyne & Wear, NE39 2PR
Tel: 01207 543884 Fax: 01207 543884
Seasonal closure: Christmas
Rooms: 2 all ensuite
Pricing: Sgl £35 Dbl £48
Room facilities: ⎙ Children: Welcome ☍
Dogs: Assistance dogs only Parking: Off-street and free
Directions: Off A1 at slip road after Metro Centre
(Concett) A694. Straight across first roundabout, A694
to Rowlands Gill. Wensley House is on right-hand side
on main road.
Map ref: Rowlands Gill 11 D1

Scarborough, North Yorkshire

Ambassador Leisure Hotel
★★★

Centre of The Esplanade, South Cliff, Scarborough,
North Yorkshire, YO11 2AY
Tel: 0500 202225 Fax: 01723 366166
Email: ask@ambassadorhotelscarborough.co.uk
Web: www.ambassadorhotelscarborough.co.uk
Rooms: 59 all ensuite ⍟ ▨ ⊗
Pricing: Sgl £29–77 Dbl £58–144
Dinner available from £19.95 CC: Accepted
Room facilities: ▢ ☎ ⎙ ✆ Access: ⍒
Conference: 2 meeting rooms (Thtr 140 max),
24hr-delegate from £75, day-delegate from £18
Children: Welcome ☍ ⍟ Dogs: Welcome
Licenses: ⍟ Leisure: Indoor pool, Spa pool,
Steam room, Solarium Parking: Off-street and free
Directions: On A64, turn right at roundabout opposite
B&Q, turn right at next roundabout, then immediately
left down Avenue Victoria to the cliff top.
Map ref: Scarborough 11 E2
See advert on opposite page

Crown Spa Hotel
★★★

Esplanade, Scarborough, North Yorkshire, YO11 2AG
Tel: 01723 357423 Fax: 01723 357404
Email: info@scarboroughhotel.com
Web: www.scarboroughhotel.com

Famous historical hotel providing excellent personal
service plus exhilarating views of South Bay, Castle &
Harbour. Home to Scarborough's finest health club and
two excellent restaurants. Ample free parking.
Rooms: 86 all ensuite ⍟ ▨ ⊗
Pricing: Sgl £45–110 Dbl £56–180
Dinner available from £18.95
CC: Accepted
Room facilities: ▢ ☎ ⎙ ✆ Access: ⍒
Conference: 7 meeting rooms (Thtr 200 max),
24hr-delegate from £75, day-delegate from £25
Children: Welcome ☍
Dogs: Welcome
Licenses: ⍟ ⍟
Leisure: Indoor pool, Gym, Health spa
Parking: Off-street and free
Directions: At south end of Valley Bridge (A165), turn
east across Valley Bridge Parade onto Belmont Road.
Continue to cliff top, hotel on right.
Map ref: Scarborough 11 E2

East Ayton Lodge Country Hotel
★★★

Moor Lane, East Ayton, Scarborough,
North Yorkshire, YO13 9EW
Tel: 01723 864227 Fax: 01723 862680
Email: ealodgehtl@cix.co.uk
Web: www.eastaytonlodgehotel.com
Seasonal closure: 2 January to 10 February
Rooms: 30 all ensuite ⍟ ▨
Dinner available
CC: Accepted
Room facilities: ▢ ☎ ⎙
Conference: 2 meeting rooms (Thtr 80 max)
Children: Welcome ☍
Dogs: Welcome
Licenses: ⍟
Parking: Off-street and free
Directions: 400 yards off the A170 Scarborough/Thirsk
road in the village of East Ayton, 3¹/₂ miles from
Scarborough.
Map ref: East Ayton 11 E2

AMBASSADOR LEISURE HOTEL

Spectacular south bay sea view rooms. Opposite famous Italian/Rose gardens.
Cliff lift to beach and spa. Conference / entertainment complex.

- Heated indoor pool with spa bath ■ Bay View Café Bar ■ Steam room ■ Fine Dine Bay View
Restaurant ■ Disability access 1:6.5 ■ Tasteful entertainment ■ Ample complimentary on-street parking

Centre of the Esplanade, South Cliff, Scarborough, North Yorkshire YO11 2AY
Tel: 01723 362841   Fax: 01723 366166

Email: ask@ambassadorhotelscarborough.co.uk   Website: www.ambassadorhotelscarborough.co.uk

Hackness Grange

★★★★ ♟♟

North Yorkshire Moors National Park, Hackness,
North Yorkshire, YO13 0JW
Tel: 01723 882345 Fax: 01723 882391
Email: hacknessgrange@englishrosehotels.co.uk
Web: www.englishrosehotels.co.uk

A Georgian country house hotel with facilities that
include an indoor pool, tennis and pitch and putt golf.
There are delightful walks and the hotel enjoys an
excellent reputation for cuisine.
Rooms: 33 all ensuite ♥ ♨
Pricing: Sgl £50–75 Dbl £110
Dinner available from £25 CC: Accepted

Room facilities: ▢ ☎ ♨
Conference: 1 meeting room (Thtr 15 max),
24hr-delegate from £95, day-delegate from £28.50
Children: Welcome ♄ ♨
Licenses: ♙♙♙ Leisure: Indoor pool, Tennis
Parking: Off-street
Directions: From A1/M1 take A64. On entering
Scarborough follow B1261 and follow Hackness sign
on right. Entering Hackness village, turn left for hotel.
Map ref: Hackness 11 E2

Palm Court Hotel

★★★

St Nicholas Cliff, Scarborough,
North Yorkshire, YO11 2ES
Tel: 01723 368161 Fax: 01723 371547
Email: palmcourt@scarborough.co.uk
Web: www.palmcourt.scarborough.co.uk
Rooms: 43 all ensuite ♨
Pricing: Sgl £50–57 Dbl £102–112
Dinner available from £16 CC: Accepted
Room facilities: ▢ ☎ ♨ Access: ♿
Conference: 4 meeting rooms (Thtr 200 max),
24hr-delegate from £75, day-delegate from £25
Children: Welcome ♄ ♨ Licenses: ♙♙♙
Leisure: Indoor pool
Parking: Off-street and free
Directions: Follow the signs for the town centre, then
the town hall. The hotel is en-route.
Map ref: Scarborough 11 E2

The Crescent Hotel

★★★ ®

The Crescent, Scarborough, North Yorkshire, YO11 2PP
Tel: 01723 360929 Fax: 01723 354126
Email: reception@thecrescenthotel.com
Web: www.thecrescenthotel.com
Rooms: 20 all ensuite 🖥 ⊗
Pricing: Dinner available from £17.50 CC: Accepted
Room facilities: ☐ ☎ ☕ ✎ Access: |↕|
Conference: 2 meeting rooms (Thtr 30 max),
24hr-delegate from £75, day-delegate from £17.50
Children: Welcome 3yrs min age
Licenses: ♦♦♦
Directions: On arrival in Scarborough town centre,
follow signs to Brunswick Centre, Museum & Art
Gallery. At Brunswick Centre, turn right into The
Crescent.
Map ref: Scarborough 11 E2

THE ROYAL HOTEL

This famous and historic hotel overlooks the beautiful South Bay and is close to the town's attractions. Restored to its Regency splendour in its public areas and now offering contemporary styled bedrooms with all the facilities of a modern resort hotel. Included is a leisure club with pool and gym. This is the obvious choice for the discerning traveller.

ST. NICHOLAS STREET, SCARBOROUGH,
NORTH YORKSHIRE, YO11 2HE

Tel: 01723 364333 Fax: 01723 500618
Email: royalhotel@englishrosehotels.co.uk
Web: www.englishrosehotels.co.uk

Sleep easy

Rest assured. Our comprehensive inspection process includes checking beds are comfortable.

The Royal Hotel

★★★

St. Nicholas Street, Scarborough,
North Yorkshire, YO11 2HE
Tel: 01723 364333 Fax: 01723 500618
Email: royalhotel@englishrosehotels.co.uk
Web: www.englishrosehotels.co.uk

Rooms: 118 all ensuite 🐾 🖥
Pricing: Sgl £55–75 Dbl £90
Dinner available from £25 CC: Accepted
Room facilities: ☐ ☎ ☕ Access: |↕|
Conference: 7 meeting rooms (Thtr 200 max),
24hr-delegate from £105, day-delegate from £33
Children: Welcome ♪ ☕
Licenses: ◬ ♦♦♦
Leisure: Indoor pool, Gym, Health spa
Map ref: Scarborough 11 E2
See advert on this page

Wrea Head Country House Hotel

★★★★ ®

Off Barmoor Lane, Scalby, Scarborough,
North Yorkshire, YO13 0PB
Tel: 01723 378211 Fax: 01723 355936
Email: wreaheadhotel@englishrosehotels.co.uk
Web: www.englishrosehotels.co.uk

Peace and tranquillity, in landscaped woodlands on
the edge of the North York Moors National Park
describe this beautifully-decorated English country
house, where fine wines and quality cuisine combine
to create the perfect retreat.
Rooms: 20 all ensuite 🐾 🖥 ⊗
Pricing: Sgl £60–75 Dbl £95
Dinner available from £25
CC: Accepted
Room facilities: ☐ ☎ ☕
Conference: 2 meeting rooms (Thtr 30 max),
24hr-delegate from £95, day-delegate from £28.50
Children: Welcome ♪ ☕

Licenses:
Parking: Off-street and free
Directions: Take A64 from A1/M1. On entering Scarborough, take A171 (Whitby Road). Pass Scalby and turn left. Hotel drive on left, after pond.
Map ref: Scalby 11 E2

Bradley Court Hotel

★★

7–9 Filey Road, Scarborough, North Yorkshire, YO11 2SE
Tel: 01723 360476 Fax: 01723 376661
Email: info@bradleycourthotel.co.uk
Web: www.bradleycourthotel.co.uk
Rooms: 40 all ensuite
Pricing: Sgl £30–50 Dbl £60–90
Dinner available from £15 CC: Accepted
Room facilities: ▢ ☎ ⬚ ✸ Access: |↟|
Conference: 1 meeting room (Thtr 100 max),
24hr-delegate from £60, day-delegate from £25
Children: Welcome ⱶ ⵜ
Licenses: ▮▮▮
Leisure: Games room
Parking: Off-street and free
Directions: Follow A64 into Scarborough. Turn right at mini roundabout after B&Q. Follow road to next mini roundabout, turn left, hotel 50 yards further on.
Map ref: Scarborough 11 E2

Clifton Hotel

★★

Queens Parade, Scarborough,
North Yorkshire, YO12 7HX
Tel: 01723 375691 Fax: 01723 371780
Email: cliftonhotel@englishrosehotels.co.uk
Web: www.englishrosehotels.co.uk

Overlooking the North Bay and close to Sea Life Centre and Atlantis Water Park. Ensuite bedrooms with direct-dial phone, TV and a welcome refreshment tray. The hotel offers ample free car parking.

Rooms: 69 all ensuite
Pricing: Sgl £35–65 Dbl £60
Dinner available from £16.95
CC: Accepted
Room facilities: ▢ ☎ ⬚
Access: |↟|
Conference: 3 meeting rooms (Thtr 120 max),
24hr-delegate from £85, day-delegate from £25
Children: Welcome ⱶ ⵜ
Licenses: ▮▮▮
Parking: Off-street and free
Directions: Follow A64 from A1/M1. Turn left at Scarborough rail station and right at Peasholm Park. Hotel is opposite Alexandra Bowls Centre.
Map ref: Scarborough 11 E2

Red Lea Hotel

★★

Prince of Wales Terrace, South Cliff, Scarborough,
North Yorkshire, YO11 2AJ
Tel: 01723 362431 Fax: 01723 371230
Email: redlea@globalnet.co.uk
Web: www.redleahotel.co.uk

Whatever the weather a warm welcome is guaranteed at the Red Lea. Situated on the South Cliff with views over gardens to the sea. Facilities include an indoor swimming pool.
Rooms: 67 all ensuite
Pricing: Sgl £34–45 Dbl £68–84
Dinner available from £15
CC: Accepted
Room facilities: ▢ ☎ ⬚
Access: |↟|
Conference: 1 meeting room (Thtr 30 max)
Children: Welcome ⱶ
Licenses: ▮▮▮
Leisure: Indoor pool, Gym, Games room
Directions: Follow signs for South Cliff. Hotel is located off the Esplanade near the cliff lift.
Map ref: Scarborough 11 E2

Northeast

Ryndle Court Hotel

 ★★

47 Northstead Manor Drive, Scarborough,
North Yorkshire, YO12 6AF
Tel: 01723 375188 Fax: 01723 375188
Email: enquiries@ryndlecourt.co.uk
Web: www.ryndlecourt.co.uk
Seasonal closure: November to February

Delightfully situated overlooking Peasholm Park near
the sea and leisure parks, comfortably furnished to a
high standard there is a relaxing coffee lounge,
residents' licensed bar and guests' car park.
Rooms: 14 all ensuite 🏊 🚭
Pricing: Sgl £40–48 Dbl £72–76
Dinner available from £10–12
CC: Accepted
Room facilities: 📺 ☕
Children: Welcome 🏠
Licenses: ♦♦♦
Parking: Off-street and free
Directions: Follow signs marked 'North Bay and
Leisure Parks' to Northstead Manor Drive.
Map ref: Scarborough 11 E2

The Whiteley Hotel

 ♦♦♦♦ ☕

99-101 Queens Parade, Scarborough,
North Yorkshire, YO12 7HY
Tel: 01723 373514 Fax: 01723 373007
Email: whiteleyhotel@bigfoot.com
Web: www.yorkshirecoast.co.uk/whiteley
Seasonal closure: 1 December to 1 February

Family-run non-smoking hotel overlooking
Scarborough's North Bay. All bedrooms are ensuite,
many with sea views. A substantial English breakfast is
served in the traditional dining room. Car park.
Rooms: 10 all ensuite 🚭
Pricing: Sgl £28.50–30.50 Dbl £47–55 CC: Accepted
Room facilities: 📺 ☕ Children: Welcome 3yrs min age
Licenses: ♦♦♦ Parking: Off-street and free
Directions: Follow signs to North Bay. By Alexandra Bowls
Centre, turn into Queens Parade. Hotel on cliff top.
Map ref: Scarborough 11 E2

Toulson Court

 ♦♦♦♦ ☒ ☕

100 Columbus Ravine, Scarborough,
North Yorkshire, YO12 7QZ
Tel: 01723 503218 Fax: 01723 503218
Email: toulsoncourt@scarborough.co.uk
Web: www.toulsoncourt.scarborough.co.uk
Rooms: 6 all ensuite 🏊
Room facilities: 📺 ☕
Children: Welcome 🏠 Dogs: Welcome
Map ref: Scarborough 11 E2

Blacksmiths Arms

 ♦♦♦

High Street, Cloughton, Scarborough,
North Yorkshire, YO13 0AE
Tel: 01723 870244
Rooms: 11 all ensuite Dinner available
Room facilities: 📺 ☕
Licenses: ♦♦♦ Parking: Off-street
Map ref: Cloughton 11 E2

Brambles Lodge

 ◆◆◆

156-158 Filey Road, Scarborough,
North Yorkshire, YO11 3AA
Tel: 01723 374613
Email: nightgales22@aol.com
Web: www.smoothhound.co.uk/hotels/brambleslodge.html
Seasonal closure: December to January
Rooms: 7 all ensuite
Pricing: Sgl £23–25 Dbl £46–50
Room facilities:
Children: Welcome 6yrs min age Dogs: Welcome
Parking: Off-street and free
Directions: From Scarborough follow the A165 across
Valley Bridge Road to Bridlington. Guest house is 1¹/₂
miles on the left past the university.
Map ref: Scarborough 11 E2

Clairmont Hotel

 ◆◆◆

20 Ryndleside, Scarborough,
North Yorkshire, YO12 6AD
Tel: 01723 362288 Fax: 01723 362288
Email: clairmonthotel@yahoo.co.uk
Web: www.clairmont.co.uk
Seasonal closure: Christmas & New Year
Rooms: 12 all ensuite
Pricing: Sgl £18–26 Dbl £36–52
Dinner available from £10 CC: Accepted
Room facilities:
Conference: 2 meeting rooms (Thtr 20 max)
Children: Welcome
Licenses: Parking: Off-street and free
Directions: Follow signs for North Bay and Leisure
Parks to Peasholm Park, Ryndleside is part of circular
road round the park.
Map ref: Scarborough 11 E2

Clarence Gardens

◆◆◆

4–5 Blenheim Terrace, Scarborough,
North Yorkshire, YO12 7HF
Tel: 01723 374884 Fax: 01723 374884
Seasonal closure: November to March
Rooms: 24 (12 ensuite)
Dinner available Room facilities:
Children: Welcome
Licenses: Leisure: Games room
Parking: Off-street and free
Directions: From the top of the North Bay, Guest House is
approximately 700 yards from the castle facing the sea.
Map ref: Scarborough 11 E2

Douglas Guest House

 ◆◆◆

153 Columbus Ravine, Scarborough,
North Yorkshire, YO12 7QZ
Tel: 01723 371311
Email: stay@douglasguesthouse.co.uk
Web: www.douglasguesthouse.co.uk

Rooms: 5 (4 ensuite)
Pricing: Sgl £22–25 Dbl £44–50
Dinner available from £7
Room facilities:
Children: Welcome 3yrs min age
Directions: From railway station along Northway
continuing over the roundabout into Columbus Ravine,
guest house is on the right-hand side.
Map ref: Scarborough 11 E2

Granby Hotel

 ◆◆◆

1-2 Granby Place, Queen Street, Scarborough,
North Yorkshire, YO11 1HL
Tel: 01723 373031 Fax: 01723 373031
Seasonal closure: October to March
Rooms: 25 all ensuite
Pricing: Sgl £25–28 Dbl £44–50
Dinner available from £8 CC: Accepted
Room facilities:
Children: Welcome
Licenses:
Parking: Off-street and free
Directions: Follow signs for town centre/castle. Queen
Street is right after mini roundabout on Castle Road.
Map ref: Scarborough 11 E2

Hotel Levante

 ◆◆◆

118 Columbus Ravine, Scarborough,
North Yorkshire, YO12 7QZ
Tel: 01723 372366
Rooms: 7 all ensuite
Pricing: Sgl £23 Dbl £46
Dinner available from £8
Room facilities:
Children: Welcome 3yrs min age
Parking: Off-street and free
Directions: From station turn onto Northway which
runs into Columbus Ravine. On the left 100m before
Peasholm Park.
Map ref: Scarborough 11 E2

Hotel Phoenix

 ◆◆◆

8/9 Rutland Terrace, Scarborough,
North Yorkshire, YO12 7JB
Tel: 01723 501150
Email: info@hotel-phoenix.co.uk
Web: www.hotel-phoenix.co.uk
Rooms: 15 all ensuite
Pricing: Dbl £25–30
Dinner available from £10–12 CC: Accepted
Room facilities: Children: Welcome
Licenses: Leisure: Holistic treatments available
Parking: Off-street and free
Directions: Hotel overlooks the North Bay at top of
Queens Parade, close to castle. Turn into hotel car
park.
Map ref: Scarborough 11 E2

Northeast

Kenways Guest House

9 Victoria Park Avenue, Scarborough,
North Yorkshire, YO12 7TR
Tel: 01723 365757 Fax: 01723 365757
Email: info@kenwaysguesthouse.co.uk
Web: www.kenwaysguesthouse.co.uk
Seasonal closure: 4 December 2005 to 11 February 2006
Rooms: 7 all ensuite 🖨 🚫
Pricing: Sgl £18–20 Dbl £36–40
Dinner available from £6
Room facilities: 🖵 ☕
Children: Welcome ⛐
Dogs: Welcome
Directions: North Bay seafront to roundabout, past
Atlantis, first left up to Peasholm Park Hotel. Victoria
Park Avenue is to the side.
Map ref: Scarborough 11 E2

Lincoln Hotel

112 Columbus Ravine, North Bay, Scarborough,
North Yorkshire, YO12 7QZ
Tel: 01723 500897 Fax: 01723 500897
Email: enquiries@lincolnhotel.net.
Web: www.lincolnhotel.net
Rooms: 7 all ensuite
Pricing: Sgl £25–35 Dbl £46–70
Dinner available from £10 CC: Accepted
Room facilities: 🖵 ☕
Children: Welcome ⼍
Licenses: ⫙
Parking: Off-street and free
Directions: Follow tourist attraction signs for North
Bay; at Peasholm roundabout last exit Columbus
Ravine; hotel is approx 400 yards on right–hand side.
Map ref: Scarborough 11 E2

Lynton Private Hotel

104 Columbus Ravine, Scarborough,
North Yorkshire, YO12 7QZ
Tel: 01723 374240
Email: watson@paul-cherryl.fsnet.co.uk
Web: www.lynton-hotel.fsnet.co.uk
Rooms: 8 all ensuite 🍴 🚫
Dinner available CC: Accepted
Room facilities: 🖵 ☕
Children: Welcome ⼍
Licenses: ⫙
Parking: Off-street and free
Directions: From the railway station take Northway. Go
straight on through two roundabouts. The Lynton Hotel
is on the left.
Map ref: Scarborough 11 E2

Newlands Hotel

80 Columbus Ravine, Scarborough,
North Yorkshire, YO12 7QU
Tel: 01723 367261
Email: newlandshotel@btconnect.com
Web: www.thenewlandshotel.co.uk
Seasonal closure: 24 December to 4 January
Rooms: 8 (5 ensuite) 🍴 🚫
Pricing: Sgl £18–20 Dbl £40–50
Room facilities: 🖵 ☕
Children: Welcome
Directions: A64 from Leeds to Scarborough, North Bay
end in between Peasholm Park and town centre.
Map ref: Scarborough 11 E2

Robyn's

139 Columbus Drive, Scarborough,
North Yorkshire, YO12 7QZ
Tel: 01723 374217
Email: info@robynsguesthouse
Web: www.robynsguesthouse.co.uk
Rooms: 6 all ensuite 🍴
Pricing: Sgl £23–30 Dbl £46
Dinner available from £10 CC: Accepted
Room facilities: 🖵 ☕
Children: Welcome ⼍
Dogs: Welcome
Map ref: Scarborough 11 E2

The Phoenix Guest House

157 Columbus Ravine, Scarborough,
North Yorkshire, YO12 7QZ
Tel: 01723 368319
Rooms: 5 all ensuite 🍴 🚫
Pricing: Sgl £22–29 Dbl £40–50
Room facilities: 🖵 ☕ Children: Welcome
Licenses: ⫙
Directions: Follow brown signs North Bay. At Peasholm
Park turn into Columbus Ravine. The Phoenix Guest
House is halfway up on left-hand side.
Map ref: Scarborough 11 E2

Tudor House Hotel

164/166 North Marine Road, Scarborough,
North Yorkshire, YO12 7HZ
Tel: 01723 361270
Seasonal closure: December
Rooms: 15 (7 ensuite) 🍴
Pricing: Sgl £16–24 Dbl £32–48 CC: Accepted
Room facilities: 🖵 ☕ Children: Welcome ⼍
Licenses: ⫙
Directions: Follow signs for cricket ground. Tudor House
150 metres away downhill from ground on the same road.
Map ref: Scarborough 11 E2

West Lodge Hotel

◆◆◆

38 West Street, Scarborough, North Yorkshire, YO11 2QP
Tel: 01723 500754
Rooms: 7 (4 ensuite)
Dinner available
CC: Accepted
Room facilities: ☐ ☕
Children: Welcome ⍊ Dogs: Welcome
Licenses: ∰
Directions: From Railway Station, follow sign for Filey
over bridge. Church on the right. West Street is opposite.
Map ref: Scarborough 11 E2

Willow Dene Hotel

◆◆◆ ✳☒

110 Columbus Ravine, North Bay, Scarborough,
North Yorkshire, YO12 7QZ
Tel: 01723 365173
Email: andy@willowdenehotel.com
Web: www.willowdenehotel.com
Seasonal closure: November to February
Rooms: 9 all ensuite
Pricing: Sgl £23–25 Dbl £46–50
Dinner available from £5–7
Room facilities: ☐ ☕
Children: Welcome 3yrs min age ⍊
Parking: Off-street and free
Directions: A64 to Falsgrave lights, right to railway
station, left through lights, across two roundabouts, on
left past church before park.
Map ref: Scarborough 11 E2

Yardley Manor Hotel

◆◆◆

65 Northstead Manor Drive, Scarborough,
North Yorkshire, YO12 6AF
Tel: 01723 365767 Fax: 01723 365767
Email: yardley@manorhotel.wanadoo.co.uk
Rooms: 14 all ensuite ☕ ⊕
Pricing: Sgl £20–28 Dbl £40–56
Dinner available from £15
CC: Accepted
Room facilities: ☐ ☕
Conference: 1 meeting room (Thtr 24 max),
24hr-delegate from £20
Children: Welcome ⍊ ☕
Dogs: Welcome
Licenses: ∰
Parking: Off-street and free
Directions: From town head for North Bay and leisure
parks. Turn left at park and left again into Northstead
Manor Drive. Hotel is on right.
Map ref: Scarborough 11 E2

Aldon Hotel

⚑ New for 2006

120 Columbus Ravine, Scarborough,
North Yorkshire, YO12 7QZ
Tel: 01723 372198
Web: www.aldon-hotel.co.uk
Rooms: 16 all ensuite ⊕
Pricing: Sgl £23–27 Dbl £23–27
CC: Accepted
Room facilities: ☐ ☕
Children: Welcome
Parking: Off-street and free
Directions: Aldon is situated near Peasholm Park,
north side of Scarborough, 5 minutes from railway
station.
Map ref: Scarborough 11 E2

Scotch Corner, North Yorkshire

Vintage Hotel and Restaurant

◆◆◆

Scotch Corner, North Yorkshire, DL10 6NP
Tel: 01748 824424 Fax: 01748 826272
Email: thevintagescotchcorner@btinternet.com
Web: www.thevintagehotel.co.uk
Seasonal closure: Christmas to New Year

Family-run roadside hotel overlooking open
countryside. Open plan rustic style bar and restaurant.
Ideal overnight stop or base for visiting Yorkshire
Dales/Moors.
Rooms: 8 (5 ensuite)
Pricing: Sgl £29.45–49 Dbl £45.50–65
Dinner available from £18–25
CC: Accepted
Room facilities: ☐ ☎ ☕
Conference: 2 meeting rooms (Thtr 50 max)
Children: Welcome ⍊
Licenses: ∰
Parking: Off-street and free
Directions: Leave A1 at Scotch Corner. Take A66
towards Penrith, Vintage Hotel 200 yards on left.
Map ref: Scotch Corner 11 D2

Northeast

Seaham, Co. Durham

Seaham Hall Hotel and Serenity Spa

★★★★ Premier

Lord Byron's Walk, Seaham, Co. Durham, SR7 7AG
Tel: 0191 516 1400 Fax: 0191 516 1410
Email: reservations@seaham-hall.com
Web: www.seaham-hall.com
Rooms: 19 all ensuite
Pricing: Sgl £195–525 Dbl £195–525
Dinner available from £40 CC: Accepted
Room facilities: Access:
Conference: 4 meeting rooms (Thtr 120 max),
day-delegate from £49.50
Children: Welcome
Licenses:
Leisure: Indoor pool, Gym, Health spa, Beauty salon
Parking: Off-street and free
Directions: Exit A1 J62. A19 south and exit B1404 left
to Seaham. At traffic lights go straight ahead onto Lord
Byron's Walk. Hotel ½ mile on right.
Map ref: Seaham 11 D1

Seahouses, Northumberland

Bamburgh Castle Hotel

★★★

Overlooking the sea, Seahouses,
Northumberland, NE68 7SQ
Tel: 01665 720283 Fax: 01665 720848
Email: bamburghcastlehotel@btinternet.com
Web: www.bamburghcastlehotel.co.uk
Seasonal closure: mid-January for 2 weeks

Enjoying a fabulous location overlooking the harbour
and sea. Log fire lounges, garden and secure car
parking. Restaurant serving freshly prepared local
produce in a friendly and hospitable atmosphere.
Rooms: 20 all ensuite
Pricing: Sgl £48.95–57.95 Dbl £85.90–105.90
Dinner available from £16.95–24.95
Room facilities:
Children: Welcome Dogs: Welcome
Licenses: Parking: Off-street and free
Directions: Follow signs for Seahouses from A1. Hotel
car park entrance is on mini roundabout opposite
Barclays Bank. (Car park barrier will rise automatically).
Map ref: Seahouses 13 F3

Olde Ship Hotel

★★

9 Main Street, Seahouses, Northumberland, NE68 7RD
Tel: 01665 720200 Fax: 01665 721383
Email: theoldeship@seahouses.co.uk
Web: www.seahouses.co.uk
Seasonal closure: Mid December to mid January
Rooms: 18 all ensuite
Pricing: Sgl £47–50 Dbl £94–100
Dinner available from £20 CC: Accepted
Room facilities:
Children: Welcome 10yrs min age
Licenses:
Leisure: Snooker/billiards, Residents' lounge
Directions: 5 miles north of Alnwick on A1. Take the
B1340 to Seahouses. The hotel is perched at the
harbour top.
Map ref: Seahouses 13 F3

Selby, North Yorkshire

The Royal Oak Inn-Hotel

◆◆◆

Main Street, Hirst Courtney, Selby,
North Yorkshire, YO8 8QT
Tel: 01757 270633 Fax: 01757 270333
Email: theroyaloakinnhotel@hotmail.com
Web: www.royaloakinn-hotel.co.uk
Rooms: 10 all ensuite
Pricing: Sgl £46.41 Dbl £67.56
Dinner available from £4.15 CC: Accepted
Room facilities:
Conference: 2 meeting rooms (Thtr 100 max)
Children: Welcome
Licenses:
Leisure: Games room Parking: Off-street and free
Directions: M62 J34 A19 north towards Selby,
crossroads at Chapel Haddlesey turn right. Hirst
Courtney 3 miles, Royal Oak centre village.
Map ref: Hirst Courtney 11 D4

Settle, North Yorkshire

Golden Lion Hotel

◆◆◆◆

Duke Street, Settle, North Yorkshire, BD24 9DU
Tel: 01729 822203 Fax: 01729 824103
Email: bookings@goldenlion.yorks.net
Web: www.yorkshirenet.co.uk/stayat/goldenlion
Rooms: 12 (10 ensuite)
Pricing: Sgl £32–39 Dbl £58–70
Dinner available from £12 CC: Accepted
Room facilities:
Conference: 1 meeting room (Thtr 12 max)
Children: Welcome
Licenses: Leisure: Games room
Parking: Off-street and free
Directions: As you enter Settle town centre from south,
hotel is on right-hand side of road, just before the
market square.
Map ref: Settle 10 C3

Sheffield, South Yorkshire

Holiday Inn Royal Victoria — Sheffield

★★★★

Victoria Station Road, Sheffield, South Yorkshire, S4 7YE
Tel: 0114 276 8822 Fax: 0114 252 6526
Email: stay@holidayinnsheffield.co.uk
Web: www.holidayinnsheffield.co.uk

A Grade II listed building, within walking distance to the city centre, with friendly service and a fine dining cuisine in the RAC award winning restaurant.
Rooms: 100 all ensuite
Pricing: Sgl £70–157.50 Dbl £70–170
Dinner available from £20
CC: Accepted
Room facilities:
Access: |↕
Conference: 17 meeting rooms (Thtr 450 max), 24hr-delegate from £150, day-delegate from £50
Children: Welcome
Licenses:
Leisure: Gym, Beauty salon
Parking: Off-street and free
Directions: Exit J33 M1 to Sheffield. At Park Square roundabout take A61N. At first set of lights turn right.
Map ref: Sheffield 8 B1

Etruria House Hotel

◆◆◆

91 Crookes Road, Broomhill, Sheffield,
South Yorkshire, S10 5BD
Tel: 0114 266 2241 Fax: 0114 267 0853
Email: etruria@waitrose.com
Seasonal closure: 24 December to 2 January
Rooms: 10 (6 ensuite)
Pricing: Sgl £36–44 Dbl £50–58
CC: Accepted
Room facilities:
Children: Welcome
Parking: Off-street and free
Directions: Leave M1 at Junction 33. Follow A57 towards Glossop for 2 miles. At traffic lights in Broomhill, turn right. Hotel 200 yards on left.
Map ref: Broomhill 8 B1

Skipton, North Yorkshire

Skipton Park Guest'otel Ltd

◆◆◆

2 Salisbury Street, Skipton,
North Yorkshire, BD23 1NQ
Tel: 01756 700640 Fax: 01756 700641
Email: derekchurch@skiptonpark.freeserve.co.uk
Web: www.skiptonpark.co.uk
Rooms: 7 all ensuite
Pricing: Sgl £40 Dbl £50
Room facilities: Parking: Off-street
Map ref: Skipton 10 C3

South Shields, Tyne & Wear

The Prestige Hotel

★★★

3 Newcastle Road, South Shields,
Tyne & Wear, NE34 9PQ
Tel: 0191 456 5500 Fax: 0191 456 4444
Email: info@theprestigehotels.com
Web: www.theprestigehotels.com

Conveniently situated off the A19, within easy reach of Newcastle, Sunderland, Durham and Newcastle airport. All rooms are furnished to a high standard to ensure a comfortable stay and include TV and radio, tea/coffee making facilities and ironing board. The Arches Restaurant and Bar provide a wide variety of cuisines. Conference, banqueting and function suites are available for both business and leisure. Reception is open 24 hours and parking for up to 200 cars is available with CCTV and a night porter on site.
Rooms: 64 all ensuite
Pricing: Sgl £60–70
Dinner available from £12.95 CC: Accepted
Room facilities: Access: |↕
Conference: 3 meeting rooms (Thtr 300 max), 24hr-delegate from £60, day-delegate from £30
Children: Welcome Dogs: Assistance dogs only
Licenses: Leisure: Games room
Parking: Off-street
Directions: From A19 take A194 to South Shields. The hotel is situated at the third roundabout on the left.
Map ref: South Shields 13 F4

Northeast

Ocean Breeze Guest House

11 Urfa Terrace, South Shields, Tyne & Wear, NE33 2ES
Tel: 0191 456 7442
Email: info@oceanbreezeguesthouse.co.uk
Web: www.oceanbreezeguesthouse.co.uk
Seasonal closure: Christmas and New Year
Rooms: 6 (3 ensuite)
Pricing: Sgl £25 Dbl £45–60
Room facilities:
Directions: Off Lawe Road (adjacent North Marine
Park) near to harbour and South Shields town centre.
Map ref: South Shields 13 F4

The Algarve Guest House

77 Ocean Road, South Shields, Tyne & Wear, NE33 2JJ
Tel: 0191 455 3783 Fax: 0191 456 6041
Rooms: 6 all ensuite
Pricing: Sgl £20–25 Dbl £40
Room facilities:
Children: Welcome   Dogs: Welcome
Map ref: South Shields 13 F4

Stockton-on-Tees, Co. Durham

Claireville

519 Yarm Road, Eaglescliffe, Co. Durham, TS16 9BG
Tel: 01642 780378 Fax: 01642 784109
Email: reception@clairevillehotel.com
Web: www.clairev.demon.com
Rooms: 18 all ensuite
Dinner available
CC: Accepted
Room facilities:
Children: Welcome
Dogs: Welcome
Licenses:
Parking: Off-street
Directions: On the A135 between the A66 (Stockton-
on-Tees) and the A19 at Yarm. Adjacent to Eaglescliffe
Golf Course.
Map ref: Eaglescliffe 11 D2

Sunderland, Tyne & Wear

Quality Hotel Sunderland

Junction A19/A184, Witney Way, Boldon,
near Sunderland, Tyne & Wear, NE35 9PE
Tel: 0191 519 1999 Fax: 0191 519 0655
Email: enquiries@hotels-sunderland.com
Web: www.choicehotelseurope.com
Rooms: 82 all ensuite
Pricing: Sgl £50–109.95 Dbl £60–143.99
Dinner available from £17.95
CC: Accepted
Room facilities:
Conference: 9 meeting rooms (Thtr 230 max),
24hr-delegate from £125, day-delegate from £34
Children: Welcome
Dogs: Welcome
Licenses:
Leisure: Indoor pool, Gym
Parking: Off-street and free
Directions: Hotel is situated on the junction between
A19 and A184, 7 miles from Newcastle train station.
Map ref: Boldon 13 F4

Tadcaster, North Yorkshire

Hazlewood Castle

Paradise Lane, Hazlewood, Tadcaster,
North Yorkshire, LS24 9NJ
Tel: 01937 535353 Fax: 01937 530630
Email: info@hazlewood-castle.co.uk
Web: www.hazlewood-castle.co.uk

This former monastery has been sensitively restored
and converted with conference centre, banqueting
suites and private dining rooms, along with cafe,
restaurant '1086' and luxury accommodation. Situated
conveniently close to Leeds and York.
Rooms: 21 all ensuite
Pricing: Sgl £120–230 Dbl £155–330
Dinner available from £16.95–44
CC: Accepted
Room facilities:
Conference: 6 meeting rooms (Thtr 160 max),
24hr-delegate from £175, day-delegate from £46
Children: Welcome
Licenses:
Parking: Off-street and free
Directions: Off A1M at A64 junction (Leeds/York). Take
A64 towards York. First left (A659) towards Tadcaster,
signs to Hazelwood Castle.
Map ref: Hazlewood 11 D3

The Presbytery Guest House

 ◆◆◆

The Old Presbytery, London Road, Saxton, Tadcaster,
North Yorkshire, LS24 9PU
Tel: 01937 557708 Fax: 01937 557392
Email: guest@presbytery.plus.com
Web: www.presbyteryguesthouse.co.uk
Rooms: 4 (3 ensuite) &
CC: Accepted
Room facilities: ▢ ☐ ☎
Conference: 1 meeting room
Children: Welcome
Parking: Off-street and free
Directions: Situated on A162 between Barkston Ash
and Scartinewell Golf Course. 2¹/₂ miles from Sherburn
in Elmet. 4 miles from Tadcaster.
Map ref: Saxton 11 D3

Thirsk, North Yorkshire

Angel Inn

 ★★

Long Street, Topcliffe, Thirsk, North Yorkshire, YO7 3RW
Tel: 01845 577237 Fax: 01845 578000
Web: www.angelinn.co.uk
Rooms: 15 all ensuite ☜
Dinner available
CC: Accepted
Room facilities: ▢ ☎ ☐
Conference: 3 meeting rooms (Thtr 150 max)
Children: Welcome ☶ ☼
Licenses: ◈ ♚
Leisure: Fishing
Parking: Off-street and free
Directions: Situated just off the A168, 3 miles from
Junction 49 A1M. 3 miles from A19.
Map ref: Topcliffe 11 D3

Thornton-in-Lonsdale, North Yorkshire

Marton Arms Hotel

 ◆◆◆◆ ✗

Thornton-in-Lonsdale, Ingleton, North Yorkshire, LA6 3PB
Tel: 01524 241281 Fax: 01524 242579
Email: mail@martonarms.co.uk
Web: www.martonarms.co.uk
Rooms: 13 all ensuite ☜ ☗ ⊗
Pricing: Sgl £39–49 Dbl £75–85
CC: Accepted
Room facilities: ▢ ☎ ☐
Conference: 1 meeting room (Thtr 50 max)
Children: Welcome ☶
Licenses: ♚
Leisure: Games room, Snooker/billiards
Parking: Off-street and free
Directions: Located at junction of A65 and A687
Skipton to Kendal road.
Map ref: Ingleton 10 B3

Tynemouth, Tyne & Wear

Grand Hotel

 ★★★★ ☕

Grand Parade, Tynemouth, Tyne & Wear, NE30 4ER
Tel: 0191 293 6666 Fax: 0191 293 6665
Email: info@grandhotel-uk.com
Web: www.grandhotel-uk.com

The Grand Hotel was originally built in 1872 as a
summer residence for the Duchess of Northumberland
and is majestically situated on a cliff top with stunning
views of the coastline.
Rooms: 44 all ensuite ☜ ☗
Pricing: Sgl £70–160 Dbl £80–160
Dinner available from £20–23 CC: Accepted
Room facilities: ▢ ☎ ☐ Access: ☷
Conference: 3 meeting rooms (Thtr 130 max),
24hr-delegate from £120, day-delegate from £28
Children: Welcome ☶ Licenses: ◈ ♚
Parking: Off-street and free
Directions: From A1 take A19 and then A1058. Follow
the signs for Tynemouth. At the seafront, turn right.
Grand Hotel is approx ¹/₂ mile.
Map ref: Tynemouth 13 F4

Wakefield, West Yorkshire

Cedar Court Hotel

★★★★★ ☕

Denby Dale Road, Calder Grove, Wakefield,
West Yorkshire, WF4 3QZ
Tel: 01924 276310 Fax: 01924 280221
Email: res@cedarcourthotels.co.uk
Web: www.cedarcourthotels.co.uk
Rooms: 150 all ensuite ☜ ☗ ⊗
Pricing: Sgl £50–145 Dbl £75–155
Dinner available from £24.50 CC: Accepted
Room facilities: ▢ ☎ ☐ ☎ ❋ Access: ☷
Conference: 19 meeting rooms (Thtr 400 max),
24hr-delegate from £160, day-delegate from £49.50
Children: Welcome Dogs: Welcome Licenses: ◈ ♚
Leisure: Indoor pool, Gym, Health spa, Beauty salon,
Snooker/billiards Parking: Off-street and free
Directions: Off Junction 39 of M1, located adjacent to
roundabout under motorway.
Map ref: Calder Grove 11 D4

Northeast

Hotel St Pierre

★★★

Barnsley Road, Newmillerdam, Wakefield,
West Yorkshire, WF2 6QG
Tel: 01924 255596 Fax: 01924 252746
Email: res@hotelstpierre.co.uk
Web: www.hotelstpierre.co.uk
Rooms: 54 all ensuite 🛏 📺 ⑤
Pricing: Sgl £49–69 Dbl £59–99
Dinner available from £19.95–25.95 CC: Accepted
Room facilities: ▢ ☎ ⑤ 📞 Access: ⏐⏐
Conference: 6 meeting rooms (Thtr 120 max),
24hr-delegate from £99, day-delegate from £29
Children: Welcome ⱶ
Licenses: ⚒ ⚌⚌ Leisure: Gym
Parking: Off-street and free
Directions: Junction 39 M1 A636 towards Wakefield.
Turn right at second roundabout, turn right onto A61
Barnsley. Hotel on left after dam.
Map ref: Newmillerdam 11 D4

Campanile
Travel Accommodation

Monckton Road, off Denby Dale Road, Wakefield,
West Yorkshire, WF2 7AL
Tel: 01924 201054 Fax: 01924 290976
Email: wakefield@envergure.co.uk
Web: www.campanile.com

Campanile hotels offer comfortable and convenient
budget accommodation and a traditional French-style
Bistro providing freshly-cooked food for breakfast,
lunch and dinner. All rooms ensuite with tea/coffee-
making facilities, DDT and TV with Sky channels.
Rooms: 77 all ensuite ⑤
Pricing: Sgl £48.45–65.95 Dbl £54.40–71.90
Dinner available from £12.95 CC: Accepted
Room facilities: ▢ ☎ ⑤ 📞
Conference: 1 meeting room (Thtr 35 max),
24hr-delegate from £70, day-delegate from £21.50
Children: Welcome ⱶ
Dogs: Welcome
Licenses: ⚌⚌
Parking: Off-street and free
Directions: Take Junction 39 M1. Towards Wakefield
Centre on A636, hotel is 1 mile from motorway on the
left side, on Monckton Road Industrial Estate.
Map ref: Wakefield 11 D4

Washington, Tyne & Wear

Campanile
Travel Accommodation

Emerson Road, District 5, Washington,
Tyne & Wear, NE37 1LE
Tel: 0191 416 5010 Fax: 0191 416 5023
Email: washington@campanile-hotels.com
Web: www.campanile.com

Campanile hotels offer comfortable and convenient
budget accommodation and a traditional French-style
Bistro providing freshly cooked food for breakfast,
lunch and dinner. All rooms ensuite with tea/coffee-
making facilities, DDT and TV with Sky channels.
Rooms: 79 all ensuite ⑤
Pricing: Sgl £43.95 Dbl £43.95
Dinner available from £7.95–15 CC: Accepted
Room facilities: ▢ ☎ ⑤ 📞
Conference: 1 meeting room (Thtr 30 max),
24hr-delegate from £70, day-delegate from £21.50
Children: Welcome ⱶ Dogs: Welcome
Licenses: ⚌⚌
Parking: Off-street and free
Directions: J64 A1(M). Follow signs for Campanile
Hotel.
Map ref: Washington 13 F4

Whitby, North Yorkshire

Saxonville Hotel

★★★★

Ladysmith Avenue, Whitby, North Yorkshire, YO21 3HX
Tel: 01947 602631 Fax: 01947 820523
Email: newtons@saxonville.co.uk
Web: www.saxonville.co.uk
Seasonal closure: December to February
Rooms: 23 all ensuite 🛏 📺 ⑤
Pricing: Sgl £56.50–61.50 Dbl £113–123
Dinner available from £22.50 CC: Accepted
Room facilities: ▢ ☎ ⑤ 📞
Conference: 2 meeting rooms (Thtr 120 max)
Children: Welcome ⱶ Licenses: ⚌⚌
Parking: Off-street and free
Directions: Follow signs for Whitby/Westcliff. At large
four-towered building turn inland into Argyle Road.
Saxonville first turning on right.
Map ref: Whitby 11 E2

Old West Cliff Hotel

★★

42 Crescent Avenue, Whitby, North Yorkshire, YO21 3EQ
Tel: 01947 603292 Fax: 01947 821716
Email: oldwestcliff@telinco.co.uk
Web: www.oldwestcliff.telinco.co.uk
Seasonal closure: December to January
Rooms: 12 all ensuite
Pricing: Sgl £51 Dbl £62
Dinner available from £16.50
CC: Accepted
Room facilities: ▢ ☕
Children: Welcome
Licenses: ♦♦♦
Directions: On approaching Whitby, follow signs for West Cliff. Hotel off the central exit of Crescent Gardens, opposite Spa and Pavillion complex.
Map ref: Whitby 11 E2

Glendale Guest House

♦♦♦♦

16 Crescent Avenue, Whitby, North Yorkshire, YO21 3ED
Tel: 01947 604242
Rooms: 5 all ensuite
Pricing: Sgl £24 Dbl £54
Dinner available from £12
Room facilities: ▢ ☕
Children: Welcome ☕
Dogs: Welcome
Licenses: ♦♦♦
Parking: Off-street and free
Directions: Railway station turn into Bagdale, proceed to roundabout at Chubb Hill, turn right to roundabout take second exit, first right Crescent Avenue.
Map ref: Whitby 11 E2

Seacliffe Hotel

♦♦♦♦

North Promenade, West Cliff, Whitby,
North Yorkshire, YO21 3JX
Tel: 01947 603139 Fax: 01947 603139
Email: julie@seacliffe.fsnet.co.uk
Web: www.seacliffe.co.uk
Rooms: 20 all ensuite
Pricing: Sgl £49.50–75 Dbl £79–86
CC: Accepted
Room facilities: ▢ ☎ ☕
Children: Welcome ♨ ☕
Dogs: Welcome
Licenses: ♦♦♦
Leisure: Games room
Parking: Off-street and free
Directions: Follow signs for West Cliff and West Cliff car park. Hotel located on sea front.
Map ref: Whitby 11 E2

Arundel House Hotel

♦♦♦

Bagdale, Whitby, North Yorkshire, YO21 1QJ
Tel: 01947 603645 Fax: 0870 1656214
Email: arundel_house@hotmail.com
Web: www.arundelhousehotel.co.uk
Rooms: 11 all ensuite
Dinner available
CC: Accepted
Room facilities: ▢ ☕
Children: Welcome ♨ ☕
Dogs: Welcome
Licenses: ♦♦♦
Parking: Off-street and free
Directions: Arundel House Hotel is situated 500 yards from the town centre and station on the A171 in the direction of Scarborough.
Map ref: Whitby 11 E2

Star Cross

♦♦♦

105 Mayfield Road, Whitby, North Yorkshire, YO21 1LT
Tel: 01947 602371
Rooms: 2 all ensuite
Pricing: Dbl £60
Room facilities: ▢ ☕
Parking: Off-street and free
Map ref: Whitby 11 E2

The Sandbeck (Private Hotel)

♦♦♦

1-2 Crescent Terrace, West Cliff, Whitby,
North Yorkshire, YO21 3EL
Tel: 01947 604012 Fax: 01947 606402
Email: dysonsandbeck@tesco.net
Web: www.whitbyonline.co.uk
Seasonal closure: December
Rooms: 24 all ensuite
Pricing: Sgl £32–34 Dbl £62–85
CC: Accepted
Room facilities: ▢ ☕
Access: |↕|
Children: Welcome ♨
Licenses: ♦♦♦
Directions: Take the A169/A171 and follow signs for West Cliff.
Map ref: Whitby 11 E2

J.M.K.

New for 2006

9 Fyling Road, Castle Park, Whitby,
North Yorkshire, YO21 3NA
Tel: 01947 603299
Rooms: 3 ⊛
Room facilities: ▢ ☕
Children: Welcome
Dogs: Welcome
Parking: Off-street and free
Map ref: Castle Park 11 E2

Northeast

Whitley Bay, Tyne & Wear

Windsor Hotel

★★★★

South Parade, Whitley Bay, Tyne & Wear, NE26 2RF
Tel: 0191 251 8888 Fax: 0191 297 0272
Email: info@windsorhotel-uk.com
Web: www.windsorhotel-uk.com

Privately owned, recently refurbished hotel with beautifully appointed bedrooms, situated between the seafront and town centre. First choice for business or pleasure.
Rooms: 69 all ensuite 🛏 🎟 ⊗
Pricing: Sgl £59–75 Dbl £65–125
Dinner available from £14.95 CC: Accepted
Room facilities: ☐ ☎ ☞ Access: |↕|
Conference: 1 meeting room (Thtr 80 max), 24hr-delegate from £89, day-delegate from £25
Children: Welcome ⼈
Licenses: ⽕⽕⽕
Parking: Off-street and free
Directions: From A1, join A19. Follow signs for A1058. Once on seafront turn left. Travel approximately 2 miles.
Map ref: Whitley Bay 13 F4

Esplanade Lodge

◆◆◆

1 Linden Terrace, Whitley Bay, Tyne & Wear, NE26 2AA
Tel: 0191 251 7557
Email: esplanadelodge@hotmail.com
Web: www.esplanadelodge.co.uk
Rooms: 9 (7 ensuite) 🛏
Pricing: Sgl £20–30 Dbl £40–60 CC: Accepted
Room facilities: ☐ ☞
Children: Welcome
Dogs: Welcome
Parking: Off-street and free
Directions: Head to the seafront (Whitley Bay). Locate the street "Esplanade" and head upwards. Lodge is at the top on the right.
Map ref: Whitley Bay 13 F4

Yarm, North Yorkshire

Judges Country House Hotel

★★★  Excellent

Kirklevington Hall, Kirklevington,
Yarm, North Yorkshire, TS15 9LW
Tel: 01642 789000 Fax: 01642 782878
Email: enquiries@judgeshotel.co.uk
Web: www.judgeshotel.co.uk

The hotel's 21 guestrooms, gourmet restaurant and private dining room sit on top of its own 31 acres of immaculate gardens. Award-winning Head Chef Neal Bullock and his team of twelve chefs take much time and trouble to source the very best in fresh local produce. Free broadband and Wi-Fi.
Rooms: 21 all ensuite 🎟 ⊗
Pricing: Sgl £153–164 Dbl £164–179
Dinner available from £32.50–45.000
CC: Accepted
Room facilities: ☐ ☎ ☞ ☎
Conference: 7 meeting rooms (Thtr 200 max), 24hr-delegate from £195, day-delegate from £45
Children: Welcome ⼈
Licenses: ⚓ ⽕⽕⽕ Leisure: Gym
Parking: Off-street and free
Directions: From the A19 take the A67 heading to Yarm and hotel is 1 mile on the left-hand side.
Map ref: Kirklevington 11 D2

York, North Yorkshire

Aldwark Manor

★★★★ Excellent

Aldwark, near Alne, York, North Yorkshire, YO61 1UF
Tel: 01347 838146 Fax: 01347 838867
Email: aldwark@marstonhotels.com
Web: www.marstonhotels.com
Rooms: 60 all ensuite 🛏 🎟 ⊗
Dinner available CC: Accepted
Room facilities: ☐ ☎ ☞ ☎
Access: |↕|
Conference: 6 meeting rooms (Thtr 300 max)

Children: Welcome ♩
Licenses: ⚐ ♙
Leisure: Indoor pool, Gym, Health spa,
Beauty salon, Golf
Parking: Off-street and free
Directions: Leave A1(M) onto A59 for York; turn left at
Green Hammerton and follow the brown tourist signs.
Map ref: Aldwark 11 D3

Dean Court Hotel

★★★★ ⚑⚑

Duncombe Place, York, North Yorkshire, YO1 7EF
Tel: 01904 625082 Fax: 01904 620305
Email: info@deancourt-york.co.uk
Web: www.deancourt-york.co.uk

In the very shadow of York Minster. Stylish designed
lounge areas, contemporary and traditionally designed
luxury accommodation. D.C.H. Award Winning
Restaurant. The Court – Café-Bistro. Free valet
parking, conference and weddings. Private dining a
speciality.
Rooms: 37 all ensuite ⚌ ⚐ ⊛
Pricing: Sgl £95–125 Dbl £125–205
Dinner available from £22.50–35
CC: Accepted
Room facilities: ⬚ ☎ ☕ ⚒
Access: ↟
Conference: 2 meeting rooms (Thtr 50 max),
24hr-delegate from £140, day-delegate from £42
Children: Welcome ♩ ⚛
Licenses: ⚐ ♙
Parking: Off-street
Directions: A64 York, A1237 York Centre. At fourth
roundabout take A19 Rawcliffe/Clifton direction. Follow
road to York Minster approx 2 miles.
Map ref: York 11 D3

Grange Hotel

★★★★ ⚑⚑⚑

Excellent

1 Clifton, York, North Yorkshire, YO30 6AA
Tel: 01904 644744 Fax: 01904 612453
Email: info@grangehotel.co.uk
Web: www.grangehotel.co.uk

Exclusive Regency townhouse just minutes from the
Minster and city centre. Luxurious accommodation,
three superb restaurants and award-winning food.
Excellent conference facilities. Private car park.
Rooms: 30 all ensuite ⚌ ⚐
Pricing: Sgl £115–260 Dbl £135–260
Dinner available from £28
CC: Accepted
Room facilities: ⬚ ☎ ☕ ⚒
Conference: 2 meeting rooms (Thtr 50 max),
24hr-delegate from £157, day-delegate from £39
Children: Welcome ♩
Licenses: ⚐ ♙
Parking: Off-street and free
Directions: On A19 York to Thirsk road, 500 yards from
city centre.
Map ref: York 11 D3

Kilima

★★★

129 Holgate Road, York, North Yorkshire, YO24 4AZ
Tel: 01904 625787 Fax: 01904 612083
Email: sales@kilima.co.uk
Web: www.kilima.co.uk
Rooms: 26 all ensuite ⚐ ⊛
Pricing: Sgl £75–78 Dbl £99–140
Dinner available from £21.95
CC: Accepted
Room facilities: ⬚ ☎ ☕ ⚒
Conference: 1 meeting room (Thtr 14 max),
24hr-delegate from £120, day-delegate from £37
Children: Welcome ♩ ⚛
Licenses: ♙
Leisure: Indoor pool, Gym, Turkish steam room
Parking: Off-street and free
Directions: Located on west side of city, on A59
Harrogate road.
Map ref: York 11 D3

Northeast

Middlethorpe Hall and Spa

★★★★ ♔♔♔ *Premier*

Bishopthorpe Road, York, North Yorkshire, YO23 2GB
Tel: 01904 641241 Fax: 01904 620176
Email: info@middlethorpe.com
Web: www.middlethorpe.com
Rooms: 29 all ensuite 🖥 ⊗
Pricing: Sgl £115–175 Dbl £175–305
Dinner available from £39–48
CC: Accepted
Room facilities: 🖥 ☎ 🕯
Access: |↕|
Conference: 4 meeting rooms (Thtr 56 max),
24hr-delegate from £170.38, day-delegate from £58.75
Children: Welcome 6yrs min age
Licenses: ⬥ ♦♦♦
Leisure: Indoor pool, Gym, Health spa, Beauty salon,
Garden walks
Parking: Off-street and free
Directions: Leave the A64 to join the A1036,
signposted York/Racecourse. Then follow smaller signs
to Bishopthorpe and Middlethorpe.
Map ref: York 11 D3

Minster Hotel

★★★

60 Bootham, York, North Yorkshire, YO30 7BZ
Tel: 01904 621267 Fax: 01904 654719
Email: book@yorkminsterhotel.co.uk
Web: www.yorkminsterhotel.co.uk
Rooms: 34 all ensuite 🍴 🖥 ⊗
Pricing: Sgl £65–95 Dbl £69–200
Dinner available from £15.95–39.95
CC: Accepted
Room facilities: 🖥 ☎ ⊃ 🕯
Access: |↕|
Conference: 3 meeting rooms (Thtr 65 max),
24hr-delegate from £120, day-delegate from £35
Children: Welcome 🍴 ☕
Dogs: Assistance dogs only
Licenses: ♦♦♦
Parking: Off-street and free
Directions: On the A19 Thirsk Road on the right-hand
side before the inner city walls.
Map ref: York 11 D3

Ice & slice?

RAC's comprehensive
inspection means we
even check drinks are
served the way
you want.

Monkbar Hotel

★★★

Monk Bar, York, North Yorkshire, YO31 7JA
Tel: 01904 638086 Fax: 01904 629195
Email: sales@monkbarhotel.co.uk
Web: www.monkbarhotel.co.uk

The perfect choice for business and leisure at the very
heart of the city. Extensive meeting facilities. Individually
designed bedrooms. Welcoming lounge and bar and
renowned restaurant. Free parking for residents.
Rooms: 99 all ensuite 🍴 🖥 ⊗
Pricing: Sgl £105–125 Dbl £140–175
Dinner available from £21–28 CC: Accepted
Room facilities: 🖥 ☎ ⊃ 🕯 Access: |↕|
Conference: 9 meeting rooms (Thtr 130 max),
24hr-delegate from £150, day-delegate from £48
Children: Welcome 🍴 ☕ Dogs: Welcome
Licenses: ⬥ ♦♦♦
Parking: Off-street and free
Directions: From A64 take A1079 exit to York. At traffic
lights turn right at the city walls. Second set of lights
straight ahead. Hotel is on the right.
Map ref: York 11 D3

Beechwood Close Hotel

★★

19 Shipton Road, York, North Yorkshire, YO30 5RE
Tel: 01904 658378 Fax: 01904 647124
Email: bch@selcom.co.uk
Web: www.beechwood-close.co.uk

A warm welcome is assured from Beverley & Graham
and their staff. Set in its own grounds, the hotel is ideal
for visiting the city and surrounding countryside.
Rooms: 14 all ensuite 🍴

Pricing: Sgl £45–52 Dbl £72–80
Dinner available from £15.75 CC: Accepted
Room facilities: ☐ ☎ ☺
Conference: 2 meeting rooms (Thtr 30 max),
24hr-delegate from £71.50, day-delegate from £18
Children: Welcome �🏃 Licenses: ⛉
Parking: Off-street and free
Directions: From Outer Ring Road (A1237), turn to city
centre at A19 Thirsk roundabout. Hotel is 1 mile on
right, just inside 30mph zone.
Map ref: York 11 D3

Blue Bridge Hotel
★★
Fishergate, York, North Yorkshire, YO10 4AP
Tel: 01904 621193 Fax: 01904 671571
Email: info@bluebridgehotel.co.uk
Web: www.bluebridgehotel.co.uk
Rooms: 20 all ensuite ☺ ☺
Pricing: Sgl £35–110 Dbl £55–160
Dinner available from £13.50–32.95 CC: Accepted
Room facilities: ☐ ☎ ☺
Conference: 2 meeting rooms (Thtr 20 max),
24hr-delegate from £90, day-delegate from £25
Children: Welcome �🏃 ☕ Dogs: Assistance dogs only
Licenses: ⛉ Parking: Off-street and free
Directions: On A19 York to Selby road, 2 miles from
outer ring road on right-hand side. Five minutes' walk
from city centre.
Map ref: York 11 D3

Knavesmire Manor

Once a Rowntree family home, the hotel
offers a tropical indoor pool, with
uninterrupted views of the famous Yorkshire
racecourse. Comfortable and well-appointed
ensuite bedrooms. Restaurant 302 has an
excellent local reputation serving local and
traditional foods.

302 Tadcaster Road, York YO24 1HE
Tel: 01904 702941 Fax: 01904 709274
knavesmire@tiscali.co.uk
www.knavesmire.co.uk

Heworth Court Hotel
★★
Heworth Green, York, North Yorkshire, YO31 7TQ
Tel: 01904 425156 Fax: 01904 415290
Email: hotel@heworth.co.uk
Web: www.visityork.com

A traditional English hotel within one mile of York
Minster with ensuite hotel accommodation, four-
posters, whisky bar, candle-lit restaurant and ample
parking. Special "short breaks" available all year.
Rooms: 28 all ensuite ☺ ☺ ☺
Pricing: Sgl £54–99 Dbl £69–125
Dinner available from £14.95 CC: Accepted
Room facilities: ☐ ☎ ☺ ☎
Conference: 1 meeting room (Thtr 50 max)
Children: Welcome �🏃
Licenses: ⛉
Parking: Off-street and free
Directions: Use outer ring road (York bypass) and turn
into York from Scarborough roundabout. Hotel is a
12-minute walk from York Minster.
Map ref: York 11 D3

Judges Lodgings
★★
9 Lendal, York, North Yorkshire, YO1 8AQ
Tel: 01904 638733 Fax: 01904 679947
Email: info@judgeslodgings.com
Web: www.judgeslodgings.com
Rooms: 14 all ensuite ☺ ☺ ☺
Pricing: Sgl £85–100 Dbl £110–180
Dinner available from £30
CC: Accepted
Room facilities: ☐ ☎ ☺
Conference: 3 meeting rooms (Thtr 40 max)
Children: Welcome �🏃 Dogs: Welcome
Licenses: ⛉ Parking: Off-street and free
Map ref: York 11 D3

Knavesmire Manor Hotel

★★

302 Tadcaster Road, York, North Yorkshire, YO24 1HE
Tel: 01904 702941 Fax: 01904 709274
Email: knavesmire@tiscali.co.uk
Web: www.knavesmire.co.uk
Rooms: 20 all ensuite
Pricing: Sgl £60–85 Dbl £79–120
Dinner available from £17
CC: Accepted
Room facilities:
Access: |↕↑
Conference: 2 meeting rooms (Thtr 30 max),
24hr-delegate from £99, day-delegate from £24.95
Children: Welcome
Dogs: Welcome
Licenses:
Leisure: Indoor pool, Health spa
Parking: Off-street and free
Directions: Take the A64 off the A1, near Tadcaster.
Follow signs to York West, then signs to Bishopthorpe
or Racecourse. Hotel opposite the Knavesmire
racecourse.
Map ref: York 11 D3
See advert on previous page

Ascot House

◆◆◆◆

80 East Parade, York, North Yorkshire, YO31 7YH
Tel: 01904 426826 Fax: 01904 431077
Email: admin@ascothouseyork.com
Web: www.ascothouseyork.com
Seasonal closure: Christmas

A family-run Victorian villa 15 minutes' walk from city
centre, Castle Museum or York Minster with rooms of
character and many four-poster or canopy beds.
Traditional English breakfasts. Residential licence,
sauna, private enclosed car park.
Rooms: 15 (12 ensuite)
Pricing: Sgl £30–60 Dbl £60–75 CC: Accepted
Room facilities:
Children: Welcome Dogs: Welcome
Licenses: Leisure: Sauna
Parking: Off-street and free
Directions: From northeast, junction A1237 and A64
(ring road) take A1036. Turn left for Heworth after
30mph sign, then right at traffic lights into East Parade.
Map ref: York 11 D3

Ashbourne House

◆◆◆◆

139 Fulford Road, York, North Yorkshire, YO10 4HG
Tel: 01904 639912 Fax: 01904 631332
Email: ashbourneh@aol.com
Web: www.ashbourne-house.com

Family-run Victorian house; ensuite rooms are
furnished in a contemporary style and fully equipped.
Licensed with a small honesty bar in a comfortable
guest lounge. Car parking. Non-smoking.
Rooms: 7 (6 ensuite)
Pricing: Sgl £45–55 Dbl £55–70 CC: Accepted
Room facilities:
Children: Welcome
Licenses: Parking: Off-street and free
Directions: On the A19 road south of the city (York to
Selby road), about one mile from the city centre.
Map ref: York 11 D3

Holly Lodge

◆◆◆◆

204–206 Fulford Road, York, North Yorkshire, YO1 4DD
Tel: 01904 646005
Web: www.thehollylodge.co.uk

Beautifully appointed Grade II listed building, 10
minutes' stroll to centre. Convenient for all York's
attractions. On-site parking. All rooms ensuite
overlooking garden or terrace. Booking recommended.
1½ miles from A64/A19 intersection.
Rooms: 5 all ensuite
Pricing: Sgl £68–98 Dbl £68–98 CC: Accepted
Room facilities:

Children: Welcome 7yrs min age
Parking: Off-street and free
Directions: On corner of Fulford Road and Wenlock, 1½ miles towards centre from A19/A64 intersection. Ten minutes' walk along A19 south from centre.
Map ref: York 11 D3

The Bloomsbury

127 Clifton, York, North Yorkshire, YO30 6BL
Tel: 01904 634031 Fax: 01904 634855
Email: info@bloomsburyhotel.co.uk
Web: www.bloomsburyhotel.co.uk
Rooms: 9 all ensuite
Pricing: Sgl £40–60 Dbl £60–90 CC: Accepted
Room facilities:
Children: Welcome Parking: Off-street and free
Directions: From A1237 North York bypass take A19 York turn at roundabout. Hotel is approximately one mile along A19 opposite the church.
Map ref: York 11 D3

The Hazelwood

24–25 Portland Street, York, North Yorkshire, YO31 7EH
Tel: 01904 626548 Fax: 01904 628032
Email: reservations@thehazelwoodyork.com
Web: www.thehazelwoodyork.com

Situated in the very heart of York yet in an extremely quiet location, an award-winning Victorian town house with private car park. Wide breakfast menu including vegetarian. Non smoking.
Rooms: 14 all ensuite
Pricing: Sgl £50–95 Dbl £80–110 CC: Accepted
Room facilities: Children: Welcome 8yrs min age
Licenses: Parking: Off-street and free
Directions: Situated just 400 yards from York Minster in residential side street, off inner ring road (Gillygate).
Map ref: York 11 D3

Barrington House Guest House

15 Nunthorpe Avenue, York, North Yorkshire, YO23 1PF
Tel: 01904 634539
Email: barringtonhouse@btinternet.com
Web: www.barringtonhouse.net
Seasonal closure: Christmas and New Year

Rooms: 7 all ensuite
Pricing: Sgl £28–35 Dbl £50–64 CC: Accepted
Room facilities: Children: Welcome
Directions: Take A1(M) to the A64 then the A1036 to Scarcroft Road, second turning on the right to Nunthorpe Avenue.
Map ref: York 11 D3

Priory Hotel

126–128 Fulford Road, York,
North Yorkshire, YO10 4BE
Tel: 01904 625280 Fax: 01904 637330
Email: reservations@priory-hotelyork.co.uk
Web: www.priory-hotelyork.co.uk
Rooms: 16 all ensuite
Pricing: Sgl £45–75 Dbl £70–95 CC: Accepted
Room facilities:
Children: Welcome Dogs: Welcome
Licenses: Parking: Off-street and free
Directions: Situated on the A19 road to Selby on south side of city. No.9 bus or 1½ miles from station.
Map ref: York 11 D3

St Denys Hotel

St Denys Road, York, North Yorkshire, YO1 1QD
Tel: 01904 622207 Fax: 01904 624800
Email: info@stdenyshotel.co.uk
Web: www.stdenyshotel.co.uk
Rooms: 13 all ensuite
Pricing: Sgl £40–75 Dbl £45–125
Dinner available from £13.95–32.95
CC: Accepted
Room facilities:
Children: Welcome Dogs: Assistance dogs only
Licenses: Parking: Off-street and free
Directions: Take A1079 for York/Hull, 2½ miles from outer ring road, around Walmgate Bar. After ½ mile turn left on one-way system. Hotel is on left, 2 minutes walk from city centre.
Map ref: York 11 D3

St Georges Hotel

6 St Georges Place, York, North Yorkshire, YO24 1DR
Tel: 01904 625056 Fax: 01904 625009
Email: sixstgeorg@aol.com
Web: www.members.aol.com/sixstgeorg
Rooms: 10 all ensuite
Pricing: Sgl £35–45 Dbl £55–63
Dinner available from £9–12 CC: Accepted
Room facilities:
Children: Welcome Dogs: Welcome
Licenses: Parking: Off-street and free
Directions: From south, take A1036. Turn left as racecourse ends on right. From north, on A59 turn right after Iron Bridge. Turn right again and second right.
Map ref: York 11 D3

Northeast

Northwest

Thwaite Flat · Sands · Carnforth · Ingleton · NORTH YOR...
Walney Island · Hornby · Austwick
Barrow-in-Furness · Morecambe · Settle · Malham · B6265
Walney · Bay · Lancaster · Forest of · Long Preston · Bolton Abbey
Island · Heysham · Ellel · Bowland · Bolton by · Gisburn · Skipton
Fleetwood · Preesall · Bowland · Barnoldswick · Earby · Silsden · Ilkley
Garstang · LANCASHIRE · Clitheroe · Colne · Keighley · Bingley
Cleveleys · Thornton · Longridge · Brockhall Village · Nelson · Haworth
Bispham · Mellor · Billington · Simonstone · Reedley · Bradford
North Shore · Langho · Burnley · Hebden · Halifax
Blackpool · Accrington · Bridge · Sowerby Br. · Elland
South Shore · Blackburn · Todmorden · Ainley Top
Blackpool · Leyland · Rawtenstall · Bacup · Huddersfield
Lytham · Clayton-le-Woods · Darwen · Ramsbottom · Rochdale
St Anne's · Southport · Chorley · Hawkshaw · Bury · Heywood · Holmfirth
Eccleston · Skelmers- · Bolton · Middleton · Oldham · Chadderton
Formby · Ormskirk · dale · Up Holland · Wigan · Farnworth · MANCHESTER
Maghull · E. Pimbo · Atherton · Leigh · Swinton · Kersal · Ashton-under-Lyne
Crosby · St Helens · Newton- · Salford · Glossop
Bootle · Knowsley · le-Willows · Eccles · Stretford · Trafford Park · Hyde
Liverpool · Wallasey · Knowsley · A57 · Warrington · Sale · Bredbury · Hayfield · Edale
Hoylake · Birkenhead · Oxton · Liverpool · Altrincham · Cheadle · Stockport · New Mills
Prestatyn · Heswall · John Lennon · Widnes · Bowdon · Bramhall · Chapel-en-le-Frith
Rhyl · Thornton Hough · Lymm · Mere · Manchester · Wilmslow · Pott · Whaley · Buxton
Rhuddlan · Neston · Runcorn · Frodsham · Intnl Airport · Knutsford · Shrigley · Bridge
Holywell · Flint · Ellesmere · Alderley · Macclesfield
St Asaph · Connah's · Port · Northwich · Over · Edge · Dovedale
Denbigh · Quay · Mollington · Peover · A54
Mold · Northop Hall · CHESHIRE · Holmes · Eaton · Congleton · Leek
Ruthin · Hawarden · Hoole · Winsford · Chapel · B5053
Llanfwrog · Caergwrle · Buckley · Chester · Middlewich · B5054
Pulford · Tarporley · Sandbach · Alsager · Biddulph
Moss · Broxton · Beeston · A51 · Crewe · Kidsgrove · Tunstall · Burslem · Swi
Wrexham · Nantwich · Newcastle-under-Lyme · Stoke-on-Trent · Kingsley · Oak...
Cefn-mawr · Malpas · Woore · Keele · Hanley · Longton · Cheadle
Ruabon · Whitchurch · STAFFOR...
Chirk · Haighton · Stone
Gledrig · Ellesmere · Market · Croxton
Whittington · Hodnet · Drayton
Wem · Adbaston · Eccleshall

Glasgow · · Edinburgh
· Newcastle
Belfast ·
Dublin · · Manchester
Birmingham ·
Cardiff · London ·

Northwest

Award winners

To help you choose somewhere really special for your stay, we've listed here all RAC Award-winning properties in this region.

Gold Ribbon Award

Premier

		pg
Gilpin Lodge Country House Hotel, Windermere	★★★	452
Green Bough Hotel, Chester	★★★	421
Holbeck Ghyll Country House Hotel, Windermere	★★★	452
Miller Howe Hotel, Windermere	★★	454
Sharrow Bay Hotel, Howtown	★★★	429
The Chester Grosvenor and Spa, Chester	★★★★★	421
The Samling, Windermere	★★★	453

Gilpin Lodge Country House Hotel, Windermere

Green Bough Hotel, Chester

Miller Howe Hotel, Windermere

Sharrow Bay Hotel, Howtown

Blue Ribbon Award

Excellent

Swinside Lodge Hotel, Keswick

White Ribbon Award

Commended

The Chester Crabwall Manor, Chester

Lakeside Hotel, Windermere

North Lakes Hotel and Spa, Penrith

Little Gem Award

Little Gem		pg
Bessiestown Country Guest House, Carlisle	♦♦♦♦♦	420
Chester Stone Villa Hotel, Chester	♦♦♦♦♦	423
Coniston Lodge, Coniston	♦♦♦♦♦	425
Hazel Bank Country House, Borrowdale	♦♦♦♦♦	418
West Vale Country Guest House, Hawkshead	♦♦♦♦♦	428

Bessiestown Country Guest House, Carlisle

Chester Stone Villa Hotel, Chester

Coniston Lodge, Coniston

Hazel Bank Country House, Borrowdale

Alderley Edge, Cheshire

The Alderley Edge Hotel

★★★★ ♞♞♞

Macclesfield Road, Alderley Edge, Cheshire, SK9 7BJ
Tel: 01625 583033 Fax: 01625 586343
Email: sales@alderleyedgehotel.com
Web: www.alderleyedgehotel.com

Following a multi-million pound refurbishment, the hotel offers all the comforts a seasoned traveller would expect, as well as special touches to make you feel at home; tea and coffee making facilities and bathrobes in superior rooms.
Rooms: 52 all ensuite ⊛
Pricing: Sgl £55–147.50 Dbl £99–175
Dinner available from £29.50
CC: Accepted
Room facilities: ▢ ☎ ▣ ☜
Access: ⎸↥
Conference: 3 meeting rooms (Thtr 90 max),
24hr-delegate from £165, day-delegate from £49.50
Children: Welcome ☩
Licenses: ⟁ ⅲ
Parking: Off-street and free
Directions: Located on B5087, just 400 yards from Alderley Edge village.
Map ref: Alderley Edge 7 E1

Alston, Cumbria

Lowbyer Manor Country House

◆◆◆◆ ☙

Hexham Road, Alston, Cumbria, CA9 3JX
Tel: 01434 381230 Fax: 01434 381425
Email: stay@lowbyer.com
Web: www.lowbyer.com
Rooms: 9 all ensuite ▣ ⊛
Pricing: Sgl £33–45 Dbl £66–90 CC: Accepted
Room facilities: ▢ ▣
Children: Welcome
Dogs: Welcome
Licenses: ⅲ
Parking: Off-street and free
Directions: From Junction 40 on M6 join A686. Hotel two minutes from Alston Town Centre on A686 towards Hexham.
Map ref: Alston 10 C1

Altrincham, Cheshire

Cresta Court

★★★

Church Street, Altrincham/Manchester,
Cheshire, WA14 4DP
Tel: 0161 927 7272 Fax: 0161 929 6548
Email: sales@cresta-court.co.uk
Web: www.cresta-court.co.uk
Rooms: 136 all ensuite ⊛ ▣ ⊛
Pricing: Sgl £55–75 Dbl £65–105
Dinner available from £15.95
CC: Accepted
Room facilities: ▢ ☎ ▣ ☜
Access: ⎸↥
Conference: 8 meeting rooms (Thtr 350 max),
24hr-delegate from £95, day-delegate from £35
Children: Welcome ☩
Dogs: Welcome
Licenses: ⟁ ⅲ
Leisure: Gym, Beauty salon
Parking: Off-street and free
Directions: Situated 200 yards from Altrincham town centre on A56. From J19 M6, take A556 towards Manchester. The hotel is on the right.
Map ref: Altrincham 7 E1
See advert on this page

Northwest

Quality Hotel Altrincham

★★★★

Langham Road, Bowdon, Altrincham, Cheshire, WA14 2HT
Tel: 0161 928 7121 Fax: 0161 927 7560
Email: enquiries@hotels-altrincham.com
Web: www.choicehotelseurope.com
Rooms: 91 all ensuite 🛏 🖥 ⊗
Pricing: Sgl £55–125 Dbl £75–145
Dinner available from £21.95
CC: Accepted
Room facilities: 🖵 ☎ 🕮 📞
Conference: 5 meeting rooms (Thtr 150 max),
24hr-delegate from £142, day-delegate from £38
Children: Welcome 🏃
Dogs: Welcome
Licenses: 🍷 🍾
Leisure: Indoor pool, Gym, Health spa
Parking: Off-street and free
Directions: Exit M6 at Junction 19. Follow A556
towards Manchester onto A56. Turn left onto B5161.
Hotel one mile on right.
Map ref: Bowdon 7 E1

Ambleside, Cumbria

The Waterhead Hotel

★★★★★

Lake Road, Ambleside, Cumbria, LA22 0ER
Tel: 015394 32566 Fax: 015394 31255
Email: waterhead@elhmail.co.uk
Web: www.elh.co.uk
Rooms: 41 all ensuite ⊗
Pricing: Sgl £103–140 Dbl £146–230
Dinner available from £30
CC: Accepted
Room facilities: 🖵 ☎ 🕮 📞
Conference: 2 meeting rooms (Thtr 35 max),
24hr-delegate from £138, day-delegate from £42
Children: Welcome 🏃 🍼
Dogs: Welcome
Licenses: 🍾
Parking: Off-street and free
Directions: From north J40 M6, from south J36; A591
to Windermere, then to Ambleside. Hotel at Waterhead
Bay opposite pier.
Map ref: Ambleside 10 B2

The big sleep

As part of our comprehensive inspection process, RAC Inspectors investigate the comfort of the beds.

Rothay Manor

★★★★

Rothay Bridge, Ambleside, Cumbria, LA22 0EH
Tel: 01539 433605 Fax: 01539 433607
Email: hotel@rothaymanor.co.uk
Web: www.rothaymanor.co.uk
Seasonal closure: 3–28 January

Enjoy comfortable, relaxed hospitality with excellent
food and wine in beautiful surroundings. Families and
disabled guests welcome. Free use of nearby leisure
centre, short breaks and special interest holidays
available.
Rooms: 19 all ensuite 🛏 🖥 ⊗
Pricing: Sgl £70–120 Dbl £125–190
Dinner available from £34–38
CC: Accepted
Room facilities: 🖵 ☎ 🕮
Conference: 1 meeting room (Thtr 22 max),
24hr-delegate from £135, day-delegate from £30
Children: Welcome 🏃 🍼
Licenses: 🍾
Leisure: Free use of nearby leisure club
Parking: Off-street and free
Directions: Exit J36 M6; follow A591 to Ambleside.
Follow signs to Coniston by turning left at traffic lights,
and again 1/4 mile later.
Map ref: Ambleside 10 B2

Queens Hotel

★★

Market Place, Ambleside, Cumbria, LA22 9BU
Tel: 01539 432206 Fax: 01539 432721
Email: enquiries@queenshotelambleside.com
Web: www.queenshotelambleside.com
Rooms: 26 all ensuite 🛏 🖥
Pricing: Sgl £31–47 Dbl £62–94
Dinner available from £15
CC: Accepted
Room facilities: 🖵 ☎ 🕮
Children: Welcome 🏃 🍼
Licenses: 🍾
Leisure: Games room
Parking: Off-street and free
Directions: From south, leave M6 at Junction 36. Take
A591 to Windermere and Ambleside. The hotel is in the
town centre.
Map ref: Ambleside 10 B2

Elder Grove

 ◆◆◆◆

Lake Road, Ambleside, Cumbria, LA22 0DB
Tel: 01539 432504 Fax: 01539 432251
Email: info@eldergrove.co.uk
Web: www.eldergrove.co.uk
Seasonal closure: Christmas
Rooms: 10 all ensuite
Pricing: Sgl £27–40 Dbl £54–80 CC: Accepted
Room facilities:
Children: Welcome Dogs: Welcome
Licenses:
Parking: Off-street and free
Directions: On the south of Ambleside, A591/Lake Road, opposite BP petrol station at the start/end of the one-way system.
Map ref: Ambleside 10 B2

Lakes Lodge

 ◆◆◆◆

Lakes Road, Ambleside, Cumbria, LA22 0DB
Tel: 01539 432240 Fax: 01539 431474
Email: u@lakeslodge.co.uk
Web: www.lakeslodge.co.uk
Rooms: 12 all ensuite
Pricing: Sgl £49–79 Dbl £69–99 CC: Accepted
Room facilities:
Conference: 1 meeting room (Thtr 15 max)
Children: Welcome
Dogs: Welcome
Licenses:
Parking: Off-street and free
Directions: Drive into Ambleside keeping in the right hand lane. Lakes Lodge on the right 50 metres before petrol station.
Map ref: Ambleside 10 B2

Appleby-in-Westmorland, Cumbria

Appleby Manor Country House Hotel

 ★★★★ Commended

Roman Road, Appleby-in-Westmorland,
Cumbria, CA16 6JB
Tel: 01768 351571 Fax: 01768 352888
Email: reception@applebymanor.co.uk
Web: www.applebymanor.co.uk
Seasonal closure: 24–26 December
Rooms: 30 all ensuite
Pricing: Sgl £80–120 Dbl £120–220 Dinner available
CC: Accepted
Room facilities:
Conference: 3 meeting rooms (Thtr 25 max)
Children: Welcome
Licenses:
Leisure: Indoor pool, Games room, Snooker/billiards
Parking: Off-street and free
Directions: Situated half a mile from the town centre on the hill towards A66, Appleby Manor overlooks the castle.
Map ref: Appleby-in-Westmorland 10 C2

Old Hall Farmhouse

 ◆◆◆◆

Bongate, Appleby-in-Westmorland,
Cumbria, CA16 6HW
Tel: 01768 351773/0800 035 0422 Fax: 01768 351773
Email: old.hall.farmhouse@lineone.net
Web: www.oldhallfarmhouse.co.uk
Rooms: 3 all ensuite
Pricing: Sgl £35 Dbl £50
Room facilities:
Dogs: Welcome
Parking: Off-street and free
Directions: 200 yards east of Royal Oak Inn on B6542 at top of hill.
Map ref: Appleby-in-Westmorland 10 C2

Barrow-in-Furness, Cumbria

Abbey House Hotel

 ★★★

Abbey Road, Barrow-in-Furness, Cumbria, LA13 0PA
Tel: 01229 838282 Fax: 01229 820403
Email: enquiries@abbeyhousehotel.com
Web: www.abbeyhousehotel.com
Rooms: 57 all ensuite
Pricing: Sgl £65–89 Dbl £108–148
Dinner available from £23.95 CC: Accepted
Room facilities: Access:
Conference: 5 meeting rooms (Thtr 300 max), 24hr-delegate from £125, day-delegate from £37.50
Children: Welcome
Dogs: Welcome
Licenses:
Parking: Off-street and free
Directions: A590 to Barrow, follow signs to Furness General Hospital, hotel less than 100 yards on left.
Map ref: Barrow-in-Furness 10 B3
See advert on following page

The Fairway Hotel

 ★★★

Hawthwaite Lane, Thwaite Flat, Barrow-in-Furness, Cumbria, LA14 4QH
Tel: 01229 461200 Fax: 01229 461209
Email: enquiries@fairway-hotel.co.uk
Web: www.fairway-hotel.co.uk
Rooms: 29 all ensuite
Pricing: Sgl £50 Dbl £75–85 Dinner available
CC: Accepted
Room facilities: Access:
Conference: 1 meeting room (Thtr 80 max)
Children: Welcome
Dogs: Assistance dogs only
Licenses:
Leisure: Golf, Games room
Parking: Off-street and free
Directions: Follow A590 to Barrow to roundabout at Park Road, pick up holiday signs to Fairway Hotel.
Map ref: Thwaite Flat 10 B3

Northwest

King Alfred Hotel

 ◆◆◆◆ ✕

Ocean Road, Walney Island, Barrow-in-Furness, Cumbria, LA14 3DU
Tel: 01229 474717 Fax: 01229 476181
Email: kingalfred@walney4.fsnet.co.uk
Web: www.thekingalfred.co.uk
Rooms: 6 all ensuite
Pricing: Sgl £30 Dbl £60
Dinner available CC: Accepted
Room facilities: 🖵 🍵
Children: Welcome ♬
Licenses: ♙♙♙
Leisure: Games room
Parking: Off-street and free
Directions: From Junction 36 M6 follow A590 to Walney Island. Left at lights on bridge. 200 yards up the hill on right.
Map ref: Walney Island 10 B3

"Stay!"

Need a pet friendly property? Look out for 'Dogs welcome' in our listings.

Bassenthwaite, Cumbria

Ravenstone Lodge

 ◆◆◆◆ ✕

Bassenthwaite, Keswick, Cumbria, CA12 4QG
Tel: 01768 776629 Fax: 01768 776629
Email: ravenstone.lodge@talk21.com
Web: www.ravenstonelodge.co.uk
Rooms: 10 (9 ensuite)
Pricing: Sgl £35–37.50 Dbl £70–75
Dinner available from £18.50 CC: Accepted
Room facilities: 🖵 🍵
Children: Welcome 8yrs min age Dogs: Welcome
Licenses: ♙♙♙ Parking: Off-street and free
Directions: Leave M6 at Junction 40. Take A66 to Keswick, then A591 towards Carlisle. Ravenstone Lodge is 4½ miles from Keswick on left-hand side.
Map ref: Keswick 10 B2

Bassenthwaite Lake, Cumbria

Lakeside Country Guest House

 ◆◆◆◆ ✕

Dubwath, Bassenthwaite Lake, near Keswick, Cumbria, CA13 9YD
Tel: 01768 776358
Email: info@lakesidebassenthwaite.co.uk
Web: www.lakesidebassenthwaite.co.uk
Seasonal closure: Christmas

Elegant, Edwardian house with private parking, superbly situated overlooking Bassenthwaite Lake and mountains. Oak panelled entrance and immaculate ensuite accommodation. Enjoy our hospitality and fine cuisine in tranquil surroundings. Hairdryer and iron available.
Rooms: 8 (7 ensuite)
Pricing: Sgl £35–40 Dbl £60–80
Dinner available from £18.50 CC: Accepted
Room facilities: 🖵 🍵
Children: Welcome ♬ ☕
Licenses: ♙♙♙
Leisure: Fishing and sailing on lake
Parking: Off-street and free
Directions: Exit M6 at J40, take A66 Keswick Cockermouth, after dual carriageway turn right at sign for Dubwath (B5291) and stay right at fork. Lakeside is 100 metres on left.
Map ref: Dubwath 10 B1

Beeston, Cheshire

The Wild Boar Hotel & Restaurant

★★★ ⫶⫶

Whitchurch Road, Beeston, near Tarporley,
Cheshire, CW6 9NW
Tel: 01829 260309 Fax: 01829 261081
Email: enquiries@wildboarhotel.com
Web: www.wildboarhotel.com
Rooms: 37 all ensuite
Pricing: Sgl £64.63 Dbl £84–105.75
Dinner available from £21.95
CC: Accepted
Room facilities: ▢ ☎ ☕ ⤦
Conference: 5 meeting rooms (Thtr 100 max),
24hr-delegate from £109, day-delegate from £25
Children: Welcome
Dogs: Welcome
Licenses: ◈ ⵜⵜ
Leisure: Golf
Parking: Off-street and free
Directions: Please refer to website: www.wildboarhotel.com
Map ref: Beeston 8 B2

Blackburn, Lancashire

Clarion Hotel & Suites Foxfields, Blackburn

★★★★

Whalley Road, Billington, Clitheroe, Lancashire, BB7 9HY
Tel: 01254 822556 Fax: 01254 824613
Email: enquiries@hotels-blackburn.com
Web: www.choicehotelseurope.com
Rooms: 44 all ensuite ⤦ ⊗
Pricing: Sgl £89–103.50 Dbl £99–112.50
Dinner available from £22.95
CC: Accepted
Room facilities: ▢ ☎ ☕ ⤦
Conference: 5 meeting rooms (Thtr 150 max),
24hr-delegate from £130, day-delegate from £35
Children: Welcome
Dogs: Welcome
Licenses: ◈ ⵜⵜ
Leisure: Indoor pool, Gym
Parking: Off-street and free
Directions: Junction 31 M6, A677 Blackburn, take A59
Clitheroe/Whalley for 10 miles, at large roundabout
take 2nd exit signed Whalley. Hotel ¹/₂ mile on right.
Map ref: Billington 10 C3

Mytton Fold Hotel & Golf Complex

★★★

Langho, near Blackburn, Lancashire, BB6 8AB
Tel: 01254 240662 Fax: 01254 248119
Email: enquiries@myttonfold.co.uk
Web: www.myttonfold.co.uk
Rooms: 28 all ensuite
Pricing: Sgl £51–57 Dbl £84–89
Dinner available from £17
CC: Accepted
Room facilities: ▢ ☎ ☕ ⤦

Conference: 6 meeting rooms (Thtr 290 max),
24hr-delegate from £89, day-delegate from £24.50
Children: Welcome
Licenses: ◈ ⵜⵜ
Leisure: Golf, Games room
Parking: Off-street and free
Directions: Leave M65 at Junction 6. Follow ring road
A459 Clitheroe 2 miles, turn right. Following A666
(Clitheroe) 3¹/₂ miles. Large roundabout. Follow Whalley
sign 500 yards on right.
Map ref: Langho 10 C3

The Avenue Hotel

★★

Brockhall Village, Old Langho, near Blackburn,
Lancashire, BB6 8AY
Tel: 01254 244811 Fax: 01254 244812
Email: bookingenquiries@theavenuehotel.co.uk
Web: www.theavenuehotel.co.uk

A modern hotel with bedrooms furnished to the
highest standard, in the heart of the Ribble Valley. A
wide range of dishes is available in our contemporary
café bar and restaurant.
Rooms: 21 all ensuite ⤦ ⊗
Pricing: Sgl £50 Dbl £60
Dinner available from £10–27
CC: Accepted
Room facilities: ▢ ☎ ☕ ⤦
Conference: 3 meeting rooms (Thtr 50 max),
24hr-delegate from £72, day-delegate from £16
Children: Welcome
Licenses: ⵜⵜ
Parking: Off-street and free
Directions: J31 M6, take A59 for 8 miles. Turn by
Northcote Manor, travel for 1 mile, turn right then first
left.
Map ref: Brockhall Village 10 C3

Are the bells ringing?

Getting married? Congratulations! Look
for the wedding bells symbol which shows
hotels licensed for civil ceremonies.

The Millstone at Mellor

Church Lane, Mellor, Blackburn,
Lancashire, BB2 7JR
Tel: 01254 813333 Fax: 01254 812628
Email: info@millstonehotel.co.uk
Web: www.millstonehotel.co.uk / www.shirehotels.com

SHIRE
HOTELS

Wonderful gem in the Lancashire countryside. An old
coaching inn, with all the comforts of a modern hotel.
Excellent reputation for home-cooked food featuring
local/regional produce in both the bar and restaurant.
Rooms: 23 all ensuite 🐕 🚭
Pricing: Sgl £72–98 Dbl £94–128
Dinner available from £15.95
CC: Accepted
Room facilities: 📺 ☎ 🍵 📞
Conference: 1 meeting room (Thtr 20 max)
Children: Welcome 🍴
Licenses: 🍷 🍶
Parking: Off-street and free
Directions: Exit J31 M6. Follow A59 towards Clitheroe.
Turn right at Mellor sign, then take second left at
roundabout up Mellor Lane.
Map ref: Mellor 10 C3

Ice & slice?

RAC's comprehensive inspection
means we even check drinks are
served the way you want.

Blackpool, Lancashire

Imperial Hotel

North Promenade, Blackpool, Lancashire, FY1 2HB
Tel: 01253 623971 Fax: 01253 751784
Email:
imperialblackpoolreservations@paramount-hotels.co.uk
Web: www.paramount-hotels.co.uk

PARAMOUNT
GROUP OF HOTELS

Historic Hotel situated on the North Promenade and
only minutes from all the local attractions.
Rooms: 181 all ensuite 🐕 🚭
Pricing: Sgl £59.50–109 Dbl £99–119
Dinner available from £21.50
CC: Accepted
Room facilities: 📺 ☎ 🍵 📞
Access: ♿
Conference: 12 meeting rooms (Thtr 600 max),
24hr-delegate from £175, day-delegate from £49
Children: Welcome 🍴
Dogs: Welcome
Licenses: 🍷 🍶
Leisure: Indoor pool, Gym, Health spa, Beauty salon
Parking: Off-street
Directions: Exit J2 M55, take A583 North Shore, follow
signs to North Promenade. The hotel is on the
seafront, north of the tower.
Map ref: Blackpool 10 B3

Gables Balmoral Hotel

Balmoral Road, South Shore, Blackpool,
Lancashire, FY4 1HR
Tel: 01253 345432 Fax: 01253 406058
Email: info@gables-balmoral.co.uk
Web: www.gables-balmoral.co.uk
Rooms: 68 all ensuite
CC: Accepted
Room facilities: Access:
Conference: 1 meeting room (Thtr 30 max)
Children: Welcome Dogs: Welcome
Licenses:
Leisure: Indoor pool, Games room
Directions: Follow signs off M55 for Blackpool Pleasure
Beach: the hotel is directly opposite the Sandcastle
Grosvenor Casino and the main entrance to the
Pleasure beach.
Map ref: South Shore 10 B3

Headlands

611–613 New South Promenade, Blackpool,
Lancashire, FY4 1NJ
Tel: 01253 341179 Fax: 01253 342047
Email: headlands@blackpool.net
Web: www.theheadlands.blackpool.net
Seasonal closure: 2–16 January
Rooms: 42 all ensuite
Pricing: Sgl £39.50–49.95 Dbl £79–99.90
Dinner available from £16 CC: Accepted
Room facilities: Access:
Children: Welcome Dogs: Welcome
Licenses:
Leisure: Snooker/billiards
Parking: Off-street and free
Directions: Take M6 to M55, turn left at first
roundabout, right at second roundabout (to
Promenade), turn right at Promenade. The Headlands
is half a mile along Promenade.
Map ref: Blackpool 10 B3

Stretton Hotel

206–214 North Promenade, Blackpool,
Lancashire, FY1 1RU
Tel: 01253 625688 Fax: 01253 752534
Email: strettonhotel@btconnect.com
Web: www.strettonhotel.co.uk
Rooms: 50 all ensuite
Pricing: Sgl £27.50–43 Dbl £51–82
Dinner available from £8.95 CC: Accepted
Room facilities: Access:
Children: Welcome
Dogs: Welcome
Licenses:
Leisure: Games room
Parking: Off-street
Directions: Take the M55 into Blackpool. Turn right
onto promenade. Hotel is 100m past North Pier.
Map ref: Blackpool 10 B3

Warwick

603 New South Promenade, Blackpool,
Lancashire, FY4 1NG
Tel: 01253 342192 Fax: 01253 405776
Web: www.theukholidaygroup.com
Seasonal closure: January
Rooms: 51 all ensuite
Pricing: Sgl £37 Dbl £74
Dinner available from £21 CC: Accepted
Room facilities:
Access:
Conference: 2 meeting rooms (Thtr 35 max),
24hr-delegate from £49, day-delegate from £18
Children: Welcome
Licenses:
Leisure: Indoor pool
Parking: Off-street and free
Directions: From the end of the M55 follow the A5230
to South Shore. Turn right at promenade. Hotel is ½
mile on right.
Map ref: Blackpool 10 B3

The Old Coach House

50 Dean Street, Blackpool, Lancashire, FY4 1BP
Tel: 01253 349195 Fax: 01253 344330
Email: blackpool@theoldcoachhouse.co.uk
Web: www.theoldcoachhouse.co.uk
Rooms: 19 all ensuite
Pricing: Dinner available from £24.99 CC: Accepted
Room facilities:
Children: Welcome
Licenses:
Leisure: Health spa
Parking: Off-street and free
Directions: M6 Junction 32, M55 to large roundabout.
Straight over, take next right, left at lights, left at next
lights, second right before car showroom, hotel on
right.
Map ref: Blackpool 10 B3

The Windsor Hotel

21 King Edward Avenue, North Shore, Blackpool,
Lancashire, FY2 9TA
Tel: 01253 353735 Fax: 01253 353735
Email: enquiries@windsorhotel.info
Web: www.windsorhotel.info
Rooms: 9 all ensuite
Pricing: Sgl £22–26 Dbl £44–52
Dinner available from £8.50 CC: Accepted
Room facilities:
Children: Welcome
Dogs: Welcome
Licenses:
Parking: Off-street and free
Directions: About 200 yards off the Queens
Promenade, take the second turning right by the Cliffs
Hotel into King Edward Avenue.
Map ref: North Shore 10 B3

Northwest

Beaucliffe

 ◆◆◆

20-22 Holmfield Road, North Shore, Blackpool,
Lancashire, FY2 9TB
Tel: 01253 351663
Rooms: 13 all ensuite
Pricing: Sgl £20–30 Dbl £40–60
Dinner available from £7
Room facilities:
Children: Welcome Dogs: Assistance dogs only
Licenses: Parking: Off-street and free
Directions: From Blackpool Tower follow the road up
the seafront towards Develys. After Synn roundabout
look for Hackey's Hotel, then turn right into King
Edward's Avenue. Hotel is 100 yards on right.
Map ref: North Shore 10 B3

Hotel Pilatus

 ◆◆◆

10 Willshaw Road, Gynn Square, North Shore,
Blackpool, Lancashire, FY2 9SH
Tel: 01253 352470 Fax: 01253 352470
Email: cynthia@pilatushotel.co.uk
Web: www.pilatushotel.co.uk
Seasonal closure: January to February
Rooms: 9 all ensuite
Pricing: Sgl £27–29 Dbl £44–48
Dinner available from £7 CC: Accepted
Room facilities:
Children: Welcome
Licenses: Parking: Off-street
Directions: From Blackpool Tower Promenade travel
past North Pier till Gynn Gardens roundabout. Turn
right Savoy Hotel, Pilatus fourth hotel down.
Map ref: North Shore 10 B3

Langwood Hotel

◆◆◆

250 Queens Promenade, Bispham, Blackpool,
Lancashire, FY2 9HA
Tel: 01253 351370
Seasonal closure: January to March
Rooms: 24 all ensuite
Pricing: Sgl £26–28 Dbl £52–56
Dinner available from £10
Room facilities:
Access:
Children: Welcome Licenses:
Parking: Off-street and free
Directions: Sea front position. Follow the sea route
north away from tower and piers.
Map ref: Bispham 10 B3

Maxime Hotel

 ◆◆◆

416-418 North Promenade, Gynn Square, Blackpool,
Lancashire, FY1 2LB
Tel: 01253 351215 Fax: 01253 354670
Email: maxime@amserve.net
Web: www.smoothhound.co.uk/hotel/maxime.html

Seasonal closure: January to February
Rooms: 30 all ensuite
Pricing: Dinner available from £15
CC: Accepted
Room facilities:
Access:
Children: Welcome Dogs: Assistance dogs only
Licenses:
Leisure: Indoor pool, Health spa
Directions: M55 roundabout, follow sign to North
Shore then to Gynn Square roundabout.
Map ref: North Shore 10 B3

Sunny Cliff Hotel

 ◆◆◆

98 Queens Promenade, Blackpool, Lancashire, FY2 9NS
Tel: 01253 351155
Seasonal closure: November to March
Rooms: 9 all ensuite
Pricing: Sgl £27–31 Dbl £54–62
Dinner available from £11
Room facilities:
Children: Welcome
Licenses: Parking: Off-street and free
Directions: 1.5 miles north of Tower along North
Promenade to large roundabout. Then past Savoy
Hotel along Queens Promenade to 98.
Map ref: Blackpool 10 B3

Westdean Hotel

◆◆◆

59 Dean Street, Blackpool, Lancashire, FY4 1BP
Tel: 01253 342904
Email: westdeanhotel@aol.com
Web: www.westdeanhotel.com
Rooms: 11 all ensuite
Pricing: Sgl £21–27 Dbl £42–54
Dinner available from £7 CC: Accepted
Room facilities: Children: Welcome
Licenses: Leisure: Games room
Parking: Off-street and free
Directions: From M55 follow south parking signs, past
Aldi and left at lights. Over Waterloo bridge, left at
lights, second right into Dean Street.
Map ref: Blackpool 10 B3

Wilmar

 ◆◆◆

42 Osborne Road, Blackpool, Lancashire, FY4 1HQ
Tel: 01253 346229
Rooms: 7 (6 ensuite)
Pricing: Sgl £20–25 Dbl £40–50
Dinner available from £6.00
Room facilities:
Children: Welcome 5yrs min age
Licenses:
Directions: On Promenade, pass South Pier towards
Pleasure Beach. Turn left immediately after pedestrian
lights. Wilmar is approximately 150m on left.
Map ref: Blackpool 10 B3

The New Central Hotel

64A Reads Avenue, Blackpool, Lancashire, FY1 4DE
Tel: 01253 623637 Fax: 01253 620857
Email: newcentral@hotmail.com
Web: www.blackpoolilluminations.com
Rooms: 47 all ensuite
Pricing: Sgl £28.68–41.18 Dbl £45.90–65.90
Dinner available from £9.95 CC: Accepted
Room facilities: ☐ ☕ Access: |↕|
Children: Welcome ↾ Dogs: Assistance dogs only
Licenses: ♦♦♦ Parking: Off-street
Directions: A583 keep heading towards town, until
C.S.L (showroom) then take the next turning on right.
Map ref: Blackpool 10 B3

Bolton by Bowland, Lancashire

Middle Flass Lodge

Settle Road, Bolton by Bowland, Clitheroe,
Lancashire, BB7 4NY
Tel: 01200 447259 Fax: 01200 447300
Email: info@middleflasslodge.fsnet.co.uk
Web: www.middleflasslodge.co.uk

Tasteful barn conversion, unrivalled views across
countryside in Forest of Bowland, peaceful location.
Always personal and professional attention. Chef
prepared cuisine in restaurant, table licence. Lounge
with store. Gardens.
Rooms: 7 all ensuite
Pricing: Sgl £36–45 Dbl £56–65
Dinner available from £20–26 CC: Accepted
Room facilities: ☐ ☕
Children: Welcome ↾ Dogs: Welcome
Licenses: ♦♦♦ Parking: Off-street and free
Directions: A59 Skipton Clitheroe bypass turn for
Sawley, follow sign Bolton-by-Bowland. At Copynook
second left signed Middle Flass Lodge, 2 miles right.
Map ref: Clitheroe 10 C3

Borrowdale, Cumbria

Borrowdale Gates Country House Hotel

Grange-in-Borrowdale, Keswick, Cumbria, CA12 5UQ
Tel: 01768 777204 Fax: 01768 777254
Email: hotel@borrowdale-gates.com

Web: www.borrowdale-gates.com
Seasonal closure: January
Rooms: 29 all ensuite
Dinner available CC: Accepted
Room facilities: ☐ ☎ ☕
Children: Welcome 12yrs min age
Licenses: ♦♦♦ Parking: Off-street and free
Directions: From Keswick follow B5289 to Grange.
Turn right over the double hump-backed bridge into
Grange village. Hotel is through village on right.
Map ref: Grange-in-Borrowdale 10 B2

Scafell Hotel

Rosthwaite, Borrowdale, Cumbria, CA12 5XB
Tel: 01768 777208 Fax: 01768 777280
Email: info@scafell.co.uk
Web: www.scafell.co.uk
Rooms: 24 all ensuite
Pricing: Sgl £28.50–46.75 Dbl £57–93.50
Dinner available from £19.95–22.95 CC: Accepted
Room facilities: ☐ ☎ ☕
Children: Welcome ↾ ⚲ Dogs: Welcome
Licenses: ◁ ♦♦♦
Leisure: Games room
Parking: Off-street and free
Directions: 6½ miles south of Keswick on B5289.
Map ref: Rosthwaite 10 B2
See advert on this page

Northwest

Hazel Bank Country House `Little Gem`

◆◆◆◆◆ ♖♖ ✕ ⬩ ☙

Rosthwaite, Borrowdale, Keswick, Cumbria, CA12 5XB
Tel: 01768 777248 Fax: 01768 777373
Email: enquiries@hazelbankhotel.co.uk
Web: www.hazelbankhotel.co.uk
Seasonal closure: Christmas

Award-winning Hazel Bank stands in 4-acre grounds
amidst the Lakeland peaks. Luxuriously appointed
ensuite bedrooms, award-winning food and excellent
wines. Attentive service and warm hospitality ensures
guests return year after year.
Rooms: 8 all ensuite 🖾 ⊗
Pricing: Sgl £33.50–62.50
Dinner available from £32.50 CC: Accepted
Room facilities: ▢ ☕
Children: Welcome 12yrs min age
Licenses: ♟ Parking: Off-street and free
Directions: From Keswick follow B5289 signposted
Borrowdale for 6 miles to Rosthwaite. On approaching
village turn left over humped-back bridge.
Map ref: Rosthwaite 10 B2

Broxton, Cheshire

Broxton Hall

★★★ ♖♖

Whitchurch Road, Broxton, Chester, Cheshire, CH3 9JS
Tel: 01829 782321 Fax: 01829 782330
Email: reservations@broxtonhall.co.uk
Web: www.broxtonhall.co.uk
Rooms: 10 all ensuite 🖾
Pricing: Dbl £80–130
Dinner available from £32.50 CC: Accepted
Room facilities: ▢ ☎ ☕
Conference: 1 meeting room (Thtr 45 max)
Children: Welcome 12yrs min age ⬩℃
Dogs: Welcome
Licenses: ◈ ♟ Parking: Off-street and free
Directions: 9 miles south of Chester on A41 towards
Whitchurch.
Map ref: Broxton 7 E2
See advert on this page

Burnley, Lancashire

Higher Trapp Country House Hotel

★★★

Trapp Lane, Simonstone, near Burnley,
Lancashire, BB12 7QW
Tel: 01282 772781 Fax: 01282 772782
Email: reception@highertrapphotel.co.uk
Web: www.highertrapphotel.co.uk
Rooms: 30 all ensuite ♥ 🖾 ⊗
Pricing: Sgl £56–62 Dbl £75–89
Dinner available from £17
CC: Accepted
Room facilities: ▢ ☎ ☕
Conference: 4 meeting rooms (Thtr 150 max),
24hr-delegate from £99, day-delegate from £25
Children: Welcome ⽊
Licenses: ◈ ♟
Parking: Off-street and free
Directions: Leave M65 at Junction 8 and take A678,
following signs for Clitheroe, through one set of traffic
lights to next. Left, following Whailey signs. A671 for
Clitheroe. Right onto School Lane (becomes Trapp
Lane). 1 mile on left.
Map ref: Simonstone 10 C3

Oaks Hotel

★★★★

Colne Road, Reedley, Burnley, Lancashire, BB10 2LF
Tel: 01282 414141 Fax: 01282 433401
Email: oaks@shirehotels.com
Web: www.shirehotels.com

SHIRE
HOTELS

A stunning Victorian mansion with a magnificent
stained glass window dominating the lobby. Ideal
location for exploring Pendle and the Ribble Valley.
Good reputation for home-cooked food featuring
local/regional produce.
Rooms: 50 all ensuite
Pricing: Sgl £77–124 Dbl £104–144
Dinner available from £22
CC: Accepted
Room facilities:
Conference: 10 meeting rooms (Thtr 120 max),
24hr-delegate from £132, day-delegate from £42
Children: Welcome
Licenses:
Leisure: Indoor pool, Gym
Parking: Off-street and free
Directions: Leave the M65 at junction 12. Follow signs
for Burnley at next three roundabouts. The Oaks is on
A682/A56 after about 1 mile.
Map ref: Reedley 10 C3

Bury, Lancashire

The Bolholt Country Park (Best Western)

★★★

Walshaw Road, Bury, Lancashire, BL8 1PU
Tel: 0161 762 4000 Fax: 0161 762 4100
Email: reservations@bolholt.co.uk
Web: www.bolholt.co.uk
Rooms: 64 all ensuite
Pricing: Sgl £55–84 Dbl £79–99
Dinner available from £15
CC: Accepted
Room facilities:
Conference: 10 meeting rooms (Thtr 350 max),
24hr-delegate from £99, day-delegate from £30

Children: Welcome
Dogs: Welcome
Licenses:
Leisure: Indoor pool, Gym, Health spa, Beauty salon,
Fishing, Games room, Steam room, Spa pool
Parking: Off-street and free
Directions: Junction 17 M60 signs for Bury, signs for
Walshaw and Tottington, situated one mile on right of
Walshaw Road.
Map ref: Bury 10 C4

Red Lion

◆◆◆

81 Ramsbottom Road, Hawkshaw, near Bury,
Lancashire, BL8 4JS
Tel: 01204 856600 Fax: 01204 853998
Email: info@redlion-hawkshaw.co.uk
Web: www.redlion-hawkshaw.co.uk
Rooms: 4 all ensuite
Pricing: Sgl £45 Dbl £60–65
Dinner available from £8
CC: Accepted
Room facilities:
Children: Welcome
Licenses:
Parking: Off-street and free
Map ref: Hawkshaw 10 C4

Buttermere, Cumbria

Bridge Hotel

★★★

Buttermere, Lake District, Cumbria, CA13 9UZ
Tel: 01768 770252 Fax: 01768 770215
Email: enquiries@bridge-hotel.com
Web: www.bridge-hotel.com
Rooms: 21 all ensuite
Pricing: Dinner available from £25
CC: Accepted
Room facilities:
Conference: 2 meeting rooms (Thtr 20 max)
Children: Welcome
Dogs: Welcome
Licenses:
Parking: Off-street and free
Directions: Take A66 around Keswick. Turn off at
Braithwaite. Head over "Newlands Pass". This brings
you down into Buttermere and the hotel.
Map ref: Buttermere 10 B2

Northwest

Carlisle, Cumbria

Crown & Mitre Hotel
★★★

English Street, Carlisle, Cumbria, CA3 8HZ
Tel: 01228 525491 Fax: 01228 514553
Email: info@crownandmitre-hotel-carlisle.com
Web: www.crownandmitre-hotel-carlisle.com
Rooms: 94 all ensuite
Pricing: Sgl £69–85 Dbl £89–120
Dinner available from £19.50–23 CC: Accepted
Room facilities: Access:
Conference: 8 meeting rooms (Thtr 400 max),
24hr-delegate from £140, day-delegate from £40
Children: Welcome Dogs: Welcome
Licenses: Leisure: Indoor pool, Jacuzzi
Parking: Off-street and free
Directions: Leave M6 motorway at J42. Take London
Road into Carlisle. First left after station. Turn right
beside Natwest Bank.
Map ref: Carlisle 10 B1

Cumbria Park
★★★

32 Scotland Road, Carlisle, Cumbria, CA3 9DG
Tel: 01228 522887 Fax: 01228 514796
Email: enquiries@cumbriaparkhotel.co.uk
Web: www.cumbriaparkhotel.co.uk
Seasonal closure: Christmas Day and Boxing Day
Rooms: 47 all ensuite
Pricing: Sgl £75–90 Dbl £97.50–125
Dinner available from £16.95
CC: Accepted
Room facilities: Access:
Conference: 6 meeting rooms (Thtr 120 max),
24hr-delegate from £105, day-delegate from £27.50
Children: Welcome
Licenses:
Leisure: Gym, Health spa, Steam room, Solarium, Sauna
Parking: Off-street and free
Directions: Leave M6 at Junction 44. Hotel is 1½ miles
down main road into Carlisle on left-hand side.
Map ref: Carlisle 13 E4

Dalston Hall Hotel
★★★★

Carlisle, Cumbria, CA5 7JX
Tel: 01228 710271 Fax: 01228 711273
Email: info@dalston-hall-hotel.co.uk
Web: www.dalston-hall-hotel.co.uk
Rooms: 12 all ensuite
Dinner available CC: Accepted
Room facilities:
Conference: 3 meeting rooms (Thtr 100 max)
Children: Welcome Licenses:
Leisure: Golf, Fishing
Parking: Off-street and free
Directions: 5 miles from junction 42 on M6, follow
signs for Dalston, 3 miles from Carlisle city centre on
B5299.
Map ref: Carlisle 13 E4

Graham Arms Hotel
★★

English Street, Longtown, near Carlisle,
The Borders, CA6 5SE
Tel: 01228 791213 Fax: 01228 791213
Email: office@grahamarms.com
Web: www.grahamarms.com
Rooms: 15 all ensuite
Pricing: Sgl £34–36 Dbl £56–65
Dinner available from £9.95 CC: Accepted
Room facilities:
Conference: 3 meeting rooms (Thtr 40 max)
Children: Welcome Dogs: Welcome
Licenses: Parking: Off-street and free
Directions: Just 6 miles from exit 44 of M6. Follow
signposts to Galashiels/The Borders Tourist Route. The
Graham Arms is about 400 yards on the right as you
enter this quaint town.
Map ref: Longtown 10 B1

Pinegrove Hotel
★★

262 London Road, Carlisle, Cumbria, CA1 2QS
Tel: 01228 524828 Fax: 01228 810941
Email: info@pinegrovehotel.co.uk
Web: www.pinegrovehotel.co.uk
Seasonal closure: Christmas Day
Rooms: 31 all ensuite
Dinner available CC: Accepted
Room facilities:
Conference: 2 meeting rooms (Thtr 120 max)
Children: Welcome Dogs: Welcome
Licenses:
Leisure: Games room
Parking: Off-street and free
Directions: Leave M6 at Junction 42, onto A6. Carlisle
Hotel is situated 1½ miles along this road on left-hand
side.
Map ref: Carlisle 13 E4

Bessiestown Country Guest House
Little Gem
◆◆◆◆◆

Bessiestown, Catlowdy, Longtown,
Carlisle, Cumbria, CA6 5QP
Tel: 01228 577219 Fax: 01228 577219
Email: info@bessiestown.co.uk
Web: www.bessiestown.co.uk

A warm welcome awaits you at this multi award winning guesthouse situated near Carlisle. In magnificent setting midway between Gretna Green and Hadrian's Wall. Beautiful ensuite bedrooms. Delicious home cooking. Indoor heated swimming pool.

Rooms: 6 all ensuite 🖨 ⊗
Pricing: Sgl £42.50 Dbl £65
Dinner available from £16
CC: Accepted
Room facilities: ▢ ☞
Children: Welcome
Licenses: ♦♦♦
Leisure: Indoor pool
Parking: Off-street and free
Directions: M6 Junction 44, A7 (or A6701) Longtown Road at Bush Hotel, 6½ miles to Penton, right onto B6318, 1½ miles Catlowdy. Bessiestown first on the left.
Map ref: Catlowdy 13 E4

Vallum House Garden Hotel

◆◆◆

Burgh Road, Carlisle, Cumbria, CA2 7NB
Tel: 01228 521860
Rooms: 9 (5 ensuite) ❤ ⊗
Pricing: Sgl £30–40 Dbl £55–65
Dinner available from £10
CC: Accepted
Room facilities: ▢ ☎ ☞
Conference: 30 meeting rooms, day-delegate from £50
Children: Welcome ♯
Dogs: Welcome
Licenses: ♦♦♦
Parking: Off-street and free
Directions: J44 M6, 2 miles to roundabout, dual carriageway, small roundabout. Right-hand fork for 1½ miles. Signpost to Burgh by Sands. Hotel 200 yards on left.
Map ref: Carlisle 13 E4

Chester, Cheshire

The Chester Grosvenor and Spa

★★★★★
Eastgate, Chester, Cheshire, CH1 1LT
Tel: 01244 324024 Fax: 01244 313246
Email: hotel@chestergrosvenor.com
Web: www.chestergrosvenor.com
Seasonal closure: 24-26 December
Rooms: 80 all ensuite 🖨 ⊗
Pricing: Sgl £180–340 Dbl £180–340
Dinner available from £55
CC: Accepted
Room facilities: ▢ ☎ ☏ ❄
Access: ⌊↑
Conference: 5 meeting rooms (Thtr 200 max), 24hr-delegate from £225, day-delegate from £60
Children: Welcome ♯
Licenses: ◇ ♦♦♦

Leisure: Gym, Health spa, Beauty salon
Parking: Off-street and free
Directions: Turn off M56 for M53 at Junction 15; turn off M53 at Junction 12 for A56. Follow signs for Chester and city centre hotels.
Map ref: Chester 7 D1

The Chester Crabwall Manor

★★★★★ 🏠🏠🏠 Excellent
Parkgate Road, Mollington,
Chester, Cheshire, CH1 6NE
Tel: 01244 851666 Fax: 01244 851400
Email: crabwallmanor@marstonhotels.com
Web: www.marstonhotels.com
Rooms: 48 all ensuite ❤ 🖨 ⊗
Dinner available
CC: Accepted
Room facilities: ▢ ☎ ☏ ☎
Conference: 8 meeting rooms (Thtr 150 max)
Children: Welcome ♯
Licenses: ◇ ♦♦♦
Leisure: Indoor pool, Gym, Health spa, Beauty salon, Snooker/billiards
Parking: Off-street and free
Directions: At the end of the M56, follow signs for Queensferry/North Wales for approximately ½ a mile, turn left at the roundabout. Crabwall Manor is 1¾ miles down this road, on the left.
Map ref: Mollington 7 D1

Green Bough Hotel

★★★ 🏠🏠🏠 Premier
60 Hoole Road, Hoole,
Chester, Cheshire, CH2 3NL
Tel: 01244 326241 Fax: 01244 326265
Email: luxury@greenbough.co.uk
Web: www.greenbough.co.uk
Rooms: 15 all ensuite 🖨 ⊗
Pricing: Sgl £89.50–179.50 Dbl £130–275
Dinner available from £40
CC: Accepted
Room facilities: ▢ ☎ ☏ ☎
Conference: 2 meeting rooms (Thtr 30 max), day-delegate from £25
Children: Welcome 13yrs min age
Licenses: ♦♦♦
Parking: Off-street and free
Directions: Take M53 to Chester. Leave at Junction 12 and take A56 to Chester city. Hotel is 1 mile from motorway.
Map ref: Hoole 7 D1

Northwest

Grosvenor Pulford Hotel

★★★

Wrexham Road, Pulford, Chester, Cheshire, CH4 9DG
Tel: 01244 570560 Fax: 01244 570809
Email: enquiries@grosvenorpulfordhotel.co.uk
Web: www.grosvenorpulfordhotel.co.uk
Rooms: 73 all ensuite
Pricing: Sgl £65–140 Dbl £75–160
Dinner available from £20
CC: Accepted
Room facilities:
Conference: 5 meeting rooms (Thtr 250 max), 24hr-delegate from £127, day-delegate from £30
Children: Welcome
Dogs: Welcome
Licenses:
Leisure: Indoor pool, Gym, Health spa, Beauty salon, Tennis, Snooker/billiards
Parking: Off-street and free
Directions: Leave M53/A55 at junction signposted A483 Chester, Wrexham & North Wales. Turn onto B5445, hotel is 2 miles on right.
Map ref: Pulford 7 D1
See advert on this page

Mill Hotel

★★★

Milton Street, Chester, Cheshire, CH1 3NF
Tel: 01244 350035 Fax: 01244 345635
Email: reservations@millhotel.com
Web: www.millhotel.com
Rooms: 129 all ensuite
Dinner available CC: Accepted
Room facilities:
Access:
Conference: 5 meeting rooms (Thtr 60 max)
Children: Welcome
Licenses:
Leisure: Indoor pool, Gym, Health spa, Beauty salon
Parking: Off-street
Directions: J12 M53 to A56 to city centre, left at second roundabout (A5268), first left Sellar Street, second left Milton Street.
Map ref: Chester 7 D1

Northop Hall Country House Hotel

★★★

Northop Hall Village, near Mold, Flintshire, CH7 6HJ
Tel: 01244 816181 Fax: 01244 814661
Email: northop@hotel-chester.com
Web: www.hotel-chester.com

Dating from 1872, steeped in history and set in acres of tranquil gardens and woodland, offering the modern comfort and service you would expect from a lovely Country House Hotel.
Rooms: 39 all ensuite
Pricing: Sgl £63–72.50 Dbl £90.50–130.50
Dinner available from £21.95
CC: Accepted
Room facilities:
Conference: 4 meeting rooms (Thtr 100 max), 24hr-delegate from £105, day-delegate from £32
Children: Welcome
Licenses:
Parking: Off-street and free
Directions: A55 Queensferry, take first exit for Buckley; at roundabout take first exit, then immediate right to Northop Hall/Ewloe Castle. 2 miles, bear left, hotel is 200 yards on left.
Map ref: Northop Hall 7 D1

Brookside Hotel

 ★★

Brook Lane, Chester, Cheshire, CH2 2AN
Tel: 01244 381943 Fax: 01244 651910
Email: info@brookside-hotel.co.uk
Web: www.brookside-hotel.co.uk
Rooms: 26 all ensuite
Dinner available
CC: Accepted
Room facilities: ▢ ☎ ▨
Children: Welcome Ħ
Licenses: ▮▮▮
Parking: Off-street and free
Directions: From city centre on A5116 Liverpool road turn right into Brook Lane. Hotel 300 yards on left, car park at rear.
Map ref: Chester 7 D1

Dene Hotel

 ★★

95 Hoole Road, Chester, Cheshire, CH2 3ND
Tel: 01244 321165 Fax: 01244 350277
Email: info@denehotel.com
Web: www.denehotel.com

VENTURE HOTELS

Ideal for exploring Chester and the surrounding countryside, The Dene is renowned for its warm and friendly welcome. Rooms include private bathrooms, direct dial telephone with modem, satellite televisions. Wi-Fi available.
Rooms: 52 all ensuite
Pricing: Sgl £49.95–70 Dbl £69.50–90
Dinner available from £7.95
CC: Accepted
Room facilities: ▢ ☎ ▨ ⌕
Conference: 1 meeting room (Thtr 20 max),
24hr-delegate from £80, day-delegate from £25

Children: Welcome Ħ
Dogs: Welcome
Licenses: ▮▮▮
Leisure: Games room, Snooker/billiards
Parking: Off-street and free
Directions: Take Junction 12 of the M53. Follow signs for A56 Hoole Road. The Dene Hotel is about 500 yards on left.
Map ref: Chester 7 D1

Chester Stone Villa Hotel — Little Gem

◆◆◆◆◆ ✄ ✓

Stone Place, Hoole, Chester, Cheshire, CH2 3NR
Tel: 01244 345014 Fax: 01244 345015
Email: enquiries@stonevillahotel.co.uk
Web: www.stonevillahotel.co.uk
Rooms: 10 all ensuite
Pricing: Sgl £45–55 Dbl £70–80
CC: Accepted
Room facilities: ▢ ☎ ▨ ⌕
Children: Welcome
Parking: Off-street and free
Directions: From M5, M6, M53, take A56. Follow past church on left. Pass through traffic lights, take second left into Stone Place. Proceed to bottom of cul-de-sac and through entrance into car park.
Map ref: Hoole 7 D1
See advert on this page

Northwest

Ba Ba Guest House

◆◆◆◆

65 Hoole Road, Hoole, Chester, Cheshire, CH2 3NJ
Tel: 01244 315047 Fax: 01244 315046
Email: reservations@babaguesthouse.co.uk
Web: www.babaguesthouse.co.uk
Rooms: 5 all ensuite
Pricing: Sgl £35–45 Dbl £65–75
CC: Accepted
Room facilities:
Children: Welcome
Parking: Off-street and free
Directions: Exit J12 M53 onto A56, signs for Chester.
The guest house is situated 1 mile from the motorway
on the left hand side.
Map ref: Hoole 7 D1

Chester Court Hotel

◆◆◆◆

48 Hoole Road, Chester, Cheshire, CH2 3NL
Tel: 01244 320779 Fax: 01244 344795
Email: info@chestercourthotel.com
Web: www.chestercourthotel.com
Rooms: 20 all ensuite
Dinner available
CC: Accepted
Room facilities:
Conference: 2 meeting rooms
Children: Welcome
Licenses:
Parking: Off-street and free
Directions: From M53 Junction 12, take A56 into
Chester. Proceed along Hoole Road (A56), and find
Chester Court Hotel on right opposite All Saints Church.
Map ref: Chester 7 D1

Hamilton Court Hotel

◆◆◆◆

Hamilton Street, Hoole, Chester, Cheshire, CH2 3JG
Tel: 01244 345387 Fax: 01244 317404
Email: hamiltoncourth@aol.com
Web: www.smoothhound.co.uk/a03588.html
Rooms: 11 all ensuite
Pricing: Sgl £30–35 Dbl £60–75
CC: Accepted
Room facilities:
Children: Welcome
Dogs: Welcome
Licenses:
Parking: Off-street and free
Directions: Come off junction 12 M53. Come over town
roundabouts heading for city centre. You will see
Oaklands Pub on left. Hamilton Street second on left.
Map ref: Hoole 7 D1

Chorley, Lancashire

Pines Hotel

★★★

Preston Road, Clayton-le-Woods, Lancashire, PR6 7ED
Tel: 01772 338551 Fax: 01772 629002
Email: mail@thepineshotel.co.uk
Web: www.thepineshotel.co.uk
Seasonal closure: 26 December

The Pines Hotel has been owned and managed since
1963 by Betty Duffin, who has a policy of catering to
customer demands and market trends. Completed in
April 2005, the Dixon Suite is a perfect example of this
ideal. The Pines has two superb suites, as well as 35
bedrooms, some with jacuzzis and four-poster beds.
Rooms: 37 all ensuite
Pricing: Sgl £75–110 Dbl £85–120
Dinner available from £10–22
CC: Accepted
Room facilities:
Conference: 5 meeting rooms (Thtr 300 max),
24hr-delegate from £115, day-delegate from £27
Children: Welcome
Licenses:
Leisure: Local gym offer, local golf club offer to
residents
Directions: M6 Junction 29 to Preston South. Right at
roundabout. Follow A6. After fourth mini roundabout,
hotel is immediately on left.
Map ref: Clayton-le-Woods 10 B4

Parr Hall Farm

◆◆◆◆

Parr Lane, Eccleston, Chorley, Lancashire, PR7 5SL
Tel: 01257 451917 Fax: 01257 453749
Email: parrhall@talk21.com
Rooms: 8 all ensuite
Pricing: Sgl £30–40 Dbl £50–60
CC: Accepted
Room facilities:
Children: Welcome
Parking: Off-street and free
Directions: M6 J27, A5209 for Parbold; immediately
right on B5250 for Eccleston. After 5 miles Parr Lane
on right, property first left.
Map ref: Eccleston 10 B4

Clitheroe, Lancashire

Brooklyn Guest House

◆◆◆◆

32 Pimlico Road, Clitheroe, Lancashire, BB7 2AH
Tel: 01200 428268 Fax: 01200 428268
Email: rg@classicfm.net
Web: www.brooklynguesthouse.co.uk
Rooms: 4 all ensuite
Pricing: Sgl £29–32 Dbl £50–55
CC: Accepted
Room facilities:
Children: Welcome
Licenses:
Directions: North of town centre. Close to roundabout
with BP garage: take Waddington Road, 200 yards.
Turn right at smaller roundabout.
Map ref: Clitheroe 10 C3

Congleton, Cheshire

Lion & Swan Hotel

★★

Swan Bank, Congleton, Cheshire, CW12 1AH
Tel: 01260 273115 Fax: 01260 299270
Email: info@lionandswan.co.uk
Web: www.lionandswan.co.uk
Rooms: 21 all ensuite
Pricing: Sgl £50 Dbl £60–70
Dinner available from £6–15
CC: Accepted
Room facilities:
Conference: 2 meeting rooms (Thtr 90 max)
Children: Welcome
Licenses:
Parking: Off-street and free
Directions: M6 J17 to Congleton, second roundabout,
third exit. Situated on one-way system at top of Swan
Bank.
Map ref: Congleton 7 E1

The Plough At Eaton

◆◆◆◆

Macclesfield Road, Eaton, Congleton,
Cheshire, CW12 2NR
Tel: 01260 280207 Fax: 01260 298377
Rooms: 8 all ensuite
Dinner available
CC: Accepted
Room facilities:
Conference: 1 meeting room (Thtr 40 max)
Children: Welcome
Licenses:
Parking: Off-street and free
Directions: Situated north of Congleton in the village of
Eton on the main Macclesfield Road.
Map ref: Eaton 7 E1

Coniston, Cumbria

Coniston Lodge　　　　Little Gem

◆◆◆◆◆

Station Road, Coniston, Cumbria, LA21 8HH
Tel: 01539 441201 Fax: 01539 441201
Email: info@coniston-lodge.com
Web: www.coniston-lodge.com
Seasonal closure: January

An RAC Little Gem winner. Beautiful scenery, peaceful
surroundings, fine home cooking and a very warm
welcome.
Rooms: 6 all ensuite
Pricing: Sgl £58.50–60.50 Dbl £90–110
Dinner available from £25
CC: Accepted
Room facilities:
Children: Welcome 10yrs min age
Licenses:
Parking: Off-street and free
Directions: Leave A593 at the crossroads close to
filling station. Turn up the hill (Station Road). Hotel is
100m on left. Park under the building.
Map ref: Coniston 10 B2

Sleep easy

Rest assured. Our comprehensive
inspection process includes
checking beds are comfortable.

The Crown

◆◆◆◆

Tilberthwaite Avenue, Coniston, Cumbria, LA21 8ED
Tel: 01539 441243 Fax: 01539 441804
Email: info@crown-hotel-coniston.com
Web: www.crown-hotel-coniston.com

A warm Lakeland welcome to the Crown Hotel situated
in the centre of Coniston village. Offering fine ales,
good food and superb hospitality. The hotel has been
completely refurbished to a very high standard to
ensure the future comfort of all our guests to enjoy the
delights of Coniston and the outlaying district.
Rooms: 12 all ensuite 🛏
Pricing: Sgl £50–75
Dinner available from £15 CC: Accepted
Room facilities: 📺 ☎ ☕
Children: Welcome 🍴
Dogs: Assistance dogs only
Licenses: ⚋ Leisure: Games room
Parking: Off-street and free
Directions: Leave the M6 at J36 onto A591 towards
Windermere, continue to Amchelscole, when in
Amchelscole take the A593 to Coniston.
Map ref: Coniston 10 B2

Crewe, Cheshire

Crewe Hall

★★★★★ 🛎🛎🛎

Weston Road, Crewe, Cheshire, CW1 6UZ
Tel: 01270 253333 Fax: 01270 253322
Email: crewehall@marstonhotels.com
Web: www.marstonhotels.com
Rooms: 65 all ensuite 🛏 🖭 🚭
Dinner available CC: Accepted
Room facilities: 📺 ☎ ☕ 🔌 Access: ⬆
Conference: 16 meeting rooms (Thtr 350 max),
24hr-delegate from £175, day-delegate from £59
Children: Welcome 🍴 Dogs: Welcome
Licenses: ⚋ ⚋
Leisure: Tennis
Parking: Off-street and free

Directions: Take Junction 16 from M6 and A50 towards
Crewe. At first roundabout take last exit (A5020). First
exit at next roundabout signposted Crewe Hall.
Map ref: Crewe 7 E2

Ellesmere Port, Cheshire

Quality Hotel Chester

★★★

Berwick Road, off Welsh Road, Little Sutton,
Ellesmere Port, Cheshire, CH66 4PS
Tel: 0151 339 5121 Fax: 0151 339 3214
Email: enquiries@quality-hotels-chester.com
Web: www.choicehotelseurope.com
Rooms: 75 all ensuite 🛏 🖭 🚭
Pricing: Sgl £70–99 Dbl £90–110
Dinner available from £18.50
CC: Accepted
Room facilities: 📺 ☎ ☕ 🔌
Access: ⬆
Conference: 6 meeting rooms (Thtr 200 max),
24hr-delegate from £110, day-delegate from £30
Children: Welcome 🍴
Dogs: Welcome
Licenses: ⚋ ⚋
Leisure: Indoor pool, Gym, Health spa, Games room
Parking: Off-street and free
Directions: Junction 5 M53 follow Queensferry, at
second set of traffic lights turn right onto A550, the
hotel is one mile on left.
Map ref: Little Sutton 7 D1

Eskdale, Cumbria

Brook House Inn

◆◆◆◆ 🍴🛏

Boot, Eskdale, Cumbria, CA19 1TG
Tel: 01946 723288 Fax: 01946 723160
Email: stay@brookhouseinn.co.uk
Web: www.brookhouseinn.co.uk
Rooms: 7 all ensuite 🛏 🚭
Pricing: Sgl £40–52.50 Dbl £60–80
Dinner available from £20
CC: Accepted
Room facilities: 📺 ☕
Children: Welcome 🍴
Licenses: ⚋ Leisure: Games room
Parking: Off-street and free
Directions: Located in Boot on the Ambleside-Eskdale
road. Please post/fax/e-mail for directions.
Map ref: Boot 10 B2

Grange-over-Sands, Cumbria

Netherwood Hotel

★★★ 🛏

Lindale Road, Grange-over-Sands, Cumbria, LA11 6ET
Tel: 01539 532552 Fax: 01539 534121
Email: enquiries@netherwood-hotel.co.uk
Web: www.netherwood-hotel.co.uk

Built in 1893, personally supervised by the Fallowfield family. Netherwood is in 17 acres of gardens overlooking Morecambe Bay, and of architectural and historical interest with superb oak panelling throughout.
Rooms: 32 all ensuite ✦ ✦
Pricing: Sgl £90 Dbl £150
Dinner available from £32 CC: Accepted
Room facilities: ▢ ☎ ☕ ✦ Access: |↕
Conference: 4 meeting rooms (Thtr 150 max),
24hr-delegate from £125, day-delegate from £40
Children: Welcome ♫ ✦ Dogs: Welcome
Licenses: ✦ ♦♦♦
Leisure: Indoor pool, Gym, Health spa, Beauty salon, Spa bath, Steam room
Parking: Off-street and free
Directions: Leave M6 at Junction 36. Take A590 for Barrow-in-Furness. Follow for Holker Hall on B5277. Netherwood is on right just before rail station.
Map ref: Grange-over-Sands 10 B3

Grasmere, Cumbria

Wordsworth Hotel

★★★★★ ♞♞
Grasmere, Cumbria, LA22 9SW
Tel: 01539 435592 Fax: 01539 435765
Email: enquiry@wordsworth-grasmere.co.uk
Web: www.grasmere-hotels.co.uk

Set in the heart of Lakeland, in magnificent surroundings, the Wordsworh Hotel has a reputation for the high quality of its food, accommodation and hospitality.
Rooms: 37 all ensuite ✦ ✦
Pricing: Sgl £90 Dbl £160
Dinner available from £39.50
CC: Accepted
Room facilities: ▢ ☎ ✦
Access: |↕
Conference: 3 meeting rooms (Thtr 100 max),
24hr-delegate from £142.50, day-delegate from £39.50
Children: Welcome ♫ ✦ ✦
Licenses: ✦ ♦♦♦
Leisure: Indoor pool, Gym
Parking: Off-street and free
Directions: From north M6 J40 for Keswick, A591 for Grasmere; from south, J36 M6 A590, then A591 as above.
Map ref: Grasmere 10 B2

Grasmere Hotel

★★★♞♞
Broadgate, Grasmere, Cumbria, LA22 9TA
Tel: 01539 435277 Fax: 01539 435277
Email: enquiries@grasmerehotel.co.uk
Web: www.grasmerehotel.co.uk
Seasonal closure: 2 January to 6 February

Charming Victorian hotel set in the midst of beautiful mountain scenery. Award-winning restaurant overlooking secluded garden through which the River Rothay flows. Outstanding service and attention to detail.
Rooms: 13 all ensuite ✦ ✦
Pricing: Sgl £30–45 Dbl £60–100
Dinner available from £25
CC: Accepted
Room facilities: ▢ ☎ ☕
Children: Welcome 10yrs min age
Dogs: Welcome
Licenses: ♦♦♦
Parking: Off-street and free
Directions: M6 junction 36 to South Lakes, A591 to Grasmere, second entrance into village. Hotel is on left, past playing fields.
Map ref: Grasmere 10 B2

Hawkshead, Cumbria

West Vale Country Guest House | Little Gem

Far Sawrey, Hawkshead,
Sawrey, Cumbria, LA22 0LQ
Tel: 01539 442817 Fax: 01539 445302
Email: enquiries@westvalecountryhouse.co.uk
Web: www.westvalecountryhouse.co.uk
Rooms: 7 (6 ensuite)
Pricing: Sgl £62–86 Dbl £114–132
Dinner available from £34
CC: Accepted
Room facilities:
Children: Welcome 12yrs min age
Licenses:
Parking: Off-street and free
Directions: West Vale is on the B5285 between
Hawkshead and the Ferry at Windermere.
Map ref: Far Sawrey 10 B2

Ivy House Hotel & Restaurant

Ambleside, Hawkshead, Cumbria, LA22 0NS
Tel: 01539 436204
Email: rob@ivyhousehotel.com
Web: www.ivyhousehotel.com
Rooms: 11 all ensuite
Pricing: Dinner available from £10
CC: Accepted
Room facilities:
Conference: 2 meeting rooms (Thtr 36 max)
Children: Welcome
Dogs: Welcome
Licenses:
Leisure: Fishing
Parking: Off-street and free
Directions: M6 J36 or J37, signs for Kendall,
Windermere, Ambleside, Coniston and then
Hawkshead.
Map ref: Hawkshead 10 B2

"Here!"

Need a pet friendly property?
Look out for 'Dogs welcome' in
our listings.

Heywood, Lancashire

The Birch Hotel
★★

Manchester Road, Heywood,
Lancashire, OL10 2QD
Tel: 01706 366137 Fax: 01706 621000
Email: birchhotel@courtesyworld.co.uk
Web: www.thebirchhotel.com

Set near Manchester airport and Central Manchester,
this business hotel offers conference and seminar
room facilities, with executive accommodation in
refurbished bedrooms. We offer weekend leisure deals
as well as Friday cabaret entertainment evenings.
Rooms: 29 all ensuite
Pricing: Sgl £58 Dbl £66 Dinner available
CC: Accepted
Room facilities:
Conference: 3 meeting rooms (Thtr 175 max)
Children: Welcome
Dogs: Welcome
Licenses:
Leisure: Complimentary pass for Esporta leisure and
health club
Parking: Off-street and free
Directions: M62 J19 Heywood turn left at Texaco
Garage. Turn left at T-junction. Hotel on left. M66 J19,
hotel 1 mile.
Map ref: Heywood 10 C4

Holmrook, Cumbria

Lutwidge Arms Hotel
★★

Holmrook, Cumbria, CA19 1UH
Tel: 01946 724230 Fax: 01946 724100
Email: ian@lutwidgearms.co.uk
Web: www.lutwidgearms.co.uk
Seasonal closure: 25 December 2005 to 2 January 2006

The Lutwidge Arms Hotel is a Victorian roadside inn with a welcoming and friendly atmosphere. Dating back to the 1850s and taking the name of the Lutwidge family of Holmrook Hall, it combined the roles of working farm and inn for many years. The hotel has been owned and personally run by the Kelly family since 1994. It provides excellent accommodation and food to a mixture of business clients and holidaymakers.

Rooms: 15 all ensuite 🐾 ⓢ
Pricing: Sgl £37–65 Dbl £55–85
Dinner available from £6.50–20 CC: Accepted
Room facilities: 🖵 ☎ 🅰 ✎
Children: Welcome ⱨ Dogs: Welcome
Licenses: ⱨⱨⱨ
Leisure: Gym, Games room, Snooker/billiards
Parking: Off-street and free
Directions: Situated on the A595 at Holmrook, 3 miles north of Muncaster Castle.
Map ref: Holmrook 10 A2

Howtown, Cumbria

Sharrow Bay Hotel
★★★ 🅡🅡🅡
Premier
Lake Ullswater, Penrith, Cumbria, CA10 2LZ
Tel: 01768 486301 Fax: 01768 486349
Email: info@sharrowbay.co.uk
Web: www.sharrowbay.co.uk

Nestling on the shores of Ullswater, enjoying one of the most breathtaking views in the country. Providing a haven for rest and relaxation with internationally-renowned cuisine within idyllic surroundings.

Rooms: 24 (23 ensuite) ⓢ
Pricing: Sgl £160 Dbl £350–500
Dinner available from £52.50
CC: Accepted
Room facilities: 🖵 ☎ ✎
Conference: 2 meeting rooms (Thtr 36 max),
24hr-delegate from £311.38, day-delegate from £76.38
Children: Welcome 13yrs min age
Dogs: Welcome
Licenses: 🜄 ⱨⱨⱨ
Parking: Off-street and free
Directions: M6 exit 40 A66 west, A592, Pooley bridge, turn right after the church towards Howtown.
Map ref: Sharrow Bay 10 B2

Kendal, Cumbria

Stonecross Manor Hotel
★★★
Milnthorpe Road, Kendal, Cumbria, LA9 5HP
Tel: 01539 733559 Fax: 01539 736386
Email: info@stonecrossmanor.co.uk
Web: www.stonecrossmanor.co.uk

Established in 1857 as an orphanage, Stonecross Manor Hotel offers easy access to town, ample car parking, local cuisine, conference and banqueting facilities, indoor swimming pool and four-poster bedrooms.

Rooms: 30 all ensuite 🐾 🖨 ⓢ
Pricing: Sgl £72.50–110 Dbl £82.50–130
Dinner available from £16–28 CC: Accepted
Room facilities: 🖵 ☎ 🅰 ✎ Access: ⱞⱞ
Conference: 3 meeting rooms (Thtr 150 max),
24hr-delegate from £99, day-delegate from £27.50
Children: Welcome ⱨ Dogs: Welcome
Licenses: 🜄 ⱨⱨⱨ Leisure: Indoor pool
Parking: Off-street and free
Directions: M6 J36, follow signs to South Kendal. Hotel on outskirts of town on left.
Map ref: Kendal 10 B2

Heaves Hotel
★★
Heaves, near Kendal, Cumbria, LA8 8EF
Tel: 01539 560396 Fax: 01539 560269
Email: hotel@heaves.freeserve.co.uk
Web: www.heaveshotel.com
Seasonal closure: 21-30 December
Rooms: 13 all ensuite 🐾 🖨
Pricing: Sgl £40–80 Dbl £60–80
Dinner available from £16–18 CC: Accepted
Room facilities: 🖵 ☎ 🅰
Conference: 3 meeting rooms (Thtr 60 max)
Children: Welcome ⱨ
Dogs: Welcome
Licenses: 🜄 ⱨⱨⱨ
Leisure: Snooker/billiards
Parking: Off-street and free
Directions: M6 Junction 36, A590 Barrow & South Lakes. After 3 miles follow A590 to roundabout, again take A590. Second junction on right (Sizergh), signs on left after turn.
Map ref: Heaves 10 B2

Northwest

Keswick, Cumbria

Derwentwater Hotel

★★★★

Portinscale, Keswick, Cumbria, CA12 5RE
Tel: 01768 772538 Fax: 01768 771002
Email: info@derwentwater-hotel.co.uk
Web: www.derwentwater-hotel.co.uk

In 16 acres of conservation grounds on the shores of Derwentwater. Providing high standards of accommodation. Award winning hospitality, pets welcome, entry to local leisure club, the perfect Lakeland retreat.
Rooms: 46 all ensuite
Pricing: Sgl £70–75 Dbl £140–200
Dinner available from £24.50
CC: Accepted
Room facilities: ☐ ☎ ☕ Access: ↥
Conference: 2 meeting rooms (Thtr 20 max), 24hr-delegate from £80, day-delegate from £30
Children: Welcome ⴕ Dogs: Welcome
Licenses: ⵌ
Leisure: Fishing, Games room, Free entry to local spa
Parking: Off-street and free
Directions: Exit J40 M6 west on A66. 150 yards past third Keswick junction, left into Portinscale, then left as road bears right.
Map ref: Portinscale 10 B2

Keswick Country House Hotel

★★★

Station Road, Keswick, Cumbria, CA12 4NQ
Tel: 0845 458 4333 Fax: 01253 754 222
Email: reservations@choicehotels.co.uk
Web: www.thekeswickcountryhousehotel.co.uk
Rooms: 74 all ensuite
Dinner available CC: Accepted
Room facilities: ☐ ☎ ☕ Access: ↥
Conference: 3 meeting rooms (Thtr 70 max)
Children: Welcome ⴕ
Licenses: ⵌ
Leisure: Snooker/billiards
Parking: Off-street and free
Directions: Exit J40 M6; A66 to Keswick; follow signs for leisure pool and museum; turn left into Station Road.
Map ref: Keswick 10 B2

Cottage in the Wood

★★★ Commended

Whinlatter Pass, Braithwaite,
Keswick, Cumbria, CA12 5TW
Tel: 01768 778409 Fax: 01768 778064
Email: info@thecottageinthewood.co.uk
Web: www.thecottageinthewood.co.uk
Seasonal closure: 2 January to February
Rooms: 10 all ensuite
Pricing: Sgl £45–50 Dbl £67.50–99
Dinner available from £20.50–25 CC: Accepted
Room facilities: ☐ ☕
Children: Welcome 8yrs min age ⴕ Licenses: ⵌ
Parking: Off-street and free
Directions: Exit the A66 after Keswick for Braithwaite. Follow signs 'Whinlatter Forest Park'. Hotel is 400 yards before forest park on right.
Map ref: Whinlatter Pass 10 B2

Highfield Hotel & Restaurant

★★★ Commended

The Heads, Keswick, Cumbria, CA12 5ER
Tel: 01768 772508 Fax: 01768 780634
Email: info@highfieldkeswick.co.uk
Web: www.highfieldkeswick.co.uk
Seasonal closure: January

Award-winning Highfield Hotel & Restaurant is located in Keswick; with fantastic views of Derwentwater and the surrounding mountains and only a few minutes walk from the town centre and the theatre by the lake.
Rooms: 18 all ensuite
Pricing: Sgl £45–65 Dbl £90–130
Dinner available from £25
CC: Accepted
Room facilities: ☐ ☎ ☕
Children: Welcome 8yrs min age
Licenses: ⵌ
Parking: Off-street and free
Directions: From A66 take second exit at roundabout. Turn left and follow to T-junction. Turn left again then right at mini roundabout. The Heads is fourth turning on right.
Map ref: Keswick 10 B2

Swinside Lodge Hotel

★★☆☆ Excellent

Grange Road, Newlands,
Keswick, Cumbria, CA12 5UE
Tel: 017687 72948 Fax: 017687 73312
Email: info@swinsidelodge-hotel.co.uk
Web: www.swinsidelodge-hotel.co.uk
Rooms: 7 all ensuite
Pricing: Sgl £95 Dbl £130–190
Dinner available from £25
CC: Accepted
Room facilities:
Children: Welcome 12yrs min age
Licenses:
Parking: Off-street and free
Directions: Leave Keswick on the A66 to
Cockermouth. Turn left signposted Portinscale.
Continue on this road for 2 miles, signposted Grange,
not Swinside.
Map ref: Newlands 10 B2
See advert on following page

Acorn House Hotel

◆◆◆◆

Ambleside Road, Keswick, Cumbria, CA12 4DL
Tel: 01768 772553 Fax: 01768 775332
Email: info@acornhousehotel.co.uk
Web: www.acornhousehotel.co.uk
Seasonal closure: 1-27 December
Rooms: 10 (9 ensuite)
Pricing: Sgl £45–60 Dbl £60–76
CC: Accepted
Room facilities:
Children: Welcome 8yrs min age
Parking: Off-street and free
Directions: 400m from town centre, opposite St John's
Church on Ambleside Road.
Map ref: Keswick 10 B2

Dalegarth House Country Hotel

◆◆◆◆

Portinscale, Keswick, Cumbria, CA12 5RQ
Tel: 01768 772817 Fax: 01768 772817
Email: allerdalechef@aol.com
Web: www.dalegarth-house.co.uk

Dalegarth offers quality accommodation, food and
wine by the resident chef proprietors in an ideal
situation close to Keswick but away from the crowds
with Lake and Mountain views.

Rooms: 10 all ensuite
Pricing: Sgl £33–35 Dbl £66–75
Dinner available from £15
CC: Accepted
Room facilities:
Children: Welcome 5yrs min age
Licenses:
Parking: Off-street and free
Directions: Approach Portinscale from A66. Enter
village, pass Farmers Arms. Dalegarth approx 100
yards on left, behind Dorothy Well.
Map ref: Portinscale 10 B2

Rickerby Grange

◆◆◆◆

Portinscale, near Keswick, Cumbria, CA12 5RH
Tel: 01768 772344 Fax: 01768 775588
Email: stay@rickerbygrange.co.uk
Web: www.rickerbygrange.co.uk
Rooms: 10 (9 ensuite)
Pricing: Sgl £35–39 Dbl £70–79
Dinner available from £15
CC: Accepted
Room facilities:
Children: Welcome 5yrs min age
Dogs: Welcome
Licenses:
Parking: Off-street and free
Directions: Bypass Keswick on A66 Cockermouth
road. Turn left at Portinscale sign. Pass Farmers Arms
Inn on left, and turn down second lane to the right.
Map ref: Portinscale 10 B2

The Paddock Guest House

◆◆◆◆

Wordsworth Street, Keswick, Cumbria, CA12 4HU
Tel: 01768 772510 Fax: 01768 772510
Email: val@thepaddock.info
Web: www.thepaddock.info
Rooms: 6 all ensuite
Pricing: Dbl £22–25
CC: Accepted
Room facilities:
Children: Welcome 5yrs min age
Licenses:
Parking: Off-street and free
Directions: A591 to town centre, pass the Dogs Inn,
under bridge, third left into Wordsworth Street.
Paddock is on the right.
Map ref: Keswick 10 B2

"I do!" Want a honeymoon hotel?
Look for our Gold, Blue, and White
Ribbon Award winning hotels.

Northwest

West View Guest House

The Heads, Keswick, Cumbria, CA12 5ES
Tel: 01768 773638
Email: info@westviewkeswick.co.uk
Web: www.westviewkeswick.co.uk

West View offers walking advice and secure cycle storage. Wet kit can be dried overnight. A massive tasty breakfast awaits all guests (smaller options available!). The view is stunning.
Rooms: 7 all ensuite
Pricing: Sgl £30–48 Dbl £60 CC: Accepted
Room facilities:
Children: Welcome 12yrs min age
Directions: From Penrith A66, second exit signed Keswick. Follow signs for Borrowdale. The Heads is opposite town centre car park.
Map ref: Keswick 10 B2

Pitcairn House

7 Blencathra Street, Keswick, Cumbria, CA12 4HW
Tel: 01768 772453 Fax: 01768 773887
Email: enquiries@pitcairnhouse.co.uk
Web: www.pitcairnhouse.co.uk
Rooms: 8 (5 ensuite)
Pricing: Sgl £25–27 Dbl £50–60
Room facilities:
Children: Welcome Dogs: Welcome
Parking: Off-street and free
Directions: From Penrith Road turn left into Station Street and immediately left again into Southey Street, Blencathra Street is second left.
Map ref: Keswick 10 B2

Swiss Court Guest House

25 Bank Street, Keswick, Cumbria, CA12 5JZ
Tel: 01768 772637 Fax: 01768 780146
Email: info@swisscourt.co.uk
Web: www.swisscourt.co.uk
Rooms: 7 all ensuite
Pricing: Sgl £26–36 Dbl £50–80
CC: Accepted Room facilities:
Children: Welcome 8yrs min age
Parking: Off-street
Directions: Swiss Court is located on the main through road in Keswick, opposite Bell Close car park and the police station. Map ref: Keswick 10 B2

Knutsford, Cheshire

Cottons Hotel & Spa
★★★★ ⓡⓡ
Manchester Road, Knutsford, Cheshire, WA16 0SU
Tel: 01565 650333 Fax: 01565 755351
Email: cottons@shirehotels.com
Web: www.shirehotels.com

SHIRE
HOTELS

Set in the Cheshire countryside, a great base for Manchester, Chester and the north-west. First-class spa with treatments and activity studios. Spacious lounges for relaxation. Good reputation for home-cooked food featuring local/regional produce.
Rooms: 109 all ensuite 🖥 ⊗
Pricing: Sgl £90–165 Dbl £130–185
Dinner available from £25 CC: Accepted
Room facilities: ▢ ☎ ☕ 🕻 Access: ⎮↿
Conference: 14 meeting rooms (Thtr 200 max), 24hr-delegate from £170, day-delegate from £59
Children: Welcome ⍧ Licenses: ◈ ⍟
Leisure: Indoor pool, Gym, Health spa, Beauty salon, Tennis Parking: Off-street and free
Directions: Just 1 mile from Junction 19 of M6, on the A50 Knutsford to Warrington road.
Map ref: Knutsford 7 E1

Mere Court Hotel
★★★★ ⓡⓡ
Warrington Road, Mere, Knutsford, Cheshire, WA16 0RW
Tel: 01565 831000 Fax: 01565 831001
Email: reservations@merecourt.co.uk
Web: www.merecourt.co.uk
Rooms: 34 all ensuite 🖥 ⊗
Pricing: Sgl £120–180 Dbl £140–190
Dinner available from £26.95 CC: Accepted
Room facilities: ▢ ☎ ☕ 🕻 Access: ⎮↿
Conference: 11 meeting rooms (Thtr 200 max), 24hr-delegate from £149, day-delegate from £49
Children: Welcome ⍧ Licenses: ◈ ⍟
Parking: Off-street and free
Map ref: Mere 7 E1
See advert on this page

Northwest

Longview Hotel

★★

Manchester Road, Knutsford, Cheshire, WA16 0LX
Tel: 01565 632119 Fax: 01565 652402
Email: enquiries@longviewhotel.com
Web: www.longviewhotel.com
Rooms: 32 all ensuite
Dinner available CC: Accepted
Room facilities:
Children: Welcome
Dogs: Welcome
Licenses:
Parking: Off-street and free
Directions: Leave M6 at Junction 19, take A556 towards Chester. After 1 mile turn left at lights. After 1¾ miles, left at roundabout and hotel is 150 yards on right. Map ref: Knutsford 7 E1

Dog Inn

♦♦♦♦

Well Bank Lane, Over Peover, Knutsford, Cheshire, WA16 8UP
Tel: 01625 861421 Fax: 01625 864800
Web: www.doginn-overpeover.co.uk
Rooms: 6 all ensuite
Pricing: Sgl £55–60 Dbl £75–80
Dinner available from £7
CC: Accepted
Room facilities:
Children: Welcome
Licenses:
Leisure: Games room
Parking: Off-street and free
Directions: From Knutsford, follow A50 Holmes Chapel Road. Turn left at "Whipping Stocks". Proceed for 2 miles.
Map ref: Over Peover 7 E1

Lancaster, Lancashire

Lancaster House Hotel

★★★★

Green Lane, Ellel, Lancaster, Lancashire, LA1 4GJ
Tel: 01524 844822 Fax: 01524 844766
Email: lancaster@elhmail.co.uk
Web: www.elh.co.uk
Rooms: 99 all ensuite
Pricing: Sgl £85.45–100.45 Dbl £120.90–149.90
Dinner available from £24.95
CC: Accepted
Room facilities:
Conference: 14 meeting rooms (Thtr 180 max), 24hr-delegate from £125, day-delegate from £37.50
Children: Welcome Dogs: Welcome
Licenses:
Leisure: Indoor pool, Gym, Beauty salon, Outdoor hot spa
Parking: Off-street and free
Directions: From Junction 33 on the M6, turn right at roundabout, and travel approximately 2 miles, where it is signposted on right.
Map ref: Ellel 10 B3

Liverpool, Merseyside

Holiday Inn Liverpool City Centre

★★★★

Lime Street, Liverpool, Merseyside, L1 1NQ
Tel: 0151 705 2705 Fax: 0151 705 2800
Email: reservations@hiliverpool.com
Web: www.hiliverpool.com
Rooms: 139 all ensuite
Pricing: Sgl £70–140 Dbl £70–140
Dinner available from £10.95–25
CC: Accepted
Room facilities: Access:
Conference: 7 meeting rooms (Thtr 400 max), 24hr-delegate from £125, day-delegate from £45
Children: Welcome
Licenses: Leisure: Gym
Parking: Off-street
Directions: Follow signs to city centre and Lime Street Station. Park in St Johns NCP car park to right of hotel.
Map ref: Liverpool 10 B4

Suites Hotel Knowsley

★★★★

Ribblers Lane, Knowsley, Prescot, Merseyside, L34 9HA
Tel: 0151 549 2222 Fax: 0151 549 1116
Email: enquiries@suiteshotelgroup.com
Web: www.suiteshotelgroup.com

The Suites Hotel Knowsley is a unique concept offering 80 suites, which consist of a bedroom with queen size bed and a comfortable lounge with a business/work area.
Rooms: 80 all ensuite
Pricing: Sgl £70–97 Dbl £75–107
Dinner available from £22
CC: Accepted
Room facilities: Access:
Conference: 14 meeting rooms (Thtr 240 max), 24hr-delegate from £130, day-delegate from £37.50
Children: Welcome

Licenses:
Leisure: Indoor pool, Gym, Sauna, Steam room,
Jacuzzis
Parking: Off-street and free
Directions: Junction 4 M57 and situated on the A580
East Lancs Road. Easy access to all major roads and
motorways.
Map ref: Knowsley 10 B4

The Liner at Liverpool

★★★

Saagar Associates, Lord Nelson Street, Liverpool,
Merseyside, L3 5QB
Tel: 0151 471 0054 Fax: 0151 707 0352
Email: reservations@theliner.co.uk
Web: www.theliner.co.uk
Rooms: 152 all ensuite
Pricing: Sgl £60–95 Dbl £75–110
Dinner available from £6.95–25
CC: Accepted
Room facilities:
Access:
Conference: 12 meeting rooms (Thtr 620 max),
24hr-delegate from £95, day-delegate from £39
Children: Welcome
Dogs: Assistance dogs only
Licenses:
Leisure: Games room, Snooker/billiards
Parking: Off-street and free
Directions: From M62/M56/M53 follow city centre
signs to Lime Street station. Hotel is next to railway
station.
Map ref: Liverpool 10 B4

Aachen Hotel

◆◆◆

89–91 Mount Pleasant, Liverpool, Merseyside, L3 5TB
Tel: 0151 709 3477/3633 Fax: 0151 709 1126
Email: enquiries@aachenhotel.co.uk
Web: www.aachenhotel.co.uk
Rooms: 17 (10 ensuite)
Pricing: Sgl £32–42 Dbl £50–60
Dinner available from £10.50–14.50
CC: Accepted
Room facilities:
Children: Welcome
Licenses:
Leisure: Snooker/billiards
Parking: Off-street and free
Directions: From M62 M56 M53, follow city centre
signs to Mount Pleasant car park.
Map ref: Liverpool 10 B4

> Ice & slice? RAC's comprehensive
> inspection means we even check drinks
> are served the way you want.

Campanile Hotel
Travel Accommodation

Chaloner Street, Queens Dock, Liverpool,
Merseyside, L3 4AJ
Tel: 0151 709 8104 Fax: 0151 709 8725
Email: liverpool@campanile-hotels.com
Web: www.campanile.com

Campanile hotels offer comfortable and convenient
budget accommodation and a traditional French-style
Bistro providing freshly-cooked food for breakfast,
lunch and dinner. All rooms ensuite with tea/coffee-
making facilities, DDT and TV with Satellite channels.
Rooms: 100 all ensuite
Pricing: Sgl £53–66 Dbl £58.95–71.90
Dinner available from £11.95 CC: Accepted
Room facilities:
Conference: 1 meeting room (Thtr 30 max),
24hr-delegate from £75, day-delegate from £21.50
Children: Welcome
Dogs: Welcome
Licenses:
Parking: Off-street and free
Directions: Follow brown tourist signs for the Albert
Dock. The Campanile Hotel is next to Queens Dock.
Map ref: Liverpool 10 B4

Loweswater, Cumbria

Grange Country House Hotel

★★

Loweswater, near Cockermouth, Cumbria, CA13 0SU
Tel: 01946 861211
Email: info@thegrange-loweswater.co.uk
Web: www.thegrange-loweswater.co.uk
Rooms: 8 all ensuite
Pricing: Sgl £40–50 Dbl £70–90
Dinner available from £20–22
Room facilities:
Children: Welcome
Dogs: Welcome
Licenses:
Parking: Off-street and free
Directions: A66 to Keswick and Cockermouth; left onto
A5086 Lamplugh/Egremont; travel 4 miles, left turn
Mockerkin village. Left for Loweswater; hotel at bottom
of hill.
Map ref: Loweswater 10 A2

Lytham St Anne's, Lancashire

Clifton Arms Hotel

★★★★

West Beach, Lytham St Anne's, Lancashire, FY8 5QJ
Tel: 01253 739898 Fax: 01253 730657
Email: welcome@cliftonarms-lytham.com
Web: www.cliftonarms-lytham.com
Rooms: 48 all ensuite ⛄ ⊗
Pricing: Sgl £100–140 Dbl £125–160
Dinner available from £25–35
CC: Accepted
Room facilities: ⬜ ☎ ⌂ ☏
Access: ⇡
Conference: 6 meeting rooms (Thtr 200 max),
24hr-delegate from £35, day-delegate from £155
Children: Welcome ♚ ⁂
Dogs: Welcome
Licenses: ⬦ ⬛
Parking: Off-street and free
Directions: From M55 Junction 4, follow signs for
A584. Hotel is situated on the seafront at Lytham.
Map ref: Lytham St Anne's 10 B4

Chadwick Hotel

★★★

South Promenade, Lytham St Anne's,
Lancashire, FY8 1NP
Tel: 01253 720061 Fax: 01253 714455
Email: sales@thechadwickhotel.com
Web: www.thechadwickhotel.com
Rooms: 75 all ensuite ⛄ ▣ ⊗
Pricing: Sgl £48–49.50 Dbl £68–76
Dinner available from £17.50 CC: Accepted
Room facilities: ⬜ ☎ ⌂ ☏
Access: ⇡
Conference: 3 meeting rooms (Thtr 70 max),
24hr-delegate from £68, day-delegate from £25
Children: Welcome ♚ ⁂
Licenses: ⬛
Leisure: Indoor pool, Gym, Health spa, Games room,
Jacuzzi, Turkish bath
Parking: Off-street and free
Directions: From M6 to M55, then follow signs to
Lytham St Anne's. Hotel is on the Promenade at St
Annes.
Map ref: Lytham St Anne's 10 B4

Be more mobile

Dial 1740 from any
mobile phone to get
up-to-the-minute RAC
traffic information.

Calls cost up to 59p per minute. Please check
with your network operator. RAC recommends
that you use 1740 to plan your journey before
you depart and park safely before using the
1740 service.

Lindum

★★

63–67 South Promenade, Lytham St Anne's,
Lancashire, FY8 1LZ
Tel: 01253 721534 Fax: 01253 721364
Email: info@lindumhotel.co.uk
Web: www.lindumhotel.co.uk
Rooms: 78 all ensuite ⛄ ⊗
Pricing: Sgl £30–55 Dbl £55–85
Dinner available from £17.50
CC: Accepted
Room facilities: ⬜ ☎ ⌂
Access: ⇡
Conference: 4 meeting rooms (Thtr 75 max),
24hr-delegate from £60, day-delegate from £17.50
Children: Welcome ♚ ⁂
Dogs: Welcome
Licenses: ⬛
Leisure: Games room
Parking: Off-street and free
Directions: Situated on the main promenade (A584) at
St Annes.
Map ref: Lytham St Anne's 10 B4

Aureol Boutique Hotel

♦♦♦♦

117 South Promenade, Lytham St Anne's,
Lancashire, FY8 1NP
Tel: 01253 781511 Fax: 01253 781302
Email: info@aureolhotel.com
Web: www.aureolhotel.com
Rooms: 4 all ensuite ⛄ ⊗
Pricing: Dinner available from £12.50
Room facilities: ⬜ ⌂
Conference: 2 meeting rooms,
24hr-delegate from £60, day-delegate from £25
Children: Welcome ♚ ⁂
Parking: Off-street and free
Directions: M6, M55 follow signs Lytham St Anne's,
passing Blackpool Airport at St Annes Square, turn
onto Promenade. Follow south to 117.
Map ref: Lytham St Anne's 10 B4

Endsleigh Hotel

♦♦♦ ⊠

315 Clifton Drive South, Lytham St Anne's,
Lancashire, FY8 1HN
Tel: 01253 725622 Fax: 01253 720072
Rooms: 15 all ensuite ⛄ ⊗
Pricing: Sgl £26–27 Dbl £52–54
Dinner available from £10
Room facilities: ⬜ ⌂
Children: Welcome ♚
Licenses: ⬛
Parking: Off-street and free
Directions: Follow signs to St Annes off M55. First
hotel east of St Annes Square shopping centre.
Map ref: Lytham St Anne's 10 B4

Strathmore Hotel

◆◆◆

305 Clifton Drive South, Lytham St Anne's,
Lancashire, FY8 1HN
Tel: 01253 725478
Rooms: 8 (5 ensuite)
Pricing: Sgl £22–28 Dbl £44–56
Room facilities: 🖵 ☕
Children: Welcome 9yrs min age ♯
Parking: Off-street and free
Directions: Follow signs to St Annes off M55.
Strathmore Hotel after 200 yards on main Blackpool to
Preston road.
Map ref: Lytham St Anne's 10 B4

Macclesfield, Cheshire

Shrigley Hall Hotel

★★★★★

Shrigley Park, Pott Shrigley, Macclesfield,
Cheshire, SK10 5SB
Tel: 01625 575757 Fax: 01625 573323
Email: shrigleyhallreservations@paramount-hotels.co.uk
Web: www.paramount-hotels.co.uk

PARAMOUNT
GROUP OF HOTELS

Set in 262 acres of rolling Cheshire countryside looking
out over the Cheshire Plain. 18th century building
boasts history and character. On edge of Peak District.
Rooms: 150 all ensuite 🛏 🔲 ⊗
Pricing: Sgl £59–118 Dbl £118
Dinner available from £25 CC: Accepted
Room facilities: 🖵 ☎ ☕ 🗝 Access: ⏏
Conference: 9 meeting rooms (Thtr 250 max),
24hr-delegate from £189, day-delegate from £62
Children: Welcome ♯ Dogs: Welcome
Licenses: ⚖ ♙
Leisure: Indoor pool, Gym, Health spa, Beauty salon,
Tennis, Golf
Parking: Off-street and free
Directions: 12 miles from Manchester Airport. Through
Macclesfield into Bollington. Follow signs for Pott
Shrigley.
Map ref: Pott Shrigley 7 F1

Chadwick House Hotel

◆◆◆

55 Beech Lane, Macclesfield, Cheshire, SK10 2DS
Tel: 01625 615558 Fax: 01625 610265
Email: chadwickhouse@ntlworld.com
Web: www.smoothhound.co.uk/hotels/chadwick.html
Rooms: 14 (12 ensuite) ⊗
Pricing: Sgl £30–40 Dbl £40–55
CC: Accepted
Room facilities: 🖵 ☎ ☕ 🗝
Children: Welcome
Parking: Off-street and free
Directions: Chadwick House is situated on A538 500
yards from town hall and centre of Macclesfield.
Map ref: Macclesfield 7 E1

Manchester

The Lowry Hotel

★★★★★ ⊗⊗⊗   ⬖ Excellent ⬗

50 Dearmans Place, Chapel Wharf, Salford,
Manchester, M3 5LH
Tel: 0161 827 4000 Fax: 0161 827 4001
Email: enquiries@thelowryhotel.com
Web: www.roccofortehotels.com
Rooms: 165 all ensuite ⊗
Pricing: Sgl £180 Dbl £190
Dinner available from £18.50
CC: Accepted
Room facilities: 🖵 ☎ ☕ 🗝 ❄
Access: ⏏
Conference: 12 meeting rooms (Thtr 350 max),
24hr-delegate from £260, day-delegate from £75
Children: Welcome ♯ ☕
Dogs: Welcome
Licenses: ⚖ ♙
Leisure: Gym, Health spa, Beauty salon
Parking: Off-street
Directions: M602 to Salford and Manchester until
Grosvenor Casino. Left at lights onto Water Street and
past Granada Studios. At end turn onto New Quay
Street/Trinity Way. At first major set of lights turn left
and follow road until Lowry Hotel sign on right.
Map ref: Manchester 10 C4

Relax & smell
the coffee

Fresh coffee,
chilled juices for
breakfast. RAC's
team of qualified
Inspectors check
them both.

Northwest

Copthorne Hotel Manchester

★★★★

Clippers Quay, Salford Quays, Manchester, M50 3SN
Tel: 0161 873 7321 Fax: 0161 877 8112
Email: roomsales.manchester@mill-cop.com
Web: www.copthornehotels.com

MILLENNIUM
HOTELS AND RESORTS

MILLENNIUM HOTELS
COPTHORNE HOTELS

At this four-star property guests enjoy spacious comfort within a peaceful location overlooking the waterfront. Ideally situated minutes from the motorway with complimentary car parking.

Rooms: 166 all ensuite
Pricing: Sgl £160–190 Dbl £160–190
Dinner available from £21 CC: Accepted
Room facilities: Access:
Conference: 8 meeting rooms (Thtr 150 max), 24hr-delegate from £170, day-delegate from £50
Children: Welcome
Licenses:
Parking: Off-street and free
Directions: From M602 follow A57/A5063 to Salford. A5063 Salford Quays onto Trafford Road. Turn right into Clippers Quay, hotel on right.
Map ref: Manchester 10 C4

The Midland

★★★★

Peter Street, Manchester, M60 2DS
Tel: 0161 236 3333 Fax: 0161 932 4107
Email: midlandsales@qhotels.co.uk
Web: www.qhotels.co.uk
Rooms: 303 all ensuite
Pricing: Sgl £90–185 Dbl £100–195
Dinner available CC: Accepted
Room facilities: Access:
Conference: 18 meeting rooms (Thtr 500 max), 24hr-delegate from £205, day-delegate from £62
Children: Welcome Dogs: Welcome
Licenses:
Leisure: Indoor pool, Gym, Health spa, Beauty salon, Squash
Directions: Enter Manchester City Centre via M602 and follow signs for the GMEX. Hotel is directly in front of the GMEX.
Map ref: Manchester 10 C4

Bredbury Hall Hotel and Country Club

★★★

Dark Lane, Goyt Valley, Bredbury,
Stockport, Cheshire, SK6 2DH
Tel: 0161 430 7421 Fax: 0161 430 5079
Email: reservations@bredburyhallhotel.co.uk
Web: www.bredburyhallhotel.co.uk
Rooms: 150 all ensuite
Pricing: Sgl £67.50–87.50 Dbl £95.50–110.50
Dinner available from £18.50
CC: Accepted
Room facilities:
Conference: 10 meeting rooms (Thtr 150 max), 24hr-delegate from £115, day-delegate from £30
Children: Welcome
Dogs: Assistance dogs only
Licenses:
Leisure: Games room, Snooker/billiards
Parking: Off-street and free
Directions: Leave M60 at Junction 25. Follow the Bredbury Hall signs. Turn right at traffic lights, then turn left after 400 yards into Osbourne Street.
Map ref: Bredbury 7 E1
See advert on this page

Golden Tulip

Waters Reach, Trafford Park, Manchester, M17 1WS
Tel: 0161 873 8899 Fax: 0161 872 6556
Email: info@goldentulipmanchester.co.uk
Web: www.goldentulipmanchester.co.uk
Rooms: 160 all ensuite
Pricing: Sgl £57–152 Dbl £69–164
Dinner available from £15–35
CC: Accepted
Room facilities:
Access:
Conference: 8 meeting rooms (Thtr 200 max),
24hr-delegate from £115, day-delegate from £39
Children: Welcome
Licenses: Parking: Off-street and free
Directions: Leave M60 J7 and follow signs to
Manchester United FC. Turn left into Sir Matt Busby
Way. Hotel is 100 yards past the stadium.
Map ref: Trafford Park 7 E1

Jurys Inn Manchester

56 Great Bridgewater Street, Manchester, M1 5LE
Tel: 0161 953 8888 Fax: 0161 953 9090
Email: bookings@jurysdoyle.com
Web: www.jurysinns.com

JURYS DOYLE
HOTELS

Rooms: 265 all ensuite
Pricing: Sgl £64.50–124.50 Dbl £64.50–124.50
Dinner available from £19
CC: Accepted
Room facilities:
Access:
Conference: 2 meeting rooms (Thtr 50 max),
24hr-delegate from £131, day-delegate from £44
Children: Welcome
Licenses:
Directions: Located 9 miles/14 km from Manchester
Airport. Piccadilly Station 1 mile. G-mex Metrolink
Station two minutes walk.
Map ref: Manchester 10 C4

Sleep easy

Rest assured. Our comprehensive
inspection process includes
checking beds are comfortable.

Monton House Hotel — Venture Hotels

116–118 Monton Road, Monton, Eccles, Manchester,
Greater Manchester, M30 9HG
Tel: 0161 789 7811 Fax: 0161 787 7609
Email: hotel@montonhousehotel.co.uk
Web: www.montonhousehotel.co.uk

VENTURE HOTELS

Superbly located hotel with 60 ensuite bedrooms. Four
miles to Manchester city centre, minutes from M602,
M60, M62. Offering excellent restaurants, bar and
conference facilities at value for money prices. Wi-Fi
available.
Rooms: 60 all ensuite
Pricing: Sgl £30–80 Dbl £40–95
Dinner available from £7.95
CC: Accepted
Room facilities:
Access:
Conference: 3 meeting rooms (Thtr 150 max),
24hr-delegate from £85, day-delegate from £25
Children: Welcome
Dogs: Welcome
Licenses:
Parking: Off-street and free
Directions: Exit M602 at J2 turn to Pendleton and take
second left onto Half Edge Lane. Hotel 1 mile on right.
Map ref: Monton 10 C4

Ascott Hotel

6 Half Edge Lane, Eccles, Manchester, M30 9GJ
Tel: 0161 950 2453 Fax: 0161 661 7063
Email: ascottmanchester@talk21.com
Web: www.ascotthotel.co.uk
Seasonal closure: Christmas
Rooms: 10 (9 ensuite)
Pricing: Sgl £42.50–55 Dbl £55–75
CC: Accepted Room facilities:
Children: Welcome Parking: Off-street and free
Directions: M60 onto M602 exit 2, follow Pendreton
signs through first lights, turn left second lights, hotel
is 1/4 mile on left. No.6 blue sign.
Map ref: Eccles 10 C4

Imperial Hotel

157 Hathersage Road, Manchester, M13 0HY
Tel: 0161 225 6500 Fax: 0161 225 6500
Email: imphotel1@aol.com
Web: www.hotelimperialmanchester.co.uk
Seasonal closure: Christmas to New Year
Rooms: 27 (21 ensuite) ⊗
Pricing: Sgl £30–40 Dbl £50
Dinner available from £8 CC: Accepted
Room facilities: ☐ ☕ Children: Welcome ♀
Licenses: ♦♦♦ Parking: Off-street and free
Directions: 1¼ miles south of city centre. By
Manchester Royal Infirmary and Manchester University.
Opposite Saint Mary's Hospital.
Map ref: Manchester 10 C4

Victoria Park Hotel

4 Park Crescent, Victoria Park, Manchester, M14 5RE
Tel: 0161 224 1399 Fax: 0161 225 4949
Email: vph.manchester@claranet.co.uk
Web: www.victoriapark-hotel.co.uk

This splendid listed building is a friendly, non-alcohol
hotel in a quiet leafy suburb, yet close to Manchester
city centre, with comfortable, traditional and spacious
ensuite, non-TV rooms.
Rooms: 19 (18 ensuite) ♨ 🖨 ⊗
Pricing: Sgl £39 Dbl £49–59
CC: Accepted
Room facilities: ☎ ☕
Children: Welcome
Directions: 1 mile from city centre. Follow signs for
Manchester University on Oxford Road, continue until
Oxford Road becomes Wilmslow Road, hotel is off this
on Park Crescent.
Map ref: Manchester 10 C4

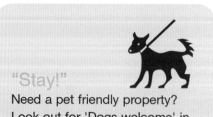

"Stay!"

Need a pet friendly property?
Look out for 'Dogs welcome' in
our listings.

Campanile Hotel
Travel Accommodation

55 Ordsall Lane, Regent Road, Salford,
Manchester, M5 4RS
Tel: 0161 833 1845 Fax: 0161 833 1847
Email: manchester@campanile-hotels.com
Web: www.campanile.com

Campanile hotels offer comfortable and convenient
budget accommodation and a traditional French-style
Bistro providing freshly-cooked food for breakfast,
lunch and dinner. All rooms ensuite with tea/coffee-
making facilities, DDT and TV with Sky channels.
Rooms: 104 all ensuite ⊗
Pricing: Sgl £56.95–75.95 Dbl £62.90–81.90
Dinner available from £12.95
CC: Accepted
Room facilities: ☐ ☎ ☕ 📞
Conference: 2 meeting rooms (Thtr 50 max),
24hr-delegate from £150, day-delegate from £25
Children: Welcome ♀
Dogs: Welcome
Licenses: ♦♦♦
Parking: Off-street and free
Directions: Leave M6 Junction 21a onto M62 to
Manchester, then M602 Salford. Continue over
roundabout onto Regent Road. Hotel on right, after
Sainsbury's.
Map ref: Salford 10 C4

Diamond Lodge
Travel Accommodation

Hyde Road (A57) East, Belle Vue,
Manchester, M18 7BA
Tel: 0161 231 0770 Fax: 0161 231 0660
Web: www.diamondlodge.co.uk
Rooms: 85 all ensuite ♨ ⊗
Pricing: Sgl £45 Dbl £45
Dinner available from £10
CC: Accepted
Room facilities: ☐ ☎ ☕
Conference: 1 meeting room (Thtr 30 max)
Children: Welcome
Licenses: ♦♦♦
Parking: Off-street and free
Directions: 2½ miles east of Manchester City Centre
on the A57 or 1½ miles west towards city J24 M60.
Manchester orbital motorway.
Map ref: Manchester 10 C4
See advert on following page

Tulip Inn Manchester
Travel Accommodation

Old Park Lane, Trafford Centre, Manchester, Lancashire, M17 8PG
Tel: 0161 755 3355 Fax: 0161 755 3344
Email: reservations@tulipinnmanchester.co.uk
Web: www.tulipinnmanchester.co.uk
Rooms: 121 all ensuite
Pricing: Dinner available from £3–30
CC: Accepted
Room facilities: Access:
Conference: 4 meeting rooms (Thtr 40 max)
Children: Welcome Licenses:
Parking: Off-street and free
Directions: Leave M60 at Junction 10 heading towards Trafford Centre. Hotel is on left-hand side.
Map ref: Manchester 10 C4

Morecambe, Lancashire

The Clarendon Hotel
★★★
Marine Road West, Morecambe, Lancashire, LA4 4EP
Tel: 01524 410180 Fax: 01524 421616
Email: clarendon@mitchellshotels.co.uk
Web: www.mitchellshotel.co.uk
Rooms: 29 all ensuite
Dinner available CC: Accepted
Room facilities: Access:
Conference: 4 meeting rooms (Thtr 90 max)
Children: Welcome Dogs: Welcome
Licenses:
Parking: Off-street and free
Directions: M6 J34 Morecambe, last roundabout by Shrimp pub first exit, follow road to promenade, turn right. Clarendon on third block.
Map ref: Morecambe 10 B3

Beach Mount Hotel
♦♦♦
395/6 Marine Road East, Morecambe, Lancashire, LA4 5AN
Tel: 01524 420753 Fax: 01524 420753
Seasonal closure: November to March
Rooms: 20 all ensuite
Pricing: Sgl £23–41.50 Dbl £42–53
CC: Accepted
Room facilities:
Children: Welcome Dogs: Welcome
Licenses:
Parking: Off-street and free
Directions: Situated on the East Promenade.
Map ref: Morecambe 10 B3

Hotel Prospect
♦♦♦
363 Marine Road East, Morecambe, Lancashire, LA4 5AQ
Tel: 01524 417819 Fax: 01524 417819
Email: peter@hotelprospect.fsnet.co.uk
Rooms: 14 all ensuite
Pricing: Sgl £17.50–19.50 Dbl £35–39
Dinner available from £9
CC: Accepted
Room facilities:
Children: Welcome Dogs: Welcome
Licenses: Parking: Off-street and free
Directions: Exit M6 Junction 34/35. Follow signs to Lancaster/Morecambe. At Morecambe, follow signs to East Promenade. Turn left at Promenade. Hotel on left.
Map ref: Morecambe 10 B3

The Marina Hotel
♦♦♦
324 Marine Road Central, Morecambe, Lancashire, LA4 5AA
Tel: 01524 423979 Fax: 01524 423979
Email: marina@marina-hotel.demon.co.uk
Web: www.marina-hotel.demon.co.uk
Rooms: 10 (6 ensuite)
Pricing: Sgl £20–30 Dbl £30–60
Dinner available from £12
CC: Accepted
Room facilities:
Children: Welcome 12yrs min age
Licenses:
Parking: Off-street and free
Directions: Follow signs for Morecambe Central Promenade. Hotel is near the new lifeboat station on the seafront.
Map ref: Morecambe 10 B3

Silverwell Hotel

20 West End Road, Morecambe, Lancashire, LA4 4DL
Tel: 01524 410532 Fax: 01524 417685
Email: silverwell@eur-isp.com
Web: www.silverwellhotel.co.uk
Rooms: 14 (6 ensuite) 🛏 🚭
Pricing: Sgl £18–21 Dbl £36–42
Dinner available from £7.50–150
CC: Accepted
Room facilities: ▢ ☕
Conference: 1 meeting room (Thtr 15 max),
24hr-delegate from £50, day-delegate from £20
Children: Welcome ⊦ Licenses: ♦♦♦
Directions: M6 J34 to Lancaster, to Morecambe, West
End, right at promenade, second right, West End Road
on left.
Map ref: Morecambe 10 B3

Newby Bridge, Cumbria

Whitewater Hotel

★★★

The Lakeland Village, Ulverston, Newby Bridge,
Cumbria, LA12 8PX
Tel: 01539 531133 Fax: 01539 531881
Email: enquiries@whitewater-hotel.co.uk
Web: www.whitewater-hotel.co.uk
Rooms: 35 all ensuite 🛏 🖨 🚭
Pricing: Sgl £80–100 Dbl £130–195
Dinner available from £23.50–25
CC: Accepted
Room facilities: ▢ ☎ ☕
Access: ⌊⌋↑
Conference: 3 meeting rooms (Thtr 80 max),
24hr-delegate from £125, day-delegate from £32
Children: Welcome ⊦ ☕
Licenses: ⟡ ♦♦♦
Leisure: Indoor pool, Gym, Health spa, Beauty salon,
Tennis, Games room, Squash court
Parking: Off-street and free
Directions: Exit M6, J36 follow A590 towards Barrow
for 16 miles. Hotel is 1 mile past Newby Bridge on
right.
Map ref: Newby Bridge 10 B2

The Knoll Country House

♦♦♦♦♦ ☐ ✕ ☖ ☕

Lakeside, Newby Bridge, near Ulverston,
Cumbria, LA12 8AU
Tel: 01539 531347 Fax: 01539 530850
Email: info@theknoll-lakeside.co.uk
Web: www.theknoll-lakeside.co.uk
Seasonal closure: 24-26 December
Rooms: 8 all ensuite 🖨 🚭
Pricing: Sgl £50–78 Dbl £70–108
Dinner available from £19.95–23.95
CC: Accepted
Room facilities: ▢ ☎ ☕ ⬚
Licenses: ♦♦♦
Parking: Off-street and free

Directions: A590 to Newby Bridge. Turn right opposite
Newby Bridge Hotel to Lakeside. 400m past the
Lakeside Hotel on left.
Map ref: Lakeside 10 B2

Lyndhurst Country House

♦♦♦♦ ✕ ☕

Newby Bridge, Cumbria, LA12 8ND
Tel: 01539 531245
Email: christine@lyndhurstcountryhouse.co.uk
Web: www.lyndhurstcountryhouse.co.uk

A relaxing, friendly country guest house set in lovely
gardens, conveniently located at the southern tip of
Lake Windermere. Comfortable ensuite bedrooms, new
guest lounge/garden room and delicious cuisine.
Rooms: 3 all ensuite 🚭
Pricing: Sgl £35 Dbl £55–60
Dinner available from £12.50
CC: Accepted
Room facilities: ▢ ☕
Children: Welcome
Licenses: ♦♦♦ Parking: Off-street and free
Directions: Lyndhurst is situated on A590 at its junction
with the A592.
Map ref: Newby Bridge 10 B2

Northwich, Cheshire

The Floatel Northwich

★★★

London Road, Northwich, Cheshire, CW9 5HD
Tel: 01606 44443 Fax: 01606 42596
Email: enquiries@hotels-northwich.com
Web: www.stop-inns.com
Rooms: 60 all ensuite 🛏 🖨 🚭
Pricing: Sgl £35–89.95 Dbl £45–110.90
Dinner available from £14.50–17.95
CC: Accepted
Room facilities: ▢ ☎ ☕ ⬚ Access: ⌊⌋↑
Conference: 4 meeting rooms (Thtr 100 max),
24hr-delegate from £90, day-delegate from £31
Children: Welcome ⊦ Dogs: Welcome
Licenses: ⟡ ♦♦♦ Parking: Off-street
Directions: Leave M6 at Junction 19 and take A556 to
Northwich/town centre and brown/white direction
signs marked Quality Hotel.
Map ref: Northwich 7 E1

Penrith, Cumbria

North Lakes Hotel and Spa

★★★★ ⅋

Commended

Ullswater Road, Penrith, Cumbria, CA11 8QT
Tel: 01768 868111 Fax: 01768 868291
Email: nlakes@shirehotels.com
Web: www.shirehotels.com

SHIRE HOTELS

Great location for exploring the lakes. Family friendly in both facilities and service. First-class spa with treatments and activity studios. Spacious lounges for relaxation. Good reputation for home-cooked food featuring local/regional produce.
Rooms: 84 all ensuite 🍴 📺 ⊗
Pricing: Sgl £87–127 Dbl £124–147
Dinner available from £25
CC: Accepted
Room facilities: 🖵 ☎ 🍵 ⚒
Access: |↟↟
Conference: 13 meeting rooms (Thtr 200 max),
24hr-delegate from £155, day-delegate from £50
Children: Welcome 升
Licenses: ⟁ ⅲ
Leisure: Indoor pool, Gym, Health spa,
Beauty salon, Games room
Parking: Off-street and free
Directions: Leave M6 at Junction 40 and follow signs for Penrith.
Map ref: Penrith 10 B1

Brandelhow Guest House

◆◆◆◆ ⅋ ℘

1 Portland Place, Penrith, Cumbria, CA11 7QN
Tel: 01768 864470
Map ref: Penrith 10 B1

Brooklands Guest House

◆◆◆◆ ⅋ ℘

2 Portland Place, Penrith, Cumbria, CA11 7QN
Tel: 01768 863395 Fax: 01768 864895
Email: enquiries@brooklandsguesthouse.com
Web: www.brooklandsguesthouse.com

Charming, elegant surroundings await any visitor to Brooklands. This beautiful, recently refurbished Victorian townhouse provides luxury ensuite rooms with all facilities. Also available, four-poster room and deluxe rooms.
Rooms: 7 all ensuite 🍴 📺 ⊗
Pricing: Sgl £30–35 Dbl £60–70
CC: Accepted
Room facilities: 🖵 🍵
Children: Welcome
Parking: Off-street and free
Directions: Exit J40 M6, follow tourist information signs, turn left at town hall into Portland Place, Brooklands 50m on the left.
Map ref: Penrith 10 B1

Are the bells ringing?

Getting married? Congratulations!
Look for the wedding bells symbol which shows hotels licensed for civil ceremonies.

Norcroft Guest House

Graham Street, Penrith, Cumbria, CA11 9LQ
Tel: 01768 862365 Fax: 01768 210425
Email: info@norcroft-guesthouse.co.uk
Web: www.norcroft-guesthouse.co.uk

Conveniently situated for M6 yet 5 minutes walk from
town centre. Norcroft Guest House offers a warm
welcome, spacious and comfortable ensuite rooms
with secure off-street parking.
Rooms: 9 all ensuite 🐾 ⊗
Pricing: Sgl £27.50–40 Dbl £55–60
Dinner available from £15
CC: Accepted
Room facilities: ▢ ⊛
Children: Welcome ♁
Dogs: Welcome
Licenses: ♦♦♦
Parking: Off-street and free
Directions: From M6 follow one-way system to town
centre, left at town hall, left into Drovers Lane, Norcroft
400 yards.
Map ref: Penrith 10 B1

Tymparon Hall

Newbiggin, Stainton, Penrith, Cumbria, CA11 0HS
Tel: 01768 483236 Fax: 01768 483236
Email: margaret@tymparon.freeserve.co.uk
Web: www.tymparon.freeserve.co.uk
Seasonal closure: December and January
Rooms: 3 all ensuite 🐾 ⊗
Dinner available
Room facilities: ⊛
Children: Welcome ♁ ⌘
Dogs: Welcome
Parking: Off-street and free
Directions: Leave M6 at Junction 40. Take A66 to
Keswick. Turn right at sign for Newbiggin. Hotel at
extreme end of village on right.
Map ref: Newbiggin 10 B1

Albany House

5 Portland Place, Penrith, Cumbria, CA11 7QN
Tel: 01768 863072 Fax: 01768 895527
Email: info@albany-house.org.uk
Web: www.albany-house.org.uk
Rooms: 5 (2 ensuite) 🐾 ⊗
Pricing: Sgl £30–37.50 Dbl £46–55 CC: Accepted
Room facilities: ▢ ⊛
Children: Welcome Dogs: Welcome
Parking: Off-street and free
Directions: Exit J40 M6, follow tourist information
signs, turn left at town hall into Portland Place. Albany
25m on the left.
Map ref: Penrith 10 B1

Preston, Lancashire

The Villa Country House Hotel

★★★ ⍟

Moss Side Lane, Wrea Green, Kirkham, Preston,
Lancashire, PR4 2PE
Tel: 01772 684347 Fax: 01772 687647
Email: info@villahotel-wreagreen.co.uk
Web: www.villahotel-wreagreen.co.uk
Rooms: 25 all ensuite 🐾 ⊗
Pricing: Sgl £65–90 Dbl £80–105
Dinner available from £10–25
CC: Accepted
Room facilities: ▢ ☎ ⊛ ✆ ❄ Access: |↥|
Conference: 2 meeting rooms (Thtr 30 max),
24hr-delegate from £100, day-delegate from £25
Children: Welcome ♁
Dogs: Welcome
Licenses: ◁ ♦♦♦
Parking: Off-street and free
Directions: Junction 3 M55, follow signs to Kirkham, at
Wrea Green follow signs to Lytham.
Map ref: Wrea Green 10 B3
See advert on following page

Brook House Hotel

★★

662 Preston Road, Clayton-Le-Woods, Chorley,
near Preston, Lancashire, PR6 7EH
Tel: 01772 336403 Fax: 01772 337369
Email: enquiries@hotel-preston-chorley.co.uk
Web: www.hotel-preston-chorley.co.uk
Rooms: 20 all ensuite 🐾 ⊗
Pricing: Sgl £40–52.95 Dbl £47.50–62.95
Dinner available from £15–25 CC: Accepted
Room facilities: ▢ ☎ ⊛
Conference: 2 meeting rooms (Thtr 70 max),
24hr-delegate from £75, day-delegate from £19.95
Children: Welcome ♁ Dogs: Welcome
Licenses: ♦♦♦
Parking: Off-street and free
Directions: From M6 Junction 29, M65 Junction 2 and
M61 Junction 9, take the A6 towards Chorley, hotel is
$1/2$ mile on the left.
Map ref: Clayton-Le-Woods 10 B4

THE VILLA

DINING ROOMS BAR AND BEDROOMS

To the Manor Born

It's rare to find a distinctive hotel in an idyllic setting, and even rarer to discover one that offers a fine dining experience to match... Yet that's exactly what's in store for visitors to The Villa, an elegant former 19th century gentleman's residence, set amidst rolling parkland and situated in the picture perfect Lancashire village of Wrea Green.

A Warm Welcome

Many visitors come to The Villa for its historic charm, air of quiet elegance and splendid location, yet often return again and again to experience the warm hospitality and excellent

personal service.

The hotel rooms are spacious and luxuriously appointed, offering stylish, comfortable accommodation. All twenty five air-conditioned rooms feature superb en-suite facilities and have been tastefully designed and furnished to create the ideal atmosphere for a relaxing visit.

Dining in Style

Residents and non-residents alike can sample the culinary delights of The Villa's superb bistro-style menu created with considerable flair by our in-house chef. The uniquely designed restaurant comprises a series of interlinked dining areas and lends itself perfectly to elegant informal entertaining, be it a relaxed lunch with friends or a romantic dinner for two.

Our mouth-watering, freshly cooked meals are complemented by a good selection of quality wines from our well stocked cellars. We set a great deal of store by the reputation of our restaurant, why not join us and enjoy a first class dining experience at The Villa.

St Andrews House Hotel

◆◆

518 Blackpool Road, Preston, Lancashire, PR2 1HY
Tel: 01772 720580 Fax: 01772 720580
Rooms: 11 (6 ensuite) ⊛
Pricing: Sgl £25–31 Dbl £40–46
Room facilities: ▢ ☕
Children: Welcome ⟊
Licenses: ▥
Parking: Off-street and free
Directions: M6/A59 to Preston. Turn right at R.A.B over
10 sets of traffic lights, 500 yards on the right.
Map ref: Preston 10 B3

Ramsbottom, Lancashire

Old Mill Hotel & Leisure Club

★★★

Springwood Street, Ramsbottom, Lancashire, BL0 9DS
Tel: 01706 822991 Fax: 01706 822291
Email: reservations@oldmill-uk.com
Web: www.oldmill-uk.com
Rooms: 29 all ensuite ⚲ ✈ ⊛
Pricing: Sgl £61 Dbl £69–76
Dinner available from £15.95
CC: Accepted
Room facilities: ▢ ☎ ☕ ☏
Conference: 3 meeting rooms (Thtr 80 max),
24hr-delegate from £99, day-delegate from £25
Children: Welcome ⟊
Licenses: ⟁ ▥
Leisure: Indoor pool, Gym, Sauna, Steam room,
Jacuzzi
Parking: Off-street and free
Directions: Close to Junction 1 on M66, 5 miles from
Bury, 15 miles from Manchester city centre.
Map ref: Ramsbottom 10 C4

Ravenglass, Cumbria

Muncaster Country Guest House

◆◆◆ ✕

Muncaster, Ravenglass, Cumbria, CA18 1RD
Tel: 01229 717693 Fax: 01229 717693
Email: ronandjan@muncastercountryguesthouse.com
Web: www.muncastercountryguesthouse.com
Rooms: 7 (2 ensuite) ⚲ ⊛
Pricing: Sgl £25–35 Dbl £45–60
Dinner available from £12–18
CC: Accepted
Room facilities: ☕
Children: Welcome ⟊
Dogs: Welcome
Licenses: ▥
Parking: Off-street and free
Directions: Situated on the A595 1 mile east of
Ravenglass, opposite main entrance to Muncaster
Castle.
Map ref: Muncaster 10 A2

Runcorn, Cheshire

Campanile Hotel
Travel Accommodation

Lowlands Road, Runcorn, Cheshire, WA7 5TP
Tel: 01928 581771 Fax: 01928 581730
Email: runcorn@louvre-hotels.co.uk
Web: www.campanile.com

Campanile hotels offer comfortable and convenient
budget accommodation and a traditional French-style
Bistro providing freshly-cooked food for breakfast,
lunch and dinner. All rooms ensuite with tea/coffee-
making facilities, DDT and TV with Sky channels.
Rooms: 53 all ensuite ✈ ⊛
Pricing: Dinner available from £5.95
CC: Accepted
Room facilities: ▢ ☎ ☕ ☏
Conference: 1 meeting room (Thtr 30 max),
24hr-delegate from £70, day-delegate from £21.50
Children: Welcome ⟊
Dogs: Welcome
Licenses: ▥
Parking: Off-street
Directions: Exit M56 at Junction 12, joining A557
towards Runcorn. Follow signs for Runcorn railway
station.
Map ref: Runcorn 7 E1

Sawrey, Cumbria

Sawrey Hotel

★★

Far Sawrey, Ambleside, Cumbria, LA22 0LQ
Tel: 01539 443425 Fax: 01539 443425
Email: sawreyhotel@btopenworld.com
Seasonal closure: Christmas
Rooms: 18 all ensuite ⚲
Pricing: Sgl £31.50–41.50 Dbl £90
Dinner available from £20.50 CC: Accepted
Room facilities: ▢ ☎ ☕
Children: Welcome ⟊ ☕
Dogs: Welcome
Licenses: ▥
Parking: Off-street and free
Directions: One mile from Windermere (Bowness) car
ferry on B5285 Hawkshead Road.
Map ref: Far Sawrey 10 B2

See advert on following page

SAWREY HOTEL

An attractive two-storey, 18th-century inn built in traditional Lake District style. Former stables converted into a bar.

FAR SAWREY,
AMBLESIDE,
CUMBRIA,
LA22 0LQ

Tel: 01539 443425
Fax: 01539 443425
Email: sawreyhotel@btopenworld.com

Shap, Cumbria

Shap Wells Hotel
★★★
Shap, Penrith, Cumbria, CA10 3QU
Tel: 01931 716628 Fax: 01931 716377
Email: manager@shapwells.com
Web: www.shapwells.com
Seasonal closure: January to mid-February
Rooms: 98 all ensuite
Dinner available
CC: Accepted
Room facilities: 🖵 ☎ 🍵
Access: |↕|
Conference: 7 meeting rooms (Thtr 170 max)
Children: Welcome �🍴
Dogs: Welcome
Licenses: ◇ ⛊
Leisure: Tennis, Games room, Snooker/billiards
Parking: Off-street and free
Directions: Exit J39 M6, then A6 for Kendal. After 1½–2 miles, hotel drive (1 mile long) on left.
Map ref: Penrith 10 B1

The big sleep
As part of our comprehensive inspection process, RAC Inspectors investigate the comfort of the beds.

Silloth, Cumbria

Golf Hotel
★★
Criffel Street, Silloth, Cumbria, CA7 4AB
Tel: 01697 331438 Fax: 01697 332582
Email: golf.hotel@virgin.net
Web: www.golfhotelsilloth.co.uk

An ideal base for the lakes, Carlisle, Roman wall and southern Scotland. Our family-run hotel overlooks the Solway Firth and is only 200 yards from Silloth-on-Solway golf club.
Rooms: 22 all ensuite
Pricing: Sgl £38.50–59 Dbl £62.30–98
Dinner available from £18.50
CC: Accepted
Room facilities: 🖵 ☎ 🍵
Conference: 2 meeting rooms (Thtr 100 max)
Children: Welcome �🍴
Dogs: Welcome
Licenses: ⛊
Leisure: Games room, Snooker/billiards
Directions: Overlooking the green in Silloth.
Map ref: Silloth 13 D4

Southport, Merseyside

Tree Tops Country House Restaurant and Hotel
★★★★ 🍴🍴
Southport Old Road, Formby, Southport,
Merseyside, L37 0AB
Tel: 01704 572430 Fax: 01704 572430
Email: sales@treetopsformby.fsnet.co.uk
Web: www.treetopsformby.co.uk
Rooms: 11 all ensuite 🖊
Pricing: Sgl £65 Dbl £110
Dinner available
CC: Accepted
Room facilities: 🖵 ☎ 🍵 📞
Conference: 2 meeting rooms (Thtr 300 max)
Children: Welcome
Licenses: ◇ ⛊
Leisure: Outdoor pool
Parking: Off-street and free
Directions: Turn off the A565 into Southport Old Road.
Map ref: Formby 10 B4

Metropole

★★

Portland Street, Southport, Merseyside, PR8 1LL
Tel: 01704 536836 Fax: 01704 549041
Email: metropole.southport@btinternet.com
Web: www.btinternet.com/~metropole.southport
Rooms: 23 all ensuite
Pricing: Sgl £25–41.50 Dbl £50–72
Dinner available from £12
CC: Accepted
Room facilities: 🖵 ☎ ☕
Children: Welcome 🍴 🕯
Dogs: Welcome
Licenses: ♟
Leisure: Snooker/billiards
Parking: Off-street and free
Directions: 100m from Southport's Lord Street, a
four-minute walk from the railway station.
Map ref: Southport 10 B4

Shelbourne Hotel

★★

1 Lord Street, Southport, Merseyside, PR8 2BH
Tel: 01704 541252 Fax: 01704 501293
Email: info@shelbourne-hotel.co.uk
Web: www.shelbourne-hotel.co.uk
Rooms: 21 all ensuite
Pricing: Sgl £40–80 Dbl £70–100
Dinner available from £11.95
CC: Accepted
Room facilities: 🖵 ☎ ☕ 📞
Conference: 2 meeting rooms (Thtr 140 max),
24hr-delegate from £45, day-delegate from £22
Children: Welcome 🍴
Dogs: Welcome
Licenses: ♟
Leisure: Games room, Snooker/billiards
Parking: Off-street and free
Directions: From south: M6 to Junction 26 then M58
Junction 3. Take A570 through Ormskirk to Southport.
From north: M6 to Junction 32 Preston, follow A59 to
A565 Southport.
Map ref: Southport 10 B4

Rosedale Hotel

◆◆◆◆

11 Talbot Street, Southport, Merseyside, PR8 1HP
Tel: 01704 530604 Fax: 01704 530604
Email: info@rosedale-hotel.co.uk
Web: www.rosedale-hotel.co.uk
Seasonal closure: Late December to early January
Rooms: 9 (8 ensuite) 🦽
Pricing: Sgl £30 Dbl £60
CC: Accepted
Room facilities: 🖵 ☕
Children: Welcome 🍴
Licenses: ♟
Parking: Off-street and free
Directions: Entering the town via A570, follow signs to
town centre into Eastbank Street. Talbot Street is on left.
Map ref: Southport 10 B4

Whitworth Falls Hotel

◆◆◆◆

16 Lathom Road, Southport, Merseyside, PR9 0JH
Tel: 01704 530074 Fax: 01704 530074
Email: whitworthfalls@rapid.co.uk
Web: www.whitworthfallshotel.com
Rooms: 12 all ensuite 🦽
Pricing: Sgl £23–30 Dbl £45–60
Dinner available from £11
CC: Accepted
Room facilities: 🖵 ☎ ☕ 📞
Children: Welcome 🍴 🕯
Dogs: Welcome
Licenses: ♟
Parking: Off-street and free
Directions: From Southport town centre, Lord Street,
head north to the fire station over the roundabout.
Take second left (Alexandra Road), and fourth right
(Lathom Road).
Map ref: Southport 10 B4

Thornton Hough, Merseyside

Thornton Hall Hotel & Health Club

★★★★

Neston Road, Thornton Hough, Merseyside, CH63 1JF
Tel: 0151 336 3938 Fax: 0151 336 7864
Email: reservations@thorntonhallhotel.com
Web: www.thorntonhallhotel.com
Rooms: 63 all ensuite 🖶 ⊗
Pricing: Sgl £132–308 Dbl £145–321
Dinner available from £28
CC: Accepted
Room facilities: 🖵 ☎ ☕ 📞
Conference: 8 meeting rooms (Thtr 435 max),
24hr-delegate from £160, day-delegate from £60
Children: Welcome 🍴
Dogs: Welcome
Licenses: ♿ ♟
Leisure: Indoor pool, Gym, Health spa,
Beauty salon, Tennis
Parking: Off-street and free
Directions: M53 junction 4 take A5151 to Clatterbridge
then B5136 to Neston. Thornton Hall is after Thornton
Hough village on the left.
Map ref: Thornton Hough 10 B4

Ullswater, Cumbria

Patterdale Hotel

★★

Patterdale, Penrith, Cumbria, CA11 0NN
Tel: 0845 458 4333 Fax: 01253 754222
Email: reservations@choice-hotels.co.uk
Web: www.patterdalehotel.co.uk
Seasonal closure: December to February
Rooms: 57 all ensuite 🦽
Pricing: Sgl £34–49.50 Dbl £67–104
Dinner available from £15.50
CC: Accepted
Room facilities: 🖵 ☎ ☕

Access:
Conference: 2 meeting rooms,
24hr-delegate from £86, day-delegate from £21
Children: Welcome ♄ ☕
Licenses: ⫯⫯⫯
Leisure: Tennis, Fishing, Croquet
Parking: Off-street and free
Directions: From M6 Junction 40, take A66 towards Keswick, at roundabout take first exit, signposted Ullswater (A592). Turn right at T-Junction. Continue through Glenridding to Patterdale.
Map ref: Patterdale 10 B2

Up Holland, Lancashire

Lancashire Manor Hotel

★★★

Prescott Road, East Pimbo, Up Holland,
Lancashire, WN8 9PU
Tel: 01695 720401 Fax: 01695 50953
Email: enquiries@hotels-skelmersdale.com
Web: www.stop-inns.com
Rooms: 55 all ensuite ♨ 🛏 ⊛
Pricing: Sgl £47.75–95.95 Dbl £75.50–151
Dinner available from £17.95
CC: Accepted
Room facilities: ▯ ☎ ☕ ☏
Conference: 7 meeting rooms (Thtr 200 max),
24hr-delegate from £109.50, day-delegate from £29.50
Children: Welcome ♄ ☕
Dogs: Welcome
Licenses: ⚖ ⫯⫯⫯
Parking: Off-street and free
Directions: M6 Junction 26, M58 Junction 5. Down to roundabout, turn left, 100 yards further turn left again. Hotel 300 yards on right.
Map ref: East Pimbo 10 B4

Wallasey, Merseyside

Grove House Hotel

★★★★ ⫯⫯

Grove Road, Wallasey, Merseyside, CH45 3HF
Tel: 0151 639 3947 Fax: 0151 639 0028
Email: reception@thegrovehouse.co.uk
Web: www.thegrovehouse.co.uk
Rooms: 14 all ensuite ♨ 🛏 ⊛
Pricing: Sgl £66.70–67.70 Dbl £83.65–110
Dinner available from £11.99–37.65
CC: Accepted
Room facilities: ▯ ☎ ☕ ☏
Conference: 2 meeting rooms (Thtr 50 max),
24hr-delegate from £92.65, day-delegate from £24.95
Children: Welcome ♄
Licenses: ⚖ ⫯⫯⫯
Parking: Off-street and free
Directions: Junction 1 M53, A554 Wallasey New Brighton; right after church onto Harrison Drive, left after Windsors Garage onto Grove Road.
Map ref: Wallasey 7 D1
See advert on this page

GROVE HOUSE HOTEL

The privately owned Grove House is situated in its own beautiful grounds in a quiet residential location of Wallasey, yet conveniently only 200 yards from the regular underground service to Liverpool and just 5 minutes to the Wallasey Tunnel and major motorway network.

Grove Road, Wallasey,
Merseyside CH45 3HF
Tel: 0151 639 3947, Fax: 0151 639 0028
Email: reception@thegrovehouse.co.uk
Web: www.thegrovehouse.co.uk

Warrington, Cheshire

The Park Royal Hotel

★★★★

Stretton Road, Stretton, Warrington, Cheshire, WA4 4NS
Tel: 01925 730706 Fax: 01925 730740
Email: parkroyal@qhotels.co.uk
Web: www.qhotels.co.uk
Rooms: 142 all ensuite ♨ ⊛
Pricing: Sgl £75–120 Dbl £85–130
Dinner available
CC: Accepted
Room facilities: ▯ ☎ ☕ ☏
Access:
Conference: 12 meeting rooms (Thtr 400 max),
24hr-delegate from £154, day-delegate from £50
Children: Welcome ♄ ☕
Dogs: Welcome
Licenses: ⚖ ⫯⫯⫯
Leisure: Indoor pool, Gym, Health spa,
Beauty salon, Tennis
Parking: Off-street and free
Directions: Exit M56 J10, A49 to Warrington. Turn right at traffic lights. Hotel 200 yards on right.
Map ref: Stretton 7 E1

Northwest

Paddington House Hotel — Venture Hotels

★★

514 Manchester Road, Warrington, Cheshire, WA1 3TZ
Tel: 01925 816767 Fax: 01925 816651
Email: hotel@paddingtonhouse.co.uk
Web: www.paddingtonhouse.co.uk

VENTURE HOTELS

Friendly, family-run Georgian house situated in its own grounds. Conveniently located close to J21 M6 and two miles from Warrington town centre. Antique-themed bar and restaurant. Wi-Fi available.
Rooms: 37 all ensuite 🍴 🖥 ⊗
Pricing: Sgl £40–85 Dbl £45–95
Dinner available from £14.95 CC: Accepted
Room facilities: 🖥 ☎ 🍵 🥂 Access: ⸾⸾⸾
Conference: 4 meeting rooms (Thtr 180 max),
24hr-delegate from £85, day-delegate from £25
Children: Welcome 🍴 🐾 Dogs: Welcome
Licenses: ⚓ ᛦ Parking: Off-street and free
Directions: Exit M6 J21. Follow signs for Warrington (A57). Continue along A57 for approximately 1 mile, hotel is on the right-hand side.
Map ref: Warrington 7 E1

Wasdale, Cumbria

Wasdale Head Inn

◆◆◆◆ 🗎 ⊠ 🗨

Wasdale, near Gosforth, Cumbria, CA20 1EX
Tel: 01946 726229 Fax: 01946 726334
Email: wasdaleheadinn@msn.com
Web: www.wasdale.com
Rooms: 13 all ensuite 🖥 ⊗
Pricing: Sgl £49–54 Dbl £98–108
Dinner available from £28 CC: Accepted
Room facilities: ☎ 🍵 🥂
Conference: 3 meeting rooms (Thtr 35 max),
24hr-delegate from £110, day-delegate from £30
Children: Welcome Dogs: Welcome
Licenses: ᛦ Parking: Off-street and free
Directions: From M6, proceed to West Cumbria. From A595, turn into Gosforth village and take left fork for Wasdale. After 1 mile bear right to climb steep hill. Inn is another 9 miles along single track road.
Map ref: Wasdale 10 B2

Whitehaven, Cumbria

Glenfield Guest House

◆◆◆◆ 🗨

Corkickle, Whitehaven, Cumbria, CA28 7TS
Tel: 01946 691911 Fax: 01946 694060
Email: glenfieldgh@aol.com
Web: www.whitehaven.org.uk/glenfield.html
Rooms: 6 all ensuite ⊗
Pricing: Sgl £32–37 Dbl £50–54
Dinner available from £4.50–8.50 CC: Accepted
Room facilities: 🖥 🍵 Children: Welcome 🍴
Dogs: Welcome Licenses: ᛦ
Directions: A5094 from Whitehaven town centre south towards Barrow. Glenfield will appear on left with unrestricted street parking opposite.
Map ref: Whitehaven 10 A2

Widnes, Cheshire

Everglades Park Hotel

★★★

Derby Road, Widnes, Cheshire, WA8 3UJ
Tel: 0151 495 5500 Fax: 0151 495 5599
Email: reservations@evergladesparkhotel.com
Web: www.evergladesparkhotel.com
Rooms: 67 all ensuite 🍴 🖥 ⊗
Pricing: Sgl £55–59 Dbl £65–69
Dinner available from £15.95–24 CC: Accepted
Room facilities: 🖥 ☎ 🍵 🥂
Conference: 11 meeting rooms (Thtr 250 max),
24hr-delegate from £99, day-delegate from £25
Children: Welcome 🍴 Dogs: Assistance dogs only
Licenses: ⚓ ᛦ
Parking: Off-street and free
Directions: From M62 J7 take the Widnes exit A557. First exit, right at first roundabout and left at next roundabout. Hotel is 200 yards on right.
Map ref: Widnes 7 E1

Wigan, Greater Manchester

Quality Hotel Wigan

★★★

Riverway, Wigan, Greater Manchester, WN1 3SS
Tel: 01942 826888 Fax: 01942 825800
Email: enquiries@hotels-wigan.com
Web: www.choicehotelseurope.com
Rooms: 88 all ensuite ⊗
Pricing: Sgl £52–91 Dbl £57–101
Dinner available from £16.95–38 CC: Accepted
Room facilities: 🖥 ☎ 🍵 🥂 Access: ⸾⸾⸾
Conference: 7 meeting rooms (Thtr 240 max),
24hr-delegate from £85, day-delegate from £27.50
Children: Welcome 🍴 Dogs: Welcome
Licenses: ⚓ ᛦ
Parking: Off-street and free
Directions: M6 northbound, take junction 25 or from M6 southbound take junction 27, follow signs for Wigan A577.
Map ref: Wigan 10 B4

Bel Air

 ★★

236 Wigan Lane, Wigan,
Greater Manchester, WN1 2NU
Tel: 01942 241410 Fax: 01942 243967
Email: belair@hotelwigan.freeserve.co.uk
Web: www.belairhotel.co.uk
Rooms: 11 all ensuite 🎿 📺
Pricing: Sgl £35–39.50 Dbl £45–49.50
Dinner available from £6.95 CC: Accepted
Room facilities: 🔲 ☎ 🍵 🌂
Children: Welcome ⓗ Dogs: Welcome
Licenses: 🍷 👬 Parking: Off-street and free
Directions: 2 miles from Junction 27 of M6. Follow A49
towards Wigan. Bel Air is on right before large
roundabout and Cherry Gardens public house.
Map ref: Wigan 10 B4

Wigton, Cumbria

Wheyrigg Hall Hotel

 ◆◆◆

Abbeytown, Wigton, near Carlisle, Cumbria, CA7 0DH
Tel: 01697 361242 Fax: 01697 361020
Rooms: 14 all ensuite 🎿
Pricing: Sgl £45 Dbl £58
Dinner available from £10 CC: Accepted
Room facilities: 🔲 ☎ 🍵
Conference: 2 meeting rooms (Thtr 100 max),
24hr-delegate from £65, day-delegate from £15
Children: Welcome ⓗ Licenses: 👬
Leisure: Games room
Parking: Off-street and free
Directions: From South J41 Penrith B5305 to Wigton,
then B5302 towards Silloth. From Carlisle A595/596,
then B5302 towards Silloth.
Map ref: Abbeytown 10 B1

Wilmslow, Cheshire

The Stanneylands Hotel

 ★★★★★ ⓡⓡ

Stanneylands Road, Wilmslow, Cheshire, SK9 4EY
Tel: 01625 525225 Fax: 01625 537282
Email: reservations@stanneylandshotel.co.uk
Web: www.stanneylandshotel.co.uk

www.primahotels.co.uk

Rooms: 31 all ensuite 🎿 📺 ⓢ
Pricing: Sgl £63–105 Dbl £85–120
Dinner available from £27.50
CC: Accepted
Room facilities: 🔲 ☎ 🍵 🌂
Conference: 4 meeting rooms (Thtr 120 max),
24hr-delegate from £140, day-delegate from £40
Children: Welcome ⓗ
Licenses: 🍷 👬

Leisure: Use of nearby leisure facilities
Parking: Off-street and free
Directions: Leave M56 at Junction 5, follow signs to
Styal. Follow B5166 and then B5358, hotel signposted
on right-hand side.
Map ref: Wilmslow 7 E1
See advert on this page

Windermere, Cumbria

Lakeside Hotel

 ★★★★ ⓡⓡⓡ

Lakeside, Newby Bridge, Cumbria, LA12 8AT
Tel: 01539 530001 Fax: 01539 531699
Email: sales@lakesidehotel.co.uk
Web: www.lakesidehotel.co.uk
Rooms: 75 all ensuite 🎿 📺 ⓢ
Dinner available
CC: Accepted
Room facilities: 🔲 ☎ 🍵
Access: 🕴
Conference: 8 meeting rooms (Thtr 100 max)
Children: Welcome ⓗ ⓒ
Licenses: 🍷 👬
Leisure: Indoor pool, Gym, Health spa, Beauty salon
Parking: Off-street and free
Directions: Leave M6 at Junction 36 and follow A590
to Newby Bridge or follow signs for Lakeside
Steamers.
Map ref: Lakeside 10 B2

Northwest

Low Wood Hotel

★★★★ 🎗

Low Wood, Windermere, Cumbria, LA23 1LP
Tel: 01539 433338 Fax: 01539 434072
Email: lowwood@elhmail.co.uk
Web: www.elh.co.uk
Rooms: 110 all ensuite 🍴 🖥 ⊘
Pricing: Sgl £103–128 Dbl £156–206
Dinner available from £29.75 CC: Accepted
Room facilities: 🖥 ☎ 🍵 🔌 Access: 🔩
Conference: 11 meeting rooms (Thtr 340 max),
24hr-delegate from £123, day-delegate from £42.50
Children: Welcome 🍴 🌡 Dogs: Welcome
Licenses: 🔷 ⚱
Leisure: Indoor pool, Gym, Health spa, Beauty salon,
Games room, Snooker/billiards
Parking: Off-street and free
Directions: Take J36 of M6 then A591 to Windermere.
Continue 2 miles. Hotel situated to the right on lake
shore.
Map ref: Low Wood 10 B2

Gilpin Lodge Country House Hotel

★★★ 🎗🎗🎗 Premier

Crook Road, near Windermere, Cumbria, LA23 3NE
Tel: 01539 488818 Fax: 01539 488058
Email: hotel@gilpinlodge.com
Web: www.gilpinlodge.com

An elegant comfortable family-run hotel in an idyllic
rural setting. No weddings or conferences. The art of
relaxation perfected. Sumptuous bedrooms, exquisite
food. See website for guided tour.
Rooms: 14 all ensuite 🖥 ⊘
Pricing: Sgl £160 Dbl £240–310
Dinner available from £42.50 CC: Accepted
Room facilities: 🖥 ☎ 🍵
Children: Welcome 7yrs min age Licenses: ⚱
Parking: Off-street and free
Directions: Leave M6 at Junction 36. Take A590/A591
to roundabout north of Kendal, then B5284 for 5 miles.
Map ref: Windermere 10 B2

Hillthwaite House

★★★ 🎗

Thornbarrow Road, Windermere, Cumbria, LA23 2DF
Tel: 01539 443636 Fax: 01539 488660
Email: reception@hillthwaite.com
Web: www.hillthwaite.com
Rooms: 31 all ensuite 🍴 🖥
Dinner available CC: Accepted
Room facilities: 🖥 ☎ 🍵
Children: Welcome 🍴 🌡
Dogs: Welcome
Licenses: ⚱
Leisure: Indoor pool
Parking: Off-street and free
Directions: Halfway between Windermere and
Bowness, turn left into Thornbarrow Road. Hillthwaite
House can be seen on skyline.
Map ref: Windermere 10 B2

Holbeck Ghyll Country House Hotel

★★★ 🎗🎗🎗 Premier

Holbeck Lane, Windermere, Cumbria, LA23 1LU
Tel: 01539 432375 Fax: 01539 434743
Email: stay@holbeckghyll.com
Web: www.holbeckghyll.com
Rooms: 20 all ensuite 🍴 🖥 ⊘
Pricing: Sgl £135–220 Dbl £190–270
Dinner available from £49.50
CC: Accepted
Room facilities: 🖥 ☎
Conference: 3 meeting rooms (Thtr 50 max),
24hr-delegate from £150, day-delegate from £45
Children: Welcome 🍴 🌡
Dogs: Welcome
Licenses: 🔷 ⚱
Leisure: Gym, Health spa, Beauty salon, Tennis,
Croquet, Putting green
Parking: Off-street and free
Directions: Leave M6 at Junction 36. Take A591 to
Windermere. Head towards Ambleside, turn right after
Brockhole (Holbeck Lane, signposted Troutbeck). Hotel
is 1/2 mile on left.
Map ref: Windermere 10 B2

"Here!"

Need a pet friendly property?
Look out for 'Dogs welcome' in
our listings.

Linthwaite House Hotel and Restaurant

★★★★ **Excellent**

Crook Road, Windermere,
The Lake District, Cumbria, LA23 3JA
Tel: 01539 488600 Fax: 01539 488601
Email: admin@linthwaite.com
Web: www.linthwaite.com

Stylish country house hotel in 14 acres with stunning views. A welcoming "unstuffy" atmosphere, award winning food, eclectic wine list and perfect location make Linthwaite the perfect place to unwind.
Rooms: 27 all ensuite
Pricing: Sgl £120–145 Dbl £140–280
Dinner available from £44 CC: Accepted
Room facilities:
Conference: 3 meeting rooms (Thtr 54 max),
24hr-delegate from £149, day-delegate from £59
Children: Welcome
Dogs: Welcome
Licenses:
Leisure: Fishing, Croquet lawn, Practice golf hole
Parking: Off-street and free
Directions: Exit M6 J36. A591 towards Windermere, then B5284 through Crook. Linthwaite is 6 miles on left, up private drive.
Map ref: Windermere 10 B2

Storrs Hall

★★★★ **Commended**

Storrs Park, Windermere, Cumbria, LA23 3LG
Tel: 01539 447111 Fax: 01539 447555
Email: storrshall@elhmail.co.uk
Web: www.elh.co.uk
Rooms: 29 all ensuite
Pricing: Sgl £105–172.50 Dbl £160–295
Dinner available from £39.50 CC: Accepted
Room facilities:
Conference: 3 meeting rooms (Thtr 30 max),
24hr-delegate from £145, day-delegate from £35
Children: Welcome 10yrs min age
Dogs: Welcome
Licenses: Leisure: Fishing
Parking: Off-street and free
Directions: Exit M6 Junction 36, A590 Windermere. At roundabout take B5284 Hawkshead via Ferry. At T-junction turn left and immediately right. At T-junction turn left onto A592. Travel 2 miles, on right.
Map ref: Storrs Park 10 B2

The Famous Wild Boar

★★★★

Crook Road, Crook, near Windermere,
Cumbria, LA23 3NF
Tel: 01539 445225 Fax: 01539 442498
Email: wildboar@elhmail.co.uk
Web: www.elh.co.uk
Rooms: 36 all ensuite
Pricing: Sgl £84.50–100 Dbl £119–150
Dinner available from £22.95 CC: Accepted
Room facilities:
Conference: 2 meeting rooms (Thtr 40 max),
24hr-delegate from £105, day-delegate from £34
Children: Welcome
Dogs: Welcome
Licenses:
Parking: Off-street and free
Directions: M6 exit 36 signed A5090/A591 to Windermere. Join B5284 to Crook. Hotel 2 miles beyond the village of Crook.
Map ref: Crook 10 B2

The Samling

★★★★  **Premier**

Ambleside Road, Windermere, Cumbria, LA23 1LR
Tel: 01539 431922 Fax: 01539 430400
Email: info@thesamling.com
Web: www.thesamling.com
Rooms: 11 all ensuite
Pricing: Sgl £195–415 Dbl £195–415
Dinner available from £45 CC: Accepted
Room facilities:
Conference: 2 meeting rooms (Thtr 40 max),
24hr-delegate from £260, day-delegate from £90
Children: Welcome
Licenses:
Parking: Off-street and free
Directions: A591 to Windermere, then on towards Ambleside. Hotel is on the right after the watersports centre.
Map ref: Windermere 10 B2

Hideaway Hotel

★★

Phoenix Way, Windermere, Cumbria, LA23 1DB
Tel: 01539 443070 Fax: 01539 443070
Email: enquiries@hideaway-hotel.co.uk
Web: www.hideaway-hotel.co.uk
Seasonal closure: January
Rooms: 15 all ensuite
Pricing: Sgl £45–62 Dbl £72–144
Dinner available from £12.95–19.95 CC: Accepted
Room facilities:
Children: Welcome Dogs: Welcome
Licenses:
Leisure: Free use of nearby leisure facilities
Parking: Off-street and free
Directions: Exit M6 J36. Take A591 towards Windermere and turn left at Ravensworth Hotel onto Phoenix Way. Hideaway 100m on the right.
Map ref: Windermere 10 B2

Northwest

Lindeth Fell Country House Hotel

 Excellent

★★★🐻🐻

Lyth Valley Road, Bowness-on-Windermere,
Cumbria, LA23 3JP
Tel: 01539 443286 Fax: 01539 447455
Email: kennedy@lindethfell.co.uk
Web: www.lindethfell.co.uk
Seasonal closure: 2-27 January

Above Lake Windermere in magnificent gardens
Lindeth Fell is beautifully situated, and offers a warm
and friendly atmosphere, superior accommodation and
superb modern English cooking, at outstanding value.
Rooms: 14 all ensuite 🍃
Pricing: Sgl £45–80 Dbl £90–160
Dinner available from £30 CC: Accepted
Room facilities: 🖵 ☎ 🍵
Conference: 1 meeting room (Thtr 12 max),
24hr-delegate from £95
Children: Welcome ♨ ⚜
Licenses: ⅲ
Parking: Off-street and free
Directions: Lindeth Fell is situated one mile south of
Bowness on the Kendal/Lyth valley Lancaster road,
which is the A5074 road, leave M6 at junction 36.
Map ref: Bowness-on-Windermere 10 B2

Miller Howe Hotel

 Premier

★★★🐻🐻🐻

Rayrigg Road, Windermere, Cumbria, LA23 1EY
Tel: 01539 442536 Fax: 01539 445664
Email: lakeview@millerhowe.com
Web: www.millerhowe.com
Rooms: 15 all ensuite ⊗
Pricing: Sgl £175 Dbl £210–360
Dinner available from £35
CC: Accepted
Room facilities: 🖵 ☎
Conference: 1 meeting room (Thtr 30 max)
Children: Welcome 8yrs min age
Dogs: Welcome
Licenses: ◈ ⅲ
Parking: Off-street and free
Directions: On A592 between Windermere and
Bowness. Ring for detailed location map or visit
website.
Map ref: Windermere 10 B2
See advert on this page

The Mortal Man

★★★🐻

Troutbeck, Windermere, Cumbria, LA23 1PL
Tel: 01539 433193 Fax: 01539 431261
Email: enquiries@themortalman.co.uk
Web: www.themortalman.co.uk
Rooms: 13 all ensuite 🖾 ⊗
Pricing: Sgl £37–45 Dbl £54–90
Dinner available from £6.95
CC: Accepted
Room facilities: 🖵 ☎ 🍵
Conference: 1 meeting room (Thtr 30 max)
Children: Welcome 5yrs min age ♨
Dogs: Welcome
Licenses: ⅲ
Leisure: Games room
Parking: Off-street
Directions: Junction 36 off the M6 take A591 to
Windermere, turn right onto A592, after 2½ miles turn
left at Troutbeck sign, right at T-junction, the inn is 800
yards on the right.
Map ref: Troutbeck 10 B2

Oakbank House Hotel

Helm Road, Bowness-on-Windermere,
Cumbria, LA23 3BU
Tel: 01539 443386 Fax: 01539 447965
Email: enquiries@oakbankhousehotel.co.uk
Web: www.oakbankhousehotel.co.uk

Only 5-diamond property in Bowness and superb lake views, great breakfast choice. Close to restaurants, shops and local attractions. Guests have use of Country Club with pool, gym, and health spa.
Rooms: 12 all ensuite
Pricing: Sgl £50–100 Dbl £50–100
CC: Accepted
Room facilities:
Children: Welcome
Licenses:
Leisure: Free membership to local country club
Parking: Off-street and free
Directions: Junction 36 of M6. A590/591 to Windermere. Follow into Bowness. After cinema on right, turn left into Helm Road. Behind Lakeland clothes shop.
Map ref: Bowness-on-Windermere 10 B2

The Beaumont

Holly Road, Windermere, Cumbria, LA23 2AF
Tel: 01539 447075 Fax: 01539 88311
Email: beaumontenquiries@btinternet.com
Web: www.lakesbeaumont.co.uk

The Beaumont provides superb quality bed and breakfast accommodation offering "comfort with a touch of class". Should you wish to have a relaxing break in the Lake District, The Beaumont is the place for you, offering superb food, sincere hospitality and tranquility yet only two minutes walk to the centre of the vibrant Lakeland village of Windermere.
Rooms: 10 all ensuite
Pricing: Sgl £40–60 Dbl £70–130
CC: Accepted
Room facilities:
Children: Welcome 10yrs min age
Licenses:
Leisure: Membership of nearby country club
Parking: Off-street and free
Directions: Follow town centre signs through one-way system, then take second left into Ellerthwaite Road and then first left into Holly Road.
Map ref: Windermere 10 B2

Fairfield

Brantfell Road, Bowness-on-Windermere,
Cumbria, LA23 3AE
Tel: 01539 446565 Fax: 01539 446565
Email: tony&liz@the-fairfield.co.uk
Web: www.the-fairfield.co.uk
Seasonal closure: Christmas

An attractive 200-year-old house set in a quiet, secluded, well-matured garden. Close to the village, lake, fells, Dales Way. Superb value.
Rooms: 9 (8 ensuite)
Pricing: Sgl £27–37 Dbl £54–84
Dinner available from £18.50
CC: Accepted
Room facilities:
Children: Welcome
Dogs: Welcome
Licenses:
Parking: Off-street
Directions: From mini roundabout in the centre of Bowness village, take road towards lake, turn left, then left again into Brantfell Road.
Map ref: Bowness-on-Windermere 10 B2

Northwest

Rosemount

◆◆◆

Lake Road, Windermere, Cumbria, LA23 2EQ
Tel: 01539 443739 Fax: 01539 448978
Email: stay@lakedistrictguesthouse.com
Web: www.lakedistrictguesthouse.com
Seasonal closure: 17-27 December
Rooms: 16 (15 ensuite) 📺
Pricing: Sgl £30–35 Dbl £50–86
CC: Accepted
Room facilities: 📺 ☕
Children: Welcome
Licenses: 👪
Leisure: Membership of Parklands leisure club for guests staying 2 nights-plus
Parking: Off-street and free
Directions: From M6 J36 take A590/591 to Windermere. Turn left onto A5074. Rosemount is on left after ¹/₂ mile.
Map ref: Windermere 10 B2

Wirral, Merseyside

RIVERHILL HOTEL
voted Best Small Hotel of the Year at Merseyside Tourism 2000 Awards

In beautiful private grounds, the award-winning Victorian Riverhill Hotel offers elegant accommodation in a convenient location in Birkenhead. The accommodation includes family rooms, and four-poster beds are also available. Looking after the outstanding menu in the Bay Tree Restaurant is resident chef Roy Evans.

Talbot Road, Oxton, Wirral, Cheshire CH43 2HJ
Tel: 0151 653 3773 Fax: 0151 653 7162
Email: reception@riverhill.co.uk
Web: www.theriverhill.co.uk

RaC
★★★
Hotel

"I do!" Want a honeymoon hotel? Look for our Gold, Blue, and White Ribbon Award winning hotels.

Riverhill Hotel

★★★★ ☕

Talbot Road, Oxton, Wirral, Merseyside, CH43 2HJ
Tel: 0151 653 3773 Fax: 0151 653 7162
Email: reception@theriverhill.co.uk
Web: www.theriverhill.co.uk
Rooms: 14 all ensuite 🍴 📺
Pricing: Sgl £79.75–89.75 Dbl £79.75–89.75
Dinner available from £18.95
CC: Accepted
Room facilities: 📺 ☎ 🛏 📞
Conference: 1 meeting room (Thtr 50 max)
Children: Welcome ⋔ ⅄
Licenses: ◁ 👪
Parking: Off-street and free
Map ref: Oxton 7 D1
See advert on this page

Workington, Cumbria

Cumberland Hotel

★★★

Station Road, Workington, Cumbria, CA14 2XQ
Tel: 01900 64401 Fax: 01900 872400
Email: cumberlandhotel@aol.com
Web: www.thecumberlandhotel.ukvt.co.uk

Country house style hotel conveniently situated close to railway station, new retail town centre, sports stadiums and Solway Coast. Excellent facilities for coach tours, business travellers and tourists alike. Award-winning services, quality restaurant.
Rooms: 29 all ensuite 🍴 📺 ⊗
Pricing: Sgl £66–70 Dbl £76–86
Dinner available from £12–36
CC: Accepted
Room facilities: 📺 ☎ 🛏 📞
Access: ♿
Conference: 3 meeting rooms (Thtr 190 max)
Children: Welcome ⋔
Dogs: Welcome
Licenses: ◁ 👪
Parking: Off-street and free
Directions: Opposite Workington railway station, close to town centre and all sports stadiums. Follow signs for rail station.
Map ref: Workington 10 A2

Wherever you go, we'll be there too.

For instant breakdown cover and the reassurance RAC gives you, wherever in the UK you're travelling to, call

0800 550 550
quoting ref: Hotel

www.rac.co.uk

Wales

Wales

Wales

Caernarfon Bay

y-C

Beddgelert
B4418
Blaenau
Ffestiniog
Llan Ffestiniog
B4407
Nefyn
B4417
Porthmadog
Penrhyndeudraeth
B4391
Edern
B4417
Criccieth
Porthmeirion
Talsarnau
Trawsfynydd
B4354
Pwllheli
GWYNEDD
Lleyn
B4413
Harlech
Llanbedr
Aberdaron
Abersoch
SNOWDONIA

Bardsey
Island
Dolgellau

Barmouth

Llwyngwril
B4405
Cemmaes
Road
Machynlleth

Tywyn
Aberdovey
W A L

CARDIGAN BAY
Borth

Aberystwyth
Ponterwyd
A44
Rhydyfelin
Chancery
Devil's Bridge
A4120
C A M B R I A N
Llanrhystud
Lledrod

Aberaeron
B4577
New Quay
CEREDIGION
Tregaron

Llangranog
Synod Inn
Aberporth
Lampeter
Cardigan
B4570
Glynarthen
Llechryd
Llanwrty
Wells
Strumble
Head
Newport
Pumsaint
Goodwick
Newcastle
Emlyn
Llando
PEMBROKESHIRE
COAST
Fishguard
Llanwrda
Llangadog Sen
St David's Head
Crymych
CARMARTHENSHIRE
St David's
Llandeloy
Wolf's
Castle
Cynwyl Elfed
Llangynin
PEMBROKESHIRE
Carmarthen
Llandeilo
Haverfordwest
St Clears
Brynamman
Abercraf
St Brides Bay
Narberth
B4314
Llansteffan
B4306
Ammanford
Broad Haven
Pendine
Kidwelly
Pontardulais
Pontardawe
Milford
Haven
Neyland
Dale
Saundersfoot
Furnace
Llanelli
Neath
Pembroke
Dock
Pembroke
Lamphey
St
Florence
Tenby
Carmarthen
Bay
Burry Port
R Loughor
Manorbier
B4320
St Govan's
Head
Gower
Swansea
Port
Talbot
Mae
Bryn
Worms Head
(Penrhyn-Gwyr)
Port-Eynon
The
Mumbles
Swansea
Bay

Porthcawl

BRISTO

Wales

Wales
Award winners

To help you choose somewhere really special for your stay, we've listed here all RAC Award-winning properties in this region.

Gold Ribbon Award

Premier

		pg
Bodysgallen Hall and Spa, Llandudno	★★★★	477
Lake Country House Hotel, Llangammarch Wells	★★★	480
Osborne House, Llandudno	Townhouse ★★★★	477
St Tudno Hotel & Restaurant, Llandudno	★★	479

Blue Ribbon Award

Excellent

		pg
Hotel Maes-y-Neuadd, Harlech	★★	475
Hotel Portmeirion, Portmeirion	★★★	486
Llangoed Hall, Brecon	★★★★	468
The St David's Hotel & Spa, Cardiff	★★★★★	470

Little Gem Award

Little Gem

		pg
Sychnant Pass House, Conwy	♦♦♦♦♦	473

Bodysgallen Hall and Spa, Llandudno

Lake Country House Hotel, Llangammarch Wells

Llangoed Hall, Brecon

Sychnant Pass House, Conwy

Aberaeron, Ceredigion

Lima House

1 Victoria Street, Aberaeron, Ceredigion, SA46 0DA
Tel: 01545 570720
Email: info@limahouse.co.uk
Web: www.limahouse.co.uk
Rooms: 3 all ensuite
Pricing: Sgl £30 Dbl £55
CC: Accepted
Room facilities:
Children: Welcome
Directions: From north after lights first left, first right.
From south before light left, then right. First large
house right-hand side.
Map ref: Aberaeron 6 B3

Abercraf, Swansea

The Abercrave Inn

145 Heol Tawe, Abercraf, Swansea, SA9 1XS
Tel: 01639 731002 Fax: 01639 730796
Email: info@abercraveinn.co.uk
Web: www.abercraveinn.co.uk

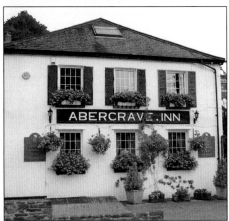

Michelin Star trained chef and staff prepare an
extensive à la carte and chef's special menu. Central
for Gower Coast and Brecon Beacons. Pony trekking,
fishing, golf, walking and caving within three minutes.
Rooms: 12 all ensuite
Pricing: Dinner available from £10.95
CC: Accepted
Room facilities:
Children: Welcome
Licenses:
Leisure: Fishing
Parking: Off-street and free
Map ref: Swansea 2 C1

Aberdovey, Gwynedd

Trefeddian Hotel

Aberdovey/Aberdyfi, Gwynedd, LL35 0SB
Tel: 01654 767213 Fax: 01654 767777
Email: info@trefwales.com
Web: www.trefwales.com
Seasonal closure: 1-23 December
Rooms: 59 all ensuite
Pricing: Sgl £45–60 Dbl £90–120
Dinner available from £25.50
CC: Accepted
Room facilities:
Access:
Children: Welcome
Dogs: Welcome
Licenses:
Leisure: Indoor pool, Beauty salon, Tennis, Games
room, Snooker/billiards
Parking: Off-street and free
Directions: ½ mile north of Aberdovey village off A493,
overlooking golf links and Cardigan Bay.
Map ref: Aberdovey 6 C3
See advert on following page

Abergele, Conwy

Kinmel Manor

St George's Road, Abergele, Conwy, LL22 9AS
Tel: 01745 832014 Fax: 01745 832014
Email: kinmelmanor@btconnect.com
Web: www.kinmelmanor.co.uk
Rooms: 51 all ensuite
Pricing: Sgl £59.50–65 Dbl £79.50–85
Dinner available from £17–22
CC: Accepted
Room facilities:
Access:
Conference: 6 meeting rooms (Thtr 300 max),
24hr-delegate from £79.50, day-delegate from £25.50
Children: Welcome
Dogs: Welcome
Licenses:
Leisure: Indoor pool, Gym, Health spa, Sauna,
Steam room
Parking: Off-street and free
Directions: Travelling on A55 turn off at junction 24.
Entrance to hotel is on the roundabout.
Map ref: Abergele 6 C1

Wales

"I do!"

Want a honeymoon
hotel? Look for our Gold,
Blue, and White Ribbon
Award winning hotels.

TREFEDDIAN HOTEL

For more than 100 years this award-winning hotel has been standing prominently overlooking golf links, sand dunes and Cardigan Bay, half a mile north of Aberdyfi (Aberdovey) village, Trefeddian is set in its own grounds and suitable for all the family.

Trefeddian is renowned for friendly attentive service, excellent meals, an extensive wine list, and spacious lounges, affording relaxing holidays.

The hotel has an indoor swimming pool, tennis court, 9-hole pitch/putt, snooker room, children's indoor/outdoor play areas, sun terraces, and lift.

Aberystwyth, Ceredigion

George Borrow Hotel

 ★★

Ponterwyd, Aberystwyth, Ceredigion, SY23 3AD
Tel: 01970 890230 Fax: 01970 890587
Email: georgeborrow@lycos.co.uk
Web: www.george-borrow.activehotels.com
Rooms: 9 all ensuite 🐾
Pricing: Sgl £35–37.50 Dbl £70–75
Dinner available from £11.95–18
CC: Accepted
Room facilities: 🖥 ☎ ☕ 🔌
Conference: 1 meeting room (Thtr 20 max)
Children: Welcome 🍴
Licenses: ⚎ Leisure: Games room
Parking: Off-street
Directions: Alongside A44, Aberystwyth side of village
of Ponterwyd, 15 mins from Aberystwyth.
Map ref: Ponterwyd 6 C3

The Marine Hotel & Leisure Suite

 ★★

Marine Terrace, Aberystwyth, Ceredigion, SY23 5AJ
Tel: 01970 612444 Fax: 01970 617435
Email: marinehotel1@btconnect.com
Web: www.marinehotelaberystwyth.com
Rooms: 44 (43 ensuite) 🐾 🛏 🚭
Pricing: Sgl £35–65 Dbl £55–95
Dinner available from £16.95–18.95
CC: Accepted Room facilities: 🖥 ☎ ☕ 🔌
Access: ♿
Conference: 5 meeting rooms (Thtr 250 max),
24hr-delegate from £110, day-delegate from £20
Children: Welcome 🍴 Dogs: Welcome
Licenses: ⚓ ⚎
Leisure: Gym, Health spa
Parking: Off-street and free
Map ref: Aberystwyth 6 C3

Blue Grass Cottages

 ♦♦♦♦ ✍

Brynglas Farm, Chancery, Aberystwyth,
Ceredigion, SY23 4DF
Tel: 01970 612799 Fax: 01970 615099
Email: blue.grass@lineone.net

Bed and Breakfast with a difference — your own
cottage and breakfast served therein. Situated in rural
countryside along the main A487, four miles south of
Aberystwyth with lovely panoramic views.

Rooms: 3 all ensuite 🐾
Pricing: Sgl £35–45 Dbl £60–80
Room facilities: 🖥 ☎ ☕
Children: Welcome 🍼
Dogs: Welcome
Parking: Off-street and free
Directions: On A487 south of Aberystwyth,
approximately 4 miles. On entering Chancery, first
entrance immediately after Chancery sign on left.
Map ref: Chancery 6 C3

Glyn-Garth Guest House

 ♦♦♦♦ ✍

South Road, Aberystwyth, Ceredigion, SY23 1JS
Tel: 01970 615050 Fax: 01970 636835
Email: glyngarth@aol.com
Web: www.glyngarthgh.cjb.net
Seasonal closure: Christmas to New Year
Rooms: 10 (6 ensuite) 🚭
Room facilities: 🖥 ☕
Children: Welcome 7yrs min age
Parking: Off-street
Directions: Close to town centre, near harbour and
castle grounds. Adjacent to South Promenade.
Map ref: Aberystwyth 6 C3

Yr Hafod

 ♦♦♦♦ ✍

1 South Marine Terrace, Aberystwyth,
Ceredigion, SY23 1JX
Tel: 01970 617579 Fax: 01970 636835
Email: johnyrhafod@aol.com
Seasonal closure: Christmas and New Year
Rooms: 7 (2 ensuite)
Pricing: Sgl £25–26 Dbl £50–66
Room facilities: 🖥 ☕
Parking: Off-street
Directions: Situated on South Promenade between
harbour and castle.
Map ref: Aberystwyth 6 C3

Nanteos Mansion B&B

 ♦♦♦

Rhydyfelin, Aberystwyth, Ceredigion, SY23 4LU
Tel: 01970 624363 Fax: 01970 626332
Email: info@nanteos.co.uk
Web: www.nanteos.co.uk
Rooms: 5 all ensuite 🛏 🚭
Pricing: Sgl £60 Dbl £100 CC: Accepted
Room facilities: 🖥 ☕
Conference: 4 meeting rooms (Thtr 150 max)
Children: Welcome Dogs: Assistance dogs only
Licenses: ⚓ ⚎
Leisure: 30 acre park, Rural walks
Parking: Off-street and free
Directions: Leave Aberystwyth southbound on A487,
first left Devil's Bridge A4120, immediate right onto
B4340 Trawsgoed. Follow signs, 1 mile on left.
Map ref: Rhydyfelin 6 C3
See advert on following page

Wales

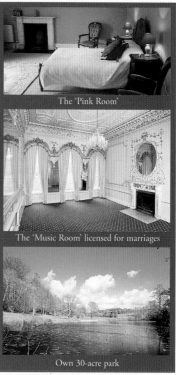
Queensbridge Hotel

♦♦♦

Victoria Terrace Promenade, Aberystwyth,
Ceredigion, SY23 2DH
Tel: 01970 612343 Fax: 01970 617452
Email: queensbridgehotel@btinternet.com
Rooms: 16 all ensuite
Pricing: Sgl £35–55 Dbl £60–80
Dinner available CC: Accepted
Room facilities: Access:
Conference: 2 meeting rooms (Thtr 40 max),
24hr-delegate from £85, day-delegate from £15
Children: Welcome Dogs: Welcome
Licenses: Parking: Off-street and free
Directions: On the sea front to the north of the
promenade.
Map ref: Aberystwyth 6 C3

Bala, Gwynedd

Plas Coch Hotel

★★

High Street, Bala, Gwynedd, LL23 7AB
Tel: 01678 520309 Fax: 01678 521135
Email: plascoch@tiscali.co.uk
Web: www.plascoch.com
Rooms: 10 all ensuite
Pricing: Sgl £43 Dbl £69 Dinner available
CC: Accepted Room facilities:
Conference: 1 meeting room (Thtr 20 max)

Children: Welcome Licenses:
Parking: Off-street and free
Directions: The hotel is in the centre of Bala High
Street. The car park is at the rear of the hotel.
Map ref: Bala 6 C2

Barmouth, Gwynedd

Bae Abermaw Country House

★★★★

Bae Abermaw, Panorama Road, Barmouth,
Gwynedd, LL42 1DQ
Tel: 01341 280550 Fax: 01341 280346
Email: enquiries@baeabermaw.com
Web: www.baeabermaw.com

The traditional Victorian exterior hides an elegant contemporary interior. The stunning views from the restaurant are matched by superb cuisine and a balanced wine selection.
Rooms: 14 all ensuite
Pricing: Sgl £88–108 Dbl £116–160
Dinner available from £25–38 CC: Accepted
Room facilities: 🖥 ☎ 🍵 🔌
Conference: 1 meeting room (Thtr 100 max)
Children: Welcome ♄ ☕ Licenses: ⚜ ♦♦♦
Leisure: Games room Parking: Off-street and free
Directions: From Dolgellau follow the A496 to Barmouth turning first right into Panorama Road and follow blue signs to Bae Abermaw.
Map ref: Barmouth 6 C2

Beaumaris, Anglesey

The Bulkeley Hotel
★★★
19 Castle Street, Beaumaris, Anglesey, LL58 8AW
Tel: 01248 810415 Fax: 01248 810146
Email: bulkeley@bestwestern.co.uk
Web: www.bulkeleyhotel.co.uk
Rooms: 43 all ensuite 🚭
Pricing: Dinner available from £19.95 CC: Accepted
Room facilities: 🖥 ☎ 🍵 🔌 Access: |↓↑|
Conference: 3 meeting rooms (Thtr 180 max),
24hr-delegate from £90.25, day-delegate £25.95
Children: Welcome ♄ Dogs: Welcome Licenses: ⚜ ♦♦♦
Parking: Off-street and free
Directions: A5, Anglesey head for Menai Bridge Town. Follow A545 to Beaumaris. In Beaumaris first right. Car park is 200m left.
Map ref: Beaumaris 6 C1
See advert on this page

Beddgelert, Gwynedd

Tanronnen Inn
★★★🍴
Beddgelert, Gwynedd, LL55 4YB
Tel: 01766 890347 Fax: 01766 890606
Email: brewery@frederic-robinson.co.uk
Web: www.frederic-robinson.co.uk
Rooms: 7 all ensuite 🚭
Pricing: Sgl £50 Dbl £90
Dinner available from £9.90 CC: Accepted
Room facilities: 🖥 ☎ 🍵 Children: Welcome ♄
Licenses: ♦♦♦ Parking: Off-street and free
Directions: Situated in village centre.
Map ref: Beddgelert 6 C2

Betws-y-Coed, Conwy

Royal Oak Hotel
★★★★🍴🍴
Betws-y-Coed, Snowdonia, Conwy, LL24 0AY
Tel: 01690 710219 Fax: 01690 710603
Email: royaloakmail@btopenworld.com

Web: www.royaloakhotel.net
Seasonal closure: 25 & 26 December
Rooms: 27 all ensuite 🚭
Pricing: Sgl £65–85 Dbl £80–135
Dinner available from £17–35 CC: Accepted
Room facilities: 🖥 ☎ 🍵 🔌
Conference: 2 meeting rooms (Thtr 50 max),
24hr-delegate from £90, day-delegate from £30
Children: Welcome ♄ Dogs: Assistance dogs only
Licenses: ⚜ ♦♦♦ Parking: Off-street and free
Directions: The hotel is situated at the village centre adjacent to the A5 London to Holyhead route.
Map ref: Betws-y-Coed 6 C1

Park Hill Hotel
★★
Llanrwst Road, Betws-y-Coed, Conwy, LL24 0HD
Tel: 01690 710540 Fax: 01690 710540
Email: welcome@park-hill-hotel.co.uk
Web: www.park-hill-hotel.co.uk
Rooms: 9 all ensuite 🛏
Pricing: Sgl £50 Dbl £56–86
Dinner available from £17.50 CC: Accepted
Room facilities: 🖥 🍵
Children: Welcome 8yrs min age
Licenses: ♦♦♦ Leisure: Indoor pool
Parking: Off-street and free
Directions: On elevated position on A470 northbound from Betws-y-Coed, ½ mile from crossing with A5/Waterloo Bridge.
Map ref: Betws-y-Coed 6 C1

Wales

Brecon, Powys

Llangoed Hall

★★★★★ 🐿🐿🐿   Excellent

Llyswen, Brecon, Powys, LD3 0YP
Tel: 01874 754525 Fax: 01874 754545
Email: enquiries@llangoedhall.com
Web: www.llangoedhall.com
Rooms: 23 all ensuite 🖥
Pricing: Sgl £150–345 Dbl £195–385
Dinner available from £45
CC: Accepted
Room facilities: 🖵 ☎
Conference: 3 meeting rooms (Thtr 80 max),
24hr-delegate from £187, day-delegate from £40
Children: Welcome 8yrs min age
Dogs: Welcome
Licenses: 🦢 ⑂
Leisure: Tennis, Snooker/billiards
Parking: Off-street and free
Directions: On A470 11 Miles north of Brecon, 11 miles
south of Builth Wells. Train: Cardiff, Hereford,
Abergavenny.
Map ref: Llyswen 7 D4
See advert on this page

Beacons

◆◆◆◆ ⑂

16 Bridge Street, Brecon, Powys, LD3 8AH
Tel: 01874 623339 Fax: 01874 623339
Email: beacons@brecon.co.uk
Web: www.thebreconbeacons.co.uk

This recently-restored listed Georgian house offers
beautifully appointed bedrooms. The candle-lit restaurant
has fine food and wines. Cosy cellar bar and private parking.
Rooms: 14 (12 ensuite) ⑂ 🖥
Pricing: Dinner available from £9.95
CC: Accepted
Room facilities: 🖵 ⑂
Children: Welcome ⑂ ⑂
Licenses: ⑂
Parking: Off-street and free
Directions: Following the A40 west through town centre,
turn left. Go downhill at traffic lights, over bridge, then
hotel is 100 yards on right.
Map ref: Brecon 7 D4

LLANGOED HALL

Set in the midst of the Wye Valley, with its own maze
and stream, Llangoed Hall really is a breath of fresh
air. One with a delicious whiff of eccentricity.

Whilst each room is individually decorated with
antique furniture and furnishings from Elanbach, the
walls are hung with art by the likes of Whistler,
Sickert and Augustus John.

Everywhere you look,
from the honesty bar in
the lounge to the
working steam engines
in the pool room, bears
testament to the tastes
and passions of owner
Sir Bernard Ashley.

LLYSWEN, BRECON, POWYS, LD3 0YP
Tel: 01874 754525   Fax: 01874 754545
Email: enquiries@llangoedhall.com
Web: www.llangoedhall.com

Usk Inn

◆◆◆◆ ⑂⑂ ⑂

Station Road, Talybont on Usk, Brecon, Powys, LD3 7JE
Tel: 01874 676251 Fax: 01874 676392
Email: stay@uskinn.co.uk
Web: www.uskinn.co.uk
Seasonal closure: Christmas
Rooms: 11 all ensuite 🖥 ⑂
Pricing: Sgl £60–75 Dbl £80–120
Dinner available from £20–29
CC: Accepted
Room facilities: 🖵 ☎ ⑂
Conference: 1 meeting room (Thtr 10 max)
Children: Welcome ⑂
Licenses: ⑂
Parking: Off-street and free
Directions: From A40, property is 6 miles east of
Brecon. Turn into Talybont on Usk. The Inn is 250
yards from the river bridge.
Map ref: Talybont on Usk 7 D4

Maeswalter

◆◆◆ ⑂

Heol Senni, near Brecon, Powys, LD3 8SU
Tel: 01874 636629
Email: Joy@maeswalter.fsnet.co.uk
Web: www.maeswalter.co.uk

A 300-year-old farmhouse situated in Brecon Beacons National Park with magnificent views against the Senni Valley. Tastefully decorated and comfortable ensuite bedrooms with tea/coffee making facilities and TV in each room.

Rooms: 4 all ensuite ⊗
Pricing: Sgl £27.50–30 Dbl £50–55
Dinner available from £15 CC: Accepted
Room facilities: ☐ ⬙ ☏
Parking: Off-street and free
Directions: A470 Brecon to Merthyr Tydfil, turn right onto A4215 Defynnog. After 2 miles turn left for Heol Senni, Maeswalter is 1½ miles on the right.
Map ref: Heol Senni 6 C4

Charming, spacious farm house of character, beautifully situated between mountains and sea, unobstructed views of Snowdonia, well-appointed bedrooms all with ensuite facilities. Jane has cookery diploma and provides excellent meals using local produce.

Rooms: 3 all ensuite ⊗
Pricing: Sgl £45 Dbl £60–70
Dinner available from £22.50
CC: Accepted
Room facilities: ☐ ⬙
Children: Welcome
Parking: Off-street and free
Directions: Caernarfon South A487, pass supermarket over bridge, first right Saron 2 miles through village through crossroads. First drive on the right.
Map ref: Saron 6 B1

Bridgend, Bridgend

Bryngarw House

◆◆◆◆ ♘♘

Bryngarw Country Park, Brynmenyn, near Bridgend, Bridgend, CF32 8UU
Tel: 01656 729009 Fax: 01656 729007
Email: bryngarwhouse@bridgend.gov.uk
Web: www.bryngarwhouse.co.uk
Rooms: 19 all ensuite ⬙ ⊗
Pricing: Dinner available from £16.95
CC: Accepted
Room facilities: ☐ ☏ ⬙
Conference: 4 meeting rooms (Thtr 80 max), 24hr-delegate from £75.50, day-delegate from £24
Children: Welcome �
Licenses: ⬙ ⬙
Parking: Off-street and free
Directions: Exit M4 J36 and follow Garw Valley signs until you see Bryngarw signs.
Map ref: Brynmenyn 3 D1
See advert on this page

Caernarfon, Gwynedd

Pengwern

◆◆◆◆ ⬙ ⬙

Saron, Llanwnda, Caernarfon, Gwynedd, LL54 5UH
Tel: 01286 831500 Fax: 01286 830741
Email: janepengwern@aol.com
Web: www.pengwern.net
Seasonal closure: November to March

Cardiff

The St David's Hotel & Spa

★★★★★ Excellent

Havannah Street, Cardiff Bay, Cardiff, CF10 5SD
Tel: 0870 4606040 Fax: 029 2031 3075
Email: reservations@thestdavidshotel.com
Web: www.roccofortehotels.com
Rooms: 132 all ensuite
Pricing: Sgl £160 Dbl £190
Dinner available from £35 CC: Accepted
Room facilities: Access:
Conference: 8 meeting rooms (Thtr 270 max), 24hr-delegate from £265, day-delegate from £75
Children: Welcome Dogs: Assistance dogs only
Licenses: Leisure: Indoor pool, Gym, Health spa, Beauty salon Parking: Off-street
Directions: Exit M4 at J33 for A4232 towards Cardiff Bay. Take Techniquest exit, turn right immediately before Techniquest into Havannah Street.
Map ref: Cardiff Bay 3 E1

Angel Hotel

★★★★

Castle Street, Cardiff, CF10 1SZ
Tel: 029 2064 9200 Fax: 029 2039 6212
Email: angelreservations@paramount-hotels.co.uk
Web: www.paramount-hotels.co.uk

PARAMOUNT
GROUP OF HOTELS

Nestled between the impressive Millennium Stadium and Cardiff Castle, the Angel Hotel is only five minutes walk from the Central Train Station.
Rooms: 102 all ensuite
Pricing: Sgl £74–88 Dbl £98
Dinner available from £18 CC: Accepted
Room facilities: Access:
Conference: 9 meeting rooms (Thtr 300 max), 24hr-delegate from £160, day-delegate from £49
Children: Welcome Dogs: Welcome
Licenses: Parking: Off-street
Directions: Exit J29 or J32 M4. Situated in Cardiff city centre, opposite Cardiff Castle.
Map ref: Cardiff 3 D1

Copthorne Hotel Cardiff Caerdydd

★★★★

Copthorne Way, Culverhouse Cross, Cardiff, CF5 6DH
Tel: 029 2059 9100 Fax: 029 2059 9080
Email: sales.cardiff@mill-cop.com
Web: www.copthornehotels.com

MILLENNIUM
HOTELS AND RESORTS
MILLENNIUM HOTELS
COPTHORNE HOTELS

In a picturesque setting just four miles from the city centre, this luxurious modern lakeside hotel offers you a warm welcome to Wales.
Rooms: 135 all ensuite
Pricing: Sgl £90–210 Dbl £100–250
Dinner available from £25 CC: Accepted
Room facilities: Access:
Conference: 8 meeting rooms (Thtr 300 max), 24hr-delegate from £175, day-delegate from £60
Children: Welcome Dogs: Welcome Licenses:
Leisure: Indoor pool, Gym, Spa bath, Sauna, Steam room
Parking: Off-street and free
Directions: J33 M4 take A4232 for 3 miles. Take first exit signposted for A48. Fourth exit off roundabout. Hotel on the left. Map ref: Culverhouse Cross 3 D1

Jurys Cardiff Hotel

★★★★

Mary Ann Street, Cardiff, CF10 2JH
Tel: 029 2034 1441 Fax: 029 2022 3742
Email: bookings@jurysdoyle.com
Web: www.jurysdoyle.com

JURYS DOYLE
HOTELS

Rooms: 146 all ensuite
Pricing: Sgl £73–190 Dbl £85–201
Dinner available from £21 CC: Accepted
Room facilities: Access:
Conference: 6 meeting rooms (Thtr 300 max), 24hr-delegate from £160, day-delegate from £41
Children: Welcome Licenses:
Parking: Off-street and free
Directions: Located 14 miles from Cardiff International Airport. Central Station only 5 mins walk. Hotel is adjacent to Cardiff International Arena.
Map ref: Cardiff 3 D1

Manor Parc Country Hotel & Restaurant

★★★

Thornhill Road, Thornhill, Cardiff, CF14 9UA
Tel: 029 2069 3723 Fax: 029 2061 4624
Email: reception@manorparchotel.fsnet.co.uk
Web: www.manorparc.com

Small select hotel with private parking set in mature
gardens with large patios overlooking Cardiff.
Conference, banqueting and restaurant facilities
offering excellent English and Continental cuisine for
the discerning guest.
Rooms: 21 all ensuite
Pricing: Dinner available from £19.50
CC: Accepted
Room facilities: 🖵 ☎ 🝠 📞
Conference: 3 meeting rooms (Thtr 100 max)
Children: Welcome
Licenses: ⟐ ⅲ Leisure: Tennis
Parking: Off-street and free
Directions: Situated on A469 on the outskirts of Cardiff,
going towards Caerphilly. Manor Parc on the left.
Map ref: Thornhill 3 D1

Quality Hotel & Suites, Cardiff

★★★

Junction 32/M4 Merthyr Road, Tongwynlais,
Cardiff, CF15 7LD
Tel: 029 2052 9988 Fax: 029 2052 9977
Email: enquiries@quality-hotels-cardiff.com
Web: www.choicehotelseurope.com
Rooms: 95 all ensuite
Pricing: Sgl £45–109.95 Dbl £55–138.90
Dinner available from £17.95
CC: Accepted
Room facilities: 🖵 ☎ 🝠 📞 ❄
Access: ⥮
Conference: 6 meeting rooms (Thtr 180 max),
24hr-delegate from £145, day-delegate from £38
Children: Welcome ⼧
Licenses: ⟐ ⅲ
Leisure: Indoor pool, Gym, Health spa, Sauna,
Steam room, Spa bath
Parking: Off-street and free
Directions: Take Junction 32 off the M4. Follow
roundabout through and take the A4054 exit for
Tongwynlais. Hotel is located on right.
Map ref: Tongwynlais 3 D1

St Mellons Hotel & Country Club

★★★

Castleton, Cardiff, CF3 2XR
Tel: 01633 680355 Fax: 01633 680399
Email: reception@stmellonshotel.co.uk
Web: www.stmellonshotel.co.uk
Rooms: 41 all ensuite
Pricing: Sgl £75–140 Dbl £90–150
Dinner available from £18
CC: Accepted
Room facilities: 🖵 ☎ 🝠 📞
Conference: 9 meeting rooms (Thtr 250 max)
Children: Welcome ⼧
Dogs: Welcome
Licenses: ⟐ ⅲ
Leisure: Indoor pool, Gym, Beauty salon, Tennis
Parking: Off-street and free
Directions: Leave M4 at Junction 28. Follow signs to
A48 Cardiff. After Castleton village, hotel is signposted
on left-hand side.
Map ref: Castleton 3 E1

Sandringham Hotel

★★

21 St Mary Street, Cardiff, CF10 1PL
Tel: 029 2023 2161 Fax: 029 2038 3998
Email: mm@sandringham-hotel.com
Web: www.sandringham-hotel.com
Seasonal closure: 24-27 December
Rooms: 28 all ensuite
Pricing: Sgl £40–100 Dbl £45–130
Dinner available from £7.45
CC: Accepted
Room facilities: 🖵 ☎ 🝠
Conference: 2 meeting rooms (Thtr 80 max),
24hr-delegate from £65, day-delegate from £15
Children: Welcome ⼧ ⅋
Licenses: ⅲ
Parking: Off-street
Directions: Exit 29 from M4, follow signs for city
centre, turn left opposite Cardiff Castle into High Street
and then proceed onto St Mary Street.
Map ref: Cardiff 3 D1

Marlborough Guest House

◆◆◆◆

98 Newport Road, Cardiff, CF2 1DG
Tel: 029 2049 2385 Fax: 029 2046 5982
Rooms: 10 all ensuite
CC: Accepted
Room facilities: 🖵 🝠
Children: Welcome ⼧
Parking: Off-street and free
Directions: Five minutes from M4 junction 29. Five
minute walk to city centre.
Map ref: Cardiff 3 D1

Wales

Campanile
Travel Accommodation

Caxton Place, Pentwyn, Cardiff, CF23 8HA
Tel: 029 2054 9044 Fax: 029 2054 9900
Email: cardiff@envergure.co.uk
Web: www.campanile.fr

Campanile hotels offer comfortable and convenient budget accommodation and a traditional French-style Bistro providing freshly-cooked food for breakfast, lunch and dinner. All rooms ensuite with tea/coffee-making facilities, DDT and TV with satellite channels.
Rooms: 47 all ensuite 🛇
Pricing: Sgl £43.50–65 Dbl £43.50–65
Dinner available from £6.25 CC: Accepted
Room facilities: 💻 ☎ 🍵 🔌
Conference: 1 meeting room (Thtr 30 max),
24hr-delegate from £70, day-delegate from £21.50
Children: Welcome 🍴 Dogs: Welcome
Licenses: 👬👬
Parking: Off-street and free
Directions: Exit J30 M4 towards Cardiff, at Pentwyn intercharge follow Brown signs to hotel.
Map ref: Pentwyn 3 E1

Cardigan, Ceredigion
Castell Malgwyn Country House Hotel
★★

Llechryd, Cardigan, Pembrokeshire, SA43 2QA
Tel: 01239 682382 Fax: 01239 682644
Email: reception@malgwyn.co.uk
Web: www.castellmalgwyn.co.uk
Rooms: 17 all ensuite 🛇 🛇
Pricing: Sgl £45–75 Dbl £65–120
Dinner available from £17.95
CC: Accepted
Room facilities: 💻 ☎ 🍵 🔌
Conference: 4 meeting rooms (Thtr 200 max),
24hr-delegate from £85, day-delegate from £25
Children: Welcome 🍴 🌜 Dogs: Welcome
Licenses: 🍷 👬👬
Leisure: Fishing
Parking: Off-street and free
Directions: From A428, at Llechryd Village, drive over River Teifi Bridge to hotel entrance. Cardigan 3 miles west of hotel.
Map ref: Llechryd 6 B4

Penbontbren Farm Hotel
★★★ 🌜

Between Glynarthen and Sarnau, near Cardigan, Ceredigion, SA44 6PE
Tel: 01239 810248 Fax: 01239 811129
Email: welcome@penbontbren.com
Web: www.penbontbren.com
Seasonal closure: January to December
Rooms: 10 all ensuite 🛇
Pricing: Sgl £63 Dbl £96
Dinner available from £15–25 CC: Accepted
Room facilities: 💻 ☎ 🍵 🔌
Conference: 1 meeting room (Thtr 25 max)
Children: Welcome 🍴 🌜
Dogs: Assistance dogs only
Licenses: 👬👬
Leisure: Snooker/billiards, Walking, Seaside, All terrain activities, Museum
Parking: Off-street and free
Directions: Travelling south from Aberystwyth on A487, take first left after Sarnau. Travelling north on A487 from Cardigan take second right about 1 mile after Tan-y-groes (signposted Penbontbren).
Map ref: Glynarthen 6 B4

Chepstow, Monmouthshire
Beaufort Hotel Chepstow
★★

Beaufort Square, Chepstow, Monmouthshire, NP16 5EP
Tel: 01291 622497 Fax: 01291 627389
Email: info@thebeauforthotel.co.uk
Web: www.beauforthotelchepstow.com
Rooms: 22 all ensuite 🛇 🛇
Dinner available CC: Accepted
Room facilities: 💻 ☎ 🍵 🔌
Conference: 3 meeting rooms (Thtr 150 max),
24hr-delegate from £75, day-delegate from £25
Children: Welcome 🍴
Licenses: 🍷 👬👬
Parking: Off-street and free
Directions: From M48, signs to Chepstow. Stay on A48. Take second left at lights by church. Hotel car park on Nelson Street.
Map ref: Chepstow 3 E1

Chirk, Wrexham
West Arms Hotel
★★★ 🌜🌜

Llanarmon-Dyffryn-Ceiriog, Llangollen, Wrexham, LL20 7LD
Tel: 01691 600612 Fax: 01691 600622
Email: bookings@thewestarms.co.uk
Web: www.thewestarms.co.uk
Rooms: 15 all ensuite 🛇 🛄
Pricing: Sgl £69.50–95 Dbl £119–174
Dinner available from £27.95 CC: Accepted
Room facilities: 💻 ☎ 🍵
Conference: 3 meeting rooms (Thtr 50 max),
24hr-delegate from £135, day-delegate from £36

Children: Welcome ♭ ⏞ℰ Dogs: Welcome
Licenses: ⚓ ⑪ Leisure: Fishing
Parking: Off-street and free
Directions: Follow B4500 from Chirk through Ceiriog
Valley for 11 miles. From Shrewsbury follow Llansilin
signs via Oswestry, then bear right.
Map ref: Llanarmon-Dyffryn-Ceiriog 7 D2

Conwy, Conwy

The Groes Inn

★★★★⏝

Tyn-y-Groes, near Conwy, Conwy, LL32 8TN
Tel: 01492 650545 Fax: 01492 650545
Email: thegroesinn@btinternet.com
Web: www.groesinn.com
Rooms: 14 all ensuite ⊞ ⊗
Pricing: Sgl £79–180 Dbl £95–219
Dinner available from £10
CC: Accepted
Room facilities: ⊡ ☎ ⊙ ⌁
Conference: 2 meeting rooms (Thtr 20 max)
Dogs: Welcome
Licenses: ⑪
Parking: Off-street and free
Directions: The town of Conwy is signed from the A55.
From there take the B5106 towards Trefriw. The Groes
is 2 miles.
Map ref: Tyn-y-Groes 6 C1

Tir-y-Coed Country House Hotel

★★★⏝

Rowen, Conwy, LL32 8TP
Tel: 01492 650219 Fax: 01492 650209
Email: info@tirycoedhotel.co.uk
Web: www.tirycoedhotel.co.uk

Surrounded by magnificent scenery in the peaceful
rural setting of a delightful Snowdonia National Park
village. Mountains, coast, castles, stately homes and
gardens nearby. Well-appointed ensuite bedrooms.
Spectacular views.
Rooms: 8 all ensuite ⊛
Pricing: Sgl £33–37 Dbl £62–70
Dinner available from £17
CC: Accepted
Room facilities: ⊡ ⊙
Children: Welcome

Dogs: Welcome
Licenses: ⑪
Parking: Off-street and free
Directions: From B5106, take signposted turning to
Rowen (unclassified road). Hotel is on fringe of village,
about 60 yards north of post office.
Map ref: Rowen 6 C1

Sychnant Pass House   Little Gem

◆◆◆◆◆ ⊞⊠ ⏝

Sychnant Pass Road, Conwy, LL32 8BJ
Tel: 01492 596868 Fax: 01492 596868
Email: bresykes@sychnant-pass-house.co.uk
Web: www.sychnant-pass-house.co.uk
Rooms: 10 all ensuite ⊛ ⊞ ⊗
Pricing: Sgl £70–140 Dbl £90–160
Dinner available from £25–27.50
CC: Accepted
Room facilities: ⊡ ⊙
Children: Welcome ♭ Dogs: Welcome
Licenses: ⚓ ⑪
Leisure: Indoor pool, Gym, Health spa, Games room,
Sauna, Hot tub
Parking: Off-street and free
Directions: Go around Conwy system past Visitors'
Centre. Take second turn on left into Upper Gate
Street: proceed up hill for 2 miles.
Map ref: Sychnant Pass 6 C1
See advert on this page

Wales

Criccieth, Gwynedd

Bron Eifion Country House Hotel

★★★ ®

Criccieth, Gwynedd, LL52 0SA
Tel: 01766 522385 Fax: 01766 522003
Email: stay@broneifion.co.uk
Web: www.broneifion.co.uk

A magnificent baronial mansion set in five acres of glorious gardens and woodlands. Close to the rugged mountains of Snowdonia. Friendly service, fresh cuisine and a well-stocked wine cellar.
Rooms: 19 all ensuite 🛏 ⊗
Pricing: Sgl £75–79 Dbl £110–140
Dinner available from £25–35
CC: Accepted
Room facilities: 🖵 ☎ ☕ ⌕
Conference: 1 meeting room (Thtr 35 max)
Children: Welcome ⍝
Licenses: ⚏
Directions: On A487 from Porthmadog go through Criccieth. Hotel is ½ mile outside Criccieth on right-hand side.
Map ref: Criccieth 6 B2

Lion Hotel

★★

Y Maes, Criccieth, Gwynedd, LL52 0AA
Tel: 01766 522460 Fax: 01766 523075
Email: info@lionhotelcriccieth.co.uk
Web: www.lionhotelcriccieth.co.uk
Rooms: 46 all ensuite 🛏 ⊗
Pricing: Sgl £37–42 Dbl £65–75
Dinner available from £15–23
CC: Accepted
Room facilities: 🖵 ☎ ☕
Access: ♿
Children: Welcome ⍝ ☕
Dogs: Welcome
Licenses: ⚏
Leisure: Games room
Parking: Off-street and free
Directions: The Lion is situated just off the A497 or B4411 in centre of Criccieth on Upper Village Green.
Map ref: Criccieth 6 B2

Glyn-Y-Coed Hotel

◆◆◆◆ ⚡ ❧

Porthmadog Road, Criccieth, Gwynedd, LL52 0HP
Tel: 01766 522870 Fax: 01766 523341
Email: juile@glyn-y-coed.co.uk
Web: www.glynycoedhotel.co.uk
Seasonal closure: 25–26 December
Rooms: 10 all ensuite 🛏 🛏 ⊗
Pricing: Sgl £45–59 Dbl £57–69
CC: Accepted
Room facilities: 🖵 ☎ ☕
Children: Welcome
Licenses: ⚏
Parking: Off-street and free
Directions: From town centre towards Porthmadog, Glyn-Y-Coed is first hotel on left (overlooking sea) and opposite the road to the beach.
Map ref: Criccieth 6 B2

Deganwy, Conwy

Deganwy Castle Hotel

★★

Station Road, Deganwy, Conwy, LL31 9DA
Tel: 01492 583555 Fax: 01492 583555
Email: deganwycastlehtl@yahoo.co.uk
Rooms: 31 all ensuite 🛏 🛏 ⊗
Pricing: Sgl £39.50–42.50 Dbl £70–76
Dinner available from £6.95–16.50
CC: Accepted
Room facilities: 🖵 ☎ ☕
Conference: 2 meeting rooms (Thtr 110 max), 24hr-delegate from £62, day-delegate from £25
Children: Welcome ⍝
Dogs: Welcome
Licenses: ⚐ ⚏
Leisure: Indoor pool, Gym, Beauty salon
Parking: Off-street and free
Directions: From Chester, exit the A55, at Deganwy/Conwy. Take the A546 passing Tesco to the centre of Deganwy village.
Map ref: Deganwy 6 C1

Denbigh, Denbighshire

Cayo Guest House

◆◆◆

74 Vale Street, Denbigh, Denbighshire, LL16 3BW
Tel: 01745 812686
Rooms: 6 (4 ensuite) ⊗
Pricing: Sgl £24–25 Dbl £48–50
CC: Accepted
Room facilities: 🖵 ☕
Children: Welcome
Dogs: Welcome
Directions: On A525, follow signs to Denbigh. At the traffic lights turn up the hill into town. Look for supermarket on right. Hotel is a little way up on left.
Map ref: Denbigh 7 D1

Devil's Bridge, Ceredigion

Hafod Arms Hotel

★★

Devil's Bridge, Aberystwyth, Ceredigion, SY23 3JL
Tel: 01970 890232 Fax: 01970 890394
Email: enquiries@hafodarms.co.uk
Web: www.hafodarms.co.uk
Seasonal closure: 15 December to 15 January
Rooms: 15 all ensuite
Dinner available
Room facilities:
Children: Welcome 10yrs min age
Licenses:
Parking: Off-street
Directions: Situated A4120 at Devil's Bridge a village
12 miles east of Aberystwyth.
Map ref: Aberystwyth 6 C3

Dolgellau, Gwynedd

Fronoleu Farm Hotel

★★

Tabor, Dolgellau, Gwynedd, LL40 2PS
Tel: 01341 422361 Fax: 01341 422023
Web: www.fronoleu.co.uk
Rooms: 11 all ensuite
Dinner available
CC: Accepted
Room facilities:
Conference: 3 meeting rooms (Thtr 150 max)
Children: Welcome
Dogs: Welcome
Licenses:
Leisure: Games room
Parking: Off-street and free
Directions: From Dolgellau town centre, follow road
past hospital. Proceed up hill. Follow Restaurant sign.
Map ref: Dolgellau 6 C2

Royal Ship Hotel

★★

Queen's Square, Dolgellau, Gwynedd, LL40 1AR
Tel: 01341 422209 Fax: 01341 421027
Email: brewery@frederic-robinson.co.uk
Web: www.frederic-robinson.co.uk
Rooms: 24 (18 ensuite)
Pricing: Sgl £47.50–50 Dbl £70–87.50
Dinner available from £9.95
CC: Accepted
Room facilities:
Children: Welcome
Licenses:
Leisure: Games room
Parking: Off-street
Directions: Situated in town centre.
Map ref: Dolgellau 6 C2

Harlech, Gwynedd

Hotel Maes-y-Neuadd

★★★

Talsarnau, near Harlech, Gwynedd, LL47 6YA
Tel: 01766 780200 Fax: 01766 780211
Email: maes@neuadd.com
Web: www.neuadd.com

Peaceful country house in Snowdonia with stunning
views of the mountains and coast. Excellent reputation
for its hospitality, fine food and wine, and well-
equipped bedrooms with a touch of luxury.
Rooms: 16 all ensuite
Pricing: Sgl £65–75 Dbl £141–235
Dinner available from £33–37
CC: Accepted
Room facilities:
Access:
Conference: 1 meeting room (Thtr 15 max),
24hr-delegate from £185, day-delegate from £45
Children: Welcome   Dogs: Welcome
Licenses:
Leisure: Croquet
Parking: Off-street and free
Directions: Three miles northeast of Harlech,
signposted on an unclassified road off B4573. Follow
brown road signs.
Map ref: Talsarnau 6 C2

Castle Cottage

◆◆◆◆◆

Y Llech, Harlech, Gwynedd, LL46 2YL
Tel: 01766 780479 Fax: 01766 781251
Email: glyn@castlecottageharlech.co.uk
Web: www.castlecottageharlech.co.uk
Seasonal closure: January
Rooms: 7 all ensuite
Pricing: Sgl £60–75 Dbl £85–110
Dinner available from £27.50
CC: Accepted
Room facilities:
Children: Welcome
Licenses:
Directions: Just off Harlech High Street, behind the Castle.
Map ref: Harlech 6 C2

Wales

Haverfordwest, Pembrokeshire

Wolfscastle Country Hotel

★★★

Wolf's Castle, Haverfordwest, Pembrokeshire, SA62 5LZ
Tel: 01437 741225 Fax: 01437 741383
Email: enquiries@wolfscastle.com
Web: www.wolfscastle.com
Seasonal closure: Christmas
Rooms: 20 all ensuite
Pricing: Sgl £59–69 Dbl £83–112
Dinner available from £16 CC: Accepted
Room facilities: 🖵 ☎ 🍵 🔌
Conference: 4 meeting rooms (Thtr 150 max)
Children: Welcome ⫪ 🐾 ۩ Dogs: Welcome
Licenses: 🌢 ⛊ Parking: Off-street and free
Directions: Situated in village of Wolf's Castle, 6 miles
north of Haverfordwest on A40.
Map ref: Wolf's Castle 6 A4

Holyhead, Anglesey

Valley Hotel

◆◆◆

London Road, Valley, Holyhead,
Isle of Anglesey, LL65 3DU
Tel: 01407 740203 Fax: 01407 740686
Email: valleyhotel@tinyworld.co.uk
Web: www.valley-hotel-anglesey.co.uk
Rooms: 20 (18 ensuite) 🍳 ⊗
Dinner available CC: Accepted
Room facilities: 🖵 ☎ 🍵
Conference: 3 meeting rooms (Thtr 120 max)
Children: Welcome ⫪ ۩ Dogs: Welcome
Licenses: ⛊ Leisure: Games room, Snooker/billiards
Parking: Off-street and free
Directions: Situated at Valley (Y Fali) on A5. Take exit 3
from A55 expressway only 4 miles from ferry port.
Map ref: Valley 6 B1

Lampeter, Ceredigion

Falcondale Mansion Hotel

★★★★

Falcondale Drive, Lampeter, Ceredigion, SA43 7RX
Tel: 01570 422910 Fax: 01570 423559
Email: info@falcondalehotel.com
Web: www.falcondalehotel.com

Nestling in fourteen acres of private gardens and
woodland, Falcondale's elegant italianate façade is
equalled by its genuinely warm and friendly welcome.
One of the most romantic places in Wales.
Rooms: 20 all ensuite
Pricing: Sgl £95–120 Dbl £130–190
Dinner available from £27.50
CC: Accepted
Room facilities: 🖵 ☎ 🍵 🔌
Access: ⛙
Conference: 2 meeting rooms (Thtr 60 max),
24hr-delegate from £110, day-delegate from £32
Children: Welcome Dogs: Welcome
Licenses: 🌢 ⛊
Parking: Off-street and free
Directions: The hotel is 500 yards west of Lampeter
centre on the A475 or 1 mile north-west of Lampeter
on the A482.
Map ref: Lampeter 6 C4

Llanbedr, Gwynedd

Ty Mawr Hotel

★★

Llanbedr, Gwynedd, LL45 2NH
Tel: 01341 241440 Fax: 01341 241440
Email: tymawrhotel@onetel.com
Web: www.tymawrhotel.org.uk
Rooms: 10 all ensuite 🍳 ⊗
Pricing: Sgl £45–50 Dbl £70
Dinner available from £15
CC: Accepted
Room facilities: 🖵 🍵
Conference: 1 meeting room (Thtr 15 max),
day-delegate from £50
Children: Welcome ⫪ Dogs: Welcome
Licenses: ⛊
Leisure: Games room
Parking: Off-street and free
Directions: Llanbedr is situated on A496 between
Barmouth and Harlech. Approaching from Barmouth,
turn right after bridge. Ty-Mawr is 100 yards up on left.
Map ref: Llanbedr 6 C2

Victoria Inn

◆◆◆◆

Llanbedr, Gwynedd, LL45 2LD
Tel: 01341 241213 Fax: 01341 241644
Email: brewery@frederic-robinson.co.uk
Web: www.frederic-robinson.com
Rooms: 5 all ensuite ⊗
Pricing: Sgl £39 Dbl £65
Dinner available from £8.50
CC: Accepted
Room facilities: 🖵 🍵
Children: Welcome ⫪
Licenses: ⛊
Parking: Off-street and free
Directions: The Victoria stands in the centre of village
of Llandbedr on the A496 coast road.
Map ref: Llanbedr 6 C2

Llandudno, Conwy

Bodysgallen Hall and Spa

★★★★★ ⓇⒶⒸ ⓇⒶⒸ ⓇⒶⒸ Premier

Llandudno, Conwy, LL30 1RS
Tel: 01492 584466 Fax: 01492 582519
Email: info@bodysgallen.com
Web: www.bodysgallen.com
Rooms: 35 all ensuite 🏊 📶 🚭
Pricing: Sgl £125–175 Dbl £175–295
Dinner available from £38–42
CC: Accepted
Room facilities: ☐ ☎ 🔌
Conference: 3 meeting rooms (Thtr 50 max),
24hr-delegate from £145, day-delegate from £50
Children: Welcome 8yrs min age
Licenses: 🍷 ♟
Leisure: Indoor pool, Gym, Health spa,
Beauty salon, Tennis
Parking: Off-street and free
Directions: Take A55 and exit at Junction 19, then
follow A470 towards Llandudno. The hotel is 1 mile on
the right.
Map ref: Llandudno 6 C1

OSBORNE HOUSE

Osborne House is located in a prime position with
glorious sea views. This 6 all suite town house has
been fabulously restored with ornate chandeliers,
original art and antiques. Romantic and luxurious,
the spacious suites have massive beds with marble
bathrooms. The award winning and stunning
Osborne's Café/Grill lit with a multitude of candles
serves superb modern style food.

17 NORTH PARADE, PROMENADE,
LLANDUDNO LL30 2LP

Tel: 01492 860330
Fax: 01492 860791

Email: sales@osbornehouse.co.uk
Web: www.osbornehouse.co.uk

RAC Dining Award
RAC ★★★★ Townhouse

Osborne House

Townhouse

★★★★ ⓇⒶⒸ Premier

17 North Parade, Llandudno, Conwy, LL30 2LP
Tel: 01492 860330 Fax: 01492 860791
Email: sales@osbornehouse.co.uk
Web: www.osbornehouse.co.uk
Seasonal closure: Christmas
Rooms: 6 all ensuite 📶
Pricing: Sgl £145–220 Dbl £145–220
Dinner available CC: Accepted
Room facilities: ☐ ☎ 🍵 🔌 ❄
Licenses: ♟
Parking: Off-street and free
Directions: Exit at Junction 19 on A55. Follow signs
Llandudno then Promenade. Osborne House is
opposite pier.
Map ref: Llandudno 6 C1
See advert on this page

Dunoon Hotel

★★★ ⓇⒶⒸ

Gloddaeth Street, Llandudno, Conwy, LL30 2DW
Tel: 01492 860787 Fax: 01492 860031
Email: reservations@dunoonhotel.co.uk
Web: www.dunoonhotel.co.uk
Seasonal closure: 27 December to mid-March

Award-winning family-run hotel of fifty years standing,
famed for its charm, elegance and warm welcome.
Lovely rooms, excellent service, good food. A short,
easy walk to shops and promenade.
Rooms: 49 all ensuite 📶
Pricing: Sgl £53–57 Dbl £74–114
Dinner available from £19.50
CC: Accepted
Room facilities: ☐ ☎ 🍵 Access: 🛗
Children: Welcome 🍴 🎮
Licenses: ♟
Parking: Off-street and free
Directions: Turn off promenade by War Memorial near
pier onto wide avenue. Hotel is 200 yards from
promenade on right.
Map ref: Llandudno 6 C1

Wales

Imperial Hotel

★★★★®

Vaughan Street, Llandudno, Conwy, LL30 1AP
Tel: 01492 877466 Fax: 01492 878043
Email: imphotel@btinternet.com
Web: www.theimperial.co.uk

Elegant Victorian hotel in central promenade position
with spectacular views of Llandudno Bay. Award-
winning restaurant using fresh local produce. Quality
accommodation. Excellent service. Ideal base for
touring north Wales.
Rooms: 98 all ensuite
Pricing: Dinner available from £25 CC: Accepted
Room facilities: 📺 ☎ 🍵 Access: 🔝
Conference: 8 meeting rooms (Thtr 150 max),
24hr-delegate from £120, day-delegate from £35
Children: Welcome 🍴 Licenses: ⚔
Leisure: Indoor pool, Gym, Health spa, Beauty salon
Parking: Off-street
Directions: Take A55 to A470, follow signs for
Llandudno, hotel is situated on the Promenade.
Map ref: Llandudno 6 C1

Ambassador Hotel

★★

Grand Promenade, Llandudno, Conwy, LL30 2NR
Tel: 01492 876886 Fax: 01492 876347
Email: reception@ambasshotel.demon.co.uk

Family-run hotel, autumn to spring breaks, Sunday
night accommodation free, first night complimentary
glass of sparkling wine and box of chocolates in room.
Ambassador passport giving discounts to attractions
and shops.

Rooms: 57 all ensuite
Pricing: Sgl £35–60 Dbl £62–86
Dinner available from £15.25 CC: Accepted
Room facilities: 📺 ☎ 🍵 📞 Access: 🔝
Conference: 1 meeting room (Thtr 35 max)
Children: Welcome 🍴
Licenses: 👬 Parking: Off-street
Directions: From A55 road to A470. Turn to
Promenade. Turn left at Promenade junction. Hotel
approx 300 yards from pier.
Map ref: Llandudno 6 C1

Esplanade Hotel

★★

Central Promenade, Llandudno, Conwy, LL30 2LL
Tel: 0800 318 688 Fax: 01492 860418
Email: info@esplanadehotel.co.uk
Web: www.esplanadehotel.co.uk
Rooms: 59 all ensuite ⊘
Dinner available
CC: Accepted
Room facilities: 📺 ☎ 🍵 📞 Access: 🔝
Conference: 5 meeting rooms (Thtr 80 max)
Children: Welcome Licenses: 👬
Parking: Off-street and free
Directions: From A55 (junction 19) follow A470 to
Llandudno. Follow brown tourist signs for beach: turn
towards Great Orme and pier.
Map ref: Llandudno 6 C1

Headlands Hotel

★★

Hill Terrace, Llandudno, Conwy, LL30 2LS
Tel: 01492 877485 Fax: 01492 874867
Web: www.headlands-hotel.com
Rooms: 15 all ensuite 📷 ⊘
Pricing: Sgl £36 Dbl £72
Dinner available from £25
CC: Accepted
Room facilities: 📺 ☎ 🍵
Children: Welcome 5yrs min age Dogs: Welcome
Licenses: 👬 Parking: Off-street and free
Map ref: Llandudno 6 C1

Royal Hotel

★★

Church Walks, Llandudno, Conwy, LL30 2HW
Tel: 01492 876476 Fax: 01492 870210
Email: royalllandudno@aol.com
Web: www.royalhotelllandudno.com
Rooms: 36 (34 ensuite) ⊛
Pricing: Sgl £30–39.50 Dbl £60–79
Dinner available from £15–25 CC: Accepted
Room facilities: 📺 ☎ 🍵 Access: 🔝
Conference: 2 meeting rooms (Thtr 100 max)
Children: Welcome 🍴
Licenses: 👬 Leisure: Games room
Parking: Off-street and free
Directions: Turn left at end of promenade, opposite pier.
Map ref: Llandudno 6 C1

Somerset Hotel

★★

Central Promenade, Llandudno, Conwy, LL30 2LF
Tel: 01492 876540 Fax: 01492 863700
Email: somerset@favroy.freeserve.co.uk
Web: www.somerset-wavecrest.co.uk
Seasonal closure: January to February
Rooms: 78 all ensuite
Pricing: Sgl £38–50 Dbl £76–100
Dinner available from £15
CC: Accepted
Room facilities: 📺 ☎ 🍵
Access: ♿
Children: Welcome ♀ Dogs: Welcome
Licenses: 🍸
Leisure: Snooker/billiards
Parking: Off-street and free
Map ref: Llandudno 6 C1

St Tudno Hotel & Restaurant

★★★   Premier

Promenade, Llandudno, Conwy, LL30 2LP
Tel: 01492 874411 Fax: 01492 860407
Email: sttudnohotel@btinternet.com
Web: www.st-tudno.co.uk

Charming seafront hotel with outstanding reputation
for fine food and wine. Elegantly and lovingly
furnished, offering the best in service and hospitality.
Host of awards for excellence. Lift, car park, indoor
heated pool.
Rooms: 19 all ensuite
Pricing: Sgl £75–90 Dbl £100–230
Dinner available
CC: Accepted
Room facilities: 📺 ☎ 🍵 🔌
Access: ♿
Conference: 2 meeting rooms (Thtr 30 max)
Children: Welcome ♀ ✂ Dogs: Welcome
Licenses: 🍸
Leisure: Indoor pool
Parking: Off-street and free
Directions: Directly opposite the pier on Llandudno's
promenade.
Map ref: Llandudno 6 C1

The Sandringham Hotel

★★

West Parade, Llandudno, Conwy, LL30 2BD
Tel: 01492 876513 Fax: 01492 877916
Map ref: Llandudno 6 C1

Warwick Hotel

★★

56 Church Walks, Llandudno, Conwy, LL30 2HL
Tel: 01492 876823 Fax: 01492 877908
Seasonal closure: 1 January to 1 March
Rooms: 14 all ensuite
Dinner available
CC: Accepted
Room facilities: 📺 🍵
Children: Welcome ♀
Dogs: Welcome
Licenses: 🍸
Parking: Off-street and free
Directions: Follow A470 to Llandudno. Drive through
town centre to T-junction, turn left onto Church Walks.
Warwick Hotel is on the right-hand side.
Map ref: Llandudno 6 C1

Abbey Lodge

◆◆◆◆◆ ✗ 🦢

14 Abbey Road, Llandudno, Conwy, LL30 2EA
Tel: 01492 878042 Fax: 01492 878042
Email: enquiries@abbeylodgeuk.com
Web: www.abbeylodgeuk.com
Seasonal closure: 15 December to 15 January
Rooms: 4 all ensuite
Pricing: Sgl £40–45 Dbl £70
Room facilities: 📺 🍵
Parking: Off-street and free
Directions: From the promenade, sea on right at
T-junction, left over two roundabouts, first right after
second roundabout, at the top turn right, Abbey Lodge
on the left.
Map ref: Llandudno 6 C1

St Hilary Hotel

◆◆◆◆ ✗

Craig-Y-Don Parade, Promenade, Llandudno,
Conwy, LL30 1BG
Tel: 01492 875551 Fax: 01492 877538
Email: info@sthilaryhotel.co.uk
Web: www.sthilaryhotel.co.uk
Seasonal closure: December to January
Rooms: 11 (9 ensuite)
Pricing: Sgl £28–39.50 Dbl £39–56
CC: Accepted
Room facilities: 📺 🍵
Children: Welcome
Licenses: 🍸
Directions: Situated on the Promenade, just 500 yards
from the North Wales Theatre, towards the Little Orme.
Map ref: Llandudno 6 C1

Karden House Hotel

◆◆◆

16 Charlton Street, Llandudno, Conwy, LL30 2AA
Tel: 01492 879347 Fax: 01492 879347
Email: technical@comset.fsnet.co.uk
Web: www.kardenhouse.com
Rooms: 10 (6 ensuite) ♨ ⊛
Pricing: Sgl £20–22 Dbl £40–44
Dinner available from £8
CC: Accepted
Room facilities: ▢ ☕
Children: Welcome ♀
Licenses: ⛾
Directions: From Llandudno railway station head down
Vaughn Street, turn left after 300 yards onto Charlton
Street. Karden House on left.
Map ref: Llandudno 6 C1

Minion Hotel

◆◆◆

21–23 Carmen Sylva Road, Llandudno, Conwy, LL30 1EQ
Tel: 01492 877740
Seasonal closure: November to March
Rooms: 10 all ensuite ⊛
Pricing: Sgl £20–22 Dbl £40–44
Dinner available from £9–10
Room facilities: ☕
Children: Welcome 3yrs min age
Dogs: Welcome
Licenses: ⛾
Parking: Off-street and free
Directions: Exit A55 onto A470 proceed to Promenade,
turn right then right at Carmen Sylva Road, Minion
situated 150 yards on right.
Map ref: Llandudno 6 C1

Llanelli, Carmarthenshire

Stradey Park Hotel

★★★ ☗☗

Furnace, Llanelli, Carmarthenshire, SA15 4HA
Tel: 01554 758171 Fax: 01554 777974
Email: reservations@stradeyparkhotel.com
Web: www.stradeyparkhotel.com
Rooms: 84 all ensuite ♨ ☐ ⊛
Pricing: Sgl £85–150 Dbl £110–150
Dinner available from £19.95
CC: Accepted
Room facilities: ▢ ☎ ☕ ☎
Access: ⌊↑
Conference: 4 meeting rooms (Thtr 300 max),
24hr-delegate from £75, day-delegate from £18.95
Children: Welcome ♀
Licenses: ⟁ ⛾
Parking: Off-street and free
Directions: Leave M4 at Junction 48. Follow signs for
Llanelli town centre then follow signs for Stradey Park
Hotel.
Map ref: Furnace 2 C1

Llangammarch Wells, Powys

Lake Country House Hotel

★★★ ☗☗☗ Premier

Llangammarch Wells, Powys, LD4 4BS
Tel: 01591 620202 Fax: 01591 620457
Email: info@lakecountryhouse.co.uk
Web: www.lakecountryhouse.co.uk

Award-winning hotel is calm and comfort epitomised;
the richly furnished sitting rooms with fine antiques,
paintings and sumptous sofas beside log fires
combine to make visitors feel like guests in a Welsh
country house.
Rooms: 19 all ensuite ♨ ⊛
Pricing: Sgl £110–170 Dbl £160–245
Dinner available from £37.50 CC: Accepted
Room facilities: ▢ ☎ Access: ⌊↑
Conference: 2 meeting rooms (Thtr 60 max),
24hr-delegate from £120, day-delegate from £35
Children: Welcome ♀ ☖ ▧
Dogs: Welcome
Licenses: ⟁ ⛾
Leisure: Indoor pool, Gym, Health spa, Beauty salon,
Tennis, Golf, Fishing, Riding, Games room,
Snooker/billiards
Parking: Off-street and free
Directions: From Builth Wells, head west on the A483
for 6 miles to Garth village. Hotel is clearly signposted
from here.
Map ref: Llangammarch Wells 6 C4

Llangefni, Anglesey

Bull Hotel

★★★

Bulkley Square, Llangefni, near Bangor,
Anglesey, LL77 7LR
Tel: 01248 722119 Fax: 01248 750488
Email: bull@welsh-historic-inns.com
Web: www.welsh-historic-inns.com
Rooms: 20 all ensuite ☐ ⊛
Pricing: Sgl £75–95 Dbl £95–115
Dinner available from £12
CC: Accepted
Room facilities: ▢ ☎ ☕ ☎
Conference: 2 meeting rooms (Thtr 40 max),
24hr-delegate from £90, day-delegate from £20

Children: Welcome ⼧
Licenses: ⫲ Parking: Off-street and free
Directions: A55 North Wales coast road, junction 6,
follow signs for Llangefni. The Bull is situated in centre
of town.
Map ref: Bangor 6 C1

Tre-Ysgawen Hall
Country House Hotel & Spa

★★★★

Capel Coch, Llangefni, Anglesey, LL77 7UR
Tel: 01248 750750 Fax: 01248 750035
Email: enquiries@treysgawen-hall.co.uk
Web: www.treysgawen-hall.co.uk
Rooms: 29 all ensuite ⊗ ⊡ ⊗
Pricing: Sgl £99.50 Dbl £158–230
Dinner available from £26 CC: Accepted
Room facilities: ⊡ ☎ ⊙ ✎
Conference: 6 meeting rooms (Thtr 200 max),
24hr-delegate from £150, day-delegate from £39.50
Children: Welcome ⼧
Licenses: ⟁ ⫲
Leisure: Indoor pool, Gym, Health spa, Beauty salon
Parking: Off-street and free
Directions: Exit junction 6 of the A55 Expressway to
Llangefni. Follow brown hotel signs to B5110 and then
quickly onto B5111.
Map ref: Capel Coch 6 B1
See advert on this page

Llangollen, Wrexham

The Hand At Llanarmon

★★

The Hand At Llanarmon, Llanarmon-Dyffryn-Ceiriog,
Ceiriog Valley, Llangollen, Wrexham, LL20 7LD
Tel: 01691 600666 Fax: 01691 600262
Email: reception@thehandhotel.co.uk
Web: www.thehandhotel.co.uk

This 16th century inn, at the heart of the glorious and
hidden Ceiriog Valley, radiates character and charm.
Superb, locally sourced food served with informal flair
and generosity every day.
Rooms: 13 all ensuite ⊗
Pricing: Sgl £47.50–60 Dbl £70–130
Dinner available from £17.50 CC: Accepted
Room facilities: ⊡ ☎ ⊙

Conference: 1 meeting room (Thtr 12 max)
Children: Welcome ⼧ Dogs: Welcome
Licenses: ⟁ ⫲ Leisure: Games room
Parking: Off-street and free
Directions: From A483 follow signs to Chirk, at centre
of Chirk follow B4500 to Ceiriog Valley, Llanarmon D.C.
approx 12 miles on.
Map ref: Llanarmon-Dyffryn-Ceiriog 7 D2

Llanwrtyd Wells, Powys

Neuadd Arms Hotel

★

The Square, Llanwrtyd Wells, Powys, LD5 4RB
Tel: 01591 610236 Fax: 01591 610610
Email: hotel@neuaddarms.fsnet.co.uk
Web: www.neuaddarmshotel.co.uk
Seasonal closure: Christmas
Rooms: 21 all ensuite ⊡ ⊗
Pricing: Sgl £30–40 Dbl £50–80
Dinner available from £13.50
CC: Accepted
Room facilities: ⊡ ⊙
Children: Welcome ⼧ ⧉ Dogs: Welcome
Licenses: ⫲ Leisure: Games room
Parking: Off-street and free
Directions: In the centre of town on the main A483,
between Builth Wells and Llandovery, also on heart of
Wales railway.
Map ref: Llanwrtyd Wells 6 C4

Wales

Machynlleth, Powys

The Wynnstay Hotel

★★

Maengwyn Street, Machynlleth, Powys, SY20 8AE
Tel: 01654 702941 Fax: 01654 703884
Email: info@wynnstay-hotel.com
Web: www.wynnstay-hotel.com
Rooms: 23 all ensuite
Pricing: Sgl £55–65 Dbl £80–110
Dinner available from £25–30
CC: Accepted
Room facilities:
Conference: 1 meeting room (Thtr 25 max)
Children: Welcome
Dogs: Welcome
Licenses:
Parking: Off-street and free
Directions: The Wynnstay Hotel is right in the centre of town, in the street opposite the clock tower. Hotel car park via Bank Street.
Map ref: Machynlleth 6 C3

Manorbier, Pembrokeshire

Castlemead Hotel

★★

Manorbier, Pembrokeshire, SA70 7TA
Tel: 01834 871358 Fax: 01834 871358
Email: castlemeadhot@aol.com
Web: www.castlemeadhotel.co.uk
Seasonal closure: January and February
Rooms: 8 all ensuite
Pricing: Sgl £50 Dbl £80
Dinner available from £16
CC: Accepted
Room facilities:
Children: Welcome
Dogs: Welcome
Licenses:
Parking: Off-street and free
Directions: Situated at bottom of village, above beach. Car park on left.
Map ref: Manorbier 2 B1

Merthyr Tydfil, Merthyr Tydfil

Bessemer Hotel

★★★

Hermon Close, Dowlais, Merthyr Tydfil, CF48 3DP
Tel: 01685 350780 Fax: 01685 352874
Email: sales@bessemerhotel.co.uk
Web: www.bessemerhotel.co.uk
Rooms: 16 all ensuite
Pricing: Sgl £55–60 Dbl £60–69
Dinner available from £9.50
CC: Accepted
Room facilities:
Access:
Conference: 2 meeting rooms (Thtr 140 max), 24hr-delegate from £150, day-delegate from £75
Children: Welcome
Dogs: Assistance dogs only
Licenses:
Parking: Off-street and free
Directions: Entering Merthyr take A4060, at roundabout, take Dowlais Industrial Estate turning. Through two roundabouts, left at third, 200 yards down to next roundabout. Hotel on the right.
Map ref: Dowlais 3 D1

The Baverstock Hotel

★★

The Heads of the Valleys Road, Merthyr Tydfil, near Aberdare, CF44 0LX
Tel: 01685 386221 Fax: 01685 723670
Email: baverstockhotel@btinternet.com
Web: www.baverstock-hotel.co.uk
Rooms: 50 all ensuite
Pricing: Sgl £45–65 Dbl £70–100
Dinner available from £12.95–17.95
CC: Accepted
Room facilities:
Conference: 5 meeting rooms (Thtr 400 max)
Children: Welcome
Dogs: Welcome
Licenses:
Parking: Off-street
Directions: Heads of the Valleys Road (A465) between Merthyr Tydfil and Aberdare, M4, M5 and M50 motorways easily accessible to hotel.
Map ref: Aberdare 3 D1

Tredegar Arms Hotel

◆◆

66 High Street, Dowlais Top, Merthyr Tydfil, CF48 3PW
Tel: 01685 377467 Fax: 01685 377467
Email: bookings@tredegararmshotel.co.uk
Web: www.tredegararmshotel.co.uk
Rooms: 8 all ensuite
Pricing: Sgl £33.50 Dbl £50
Dinner available from £5.95–12.95
CC: Accepted
Room facilities:
Children: Welcome
Dogs: Welcome
Licenses:
Parking: Off-street and free
Directions: A465 to Merthyr Tydfil. Left at junction of A465/A4060, onto A4102 to Dowlais, hotel 300 yards on left.
Map ref: Dowlais Top 3 D1

"Here!"

Need a pet friendly property? Look out for 'Dogs welcome' in our listings.

Milford Haven, Pembrokeshire

Belhaven House Hotel Limited

29 Hamilton Terrace (A4076), Milford Haven,
Pembrokeshire, SA73 3JJ
Tel: 01646 695983 Fax: 01646 690787
Email: bruce@westwaleshotels.com
Web: www.west-wales-hotels.com
Seasonal closure: 22–29 December
Rooms: 9 (7 ensuite)
Pricing: Sgl £35–55 Dbl £45–70
Dinner available from £6.95–19
CC: Accepted
Room facilities:
Children: Welcome
Dogs: Welcome
Licenses:
Parking: Off-street and free
Directions: Opposite the Cenotaph on the A4076 300
yards from town hall above the marina and waterway.
Map ref: Milford Haven 2 B1

Neath, Neath Port Talbot

Castle Hotel

The Parade, Neath, Neath Port Talbot, SA11 1RB
Tel: 01639 641119 Fax: 01639 641624
Email: info@castlehotelneath.co.uk
Web: www.castlehotelneath.co.uk
Rooms: 29 all ensuite
Dinner available
CC: Accepted
Room facilities:
Conference: 3 meeting rooms (Thtr 160 max)
Children: Welcome
Licenses:
Parking: Off-street
Directions: Leave M4 at J43. Follow signs for Neath,
hotel 200 yards past railway station on right. Car park
20 yards further on left.
Map ref: Neath 3 D1

Sleep easy

Rest assured. Our comprehensive
inspection process includes
checking beds are comfortable.

Nefyn, Gwynedd

Woodlands Hall Hotel

Edern, Nefyn, Gwynedd, LL53 6JB
Tel: 01758 720425
Web: www.woodlandshall.co.uk

Woodlands Hall Hotel is located in a secluded position
in Edern on the beautiful Lleyn Peninsula. Set in seven
acres of tree-scattered grounds, it is an ideal spot to
unwind. There are two bars, a restaurant and a well
stocked wine cellar. Special event or function
packages are available.
Rooms: 13 all ensuite
Pricing: Sgl £32.50–37.50 Dbl £65
Dinner available from £19.50–25
CC: Accepted
Room facilities:
Conference: 1 meeting room
Children: Welcome
Dogs: Welcome
Licenses:
Leisure: Games room, Snooker/billiards,
Childrens' play area
Parking: Off-street and free
Map ref: Edern 6 B2

New Quay, Ceredigion

Brynarfor Hotel

New Road, New Quay, Ceredigion, SA45 9SB
Tel: 01545 560358 Fax: 01545 561204
Email: enquiries@brynarfor.co.uk
Web: www.brynarfor.co.uk
Seasonal closure: November to February
Rooms: 7 all ensuite
Pricing: Sgl £35–39 Dbl £60–80
Dinner available from £12
CC: Accepted
Room facilities:
Children: Welcome
Licenses:
Leisure: Games room
Parking: Off-street and free
Directions: A487 to Llanarth, B4342 New Quay. Hotel
left overlooking sea, before town.
Map ref: New Quay 6 B3

Wales

Newport

The Celtic Manor Resort

★★★★★ ♛♛♛

Coldra Woods, Newport, NP18 1HQ
Tel: 01633 413000 Fax: 01633 410269
Email: postbox@celtic-manor.com
Web: www.celtic-manor.com
Rooms: 330 all ensuite
Pricing: Sgl £160–1110 Dbl £192–1142
Dinner available from £95 CC: Accepted
Room facilities: 🖵 ☎ 🍵 🛎 ❄ Access: ♿
Conference: 40 meeting rooms (Thtr 1500 max)
Children: Welcome 🍴 🛝 Licenses: 🎫 ♟
Leisure: Indoor pool, Gym, Health spa, Beauty salon,
Tennis, Golf, Snooker/billiards
Parking: Off-street and free
Directions: Exit M4 at Junction 24. At roundabout exit
A48 towards Newport. Follow brown signs turning right
to the resort after 100 yards.
Map ref: Coldra Woods 3 E1

The Parkway Hotel

★★★★

Cwmbran Drive, Cwmbran, Newport, Torfaen, NP44 3UW
Tel: 01633 871199 Fax: 01633 869160
Email: enquiries@parkwayhotel.co.uk
Web: www.bw-parkwayhotel.co.uk

This privately owned hotel has recently been refurbished
and offers a very high standard of accommodation in
executive bedrooms with marble bathrooms. Fully
equipped leisure club with indoor heated pool.
Rooms: 70 all ensuite
Pricing: Sgl £70–118 Dbl £90–146
Dinner available from £18.95–50 CC: Accepted
Room facilities: 🖵 ☎ 🍵 🛎
Conference: 7 meeting rooms (Thtr 500 max),
24hr-delegate from £87.50, day-delegate from £29.75
Children: Welcome 🍴 ⛲ Dogs: Welcome
Licenses: 🎫 ♟
Leisure: Indoor pool, Gym, Health spa, Sauna,
Steam room, Sunbathing patio
Parking: Off-street and free
Directions: From M4 take J25A (west). J26 (East) then
A4042/A4051 towards Cwmbran. At mini roundabout
take third exit, then first right.
Map ref: Cwmbran 3 E1

Kings Hotel

★★★

High Street, Newport, NP20 1QU
Tel: 01633 842020 Fax: 01633 244667
Email: kings.mc@virgin.net
Web: www.thekingshotelnewport.co.uk
Seasonal closure: 24 December to 2 January
Rooms: 61 all ensuite 🍵 🛎
Pricing: Sgl £75–85 Dbl £98–110 Dinner available
CC: Accepted
Room facilities: 🖵 ☎ 🍵 🛎 Access: ♿
Conference: 5 meeting rooms (Thtr 300 max)
Children: Welcome 🍴
Licenses: 🎫 ♟ Leisure: Snooker/billiards
Parking: Off-street and free
Directions: From Junction 26 of M4, drive towards city
centre (A4051). At main roundabout take third exit to
the hotel.
Map ref: Newport (Newport) 3 E1
See advert on opposite page

The Inn At The Elm Tree

◆◆◆◆ ♛♛ ✂ ⚲

St Brides, Wentlooge, Newport, NP10 8SQ
Tel: 01633 680225 Fax: 01633 681035
Email: inn@the-elm-tree.co.uk
Web: www.the-elm-tree.co.uk
Rooms: 10 all ensuite 🛏 🛎
Pricing: Sgl £80–90 Dbl £90–130
Dinner available from £12.50 CC: Accepted
Room facilities: 🖵 ☎ 🍵 🛎
Conference: 2 meeting rooms (Thtr 20 max),
24hr-delegate from £125, day-delegate from £35
Children: Welcome 10yrs min age
Dogs: Welcome
Licenses: ♟ Parking: Off-street and free
Directions: Exit M4 at Junction 28. Take A48 to B4239
2 miles along country lane. We are on S-bend in St
Brides village on left.
Map ref: St Brides 3 E1

Pembroke, Pembrokeshire

Wheeler's Old King's Arms Hotel

★★★ ♛♛

Main Street, Pembroke, Pembrokeshire, SA71 4JS
Tel: 01646 683611 Fax: 01646 682335
Email: reception@oldkingsarmshotel.freeserve.co.uk
Web: www.oldkingsarmshotel.co.uk
Rooms: 18 all ensuite
Pricing: Sgl £40–55 Dbl £65
Dinner available from £15.95–25
CC: Accepted
Room facilities: 🖵 ☎ 🍵 🛎
Children: Welcome 🍴 ⛲ Dogs: Welcome
Licenses: ♟ Parking: Off-street and free
Directions: M4 to Carmarthen, A477 to Pembroke. Turn
left for Pembroke. At roundabout, follow town centre
sign. Turn right onto the Parade. Car park is
signposted.
Map ref: Pembroke 2 B1

Penarth, Vale of Glamorgan

Glendale Hotel

10 Plymouth Road, Penarth,
Vale of Glamorgan, CF64 3DH
Tel: 029 2070 6701 Fax: 029 2070 9269
Web: www.infotel.co.uk
Rooms: 22 (17 ensuite)
Pricing: Sgl £33.50–45 Dbl £55–75
Dinner available from £14.75
CC: Accepted
Room facilities: ▢ ☎ 🖥
Children: Welcome ⼁ ⽷
Licenses: 👬
Directions: Penarth town centre, 4 miles west of Cardiff
(approach via M4 junction 33).
Map ref: Penarth 3 D1

Port Talbot, Neath Port Talbot

Aberavon Beach Hotel

Port Talbot, Swansea Bay,
Neath Port Talbot, SA12 6QP
Tel: 01639 884949 Fax: 01639 897885
Email: sales@aberavonbeach.com
Web: www.aberavonbeach.com

Modern hotel close to M4 and 7 miles from centre of
Swansea. Seafront location with views across Swansea
Bay. Comfortable bedrooms, elegant restaurant with fine
food, conference facilities and friendly staff.
Rooms: 52 all ensuite ⼁ ⼁
Pricing: Sgl £80–105 Dbl £90–120
Dinner available from £21
CC: Accepted
Room facilities: ▢ ☎ 🖥 ⼁
Access: 👬
Conference: 6 meeting rooms (Thtr 400 max),
24hr-delegate from £110, day-delegate from £34
Children: Welcome ⼁ ⽷ Dogs: Welcome
Licenses: ⼁ 👬
Leisure: Indoor pool, Health spa, Games room, Sauna
Parking: Off-street and free
Directions: Leave M4 at Junction 41, take A48 and
follow signs for Aberavon and Hollywood Park.
Map ref: Port Talbot 3 D1

Portmeirion, Gwynedd

Castell Deudraeth

Portmeirion, Gwynedd, LL48 6ET
Tel: 01766 770000 Fax: 01766 771331
Email: hotel@portmeirion-village.com
Web: www.portmeirion-village.com
Rooms: 11 all ensuite ⼁
Pricing: Sgl £175 Dbl £205
Dinner available
CC: Accepted
Room facilities: ▢ ☎ 🖥 ⼁
Access: 👬
Conference: 2 meeting rooms (Thtr 30 max)
Children: Welcome ⼁
Licenses: ⼁ 👬
Leisure: Outdoor pool, Tennis
Parking: Off-street and free
Directions: Off A487 at Minffordd between
Penrhyndeudraetu and Porthmadog.
Map ref: Portmeirion 6 C2

Wales

Hotel Portmeirion

★★★★

Portmeirion, Gwynedd, LL48 6ET
Tel: 01766 770000 Fax: 01766 771331
Email: hotel@portmeirion-village.com
Web: www.portmeirion-village.com
Rooms: 51 all ensuite
Pricing: Sgl £112.50–175 Dbl £173–283
Dinner available from £37.50 CC: Accepted
Room facilities: ☐ ☎ 📞 Access: |↓|
Conference: 4 meeting rooms (Thtr 100 max)
Children: Welcome ⼑ ⅀ Licenses: ⚖ ⅏
Leisure: Outdoor pool, Golf Parking: Off-street and free
Directions: Off the A487 at Minffordd between
Penrhyndeudraeth and Porthmadog.
Map ref: Portmeirion 6 C2

Rhos-on-Sea, Conwy

Plas Rhos

◆◆◆◆◆

53 Cayley Promenade, Rhos-on-Sea, Colwyn Bay,
Conwy, LL28 4EP
Tel: 01492 543698 Fax: 01492 540088
Email: info@plasrhos.co.uk
Web: www.plasrhos.co.uk
Seasonal closure: 21 December to 31 January
Rooms: 8 all ensuite 📺 ⊗
Pricing: Sgl £38–55 Dbl £60–85 CC: Accepted
Room facilities: ☐ ☕ 📞
Children: Welcome 12yrs min age Licenses: ⅏
Parking: Off-street and free
Directions: Exit A55 at Rhos-on-Sea, follow promenade
signs. At seafront fourth building on the left.
Map ref: Colwyn Bay 6 C1

The Northwood

◆◆◆

47 Rhos Road, Rhos-on-Sea, Colwyn Bay,
Conwy, LL28 4RS
Tel: 01492 549931
Email: welcome@thenorthwood.co.uk
Web: www.thenorthwood.co.uk

The Northwood is a very friendly, family run guest house
situated in the heart of lovely Rhos-on-Sea. We have 12
tasteful, newly furnished rooms and an excellent chef.

Rooms: 12 (11 ensuite) 🐾
Pricing: Sgl £28–40 Dbl £56–80
Dinner available from £12–18 CC: Accepted
Room facilities: ☐ ☕ 📞
Children: Welcome ⼑
Dogs: Welcome
Licenses: ⅏
Parking: Off-street and free
Directions: Leave the A55 at J22 and go down the slip
road to the T-junction. Turn right and go under the A55
to the sea front. Turn left and follow the seaside past
the pier until you can see the harbour and the small
boats. Turn left into Rhos Road and you will see us
175 yards on the left.
Map ref: Rhos-on-Sea 6 C1

Ruabon, Wrexham

Wynnstay Arms Hotel

★★

High Street, Ruabon, near Wrexham, LL14 6BL
Tel: 01978 822187 Fax: 01978 820093
Rooms: 9 all ensuite ⊗
Pricing: Sgl £37.50 Dbl £55
Dinner available from £8 CC: Accepted
Room facilities: ☐ ☎ ☕
Conference: 2 meeting rooms (Thtr 100 max)
Children: Welcome ⼑
Licenses: ⅏
Parking: Off-street and free
Directions: Take A483 between Wrexham and
Oswestry. Leave at exit A539 Whitchurch. Ruabon
approximately 1 mile from exit.
Map ref: Ruabon 7 D2

Ruthin, Denbighshire

Ruthin Castle

★★★★

Corwen Road, Ruthin, Denbighshire, LL15 2NU
Tel: 01824 702664 Fax: 01824 705978
Email: reservations@ruthincastle.co.uk
Web: www.ruthincastle.co.uk

Originally built by Edward I in 1282. Set in 35 acres
including ruins, dungeons and gardens. It has two
magnificent lounges, oak panelled entrance hall and
bar in the library.

Rooms: 58 all ensuite
Pricing: Sgl £59–92.50 Dbl £79–180
Dinner available from £23.50
CC: Accepted
Room facilities: ☐ ☎ ☕
Access: ⬆
Conference: 6 meeting rooms (Thtr 140 max),
24hr-delegate from £142, day-delegate from £42
Children: Welcome ⎋
Licenses: ⬥ ⣿
Leisure: Gym, Beauty salon, Fishing, Snooker/billiards
Parking: Off-street and free
Directions: A494 to Ruthin; castle at end of Castle
Street, just off town square.
Map ref: Ruthin 7 D1

Woodlands Hall Hotel
★★★ ⓡⓡ
Llanfwrog, Ruthin, Denbighshire, LL15 2AN
Tel: 01824 705107 Fax: 01824 704817
Email: info@woodlandshallhotel.co.uk
Web: www.woodlandshallhotel.co.uk

This family run hotel is set in parkland overlooking the
Vale of Clwyd. Six luxury bedrooms furnished to a high
standard. A choice of two restaurants with fabulous
wood carvings throughout.
Rooms: 6 all ensuite ⬥ ⊘
Pricing: Sgl £41–57 Dbl £55.50–62
Dinner available from £12.50–27
CC: Accepted
Room facilities: ☐ ☎ ☕ ⬥
Conference: 1 meeting room (Thtr 30 max),
24hr-delegate from £90, day-delegate from £30
Children: Welcome ⎋
Dogs: Welcome
Licenses: ⣿
Leisure: Gym, Health spa, Tennis, Snooker/billiards
Parking: Off-street and free
Directions: On reaching Ruthin take the B5105 Cerrig-
Y-Drudion Road. Turning right at the Cross Keys Inn,
signposted to Bontuchel. The Hall is signposted ³/₄
mile on the left.
Map ref: Llanfwrog 7 D2

Saundersfoot, Pembrokeshire

St Bride's Hotel
★★★★ ⓡ
St Bride's Hill, Saundersfoot, Pembrokeshire, SA69 9NH
Tel: 01834 812304 Fax: 01834 811766
Email: reservations@stbrideshotel.com
Web: www.stbrideshotel.com
Rooms: 35 all ensuite ⬥ ⊘
Pricing: Sgl £85–130 Dbl £130–240 Dinner available
CC: Accepted
Room facilities: ☐ ☎ ☕ ⬥ Access: ⬆
Conference: 3 meeting rooms (Thtr 120 max),
24hr-delegate from £135, day-delegate from £35
Children: Welcome ⎋ ⊹ Dogs: Welcome
Licenses: ⬥ ⣿
Leisure: Indoor pool, Outdoor pool, Health spa
Parking: Off-street and free
Directions: Travel west along M4 to Carmarthen. A477
towards Tenby. Saundersfoot is 4 miles before Tenby.
Enter village: hotel overlooks harbour on the clifftop.
Map ref: Saundersfoot 2 B1

Merlewood Hotel
★★
St Bride's Hill, Saundersfoot, Pembrokeshire, SA69 9NP
Tel: 01834 812421 Fax: 01834 812421
Email: merlehotel@aol.com
Web: www.merlewood.co.uk
Seasonal closure: November to February
Rooms: 28 all ensuite ⬥ ⊘
Pricing: Dinner available from £14.95
CC: Accepted
Room facilities: ☐ ☕
Conference: 1 meeting room (Thtr 100 max)
Children: Welcome ⎋
Licenses: ⣿
Leisure: Outdoor pool, Games room
Parking: Off-street and free
Directions: From Carmarthen, travel west towards
Tenby. At Begelly roundabout take turning for
Saundersfoot. Hotel just out of Saundersfoot centre,
on right as you reach top of St Bride's Hill.
Map ref: Saundersfoot 2 B1

Woodlands Hotel
◆◆◆◆ ⊘ ⓡ
St Bride's Hill, Saundersfoot, Pembrokeshire, SA69 9NP
Tel: 01834 813338 Fax: 01834 811480
Email: mail@hotelwoodlands.co.uk
Web: www.hotelwoodlands.co.uk
Seasonal closure: November to March
Rooms: 10 all ensuite ⬥ ⊘
Pricing: Sgl £35–50 Dbl £50–68
Dinner available from £6–18 CC: Accepted
Room facilities: ☐ ☕
Children: Welcome ⎋
Licenses: ⣿ Parking: Off-street and free
Directions: From centre of village, take road to Tenby.
500 yards up hill, hotel is on right.
Map ref: Saundersfoot 2 B1

Wales

St Clears, Carmarthenshire

Coedllys Country House

◆◆◆◆◆

Coedllys Uchaf, Llangynin, St Clears,
Carmarthenshire, SA33 4JY
Tel: 01994 231455 Fax: 01994 231441
Email: keith@harber.fsworld.co.uk
Web: www.coedllyscountryhouse.co.uk
Seasonal closure: Christmas

Tranquility, luxury, escapism, romance. Let us spoil you at our award-winning country house guest accommodation. Sleep well in sumptious antique beds, indulge and pamper yourself with all our extras.
Rooms: 3 all ensuite
Pricing: Sgl £42.50 Dbl £70
Dinner available from £16–23 CC: Accepted
Room facilities:
Children: Welcome 10yrs min age
Dogs: Welcome
Leisure: Indoor pool, Gym, Health spa
Parking: Off-street and free
Directions: From St Clears follow sign to Chocolate Farm/Llangynin. Immediately past Llangynin sign, 30mph sign on left. Turn left, 200 yards along track then turn left.
Map ref: Llangynin 6 B4

St David's, Pembrokeshire

Lochmeyler Farm Guest House

◆◆◆◆◆

Llandeloy, Pen-y-Cwm, near Solva, St David's,
Pembrokeshire, SA62 6LL
Tel: 01348 837724 Fax: 01348 837622
Email: stay@lochmeyler.co.uk
Web: www.lochmeyler.co.uk
Rooms: 15 all ensuite
Pricing: Sgl £25–45 Dbl £50–70
Dinner available from £15 CC: Accepted
Room facilities:
Children: Welcome Dogs: Welcome
Licenses: Parking: Off-street and free
Directions: From Fishguard, follow A487 St David's road to Mathry, turn left and follow road to Llandeloy. From Haverfordwest, follow A487 to Pen-y-Cwm, turn right to Llandeloy.
Map ref: Llandeloy 6 A4

Y Glennydd Hotel

◆◆◆

51 Nun Street, St David's, Pembrokeshire, SA62 6NU
Tel: 01437 720576 Fax: 01437 720184
Web: www.yglennyddhotel.co.uk
Seasonal closure: December and January
Rooms: 10 (8 ensuite)
Pricing: Sgl £30–40 Dbl £50–60
Dinner available from £18 CC: Accepted
Room facilities:
Children: Welcome
Licenses:
Parking: Off-street and free
Directions: 800 metres from Cross Square, next door to fire station.
Map ref: St David's 6 A4

Swansea

Beaumont Hotel

★★★

72–73 Walter Road, Swansea, SA1 4QA
Tel: 01792 643956 Fax: 01792 643044
Email: info@beaumonthotel.co.uk
Web: www.beaumonthotel.co.uk
Rooms: 16 all ensuite
Pricing: Sgl £45–75 Dbl £65–90
Dinner available from £10–20
CC: Accepted
Room facilities:
Conference: 1 meeting room (Thtr 40 max)
Children: Welcome Dogs: Welcome
Licenses:
Parking: Off-street and free
Directions: M4 J42, A483; right at traffic lights at Tesco, left at roundabout; first right, top of the road, turn left.
Map ref: Swansea 2 C1
See advert on opposite page

Windsor Lodge Hotel & Restaurant

★★★

Mount Pleasant, Swansea, SA1 6EG
Tel: 01792 642158 Fax: 01792 648996
Email: reservations@windsor-lodge.co.uk
Web: www.windsor-lodge.co.uk
Seasonal closure: 24-25 December
Rooms: 19 all ensuite
Pricing: Sgl £50–65 Dbl £65–75
Dinner available from £20 CC: Accepted
Room facilities:
Conference: 1 meeting room (Thtr 30 max)
Children: Welcome
Dogs: Welcome
Licenses:
Parking: Off-street and free
Directions: M4 Junction 42, A483 to Sainsbury's. Turn right at traffic lights beyond Sainsbury's. Turn left at railway station, then immediately right after second lights.
Map ref: Swansea 2 C1

Crescent Guest House

 ✦✦✦✦

132 Eaton Crescent, Uplands, Swansea, SA1 4QR
Tel: 01792 466814 Fax: 01792 466814
Email: jonesthecresent@aol.com
Web: www.crescentguesthouse.co.uk
Seasonal closure: Christmas to New Year
Rooms: 6 all ensuite 🍴 🚭
Pricing: Sgl £34–36 Dbl £54–56 CC: Accepted
Room facilities: 🖵 🍵
Children: Welcome Parking: Off-street and free
Directions: From railway station, take A4118 to St James'
Church, then first left, first right into Eaton Crescent.
Map ref: Swansea 2 C1

Grosvenor House

✦✦✦✦

Mirador Crescent, Uplands, Swansea, SA2 0QX
Tel: 01792 461522 Fax: 01792 461522
Email: enquiries@grosvenor-guesthouse.co.uk
Web: www.grosvenor-guesthouse.co.uk
Seasonal closure: Christmas and New Year
Rooms: 7 all ensuite 🍴 🚭
Pricing: Sgl £33–38 Dbl £55–62 CC: Accepted
Room facilities: 🖵 🍵
Children: Welcome
Parking: Off-street and free
Directions: Off A4118, 1 mile from Swansea railway
station travelling west, take the third turning on the
right, after St James' Church.
Map ref: Swansea 2 C1

Alexander Hotel

✦✦✦

3 Sketty Road, Uplands, Swansea, SA2 0EU
Tel: 01792 470045 Fax: 01792 476012
Email: reception@alexander-hotel.co.uk
Web: www.alexander-hotel.co.uk
Seasonal closure: Christmas to New Year
Rooms: 7 (6 ensuite) 🚭
Pricing: Sgl £38–40 Dbl £62–65 CC: Accepted
Room facilities: 🖵 ☎ 🍵
Children: Welcome 🍴 Dogs: Welcome
Licenses: 👥
Leisure: Games room
Directions: On A4118, in the Uplands area of Swansea.
On left-hand side at the beginning of Sketty Road, as
you leave the Uplands towards Sketty.
Map ref: Swansea 2 C1

Hurst Dene Hotel

✦✦✦

10 Sketty Road, Uplands, Swansea, SA2 0LJ
Tel: 01792 280920 Fax: 01792 280920
Email: hurstdenehotel@yahoo.co.uk
Web: www.hurstdene.co.uk

A recently refurbished three diamonds establishment,
where bedrooms are tastefully appointed with TV, tea/
coffee facilities. Private parking available. We offer
easy access to city centre and Gower Peninsular.
Rooms: 10 (8 ensuite) 🍴 🚭
Pricing: Sgl £26–35 Dbl £52–60
CC: Accepted
Room facilities: 🖵 🍵
Children: Welcome 🍴 ☕
Parking: Off-street and free
Directions: From M4 junction 42 take A483 towards the
city centre. You can find Hurst Dene on Sketty Road
Uplands A4118.
Map ref: Swansea 2 C1

Wales

Rock Villa

1 George Bank, Southend, Mumbles,
Swansea, SA3 4EQ
Tel: 01792 366794
Email: rockvilla@tinyworld.co.uk
Web: users.tinyworld.co.uk/rockvilla
Seasonal closure: 21 December to 3 January

Rock Villa, small friendly guest house situated on the
seafront within walking distance of beach, bowling
greens, tennis courts and shops. Ideal for water-skiing,
surfing or sailing. Centrally-heated rooms.
Rooms: 6 (4 ensuite) 📠
Pricing: Sgl £26–30 Dbl £54–60
CC: Accepted
Room facilities: 💻 ☕
Children: Welcome 4yrs min age ♀
Dogs: Welcome
Parking: Off-street and free
Directions: M4 Junction 42 A483 to Swansea.
Approximately 4¹/₂ miles A4067 to Mumbles. Next to
George Restaurant and Hotel.
Map ref: Swansea 2 C1

Tenby, Pembrokeshire

Atlantic Hotel

★★★★
The Esplanade, Tenby, Pembrokeshire, SA70 7DU
Tel: 01834 842881 Fax: 01834 842881
Email: enquiries@atlantic-hotel.uk.com
Web: www.atlantic-hotel.uk.com
Seasonal closure: Approx 18 December 2006 to
8 February 2007
Rooms: 42 all ensuite 📶 📀
Pricing: Sgl £72–76 Dbl £96–160
Dinner available from £22
CC: Accepted
Room facilities: 💻 ☎ ☕
Access: ⏛
Children: Welcome ♀
Dogs: Welcome
Licenses: 👪
Leisure: Indoor pool, Health spa, Spa bath, Steam room
Parking: Off-street and free
Directions: Keep town walls on left, then turn right at
Esplanade. Hotel is halfway along on your right.
Map ref: Tenby 2 B1

Fourcroft Hotel

★★★
North Beach, Tenby, Pembrokeshire, SA70 8AP
Tel: 01834 842886 Fax: 01834 842888
Email: bookings@fourcroft-hotel.co.uk
Web: www.fourcroft-hotel.co.uk
Rooms: 40 all ensuite 📶 📀
Pricing: Sgl £40–65 Dbl £80–130
Dinner available from £22
CC: Accepted
Room facilities: 💻 ☎ ☕ 🔌
Access: ⏛
Conference: 3 meeting rooms (Thtr 80 max),
24hr-delegate from £120, day-delegate from £20
Children: Welcome ♀ 🍼
Dogs: Welcome
Licenses: 🍷 👪
Leisure: Outdoor pool, Health spa, Games room,
Snooker/billiards, Giant chess, Human gyroscope
Parking: Off-street
Directions: After 'Welcome to Tenby' signs, fork left
towards North Beach. Down a gentle hill, around a
right-handed sweeping bend, up a hill. At seafront turn
sharp left. Fourcroft is 150 yards along on left.
Map ref: Tenby 2 B1

Heywood Mount Hotel & Spa Leisure Suite

★★★★ 🍷🍷
Heywood Lane, Tenby, Pembrokeshire, SA70 8DA
Tel: 01834 842087 Fax: 01834 842113
Email: reception@heywoodmount.co.uk
Web: www.heywoodmount.co.uk
Seasonal closure: 24-26 December
Rooms: 29 all ensuite 📶 📠 📀
Pricing: Sgl £50–130 Dbl £90–170
Dinner available from £16
CC: Accepted
Room facilities: 💻 ☎ ☕ 🔌
Conference: 3 meeting rooms (Thtr 100 max),
24hr-delegate from £135, day-delegate from £22
Children: Welcome 3yrs min age ♀
Dogs: Assistance dogs only
Licenses: 🍷 👪
Leisure: Indoor pool, Gym, Health spa, Beauty salon,
Games room, Sauna, Jacuzzi
Parking: Off-street and free
Directions: Passing 'Welcome to Tenby' sign look for a
brown National Trust sign directing you to Heywood
Mount.
Map ref: Tenby 2 B1

Lamphey Court Hotel & Spa

★★★★ 🍷
Lamphey, Pembroke, Pembrokeshire, SA71 5NT
Tel: 01646 672273 Fax: 01646 672480
Email: info@lampheycourt.co.uk
Web: www.lampheycourt.co.uk
Rooms: 39 all ensuite 📶 📀
Pricing: Sgl £78–90 Dbl £110–155
Dinner available from £25

CC: Accepted
Room facilities:
Conference: 2 meeting rooms (Thtr 80 max),
24hr-delegate from £140, day-delegate from £35
Children: Welcome
Licenses:
Leisure: Indoor pool, Gym, Health spa,
Beauty salon, Tennis
Parking: Off-street and free
Directions: M4 to Carmarthen, A40 to St Clears, A477
to Pembroke. Turn left at Milton Village. In Lamphey
turn right at road sign. Entrance next to Bishop's
Palace.
Map ref: Lamphey 2 B1

Greenhills Country Hotel

★★

St Florence, Tenby, Pembrokeshire, SA70 8NB
Tel: 01834 871291 Fax: 01834 871948
Email: enquiries@greenhillshotel.co.uk
Web: www.greenhillshotel.co.uk
Seasonal closure: December to March
Rooms: 28 all ensuite
Dinner available
Room facilities:
Children: Welcome
Licenses:
Leisure: Outdoor pool, Games room
Parking: Off-street
Directions: In St Florence, pass church on right. Turn
left at hotel signpost. Hotel 250 yards further on.
Map ref: St Florence 2 B1

Broadmead Hotel

Heywood Lane, Tenby, Pembrokeshire, SA70 8DA
Tel: 01834 842641 Fax: 01834 845757
Web: www.broadmeadhoteltenby.com
Seasonal closure: December to March

Established 23 years and personally supervised by
proprietors. Set in tranquil surroundings, ample
parking, easy walking distance to town and beaches.
High standards of service and cuisine offering
excellent value.
Rooms: 20 all ensuite
Pricing: Sgl £30–46 Dbl £60–72
Dinner available from £16–18
CC: Accepted

Room facilities:
Children: Welcome
Licenses:
Parking: Off-street
Directions: On arrival in Tenby turn right into
Serpentine Road following signs for Broadmead. Turn
right again into Heywood Lane.
Map ref: Tenby 2 B1

Trefriw, Conwy

Princes Arms Hotel

★★★

Trefriw, Conwy, LL27 0JP
Tel: 01492 640592 Fax: 01492 640559
Email: enquiries@princes-arms.co.uk
Web: www.princes-arms.co.uk
Rooms: 9 all ensuite
Pricing: Sgl £48–58 Dbl £76–90
Dinner available from £20–25
CC: Accepted
Room facilities:
Conference: 2 meeting rooms (Thtr 30 max),
24hr-delegate from £95, day-delegate from £25
Children: Welcome
Dogs: Assistance dogs only
Licenses:
Parking: Off-street and free
Directions: From Betws-y-Coed head north on the
B5106 to Trefriw. From Conwy head south on the
B5106 from Conwy Castle down to Trefriw.
Map ref: Trefriw 6 C1

Usk, Monmouthshire

Glen-yr-Afon House Hotel

★★★★

Pontypool Road, Usk, Monmouthshire, NP15 1SY
Tel: 01291 672302 Fax: 01291 672597
Email: enquiries@glen-yr-afon.co.uk
Web: www.glen-yr-afon.co.uk
Rooms: 28 all ensuite
Dinner available CC: Accepted
Room facilities:
Access:
Conference: 7 meeting rooms (Thtr 200 max)
Children: Welcome
Dogs: Welcome
Licenses:
Parking: Off-street and free
Directions: Follow A472 through Usk high street over
river bridge follow road around to the right 200 yards
on left.
Map ref: Usk 3 E1

Wales

Welshpool, Powys

Lane Farm

◆◆◆◆

Criggion, Welshpool, Powys, SY5 9BG
Tel: 01743 884288 Fax: 01743 885126
Email: lane.farm@ukgateway.net
Web: www.lanefarmbedandbreakfast.co.uk
Seasonal closure: 23–27 December

Warm welcome assured on working organic farm in tranquil location, nestling beneath the Breidden Hills between Shrewsbury and Welshpool. Two ground floor bedrooms. Mountains, coast, castles, stately homes and gardens nearby.
Rooms: 4 all ensuite ⊛
Pricing: Sgl £35 Dbl £50
Room facilities:
Children: Welcome
Leisure: Fishing
Parking: Off-street and free
Directions: Situated on B4393 between Crew Green and Llandrinio, 12 miles from Shrewsbury, 9 miles from Welshpool.
Map ref: Criggion 7 D2

Wrexham, Wrexham

Moreton Park Lodge

★★★

Moreton Park, Gledrid, Chirk, Wrexham, LL14 5DG
Tel: 01691 776666 Fax: 01691 776655
Email: reservations@moretonpark.com
Web: www.moretonpark.com
Rooms: 46 all ensuite ⊛ ⊛
Dinner available
CC: Accepted
Room facilities: ⬚ ☎ ⊿ ☏
Conference: 1 meeting room (Thtr 8 max)
Children: Welcome ⊩
Licenses: ⚶
Parking: Off-street and free
Directions: At intersection of A5 and B5070, 3 miles north of Oswestry, 8 miles south of Wrexham.
Map ref: Gledrid 7 D2

Y Felinheli, Gwynedd

Hotel Plas Dinorwic

◆◆◆◆

Fford Siabod, Menai Marina, Y Felinheli, Gwynedd, LL56 4XA
Tel: 01248 670559 Fax: 01248 670300
Email: plasdinorwic@btconnect.com
Web: www.hotelplasdinorwic.com
Seasonal closure: Christmas day
Rooms: 24 all ensuite ⊛ ⊛
Pricing: Sgl £50–60 Dbl £60–75
Dinner available
CC: Accepted
Room facilities: ⬚ ⊿
Conference: 1 meeting room (Thtr 40 max)
Children: Welcome ⊩ Dogs: Assistance dogs only
Licenses: ⚶ Leisure: Indoor pool
Parking: Off-street and free
Directions: A55 J10. Follow signs for Caernarfen. At mini-roundabout take first exit left and take second exit at next roundabout for Y Felinheli. Turn right opposite Halfway House pub and into the marina. Hotel is across the bridge on top of the hill.
Map ref: Y Felinheli 6 C1

Ice & slice?

RAC's comprehensive inspection means we even check drinks are served the way you want.

The big sleep

As part of our comprehensive inspection process, RAC Inspectors investigate the comfort of the beds.

Members

Look into bigger car insurance savings

Our new, 'Direct' approach means a more tailored quote for you

RAC Direct Insurance offers you:

✔ Extra discounts for RAC members

✔ Up to 70% no claims discount

✔ Windscreen repair or replacement

✔ Personal injury cover for you and your partner

✔ Optional courtesy car while yours is being repaired

✔ Optional cover for up to 90 days while you're driving anywhere in the EU.

Call now for bigger savings

0800 015 2284

Quoting ref RAC4

People behind people behind the wheel

⌐aC
direct insurance

For Breakdown, **Insurance**, BSM Lessons, **Injury Claims** and Windscreen repairs **call 08000 966 000**

Scotland

Glasgow • • Edinburgh

• Newcastle

Belfast •

Dublin •   • Manchester

Birmingham •

Cardiff •   London •

Cape Wrath

Butt of Lewis
(Rubha Robhanais)
Port Nis

North-west
Sutherland

Càrlabhagh
Stornoway
(Steòrnabhagh)

Port Nan
Giuran
Eye Peninsula
(An Rubha)

Laxford Bridge
Scourie

Eddrachillis
Bay

ISLE OF LEWIS
(EILEAN LEODHAIS)

Enard
Bay

Lochinver   Inchnadamph
Assynt-
Coigach

OUTER
HEBRIDES

Baile Ailein

THE MINCH

Ledmore

Scarp

Loch
Langabhat

3 hours

Ullapool

South Lewis, Harris
& North Uist

Taransay
(Tarasaigh)

Tarbert
(Tairbeart)

Scalpay
(Scalpaigh)

Laide

Fionn
Loch

Pabbay
(Pabaigh)

Harris
(Na Hearadh)

Poolewe

Roghadal

Gairloch

Wester Ross

Loch
Fannich

Gorston

North Uist
(Uibhist a Tuath)

THE LITTLE MINCH

Kinlochewe

A832

Tigh A
Ghearraidh
Lochmaddy
(Loch nam Madadh)

Trotternish
Staffin

2 hrs

Uig

Loch
Snizort

Rona

Loch
Torridon

Achnasheen

Benbecula
(Beinn na Faoghla)

Creag

WESTERN ISLES

Dunvegan

Portree

Shieldaig

HIGHLAND

Loch Monar

R Farrar

South Uist
(Uibhist a Deas)

Bracadale

Raasay

Lochcarron

Loch
Carron

Loch
Mullardoch

Cannich

South Uist
Machair

Lochboisdale
(Loch Baghasdail)

ISLE OF
SKYE

Drynoch

Sligachan

Cuillin
Hills

Broadford

Kyle of
Lochalsh   H

Kintail   Glen Affric

Shiel Bridge

Cluanie Inn

Invermor

Sound of Barra

Soay

Isleornsay

Glen Moriston

R Moriston

Castlebay
(Bàgh a'Chaisteil)

2 hrs

Barra (Barraigh)

Canna

Sound of Canna

Ardvasar

Knoydart

Loch
Quoich

R Garry

Invergar

OUTER HEBRIDES

Rùm

Loch
Lochy

Lochnoch

Mingulay
(Miughlaigh)

6 hours

Sound of Rum

Mallaig

Loch Morar

Loch Arkaig

Spean Bridge

R Spean

5 hours

Muck

Eigg

Arisaig

Glenfinnan

Loch Eil

Sound of

For
Shetland Islands
see third page
following

Scotland

Mull Head

North
Ronaldsay

North Ronaldsay Firth

Westray

The
North
Sound

Start Point

Westray Firth

Sanday

Rousay

Sanday
Sound

Birsay

Eday

Stronsay

Twatt

Stronsay
Firth

Shapinsay

ORKNEY
ISLANDS

Finstown

Stromness

Kirkwall

MAINLAND

Hoy and
West Mainland

St Mary's
Scapa
Flow

Rora Head

HOY

Burray

S Walls

South
Ronaldsay

Burwick

PENTLAND

FIRTH

Dunnet Head

2 hrs

Duncansby Head

Scrabster

John
o'Groats

Strathy Point

Melvich

Thurso

Castletown

Durness

Reay

Sinclair's Bay

Bettyhill

Golval

Eriboll

Tongue

Halkirk

Kyle of
Tongue

North-west
Sutherland

Loch
Loyal

Wick

Syre

River Thurso

Altnaharra

L Naver

B873

Latheron

Lybster

Kinbrace

Dunbeath

Inchnadamph

Helmsdale

Ledmore

Dalchork

Lairg

Brora

Oykel
Bridge

R Oykel

Golspie

Bonar Bridge

Dornoch

Dornoch Firth

Dornoch
Firth

Tain

Alness

MORAY FIRTH

Lossiemouth

Spey Bay

Portknockie

Cullen

Kinnaird Head

Invergordon

Burghead

Findochty

Buckie

Rosehearty

Fraserburgh

Cromarty

Elgin

Lhanbryde

Portsoy

Banff

Macduff

Gorstan

Dingwall

Fortrose

Nairn

Forres

Fochabers

Keith

Aberchirder

Turriff

Mintlaw

Contin

Muir of Ord

Avoch

Rothes

Aberdour

Peterhead

Beauly

Inverness

Charlestown
of Aberlour

Dufftown

Huntly

Elon

Tomatin

Grantown-
on-Spey

MORAY

Rhynie

Oldmeldrum

Drumnadrochit

Carrbridge

Tomintoul

B9002

Inverurie

Kintore

Dyce

Invermoriston

Nethy
Bridge

Alford

Monymusk

R Moriston

Aviemore

Whitebridge

Fort Augustus

CAIRNGORMS
The Cairngorm
Mountains

ABERDEENSHIRE

Aberdeen

Invergarry

Newtonmore

Kingussie

Aboyne

Peterculter

Lochlochy

Maryculter

n Bridge

Braemar

Ballater

Banchory

Stonehaven

Dalwhinnie

SCOTLAND

Scotland

Note:
Dark blue dots represent the location of RAC-inspected accommodation

MORAY FIRTH

MORAY

ABERDEENSHIRE

CAIRNGORMS
The Cairngorm Mountains

GRAMPIAN MOUNTAINS

SCOTLAND

ANGUS

PERTH AND KINROSS

TAY

LOCH LOMOND & THE TROSSACHS
STIRLING

FIFE

St Andrews Bay

Fife Ness

FIRTH OF FORTH

EDINBURGH

WEST LOTHIAN

MIDLOTHIAN

SCOTTISH BORDERS

Upper Tweeddale

Eildon & Leaderfoot

EAST AYRSHIRE

S LANARKSHIRE

DUMFRIES AND GALLOWAY

GALLOWAY

NORTHUMBERLAND

NORTHUMBER...

Holy Island

Kinnaird Head

St Abb's Head

Tain, Alness, Invergordon, Cromarty, Dingwall, Strathpeffer, Contin, Muir of Ord, Beauly, Inverness, Fortrose, Avoch, Nairn, Forres, Elgin, Lossiemouth, Burghead, Lhanbryde, Fochabers, Spey Bay, Portknockie, Findochty, Buckie, Cullen, Banff, Macduff, Rosehearty, Fraserburgh, Mintlaw, Peterhead, Ellon, Oldmeldrum, Inverurie, Kintore, Dyce, Aberdeen, Peterculter, Maryculter, Banchory, Aboyne, Ballater, Braemar, Stonehaven, Inverbervie, Laurencekirk, Brechin, Montrose, Arbroath, Carnoustie, Dundee, Forfar, Kirriemuir, Glamis, Meigle, Coupar Angus, Blairgowrie, Rattray, Alyth, Perth, Scone, Newport-on-Tay, St Andrews, Crail, Kilrenny, Anstruther, Pittenweem, Cupar, Ladybank, Leven, Methil, Buckhaven, Glenrothes, Kirkcaldy, Burntisland, Cowdenbeath, Dunfermline, Kinross, Falkland, Auchtermuchty, Newburgh, Bridge of Earn, Auchterarder, Blackford, Crieff, Comrie, St Fillans, Aberfeldy, Kenmore, Pitlochry, Kirkmichael, Bridge of Cally, Dunkeld, Blair Atholl, Kinloch Rannoch, Killin, Lochearnhead, Tyndrum, Crianlarich, Tarbet, Luss, Alexandria, Dumbarton, Milngavie, Bishopbriggs, Kirkintilloch, Clydebank, Glasgow, Paisley, Barrhead, Johnstone, Beith, Kilwinning, Stevenston, Kilmarnock, Galston, Darvel, Mauchline, Cumnock, New Cumnock, Sanquhar, Thornhill, Moffat, Beattock, Lockerbie, Langholm, Canonbie, Longtown, Gretna, Annan, Dumfries, Dalbeattie, Castle Douglas, Gatehouse of Fleet, Newton Stewart, New Galloway, Moniaive, Carsphairn, Dalmellington, Maybole, Ayr, Prestwick, Troon, Irvine, Stewarton, East Kilbride, Hamilton, Motherwell, Wishaw, Airdrie, Coatbridge, Shotts, Whitburn, Bathgate, Armadale, Livingston, Cumbernauld, Falkirk, Grangemouth, Bo'ness, Linlithgow, Queensferry, Musselburgh, Dalkeith, Bonnyrigg, Loanhead, Penicuik, Peebles, Innerleithen, Galashiels, Melrose, Selkirk, Hawick, Jedburgh, St Boswells, Dryburgh, Kelso, Coldstream, Greenlaw, Duns, Ayton, Eyemouth, Berwick-upon-Tweed, Wooler, Belford, Bamburgh, Seahouses, Otterburn, Bellingham, Haltwhistle, Brampton, Carlisle

Loch Ness, Loch Rannoch & Glen Lyon, Loch Tummel, Loch Tay, Loch Katrine, Loch Lomond, Firth of Tay, Firth of Forth, River Dee, River Don, River Spey, River Tay, River Earn, R Teviot, R Tweed

Scotland

Scotland

Scotland

Award winners

To help you choose somewhere really special for your stay, we've listed here all RAC Award-winning properties in this region.

Gold Ribbon Award

Premier

		pg
Balbirnie House, Markinch	★★★★	534
Highland Cottage, Isle of Mull	★★	528
Inverlochy Castle Hotel, Fort William	★★★★	518
Kinnaird, Dunkeld	★★★	512

Balbirnie House, Markinch

Highland Cottage, Isle of Mull

Inverlochy Castle Hotel, Fort William

Blue Ribbon Award

Excellent

White Ribbon Award

Commended

Cuillin Hills Hotel, Isle of Skye

Darroch Learg, Ballater

Culloden House Hotel, Inverness

Comlongon Castle Hotel, Dumfries

Little Gem Award

Little Gem		pg
Ards House, Oban	♦♦♦♦	536
Craigadam, Castle Douglas	♦♦♦♦♦	510
Glenbervie Guest House, Oban	♦♦♦♦	536
Kirkton House, Helensburgh	♦♦♦♦♦	524
Well View Hotel, Moffat	♦♦♦♦♦	535

Ards House, Oban

Craigadam, Castle Douglas

Kirkton House, Helensburgh

Aberdeen

Copthorne Hotel Aberdeen

★★★★ ⓡ

122 Huntly Street, Aberdeen, AB10 1SU
Tel: 01224 630404 Fax: 01224 640573
Email: sales.aberdeen@mill-cop.com
Web: www.copthornehotels.com

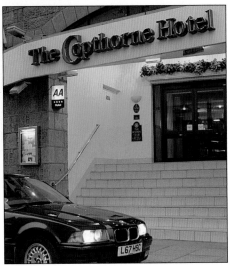

Located in the West End of the city centre, this hotel is renowned for its impeccable service. The hotel offers complimentary parking. Weekend rates are also available.
Rooms: 89 all ensuite 🛏 Ⓢ
Pricing: Sgl £60–220 Dbl £80–235
Dinner available from £17 CC: Accepted
Room facilities: 🖥 ☎ ☕ ✎
Access: Ⅲ
Conference: 3 meeting rooms (Thtr 200 max),
24hr-delegate from £145, day-delegate from £36
Children: Welcome ⼍
Dogs: Welcome
Licenses: ◁ ⅲ
Parking: Off-street and free
Directions: Travelling from South, take second left at roundabout, right at next roundabout. Follow Holburn Street for 2 miles. Turn onto Union Street, and take first left, second right.
Map ref: Aberdeen 15 F3

Maryculter House Hotel

★★★

South Deeside Road, Maryculter, Aberdeen, AB12 5GB
Tel: 01224 732124 Fax: 01224 733510
Email: reservations@maryculterhousehotel.com
Web: www.maryculterhousehotel.com

This picturesque country house on Royal Deeside dates from 1225. The ideal setting for that tranquil break, be it business or pleasure. Old world charm, genuine homely atmosphere and quality Scottish food.
Rooms: 40 all ensuite 🛏 ✉ Ⓢ
Pricing: Sgl £65–140
Dinner available from £25 CC: Accepted
Room facilities: 🖥 ☎ ☕ ✎
Conference: 7 meeting rooms (Thtr 200 max),
24hr-delegate from £140, day-delegate from £40
Children: Welcome ⼍ Dogs: Welcome
Licenses: ◁ ⅲ
Leisure: Gym
Parking: Off-street and free
Directions: Entering Aberdeen from south (A90). Take B9077 for five miles. Hotel located one mile past Mill Inn bridge on the right.
Map ref: Maryculter 15 F3

The Burnett Arms Hotel

Historic coaching inn ideally situated for touring Royal Deeside and the northeast of Scotland. 18 miles from Aberdeen and 16 miles from Dyce International Airport (ABZ).

Facilities include two function suites, restaurant, two bars. Surrounding area of Scotland renowned for its breathtaking beauty and golf courses. Golf nearby.

Weekend rates available

25 High Street, Banchory AB31 5TD
Tel: 01330 824944   Fax: 01330 825553
Email: theburnett@btconnect.com
Website: www.burnettarms.co.uk

Scotland

The Jays Guest House

◆◆◆◆

422 King Street, Aberdeen, AB24 3BR
Tel: 01224 638295 Fax: 01224 638360
Email: alice@jaysguesthouse.co.uk
Web: www.jaysguesthouse.co.uk
Rooms: 10 all ensuite ♿
Pricing: Sgl £40–50 Dbl £70–80
CC: Accepted
Room facilities: 🖥 📠
Children: Welcome 12yrs min age
Parking: Off-street and free
Directions: From East End of Union Street, turn left
onto King Street and the Jays Guest House is approx
³/₄ mile from this junction.
Map ref: Aberdeen 15 F3

The Spires Serviced Apartments

◆◆◆◆

531 Great Western Road, Aberdeen, AB10 6PE
Tel: 0845 270 0090 Fax: 01224 310092
Email: book@thespires.co.uk
Web: www.thespires.co.uk
Rooms: 53 all ensuite
Pricing: Sgl £85–105 Dbl £65–125
CC: Accepted
Room facilities: 🖥 📠
Children: Welcome
Parking: Off-street and free
Directions: At the junction of Anderson Drive/Great
Western Road. If coming from South turn left. If
coming from the North turn right. The Apartments are
200 yards on the left opposite Mannofield Church.
Map ref: Aberdeen 15 F3

Cedars Private Hotel

◆◆◆

339 Great Western Road, Aberdeen, AB10 6NW
Tel: 01224 583225 Fax: 01224 585050
Email: reservations@cedars-private-hotel.freeserve.co.uk
Web: www.cedars-private-hotel.freeserve.co.uk
Rooms: 12 all ensuite ♿ ♿
Pricing: Sgl £30–45 Dbl £50–54
CC: Accepted
Room facilities: 🖥 ☎ 📠
Children: Welcome
Dogs: Welcome
Leisure: Snooker/billiards
Parking: Off-street and free
Directions: Great Western Road crosses Anderson
Drive, which is the city ring road.
Map ref: Aberdeen 15 F3

Be more mobile Dial 1740 from any
mobile phone to get up-to-the-
minute RAC traffic information.

Calls cost up to 59p per minute. Please check with your network operator.

Aberfeldy, Perth & Kinross

Moness House Hotel & Country Club

★★★

Crieff Road, Aberfeldy, Perth & Kinross, PH15 2DY
Tel: 0870 443 1460 Fax: 0870 443 1461
Email: info@moness.com
Web: www.moness.com

Set within 35 acres of woodland, Moness offers
comfortable, quaint rooms, each with its own ensuite.
Breakfast, lunch and dinner available. Guests receive
membership of the on-site leisure club, which includes
an indoor heated pool.
Rooms: 12 all ensuite
Pricing: Sgl £43–67 Dbl £56–104
Dinner available from £9–25 CC: Accepted
Room facilities: 🖥 ☎ 📠
Conference: 2 meeting rooms (Thtr 200 max),
24hr-delegate from £90, day-delegate from £25
Children: Welcome �🍴 Licenses: 🔔 👥
Leisure: Indoor pool, Games room, Snooker/billiards
Parking: Off-street and free
Directions: Follow A9 north from Perth towards
Inverness, turn right at Ballinluig A827 to Aberfeldy.
Turn left A826 at traffic lights in Aberfeldy, Moness is
200m on left.
Map ref: Aberfeldy 13 D1

Airdrie, North Lanarkshire

Tudor Hotel

★★★

39-49 Alexander Street, Airdrie,
North Lanarkshire, ML6 0BA
Tel: 01236 764144 Fax: 01236 747589
Web: www.tudor-hotel.co.uk
Rooms: 20 all ensuite ♿ 📠
Pricing: Sgl £45 Dbl £65
Dinner available from £15.95 CC: Accepted
Room facilities: 🖥 ☎ 📠 ☎
Conference: 3 meeting rooms (Thtr 250 max)
Children: Welcome �🍴 Licenses: 🔔 👥
Parking: Off-street and free
Directions: On the main A89 near town centre, Airdrie
train station behind hotel.
Map ref: Airdrie 13 D2

Anstruther, Fife

The Waterfront
Restaurant with Rooms

18/20 Shore Street, Anstruther, Fife, KY10 3EA
Tel: 01333 312200 Fax: 01333 312288
Email: chris@anstruther-waterfront.co.uk
Web: www.anstruther-waterfront.co.uk

Overlooking Anstruther Harbour and marina, The Waterfront boasts a stylish restaurant with eight ensuite rooms around a courtyard. We also have a luxury self catering apartment sleeping eight. Open all year.
Rooms: 8 all ensuite
Pricing: Sgl £25–40 Dbl £50–80
Dinner available from £8–20
CC: Accepted
Room facilities:
Children: Welcome
Dogs: Assistance dogs only
Licenses:
Parking: Off-street and free
Directions: Located on Shore Street facing the harbour.
Map ref: Anstruther 13 E2

Spindrift

Pittenweem Road, Anstruther, Fife, KY10 3DT
Tel: 01333 310573 Fax: 01333 310573
Email: info@thespindrift.co.uk
Web: www.thespindrift.co.uk
Seasonal closure: Christmas

The Spindrift owned and run by Kenneth and Christine Lawson offers comfortable, superbly furnished rooms. An ambience that speaks of friendly service, a warm welcome and freshly prepared food.
Rooms: 8 all ensuite
Pricing: Sgl £38–46 Dbl £56–72
Dinner available from £20
CC: Accepted
Room facilities:
Children: Welcome 10yrs min age
Dogs: Welcome
Licenses:
Parking: Off-street and free
Directions: Approaching Anstruther from the west, the Spindrift is first on the left. From the east, it is last on the right.
Map ref: Anstruther 13 E2

Arbroath, Angus

Hotel Seaforth
★★

Dundee Road, Arbroath, Angus, DD11 1QF
Tel: 01241 872232 Fax: 01241 877473
Email: hotelseaforth@ukonline.co.uk
Web: www.hotelseaforth.co.uk

An ideal location for golfing, sea angling and shooting. Hotel Seaforth offers splendid accommodation in 19 ensuite bedrooms, most of them overlooking the sea. Relax in the fully equipped leisure centre, or our bar and restaurant.
Rooms: 19 all ensuite
Pricing: Sgl £49.50–55 Dbl £65–69.50
Dinner available from £12.50
CC: Accepted
Room facilities:
Conference: 3 meeting rooms (Thtr 120 max), 24hr-delegate from £68, day-delegate from £12.50
Children: Welcome
Dogs: Welcome
Licenses:
Leisure: Indoor pool, Gym, Snooker/billiards
Parking: Off-street and free
Directions: Hotel Seaforth is on the A92, main road from Dundee to Aberdeen, facing the sea.
Map ref: Arbroath 13 E1

Scotland

Auchencairn, Dumfries & Galloway

Balcary Bay Hotel

★★★☆☆

Shore Road, Auchencairn, Dumfries & Galloway, DG7 1QZ
Tel: 01556 640217 Fax: 01556 640272
Email: reservations@balcary-bay-hotel.co.uk
Web: www.balcary-bay-hotel.co.uk
Seasonal closure: Late December to 1 February
Rooms: 20 all ensuite
Pricing: Sgl £63 Dbl £118–140
Dinner available from £31 CC: Accepted
Room facilities: 🖵 ☎ 🛇
Children: Welcome 🍴 ⚲ Dogs: Welcome
Licenses: 🏮
Parking: Off-street and free
Directions: The hotel is located off the A711 Dumfries-Kirkudbright road, two miles out of Auchencairn along the shore road.
Map ref: Auchencairn 13 D4
See advert on this page

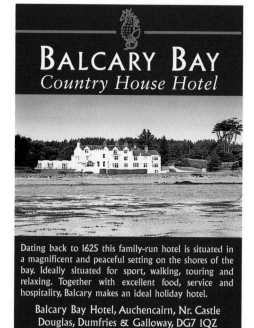

BALCARY BAY
Country House Hotel

Dating back to 1625 this family-run hotel is situated in a magnificent and peaceful setting on the shores of the bay. Ideally situated for sport, walking, touring and relaxing. Together with excellent food, service and hospitality, Balcary makes an ideal holiday hotel.

Balcary Bay Hotel, Auchencairn, Nr. Castle Douglas, Dumfries & Galloway, DG7 1QZ
Tel: (01556) 640217/640311 Fax: (01556) 640272
Email: reservations@balcary-bay-hotel.co.uk
Website: www.balcary-bay-hotel.co.uk

Aviemore, Highland

Ravenscraig Guest House

◆◆◆◆

141 Grampian Road, Aviemore, Highland, PH22 1RP
Tel: 01479 810278 Fax: 01479 810210
Email: info@aviemoreonline.com
Web: www.aviemoreonline.com
Rooms: 12 all ensuite 🍴 🛇
Pricing: Sgl £25–35 Dbl £50–70 CC: Accepted
Room facilities: 🖵 🛇
Children: Welcome
Parking: Off-street and free
Directions: Situated towards the quieter north end of Aviemore's main street. Opposite the war memorial, seven minutes walk from railway station.
Map ref: Aviemore 15 D3

Ayr, South Ayrshire

Enterkine Country House

★★★☆☆ Excellent

Annbank, By Ayr, South Ayrshire, KA6 5AL
Tel: 01292 520580 Fax: 01292 521582
Email: mail@enterkine.com
Web: www.enterkine.com
Rooms: 12 all ensuite 🛇
Pricing: Sgl £55–110 Dbl £110–160
Dinner available from £21.95–37 CC: Accepted
Room facilities: 🖵 ☎ 🛇 Access: ⏏
Conference: 5 meeting rooms (Thtr 60 max),
24hr-delegate from £140, day-delegate from £26
Dogs: Welcome Licenses: 🜊 🏮
Leisure: Fishing Parking: Off-street and free
Directions: Follow A77 to Ayr then follow B743 Mauchline Mossblown. Then follow B744 Annbank. Enterkine is on the outskirts of Annbank on road to Coylton.
Map ref: Annbank 12 C3

Dunduff Farm

◆◆◆◆◆ ⚲

Dunure, Ayr, South Ayrshire, KA7 4LH
Tel: 01292 500225 Fax: 01292 500222
Email: gemmelldunduff@aol.com
Web: www.gemmelldunduff.co.uk

Dunduff Farm is an ideal location for exploring south west Scotland and its attractions, including Culzean Castle, Robert Burns' Cottage, Burns' Heritage Trail and Ayrshire's finest golf courses. Homely and comfortable accommodation.
Rooms: 3 (2 ensuite) 🛇
Pricing: Sgl £35 Dbl £54 CC: Accepted
Room facilities: 🖵 🛇 Children: Welcome 16yrs min age
Leisure: Fishing Parking: Off-street and free
Directions: 6 miles south of Ayr past school on A719.
Map ref: Dunure 12 C3

Horizon Hotel

Esplanade, Ayr, South Ayrshire, KA7 1DT
Tel: 01292 264384 Fax: 01292 264011
Email: reception@horizonhotel.com
Web: www.horizonhotel.com

Ayr's only seafront hotel, five minutes from the vibrant town centre. Dine in our conservatory restaurant, friendly atmosphere. Golfers' paradise.
Rooms: 20 all ensuite
Pricing: Sgl £35–85 Dbl £70–130
Dinner available from £18 CC: Accepted
Room facilities: Access:
Conference: 2 meeting rooms (Thtr 180 max), 24hr-delegate from £89.50, day-delegate from £19.95
Children: Welcome Dogs: Welcome
Licenses: Parking: Off-street and free
Directions: Enter Ayr following seafront signs. Hotel at north end of esplanade between pavilion and Citadel Leisure Centre. Map ref: Ayr 12 C3

Belmont Guest House

15 Park Circus, Ayr, South Ayrshire, KA7 2DJ
Tel: 01292 265588 Fax: 01292 290303
Email: belmontguesthouse@btinternet.com
Web: www.belmontguesthouse.co.uk

Enjoy a stay at Belmont, a traditional Scottish townhouse built in 1877 in a quiet tree-lined conservation area. Our ideal location provides easy access to Ayr's shopping centre and seafront.
Rooms: 5 all ensuite
Pricing: Sgl £28–30 Dbl £52–54 CC: Accepted
Room facilities: Children: Welcome

Dogs: Welcome Parking: Off-street and free
Directions: A70 Holmston Road, double roundabout, Parkhouse Street, traffic lights. Left at traffic lights. First right Bellvue Street, right Park Circus.
Map ref: Ayr 12 C3

Ballachulish, Argyll & Bute

Lyn-Leven Guest House

West Laroch, Ballachulish, Argyll & Bute, PH49 4JP
Tel: 01855 811392 Fax: 01855 811600
Web: www.lynleven.co.uk
Seasonal closure: Christmas

A warm Highland welcome awaits you at our award-winning family-run guest house, only one mile from lovely Glencoe. We are situated with attractive gardens overlooking Loch Leven. Private parking.
Rooms: 12 all ensuite
Pricing: Sgl £25–35 Dbl £50–60
Dinner available from £9–10
CC: Accepted Room facilities:
Children: Welcome Dogs: Welcome
Licenses: Parking: Off-street and free
Directions: Take A82 to Glencoe and continue for 1 mile. West Laroch sign on left to Ballachulish.
Map ref: Ballachulish 14 C4

Ballater, Aberdeenshire

Darroch Learg

★★★★

Excellent

Braemar Road, Ballater, Aberdeenshire, AB35 5UX
Tel: 01339 755443 Fax: 01339 755252
Email: info@darroch-learg.demon.co.uk
Web: www.darrochlearg.co.uk
Seasonal closure: January
Rooms: 17 all ensuite
Dinner available CC: Accepted
Room facilities:
Conference: 3 meeting rooms, 24hr-delegate from £130, day-delegate from £30
Children: Welcome Dogs: Welcome
Parking: Off-street and free
Directions: Approaching Ballater on A93 from Braemar, turn left into driveway just past 30mph signs.
Map ref: Ballater 15 E3

Scotland

Balloch, West Dunbartonshire

Sunnyside B & B

Sunnyside, 35 Main Street, Bonhill, near Balloch,
Alexandria, West Dunbartonshire, G83 9JX
Tel: 01389 750282
Email: sunnyside@i12.com
Rooms: 3 all ensuite
Pricing: Sgl £18–30 Dbl £40–60
Room facilities:
Children: Welcome
Dogs: Welcome
Parking: Off-street and free
Directions: Phone or e-mail. Directions will be sent via
1st class mail, e-mail or fax.
Map ref: Alexandria 12 C2

Banchory, Aberdeenshire

Banchory Lodge Hotel

Dee Street, Banchory, Aberdeenshire, AB31 5HS
Tel: 01330 822625 Fax: 01330 825019
Email: enquiries@banchorylodge.co.uk
Web: www.banchorylodge.co.uk

Situated beside the River Dee in a tranquil picturesque
setting, this country house retains a hospitable homely
atmosphere with comfort, luxury and charm. Open
fires and fresh flowers.
Rooms: 22 all ensuite
Pricing: Sgl £85–90 Dbl £150–160
Dinner available from £24.50
CC: Accepted
Room facilities:
Conference: 3 meeting rooms (Thtr 50 max),
24hr-delegate from £110, day-delegate from £35
Children: Welcome
Dogs: Welcome
Licenses:
Leisure: Fishing, Games room
Parking: Off-street and free
Directions: A93 from Aberdeen, turn left at traffic lights
in Banchory, from south A957 from Stonehaven to
Banchory.
Map ref: Banchory 15 F3

Raemoir House Hotel

★★★★
Banchory, Aberdeenshire, AB31 4ED
Tel: 01330 824884 Fax: 01330 822171
Email: relax@raemoir.com
Web: www.raemoir.com

Welcome to Raemoir, one of the most beautiful
Country House Hotels in the Highlands - a very special
place famed for its hospitality for decades. Raemoir is
situated in 3,500 acres of Parkland and Forest in
Beautiful Royal Deeside - surrounded by Romantic
Castles, but only 20 minutes away from Aberdeen
Airport and within easy reach of the City Centre.
Rooms: 20 all ensuite
Pricing: Dinner available from £26
CC: Accepted
Room facilities:
Conference: 2 meeting rooms (Thtr 50 max),
24hr-delegate from £105, day-delegate from £30
Children: Welcome
Dogs: Welcome
Licenses:
Leisure: Health spa, Beauty salon, Tennis, Golf
Parking: Off-street and free
Directions: 20 miles west of Aberdeen. From A93 to
Banchory, turn right onto A980 Torphins road. After
1½ miles, hotel is opposite T-junction.
Map ref: Banchory 15 F3

Burnett Arms Hotel

★★
25 High Street, Banchory, Aberdeenshire, AB31 5TD
Tel: 01330 824944 Fax: 01330 825553
Email: theburnett@btconnect.com
Web: www.burnettarms.co.uk
Rooms: 16 all ensuite
Pricing: Sgl £50–67 Dbl £71–92
Dinner available from £16
CC: Accepted
Room facilities:
Conference: 2 meeting rooms (Thtr 100 max),
24hr-delegate from £95, day-delegate from £24
Children: Welcome
Dogs: Welcome
Licenses:
Parking: Off-street and free
Directions: On A93 west of Aberdeen in Banchory
town centre. Northern side of street.
Map ref: Banchory 15 F3
See advert under Aberdeen listings

Beauly, Highland

Lovat Arms Hotel

★★★

Main Street, Beauly, Highland, IV4 7BS
Tel: 01463 782313 Fax: 01463 782862
Email: info@lovatarms.com
Web: www.lovatarms.com
Rooms: 22 all ensuite
Pricing: Sgl £40–60 Dbl £60–120
Dinner available from £25
CC: Accepted
Room facilities: ▢ ☎ ▣ ▟
Conference: 2 meeting rooms (Thtr 60 max)
Children: Welcome ♀
Dogs: Welcome
Licenses: ◈ ♙
Leisure: Beauty salon, Fishing, Games room
Parking: Off-street and free
Directions: Take A9 to Inverness, cross Kessock
Bridge, stay on A9 till Tore roundabout. Take first left
on A832 to Muir-of-ord, left on A862 to Beauly Hotel at
one end off village square.
Map ref: Beauly 15 D3
See advert on this page

Heathmount Guest House

◆◆◆◆

Station Road, Beauly, Highland, IV4 7EQ
Tel: 01463 782411
Seasonal closure: Christmas and New Year
Rooms: 5 ⊗
Pricing: Sgl £20–25 Dbl £40–50
CC: Accepted
Room facilities: ▢ ▣
Children: Welcome
Parking: Off-street and free
Directions: 20m from post office on main road through
Beauly village.
Map ref: Beauly 15 D3

Blairgowrie, Perth & Kinross

Angus Hotel

★★★

Wellmeadow, Blairgowrie, Perth & Kinross, PH10 6NH
Tel: 01250 872455 Fax: 01250 875615
Email: reservations@theangushotel.com
Web: www.theangushotel.com
Rooms: 81 all ensuite ⬥
Pricing: Dinner available from £18.95
CC: Accepted
Room facilities: ▢ ☎ ▣
Access: ⊬
Conference: 5 meeting rooms (Thtr 180 max),
24hr-delegate from £49, day-delegate from £19
Children: Welcome ♀ ⌀
Dogs: Welcome
Licenses: ◈ ♙
Leisure: Indoor pool, Beauty salon, Games room
Parking: Off-street and free

LOVAT ARMS HOTEL

Our Taste of Scotland Kitchen provides
an excellent variety of cuisine, much of it
produced on our own farm. Our
bedrooms are all furnished in clan tartans
which adds to the family atmosphere. The
Garden and Ceilidh rooms provide
excellent areas for small meetings and
functions for up to about 60 people.

BEAULY, Nr. INVERNESS IV4 7BS

Tel: 01463 782313   Fax: 01463 782862
Email: info@lovatarms.com
Website: www.lovatarms.com

Directions: The Angus Hotel overlooks the
Wellmeadow in the centre of Blairgowrie, 16 miles
north of Perth on A93.
Map ref: Blairgowrie 13 D1

Bonar Bridge, Highland

Kyle House

◆◆◆

Dornoch Road, Bonar Bridge, Highland, IV24 3EB
Tel: 01863 766360 Fax: 01863 766360
Email: kylehouse360@msn.com
Seasonal closure: November to January
Rooms: 6 (3 ensuite) ⊗
Pricing: Sgl £25 Dbl £50
Room facilities: ▢ ▣
Children: Welcome 4yrs min age
Parking: Off-street and free
Directions: On A949, fourth house past newsagents on
left northbound. Fourth house on right entering village
from east side.
Map ref: Bonar Bridge 15 D2

Are the bells ringing?

Getting married? Congratulations! Look
for the wedding bells symbol which shows
hotels licensed for civil ceremonies.

Scotland

Bothwell, South Lanarkshire

Bothwell Bridge Hotel

★★★

89 Main Street, Bothwell, South Lanarkshire, G71 8EU
Tel: 01698 852246 Fax: 01698 854686
Email: enquiries@bothwellbridge-hotel.com
Web: www.bothwellbridge-hotel.com
Rooms: 90 all ensuite
Pricing: Sgl £65–70 Dbl £75–150
Dinner available from £15.50 CC: Accepted
Room facilities: ▢ ☎ ☕ ✎ Access: ♿
Conference: 5 meeting rooms (Thtr 200 max)
Children: Welcome ♁ ☕ Licenses: ◈ ♙
Directions: Exit at junction 5 on M74, follow sign for
East Kilbride. At large roundabout follow signs for
Bothwell, at mini roundabout turn right, hotel is on the
main street after the shops on the right-hand side.
Map ref: Bothwell 12 C2
See advert on this page

Bothwell Bridge Hotel

89 Main Street, Bothwell, G71 8EU
Glasgow, South Lanarkshire
Tel: 01698 852246 Fax: 01698 854686
Email: enquiries@bothwellbridge-hotel.com
Web: www.bothwellbridge-hotel.com

Set in the quiet village of Bothwell this charming
hotel offers the tranquillity of country life while
being centrally located. Comfortable modern
ensuite rooms. Only 15 minutes from Glasgow's
centre or 40 minutes from Edinburgh. Access is
readily available from M8 and M74 Junction 5.
International restaurant & casual dining. The hotel
specialises in conferences and functions.

Campbeltown, Argyll & Bute

Dunvalanree

◆◆◆◆◆ ☷☷ ✖ ☕

Port Righ, Carradale, Campbeltown,
Argyll & Bute, PA28 6SE
Tel: 01583 431226 Fax: 01583 431339
Email: bookin@dunvalanree.com
Web: www.dunvalanree.com

Rooms: 7 (5 ensuite)
Dinner available CC: Accepted
Room facilities: ▢ ☕
Children: Welcome ♁ ☕
Dogs: Welcome
Licenses: ◈ ♙
Parking: Off-street and free
Directions: From Tarbert take A83 towards
Campbeltown. Turn left onto B8001 towards Skipness
but follow signs to Carradale. After 20 miles in
Carradale turn left then right after the bus stop.
Map ref: Port Righ 12 B3

Castle Douglas, Dumfries & Galloway

Kings Arms Hotel

★★

St Andrews Street, Castle Douglas,
Dumfries & Galloway, DG7 1EL
Tel: 01556 502626 Fax: 01556 502097
Email: david@galloway-golf.co.uk
Web: www.galloway-golf.co.uk
Seasonal closure: 25–26 December and 1–3 January
Rooms: 10 (9 ensuite) ☷ ☕
Pricing: Sgl £44–58 Dbl £66–70
Dinner available from £14.95–27.50
CC: Accepted
Room facilities: ▢ ☕
Conference: 1 meeting room (Thtr 24 max),
24hr-delegate from £75
Children: Welcome ♁
Dogs: Welcome
Licenses: ♙
Parking: Off-street and free
Directions: From A75 turn off at sign for Castle
Douglas. Go down main street to town clock, turn left.
Hotel 100 yards on left.
Map ref: Castle Douglas 13 D4

Craigadam   Little Gem

◆◆◆◆◆ ☷ ✖ ☕

Craigadam, Kirkpatrick Durham, Castle Douglas,
Dumfries & Galloway, DG7 3HU
Tel: 01556 650233 Fax: 01556 650233
Email: inquiry@craigadam.com
Web: www.craigadam.com
Rooms: 10 all ensuite ☷ ☕
Dinner available
CC: Accepted
Room facilities: ▢ ☕
Children: Welcome ♁ ☕
Dogs: Welcome
Licenses: ◈ ♙
Leisure: Beauty salon, Fishing, Snooker/billiards
Parking: Off-street and free
Directions: Leave Dumfries on A75 towards Castle
Douglas. At Crocketford (10 miles) turn onto A712:
property is 2 miles on the right.
Map ref: Craigadam 13 D4

Crinan, Argyll & Bute

Crinan Hotel

★★★★ ⱤⱤ

By Lochgilphead, Crinan, Argyll & Bute, PA31 8SR
Tel: 01546 830261 Fax: 01546 830292
Email: nryan@crinanhotel.com
Web: www.crinanhotel.com
Seasonal closure: Mid December to end of January
Rooms: 20 all ensuite ⬥ ⊗
Dinner available
CC: Accepted
Room facilities: 🖵 ☎ 🛏 Access: |↕|
Conference: 2 meeting rooms (Thtr 60 max)
Children: Welcome ⱨ Dogs: Welcome
Licenses: ◆ ⱨⱨⱨ Leisure: Beauty salon, Fishing, Riding
Parking: Off-street and free
Directions: Airport, M8 westbound, Erskine Bridge,
then A82 to Tarbet, then A83, at Lochgilphead A816,
after 2 miles A841 to Crinan.
Map ref: Crinan 12 C2

Drymen, Stirlingshire

The Buchanan Arms Hotel and Leisure Club

★★★ Ɽ

Drymen, Stirlingshire, G63 0BQ
Tel: 01360 660588 Fax: 01360 660943
Email: enquiries@buchananarms.co.uk
Web: www.stonefieldhotels.com

In the heart of a conservation village near Loch
Lomond, The Buchanan seems to soak up the mood
of the beautiful surrounding countryside. Comfort, fine
dining and modern leisure facilities.
Rooms: 52 all ensuite ⬥ 🗔 ⊗
Pricing: Sgl £60–100 Dbl £130–160
Dinner available from £22.50 CC: Accepted
Room facilities: 🖵 ☎ 🛏
Conference: 8 meeting rooms (Thtr 150 max),
24hr-delegate from £117.50, day-delegate from £35
Children: Welcome ⱨ 🎠 Dogs: Welcome
Licenses: ◆ ⱨⱨⱨ
Leisure: Indoor pool, Gym, Health spa, Beauty salon
Parking: Off-street and free
Directions: M8 to Glasgow follow signs to Clyde
tunnel, then A81 to Aberfoyle Bearsden Cross
roundabout, take A809 follow signs for Drymen.
Map ref: Drymen 12 C2

Dumfries, Dumfries & Galloway

Cairndale Hotel and Leisure Club

★★★

English Street, Dumfries,
Dumfries & Galloway, DG1 2DF
Tel: 01387 254111 Fax: 01387 250555
Email: sales@cairndale.fsnet.co.uk
Web: www.cairndalehotel.co.uk

The Cairndale Hotel & Leisure Club is conveniently
situated close to Dumfries town centre and offers
outstanding cabaret entertainment packages including
tribute weekends and Scottish entertainment.
Rooms: 91 all ensuite ⬥ 🗔 ⊗
Pricing: Sgl £59–89 Dbl £79–109
Dinner available
CC: Accepted
Room facilities: 🖵 ☎ 🛏
Access: |↕|
Conference: 10 meeting rooms (Thtr 300 max)
Children: Welcome ⱨ 🎠
Dogs: Welcome
Licenses: ◆ ⱨⱨⱨ
Leisure: Indoor pool, Gym, Health spa, Beauty salon
Parking: Off-street and free
Directions: From south, A76 into Dumfries via Annan
Road then English Street. From north, leave M74 at
Beattock then to Dumfries via A701. First left mini-
roundabout, straight on 1/2 mile, hotel in front of traffic
lights. From west follow bypass then right for Dumfries
at A701 junction.
Map ref: Dumfries 13 D4

Scotland

"Stay!"
Need a pet friendly property?
Look out for 'Dogs welcome' in
our listings.

Comlongon Castle Hotel

★★★★

Commended

Clarencefield, Dumfries & Galloway, DG1 4NA
Tel: 01387 870283 Fax: 01387 870266
Email: reception@comlongon.co.uk
Web: www.comlongon.com
Seasonal closure: January

A privately run family concern, Comlongon Castle offers a unique blend of history and privacy in over 120 acres of secluded grounds. Near the Scottish/English border, the setting, facilities and atmosphere make it a place to remember and revisit.
Rooms: 14 all ensuite 🛏 🖨 🚭
Pricing: Sgl £80–150 Dbl £100–210
Dinner available from £35 CC: Accepted
Room facilities: 🖥 ☎ ☕
Conference: 2 meeting rooms (Thtr 50 max),
24hr-delegate from £130, day-delegate from £60
Children: Welcome ♬ 🐴 Dogs: Assistance dogs only
Licenses: 🍷 🕴
Parking: Off-street and free
Directions: At England/Scotland border, take A75 to Annan, then left onto B724. After 8 miles, at Clarencefield turn left down private drive.
Map ref: Clarencefield 13 D4

Hetland Hall Hotel

★★★
Carrutherstown, Dumfries & Galloway, DG1 4JX
Tel: 01387 840201 Fax: 01387 840211
Email: info@hetlandhallhotel.co.uk
Web: www.hetlandhallhotel.co.uk

Magnificent country house hotel set amidst 18 acres of private parkland with sweeping views over the Solway Firth. A heated swimming pool, sauna, steam room and fully equipped gym are available to all guests.
Rooms: 30 all ensuite 🛏 🖨 🚭
Pricing: Sgl £65–79 Dbl £79–103
Dinner available from £19.95
CC: Accepted
Room facilities: 🖥 ☎ ☕ 🔌
Conference: 4 meeting rooms (Thtr 200 max),
24hr-delegate from £90, day-delegate from £19
Children: Welcome ♬ 🍼 Dogs: Welcome
Licenses: 🍷 🕴
Leisure: Indoor pool, Gym, Pitch and putt, Sauna, Steam room Parking: Off-street and free
Directions: On A75 Euroroute, 8 miles east of Dumfries and 15 miles west of Gretna Green.
Map ref: Carrutherstown 13 D4

Dunfermline, Fife

King Malcolm Hotel

★★★
Laburnam Road, Dunfermline, Fife, KY11 8DS
Tel: 01383 722611 Fax: 01383 730865
Email: info@kingmalcolm-hotel-dunfermline.com
Web: www.peelhotel.com
Rooms: 48 all ensuite 🚭
Pricing: Sgl £106.50 Dbl £143
Dinner available from £17.50–19.95
CC: Accepted
Room facilities: 🖥 ☎ ☕
Conference: 3 meeting rooms (Thtr 150 max),
day-delegate from £33
Children: Welcome ♬ 🍼 Dogs: Welcome
Licenses: 🕴 Leisure: Games room
Parking: Off-street and free
Directions: M90 J2, follow signs for Dunfermline on A823. At third roundabout, hotel is on right-hand side.
Map ref: Dunfermline 13 D2

Dunkeld, Perth & Kinross

Kinnaird

★★★★★ 🦌🦌🦌

Premier

Kinnaird Estate, by Dunkeld, Perth & Kinross, PH8 0LB
Tel: 01796 482440 Fax: 01796 482289
Email: enquiry@kinnairdestate.com
Web: www.kinnairdestate.com
Rooms: 9 all ensuite 🖨 🚭
Dinner available CC: Accepted
Room facilities: 🖥 ☎ 🔌 Access: 🕴
Conference: 1 meeting room (Thtr 20 max)
Children: Welcome 12yrs min age Dogs: Welcome
Licenses: 🍷 🕴
Leisure: Health spa, Beauty salon, Tennis, Fishing, Snooker/billiards
Parking: Off-street and free
Directions: Travel north on A9 past Perth and Dunkeld. Turn left onto B898. The Kinnaird is four miles along on right. Map ref: Dunkeld 13 D1

THE ROYAL TERRACE
RAC★★★★ HOTEL

This charming hotel forms part of a quiet Georgian terrace, just five minutes walk from the historical centre of Edinburgh. The 107 well equipped bedrooms offer a variety of styles, either overlooking the terrace gardens or with views over the Firth of the Forth. Whether your stay is for business or for pleasure, The Royal Terrace Hotel will help you relax in style.

18 Royal Terrace, Edinburgh, EH7 5AQ
Tel: 0131 524 5107 Fax: 0131 557 5334

Email: reservations@royalterracehotel.co.uk
Web: www.royalterracehotel.co.uk

Duns Berwickshire, Scottish Borders

St Albans

Clouds, Duns, Scottish Borders, TD11 3BB
Tel: 01361 883285 Fax: 01361 884534
Email: st_albans@ukf.net
Web: www.scotlandbordersbandb.co.uk
Rooms: 2 ⊗
Pricing: Sgl £35–40 Dbl £64–70
CC: Accepted
Room facilities: ☐ ☕
Children: Welcome 12yrs min age
Dogs: Welcome
Directions: Clouds is a lane immediately behind the police station which is situated in Newtown Street.
Map ref: Duns 13 E2

Edinburgh

The Balmoral
★★★★★
1 Princes Street, Edinburgh, EH2 2EQ
Tel: 0870 460 7040/0131 556 2414
Fax: 0131 557 3747
Email: reservations@thebalmoralhotel.com
Web: www.roccofortehotels.com
Rooms: 188 all ensuite ⊗
Pricing: Sgl £139–164 Dbl £204–255
Dinner available from £25

CC: Accepted
Room facilities: ☐ ☎ ☏ ☼
Access: ⌊↕
Conference: 10 meeting rooms (Thtr 350 max), 24hr-delegate from £265, day-delegate from £65
Children: Welcome ╫ ☕ Dogs: Assistance dogs only
Licenses: ⚖ ♟
Leisure: Indoor pool, Gym, Health spa
Parking: Off-street
Directions: Follow signs to city centre. The Balmoral is located at the east end of Princes Street, adjacent to Waverley station.
Map ref: Edinburgh 13 D2

Carlton Hotel
★★★★
19 North Bridge, Edinburgh, EH1 1SD
Tel: 0131 472 3000 Fax: 0131 556 2691
Email: carltonreservations@paramount-hotels.co.uk
Web: www.paramount-hotels.co.uk

PARAMOUNT
GROUP OF HOTELS

Right in the heart of Edinburgh, the Carlton Hotel is just a few minutes walk from Waverley train station and within easy access of famous monuments and historical attractions.
Rooms: 189 all ensuite ⊗ ⊗
Pricing: Sgl £138 Dbl £138
Dinner available from £15 CC: Accepted
Room facilities: ☐ ☎ ☏ ☼ Access: ⌊↕
Conference: 9 meeting rooms (Thtr 300 max), 24hr-delegate from £180, day-delegate from £55
Children: Welcome ╫ ☃ Dogs: Welcome
Licenses: ⚖ ♟
Leisure: Indoor pool, Gym, Health spa
Parking: Off-street
Directions: Follow signs for Waverley train station; hotel is situated above North Bridge.
Map ref: Edinburgh 13 D2

The Royal Terrace Hotel

★★★★

18 Royal Terrace, Edinburgh, EH7 5AQ
Tel: 0131 557 3222 Fax: 0131 557 5334
Email: reservations@royalterracehotel.co.uk
Web: www.royalterracehotel.co.uk

www.primahotels.co.uk

Rooms: 107 all ensuite 🛏 🖥 ⊗
Pricing: Sgl £70–115 Dbl £80–175
Dinner available from £22.50 CC: Accepted
Room facilities: 📺 ☎ ☕ 🌿 Access: 🛗
Conference: 5 meeting rooms (Thtr 100 max),
24hr-delegate from £140, day-delegate from £35
Children: Welcome ☒
Licenses: 🍷 ⅲ
Leisure: Indoor pool, Gym, Beautiful Edwardian
terraced gardens
Directions: Northeast from Princes Street, located off
Leith Walk, 8 miles from airport, 1/2 mile from Waverley
station on Royal Terrace.
Map ref: Edinburgh 13 D2
See advert on previous page

Braid Hills Hotel

★★★★ ⊞

134 Braid Road, Edinburgh, EH10 6JD
Tel: 0131 447 8888 Fax: 0131 452 8477
Email: bookings@braidhillshotel.co.uk
Web: www.braidhillshotel.co.uk
Rooms: 67 all ensuite 🛏 🖥 ⊗
Dinner available CC: Accepted
Room facilities: 📺 ☎ ☕ 🌿
Conference: 2 meeting rooms (Thtr 100 max)
Children: Welcome ☒
Licenses: 🍷 ⅲ
Parking: Off-street
Directions: From city bypass take A702 Lothianburn
Junction signposted to City Centre. Braid Hills Hotel
approximately one mile on right-hand side.
Map ref: Edinburgh 13 D2

Dalhousie Castle

★★★★ ⊞⊞

Bonnyrigg, near Edinburgh, Midlothian, EH19 3JB
Tel: 01875 820 153 Fax: 01875 821 936
Email: info@dalhousiecastle.co.uk
Web: www.dalhousiecastle.co.uk
Rooms: 35 all ensuite 🛏 🖥 ⊗
Pricing: Sgl £125–265 Dbl £175–335
Dinner available from £38
CC: Accepted
Room facilities: 📺 ☎ ☕
Conference: 6 meeting rooms (Thtr 120 max),
24hr-delegate from £200, day-delegate from £45
Children: Welcome ☒
Dogs: Welcome

Licenses: 🍷 ⅲ
Leisure: Health spa, Beauty salon, Fishing, Dalhousie
Castle Falconry Mews
Parking: Off-street and free
Directions: Dalhousie Castle is located on the B704,
1 mile from the A7 at Newtongrange, 4 miles south
from the A720 city bypass.
Map ref: Bonnyrigg 13 D2

Jurys Inn Edinburgh

★★★

43 Jeffrey Street, Edinburgh, EH1 1DH
Tel: 0131 200 3300 Fax: 0131 200 0400
Email: bookings@jurysdoyle.com
Web: www.jurysinns.com
Seasonal closure: 24-25 December

JURYS DOYLE
HOTELS

Rooms: 186 all ensuite ⊗
Pricing: Sgl £50–200 Dbl £50–200
Dinner available from £15 CC: Accepted
Room facilities: 📺 ☎ ☕ 🌿
Access: 🛗
Conference: 5 meeting rooms (Thtr 50 max),
24hr-delegate from £135, day-delegate from £35
Children: Welcome ☒
Licenses: ⅲ
Parking: Off-street
Directions: Located 9 miles/14.4 km from airport. Just
two minutes walk from Waverley Station.
Map ref: Edinburgh 13 D2

Old Waverley Hotel

★★★

43 Princes Street, Edinburgh, EH2 2BY
Tel: 0131 556 4648 Fax: 0131 557 6316
Email: reservations@oldwaverley.co.uk
Web: www.oldwaverley.co.uk

The Old Waverley Hotel is centrally positioned on
famous Princes Street. There are 80 comfortable
ensuite bedrooms, many have views of the Castle.
Both Cranstons Restaurant and the Abbotsford
Lounge Bar are light and airy with superb views. Both
offer excellent cuisine and service. £1.75m
refurbishment has been spent to date.

Rooms: 80 all ensuite
Pricing: Sgl £80–130 Dbl £95–175
Dinner available from £12.50
CC: Accepted
Room facilities:
Access:
Children: Welcome
Licenses:
Directions: Follow signs for Edinburgh Waverley train station. Hotel is located on the opposite side on Princes Street.
Map ref: Edinburgh 13 D2

Kew House

1 Kew Terrace, Murrayfield, Edinburgh, EH12 5JE
Tel: 0131 313 0700 Fax: 0131 313 0747
Email: info@kewhouse.com
Web: www.kewhouse.com
Rooms: 6 all ensuite
Pricing: Sgl £70–75 Dbl £78–135
Dinner available from £15
CC: Accepted
Room facilities:
Children: Welcome
Dogs: Welcome
Licenses:
Parking: Off-street and free
Directions: Directly on A8 route 1 mile west of Princes Street and on main route from airport.
Map ref: Murrayfield 13 D2

The Knight Residence

12 Lauriston Street, Edinburgh, EH3 9DJ
Tel: 0131 622 8120 Fax: 0131 622 7363
Email: info@theknightresidence.co.uk
Web: www.theknightresidence.co.uk

Stylish aparthotel in the centre of Edinburgh. One, two and three bedroom apartments with kitchen, bathrooms, living room with dining area and private parking. Daily maid service, on-site concierge.
Rooms: 19 all ensuite
Pricing: Sgl £85–155 Dbl £95–165
CC: Accepted
Room facilities:
Access:

Children: Welcome
Parking: Off-street and free
Directions: Located close to Edinburgh Castle between the grassmarket and Lothian Road. Call for directions or visit the website.
Map ref: Edinburgh 13 D2

Allison House

17 Mayfield Gardens, Edinburgh, EH9 2AX
Tel: 0131 667 8049 Fax: 0131 667 5001
Email: info@allisonhousehotel.com
Web: www.allisonhousehotel.com
Rooms: 11 (10 ensuite)
Pricing: Sgl £40–55 Dbl £60–100
CC: Accepted
Room facilities:
Children: Welcome
Dogs: Welcome
Parking: Off-street and free
Directions: Situated on the south side of Edinburgh, 1 mile from city centre on A701.
Map ref: Edinburgh 13 D2

Ashlyn Guest House

42 Inverleith Row, Edinburgh, EH3 5PY
Tel: 0131 552 2954 Fax: 0131 552 2954
Email: reservations@ashlyn-edinburgh.com
Web: www.ashlyn-edinburgh.com
Rooms: 7 (5 ensuite)
Pricing: Sgl £27.50–35 Dbl £55–80
CC: Accepted
Room facilities:
Children: Welcome 7yrs min age
Directions: Situated 1 mile north of Princes Street, adjacent to Royal Botanical Gardens, opposite Heriott rugby ground.
Map ref: Edinburgh 13 D2

Corstorphine Lodge Hotel

186 St John's Road, Corstorphine,
Edinburgh, EH12 8SG
Tel: 0131 476 7116 Fax: 0131 476 7117/539 4945
Email: corstlodge@aol.com
Web: www.corstorphinehotels.co.uk
Rooms: 17 all ensuite
Pricing: Sgl £29–69 Dbl £49–129
CC: Accepted
Room facilities:
Children: Welcome
Parking: Off-street and free
Directions: From city head out along A8 into Corstorphine. From M8 or bypass, head for bypass north exit, along A8 into Corstorphine. From north, head for A8 into Corstorphine.
Map ref: Corstorphine 13 D2

Scotland

Southside Guest House

8 Newington Road, Edinburgh, EH9 1QS
Tel: 0131 668 4422 Fax: 0131 667 7771
Map ref: Edinburgh 13 D2

Ardleigh Guest House

260 Ferry Road, Trinity, Edinburgh, EH5 3AN
Tel: 0131 552 1833 Fax: 0131 552 4951
Email: info@ardleighhouse.com
Web: www.ardleighhouse.com
Rooms: 7 (5 ensuite) 🛏️ 📺 ⊗
Pricing: Sgl £25–50 Dbl £45–100 CC: Accepted
Room facilities: 🖥️ ☕
Children: Welcome 2yrs min age
Directions: From A720 M8 follow A90 to Barnton. Right
into Queensferry Road, Telford Road to Ferry Road
towards Leith. Opposite Golden Acre.
Map ref: Edinburgh 13 D2

Boisdale Hotel

9 Coates Gardens, Edinburgh, EH12 5LG
Tel: 0131 337 1134 Fax: 0131 313 0048
Rooms: 10 all ensuite 🛏️ ⊗
Pricing: Sgl £30–40 Dbl £60–80 CC: Accepted
Room facilities: 🖥️ ☕
Children: Welcome ⯑ ⯑ Dogs: Welcome
Map ref: Edinburgh 13 D2

Cumberland Hotel

1 West Coates, Edinburgh, EH12 5JQ
Tel: 0131 337 1198 Fax: 0131 539 4945
Email: cumblhotel@aol.com
Web: www.cumberlandhotel-edinburgh.com
Rooms: 17 all ensuite 🛏️ 📺 ⊗
Pricing: Sgl £39–99 Dbl £49–129 CC: Accepted
Room facilities: 🖥️ ☕
Conference: 1 meeting room (Thtr 20 max)
Children: Welcome ⯑
Licenses: ⛽ Parking: Off-street and free
Directions: From airport: A8 towards Haymarket. From
city centre head for West End past the Haymarket
Station. Hotel is 200 yards on the right.
Map ref: Edinburgh 13 D2

Galloway Guest House

22 Dean Park Crescent, Edinburgh, EH4 1PH
Tel: 0131 332 3672 Fax: 0131 332 3672
Email: galloway_theclarks@hotmail.com
Rooms: 10 (6 ensuite) 🛏️
Pricing: Sgl £25–60 Dbl £40–80 CC: Accepted
Room facilities: 🖥️ ☕
Children: Welcome ⯑ Dogs: Welcome
Directions: 1km from Princes Street/West End on A9.
Map ref: Edinburgh 13 D2

Thrums Hotel

14 Minto Street, Edinburgh, EH9 1RQ
Tel: 0131 667 5545/8545 Fax: 0131 667 8707
Email: info@thrumshotel.com
Web: www.thrumshotel.com
Rooms: 14 all ensuite 🛏️ ⊗
Pricing: Sgl £35–50 Dbl £50–110 CC: Accepted
Room facilities: 🖥️ ☎️ ☕
Children: Welcome Dogs: Assistance dogs only
Licenses: ⛽
Leisure: Wireless internet access
Parking: Off-street and free
Directions: Follow city bypass to Edinburgh South,
then take A7/A701 to Newington.
Map ref: Edinburgh 13 D2

Western Manor House Hotel

92 Corstorphine Road, Murrayfield, Edinburgh, EH12 6JG
Tel: 0131 538 7490 Fax: 0131 538 7490
Email: info@westernmanorhousehotel.co.uk
Web: www.westernmanorhousehotel.co.uk
Rooms: 11 (7 ensuite) 🛏️ ⊗
Pricing: Sgl £40–50 Dbl £60–90
Dinner available from £10 CC: Accepted
Room facilities: 🖥️ ☕
Conference: 1 meeting room
Children: Welcome ⯑
Licenses: ⛽

Parking: Off-street and free
Directions: Situated on main route from airport to city centre near zoo and Murrayfield Stadium. Approximately two miles from city centre.
Map ref: Murrayfield 13 D2

Averon City Centre Guest House

44 Gilmore Place, Edinburgh, EH3 9NQ
Tel: 0131 229 9932
Email: info@averon.co.uk
Web: www.averon.co.uk

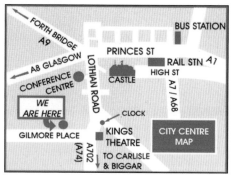

Comfortable guest house located in Central Edinburgh near Edinburgh Castle and Princes Street. Comfortable ensuite rooms in traditional Georgian villa built in 1750. Ideal location for visiting Edinburgh with private car park.
Rooms: 12 (8 ensuite) ⛵ CC: Accepted
Room facilities: ▢ ☕ Children: Welcome
Parking: Off-street
Directions: From Princes Street go up Lothian Road and turn right at the Kings Theatre.
Map ref: Edinburgh 13 D2

Edzell, Angus

Glenesk Hotel

High Street, Edzell, Angus, DD9 7TF
Tel: 01356 648319 Fax: 01356 647333
Email: gleneskhotel@btconnect.com
Web: www.gleneskhotel.co.uk
Rooms: 24 all ensuite ⛵
Pricing: Sgl £65–75 Dbl £100–110
Dinner available from £25–30 CC: Accepted
Room facilities: ▢ ☎ ☕
Conference: 3 meeting rooms (Thtr 120 max), 24hr-delegate from £85, day-delegate from £20
Children: Welcome ⫚ Dogs: Welcome
Licenses: ⟁ ⦙⦙⦙
Leisure: Indoor pool, Gym, Golf, Games room, Snooker/billiards
Parking: Off-street and free
Directions: 3 miles off A90. 30 miles north of Dundee. 40 miles south of Aberdeen.
Map ref: Edzell 15 E4
See advert on opposite page

Falkirk, Stirlingshire

The Antonine Hotel

★★

1 Manor Street, Falkirk, Stirlingshire, FK1 1NT
Tel: 01324 624066 Fax: 01324 611785
Email: sales@antoninehotel.com
Web: www.antonine.com
Rooms: 33 all ensuite ⦿
Pricing: Sgl £49.95 Dbl £69.95
Dinner available from £5.99–20
CC: Accepted
Room facilities: ▢ ☎ ☕
Access: ⦙⦙⦙
Conference: 3 meeting rooms (Thtr 120 max)
Children: Welcome ⫚
Dogs: Assistance dogs only
Licenses: ⦙⦙⦙
Parking: Off-street and free
Map ref: Falkirk 13 D2

Falkland, Fife

Covenanter Hotel

◆◆◆☂☂

The Square, Falkland, Fife, KY15 7BU
Tel: 01337 857224 Fax: 01337 857163
Email: convenanterhotel@aol.com
Web: www.covenanterhotel.com
Rooms: 5 all ensuite ⛵ ⦿
Pricing: Sgl £42–45 Dbl £52–65
Dinner available from £12
CC: Accepted
Room facilities: ▢ ☕
Conference: 2 meeting rooms (Thtr 35 max)
Children: Welcome ⫚
Licenses: ⦙⦙⦙
Parking: Off-street and free
Directions: In main square of Falkland just opposite Parish Church and few yards from palace.
Map ref: Falkland 13 D2

Scotland

Fintry, Stirling

Culcreuch Castle Hotel

★★★

Culcreuch Castle & Country Park, Fintry,
Stirling, G63 0LW
Tel: 01360 860555 Fax: 01360 860556
Email: info@culcreuch.com
Web: www.culcreuch.com

Romantic 700 year old castle set in 1600 acres of
parkland encompassed by stunning Highland scenery.
Ensuite four poster bedrooms, candlelit dinners, log
fires, cosy bar, welcoming staff.
Rooms: 14 all ensuite
Pricing: Sgl £70–115 Dbl £90–180
Dinner available from £27.50 CC: Accepted
Room facilities:
Conference: 4 meeting rooms (Thtr 150 max),
24hr-delegate from £97.50, day-delegate from £27.50
Children: Welcome
Licenses: Leisure: Fishing
Parking: Off-street and free
Directions: From Stirling take A811 west to Kippen,
then B822 southwest to Fintry. From Glasgow take
A81 north to Killearn, then B818 east to Fintry.
Map ref: Fintry 12 C2

Forres, Moray

Ramnee Hotel

★★★★

Victoria Road, Forres, Moray, IV36 3BN
Tel: 01309 672410 Fax: 01309 673392
Email: ramneehotel@btconnect.com
Web: www.ramneehotel.com
Rooms: 20 all ensuite
Pricing: Dinner available from £24
Room facilities:
Conference: 3 meeting rooms (Thtr 120 max),
24hr-delegate from £124.50, day-delegate from £24.50
Children: Welcome Dogs: Welcome
Licenses:
Leisure: Facilities of sister hotel, Leisure club
Parking: Off-street
Directions: From A96 Inverness-Aberdeen road at
Forres, turn left onto Forres bypass east of town. Hotel
is 500m on right.
Map ref: Forres 15 E2

Fort William, Highland

Inverlochy Castle Hotel

★★★★★

Torlundy, Fort William, Highland, PH33 6SN
Tel: 01397 702177 Fax: 01397 702953
Email: info@inverlochy.com
Web: www.inverlochycastlehotel.com
Seasonal closure: 6 January to 4 February

Inverlochy Castle built in 1863 near the site of the original
XIIIth century fortress, nestles in the foothills of Ben Nevis,
sitting amidst some of Scotland's finest scenery once
enjoyed by Queen Victoria herself. The beauty and
tranquility of the castle's setting is remarkable, and in
keeping with the grandeur of its surroundings.
Rooms: 18 all ensuite
Pricing: Sgl £300–410 Dbl £360–580
Dinner available from £52.50 CC: Accepted
Room facilities:
Conference: 3 meeting rooms (Thtr 50 max),
24hr-delegate from £280
Children: Welcome Dogs: Welcome
Licenses:
Leisure: Tennis, Fishing, Games room,
Snooker/billiards
Parking: Off-street and free
Directions: Accessible from the A82 trunk road from
Glasgow to Fort William. 3 miles north of Fort William,
towards Inverness on the A82.
Map ref: Torlundy 14 C4

Grand Hotel

★★★★

Gordon Square, Fort William, Highland, PH33 6DX
Tel: 01397 702928 Fax: 01397 702928
Email: grandhotel.scotland@virgin.net
Web: www.grandhotel-scotland.co.uk
Seasonal closure: 30 December to 10 February
Rooms: 30 all ensuite
Pricing: Sgl £39.50–49.50 Dbl £59–79
Dinner available from £20 CC: Accepted
Room facilities: Children: Welcome
Licenses:
Parking: Off-street and free
Directions: Located in the town centre at the west end
of the pedestrianised high street. Parking is to front
and rear of hotel.
Map ref: Fort William 14 C4

Moorings Hotel

★★★★

Banavie, Fort William, Highland, PH33 7LY
Tel: 01397 772797 Fax: 01397 772441
Email: reservations@moorings-fortwilliam.co.uk
Web: www.moorings-fortwilliam.co.uk
Rooms: 28 all ensuite 🛇 🚭
Pricing: Sgl £43–110 Dbl £86–130
Dinner available from £26
CC: Accepted
Room facilities: 🖵 ☎ ☕ 📞
Conference: 1 meeting room (Thtr 120 max),
24hr-delegate from £125, day-delegate from £15
Children: Welcome � Dogs: Welcome
Licenses: ⬦ ♦♦♦
Parking: Off-street and free
Directions: Follow A82, turn onto A830 for approx one
mile, turn right into B8004 Banavie.
Map ref: Banavie 14 C4

Distillery House

◆◆◆◆ ✖

North Road, Nevis Bridge, Fort William,
Highland, PH33 6LR
Tel: 01397 700103 Fax: 01397 702980
Email: disthouse@aol.com
Web: www.visit-fortwilliam.co.uk/Distillery-House
Rooms: 10 all ensuite 🛇 🚭
Pricing: Sgl £25–40 Dbl £50–95
CC: Accepted
Room facilities: 🖵 ☕
Children: Welcome
Dogs: Welcome
Parking: Off-street and free
Directions: From the north, turn right at second set of
traffic lights. From the south, the hotel is on the left
after Glen Nevis roundabout, which is the third
roundabout.
Map ref: Nevis Bridge 14 C4

Galashiels, Scottish Borders

Kingsknowes Hotel

★★★★

1 Selkirk Road, Galashiels, Scottish Borders, TD1 3HY
Tel: 01896 758375 Fax: 01896 750377
Email: enquiries@kingsknowes.co.uk
Web: www.kingsknowes.co.uk
Rooms: 12 all ensuite 🛇 🚭
Pricing: Sgl £59–75 Dbl £89–110
Dinner available from £17.50
CC: Accepted
Room facilities: 🖵 ☎ ☕ 📞
Conference: 3 meeting rooms (Thtr 60 max),
24hr-delegate from £72.75, day-delegate from £13.75
Children: Welcome � 🐾 Dogs: Welcome
Licenses: ⬦ ♦♦♦
Parking: Off-street and free
Directions: From Edinburgh, or Junction 40 of M6, follow A7
to Galashiels. From Newcastle, follow A68 to Galashiels.
Map ref: Galashiels 13 E3

Glasgow

Millennium Hotel Glasgow

★★★★★

40 George Square, Glasgow, G2 1DS
Tel: 0141 332 6711 Fax: 0141 332 4264
Email: reservations.glasgow@mill-cop.com
Web: www.millenniumhotels.com

MILLENNIUM
HOTELS AND RESORTS

MILLENNIUM HOTELS
COPTHORNE HOTELS

A Victorian building at the heart of this vibrant and
welcoming city, offers a relaxed environment with
contemporary interiors, complemented by a
fashionable conservatory overlooking George Square.
Rooms: 117 all ensuite 🛇 🚭
Pricing: Sgl £190.75 Dbl £206.50
Dinner available from £15 CC: Accepted
Room facilities: 🖵 ☎ ☕ 📞 ❄ Access: ♿
Conference: 6 meeting rooms (Thtr 40 max),
24hr-delegate from £165, day-delegate from £45
Children: Welcome �
Licenses: ♦♦♦
Directions: Exit M8 Junction 15, straight through four
sets traffic lights, turn left at fifth, George Square is
directly ahead.
Map ref: Glasgow 12 C2

Dalmeny Park Country House Hotel

★★★

Lochilbo Road, Glasgow, G78 1LG
Tel: 0141 881 9211 Fax: 0141 881 9214
Email: luxury@dalmenypark.com
Web: www.dalmenypark.com
Rooms: 20 all ensuite 📠 🚭
Pricing: Sgl £67–87 Dbl £87–175
Dinner available from £14 CC: Accepted
Room facilities: 🖵 ☎ ☕
Conference: 4 meeting rooms (Thtr 250 max),
24hr-delegate from £128, day-delegate from £28
Children: Welcome � Dogs: Welcome
Licenses: ⬦ ♦♦♦
Parking: Off-street and free
Directions: Follow A736 through Barrhead towards
Irvine. Hotel is on the right as you leave Barrhead.
Map ref: Glasgow 12 C2

Scotland

Jurys Glasgow Hotel

★★★

Great Western Road, Glasgow, G12 0XP
Tel: 0141 334 8161 Fax: 0141 334 3846
Email: bookings@jurysdoyle.com
Web: www.jurysdoyle.com

JURYS DOYLE
H O T E L S

Rooms: 137 all ensuite ⊗
Pricing: Sgl £51–145 Dbl £60–154
Dinner available from £20.50 CC: Accepted
Room facilities: ▢ ☎ ⊙ ⌁ Access: ♿
Conference: 5 meeting rooms (Thtr 140 max),
24hr-delegate from £132, day-delegate from £29
Children: Welcome ♀
Licenses: ⚖ ♦♦♦
Leisure: Indoor pool, Gym, Health spa
Parking: Off-street and free
Directions: Located 7 miles/11 km from Glasgow
International Airport. Central Station 3 miles/5 km, just
10 mins from bustling city centre.
Map ref: Glasgow 12 C2

Jurys Inn Glasgow

★★★

80 Jamaica Street, Glasgow, G1 4QE
Tel: 0141 314 4800 Fax: 0141 314 4888
Email: bookings@jurysdoyle.com
Web: www.jurysinns.com
Seasonal closure: 24-26 December

JURYS DOYLE
H O T E L S

Rooms: 321 all ensuite ⚒ ⊗
Pricing: Sgl £150 Dbl £159
Dinner available from £19
CC: Accepted
Room facilities: ▢ ☎ ⊙ ⌁ ❋ Access: ♿
Conference: 10 meeting rooms (Thtr 90 max),
24hr-delegate from £116, day-delegate from £37
Children: Welcome ♀ Licenses: ♦♦♦
Directions: Exit 19 off M8 onto Bothwell Street. Left
onto Hope Street. Right onto West George Street.
Right onto Renfield Street leads to Jamaica Street.
Map ref: Glasgow 12 C2

Kings Park Hotel

★★★

Mill Street, Rutherglen, Glasgow, G73 2AR
Tel: 0141 647 5491 Fax: 0141 613 3022
Email: info@kingsparkhotel.com
Web: www.kingsparkhotel.com
Rooms: 26 all ensuite ⊗
Pricing: Sgl £45–100 Dbl £60–110
Dinner available from £21
CC: Accepted
Room facilities: ▢ ☎ ⊙ ⌁
Conference: 3 meeting rooms (Thtr 220 max),
24hr-delegate from £95, day-delegate from £20
Children: Welcome ♀ ⚙ Dogs: Welcome

Licenses: ⚖ ♦♦♦ Parking: Off-street and free
Directions: Follow A730 from Glasgow towards East
Kilbride. Hotel is situated on the left in the suburb on
Rutherglen.
Map ref: Rutherglen 12 C2

Quality Hotel Glasgow

★★★

99 Gordon Street, Glasgow, G1 3SF
Tel: 0141 221 9680 Fax: 0141 226 3948
Email: enquiries@quality-hotels-glasgow.com
Web: www.choicehotelseurope.com
Rooms: 222 all ensuite ⚒ ⊗
Pricing: Sgl £122.20 Dbl £144.65–155.15
Dinner available from £14.95
CC: Accepted
Room facilities: ▢ ☎ ⊙ ⌁ Access: ♿
Conference: 21 meeting rooms (Thtr 600 max),
24hr-delegate from £126, day-delegate from £35
Children: Welcome ♀ Dogs: Welcome
Licenses: ⚖ ♦♦♦
Leisure: Indoor pool, Gym, Health spa, Beauty salon
Parking: Off-street
Directions: From M8 Westbound take Junction 19 onto
Argyle Street and left onto Oswald Street. NCP car
park on right.
Map ref: Glasgow 12 C2

Sherbrooke Castle Hotel

★★★★ ⚘ ⚘

11 Sherbrooke Avenue, Pollokshields, Glasgow, G41 4PG
Tel: 0141 427 4227 Fax: 0141 427 5685
Email: mail@sherbrooke.co.uk
Web: www.sherbrooke.co.uk
Rooms: 21 all ensuite ⚒ ⊞ ⊗
Dinner CC: Accepted
Room facilities: ▢ ☎ ☎ ⊙
Conference: 4 meeting rooms (Thtr 200 max)
Children: Welcome ♀ Dogs: Welcome
Licenses: ⚖ ♦♦♦
Parking: Off-street and free
Directions: Close to Junction 1 M77. Close to
Junctions 22 and 23 from City M8. Close to Junction
27 from Glasgow Airport.
Map ref: Pollokshields 12 C2

Smiths Hotel

★★★

David Donnelly Place, Kirkintilloch, Glasgow, G66 1DD
Tel: 0141 7750398 Fax: 0141 7767643
Email: reception@smithshotel.com
Web: www.smithshotel.com
Rooms: 20 all ensuite ⚒ ⊗
Pricing: Sgl £50–60 Dbl £60–75
Dinner available from £7.95–12.95
CC: Accepted
Room facilities: ▢ ⊙
Conference: 3 meeting rooms (Thtr 200 max),
24hr-delegate from £100, day-delegate from £100
Children: Welcome ♀

Licenses: Leisure: Golf, Games room
Parking: Off-street and free
Directions: Exit 2 of M80 onto Lenzie Road. Follow road ahead at two mini-roundabouts, under railway bridge. Follow signs for Kirkintilloch.
Map ref: Kirkintilloch 12 C2
See advert on this page

The Glynhill Hotel & Leisure Club
★★★

169 Paisley Road, Renfrew, near Glasgow Airport, Glasgow, PA4 8XB
Tel: 0141 886 5555 Fax: 0141 885 2838
Email: glynhillleisurehotel@msn.com
Web: www.glynhill.com
Rooms: 145 all ensuite
Pricing: Sgl £79–125 Dbl £85–250
Dinner available from £21–25
CC: Accepted
Room facilities:
Conference: 1 meeting room (Thtr 400 max), 24hr-delegate from £125, day-delegate from £27
Children: Welcome
Dogs: Assistance dogs only
Licenses:
Leisure: Indoor pool, Gym, Health spa, Beauty salon
Parking: Off-street and free
Directions: On M8 towards Glasgow Airport, turn off at J27. Take A741 towards Renfrew Cross. Hotel on right.
Map ref: Renfrew 12 C2

The Lomond Hotel
◆◆◆

6 Buckingham Terrace, Great Western Road, Glasgow, G12 8EB
Tel: 0141 339 2339 Fax: 0141 339 0477
Email: info@lomondhotel.co.uk
Web: www.lomondhotel.co.uk
Rooms: 17 (6 ensuite)
Pricing: Sgl £25–45 Dbl £44–60
CC: Accepted
Room facilities:
Children: Welcome
Parking: Off-street and free
Directions: M8 J17 onto A82 (Great Western Road). Halfway along turn left into Buckingham Terrace.
Map ref: Glasgow 12 C2

The Merchant Lodge
◆◆◆

52 Virginia Street, Glasgow, G1 1TY
Tel: 0141 552 2424 Fax: 0141 552 4747
Email: reservations@merchantlodgehotel.com
Web: www.merchantlodgehotel.com
Rooms: 40 all ensuite
Pricing: Sgl £40–50 Dbl £62–80
CC: Accepted
Room facilities: Access:
Children: Welcome
Dogs: Welcome
Map ref: Glasgow 12 C2

Scotland

The Townhouse Hotel

 ◆◆◆

21 Royal Crescent, Glasgow, G3 7SL
Tel: 0141 332 9009 Fax: 0141 353 2143
Email: reservations@thetownhousehotelglasgow.com
Web: www.thetownhousehotelglasgow.com
Rooms: 19 (17 ensuite)
Room facilities: ☐ ☎ ☕
Children: Welcome
Dogs: Welcome
Parking: Off-street and free
Map ref: Glasgow 12 C2

Charing Cross Guest House

 ◆◆

310 Renfrew Street, Glasgow, G3 6UW
Tel: 0141 332 2503 Fax: 0141 353 3047
Email: enquiries@charing-x.com
Web: www.charing-x.com
Rooms: 25 (10 ensuite)
CC: Accepted
Room facilities: ☐ ☎ ☕ ⬚ Children: Welcome
Parking: Off-street
Directions: Exit J18 M8, Charing Cross, take first left
for Sauchiehall Street and then two first lefts onto
Renfrew Street.
Map ref: Glasgow 12 C2

Georgian House

◆

29 Buckingham Terrace, Great Western Road,
Kelvinside, Glasgow, G12 8ED
Tel: 0141 339 0008
Email: thegeorgianhouse@yahoo.com
Web: www.thegeorgianhousehotel.com

This restored Georgian town house residence retains
many original features to create stylish comfort in the
midst of the vibrant West End. Overlooking the Botanic
Garden, close to restaurants, theatres and major
sights.

Rooms: 12 (9 ensuite) ⬚ ⬚ ⬚
CC: Accepted
Room facilities: ☐ ☕ ⬚
Children: Welcome ⬚ ⬚
Parking: Off-street and free
Directions: Exit Junction 17, M8, onto Great Western
Road. 1½ miles, right at Botanic Gardens 360° at
roundabout, second left Buckingham Terrace.
Map ref: Kelvinside 12 C2

Campanile Glasgow
Travel Accommodation

10 Tunnel Street, Glasgow, G3 8HL
Tel: 0141 287 7700 Fax: 0141 287 7701
Email: glasgow@campanile.com
Web: www.campanile.com

Campanile hotels offer comfortable and convenient
budget accommodation and a traditional French-style
Bistro providing freshly-cooked food for breakfast,
lunch and dinner. All rooms ensuite with tea/coffee-
making facilities, DDT and TV with satellite channels.
Rooms: 106 all ensuite ⬚
Pricing: Sgl £51.90–85 Dbl £57.85–85
Dinner available from £13
CC: Accepted
Room facilities: ☐ ☎ ☕ ❄
Access: ⬚
Conference: 5 meeting rooms (Thtr 120 max),
24hr-delegate from £88, day-delegate from £25
Children: Welcome ⬚
Dogs: Welcome
Licenses: ⬚
Parking: Off-street and free
Directions: Exit 19 on the M8. Follow SECC signs.
Map ref: Glasgow 12 C2

Sleep easy

Rest assured. Our com-
prehensive inspection
process includes
checking beds are
comfortable.

Grantown-on-Spey, Moray

Culdearn House Hotel

★★

Woodlands Terrace, Grantown-on-Spey,
Moray, PH26 3JU
Tel: 01479 872106 Fax: 01479 873641
Email: enquiries@culdearn.com
Web: www.culdearn.com
Seasonal closure: December to February

Small privately-owned country hotel, situated in the
heart of Speyside offering a blend of warmth, elegance
and informality. With just seven bedrooms each guest
is welcomed as a friend.
Rooms: 7 all ensuite ☺
Pricing: Sgl £45–55 Dbl £90–110
Dinner available from £30
CC: Accepted
Room facilities: ☐ ☕
Children: Welcome 12yrs min age
Licenses: ♦♦♦
Parking: Off-street and free
Directions: Enter Grantown from southwest on A95.
Turn left at 30mph sign. House opposite.
Map ref: Grantown-on-Spey 15 E3

The Pines

★★★☺☺ Commended

Woodside Avenue, Grantown-on-Spey,
Moray, PH26 3JR
Tel: 01479 872092 Fax: 01479 872092
Email: info@thepinesgrantown.co.uk
Web: www.thepinesgrantown.co.uk
Seasonal closure: November to February
Rooms: 8 all ensuite ☺
Pricing: Sgl £55–73 Dbl £90–125
Dinner available from £30
CC: Accepted
Room facilities: ☐ ☕
Children: Welcome 12yrs min age
Dogs: Welcome
Licenses: ♦♦♦
Parking: Off-street and free
Directions: On entering the town from the south take
A939 to Tomintoul, then turn first right.
Map ref: Grantown-on-Spey 15 E3

Ravenscourt House Hotel

◆◆◆◆◆

Seafield Avenue, Grantown-on-Spey, Moray, PH26 3JG
Tel: 01479 872286 Fax: 01479 873260
Rooms: 8 all ensuite ☺☺ ☺
Pricing: Sgl £35–40 Dbl £76–90 Dinner available
CC: Accepted
Room facilities: ☐ ☕
Children: Welcome Dogs: Welcome
Licenses: ♦♦♦
Parking: Off-street and free
Directions: Turn left at Bank of Scotland. Ravenscourt
is 200m on right-hand side.
Map ref: Grantown-on-Spey 15 E3

Gretna, Dumfries & Galloway

Gretna Chase Hotel

★★★

Sark Bridge, Gretna, Dumfries & Galloway, DG16 5JB
Tel: 01461 337517 Fax: 01461 337766
Email: enquiries@gretnachase.co.uk
Web: www.gretnachase.co.uk
Rooms: 20 all ensuite ☺☺ ☺ ☺
Pricing: Sgl £69–99 Dbl £92.50–185 Dinner available
CC: Accepted
Room facilities: ☐ ☎ ☕ ☕
Children: Welcome ♦ Licenses: ♦♦♦
Parking: Off-street and free
Directions: 6 miles north of J44, take slip road for
Gretna. Turn left at junction; hotel is 600 yards on right.
Map ref: Gretna 13 D4

Solway Lodge Hotel

★★

Annan Road, Gretna, Dumfries & Galloway, DG16 5DN
Tel: 01461 338266 Fax: 01461 337791
Web: www.solwaylodge.co.uk
Rooms: 10 all ensuite ☺ CC: Accepted
Room facilities: ☐ ☎ ☕
Children: Welcome Dogs: Welcome
Licenses: ♦♦♦ Parking: Off-street
Directions: From south, take second exit at roundabout
('Town'). Lodge 200m on right.
Map ref: Gretna 13 D4

Surrone House Hotel

◆◆◆

Annan Road, Gretna, Dumfries & Galloway, DG16 5DL
Tel: 01461 338341 Fax: 01461 338341
Email: enquiries@surronehouse.co.uk
Web: www.surronehouse.co.uk
Rooms: 7 (6 ensuite) ☺☺ ☺ ☺
Pricing: Sgl £45–50 Dbl £55–60
Dinner available from £10.50 CC: Accepted
Room facilities: ☐ ☕ Children: Welcome
Licenses: ♦♦♦ Parking: Off-street and free
Directions: On main road through Gretna (not the
bypass).
Map ref: Gretna 13 D4

Scotland

Haddington, East Lothian

Eaglescairnie Mains

By Gifford, Haddington, East Lothian, EH41 4HN
Tel: 01620 810491 Fax: 01620 810491
Email: williams.eagles@btinternet.com
Web: www.eaglescairnie.com
Seasonal closure: Christmas week

Beautifully furnished farmhouse on a 350-acre
conservation award-winning working farm – tranquility,
stunning views, farm walks. 30 minutes from
Edinburgh, the Borders, golf courses galore, Seabird
Centre, Glenkinche distillery and Concord.
Rooms: 3 all ensuite
Pricing: Sgl £35–45 Dbl £60–70
CC: Accepted
Room facilities:
Children: Welcome
Dogs: Welcome
Leisure: Tennis, Farm walks
Parking: Off-street and free
Directions: A1 Haddington; B6368 Bolton and Humbie;
1/4 mile after Bolton fork left signed Eaglescairnie. 1/2
mile up hill on left.
Map ref: Haddington 13 E2

Helensburgh, Argyll & Bute

Kirkton House   Little Gem

Darleith Road, Cardross, Argyll & Bute, G82 5EZ
Tel: 01389 841951 Fax: 01389 841868
Email: rac@kirktonhouse.co.uk
Web: www.kirktonhouse.co.uk
Seasonal closure: December and January

Converted 18th century farmstead in tranquil country
setting with panoramic views of the Clyde and
surrounding hills, informal and unpretentious, ideal
base for Loch Lomond, Glasgow and the West
Highland.
Rooms: 6 all ensuite
Pricing: Sgl £37.50–40 Dbl £50–60
CC: Accepted
Room facilities:
Children: Welcome
Dogs: Welcome
Licenses:
Parking: Off-street
Directions: Turn north off A814 at the west end of
Cardross Village, up Darleith Road. Kirkton is 1/2 mile
on right.
Map ref: Cardross 12 C2

Halkirk, Highland

Ulbster Arms Hotel

Bridge Street, Halkirk, Highland, KW12 6XY
Tel: 01847 831641 Fax: 01847 831206
Email: ulbster-arms@ecosse.net
Web: www.ulbsterarms.co.uk
Rooms: 10 all ensuite
Dinner available CC: Accepted
Room facilities:
Conference: 1 meeting room (Thtr 14 max)
Children: Welcome
Dogs: Welcome
Licenses:
Leisure: Fishing
Parking: Off-street
Directions: 5 miles from main town of Thurso, 13 miles
from Dounreay.
Map ref: Halkirk 15 E1

Innerleithen, Scottish Borders

Corner House Hotel

1 Chapel Street, Innerleithen, Tweedale,
Scottish Borders, EH44 6HN
Tel: 01896 831181 Fax: 01896 831182
Email: cornerhousehotel@talk21.com
Seasonal closure: one week in October
Rooms: 6 all ensuite
Dinner available
CC: Accepted
Room facilities:
Children: Welcome
Dogs: Welcome
Licenses:
Parking: Off-street
Directions: Follow A703 from Edinburgh to Peebles,
then take the A72 to Innerleithen, approximately 25
miles.
Map ref: Innerleithen 13 D3

Invergarry, Highland

Glengarry Castle Hotel

★★★

Invergarry, Highland, PH35 4HW
Tel: 01809 501254 Fax: 01809 501207
Email: castle@glengarry.net
Web: www.glengarry.net
Seasonal closure: mid-November to mid-March
Rooms: 26 (25 ensuite) 🗗 ⊛
Pricing: Sgl £58–85 Dbl £86–160
Dinner available from £28
CC: Accepted
Room facilities: 🗖 ☎ 🕾 🔧
Children: Welcome ⏰ ۩
Dogs: Welcome
Licenses: ﷺ
Leisure: Tennis, Fishing
Parking: Off-street and free
Directions: Located on the A82, overlooking Loch
Oich, 1 mile from Invergarry.
Map ref: Invergarry 14 C3

Inverness, Highland

Culloden House Hotel

Commended

★★★★★

Milton of Culloden, Culloden, Inverness,
Inverness-shire, IV2 7BZ
Tel: 01463 790461 Fax: 01463 792181
Email: info@cullodenhouse.co.uk
Web: www.cullodenhouse.co.uk
Seasonal closure: Christmas

A lodging of Bonnie Prince Charlie in the 1700s, today
this handsome Palladian country house stands in 40
acres of elegant lawns and parkland. Inside, the
magnificent drawing-room has many fine antiques and
a large open fire.
Rooms: 28 all ensuite 🍽 🗗 ⊛
Pricing: Sgl £85–285 Dbl £140–290
Dinner available from £30–40
CC: Accepted
Room facilities: 🗖 ☎ 🕾
Conference: 3 meeting rooms (Thtr 60 max),
24hr-delegate from £150, day-delegate from £30
Children: Welcome 10yrs min age ⏰ ۩
Dogs: Welcome
Licenses: ﷺ ۩   Leisure: Tennis
Parking: Off-street and free
Directions: Follow A96, take turning for Culloden,
Smithton and Balloch. Through two sets of traffic
lights, turn left at church, continue 200 yards.
Map ref: Culloden 15 D3

Loch Ness House Hotel

★★★

Glenurquhart Road, Inverness, Highland, IV3 8JL
Tel: 01463 231248 Fax: 01463 239327
Email: lnhhchris@aol.com
Web: www.smoothhound.co.uk/hotels/lochness.html
Rooms: 22 all ensuite 🍽 🗗
Dinner available
CC: Accepted
Room facilities: 🗖 ☎ 🕾
Children: Welcome ⏰
Dogs: Welcome
Licenses: ﷺ ۩
Parking: Off-street and free
Directions: Situated on A82 (Fort William). From A9,
turn left at Longman roundabout, follow A82 signs for
2½ miles. Beside Torvean golf course and Caledonian
Canal.
Map ref: Inverness 15 D3

Lochardil House Hotel

★★★★

Stratherrick Road, Inverness, Highland, IV2 4LF
Tel: 01463 235995 Fax: 01463 713394
Email: reservations@lochardil.co.uk
Web: www.bw-lochardilhouse.co.uk
Seasonal closure: 24 December to 4 January
Rooms: 12 all ensuite ⊛
Pricing: Sgl £85–95 Dbl £115
Dinner available from £20
CC: Accepted
Room facilities: 🗖 ☎ 🕾 🔧
Conference: 4 meeting rooms (Thtr 200 max),
day-delegate from £37.60
Children: Welcome ⏰
Dogs: Assistance dogs only
Licenses: ﷺ ۩
Parking: Off-street and free
Directions: From A9 police HQ take Sir Walter Scott
Drive through more roundabouts. Turn right onto
Straterrick Road. Hotel is 500 yards.
Map ref: Inverness 15 D3

Scotland

Priory Hotel

★★★

The Square, Beauly, Highland, IV4 7BX
Tel: 01463 782309 Fax: 01463 782531
Email: reservations@priory-hotel.com
Web: www.priory-hotel.com

Located in the picturesque village square of Beauly,
The Priory is an ideal touring base for all visitors. Our
regular corporate customers always enjoy the excellent
quality accommodation, food and service.
Rooms: 36 all ensuite 🛏 🚭
Pricing: Sgl £42.50–52.50 Dbl £42.50–52.50
Dinner available from £12.50–250
CC: Accepted
Room facilities: 🖵 ☎ ☕ 🐾 Access: ♿
Children: Welcome ♁ ☕
Dogs: Assistance dogs only
Licenses: ◈ ♨
Leisure: Games room, Snooker/billiards
Parking: Off-street and free
Directions: A9 bypass Inverness approximately 5 miles
to Tore roundabout. Exit first left, follow sign for
Beauly. Hotel is in village square.
Map ref: Beauly 15 D3

Royal Highland Hotel

★★★

Station Square, 18 Academy Street, Inverness,
Highland, IV1 1LG
Tel: 01463 231926 Fax: 01463 710705
Email: info@royalhighlandhotel.co.uk
Web: www.royalhighlandhotel.co.uk

A non-smoking guest house within walking distance of
the town centre, with a reputation for good food, warm
welcome and Highland hospitality. All rooms are
furnished to a high standard with guests' comfort a
priority.
Rooms: 70 all ensuite 🛏 🚭 🚭
Pricing: Sgl £89.95–99.95 Dbl £129.95–149.95
Dinner available from £20–30 CC: Accepted
Room facilities: 🖵 ☎ ☕ 🐾
Access: ♿
Conference: 3 meeting rooms (Thtr 200 max),
24hr-delegate from £99, day-delegate from £28
Children: Welcome ♁ Dogs: Welcome
Licenses: ◈ ♨
Parking: Off-street and free
Directions: Follow signs for city centre, hotel is
adjacent to railway station.
Map ref: Inverness 15 D3

Moyness House

◆◆◆◆◆

6 Bruce Gardens, Inverness, Highland, IV3 5EN
Tel: 01463 233836 Fax: 01463 233836
Email: stay@moyness.co.uk
Web: www.moyness.co.uk

Top awards (Visit Scotland 5 Stars, AA 5 Diamonds).
Beautiful Victorian villa, conveniently located in quiet
street near city centre, Edencourt Theatre, and
riverside. 7 charming rooms, all ensuite. Ample
parking.
Rooms: 7 all ensuite 🚭
Pricing: Sgl £35–38 Dbl £70–76 CC: Accepted
Room facilities: 🖵 ☕
Children: Welcome Dogs: Welcome
Parking: Off-street and free
Directions: From A9 (North/South) or A862 follow signs
for A82, Fort William Road. From A82, Bruce Gardens
opposite Highland Council Offices.
Map ref: Inverness 15 D3

Westbourne Guest House

50 Huntly Street, Inverness, Highland, IV3 5HS
Tel: 01463 220700 Fax: 01463 220700
Email: richard@westbourne.org.uk
Web: www.westbourne.org.uk
Rooms: 10 all ensuite
Pricing: Sgl £30–40 Dbl £60–80 CC: Accepted
Room facilities:
Children: Welcome Dogs: Welcome
Parking: Off-street and free
Directions: Leave A9 at A82. Proceed straight over
three roundabouts, cross Friars Bridge. Take first left
into Wells Street, then into Huntly Street.
Map ref: Inverness 15 D3
See advert on following page

Inverurie, Aberdeenshire

Strathburn Hotel

★★★

Burghmuir Drive, Inverurie, Aberdeenshire, AB51 4GY
Tel: 01467 624422 Fax: 01467 625133
Email: strathburn@btconnect.com
Web: www.strathburn-hotel.co.uk
Seasonal closure: 25-26 December and 1-2 January
Rooms: 25 all ensuite
Pricing: Sgl £55–75 Dbl £75–95
Dinner available from £18.75 CC: Accepted
Room facilities:
Conference: 1 meeting room (Thtr 30 max),
24hr-delegate from £105, day-delegate from £18
Children: Welcome Dogs: Welcome
Licenses: Parking: Off-street and free
Directions: From Aberdeen Airport head north on A96
for 10 miles. Blackhall roundabout (Safeways) turn
right then left at next roundabout.
Map ref: Inverurie 15 F3

Isle of Arran, North Ayrshire

Kinloch Hotel

★★★

Blackwaterfoot, Brodick, Isle of Arran,
North Ayrshire, KA27 8ET
Tel: 01770 860444 Fax: 01770 860447
Email: reservations@kinlochhotel.eclipse.co.uk
Web: www.kinloch-arran.com
Rooms: 43 all ensuite
Dinner available CC: Accepted
Room facilities:
Access:
Conference: 3 meeting rooms (Thtr 150 max)
Children: Welcome Dogs: Welcome
Licenses:
Leisure: Indoor pool, Gym, Beauty salon, Games room,
Snooker/billiards
Parking: Off-street and free
Directions: Ferry from Ardrossan; take B880 and follow
signs for Blackwaterfoot. Hotel is in centre of village.
Map ref: Blackwaterfoot 12 B3

Isle of Islay, Argyll & Bute

Port Askaig Hotel

★★

Port Askaig, Isle of Islay, Argyll & Bute, PA46 7RD
Tel: 01496 840245 Fax: 01496 840295
Email: hotel@portaskaig.co.uk
Web: www.portaskaig.co.uk

This 400-year-old inn overlooks the Sound-of-Islay, the
picturesque harbour and lifeboat station. Situated in
own gardens. The best of home-cooked food. Bars
open all day.
Rooms: 8 (6 ensuite)
Pricing: Sgl £25–34 Dbl £50–85
Dinner available from £25
CC: Accepted
Room facilities:
Conference: 1 meeting room,
24hr-delegate from £60, day-delegate from £20
Children: Welcome 5yrs min age
Dogs: Welcome
Licenses:
Leisure: Snooker/billiards, Occasional live music.
Parking: Off-street and free
Directions: Harbourside at Port Askaig ferry terminal.
From Port Ellen terminal or from Islay airport follow
straight route through Bowmore and Bridgend.
Map ref: Port Askaig 12 A2

"I do!"

Want a honeymoon hotel? Look
for our Gold, Blue, and White
Ribbon Award winning hotels.

Scotland

WESTBOURNE GUEST HOUSE

Situated overlooking the River Ness. Clean, comfortable, friendly accommodation. All rooms individually decorated to a high standard with a Tartan theme. Five minutes walk from city centre. Easy access to Bus, Train & Airport. Ideal location for touring the Highlands. Richard & Nan look forward to welcoming you to Westbourne.

50 Huntly Street, Inverness, Highland, IV3 5HS
Tel: 01463 220700 Fax: 01463 220700
Email: richard@westbourne.org.uk
Web: www.westbourne.org.uk

Isle of Mull, Argyll & Bute

The Western Isles Hotel

★★★

Tobermory, Isle of Mull, Argyll & Bute, PA75 6PR
Tel: 01688 302012 Fax: 01688 302297
Email: wihotel@aol.com
Web: www.mullhotel.com
Seasonal closure: 18–28 December

A Victorian hotel with stunning views overlooking the Sound of Mull. Situated above picturesque Tobermory, offering good food, fine wines and whiskies, this is a haven of comfort and relaxation.
Rooms: 28 all ensuite
Pricing: Sgl £49–55 Dbl £98–134
Dinner available from £32.95

CC: Accepted
Room facilities:
Conference: 2 meeting rooms (Thtr 60 max), 24hr-delegate from £93, day-delegate from £30
Children: Welcome
Dogs: Welcome
Licenses:
Parking: Off-street and free
Directions: Ferry from Oban to Craignure, turn right to Tobermory, left turn into Backbrae from Main Street and first right.
Map ref: Tobermory 12 A1

Highland Cottage
★★★★ Premier

Breadalbane Street, Tobermory, Isle of Mull, Argyll & Bute, PA75 6PD
Tel: 01688 302030 Fax: 01688 302727
Email: davidandjo@highlandcottage.co.uk
Web: www.highlandcottage.co.uk
Seasonal closure: Restricted opening in winter

Cosy family-run hotel in Upper Tobermory conservation area. Four-poster beds and elegant lounges. Unrivalled hospitality from resident owners. Wildlife, walking, superb scenery or just relax!
Rooms: 6 all ensuite
Pricing: Sgl £96–130 Dbl £125–165
Dinner available from £35
CC: Accepted
Room facilities:
Children: Welcome 9yrs min age
Dogs: Welcome
Licenses:
Parking: Off-street and free
Directions: From roundabout at top of town go straight across stone bridge. Immediately turn right. Hotel is on right opposite fire station.
Map ref: Tobermory 12 A1

"Here!"

Need a pet friendly property? Look out for 'Dogs welcome' in our listings.

Isle of Skye, Highland

Cuillin Hills Hotel

★★★

Portree, Isle of Skye, Highland, IV51 9QU
Tel: 01478 612003 Fax: 01478 613092
Email: info@cuillinhills-hotel-skye.co.uk
Web: www.cuillinhills-hotel-skye.co.uk
Rooms: 27 all ensuite
Pricing: Sgl £55–75 Dbl £110–230
Dinner available from £31.50–340
CC: Accepted
Room facilities:
Conference: 2 meeting rooms (Thtr 140 max),
24hr-delegate from £160, day-delegate from £18
Children: Welcome
Licenses:
Parking: Off-street and free
Directions: Turn right 1/4 mile north of Portree off the
A855 and follow signs for the hotel.
Map ref: Portree 14 B3
See advert on this page

Hotel Eilean Iarmain

★★

Isleornsay, Sleat, Isle of Skye, Highland, IV43 8QR
Tel: 01471 833332 Fax: 01471 833275
Email: bookings@eilean-iarmain.co.uk
Web: www.eileaniarmain.co.uk
Rooms: 16 all ensuite
Dinner available
Room facilities:
Children: Welcome
Dogs: Welcome Licenses:
Leisure: Fishing
Parking: Off-street
Directions: Arriving by car, cross the Skye Bridge.
Follow A850 for 7 miles, turn left onto A851 for 8
miles. Turn left at Isleornsay Road sign and drive to the
hotel on the harbour front (1/2 mile).
Map ref: Isleornsay 14 B3

Royal Hotel

★★

Bank Street, Portree, Isle of Skye, Highland, IV51 9BU
Tel: 01478 612525 Fax: 01478 613198
Email: info@royal-hotel-skye.com
Web: www.royal-hotel-skye.com
Rooms: 21 all ensuite
Pricing: Sgl £59–67.50 Dbl £76–99
Dinner available from £19.50–27
CC: Accepted
Room facilities:
Children: Welcome Dogs: Welcome
Licenses:
Leisure: Gym, Beauty salon
Parking: Off-street and free
Directions: Follow A87 from Kyle of Lochalsh across
Skye bridge to Portree. Follow A855 right. Hotel
approximately 1km on left overlooking harbour.
Map ref: Portree 14 B3

Scotland

Toravaig House Hotel

Knock Bay, Teangue Sleat, Isle of Skye,
Highland, IV44 8RE
Tel: 01471 820200 Fax: 01471 833231
Email: info@skyehotel.co.uk
Web: www.skyehotel.co.uk

Contemporary styled country house hotel with
splendid restaurant in the 'Garden of Skye'. Superb
views, sleigh beds, Sky TV in ensuite rooms, open fire.
Personally run and managed. Awarded 'Scottish Island
Hotel of the Year 2005', Red H for Hospitality and
Silver Plate for Dining (Hotel Review-Scotland).
Rooms: 9 all ensuite
Pricing: Sgl £69.50–95 Dbl £110–140
Dinner available from £22
CC: Accepted
Room facilities:
Conference: 1 meeting room,
24hr-delegate from £85, day-delegate from £25
Children: Welcome 10yrs min age
Licenses:
Parking: Off-street and free
Directions: Travel to Skye. Cross bridge, travel 7 miles,
turn left to Armadale. Hotel 11 miles on main A851. Or
3 miles north of Armadale ferry port.
Map ref: Knock Bay 14 B3

Jedburgh, Scottish Borders

Ferniehirst Mill Lodge

Jedburgh, Scottish Borders, TD8 6PQ
Tel: 01835 863279 Fax: 01835 863279
Email: ferniehirstmill@aol.com
Web: www.ferniehirstmill.co.uk
Rooms: 7 all ensuite
Pricing: Sgl £25 Dbl £50
Dinner available from £15
CC: Accepted
Room facilities:
Children: Welcome Dogs: Welcome
Licenses:
Leisure: Fishing, Riding
Parking: Off-street and free
Directions: 2¹/₂ miles south of Jedburgh, 8 miles north
of Scottish border, ¹/₃ mile off A68 on east side.
Map ref: Jedburgh 13 E3

Kelso, Scottish Borders

Cross Keys Hotel

36–37 The Square, Kelso, Scottish Borders, TD5 7HL
Tel: 01573 223303 Fax: 01573 225792
Email: cross-keys-hotel@easynet.co.uk
Web: www.cross-keys-hotel.co.uk
Rooms: 27 all ensuite
Pricing: Sgl £45.90–58 Dbl £48–98
Dinner available from £10–25
CC: Accepted
Room facilities:
Access:
Conference: 40 meeting rooms (Thtr 250 max),
24hr-delegate from £89, day-delegate from £15
Children: Welcome   Dogs: Welcome
Licenses:
Parking: Off-street and free
Map ref: Kelso 13 E3

Ednam House Hotel

Bridge Street, Kelso, Scottish Borders, TD5 7HT
Tel: 01573 224168 Fax: 01573 226319
Email: contact@ednamhouse.com
Web: www.ednamhouse.com
Seasonal closure: 24 December to 6 January
Rooms: 32 all ensuite
Pricing: Dinner available from £15
CC: Accepted
Room facilities:
Conference: 2 meeting rooms (Thtr 200 max)
Children: Welcome   Dogs: Welcome
Licenses:
Leisure: Games room
Parking: Off-street
Directions: Off the town square on Bridge Street
leading to the Abbey.
Map ref: Kelso 13 E3

Kilchrenan, Argyll & Bute

Ardanaiseig Hotel

Kilchrenan, Taynuilt, Argyll & Bute, PA35 1HE
Tel: 01866 833333 Fax: 01866 833222
Email: ardanaiseig@clara.net
Web: www.ardanaiseig.com
Rooms: 16 all ensuite
Dinner available CC: Accepted
Room facilities:
Children: Welcome   Dogs: Welcome
Licenses:
Leisure: Tennis, Fishing, Games room,
Snooker/billiards
Parking: Off-street and free
Directions: A85 Crialairich Oban turn off at Taynuilt,
B845 to Kilchrenan, turn left at pub to Ardanaiseig,
3 miles down the road.
Map ref: Ardanaiseig 12 B1

Taychreggan Hotel

★★★

Taynuilt, Kilchrenan, Argyll & Bute, PA35 1HQ
Tel: 01866 833211/366 Fax: 01866 833244
Email: info@taychregganhotel.co.uk
Web: www.tacyhregganhotel.co.uk
Rooms: 20 all ensuite
Pricing: Sgl £117 Dbl £127–250
Dinner available from £37.50
CC: Accepted
Room facilities:
Conference: 3 meeting rooms (Thtr 20 max)
Children: Welcome 14yrs min age
Dogs: Welcome
Licenses:
Leisure: Fishing, Snooker/billiards
Parking: Off-street and free
Directions: From Glasgow follow M8 to Erskine Bridge, then A82 to Tyndrum. Take A85 to Taynuilt, then B845 to Kilchrenan.
Map ref: Kilchrenan 12 B1
See advert on following page

TAYCHREGGAN

Award-winning lochside hotel set amid breathtaking Argyll scenery. Excellent wine list, shamefully large malt whisky selection. Walk, fish or simply do nothing. Just peace and tranquility.

Taynuilt, Kilchrenan,
Argyll & Bute, PA35 1HQ
Tel: 01866 833211/366
Fax: 01866 833244
info@taychregganhotel.co.uk
www.taychregganhotel.co.uk

Ice & slice? RAC's comprehensive inspection means we even check drinks are served the way you want.

Killearn, Stirlingshire

Black Bull Hotel

★★★

2 The Square, Killearn, Stirlingshire, G63 9NG
Tel: 01360 550215 Fax: 01360 550143
Email: sales@blackbullhotel.com
Web: www.blackbullhotel.com
Rooms: 14 all ensuite
Pricing: Sgl £55–70 Dbl £70–95
Dinner available from £9.95–29.50
CC: Accepted
Room facilities:
Conference: 4 meeting rooms (Thtr 60 max), 24hr-delegate from £105, day-delegate from £29.95
Children: Welcome
Dogs: Welcome
Licenses:
Parking: Off-street and free
Directions: From South: M8 J25, through Clyde tunnel and stay on A739, following Aberfoyle signs. Take A81 through Strathblane and take Killearn turning. At top of hill turn left for Black Bull. From Northeast: A811 west from Stirling towards Erskine Bridge, 2 miles after Buchylyvie turn onto A875. Go through Balfron to reach Killearn. From Northwest: A82 past Loch Lomond, follow signs for Balloch and A811. Take A809 (Glasgow) rightwards before Drymen and after 2 miles turn left for B834 to Killearn.
Map ref: Killearn 12 C2

Kingussie, Highland

The Cross At Kingussie
Restaurant with Rooms

Excellent

Tweed Mill Brae, Ardbroilach, Kingussie, Highland, PH21 1LB
Tel: 01540 661166 Fax: 01540 661080
Email: relax@thecross.co.uk
Web: www.thecross.co.uk
Seasonal closure: Christmas to January, except Hogmanay
Rooms: 8 all ensuite
Pricing: Sgl £90–190 Dbl £120–200
Dinner available from £35
CC: Accepted
Room facilities:
Conference: 1 meeting room (Thtr 20 max), 24hr-delegate from £120, day-delegate from £40
Children: Welcome 8yrs min age
Licenses:
Leisure: Pétanque
Parking: Off-street and free
Directions: At traffic lights in centre of Kingussie, turn uphill and travel along Arbroilach Road for 200 metres. Hotel on left.
Map ref: Kingussie 15 D3

Kirkcaldy, Fife

Dean Park Hotel

★★★

Chapel Level, Kirkcaldy, Fife, KY2 6QW
Tel: 01592 261635 Fax: 01592 261371
Email: info@deanparkhotel.co.uk
Web: www.deanparkhotel.co.uk
Rooms: 34 all ensuite
Dinner available CC: Accepted
Room facilities: Access:
Conference: 6 meeting rooms (Thtr 300 max)
Children: Welcome Licenses:
Parking: Off-street and free
Directions: Take A92 Edinburgh-Dunfermline road to Kirkcaldy. Take A910 to first roundabout.
Map ref: Kirkcaldy 13 D2

Strathearn Hotel

★★

2 Wishart Place, Kirkcaldy, Fife, KY1 2AS
Tel: 01592 652210 Fax: 01592 654731
Web: www.thestrathearnhotel.com
Rooms: 18 all ensuite
Dinner available CC: Accepted
Room facilities:
Conference: 5 meeting rooms (Thtr 120 max)
Children: Welcome
Licenses: Parking: Off-street and free
Directions: Exit the A92 towards East Kirkcaldy. At third roundabout, turn left onto A955. Turn left on sighting our four flagpoles.
Map ref: Kirkcaldy 13 D2

Kyle, Highland

Lochalsh Hotel

★★★

Ferry Road, Kyle of Lochalsh, Highland, IV40 8AF
Tel: 01599 534202 Fax: 01599 534881
Email: mdmacrae@lochalsh-hotel.demon.co.uk
Web: www.lochalshhotel.com

A family-owned hotel overlooking the Isle of Skye. An oasis of comfort and good living in the Scottish Highlands, with 38 bedrooms — all ensuite.
Rooms: 38 all ensuite
Pricing: Sgl £40–75 Dbl £75–140
Dinner available from £22 CC: Accepted
Room facilities: Access:
Conference: 1 meeting room (Thtr 50 max)
Children: Welcome Dogs: Welcome
Licenses:
Parking: Off-street and free
Directions: From south, turn left at Kyle traffic lights. Hotel 75m from lights.
Map ref: Kyle of Lochalsh 14 B3

Langbank, Renfrewshire

Gleddoch House Hotel

★★★★

Old Greenock Road, Langbank, Renfrewshire, PA14 6YE
Tel: 01475 540711 Fax: 01475 540201
Email: reservations@gleddochhouse.com
Web: www.gleddochhouse.com
Rooms: 72 all ensuite
Dinner available CC: Accepted
Room facilities:
Conference: 4 meeting rooms (Thtr 100 max)
Children: Welcome Dogs: Welcome
Licenses:
Leisure: Indoor pool, Gym, Beauty salon, Golf, Fishing, Riding
Parking: Off-street and free
Directions: From Glasgow take M8 (Greenock), then B789 Houston Langbank exit. Follow signs for Gleddoch House.
Map ref: Langbank 12 C2

Lerwick, Shetland Isles

Glen Orchy House

◆◆◆◆

20 Knab Road, Lerwick,
Shetland Isles, ZE1 0AX
Tel: 01595 692031 Fax: 01595 692031
Email: glenorchy.house@virgin.net
Web: www.guesthouselerwick.com
Rooms: 22 all ensuite ⊛
Pricing: Sgl £42.50–45 Dbl £69
Dinner available from £17
CC: Accepted
Room facilities: ▢ ☎ ⬭ ❄
Children: Welcome ⼌
Dogs: Welcome
Licenses: ♔♔♔
Parking: Off-street and free
Directions: Follow main route until Church/Knab
Road/Annsbrae/Greenfield junction. Turn right from
south, straight ahead from north, onto Knab Road.
Map ref: Lerwick 13 F2
See advert on opposite page

Livingston, West Lothian

Ashcroft Farmhouse

◆◆◆◆◆

East Calder, Livingston, West Lothian, EH53 0ET
Tel: 01506 881810 Fax: 01506 884327
Email: scottashcroft7@aol.com
Web: www.ashcroftfarmhouse.com
Rooms: 6 all ensuite ⬚ ⊛
Pricing: Sgl £48–60 Dbl £64–70
CC: Accepted
Room facilities: ▢ ⬭
Children: Welcome 5yrs min age ⼌
Parking: Off-street and free
Directions: On B7015 half a mile east of East Calder.
Map ref: East Calder 13 D2

Lochgilphead, Argyll & Bute

Stag Hotel and Restaurant

★★

Argyll Street, Lochgilphead, Argyll & Bute, PA31 8NE
Tel: 01546 602496 Fax: 01546 603549
Email: reservations@staghotel.com
Web: www.staghotel.com
Rooms: 18 all ensuite ⬚
Dinner available CC: Accepted
Room facilities: ▢ ☎ ⬭
Conference: 2 meeting rooms (Thtr 48 max)
Children: Welcome ⼌ ☼
Licenses: ♔♔♔
Leisure: Games room
Directions: A82/83 Glasgow Campbeltown
Lochgilphead town centre mini roundabout turn right
Argyll Street, hotel at junction Lorne Street and Argyll
Street corner.
Map ref: Lochgilphead 12 B2

Lochinver, Highland

Inver Lodge Hotel

★★★★ ⬕⬕
Lochinver, Highland, IV27 4LU
Tel: 01571 844496 Fax: 01571 844395
Email: stay@inverlodge.com
Web: www.inverlodge.com
Seasonal closure: December to March

Our foreground is Lochinver Bay and the Minch: our
backdrop, the great peaks of Sutherland: Canisp and
Suilven. The hotel combines modern facilities and comforts
with the traditional ambience of a Highland lodge.
Rooms: 20 all ensuite ⊛
Pricing: Sgl £80–100 Dbl £150
Dinner available from £40 CC: Accepted
Room facilities: ▢ ☎ ⬭
Children: Welcome 10yrs min age ⼌ Dogs: Welcome
Licenses: ⬙ ♔♔♔ Leisure: Fishing, Snooker/billiards
Parking: Off-street and free
Directions: On entering Lochinver, head towards
pier/harbour. Take first left after tourist information
centre for private road to hotel.
Map ref: Lochinver 14 C1

Mallaig, Highland

West Highland Hotel

★★
Mallaig, Highland, PH41 4QZ
Tel: 01687 462210 Fax: 01687 462130
Email: westhighland.hotel@virgin.net
Web: www.westhighlandhotel.co.uk
Seasonal closure: November to April
Rooms: 39 all ensuite ⬗ ⊛
Pricing: Sgl £40–50 Dbl £70–80
Dinner available from £16 CC: Accepted
Room facilities: ▢ ⬭
Conference: 1 meeting room (Thtr 100 max)
Children: Welcome ⼌ Dogs: Welcome
Licenses: ⬙ ♔♔♔ Parking: Off-street and free
Directions: From Fort William, turn right at roundabout,
then first right uphill. From Skye ferry, turn left at
roundabout, then first right uphill.
Map ref: Mallaig 14 B3

Scotland

Markinch, Fife

Balbirnie House

★★★★ *Premier*

Balbirnie Park, Markinch, By Glenrothes, Fife, KY7 6NE
Tel: 01592 610066 Fax: 01592 610529
Email: info@balbirnie.co.uk
Web: www.balbirnie.co.uk
Rooms: 30 all ensuite
Pricing: Dinner available from £32.50 CC: Accepted
Room facilities:
Conference: 8 meeting rooms (Thtr 250 max),
24hr-delegate from £162, day-delegate from £42
Children: Welcome Dogs: Welcome
Licenses: Leisure: Golf
Parking: Off-street and free
Directions: From Edinburgh, follow signs for Forth Road
Bridge (M90). Leave at Junction 2a and take A92. Follow
signs to Glenrothes. Across third roundabout, turn right
at signs for Balbirnie Park.
Map ref: Markinch 13 D2

Maybole, South Ayrshire

Ladyburn

★★ *Excellent*

Ladyburn, Maybole, South Ayrshire, KA19 7SG
Tel: 01655 740585 Fax: 01655 740580
Email: jh@ladyburn.co.uk
Web: www.ladyburn.co.uk
Seasonal closure: Restricted opening November to March
Rooms: 5 all ensuite
Pricing: Sgl £70–100 Dbl £140–190
Dinner available from £32.50 CC: Accepted
Room facilities:
Licenses:
Parking: Off-street
Directions: A77, B7024 to Crosshill. Right at war
memorial, left after 2 miles. After a further ³/₄ mile,
Ladyburn is on the right.
Map ref: Ladyburn 12 C3

Melrose, Scottish Borders

Dryburgh Abbey Hotel

★★★

St Boswells, Melrose, Scottish Borders, TD6 0RQ
Tel: 01835 822261 Fax: 01835 823945
Email: enquiries@dryburgh.co.uk
Web: www.dryburgh.co.uk
Rooms: 38 all ensuite
Dinner available CC: Accepted
Room facilities: Access:
Conference: 3 meeting rooms (Thtr 140 max)
Children: Welcome Dogs: Welcome
Licenses: Leisure: Indoor pool, Fishing
Parking: Off-street and free
Directions: Take A68 to St Boswells. Turn onto B6404
and head through village. After 2 miles turn left on to
B6356. Continue for 2 miles to hotel entrance.
Map ref: Dryburgh 13 E3

Braidwood B&B

◆◆◆◆

Buccleuch Street, Melrose, Scottish Borders, TD6 9LD
Tel: 01896 822488 Fax: 01896 822148
Email: enquiries@braidwoodmelrose.co.uk
Web: www.braidwoodmelrose.co.uk
Rooms: 4 (2 ensuite)
Pricing: Sgl £25–40 Dbl £50–55
Room facilities:
Children: Welcome Dogs: Welcome
Directions: Centrally situated next to Post Office and
close to Abbey.
Map ref: Melrose 13 E3

Moffat, Dumfries & Galloway

Moffat House Hotel

★★★

High Street, Moffat, Dumfries & Galloway, DG10 9HL
Tel: 01683 220039 Fax: 01683 221288
Email: moffat@talk21.com
Web: www.moffathouse.co.uk
Rooms: 20 all ensuite
Pricing: Sgl £57–67 Dbl £84–105
Dinner available
CC: Accepted
Room facilities:
Conference: 3 meeting rooms (Thtr 90 max),
24hr-delegate from £109, day-delegate from £28

MOFFAT HOUSE HOTEL

Gracious 18c John Adams mansion set in its
own grounds and situated in the centre of the
picturesque village of Moffat, halfway between
Carlisle and Glasgow and 25 min. drive from
Gretna Green.

Relaxed, friendly atmosphere, excellent food
and service.

Beautiful surrounding countryside, golf, fishing
and riding.

HIGH STREET, MOFFAT, DUMFRIES &
GALLOWAY, DG10 9HL

Tel: 01683 220039   Fax: 01683 221288
Email: moffat@talk21.com
Web: www.moffathouse.co.uk

Children: Welcome Dogs: Welcome
Licenses:
Parking: Off-street and free
Directions: Turn off M74 at Junction 15. One mile to Moffat. Located in Town Square.
Map ref: Moffat 13 D3
See advert on opposite page

Famous Star Hotel

★★

44 High Street, Moffat, Dumfries & Galloway, DG10 9EF
Tel: 01683 220156 Fax: 01683 221524
Email: tim@famousstarhotel.com
Web: www.famousstarhotel.com
Rooms: 8 all ensuite
Pricing: Sgl £50–60 Dbl £60–75
Dinner available from £6 CC: Accepted
Room facilities:
Children: Welcome  Dogs: Assistance dogs only
Licenses: Leisure: Games room
Directions: Situated 1 mile off M74 Junction 15. The hotel is on the right-hand side in the town centre.
Map ref: Moffat 13 D3

Well View Hotel — Little Gem

◆◆◆◆◆

Ballplay Road, Moffat, Dumfries & Galloway, DG10 9JU
Tel: 01683 220184 Fax: 01683 220088
Email: info@wellview.co.uk
Web: www.wellview.co.uk
Rooms: 6 all ensuite
Dinner available CC: Accepted
Room facilities:
Conference: 2 meeting rooms (Thtr 16 max)
Children: Welcome Dogs: Welcome
Licenses: Parking: Off-street and free
Directions: From Moffat, A708 for Selkirk. 1/2 mile left into Ballplay Road, then 300 yards on right.
Map ref: Moffat 13 D3

Monymusk, Aberdeenshire

Grant Arms Hotel

◆◆

Monymusk, Inverurie, Aberdeenshire, AB51 7HJ
Tel: 01467 651226 Fax: 01467 651494
Email: info@monymusk.com
Web: www.monymusk.com/grantarms.html
Seasonal closure: January
Rooms: 13 all ensuite
Pricing: Sgl £60 Dbl £70 Dinner available
CC: Accepted
Room facilities:
Children: Welcome Licenses:
Leisure: Access to 10 miles of fly-fishing on Monymusk fishings of River Don
Directions: Take the A96 to Inverurie, then the B994 to Kemnay, then the B993 to Monymusk. Turn right into the village.
Map ref: Inverurie 15 F3

Motherwell, North Lanarkshire

Alona Hotel

★★★★

Strathclyde Country Park, Motherwell, North Lanarkshire, ML1 3RT
Tel: 01698 333888 Fax: 01698 338720
Web: www.alonahotel.co.uk
Rooms: 51 all ensuite
Dinner available
CC: Accepted
Room facilities:
Access:
Conference: 4 meeting rooms (Thtr 130 max)
Children: Welcome Dogs: Welcome
Licenses:
Parking: Off-street and free
Directions: Exit M74 at junction 5. Enter Strathclyde Country Park. Hotel located 300 yards on left-hand side.
Map ref: Motherwell 13 D2

Nethy Bridge, Highland

Nethybridge Hotel

★★

Nethy Bridge, Highland, PH25 3DP
Tel: 01479 821203 Fax: 01479 821686
Email: salesnethybridge@strathmorehotels.com
Web: www.strathmorehotels.com
Rooms: 69 all ensuite
Dinner available CC: Accepted
Room facilities:
Access:
Children: Welcome
Dogs: Welcome
Licenses:
Leisure: Games room
Parking: Off-street
Map ref: Nethy Bridge 15 D3

Newtonmore, Highland

Glen Hotel

★★

Main Street, Newtonmore, Highland, PH20 1DD
Tel: 01540 673203 Fax: 01540 673235
Email: room@theglenhotel.co.uk
Web: www.theglenhotel.co.uk
Rooms: 10 all ensuite
Pricing: Sgl £27.50–32.50 Dbl £55–65
Dinner available from £5
CC: Accepted
Room facilities:
Conference: 1 meeting room (Thtr 25 max)
Children: Welcome
Licenses:
Leisure: Games room
Parking: Off-street and free
Directions: Halfway between Perth and Inverness, just off the A9.
Map ref: Newtonmore 15 D3

Scotland

Oban, Argyll & Bute

Royal Hotel

★★

Argyll Square, Oban, Argyll & Bute, PA34 4BE
Tel: 01631 563021 Fax: 01631 562811
Email: salesroyaloban@strathmorehotels.com
Web: www.strathmorehotels.com
Rooms: 91 all ensuite
Dinner available CC: Accepted
Room facilities: Access:
Conference: 2 meeting rooms (Thtr 120 max)
Children: Welcome Dogs: Welcome
Licenses: Parking: Off-street
Directions: In town centre, five minutes from
ferry/rail/bus terminals.
Map ref: Oban 12 B1

Ards House   Little Gem

♦♦♦♦

Oban, Connel, Argyll & Bute, PA37 1PT
Tel: 01631 710255 Fax: 01631 710857
Email: info@ardshouse.com
Web: www.ardshouse.com
Seasonal closure: 24 December to 3 January

Five minutes from Oban in a truly idyllic location with
stunning views and incredible sunsets. Ideal base for
touring or to simply relax and unwind. Exclusively for
non smokers.
Rooms: 4 all ensuite
Pricing: Sgl £45–65 Dbl £66–85
CC: Accepted
Room facilities:
Children: Welcome 8yrs min age
Dogs: Welcome
Parking: Off-street and free
Directions: 5 miles before Oban on A85 just after
junction A828 Fort William.
Map ref: Connel 12 B1

Glenbervie Guest House   Little Gem

♦♦♦♦

Dalriach Road, Oban, Argyll & Bute, PA34 5JD
Tel: 01631 564770 Fax: 01631 566723
Email: glenbervie@lineone.net
Seasonal closure: December to January
Rooms: 8 (6 ensuite)
Pricing: Sgl £25–35 Dbl £50–70

Dinner available from £12–15
Room facilities:
Children: Welcome 5yrs min age
Licenses:
Parking: Off-street and free
Directions: A85 from Glasgow to Oban. First left to
Kingsknoll Hotel, straight over crossroads, the leisure
centre is on the left and the hotel is on the right.
Map ref: Oban 12 B1

The Old Manse Guest House

♦♦♦♦

Dalriach Road, Oban, Argyll & Bute, PA34 5JE
Tel: 01631 564886
Email: oldmanse@obanguesthouse.co.uk
Web: www.obanguesthouse.co.uk

Fine Victorian villa with magnificent sea views over
Oban Bay and beautiful gardens. Minutes from town.
Special occasion and off-peak breaks available.
Private parking.
Rooms: 6 all ensuite
Pricing: Dbl £52–72 CC: Accepted
Room facilities:
Directions: A85 into Oban. Left at Kings Knoll Hotel,
following signs to leisure centre. Old Manse 200 yards
on right past leisure centre.
Map ref: Oban 12 B1

Onich, Highland

Onich Hotel

★★★

Onich, Highland, PH33 6RY
Tel: 01855 821214 Fax: 01855 821484
Email: enquiries@onich-fortwilliam.co.uk
Web: www.onich-fortwilliam.co.uk
Seasonal closure: Christmas
Rooms: 25 all ensuite
Pricing: Sgl £37–57 Dbl £74–130
Dinner available from £28
CC: Accepted
Room facilities:
Conference: 1 meeting room (Thtr 30 max),
24hr-delegate from £125, day-delegate from £25
Children: Welcome Dogs: Welcome

Licenses:
Leisure: Games room, Snooker/billiards, Spa bath
Parking: Off-street and free
Directions: The Onich Hotel is situated on the A82 in the village of Onich, overlooking Loch Linnhe, 12 miles south of Fort William.
Map ref: Onich 14 C4

Perth, Perth & Kinross

Murrayshall House Hotel and Golf Courses
★★★★ 🎍🎍🎍
Scone, Perth, Perth & Kinross, PH2 7PH
Tel: 01738 551171 Fax: 01738 552595
Email: info@murrayshall.co.uk
Web: www.murrayshall.co.uk
Rooms: 41 all ensuite
Dinner available CC: Accepted
Room facilities:
Conference: 6 meeting rooms (Thtr 200 max)
Children: Welcome Dogs: Welcome
Licenses:
Leisure: Gym, Tennis, Golf
Parking: Off-street and free
Directions: From Perth take A94 to Coupar Angus. Turn right off A94 just before the village of Scone. Follow country road for 1½ miles.
Map ref: Scone 13 D1

Quality Hotel Perth
★★★
Leonard Street, Perth, Perth & Kinross, PH2 8HE
Tel: 01738 624141 Fax: 01738 639912
Email: enquiries@hotels-perth.com
Web: www.choicehotelseurope.com
Rooms: 70 all ensuite
Pricing: Dinner available from £17.95
CC: Accepted
Room facilities: Access:
Conference: 7 meeting rooms (Thtr 450 max), 24hr-delegate from £99, day-delegate from £29.50
Children: Welcome Dogs: Welcome
Licenses:
Parking: Off-street and free
Directions: From M90/A90, turn left into Marshall Place, which runs into Kings Place, then Leonard Street. Adjacent to railway station.
Map ref: Perth 13 D1

Salutation Hotel
★★★
South Street, Perth, Perth & Kinross, PH2 8PH
Tel: 01738 630066 Fax: 01738 633598
Email: salessalutation@strathmorehotels.com
Web: www.strathmorehotels.com
Rooms: 84 all ensuite
Pricing: Sgl £40–80 Dbl £70–100
Dinner available from £17.95 CC: Accepted
Room facilities: Access:
Conference: 6 meeting rooms (Thtr 250 max),

24hr-delegate from £80, day-delegate from £20
Children: Welcome Dogs: Welcome
Licenses:
Directions: Situated in the centre of Perth, M85 from Dundee, A9 from Inverness, A9 from Stirling/Glasgow, M90 from Edinburgh.
Map ref: Perth 13 D1

Clunie Guest House
◆◆◆
12 Pitcullen Crescent, Perth, Perth & Kinross, PH2 7HT
Tel: 01738 623625 Fax: 01738 623238
Email: ann@clunieguesthouse.co.uk
Web: www.clunieguesthouse.co.uk
Rooms: 7 all ensuite
Pricing: Sgl £25–33 Dbl £46–55 CC: Accepted
Room facilities:
Children: Welcome
Dogs: Welcome Parking: Off-street and free
Directions: Situated on A94 Perth/Couper Angus road. Leave M90 at Junction 11 and follow signs for A94.
Map ref: Perth 13 D1

Pitlochry, Perth & Kinross

Balrobin Hotel
★★
Higher Oakfield, Pitlochry, Perth & Kinross, PH16 5HT
Tel: 01796 472901 Fax: 01796 474200
Email: info@balrobin.co.uk
Web: www.balrobin.co.uk
Seasonal closure: October to March
Rooms: 14 all ensuite
Pricing: Sgl £40.50–49.50 Dbl £68–81
Dinner available from £18 CC: Accepted
Room facilities:
Children: Welcome 5yrs min age Dogs: Welcome
Licenses: Parking: Off-street and free
Directions: From centre of town, follow brown tourist signs.
Map ref: Pitlochry 15 D4

Knockendarroch House Hotel
★★ 🎍🎍
Higher Oakfield, Pitlochry, Perth & Kinross, PH16 5HT
Tel: 01796 473473 Fax: 01796 474068
Email: info@knockendarroch.co.uk
Web: www.knockendarroch.co.uk
Seasonal closure: November to February
Rooms: 12 all ensuite
Pricing: Dbl £92–104
Dinner available from £23 CC: Accepted
Room facilities:
Children: Welcome 10yrs min age
Licenses: Parking: Off-street and free
Directions: Enter Pitlochry from A9 on main street (Atholl Road), take Bonnethill Road, Tobergargan Road, then Higher Oakfield; three minutes walk from town centre.
Map ref: Pitlochry 15 D4

Scotland

Poolewe, Highland

Pool House

By Inverewe Garden, Poolewe, Highland, IV22 2LD
Tel: 01445 781272 Fax: 01445 781403
Email: enquiries@poolhousehotel.com
Web: www.poolhousehotel.com
Rooms: 6 all ensuite
Pricing: Sgl £165–175 Dbl £285–500
Dinner available from £45–48
CC: Accepted
Room facilities:
Children: Welcome 14yrs min age
Dogs: Assistance dogs only
Licenses:
Leisure: Games room, Snooker/billiards
Parking: Off-street and free
Directions: 6 miles north of Gairloch on the A832
situated by the bridge in Poolewe, by the River Ewe.
Map ref: Poolewe 14 C2

Rosebank, South Lanarkshire

Popinjay Hotel

Lanark Road, Rosebank, South Lanarkshire, ML8 5QB
Tel: 01555 860441 Fax: 01555 860204
Email: sales@popinjayhotel.co.uk
Web: www.popinjayhotel.co.uk
Rooms: 38 all ensuite
Pricing: Dinner available from £21.50
CC: Accepted
Room facilities: Access:
Conference: 2 meeting rooms (Thtr 160 max),
24hr-delegate from £99, day-delegate from £45
Children: Welcome Dogs: Welcome
Licenses:
Leisure: Fishing
Parking: Off-street and free
Directions: 4 miles from M74, on the A72 between
Hamilton and Lanark.
Map ref: Rosebank 13 D2

Sorn, East Ayrshire

The Sorn Inn
Restaurant with Rooms

35 Main Street, Sorn, East Ayrshire, KA5 6HU
Tel: 01290 551305 Fax: 01290 553470
Email: craig@sorninn.com
Web: www.sorninn.com
Rooms: 4 all ensuite
Pricing: Sgl £50 Dbl £70–90
Dinner available from £22
CC: Accepted
Room facilities:
Children: Welcome
Licenses:
Parking: Off-street and free

Directions: From North M77/A77 to A76 turnoff follow
A76 to Mauchline. Turn left B743 to Sorn from South
A76 to Mauchline.
Map ref: Sorn 12 C3

Spean Bridge, Highland

Letterfinlay Lodge Hotel

Lochlochy, Spean Bridge, Highland, PH34 4DZ
Tel: 01397 712622
Email: info@letterfinlaylodgehotel.com
Web: www.letterfinlaylodgehotel.com
Seasonal closure: November to mid-March
Rooms: 13 (9 ensuite)
Dinner available from £23
CC: Accepted
Room facilities:
Children: Welcome Dogs: Welcome
Licenses:
Leisure: Fishing, Games room, Snooker/billiards
Parking: Off-street and free
Directions: 7 miles north of Spean Bridge, on shore of
Lochlochy on the A82.
Map ref: Lochlochy 14 C4

Smiddy House

Roy Bridge Road, Spean Bridge, Highland, PH34 4EU
Tel: 01397 712335 Fax: 01397 712043
Email: enquiry@smiddyhouse.co.uk
Web: www.smiddyhouse.co.uk
Seasonal closure: November

Situated in the village, Smiddy House offers true
Scottish hospitality. Bedrooms are tastefully furnished
with quality fabrics. Russell's restaurant offers quality
cuisine using the finest of local produce.
Rooms: 4 all ensuite
Pricing: Sgl £35–55 Dbl £55–70
Dinner available from £19.50 CC: Accepted
Room facilities:
Children: Welcome Dogs: Welcome
Licenses: Parking: Off-street and free
Directions: 10 miles north of Fort William, along the
A82 till you come to Spean Bridge. Go over the Spean
Bridge and you will find Smiddy House on the corner.
Map ref: Spean Bridge 14 C4

St Andrews, Fife

Bellcraig Guest House

♦♦♦

8 Murray Park, St Andrews, Fife, KY16 9AW
Tel: 01334 472962 Fax: 01334 472962
Email: bellcraig1@aol.com
Web: www.bellcraig.co.uk
Rooms: 6 (5 ensuite)
Pricing: Sgl £35–40 Dbl £40–45 CC: Accepted
Room facilities:
Children: Welcome
Directions: On entering St Andrews, carry on at second roundabout, left at first traffic lights, left through car park onto one-way system. Bellcraig is second house on right.
Map ref: St Andrews 13 E1

Stirling

Stirling Highland Hotel

★★★★

Spittal Street, Stirling, FK8 1DU
Tel: 01786 272727 Fax: 01786 272829
Email: stirlingreservations@paramount-hotels.co.uk
Web: www.paramount-hotels.co.uk

PARAMOUNT
GROUP OF HOTELS

The former High School of Stirling, the Stirling Highland Hotel has retained many original features and is full of character and charm.
Rooms: 96 all ensuite
Pricing: Sgl £74–118 Dbl £98–118
Dinner available from £24.50
CC: Accepted
Room facilities:
Access:
Conference: 6 meeting rooms (Thtr 100 max), 24hr-delegate from £46, day-delegate from £155
Children: Welcome
Dogs: Welcome
Licenses:
Leisure: Indoor pool, Gym, Health spa, Beauty salon
Parking: Off-street
Directions: Exit J10 M9 and follow signs for Stirling Castle. The hotel is 100 yards from the castle on Spittal Street.
Map ref: Stirling 13 D2

Royal Hotel

★★★

55 Henderson Street, Bridge of Allan, Stirling, FK9 4HG
Tel: 01786 832284 Fax: 01786 834377
Email: stay@royal-stirling.co.uk
Web: www.royal-stirling.co.uk
Rooms: 32 all ensuite
Pricing: Dinner available from £23.50
CC: Accepted
Room facilities:
Access:
Conference: 4 meeting rooms (Thtr 150 max), 24hr-delegate from £140, day-delegate from £40
Children: Welcome
Dogs: Assistance dogs only
Licenses:
Parking: Off-street and free
Directions: Leave M9 at Junction 11. At large roundabout, take fourth turning which is signposted Bridge of Allan. Follow this road (A9) into the village centre. Hotel is on left.
Map ref: Bridge of Allan 13 D2

Strathpeffer, Highland

Brunstane Lodge Hotel

♦♦♦♦

Golf Course Road, Strathpeffer, Highland, IV14 9AT
Tel: 01997 421261 Fax: 01997 421272
Email: chris@guichot.freeserve.co.uk
Web: www.brunstanelodge.com
Rooms: 6 all ensuite
Pricing: Sgl £43–55 Dbl £72–74
Dinner available from £7.95
CC: Accepted
Room facilities:
Conference: 1 meeting room, 24hr-delegate from £56.95, day-delegate from £17.95
Children: Welcome
Licenses:
Parking: Off-street and free
Directions: From Dingwall carry on the A834 to village centre. At crossroads turn right up golf course road.
Map ref: Strathpeffer 15 D2

Tarbert, Argyll & Bute

Stonefield Castle Hotel

★★★★ ⌖⌖

Loch Fyne, Tarbert, Argyll & Bute, PA29 6YJ
Tel: 01880 820836 Fax: 01880 820929
Email: enquiries@stonefieldcastle.co.uk
Web: www.stonefieldhotels.com

Awarded restaurant with one of the finest views over Loch Fyne and the west coast. 60 acres of woodland gardens renowned for their rare and exotic plants and shrubs.
Rooms: 33 all ensuite ⌖ ⌖ ⌖
Pricing: Sgl £80–125 Dbl £110–250
Dinner available from £30
CC: Accepted
Room facilities: ▢ ☎ ⌖
Access: |↕|
Conference: 4 meeting rooms (Thtr 150 max), 24hr-delegate from £120, day-delegate from £37.50
Children: Welcome ⼁ ⌖ Dogs: Welcome
Licenses: ⌖ ⼀⼀⼀
Leisure: Fishing, Snooker/billiards
Parking: Off-street and free
Directions: From Glasgow, A82 then A83 from Loch Lomond. Entrance is on the left-hand side, two miles north of the village of Tarbert.
Map ref: Tarbert 12 B2

Columba Hotel

★★ ⌖⌖

East Pier Road, Tarbert, Loch Fyne, Argyll & Bute, PA29 6UF
Tel: 01880 820808 Fax: 01880 820808
Email: info@columbahotel.com
Web: www.columbahotel.com
Seasonal closure: Christmas
Rooms: 10 all ensuite ⌖
Dinner available
CC: Accepted
Room facilities: ▢ ⌖
Conference: 1 meeting room (Thtr 30 max)
Children: Welcome ⼁ ⌖ ⌖ Dogs: Welcome
Licenses: ⼀⼀⼀ Leisure: Games room
Parking: Off-street
Directions: As you enter Tarbert on A83, turn left around the harbour. Columba Hotel is ½ mile from junction.
Map ref: Tarbert 12 B2

Troon, South Ayrshire

Marine Hotel

★★★★ ⌖

Crosbie Road, Troon, South Ayrshire, KA10 6HE
Tel: 01292 314444 Fax: 01292 316922
Email: marinereservations@paramount-hotels.co.uk
Web: www.paramount-hotels.co.uk

PARAMOUNT
GROUP OF HOTELS

Only 40 minutes from Glasgow, set on the beautiful Ayrshire Coast overlooking Royal Troon Golf Course.
Rooms: 90 all ensuite ⌖ ⌖ ⌖
Pricing: Sgl £128 Dbl £128
Dinner available from £20 CC: Accepted
Room facilities: ▢ ☎ ⌖ ⌖
Access: |↕|
Conference: 6 meeting rooms (Thtr 200 max), 24hr-delegate from £170, day-delegate from £48
Children: Welcome ⼁ ⌖
Dogs: Welcome
Licenses: ⌖ ⼀⼀⼀
Leisure: Indoor pool, Gym, Health spa, Beauty salon
Parking: Off-street
Directions: Take M77/A77 to Prestwick airport. Turn right at B749 to Troon. Hotel is on left by Royal Troon golf club.
Map ref: Troon 12 C3

The big sleep

As part of our comprehensive inspection process, RAC Inspectors investigate the comfort of the beds.

Turnberry, South Ayrshire

The Westin-Turnberry Resort

★★★★★ ♟♟♟

Turnberry, South Ayrshire, KA26 9LT
Tel: 01655 331000 Fax: 01655 331706
Email: turnberry@westin.com
Web: www.westin.com/turnberry
Seasonal closure: Christmas

The world renowned 5 star Westin Turnberry Resort is located in spectacular coastal surroundings with unrivalled facilities. Including world class golf on the famous links courses, The Colin Montgomery Links Golf Academy, an award-winning Spa, excellent conference facilities, an exclusive development of luxury lodges and cottages and a variety of outdoor pursuits without peer.
Rooms: 221 all ensuite ⬛ ⊗
Pricing: Sgl £135–320 Dbl £159–375
Dinner available from £25
CC: Accepted
Room facilities: ▢ ☎ ☕ ⬉
Access: |↓↑
Conference: 14 meeting rooms (Thtr 275 max), 24hr-delegate from £280, day-delegate from £60
Children: Welcome ♿ ☕
Dogs: Welcome
Licenses: ⚘ ♟♟♟
Leisure: Indoor pool, Gym, Health spa, Beauty salon, Tennis, Golf, Fishing, Riding, Games room, Snooker/billiards, Archery, Quad-biking
Parking: Off-street and free
Directions: Turnberry is located just off the A77 Glasgow to Stranraer road, 17 miles south of Ayr.
Map ref: Turnberry 12 C3

Malin Court Hotel
★★★★♟♟
Turnberry, Girvan, South Ayrshire, KA26 9PB
Tel: 01655 331457 Fax: 01655 331072
Email: info@malincourt.co.uk
Web: www.malincourt.co.uk
Rooms: 18 all ensuite ⊗
Pricing: Sgl £72–82 Dbl £104–124
Dinner available from £12
CC: Accepted
Room facilities: ▢ ☎ ☕ ⬉
Access: |↓↑

Conference: 3 meeting rooms (Thtr 200 max), 24hr-delegate from £65.50, day-delegate from £21.95
Children: Welcome ♿
Licenses: ⚘ ♟♟♟
Parking: Off-street and free
Directions: On A77 take Ayr exit. From Ayr, take the A719 to Turnberry and Maidens.
Map ref: Turnberry 12 C3

Wick, Highland

Mackay's Hotel
★★
Union Street, Wick, Highland, KW1 5ED
Tel: 01955 602323 Fax: 01955 605930
Web: www.mackayshotel.co.uk
Rooms: 30 all ensuite ♨ ⬛ ⊗
Pricing: Sgl £55–85 Dbl £80–120
Dinner available CC: Accepted
Room facilities: ▢ ☎ ☕ ⬉
Access: |↓↑
Conference: 2 meeting rooms (Thtr 120 max)
Children: Welcome ♿
Dogs: Assistance dogs only
Licenses: ⚘ ♟♟♟
Directions: On the main road A99 north, towards town centre. Turn right at mini roundabout, directly before bridge across river. Hotel is on left, opposite hospital.
Map ref: Wick 15 E1

Inverlochy Castle Hotel, Fort William

Scotland

Northern Ireland

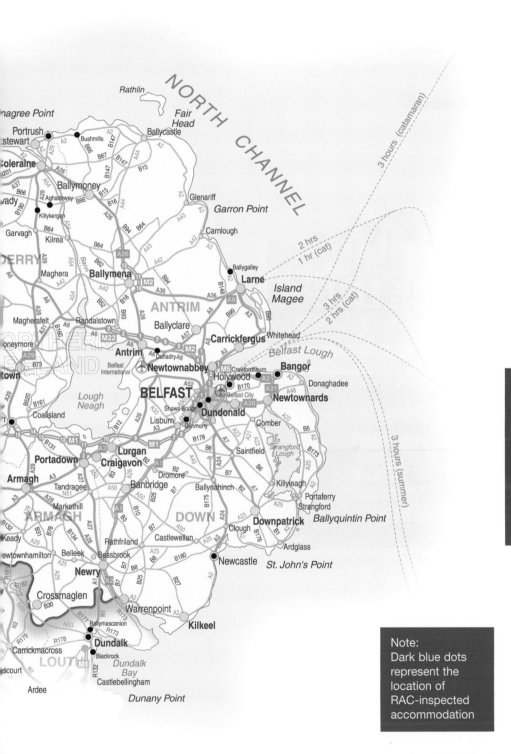

Northern Ireland

Note:
Dark blue dots represent the location of RAC-inspected accommodation

Northern Ireland

Award winners

To help you choose somewhere really special for your stay, we've listed here the RAC Award-winning hotel in this region.

Blue Ribbon Award

		pg
The Old Inn, Bangor	★★★	545

The Old Inn, Bangor

The Old Inn, Bangor

Bangor, Co. Down

Marine Court Hotel
★★★★

The Marina, 18-20 Quay Street,
Bangor, Co. Down, BT20 5ED
Tel: 028 9145 1100 Fax: 028 9145 1200
Email: marinecourt@btconnect.com
Web: www.marinecourthotel.net
Seasonal closure: 25 December
Rooms: 52 all ensuite
Pricing: Sgl £80–90 Dbl £90–100
Dinner available from £8.95 CC: Accepted
Room facilities: Access:
Conference: 4 meeting rooms (Thtr 300 max),
24hr-delegate from £129.25, day-delegate from £23.50
Children: Welcome Licenses:
Leisure: Indoor pool, Gym, Health spa
Parking: Off-street and free
Directions: A2 from Belfast to Bangor. Located on sea front facing marina.
Map ref: Bangor 17 F2

The Old Inn
★★★★

11-15 Main Street, Crawfordsburn, Co. Down, BT19 1JH
Tel: 028 9185 3255 Fax: 028 9185 2775
Email: info@theoldinn.com
Web: www.theoldinn.com
Seasonal closure: 24 December

Unique accommodation in Ireland's oldest coaching inn. 31 individually styled bedrooms & garden cottage. Award winning 1614 restaurant or Churn bistro for casual dining. Cosy fires, relaxing atmosphere — RAC Blue Ribbon Winner 2003, 2004 and 2005.
Rooms: 31 all ensuite
Pricing: Sgl £85–200 Dbl £85–200
Dinner available from £19.50–30 CC: Accepted
Room facilities:
Conference: 2 meeting rooms (Thtr 100 max),
24hr-delegate from £120, day-delegate from £30
Children: Welcome
Licenses:
Parking: Off-street and free
Directions: From Belfast take the A2 towards Bangor. Three miles past Holywood, take the B20 to Crawfordsburn. The Old Inn is on the left-hand side on the main street.
Map ref: Crawfordsburn 17 F2

Bangor Bay Inn
★★★

10-12 Seacliff Road, Bangor, Co. Down, BT20 5EY
Tel: 028 9127 0696 Fax: 028 9127 1678
Email: bangorinn@aol.com
Web: www.bangorbayinn.com
Seasonal closure: Christmas Day, Boxing Day and New Year's Day

Double fronted late 19th century home. Sympathetically integrating old world charm with state-of-the-art ensuite rooms. Excellent dining and licensed lounge bar overlooking The Marina, 25 minutes from centre of Belfast.
Rooms: 15 all ensuite
Pricing: Sgl £45–65 Dbl £65–90
Dinner available from £7.95–15.95
CC: Accepted
Room facilities:
Children: Welcome
Licenses:
Parking: Off-street and free
Directions: Twelve miles from Belfast straight through Bangor Town Centre to seafront, go straight along Marina ½ mile. Opposite Lifeboat Station and North Pier.
Map ref: Bangor 17 F2

Are the bells ringing?

Getting married? Congratulations! Look for the wedding bells symbol which shows hotels licensed for civil ceremonies.

Northern Ireland

Belcoo, Co. Fermanagh

Customs House Country Inn

◆◆◆◆ ॒ ✑

25-27 Main Street, Belcoo, Co. Fermanagh, BT93 5FB
Tel: 028 6638 6285 Fax: 028 6638 6936
Email: info@customshouseinn.com
Web: www.customshouseinn.com

Award-winning country inn situated on the shores of
Lough McNean in the idyllic village of Belcoo. This
superb family-run facility, with its warm welcome, will
not disappoint.
Rooms: 9 all ensuite ⊛
Pricing: Sgl £40–50 Dbl £60–80
Dinner available from £18.95–22.95
CC: Accepted
Room facilities: ☐ ☎ ◷ ☖ Access: ⌊↑
Conference: 2 meeting rooms (Thtr 60 max),
24hr-delegate from £50, day-delegate from £10
Children: Welcome ♯ ⅀ℂ
Dogs: Assistance dogs only
Licenses: ♦♦♦
Directions: Take A4 from Enniskillen, sign posted Sligo,
for 12 miles. Hotel located on main street in Belcoo
village.
Map ref: Belcoo 16 C3

Belfast, Co. Antrim

Hastings Culloden Estate and Spa

★★★★★ ॒॒

Bangor Road, Holywood, Belfast, Co. Antrim, BT18 0EX
Tel: 028 9042 1066 Fax: 028 9042 6777
Email: res@cull.hastingshotels.com
Web: www.hastingshotels.com
Rooms: 79 all ensuite ⊛ ⟁ ⊛
Pricing: Sgl £188–208 Dbl £246–636
Dinner available from £40 CC: Accepted
Room facilities: ☐ ☎ ◷ ☖ Access: ⌊↑
Conference: 8 meeting rooms (Thtr 500 max),
24hr-delegate from £246.75, day-delegate from £64.63
Children: Welcome ♯
Licenses: ◬ ♦♦♦
Leisure: Indoor pool, Gym, Health spa, Beauty salon
Parking: Off-street and free
Directions: 6 miles from Belfast city centre via A2,
signposted Bangor.
Map ref: Holywood 17 F2

Dunadry Hotel and Country Club

★★★★ ॒

2 Islandreagh Drive, Dunadry, Co. Antrim, BT41 2HA
Tel: 028 9038 5050 Fax: 028 9038 5055
Email: reservations@mooneyhotelgroup.com
Web: www.dunadry.com
Seasonal closure: 24-26 December
Rooms: 83 all ensuite ⊛ ⊛
Pricing: Dinner available from £10 CC: Accepted
Room facilities: ☐ ☎ ◷ ☖ Access: ⌊↑
Conference: 6 meeting rooms (Thtr 50 max)
Children: Welcome ♯ ⅀ℂ
Licenses: ◬ ♦♦♦
Leisure: Indoor pool, Gym, Health spa, Beauty salon
Parking: Off-street and free
Directions: From Belfast take M2, follow signs to
Templepatrick and Belfast International Airport. Take
A57, turn left to Templepatrick. At roundabout go
straight through Templepatrick. Second turn next
roundabout. Dunadry is 1 mile on left.
Map ref: Dunadry 17 E2

Hastings Europa Hotel

★★★★ ॒

Great Victoria Street, Belfast, Co. Antrim, BT2 7AP
Tel: 028 9027 1066 Fax: 028 9026 6099
Email: res@eur.hastingshotels.com
Web: www.hastingshotels.com
Seasonal closure: 24–25 December
Rooms: 240 all ensuite
Pricing: Sgl £106–136 Dbl £126–191
Dinner available from £15–26.50 CC: Accepted
Room facilities: ☐ ☎ ◷ ☖ Access: ⌊↑
Conference: 16 meeting rooms (Thtr 500 max),
24hr-delegate from £176.25, day-delegate from £47
Children: Welcome ♯
Licenses: ◬ ♦♦♦
Directions: From M1 and M2 take West Link to
Grosvenor Road junction. Left onto Grosvenor Road,
right onto Boyne Bridge, then first left, Glengall Street.
Hotel is beside Grand Opera House.
Map ref: Belfast 17 F2

Hastings Stormont Hotel

★★★★ ॒

Upper Newtownards Road, Belfast, Co. Antrim, BT4 3LP
Tel: 028 9065 1066 Fax: 028 9048 0240
Email: res@stor.hastingshotels.com
Web: www.hastingshotels.com
Rooms: 105 all ensuite ⊛
Pricing: Sgl £70–134 Dbl £90–170
Dinner available from £20 CC: Accepted
Room facilities: ☐ ☎ ◷ ☖ Access: ⌊↑
Conference: 16 meeting rooms (Thtr 500 max),
24hr-delegate from £170.38, day-delegate from £44.65
Children: Welcome ♯ Licenses: ◬ ♦♦♦
Parking: Off-street and free
Directions: From Belfast city centre, follow A2 to
Newtownards. Turn right at Stormont Parliament
Buildings.
Map ref: Belfast 17 F2

Ramada Belfast

★★★★

117 Milltown Road, Shaws Bridge, Belfast,
Co. Antrim, BT8 7XP
Tel: 028 9092 3500 Fax: 028 9092 3600
Email: mail@ramadabelfast.com
Web: www.ramadabelfast.com
Rooms: 120 all ensuite 🕸
Pricing: Sgl £65–115 Dbl £79–140
Dinner available from £10 CC: Accepted
Room facilities: 🖵 ☎ 🍵 ✆ ❋ Access: ⬆⬇
Conference: 14 meeting rooms (Thtr 900 max),
24hr-delegate from £145, day-delegate from £39.50
Children: Welcome 🍴 Dogs: Assistance dogs only
Licenses: ⬨ ⫙ Leisure: Indoor pool, Gym, Health
spa, Beauty salon, Games room, Snooker/billiards
Parking: Off-street and free
Directions: The Ramada Belfast is set in the tranquil Lagan
Valley Regional Park just 3 miles from the city centre.
Map ref: Shaws Bridge 17 F2

Balmoral Hotel

★★★

Blacks Road, Dunmurry, Belfast, Co. Antrim, BT10 0NF
Tel: 028 9030 1234 Fax: 028 9060 1455
Email: info@balmoralhotelbelfast.co.uk
Web: www.balmoralhotelbelfast.com
Seasonal closure: 24-26 December

Within easy access of the M1 and on the main Dublin
route, the Balmoral Hotel offers 40 ensuite bedrooms, 8 of
which are equipped with disabled facilities. Designed with
the guest in mind, each room features remote TV, Radio,
DD Telephone and Hospitality Tray. From the moment you
arrive you can expect the warmest of welcomes. The
hotel offers spacious lounges and food is served all day in
the Lady Anne and Glenriver restaurants.
Rooms: 40 all ensuite 🕸
Pricing: Sgl £40–65 Dbl £55–85
Dinner available from £15 CC: Accepted
Room facilities: 🖵 ☎ 🍵
Conference: 3 meeting rooms (Thtr 300 max),
day-delegate from £90
Children: Welcome 🍴 Licenses: ⫙
Leisure: Games room Parking: Off-street and free
Directions: From Belfast take M1 motorway. Take
second exit, signposted Dunmurry. Take right at lights.
Straight through second lights, hotel on left.
Map ref: Dunmurry 17 F2

Days Hotel Belfast

★★★

40 Hope Street, Belfast, Co. Antrim, BT12 5EE
Tel: 028 90 242494 Fax: 028 90 242495
Email: reservations@dayshotelbelfast.com
Web: www.dayshotelbelfast.com
Rooms: 244 all ensuite 🕸
Dinner available CC: Accepted
Room facilities: 🖵 ☎ 🍵 ✆
Access: ⬆⬇
Conference: 8 meeting rooms (Thtr 80 max)
Children: Welcome 12yrs min age
Licenses: ⫙
Parking: Off-street and free
Directions: Follow signs for Westlink. Take exit into
Grosvenor Road to the city centre. Turn right at first
set of traffic lights. Proceed over bridge and take next
left onto Hope Street. Hotel is on right-hand side.
Map ref: Belfast 17 F2

Dukes Hotel

★★★

65-67 University Street, Belfast, Co. Antrim, BT7 1HL
Tel: 028 9023 6666 Fax: 028 9023 7177
Email: info@dukes-hotel-belfast.co.uk
Web: www.welcome-group.co.uk

Centrally located modern hotel with twelve ensuite
bedrooms with direct-dial telephones, satellite television,
hairdryers and tea and coffee facilities. Sauna on
request. Award-winning Chinese restaurant on site.
Rooms: 12 all ensuite 🖥 🕸
Pricing: Sgl £65–70 Dbl £70–80
Dinner available from £30
CC: Accepted
Room facilities: 🖵 ☎ 🍵 ✆ Access: ⬆⬇
Conference: 3 meeting rooms (Thtr 150 max),
24hr-delegate from £120, day-delegate from £27.50
Children: Welcome 🍴
Licenses: ⫙
Leisure: Gym
Directions: From the M1 follow signs for city
centre/Queen's University. The hotel is located directly
behind Queen's University on junction Botanic
Avenue/University Street.
Map ref: Belfast 17 F2

Northern Ireland

Jurys Inn Belfast

★★★

Fisherwick Place, Great Victoria Street, Belfast,
Co. Antrim, BT2 7AP
Tel: 028 9053 3500 Fax: 028 9053 3511
Email: bookings@jurysdoyle.com
Web: www.jurysinns.com
Seasonal closure: 24-26 December

JURYS DOYLE
HOTELS

Rooms: 190 all ensuite ⊛
Pricing: Sgl £73–118 Dbl £81–126
Dinner available from £17 CC: Accepted
Room facilities: ▢ ☎ ☕ ☎ Access: ♿
Conference: 6 meeting rooms (Thtr 30 max),
24hr-delegate from £126, day-delegate from £34
Children: Welcome
Licenses: ♦♦♦
Parking: Off-street
Directions: Located 2 miles from Belfast City Airport.
Great Victoria Station 2 mins walk. Inn is adjacent to
Opera House and City Hall.
Map ref: Belfast 17 F2

Tara Lodge

♦♦♦♦ ☙

36 Cromwell Road, Belfast, Co. Antrim, BT7 1JW
Tel: 028 9059 0900 Fax: 028 9059 0901
Email: info@taralodge.com
Web: www.taralodge.com
Seasonal closure: 25-28 December & 11-14 July

Tara Lodge is an exclusive development that offers
warm and genuine hospitality in tasteful contemporary
surroundings. High quality service and facilities, secure
car parking with a city centre location.
Rooms: 19 all ensuite ⊛
Pricing: Sgl £52.50–62.50 Dbl £65–70 CC: Accepted
Room facilities: ▢ ☎ ☕ ☎ Access: ♿
Conference: 1 meeting room
Children: Welcome
Parking: Off-street and free
Directions: M2 to exit roundabout, fifth exit towards
Boucher Road, first left, exit next roundabout, at traffic
lights take left, turn right 600 yards after next left, next
right along Queens University. Turn left into Botanic
Avenue, take third right into Cromwell Road.
Map ref: Belfast 17 F2

Bushmills, Co. Antrim

Bushmills Inn Hotel

★★★★ ☙☙

9 Dunluce Road, Bushmills, Co. Antrim, BT57 8QG
Tel: 028 2073 3000 Fax: 028 2073 2048
Email: mail@bushmillsinn.com
Web: www.bushmillsinn.com
Seasonal closure: Christmas Day

"A living museum of Ulster hospitality." Turf fires, gas
lights and aged timbers set the tone for this legendary
coaching inn & mill house at the gateway to the Giant's
Causeway.
Rooms: 32 all ensuite ☙ ☙ ⊛
Pricing: Sgl £68–148 Dbl £98–248
Dinner available from £28
CC: Accepted
Room facilities: ▢ ☎ ☕ ☎
Conference: 3 meeting rooms (Thtr 40 max),
24hr-delegate from £98, day-delegate from £25
Children: Welcome ♒ ☕
Licenses: ♦♦♦
Parking: Off-street and free
Directions: On the A2 Antrim coast road in Bushmills
village with main entrance as you cross the River
Bush.
Map ref: Bushmills 17 E1

Clogher, Co. Tyrone

Corick Country House

♦♦♦♦ ☙☙

20 Corick Road, Clogher, Co. Tyrone, BT76 0BZ
Tel: 028 8554 8216 Fax: 028 8554 9531
Email: corickcountryhouse@btinternet.com
Web: www.corickcountryhouse.com
Rooms: 10 all ensuite ☙ ⊛
Pricing: Sgl £55 Dbl £90
Dinner available from £19.95 CC: Accepted
Room facilities: ▢ ☎ ☕
Conference: 4 meeting rooms (Thtr 200 max),
24hr-delegate from £62, day-delegate from £22
Children: Welcome ♒ ☕ Dogs: Welcome
Licenses: ◬ ♦♦♦ Leisure: Fishing, Riding
Parking: Off-street and free
Directions: Corick House is located off the main A4
Belfast to Enniskillen Road. Between Augher to
Clogher. Turn on right hand side. Signpost on A4.
Map ref: Clogher 17 D2

Coleraine, Co. Londonderry

Brown Trout Golf & Country Inn

★★

Agivey Road, Aghadowey, Co. Londonderry, BT51 4AD
Tel: 028 7086 8209 Fax: 028 7086 8878
Email: jane@browntroutinn.com
Web: www.browntroutinn.com
Rooms: 15 all ensuite
Pricing: Sgl £55–65 Dbl £65–90
Dinner available from £16–20 CC: Accepted
Room facilities: ☐ ☎ ☕ Access: ॥
Conference: 2 meeting rooms (Thtr 40 max),
24hr-delegate from £75, day-delegate from £20
Children: Welcome ⊓ ⌁ Dogs: Welcome
Licenses: ⅲ
Leisure: Gym, Golf, Fishing
Parking: Off-street and free
Directions: On intersection of A54 B66 7 miles south of
Coleraine.
Map ref: Aghadowey 17 E1

Heathfield Farm

◆◆◆◆

31 Drumcroone Road, Killykergan, Coleraine,
Co. Londonderry, BT51 4EB
Tel: 028 2955 8245 Fax: 028 2955 8245
Email: relax@heathfieldfarm.com
Web: www.heathfieldfarm.com
Rooms: 3 all ensuite
Pricing: Sgl £30 Dbl £50
CC: Accepted
Room facilities: ☐ ☕
Dogs: Welcome Leisure: Fishing
Parking: Off-street and free
Directions: On A29 Garvagh/Coleraine road. 2 miles
north of Garvagh, 7 miles south of Coleraine.
Map ref: Killykergan 17 E1

Dungannon, Co. Tyrone

Stangmore Country House

◆◆◆◆◆ ⌨ ⌁

65 Moy Road, Dungannon, Co. Tyrone, BT71 7DT
Tel: 028 8772 5600 Fax: 028 8772 6644
Email: info@stangmorecountryhouse.com
Web: www.stangmorecountryhouse.com
Rooms: 9 all ensuite ⊛
Pricing: Sgl £60–75 Dbl £80–100
Dinner available from £21.50
CC: Accepted
Room facilities: ☐ ☎ ☕
Conference: 1 meeting room (Thtr 40 max),
24hr-delegate from £85, day-delegate from £25
Children: Welcome ⊓
Licenses: ⅲ
Parking: Off-street and free
Directions: From M1 motorway take the exit at Junction 15.
At the roundabout follow signs for Dungannon. Stangmore
is 250 yards on the left from the roundabout (signposted).
Map ref: Dungannon 17 E2

Enniskillen, Co. Fermanagh

Killyhevlin Hotel

★★★★ ⌁

Killyhevlin, Enniskillen, Co. Fermanagh, BT74 6RW
Tel: 028 6632 3481 Fax: 028 6632 4726
Email: info@killyhevlin.com
Web: www.killyhevlin.com
Seasonal closure: 24–25 December
Rooms: 70 all ensuite ⊛ ⊠ ⊛
Pricing: Sgl £90–125 Dbl £120–165
Dinner available from £24.95–32.95 CC: Accepted
Room facilities: ☐ ☎ ☕ ⌕ Access: ॥
Conference: 7 meeting rooms (Thtr 500 max)
Children: Welcome 12yrs min age ⊓ ⌁
Dogs: Welcome Licenses: ⅲ
Leisure: Indoor pool, Gym, Health spa, Beauty salon,
Fishing, Aerobics studio, Outdoor hot tub, Jacuzzi,
Steam room, Sauna Parking: Off-street and free
Directions: Situated on A4, due east of Enniskillen on
main Belfast road, 1km from Enniskillen town.
Map ref: Enniskillen 17 D3

Feeny, Co. Londonderry

Drumcovitt House and Barn

◆◆◆◆ ⌁

704 Feeny Road, Feeny, Co. Londonderry, BT47 4SU
Tel: 028 7778 1224 Fax: 028 7778 1224
Email: drumcovitt.feeny@btinternet.com
Web: www.drumcovitt.com

Listed Georgian house situated in the foothills of the
Sperrin Mountains, stunning views, ideal for visiting Derry
City, Donegal and the Giant's Causeway. Centrally
heated. Log fires. Relax. Stroll. Birdwatch. Return again
and again.
Rooms: 9 (3 ensuite) ⊛
Pricing: Sgl £24–28 Dbl £48–56
Dinner available from £15–20 CC: Accepted
Room facilities: ☐ ☎ ☕ ⌕
Children: Welcome ⊓ ⌁ Dogs: Welcome
Licenses: ⌂
Leisure: Games room, Snooker/billiards
Parking: Off-street and free
Directions: From A6 Belfast-Derry road, a quarter-mile
west of Dungiven take the B74 to Feeny. After 3¹⁄₂
miles, Drumcovitt is on the right.
Map ref: Feeny 17 D1

Northern Ireland

Larne, Co. Antrim

Hastings Ballygally Castle Hotel

★★★

274 Coast Road, Ballygally, Co. Antrim, BT40 2QZ
Tel: 028 2858 1066 Fax: 028 2858 3681
Email: res@bgc.hastingshotels.com
Web: www.hastingshotels.com
Rooms: 44 all ensuite
Pricing: Sgl £90–125 Dbl £130–150
Dinner available from £22
CC: Accepted
Room facilities:
Access:
Conference: 4 meeting rooms (Thtr 200 max),
24hr-delegate from £129.25, day-delegate from £44.06
Children: Welcome
Licenses:
Parking: Off-street and free
Directions: 20 miles north of Belfast on the Antrim
coast road (M2 from Belfast, then A8 to Larne). 4 miles
north of Larne on Antrim coast.
Map ref: Ballygally 17 F2

Limavady, Co. Londonderry

Radisson SAS Roe Park Resort

★★★★★

Roe Park, Limavady, Co. Londonderry, BT49 9LB
Tel: 028 7772 2222 Fax: 028 7772 2313
Email: reservations@radissonroepark.com
Web: www.radissonroepark.com

The north coast's only 4-star deluxe resort. Old and
new combine to create a world class resort featuring
118 bedrooms and suites. Indoor heated pool,
unrivalled leisure spa with an extensive range of
treatments, an excellent 18-hole parkland golf course,
driving range and indoor golf academy, the award-
winning Greens Restaurant serving classic fare with
Irish flair and the relaxed charm that is the Coach
House Brasserie.
Rooms: 118 all ensuite
Pricing: Sgl £90 Dbl £130
Dinner available from £23–31
CC: Accepted
Room facilities:
Access:
Conference: 7 meeting rooms (Thtr 400 max),
24hr-delegate from £115, day-delegate from £26
Children: Welcome
Leisure: Indoor pool, Gym, Beauty salon, Golf, Games
room, Snooker/billiards
Parking: Off-street and free
Directions: Situated on A2 Londonderry-Limavady
Road, 16 miles from Londonderry, 1 mile from
Limavady. Resort is 10 miles from city of Derry and 45
miles from Belfast airport.
Map ref: Limavady 17 E1

Ballycarton House

♦♦♦♦

239 Seacoast Road, Limavady,
Co. Londonderry, BT49 0HZ
Tel: 028 7775 0216 Fax: 028 7775 0231
Email: stay@ballycartonhouse.com
Web: www.ballycartonhouse.com
Rooms: 6 all ensuite
Pricing: Sgl £30 Dbl £56
Dinner available from £15
CC: Accepted
Room facilities:
Children: Welcome
Leisure: Internet access available
Parking: Off-street and free
Directions: Situated 5 miles north of Limavady on the
A2 coast road to Coleraine. Follow signs for car ferry
from Limavady.
Map ref: Limavady 17 E1

Londonderry, Co. Londonderry

Hastings Everglades Hotel

★★★★

Prehen Road, Waterside, Londonderry,
Co. Londonderry, BT47 2NH
Tel: 028 7132 1066 Fax: 028 7134 9200
Email: res@egh.hastingshotels.com
Web: www.hastingshotels.com
Rooms: 64 all ensuite
Pricing: Sgl £70–100 Dbl £80–130
Dinner available from £19.95
CC: Accepted
Room facilities:
Access:
Conference: 5 meeting rooms (Thtr 400 max),
24hr-delegate from £99, day-delegate from £30
Children: Welcome
Licenses:
Parking: Off-street and free
Directions: Follow main A6 route to Londonderry.
Follow signs for Strabane/Omagh. Go ahead at traffic
lights at bridge. Hotel second left.
Map ref: Londonderry 17 D1

Tower Hotel Derry

★★★★ ®

Butcher Street, Londonderry,
Co. Londonderry, BT48 6HL
Tel: 048 7137 1000 Fax: 048 7137 1234
Email: reservations@thd.ie
Web: www.towerhotelgroup.com
Seasonal closure: 24–27 December
Rooms: 93 all ensuite 🏊
Pricing: Sgl £105 Dbl £130
Dinner available from £15
Room facilities: 🖥 ☎ 🍵 📞
Access: ♿
Conference: 5 meeting rooms (Thtr 250 max)
Children: Welcome 🎠
Licenses: ◇ 👯
Leisure: Gym
Parking: Off-street and free
Map ref: Londonderry 17 D1

Newcastle, Co. Down

Hastings Slieve Donard Hotel

★★★★★ ®

Downs Road, Newcastle, Co. Down, BT33 0AH
Tel: 028 4372 1066 Fax: 028 4372 1166
Email: res@sdh.hastingshotels.com
Web: www.hastingshotels.com
Rooms: 124 all ensuite 🏊
Pricing: Sgl £145–205 Dbl £165–225
Dinner available from £29.50
CC: Accepted
Room facilities: 🖥 ☎ 🍵 📞
Access: ♿
Conference: 16 meeting rooms (Thtr 900 max),
24hr-delegate from £176.25, day-delegate from £58.75
Children: Welcome 🎠 🍼
Licenses: ◇ 👯
Leisure: Indoor pool, Gym, Health spa, Beauty salon,
Games room
Parking: Off-street and free
Directions: From Belfast, take A24 and follow signs to
Newcastle. From Dublin, take R174 to Newry then A2
and follow signs to Newcastle.
Map ref: Newcastle 17 F3

Relax & smell the coffee

Fresh coffee, chilled juices for breakfast. RAC's team of qualified Inspectors check them both.

Burrendale Hotel & Country Club

★★★ ®®

51 Castlewellan Road, Newcastle,
Co. Down, BT33 0JY
Tel: 028 4372 2599 Fax: 028 4372 2328
Email: reservations@burrendale.com
Web: www.burrendale.com

Nestling between the majestic Mourne Mountains and
the glimmering Irish Sea lies The Burrendale Hotel. Relax
in our leisure club or unwind in our health clinic. Only five
minutes from the famous Royal County Down.
Rooms: 69 all ensuite 🏊 🚭
Pricing: Sgl £75–95 Dbl £110–130
Dinner available from £16–26
CC: Accepted
Room facilities: 🖥 ☎ 🍵 📞
Access: ♿
Conference: 8 meeting rooms (Thtr 300 max),
24hr-delegate from £125, day-delegate from £37
Children: Welcome 14yrs min age 🎠 🍼
Licenses: ◇ 👯
Leisure: Indoor pool, Gym, Health spa, Beauty salon,
Games room
Parking: Off-street and free
Directions: From Belfast, take A24 to Newcastle, then
A50 Castlewellan Road. From Belfast, 45 minutes;
from Newry, 40 minutes; from Dublin, 90 minutes.
Map ref: Newcastle 17 F3

Portrush, Co. Antrim

Albany Lodge Guest House

◆◆◆◆ 🍴 ✍ ®

2 Eglington Street, Portrush, Co. Antrim, BT56 8DX
Tel: 028 7082 3492 Fax: 028 7082 1227
Email: info@albanylodgeni.co.uk
Web: www.albanylodgeni.co.uk
Rooms: 10 all ensuite 📺 🚭
Pricing: Sgl £45–120 Dbl £90–140
Dinner available from £12.50–20
CC: Accepted
Room facilities: 🖥 ☎ 🍵 📞
Directions: Follow signs "Town Centre". Pass harbour,
follow main street to Y-junction. Albany Lodge first
house on right beside Presbyterian church.
Map ref: Portrush 17 E1

Northern Ireland

Harbour Heights

◆◆◆◆ ✳🖂

17 Kerr Street, Portrush, Co. Antrim, BT56 8DG
Tel: 028 7082 2765 Fax: 028 7082 2558
Email: info@harbourheightsportrush.com
Web: www.harbourheightsportrush.com

Located in an area of outstanding natural beauty —
Giant's Causeway World Heritage Site, Royal Portrush
Golf Club. Golf, wedding parties of 15–20 persons.
Spectacular sea views.
Rooms: 11 (9 ensuite) 🚭
Pricing: Sgl £32.50 Dbl £60–65
Dinner available from £10
CC: Accepted
Room facilities: ▢ ☎ 🖥 📞
Children: Welcome 🪑 🍼
Directions: Leave M2, A26 North follow signs
Coleraine, follow signs Portrush, follow signs Harbour,
150 yards on right-hand side of Kerr Street.
Map ref: Portrush 17 E1

Beulah Guest House

◆◆◆ ✳🖂

16 Causeway Street, Portrush, Co. Antrim, BT56 8AB
Tel: 028 7082 2413 Fax: 028 7082 5900
Email: stay@beulahguesthouse.com
Web: www.beulahguesthouse.com
Seasonal closure: 23-29 December
Rooms: 10 (9 ensuite) 🚭
Pricing: Sgl £25–48 Dbl £50–60
Dinner available from £12.50
CC: Accepted
Room facilities: ▢ 🖥
Children: Welcome 🪑
Parking: Off-street and free
Directions: Approaching Portrush, follow sign for
Bushmills/East Strand car park, bringing you to
Causeway Street (do not take town centre). Guest
house approximately 300 metres on left.
Map ref: Portrush 17 E1

Drumcovitt House and Barn, Feeny

Republic of Ireland

Tory
Tory Sound

Bloody Foreland
R257
Falc
C
Bunbeg
Gweedore
Aran
Dungloe
DERRYVEAGH
N
DO
Mass
R250
Glenties
Rossan Point
Glencolumbkille
Ardara
R252
Lough
Esker
Carrick
R263
Lough Esker
N56
Donega

Donegal Bay
Ballyshannon
Bundoran
Balleek
N15
A46

Erris Head
Downpatrick Head
Killala
Bay
Sligo Bay
Sligo
N15
Manorhamilton
Belmullet
R314
R287
Sligo
R292
R286
N16
The
Mullet
R313
R315
R314
Dromore
West
L. Gill
R287
Bangor Erris
Crossmolina
Ballina
Enniscrone
SLIEVE GAMPH
Lisduff
Ballysadare
LEITRIM
N59
SLIGO
Riverstown
R290
Blacksod
Bay
Ballycroy
Lough
Conn
MTS
N17
Lough
Arrow
Lough
Aller
Achill Head
Keel
R312
R316
Foxford
N5
Tubbercurry
R294
Drumsha
Achill
Island
Mulrany
R317
R315
Charlestown
R293
R294
Boyle
N4
Drumsha
Clare
Newport
R310
N5
Swinford
Knock
International
N17
Ballaghaderreen
N5
R581
Leitrim
Carrick-on-
Shannon
Fena
Clew
Bay
Castlebar
Killamagh
R324
R322
R325
Frenchpark
R370
R208
Louisburgh
R335
R311
Westport
R330
Balla
R321
N17
Knock
N83
R293
R325
R369
R371
Inishturk
MAYO
Partry
Claremorris
Ballyhaunis
ROSCOMMON
Castlerea
Tulsk
N5
Inishbofin
Killary
Harbour
Renvyle
Aasleagh
Lough
Carra
B331
R327
R327
R360
Ballymoe
R367
N60
Letterfrack
N59
Clonbur
R345
Ballinrobe
R332
Dunmore
R360
R362
R362
R366
Roscommon
R392
Clifden
Connemara
National Park
CONNEMARA
Recess
Cong
Lough
Corrib
N84
N17
R384
Athleague
N61
Slyne Head
Maam Cross
N59
Headford
N17
Tuam
R332
N63
Lough Ree
Roundstone
R340
Cashel
R341
Oughterard
N59
Mount
Bellew
R550
R363
Westmeath
R362
Carna
Moycullen
Claregalway
R348
Ballinasloe
N6
Athlone
Bushypark
Camaroe
Spiddal
R336
Saithill
Galway
Athenry
GALWAY
N6
N65
Gorumna Is.
Oranmore
R347
R348
R357
Galway Bay
Kilcolgan
N6
Loughrea
R355
R356
Ologhan
Aran Islands
Inishmore
N67
Kinvara
N18
R361
SLIEVE
AUGHTY
MTS
R489
Inishmaan
Ballyvaughan
Knocknagrough
Gregans
Castle
Gort
R353
R351
Portumna
R440
Birr
Inisheer
Doolin
R477
R460
R466

Note:
Dark blue dots represent the location of RAC-inspected accommodation

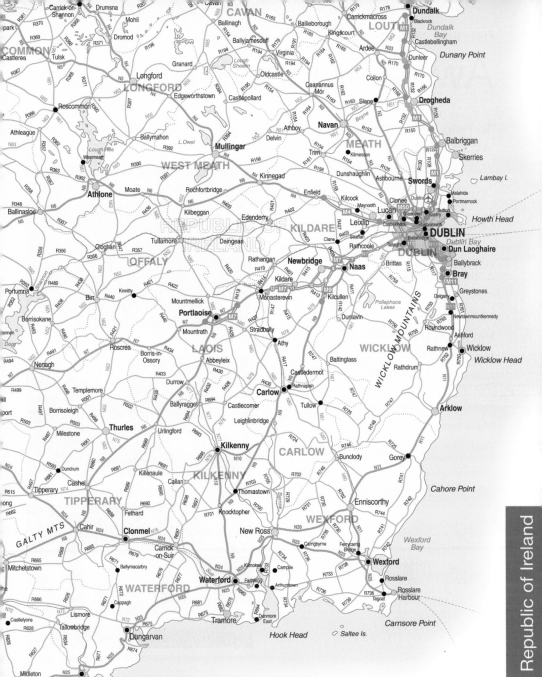

Republic of Ireland

Award winners

To help you choose somewhere really special for your stay, we've listed here all RAC Award-winning properties in this region.

Gold Ribbon Award

Premier

Caragh Lodge, Caragh Lake

Cashel House Hotel, Cashel

Dunbrody Country House Hotel & Spa, Arthurstown

The K Club, Straffan

Blue Ribbon Award

Excellent

		pg
Ballygarry House, Tralee	★★★★	606
Gregans Castle Hotel, Ballyvaughan	★★★	564
Herbert Park Hotel, Dublin	★★★★	578
Inchydoney Island Lodge & Spa, Cork	★★★★	571
Kelly's Resort Hotel, Rosslare	★★★★	604
Killashee House Hotel & Villa Spa, Naas	★★★★	601
Kingsley Hotel, Cork	★★★★	571
Moyglare Manor Hotel, Maynooth	★★★	600
Tinakilly House Hotel, Wicklow	★★★	610

White Ribbon Award

Commended

		pg
Ardagh Hotel & Restaurant, Clifden	★★★	569
Cahernane House Hotel, Killarney	★★★★	593
Crowne Plaza, Dublin Airport Dublin 9	★★★★	577
Killarney Royal, Killarney	★★★★	593
Knockranny House Hotel, Westport	★★★★	608
Renvyle House Hotel, Clifden	★★★	569
Sea View House Hotel, Ballylickey	★★★	563

Gregans Castle Hotel, Ballyvaughan

Herbert Park Hotel, Dublin

Knockranny House Hotel, Westport

Renvyle House Hotel, Clifden

Little Gem Award

Little Gem		pg
Ahernes Seafood Restaurant & Accommodation, Yougal	♦♦♦♦♦	611
Ashlee Lodge, Blarney	♦♦♦♦♦	566
Ballymaloe House, Midleton	♦♦♦♦♦	600
Ballyvolane House, Fermoy	♦♦♦♦♦	588
Byrne Mal Dua House, Clifden	♦♦♦♦♦	570
Churchtown House, Rosslare	♦♦♦♦♦	604
Coopershill House, Riverstown	♦♦♦♦♦	603
Coursetown Country House, Athy	♦♦♦♦♦	562
Earls Court House, Killarney	♦♦♦♦♦	595
Fairview Guest House, Killarney	♦♦♦♦♦	595
Glasha, Ballymacarbry	♦♦♦♦♦	563
Kilmokea Country Manor and Gardens, Campile	♦♦♦♦♦	566
Mount Royd Country Home, Carrigans	♦♦♦♦♦	568
Pembroke Townhouse, Dublin	♦♦♦♦♦	584
The Castle Country House, Dungarvan	♦♦♦♦♦	588
Trinity Lodge, Dublin	♦♦♦♦	586

Ahernes Seafood Restaurant & Accommodation, Yougal

Ashlee Lodge, Blarney

Ballymaloe House, Midleton

Churchtown House, Rosslare

Achill Island, Co. Mayo

Achill Cliff House Hotel

★★★ ®

Keel, Achill Island, Co. Mayo
Tel: +353(0)98 43400 Fax: +353(0)98 43007
Email: info@achillcliff.com
Web: www.achillcliff.com
Seasonal closure: 24–26 December
Rooms: 10 all ensuite ⊛
Pricing: Sgl €35–100 Dbl €70–100
Dinner available from €25–35 CC: Accepted
Room facilities: ▢ ☎ ◎ ↳
Conference: 1 meeting room (Thtr 40 max)
Children: Welcome 10yrs min age ⫪ Licenses: ♣♣♣
Leisure: Sauna Parking: Off-street and free
Directions: From Castlebar to Newport, Mulranny Achill
Sound and 11 miles further, on the right side of road in
Keel is Achill Cliff House Hotel.
Map ref: Keel 16 A3

Adare, Co. Limerick

Ballycannon Lodge

◆◆◆◆ ✳⧅

Adare Croagh, Co. Limerick
Tel: +353(0)69 64084 Fax: +353(0)69 64084
Email: info@ballycannonlodge.com
Web: www.ballycannonlodge.com
Rooms: 11 all ensuite ⊛ ⊛
Pricing: Dinner available from €15 CC: Accepted
Room facilities: ▢ ◎
Children: Welcome ⫪ Licenses: ♣♣♣
Parking: Off-street and free
Map ref: Adare 18 C2
See advert on this page

Berkeley Lodge

◆◆◆◆ ✳⧅

Station Road, Adare, Co. Limerick
Tel: +353(0)61 396857 Fax: +353(0)61 396857
Email: berlodge@iol.ie
Web: www.adare.org
Rooms: 6 all ensuite ⊛ ⊛
Pricing: Sgl €58 Dbl €70 CC: Accepted
Room facilities: ▢ ◎
Children: Welcome 2yrs min age ⫪
Parking: Off-street and free
Directions: Take route N21 (Limerick) via Killarney to
Adare. Turn right at roundabout. Hotel is fifth house on
the right after petrol station.
Map ref: Adare 18 C2

Coatesland House Guesthouse (Hogans)

◆◆◆◆ ✳⧅ ☙

Tralee/Killarney Road (N21), Adare, Co. Limerick
Tel: +353(0)61 396372 Fax: +353(0)61 396833
Email: coatesfd@indigo.ie
Web: http://indigo.ie/~coatesfd/
Seasonal closure: 10 to 28 December

Rooms: 6 all ensuite ⊛ ⊛ CC: Accepted
Room facilities: ▢ ☎ ◎ Children: Welcome ⫪ ⟐
Dogs: Welcome Parking: Off-street and free
Directions: 1 km from village centre. Left side, beside
Doherty Farm machinery yard on N21 Tralee road.
Map ref: Adare 18 C2

Arthurstown, Co. Wexford

Dunbrody Country House Hotel & Spa

★★★ ® ® ® *Premier*

Arthurstown, near Waterford, Co. Wexford
Tel: +353(0)51 389600 Fax: +353(0)51 389601
Email: dunbrody@indigo.ie
Web: www.dunbrodyhouse.com
Seasonal closure: 20–26 December
Rooms: 22 all ensuite ⊛
Pricing: Sgl €135–250 Dbl €225–325
Dinner available from €55 CC: Accepted
Room facilities: ▢ ☎ ↳
Conference: 1 meeting room (Thtr 70 max)
Children: Welcome ⟐ Licenses: ⟲ ♣♣♣
Leisure: Health spa, Beauty salon, Cookery school
Parking: Off-street and free
Directions: From Dublin via M11/N11 to Wexford and
R733 to Arthurstown. From Cork N25 via Waterford
and passage east car ferry Ballyhack.
Map ref: Arthurstown 19 E3
See advert on following page

Republic of Ireland

DUNBRODY COUNTRY HOUSE HOTEL & SPA

Set in 200 acres of beautiful parkland, Dunbrody is an enchantingly intimate 1830s Georgian manor. Ancestral home to the Chichester family, the house has a long and established tradition of hospitality. Crackling log fires in period fireplaces, relaxed elegance, Dunbrody is a charming hotel with character and atmosphere of its own. Rates from €125 pps DBB.

ARTHURSTOWN, NEW ROSS,
CO. WEXFORD, IRELAND

Tel: +353(0)51 389600
Fax: +353(0)51 389601

Email: dunbrody@indigo.ie
Web: www.dunbrodyhouse.com

RaC
★★★
Hotel
Gold Ribbon Award

RAC
Dining
Award 🍴🍴🍴

Athlone, Co. Westmeath

Hodson Bay Hotel
★★★ 🏠

Athlone, Co. Westmeath
Tel: +353(0)90 6442000 Fax: +353(0)90 6442020
Email: info@hodsonbayhotel.com
Web: www.hodsonbayhotel.com

A very popular hotel located on the shores of Lough Ree. It offers panoramic views and very comfortable rooms. Ample secure car parking is available.
Rooms: 180 all ensuite 🛏️
Pricing: Sgl €70–200 Dbl €110–320
Dinner available from €39
CC: Accepted
Room facilities: 📺 ☎️ 🍵 🔌
Access: ♿
Conference: 14 meeting rooms (Thtr 1500 max),

day-delegate from €23
Children: Welcome 🍴
Dogs: Assistance dogs only
Licenses: 🍷 🍸
Leisure: Indoor pool, Gym, Health spa, Beauty salon, Golf, Thermal and treatment spa, Outdoor hot-tub
Parking: Off-street and free
Directions: The hotel is located off the N61 Roscommon Road just 5 minutes from Athlone Town, 90 minutes from Dublin International Airport.
Map ref: Athlone 19 D1

Athy, Co. Kildare

Coursetown Country House   `Little Gem`
◆◆◆◆◆ ✂️ 🍷

Stradbally Road, Athy, Co. Kildare
Tel: +353(0)59 86 31101 Fax: +353(0)59 86 32740
Email: coursetown@hotmail.com
Web: www.coursetown.com
Seasonal closure: 20 December to 6 January
Rooms: 4 all ensuite 🔌
Pricing: Sgl €75 Dbl €110
CC: Accepted
Room facilities: 📺 ☎️ 🍵
Dogs: Welcome
Parking: Off-street and free
Directions: Turn off N78 at Athy or N80 at Stradbally onto R428. House is 3km from Athy and 9km from Stradbally.
Map ref: Athy 19 E2

Ballinamore, Co. Leitrim

Riversdale Farm Guesthouse
◆◆◆◆ ✂️

Ballinamore, Co. Leitrim
Tel: +353(0)71 9644122 Fax: +353(0)71 9644813
Email: riversdaleguesthouse@eircom.net
Web: www.riversdale.biz
Seasonal closure: 30 November to 31 January
Rooms: 13 all ensuite 🛏️ 🔌
Pricing: Sgl €40–48 Dbl €80
Dinner available from €18 CC: Accepted
Room facilities: ☎️ 🍵
Conference: 1 meeting room (Thtr 20 max)
Children: Welcome 3yrs min age 🍴 🍼
Licenses: 🍸
Leisure: Indoor pool, Gym, Fishing, Games room, Sauna, Squash
Parking: Off-street and free
Directions: From centre Ballinamore on R202 follow signpost Riversdale or Carrigallen. Riversdale is 1½ miles on left, sign at entrance.
Map ref: Ballinamore 17 D3

Ballycotton, Co.Cork

Bayview Hotel

★★★

Ballycotton, Co. Cork
Tel: +353(0)21 4646746 Fax: +353(0)21 4646075
Email: res@thebayviewhotel.com
Web: www.thebayviewhotel.com
Seasonal closure: November to March
Rooms: 35 all ensuite ⚑ ⊗
Pricing: Dinner available from €48.50
CC: Accepted
Room facilities: ▢ ☎ ⊙ ⦀
Access: |↥|
Conference: 2 meeting rooms (Thtr 40 max)
Children: Welcome ⼍ ⫝̸ Dogs: Assistance dogs only
Licenses: ⵗ
Parking: Off-street and free
Directions: At Castlemantyr on the N25, turn onto the
R632. Follow the signs for Ballycotton.
Map ref: Ballycotton 19 D4

Ballyheigue, Co. Kerry

White Sands Hotel

★★★

Ballyheigue, Co. Kerry
Tel: +353(0)66 33357 Fax: +353(0)66 713357
Email: whitesands@eircom.net
Web: www.irishcountryhotels.com
Seasonal closure: 1 November to 31 March
Rooms: 81 all ensuite
Directions: Located in the town of Ballyheigh on the
R551 between Tralee and Ballybunnon.
Map ref: Ballyheigue 18 B3

Ballylickey, Co. Cork

Sea View House Hotel

★★★

Ballylickey, Bantry, Co. Cork
Tel: +353(0)27 50462 Fax: +353(0)27 51555
Email: info@seaviewhousehotel.com
Web: www.seaviewhousehotel.com
Seasonal closure: Mid November to mid March

Set in private grounds in the village of Ballylickey in
West Cork, this charming country house is renowned
for its tranquility and unique beauty and is a welcome
retreat for the leisure or business traveller.
Rooms: 25 all ensuite ⚑
Pricing: Sgl €80–100 Dbl €140–200
Dinner available from €45–50
CC: Accepted
Room facilities: ▢ ☎ ⦀
Conference: 1 meeting room (Thtr 20 max)
Children: Welcome ⼍ ⫝̸
Dogs: Welcome
Licenses: ⵗ
Directions: On main route N71, 3 miles from Bantry,
7 miles from Glengariff.
Map ref: Bantry 18 B4

Ballymacarbry, Co. Waterford

Glasha   Little Gem

◆◆◆◆◆ ⊠⊙

Ballymacarbry, via Clonmel, Co. Waterford
Tel: +353(0)52 36108 Fax: +353(0)52 36108
Email: glasha@eircom.net
Web: www.glashafarmhouse.com
Seasonal closure: 1-28 December

This is a very popular award-winning guest house set
in the quiet town of Ballymacarbry. All rooms are very
comfortable. This is an ideal base from which to
explore the counties of Waterford and Tipperary.
Rooms: 8 all ensuite ⊗
Pricing: Sgl €100–120 Dbl €100–120
Dinner available from €25
CC: Accepted
Room facilities: ▢ ⊙
Leisure: Fishing
Parking: Off-street
Directions: Take the 671 between Clonmel and
Dungarvan, there are 3 signs for Glasha on the 671.
Map ref: Ballymacarbry 19 D3

"Stay!"

Need a pet friendly property? Look
out for 'Dogs welcome' in our listings.

Republic of Ireland

Hanoras Cottage, Country House & Restaurant

◆◆◆◆◆ �?�?✕☐

Nire Valley, Ballymacarbry, Co. Waterford
Tel: +353(0)52 36134 Fax: +353(0)52 36540
Email: hanorascottage@eircom.net
Web: www.hanorascottage.com
Rooms: 10 all ensuite ⊗
Pricing: Dbl € 160–250 Dinner available
CC: Accepted
Room facilities: ☐ ☎ ☕
Licenses: ♦♦♦
Leisure: Health spa
Parking: Off-street and free
Directions: From Clonmel or Dungarvan take R672 to Ballymacarbry. Turn off at Melody's Pub. Hotel is signposted from there, directly beside the Nire Church.
Map ref: Ballymacarbry 19 D3

Ballysadare, Co. Sligo

Seashore House

◆◆◆◆ ✕☐ ❦

Off Ballina Road (N59), Lisduff, Ballysadare, Co. Sligo
Tel: +353(0)71 9167827 Fax: +353(0)71 9167827
Email: seashore@oceanfree.net
Web: www.seashoreguests.com
Rooms: 5 (4 ensuite) ⊗
Pricing: Sgl € 45–50 Dbl € 70–75
Room facilities: ☐
Leisure: Tennis, Birdwatching facilities
Directions: Turn off N4 taking N59 towards Ballysadare village. N59 at bridge in Ballysadare, travel 4km west. Seashore sign is clearly visible on right around a bend.
Map ref: Lisduff 16 C3

Are the bells ringing?

Getting married? Congratulations! Look for the wedding bells symbol which shows hotels licensed for civil ceremonies.

Ballyvaughan, Co. Clare

Gregans Castle Hotel

★★★★ �?�? Excellent

Ballyvaughan, Co. Clare
Tel: +353(0)65 7077005 Fax: +353(0)65 7077111
Email: stay@gregans.ie
Web: www.gregans.ie
Seasonal closure: 23 October 2005 to 6 April 2006

Situated in the Burren, a unique area of Ireland with limestone scenery stretching up to Galway Bay and the Arran Islands beyond. This hotel offers traditional Irish hospitality in a relaxing environment with turf fires and genuine warm smiles.
Rooms: 21 all ensuite ⊗ ✉ ⊗
Pricing: Sgl € 120–178 Dbl € 170–210
Dinner available from € 27–52
CC: Accepted
Room facilities: ☎
Conference: 1 meeting room (Thtr 20 max)
Children: Welcome ♯ ☕
Licenses: ♦♦♦
Parking: Off-street and free
Directions: 3¹/₂ miles south of Ballyvaughan village on road N67, approx 1 hour from Shannon International Airport.
Map ref: Gregans Castle 18 B1

Rusheen Lodge

◆◆◆◆◆ ✕☐ ❦

Knocknagrough, Ballyvaughan, Co. Clare
Tel: +353(0)65 7077092 Fax: +353(0)65 7077152
Email: rusheen@iol.ie
Web: www.rusheenlodge.com
Seasonal closure: December to January
Rooms: 9 all ensuite ⊗ ⊗
Pricing: Sgl € 55–68 Dbl € 80–96
CC: Accepted
Room facilities: ☐ ☎ ☕
Children: Welcome ☕
Parking: Off-street and free
Directions: From Ballyvaughan village, take N67 south for ³/₄ km. Rusheen Lodge is on the left-hand side of the road.
Map ref: Knocknagrough 18 B1

Bantry, Co. Cork

Westlodge Hotel

★★★

Bantry, Co. Cork
Tel: +353(0)27 50360 Fax: +353(0)27 50438
Email: reservations@westlodgehotel.ie
Web: www.westlodgehotel.ie

This modern hotel is popular with both the leisure and corporate market and is close to the picturesque Bantry Bay. All rooms are comfortable and the hotel has modern leisure facilities.
Rooms: 90 all ensuite 🐾 ⊗
Pricing: Sgl €80–95 Dbl €130–170
Dinner available from €36
CC: Accepted
Room facilities: 🖵 ☎ ☺
Access: 🚻
Conference: 3 meeting rooms (Thtr 300 max)
Children: Welcome 🍴 🐴 ⁙
Licenses: ⟁ ⚯
Leisure: Indoor pool, Gym, Health spa, Tennis, Snooker/billiards
Parking: Off-street and free
Map ref: Bantry 18 B4

Blarney, Co. Cork

Blarney Castle

★★★

Village Green, Blarney, Co. Cork
Tel: +353(0)21 4385116 Fax: +353(0)21 4385542
Email: info@blarneycastlehotel.com
Web: www.blarneycastlehotel.com
Seasonal closure: Christmas Day only

Situated in the heart of Blarney town this is a small family run hotel. All rooms are very comfortable and it is an ideal base from which to explore the Cork and Kerry regions.
Rooms: 13 all ensuite 🐾 ⊗
Pricing: Sgl €60–85 Dbl €110–130
Dinner available from €25.50
CC: Accepted
Room facilities: 🖵 ☎ ☺ 🗝 ❄
Conference: 2 meeting rooms (Thtr 100 max)
Children: Welcome 🍴
Licenses: ⚯
Parking: Off-street and free
Directions: From the N20 take a left for Blarney and hotel is located in the village on the left-hand side.
Map ref: Blarney 18 C4

Belturbet, Co. Cavan

Church View Guest House

◆◆◆◆ ✱✍

8 Church Street, Belturbet, Cavan, Co. Cavan
Tel: +353(0)49 95 22358
Web: www.churchviewguesthouse.com
Rooms: 8 (7 ensuite) 🐾 ⊗
Pricing: Sgl €30–35 Dbl €60–70
CC: Accepted
Room facilities: 🖵
Children: Welcome
Parking: Off-street and free
Directions: Church View Guest House is situated in Belturbet, Co. Cavan, 1³/₄ hours from Belfast and Dublin.
Map ref: Cavan 17 D3

The big sleep

As part of our comprehensive inspection process, RAC Inspectors investigate the comfort of the beds.

Republic of Ireland

Ashlee Lodge   `Little Gem`

◆◆◆◆◆ ✕🗇 ♔

Tower, Blarney, Co. Cork
Tel: +353(0)21 4385346 Fax: +353(0)21 4385726
Email: info@ashleelodge.com
Web: www.ashleelodge.com

This charming 4-star private hotel is a rare find, striking
the perfect balance between traditional comfort and a
contemporary atmosphere. A winner of numerous national
awards, boasting some of the finest bedrooms in Ireland.
Rooms: 10 all ensuite 🚭
Pricing: Sgl €85–125 Dbl €140–200
Dinner available from €30
CC: Accepted
Room facilities: 💻 ☎ 🗇 ☕ ❋
Children: Welcome   Dogs: Welcome
Licenses: ♦♦♦
Leisure: Health spa, Sauna
Parking: Off-street and free
Directions: Located on Blarney-Killarney road R617, in
the village of Tower, just outside Blarney village.
Map ref: Blarney 18 C4

Bray, Co. Wicklow

The Royal Hotel & Leisure Centre

★★★

Main Street, Bray, Co. Wicklow
Tel: +353(0)1 2862935 Fax: +353(0)1 2867373
Email: reservations@royalhotel.ie
Web: www.royalhotel.ie
Rooms: 98 all ensuite 🐾 🚭
Pricing: Dinner available from €25–28
CC: Accepted
Room facilities: 💻 ☎ 🗇 ☕
Access: ⏏
Conference: 6 meeting rooms (Thtr 500 max),
24hr-delegate from €160, day-delegate from €45
Children: Welcome ✛ 🐎
Licenses: ◈ ♦♦♦
Leisure: Indoor pool, Gym, Beauty salon, Golf,
Games room
Parking: Off-street
Map ref: Bray 19 F1

Campile, Co. Wexford

Kilmokea Country Manor and Gardens   `Little Gem`

◆◆◆◆◆ ✕🗇 ♔

Kilmokea, Great Island, Campile, Co. Wexford
Tel: +353(0)51 388109 Fax: +353(0)51 388776
Email: kilmokea@eircom.net
Web: www.kilmokea.com and www.ireland4food.net
Rooms: 6 (5 ensuite) 🐾 🚭
Pricing: Sgl €115–160 Dbl €170–260
Dinner available from €45–60
CC: Accepted
Room facilities: ☎ 🗇
Conference: 1 meeting room (Thtr 60 max)
Children: Welcome ✛ 🍼
Dogs: Welcome ✛
Licenses: ♦♦♦
Leisure: Indoor pool, Gym, Health spa, Tennis, Fishing,
Games room, Jacuzzi, Sauna, Aromatherapy
Parking: Off-street and free
Directions: Take R733 towards Campile. Follow brown
signs to Kilmokea Gardens.
Map ref: Kilmokea 19 E3

Caragh Lake, Co. Kerry

Caragh Lodge

★★ 🛏🛏🛏   Premier

Caragh Lake, Killorglin, Co. Kerry
Tel: +353(0)66 9769115 Fax: +353(0)66 9769316
Email: caraghl@iol.ie
Web: www.caraghlodge.com
Seasonal closure: Mid October to end April

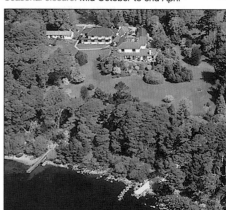

A well established owner-run hotel that has been much
extended and improved over the years. It boasts light,
comfortable rooms, very good food, a friendly team of
staff and wonderfully picturesque location on the
shores of Caragh Lake.
Rooms: 15 all ensuite 🚭
Pricing: Sgl €140 Dbl €195–350
Dinner available from €45
CC: Accepted
Room facilities: ☎

Children: Welcome 12yrs min age
Licenses:
Leisure: Fishing
Parking: Off-street and free
Directions: From Killorglin, take N70 towards Glenbeigh.
Turn left after 3 miles at signpost 'Caragh Lodge'. Turn
left at end of road. Caragh Lodge on right.
Map ref: Killorglin 18 B3

Carlow Town, Co. Carlow

Barrowville Town House

♦♦♦♦♦

Kilkenny Road, Carlow Town, Co. Carlow
Tel: +353(0)59 9143324 Fax: +353(0)59 9141953
Email: barrowvilletownhouse@eircom.net
Web: www.barrowvillehouse.com

Five-diamond Georgian listed town house. Well
appointed bedrooms. Traditional or buffet breakfast
served in conservatory overlooking gardens. Excellent
location for golf and touring Southeast/Midlands.
Rooms: 7 all ensuite
Pricing: Sgl €55–65 Dbl €90–95
CC: Accepted
Room facilities:
Parking: Off-street and free
Directions: On N9 south side of Carlow Town at fifth
traffic light on right. Travelling north 50 metres, before
first right, on left.
Map ref: Carlow 19 E2

Celtic B & B

♦♦♦

34 Hillview Drive, Rathnapish, Carlow Town,
Co. Carlow
Tel: +353(0)59 9135762 Fax: +353(0)59 9135762
Email: celticaccommodation@eircom.net
Seasonal closure: Christmas to New Year
Rooms: 6 (5 ensuite)
Room facilities:
Children: Welcome
Parking: Off-street and free
Directions: Main Dublin to Carlow road, pass through
roundabout to town, 1st B&B on left-hand side, 10
minute walk to town centre.
Map ref: Rathnapish 19 E2

Carraroe, Co. Galway

Hotel Carraroe

★★

Carraroe, Co. Galway
Tel: +353(0)91 595116 Fax: +353(0)91 595187
Map ref: Carraroe 18 B1

Carrick-on-Shannon, Co. Leitrim

The Landmark Hotel

★★★★

Carrick-on-Shannon, Co. Leitrim
Tel: +353 (0)71 9622222 Fax: +353 (0)71 9622233
Email: landmarkhotel@eircom.net
Web: www.thelandmarkhotel.com

The hotel overlooks the River Shannon and its
picturesque marina, just a stroll from the town. Offering
luxurious accommodation, the Boardwalk Café and
Bar, Ferrari's Bistro – with innovative cuisine,
conference and banqueting facilities.
Rooms: 50 all ensuite
Pricing: Sgl €125–153 Dbl €189–245
Dinner available from €45
CC: Accepted
Room facilities:
Access:
Conference: 6 meeting rooms (Thtr 450 max)
Children: Welcome
Licenses:
Parking: Off-street and free
Directions: Located on the N4 Sligo-Dublin road.
Approaching Carrick from Dublin, take the first exit off
the roundabout and the hotel is on the right-hand side.
Map ref: Carrick-on-Shannon 16 C3

Republic of Ireland

Carrigaline, Co. Cork

Carrigaline Court Hotel & Leisure Centre

★★★★

Main Street, Carrigaline, Co. Cork
Tel: +353(0)21 4852100 Fax: +353(0)21 4371103
Email: reception@carrigcourt.com
Web: www.carrigcourt.com
Seasonal closure: 25-26 December
Rooms: 91 all ensuite
Pricing: Sgl €115 Dbl €178
Dinner available from €35 CC: Accepted
Room facilities: ▢ ☎ ☕ ✎
Access: ♿
Conference: 5 meeting rooms (Thtr 350 max),
24hr-delegate from €163, day-delegate from €35
Children: Welcome 🍴 🎠
Licenses: ⚓ ♟
Leisure: Indoor pool, Gym, Beauty salon, Jacuzzi,
Steam room, Sauna
Parking: Off-street and free
Directions: Follow the south ring road until the
Shannonpark roundabout, then follow prominent signs
for Carrigaline, located 15 mins drive from city centre.
Map ref: Carrigaline 18 C4

Carrigans, Co. Donegal

Mount Royd Country Home   Little Gem

♦♦♦♦♦ 🍴 ☕

Carrigans, near Derry, Co. Donegal
Tel: +353(0)74 9140163 Fax: +353(0)74 9140400
Email: jmartin@mountroyd.com
Web: www.mountroyd.com
Seasonal closure: December and January

You can be assured of old style hospitality in our
charming, award-winning home. Very central for
touring the north-west. Derry city 9km, airport 25
minutes. Top 20 AA Landlady 2005.
Rooms: 4 all ensuite
Pricing: Sgl €35–40 Dbl €57–65
Room facilities: ▢ ☕
Children: Welcome 12yrs min age 🍴
Parking: Off-street and free
Directions: Carrigans signposted off N13 and N14 on
R236. From Londonderry take A40. Mount Royd in
Carrigans village.
Map ref: Carrigans 17 D1

Cashel, Co. Galway

Cashel House Hotel   Premier

★★★ ♟♟♟

Cashel, Connemara, Co. Galway
Tel: +353(0)95 31001 Fax: +353(0)95 31077
Email: info@cashel-house-hotel.com
Web: www.cashel-house-hotel.com
Seasonal closure: 5 January to 5 February

An oasis of elegance, charm and good food
surrounded by 10 acres of one of Ireland's best
gardens and 1,500 square miles of Connemara's
unspoilt mountains and boglands.
Rooms: 32 all ensuite 🚗
Pricing: Sgl €85–125 Dbl €170–310
Dinner available from €49 CC: Accepted
Room facilities: ▢ ☎ ☕ ✎
Children: Welcome 🍴 🎠 Dogs: Welcome
Licenses: ♟
Leisure: Tennis, Garden, Hill walking
Parking: Off-street and free
Directions: Take N59 from Galway, 1 mile after Recess
take left turn. Hotel is signposted from there.
Map ref: Cashel 19 D3

Castlebar, Co. Mayo

Lynch Breaffy House Spa & Suites

★★★

Castlebar, Co. Mayo
Tel: +353(0)65 6823000 Fax: +353(0)65 6823759
Email: reservations@lynchotels.com
Web: www.lynchotels.com
Rooms: 125 all ensuite
Pricing: Dinner available from €30 CC: Accepted
Room facilities: ▢ ☎ ☕ ✎
Access: ♿
Conference: 7 meeting rooms (Thtr 500 max),
24hr-delegate from €185, day-delegate from €50
Children: Welcome 🍴 🎠
Dogs: Assistance dogs only
Licenses: ⚓ ♟
Leisure: Indoor pool, Gym, Health spa, Beauty salon
Parking: Off-street and free
Directions: Lynch Breaffy House Spa & Suites is
located only 4km outside Castlebar town on the N60
going towards Tuam and Galway.
Map ref: Castlebar 16 B3

Castlemartyr, Co. Cork

Garryvoe Hotel

★★

Castlemartyr, Co. Cork
Tel: +353(0)21 4646718 Fax: +353(0)21 4646824
Email: res@garryvoehotel.com
Web: www.garryvoehotel.com
Seasonal closure: 24 December
Rooms: 50 all ensuite
Pricing: Dinner available from €34 CC: Accepted
Room facilities:
Conference: 4 meeting rooms (Thtr 300 max)
Children: Welcome
Dogs: Assistance dogs only
Licenses:
Leisure: Tennis
Parking: Off-street and free
Directions: At Castlemartyr on the N25, main Cork to
Waterford Road, turn onto the R632 in the direction of
Garryvoe.
Map ref: Castlemartyr 19 D4

Clifden, Co. Galway

Alcock & Brown Hotel

★★★

The Square, Clifden, Co. Galway
Tel: +353(0)95 21206 Fax: +353(0)95 21842
Email: alcockandbrown@eircom.net
Web: www.alcockandbrown-hotel.com
Seasonal closure: 22–26 December
Rooms: 19 all ensuite
Pricing: Sgl €75–99 Dbl €110–268
Dinner available from €25 CC: Accepted
Room facilities: Children: Welcome
Dogs: Welcome
Licenses:
Directions: From Dublin take N6 to Galway, then N59
to Clifden. Hotel is in centre of village.
Map ref: Clifden 16 A4

Ardagh Hotel & Restaurant

★★★
Commended

Ballyconneely Road, Clifden, Co. Galway
Tel: +353(0)95 21384 Fax: +353(0)95 21314
Email: ardaghhotel@eircom.net
Web: www.ardaghhotel.com
Seasonal closure: November to March
Rooms: 21 all ensuite
Pricing: Dinner available from €38–49.50
CC: Accepted
Room facilities:
Children: Welcome Dogs: Welcome
Licenses:
Leisure: Games room, Snooker/billiards
Parking: Off-street
Directions: From Clifden Town follow signs to
Ballyconneely. Ardagh Hotel is 2 miles out of Clifden.
Map ref: Clifden 16 A4

Clifden Station House

★★★

Clifden, Connemara, Co. Galway
Tel: +353(0)95 21699 Fax: +353(0)95 21667
Email: reservations@clifdenstationhouse.com
Web: www.clifdenstationhouse.com
Seasonal closure: Christmas
Rooms: 78 all ensuite
Dinner available CC: Accepted
Room facilities:
Access:
Conference: 3 meeting rooms (Thtr 300 max)
Children: Welcome
Licenses:
Leisure: Indoor pool, Gym, Beauty salon, Games room
Parking: Off-street and free
Directions: N59 from Galway city.
Map ref: Clifden 16 A4

Renvyle House Hotel

★★★
Commended

Renvyle, Connemara, Co. Galway
Tel: +353(0)95 43511 Fax: +353(0)95 43515
Email: info@renvyle.com
Web: www.renvyle.com
Seasonal closure: January to February
Rooms: 69 all ensuite
Pricing: Sgl €30–199 Dbl €50–310
Dinner available from €45
CC: Accepted
Room facilities:
Conference: 2 meeting rooms (Thtr 120 max)
Children: Welcome Dogs: Welcome
Licenses:
Leisure: Outdoor pool, Tennis, Golf, Fishing, Riding,
Snooker/billiards
Parking: Off-street and free
Directions: Take N59 west from Galway. At Recess turn
right, at Kylemore turn left. At Letterfrack turn right.
Continue for 5 miles.
Map ref: Renvyle 16 A4

Buttermilk Lodge Guest House

◆◆◆◆◆

Westport Road, Clifden, Co. Galway
Tel: +353(0)95 21951 Fax: +353(0)95 21953
Email: buttermilklodge@eircom.net
Web: www.buttermilklodge.com
Seasonal closure: 3 January to 3 February
Rooms: 11 all ensuite
Pricing: Sgl €45–70 Dbl €70–90
CC: Accepted
Room facilities:
Children: Welcome 5yrs min age
Leisure: Own farm nearby for guests to visit,
Connemara ponies and sheep
Parking: Off-street and free
Directions: From Galway, turn right at Esso station;
Buttermilk is 400 metres on left. From Westport,
Buttermilk is on right 100 metres after 'Clifden' sign.
Map ref: Clifden 16 A4

Republic of Ireland

Byrne Mal Dua House `Little Gem`

◆◆◆◆◆

Galway Road, Clifden, Connemara, Co. Galway
Tel: +353(0)95 21171 Fax: +353(0)95 21739
Email: info@maldua.com Web: www.maldua.com
Rooms: 14 all ensuite
Pricing: Sgl €45–85 Dbl €90–165 CC: Accepted
Room facilities:
Conference: 3 meeting rooms (Thtr 30 max)
Children: Welcome Dogs: Assistance dogs only
Licenses: Leisure: Basketball
Parking: Off-street and free
Directions: Located on the Galway Road (N59), 1 km
from Clifden.
Map ref: Clifden 16 A4

Highfield Lodge

◆◆◆◆

Dooneen Road, Clifden, Co. Galway
Tel: +353(0)95 22283
Email: highfield@highfieldlodge.com
Web: www.highfieldlodge.com
Seasonal closure: 1 October to 7 March
Rooms: 4 all ensuite
Room facilities:
Children: Welcome 7yrs min age
Parking: Off-street and free
Directions: Seven minutes walk from town centre on
Dooneen Road overlooking Clifden.
Map ref: Clifden 16 A4

Benview House

◆◆◆

Bridge Street, Clifden, Co. Galway
Tel: +353(0)95 21256 Fax: +353(0)95 21226
Email: benviewhouse@ireland.com
Web: www.benviewhouse.com

Charming mid-19th century town of immense character.
Our family has been extending traditional family hospitality
to our guests continuously since 1926. Recommended by
Frommer and Le Petit Fute guides.
Rooms: 9 all ensuite
Pricing: Sgl €30–50 Dbl €60–76
CC: Accepted
Room facilities:
Children: Welcome
Directions: Take N59 to Clifden Town. Located on
Bridge Street, just off N59 and close to town centre.
Map ref: Clifden 16 A4

Clonbur, Co. Galway

Fairhill House Hotel

★★★

Clonbur, Co. Galway
Tel: +353(0)94 954 6176 Fax: +353(0)94 954 6176
Email: fairhillhouse@eircom.net
Web: www.fairhillhouse.com
Seasonal closure: Christmas day
Rooms: 20 all ensuite
Pricing: Sgl £65–85 Dbl £90–130
Dinner available from £30 CC: Accepted
Room facilities: Access:
Conference: 2 meeting rooms (Thtr 250 max),
24hr-delegate from £55
Children: Welcome Dogs: Assistance dogs only
Licenses:
Parking: Off-street and free
Directions: 30 miles from Galway and then onto
Headford Cross, then Clonbur. Hotel is 1 hour from
Knock (airport) and 8 miles from Ballinrobe.
Map ref: Clonbur 16 B4

Clonmel, Co. Tipperary

Hotel Minella

★★★★

Coleville Road, Clonmel, Co. Tipperary
Tel: +353(0)52 22388 Fax: +353(0)52 24381
Email: frontdesk@hotelminella.ie
Web: www.hotelminella.ie
Seasonal closure: 23-28 December
Rooms: 70 all ensuite
Dinner available CC: Accepted
Room facilities: Access:
Conference: 5 meeting rooms (Thtr 500 max)
Children: Welcome
Licenses: Leisure: Indoor pool, Gym, Tennis
Parking: Off-street and free
Directions: On arrival in Clonmel, cross the river to the
south side. Hotel Minella is to the east of the town.
Map ref: Clonmel 19 D3

Connemara, Co. Galway

Carna Bay Hotel

★★★

Carna, Connemara, Co. Galway
Tel: +353(0)95 32255 Fax: +353(0)95 32530
Email: carnabay@iol.ie
Web: www.carnabay.com
Rooms: 26 all ensuite
Dinner available CC: Accepted
Room facilities:
Conference: 1 meeting room (Thtr 60 max)
Children: Welcome Dogs: Welcome
Licenses:
Parking: Off-street and free
Directions: From Galway City take N59. Clifden Road
turn left at Marny Cross for Carna.
Map ref: Carna 16 A4

Zetland Country House Hotel

★★★ ♙♙

Cashel Bay, Connemara, Co. Galway
Tel: +353(0)95 31111 Fax: +353(0)95 31117
Email: zetland@iol.ie
Web: www.zetland.com
Rooms: 20 all ensuite 🛏 🗗 ⊗
Dinner available
CC: Accepted
Room facilities: ▢ ☎ 🍵
Conference: 1 meeting room (Thtr 20 max)
Children: Welcome �🍴 Dogs: Welcome
Licenses: ⚖ ♔♔♔
Leisure: Tennis, Snooker/billiards
Parking: Off-street and free
Directions: From Galway take N59 direction Clifden. 2
miles after Recess left on R340. 4 miles right on R342.
Map ref: Cashel Bay 18 B1

The Anglers Return

◆◆◆◆

Toombeola, Roundstone, Connemara, Co. Galway
Tel: +353(0)95 31091 Fax: +353(0)95 31091
Web: www.anglersreturn.itgo.com
Seasonal closure: December to February
Rooms: 5 (1 ensuite) 🛏 ⊗
Room facilities: 🍵
Conference: 1 meeting room
Children: Welcome 7yrs min age 🍼
Leisure: Fishing, Free trout fishing. Walks on site
Parking: Off-street and free
Directions: From Galway, N59 Galway/Clifden road,
turn left on R341, Ballynahinch/Roundstone road, for 4
miles. The Anglers Return is on left overlooking river.
Map ref: Toombeola 18 B1

Cork, Co. Cork

Hayfield Manor

★★★★★ ♙♙♙ *Premier*

Perrott Avenue, College Road, Cork, Co. Cork
Tel: +353(0)21 484 5900 Fax: +353(0)21 431 6839
Email: enquiries@hayfieldmanor.ie
Web: www.hayfieldmanor.ie
Rooms: 88 all ensuite ⊗
Pricing: Sgl €380 Dbl €380
Dinner available from €40–65 CC: Accepted
Room facilities: ▢ ☎ 🗝 ❄
Access: |↕|
Conference: 6 meeting rooms (Thtr 110 max)
Children: Welcome �🍴 🍼
Dogs: Assistance dogs only
Licenses: ♔♔♔
Leisure: Indoor pool, Gym, Health spa, Beauty salon,
Outdoor hot tub
Parking: Off-street
Directions: Travelling west from city centre, take N70
for Killarney. Turn left at university gates off Western
Road. At top of road turn right and immediately left;
hotel at top of avenue.
Map ref: Cork 18 C4

Inchydoney Island Lodge & Spa

★★★★ ♙♙♙ *Excellent*

Inchydoney Island, Clonakilty, Co. Cork
Tel: +353(0)23 33143/21107 Fax: +353(0)23 35229
Email: reservations@inchydoneyisland.com
Web: www.inchydoneyisland.com
Seasonal closure: 25–26 December
Rooms: 67 all ensuite 🛏 ⊗
Pricing: Sgl €210–215 Dbl €320–340
Dinner available from €55 CC: Accepted
Room facilities: ▢ ☎ 🍵 🗝 Access: |↕|
Conference: 6 meeting rooms (Thtr 300 max),
24hr-delegate from €210, day-delegate from €56
Children: Welcome �🍴 🍼 Licenses: ♔♔♔
Leisure: Indoor pool, Gym, Health spa, Beauty salon,
Games room, Snooker/billiards, Thalasso spa, Surfing
Parking: Off-street and free
Directions: Take N71 from Cork to Clonakilty. Follow
signs to Inchydoney.
Map ref: Inchydoney Island 18 C4

Kingsley Hotel

★★★★ ♙♙♙ *Excellent*

Victoria Cross, Cork, Co. Cork
Tel: +353(0)21 4800 555 Fax: +353(0)21 4800 527
Email: resv@kingsleyhotel.com
Web: www.kingsleyhotel.com

Overlooking the river bank and 5 minutes from the city
centre, this hotel offers elegant bedrooms, richly
adorned public areas, good leisure facilities and
attentive friendly service. Award-winning food, most
notably seafood, served in Otters Restaurant. Spa, 80
new bedrooms and 18 apartments for spring 2006.
Rooms: 69 all ensuite 🛏 🗗
Pricing: Sgl €145–230 Dbl €175–350
Dinner available from €45
CC: Accepted
Room facilities: ▢ ☎ 🍵 🗝 ❄ Access: |↕|
Conference: 11 meeting rooms (Thtr 150 max)
Children: Welcome �🍴
Licenses: ⚖ ♔♔♔
Leisure: Indoor pool, Gym, Health spa, Beauty salon
Directions: Located on the N22 at Victoria Cross 1 km
from Cork City Centre, 5km from Cork Airport.
Map ref: Cork 18 C4

Republic of Ireland

Midleton Park Hotel and Spa

★★★★ ⌾⌾

Old Cork Road, Midleton, Co. Cork
Tel: +353(0)21 4635111 Fax: +353(0)21 4635101
Email: resv@midletonpark.com
Web: www.midletonpark.com
Rooms: 80 all ensuite ⊗
Pricing: Sgl €95–115 Dbl €135–160
Dinner available from €35 CC: Accepted
Room facilities: ▢ ☎ ⊗ ✆ Access: ⌊↑
Conference: 5 meeting rooms (Thtr 300 max),
24hr-delegate from €155
Children: Welcome 冇 Licenses: ⌂ ⋔
Leisure: Indoor pool, Gym, Health spa, Beauty salon
Parking: Off-street and free
Directions: Located off the N25 between Cork and
Waterford just 15 miles from Cork Airport via Jack
Lynch Tunnel.
Map ref: Midleton 18 C4
See advert on this page

Ambassador Hotel Best Western

★★★ ⌾

St. Lukes, Cork City, Co. Cork
Tel: +353(0)21 4551996 Fax: +353(0)21 4551997
Email: reservations@ambassadorhotel.ie
Web: www.ambassadorhotel.ie
Seasonal closure: 24 & 26 December
Rooms: 58 all ensuite ⋈ ⊗

Dinner available CC: Accepted
Room facilities: ▢ ☎ ⊗ ✆ Access: ⌊↑
Conference: 5 meeting rooms (Thtr 220 max)
Children: Welcome 冇 Licenses: ⋔
Leisure: Gym Parking: Off-street and free
Directions: Take a left turn at end of Maclurtoun Street
at lights, proceed up Summerhill and take left turn at St
Luke's Cross.
Map ref: Cork 18 C4

Jurys Inn Cork

★★★

Anderson's Quay, Cork, Co. Cork
Tel: +353(0)21 427 6444 Fax: +353(0)21 427 6144
Email: jurysinncork@jurysdoyle.com
Web: www.jurysinns.com
Seasonal closure: 23-26 December

JURYS DOYLE
HOTELS

Rooms: 133 all ensuite ⊗
Pricing: Sgl €161.50 Dbl €173
Dinner available from €25 CC: Accepted
Room facilities: ▢ ☎ ⊗ ✆ Access: ⌊↑
Conference: 1 meeting room (Thtr 25 max)
Children: Welcome 冇 Licenses: ⋔
Directions: Located 4 miles/6 km from airport. Follow
signs for City Centre.
Map ref: Cork 18 C4

The Gresham Metropole

 ★★★

MacCurtain Street, Cork, Co. Cork
Tel: +353(0)21 4508122 Fax: +353(0)21 4506450
Email: info@gresham-metropolehotel.com
Web: www.gresham-hotels.com

Long established centrally located hotel. Offering a great deal of period charm, comfortable rooms and good food.
Rooms: 113 all ensuite
Pricing: Sgl €90–260 Dbl €90–260
Dinner available from €30–50
CC: Accepted
Room facilities: 📺 ☎ 🍵 �ॄ
Access: |↕|
Conference: 12 meeting rooms (Thtr 500 max), 24hr-delegate from €170, day-delegate from €75
Children: Welcome 🎠
Licenses: 🕴
Leisure: Indoor pool, Gym, Beauty salon, Sauna, Jacuzzi, Steam room, Solarium
Parking: Off-street and free
Directions: Hotel entrance is on MacCurtain Street. Rear of hotel clearly visible from Patrick's Quay. Free parking for guests at check-in.
Map ref: Cork 18 C4

Crawford House

◆◆◆◆ ⚹

Western Road, Cork, Co. Cork
Tel: +353(0)21 4279000 Fax: +353(0)21 4279927
Email: info@crawfordguesthouse.com
Web: www.crawfordguesthouse.com
Rooms: 12 all ensuite ⊛
CC: Accepted
Room facilities: 📺 ☎ 🍵 �ॄ
Children: Welcome 🎠
Parking: Off-street and free
Directions: Ten-minute walk from city centre. Located directly across from University College, Cork. N8 from Dublin, N22 from Kerry.
Map ref: Cork 18 C4

Garnish House

◆◆◆◆ ⚹ ⚭

Western Road, Cork City 21, Co. Cork
Tel: +353(0)21 4275111 Fax: +353(0)21 4273872
Email: garnish@iol.ie Web: www.garnish.ie
Rooms: 20 (14 ensuite) ⊛ ⊛ CC: Accepted
Room facilities: 📺 ☎ 🍵 Children: Welcome 🎠 🧸 🍼
Dogs: Welcome Parking: Off-street
Directions: N8 from Dublin, N22 from Kerry. Close to bus and rail stations, opposite Cork University, 20 min drive from Cork airport.
Map ref: Cork 18 C4

Killarney Guest House

◆◆◆◆ ⚹

Western Road, Cork, Co. Cork
Tel: +353(0)21 4270290 Fax: +353(0)21 4271010
Email: killarneyhouse@iol.ie
Web: killarneyguesthouse.com
Rooms: 19 all ensuite ⊛ CC: Accepted
Room facilities: 📺 ☎ 🍵 Children: Welcome 🎠
Parking: Off-street and free
Directions: 10 minutes' walk from city centre and across from Cork University. N8 from Dublin and N22 from Kerry.
Map ref: Cork 18 C4

Lancaster Lodge

◆◆◆◆ ⚹

Lancaster Quay, Western Road, Cork, Co. Cork
Tel: +353(0)21 4251125 Fax: +353(0)21 4251126
Email: info@lancasterlodge.com
Web: www.lancasterlodge.com
Seasonal closure: 22-26 December
Rooms: 39 all ensuite
Pricing: Sgl €85–130 Dbl €110–160
CC: Accepted Room facilities: 📺 ☎ 🍵 ﹄
Access: |↕| Children: Welcome
Parking: Off-street and free
Directions: Cork City Centre, 20 minutes from airport, adjacent to Jury's Hotel.
Map ref: Cork 18 C4

Lotamore House

◆◆◆◆ ⚹ ⚭

Tivoli, Cork, Co. Cork
Tel: +353(0)21 4822344 Fax: +353(0)21 4822219
Email: lotamore@iol.ie
Web: www.lotamorehouse.com
Rooms: 20 all ensuite ⊛ ⊟ ⊛
CC: Accepted Room facilities: 📺 ☎ ﹄
Conference: 1 meeting room (Thtr 40 max), 24hr-delegate from €150, day-delegate from €40
Children: Welcome 🎠 Dogs: Assistance dogs only
Licenses: 🕴 Parking: Off-street and free
Directions: Depart Cork for Dublin on N8, 1 mile outside city pass Silversprings Hotel on left. Continue halfway down dual carriageway. Lotamore House is well signposted on right.
Map ref: Tivoli 18 C4

Westview Apartments

◆◆◆◆

Apt. 7 Westview House, 16 Washington Street,
Cork, Co. Cork
Tel: +353(0)21 494 4910
Email: info@westview.ie
Web: www.westview.ie
Seasonal closure: 24-26 December
Rooms: 4 all ensuite
Pricing: Sgl €150 Dbl €200 CC: Accepted
Room facilities: Access:
Children: Welcome Dogs: Assistance dogs only
Licenses: Parking: Off-street
Directions: From Cork airport, left at roundabout, third
exit Kinsale roundabout (city centre), left at third set of
lights. Through next lights, right at next, and follow
road along George's Quay. Right over first bridge, left
at lights (South Mall). Past park on Grand Parade, left
at lights onto Washington Street and Westview is on
left after Courthouse.
Map ref: Cork 18 C4

Rose Lodge

◆◆◆

Mardyke Walk, off Western Road, Cork, Co. Cork
Tel: +353(0)21 4272958 Fax: +353(0)21 4274089
Email: info@roselodge.net
Web: www.roselodge.net
Rooms: 16 all ensuite
CC: Accepted
Room facilities:
Children: Welcome
Directions: Take Washington Street, onto Western
Road, take right at university college, first house on
right.
Map ref: Cork 18 C4

Delgany, Co. Wicklow

Glenview Hotel

★★★★

Glen-O-The-Downs, Delgany, Co. Wicklow
Tel: +353(0)1 2873399 Fax: +353(0)1 2877511
Email: sales@glenviewhotel.com
Web: www.glenviewhotel.com
Rooms: 70 all ensuite
Pricing: Sgl €121–160 Dbl €150–240
Dinner available from €15–45
CC: Accepted
Room facilities:
Access:
Conference: 5 meeting rooms (Thtr 200 max)
Children: Welcome 12yrs min age
Licenses:
Leisure: Indoor pool, Gym, Beauty salon
Parking: Off-street and free
Directions: Take N11 southbound towards Wexford.
After village of Kilmacanogne, continue southbound for
approximately 1 mile, take left exit after Ecoshop to
hotel.
Map ref: Delgany 19 F2

Dingle, Co. Kerry

Dingle Benners Hotel

◆◆◆◆◆

Main Street, Dingle, Co. Kerry
Tel: +353(0)66 9151638 Fax: +353(0)66 9151412
Email: reservations@dinglebenners.com
Web: www.dinglebenners.com
Rooms: 52 all ensuite
Pricing: Sgl €85–150 Dbl €120–225
Dinner available from €20–55
CC: Accepted
Room facilities:
Access:
Children: Welcome
Dogs: Assistance dogs only
Licenses:
Parking: Off-street and free
Directions: From N86 at roundabout take right. At end
of street take left up Main Street. Halfway up on left.
Map ref: Dingle 18 A3

Milltown House

◆◆◆◆◆

Dingle, Co. Kerry
Tel: +353(0)66 9151372 Fax: +353(0)66 9151095
Email: info@milltownhousedingle.com
Web: www.milltownhousedingle.com
Seasonal closure: 28 October to 27 April
Rooms: 10 all ensuite
Pricing: Sgl €90–125 Dbl €100–150
CC: Accepted
Room facilities:
Children: Welcome 12yrs min age
Parking: Off-street and free
Directions: Leave Dingle on Sleahead Drive Road. Take
next two left turns. Milltown House less than 1 mile
west of Dingle town.
Map ref: Dingle 18 A3

Alpine House Guest House

◆◆◆◆

Mail Road, Dingle, Co. Kerry
Tel: +353(0)66 9151250 Fax: +353(0)66 9151966
Email: alpinedingle@eircom.net
Web: www.alpineguesthouse.com
Rooms: 10 all ensuite
Pricing: Sgl €35–65 Dbl €60–95
CC: Accepted
Room facilities:
Children: Welcome 5yrs min age
Parking: Off-street and free
Directions: On route N86 at entrance to Dingle town.
2 minutes' walk from town centre.
Map ref: Dingle 18 A3

Inch Beach Guest House

◆◆◆◆

Inch Beach, Inch, Co. Kerry
Tel: +353(0)66 9158333 Fax: +353(0)66 9158388
Email: inch@iol.ie
Web: www.inchbeachguesthouse.com
Seasonal closure: 25-26 December
Rooms: 9 all ensuite ♨ ⊗
CC: Accepted
Room facilities: ▢ ☎ ⬛
Children: Welcome 6yrs min age Ħ
Parking: Off-street and free
Directions: Take R561 towards Castlemaine/Dingle
17 km beyond Castlemaine lies Inch Beach Guest
House situated on the right overlooking the beach.
Map ref: Dingle 18 A3

Donegal, Co. Donegal

Harvey's Point Country Hotel

★★★★★

Lough Eske, Donegal, Co. Donegal
Tel: +353(0)74 9722208 Fax: +353(0)74 9722352
Email: info@harveyspoint.com
Web: www.harveyspoint.com
Seasonal closure: Sunday night, Monday, Tuesday,
November to March

Nestling on the edge of the shimmering Lough Eske,
beneath the majesty of the Blue Stack Mountains,
Harvey's Point is an island of serenity where the warmest
of welcomes awaits those who seek sanctuary.
Rooms: 60 all ensuite ⬛ ⊗
Pricing: Sgl €114–195 Dbl €290–390
Dinner available from €50
CC: Accepted
Room facilities: ▢ ☎ ⬛ ☏
Access: ⚿
Conference: 3 meeting rooms (Thtr 250 max),
24hr-delegate from €150, day-delegate from €35
Dogs: Welcome
Licenses: ⚿
Leisure: Fishing
Parking: Off-street and free
Directions: 6km outside Donegal town.
Map ref: Lough Eske 16 C2

The Milford Inn Hotel

★★★⬛

Letterkenny Road, Milford, Co. Donegal
Tel: +353(0)7491 53313 Fax: +353(0)7491 53388
Email: milfordinnhotel@eircom.net
Web: www.milfordinnhotel.com

On the outskirts of the small town of Milford, this
modern hotel has spacious well-appointed rooms,
many offering views of the surrounding countryside.
The traditional style bar is full of character and the
hotel has a well-earned reputation for its home
cooking.
Rooms: 33 all ensuite
Pricing: Sgl €35–90 Dbl €75–130
Dinner available from €15–30
CC: Accepted
Room facilities: ▢ ☎ ⬛ ☏
Access: ⚿
Conference: 5 meeting rooms (Thtr 450 max)
Children: Welcome Ħ ✳
Licenses: ⚿ ⚿
Leisure: Beauty salon
Parking: Off-street and free
Directions: From the town of Letterkenny follow signs
for Milford/Downings through Ramelton Town. Turn left
at bridge, hotel is 4 miles on left.
Map ref: Milford 17 D1

Republic of Ireland

Ardeevin

Lough Eske, Barnesmore, Donegal, Co. Donegal
Tel: +353(0)74 9721790 Fax: +353(0)74 9721790
Email: seanmcginty@eircom.net
Web: www.members.tripod.com/~Ardeevin
Seasonal closure: 1 December to 17 March

Charming country residence, overlooking Lough Eske
and Donegal Bay. Surrounded by Bluestack Mountains
with Sligo Mountains close by. All bedrooms have a
panoramic view of Lough Eske with its salmon, brown
trout and char. Ther are many forest walks and several
small lakes in the mountains within walking distance.
Convenient to beaches and golf course, horse riding
within 8km.
Rooms: 6 all ensuite
Pricing: Sgl €40–45 Dbl €60–65
Room facilities:
Children: Welcome 10yrs min age
Parking: Off-street and free
Directions: Take N15 from Donegal Town,
Derry/Letterkenny road for 4km. Turn left at sign for
Ardeevin (past garage).
Map ref: Lough Eske 16 C2

Doolin, Co. Clare

Cullinans Seafood Restaurant & Guest House

Doolin, Co. Clare
Tel: +353(0)65 7074183 Fax: +353(0)65 7074239
Email: cullinans@eircom.net
Web: www.cullinansdoolin.com
Rooms: 8 all ensuite
Pricing: Sgl €40–70 Dbl €60–90
Dinner available from €27.50
CC: Accepted
Room facilities:
Children: Welcome
Licenses:
Leisure: Fishing
Parking: Off-street and free
Directions: Situated in the centre of Doolin within 5
minutes walk to the pubs.
Map ref: Doolin 18 B2

Dublin

Merrion Hotel

★★★★★ Premier

Upper Merrion Street, Dublin 2
Tel: +353(0)1 603 0600 Fax: +353(0)1 603 0700
Email: info@merrionhotel.com
Web: www.merrionhotel.com
Rooms: 142 all ensuite
Pricing: Sgl €370–390 Dbl €390–410
Dinner available from €35
CC: Accepted
Room facilities:
Access:
Conference: 6 meeting rooms (Thtr 50 max),
24hr-delegate from €390, day-delegate from €110
Children: Welcome
Licenses:
Leisure: Indoor pool, Gym, Health spa, Beauty salon
Parking: Off-street
Directions: Situated at the top of Upper Merrion Street
on left, opposite government buildings, in the heart of
Dublin city.
Map ref: Dublin 19 F1

The Berkeley Court

★★★★★

Lansdowne Road, Dublin 4
Tel: +353(0)1 6653200 Fax: +353(0)1 6617238
Email: berkeleycourt@jurysdoyle.com
Web: www.jurysdoyle.com

JURYS DOYLE
HOTELS

Rooms: 186 all ensuite
Pricing: Sgl €178–460 Dbl €204–531
Dinner available from €45
CC: Accepted
Room facilities:
Access:
Conference: 10 meeting rooms (Thtr 400 max),
24hr-delegate from €372, day-delegate from €103
Children: Welcome 12yrs min age
Licenses:
Parking: Off-street
Directions: Follow signs to city centre. East Link toll,
over bridge. Follow signs for RDS. Turn right at Jurys
Hotel. Berkeley is on right.
Map ref: Dublin 19 F1

The Westbury Hotel

★★★★★

Grafton Street, Dublin 2
Tel: +353(0)1 6791122 Fax: +353(0)1 6797078
Email: westbury@jurysdoyle.com
Web: www.jurysdoyle.com

JURYS DOYLE
HOTELS

Rooms: 204 all ensuite

Pricing: Sgl €254–480 Dbl €280–552
Dinner available from €35–65
CC: Accepted
Room facilities: ⬜ ☎ 📞 ❄
Access: ⬆
Conference: 9 meeting rooms (Thtr 250 max),
24hr-delegate from €341, day-delegate from €96
Children: Welcome ⍑
Licenses: ⬥ ⬛
Leisure: Gym
Parking: Off-street and free
Directions: Follow the signs to city centre. From south
Great Georges Street onto Exchequer Street, second
right into Clarendon Street, next left.
Map ref: Dublin 19 F1

Castleknock Hotel & Country Club
★★★★
Porterstown Road, Castleknock, Dublin 15
Tel: +353(0)1 6406300 Fax: +353(0)1 6406303
Email: reservations@chcc.ie
Web: www.towerhotelgroup.com
Seasonal closure: 24-26 December
Rooms: 144 all ensuite ⊗
Pricing: Sgl €195 Dbl €245
Dinner available from €45
CC: Accepted
Room facilities: ⬜ ☎ ⊕ 📞
Access: ⬆
Conference: 9 meeting rooms (Thtr 400 max)
Children: Welcome ⍑
Licenses: ⬥ ⬛
Leisure: Indoor pool, Gym, Health spa,
Beauty salon, Golf
Parking: Off-street and free
Directions: Follow N3 out of Dublin City. Take turn for
Castleknock. Turn left at Myos pub. Take next left onto
Porterstown Road.
Map ref: Castleknock 19 F1

Crowne Plaza, Dublin Airport
★★★★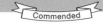
Commended
Northwood Park, Santry Demesne, Santry, Dublin 9
Tel: +353(0)1 8628888 Fax: +353(0)1 8628800
Email: info@crowneplazadublin.ie
Web: www.cpdublin-airport.com
Seasonal closure: 24-25 December

The Crowne Plaza is situated in a mature parkland
setting of 120 acres, 5 minutes from the airport and
only 15 minutes from the city centre.
Rooms: 204 all ensuite ⊗ 📺 ⊗
Pricing: Sgl €150–360 Dbl €160–380
Dinner available from €33
CC: Accepted
Room facilities: ⬜ ☎ ⊕ 📞 ❄ Access: ⬆
Conference: 12 meeting rooms (Thtr 240 max),
24hr-delegate from €240, day-delegate from €60
Children: Welcome ⍑
Licenses: ⬛
Leisure: Gym
Parking: Off-street and free
Directions: From Dublin Airport M1 to City Centre,
Santry exit off motorway, third exit off the roundabout.
Straight through traffic lights, right at next lights. Next
lights left into Northwood Park. Hotel on right.
Map ref: Santry 19 F1

Grand Hotel
★★★★
Malahide, Co. Dublin
Tel: +353(0)1 8450000 Fax: +353(0)1 8450987
Email: info@thegrand.ie
Web: www.thegrand.ie
Seasonal closure: Christmas

The Grand Hotel is a large period property located in the
centre of Malahide. It offers extensive business and
conference facilities along with an up-to-date leisure
complex. All rooms are comfortable and well designed.
Rooms: 150 all ensuite ⊗
Pricing: Sgl €130–230 Dbl €170–290
Dinner available from €40–45
CC: Accepted
Room facilities: ⬜ ☎ ⊕ 📞 Access: ⬆
Conference: 16 meeting rooms (Thtr 500 max),
24hr-delegate from €225, day-delegate from €35
Children: Welcome ⍑
Licenses: ⬥ ⬛
Leisure: Indoor pool, Gym, Health spa, Beauty salon
Parking: Off-street and free
Directions: From Dublin airport, go northwards on Belfast
road; turn right for Malahide at appropriate roundabout.
Map ref: Malahide 19 F1

Republic of Ireland

Herbert Park Hotel

★★★★★ ♔♔♔   Excellent

Ballsbridge, Dublin 4
Tel: +353(0)1 6672200 Fax: +353(0)1 6672595
Email: reservations@herbertparkhotel.ie
Web: www.herbertparkhotel.ie
Rooms: 153 all ensuite ⊗
Pricing: Sgl €138–249 Dbl €157–313
Dinner available from €45
CC: Accepted
Room facilities: ▢ ☎ ✆ ✳
Access: ᴌᴌ
Conference: 4 meeting rooms (Thtr 100 max),
24hr-delegate from €275, day-delegate from €78
Children: Welcome ♄ ⅋
Licenses: ♦♦♦
Leisure: Gym, Tennis
Parking: Off-street and free
Directions: From Nassau Street go straight out of
Mount Street and Northumberland Road into
Ballsbridge; first turn right after the bridge, next right.
Map ref: Ballsbridge 19 F1
See advert on this page

Jurys Ballsbridge Hotel and The Towers

★★★★ ♔

Pembroke Road, Ballsbridge, Dublin 4
Tel: +353(0)1 660 5000 Fax: +353(0)1 660 5540
Email: bookings@jurysdoyle.com
Web: www.jurysdoyle.com

JURYS DOYLE
HOTELS

Rooms: 501 all ensuite ⊗
Pricing: Sgl €156–441 Dbl €176–503
Dinner available from €25.20
CC: Accepted
Room facilities: ▢ ☎ ☕ ✆
Access: ᴌᴌ
Conference: 22 meeting rooms (Thtr 850 max),
24hr-delegate from €189, day-delegate from €83
Children: Welcome ♄ ⅋
Licenses: ◁ ♦♦♦
Leisure: Indoor pool, Outdoor pool, Gym,
 Health spa, Beauty salon
Parking: Off-street and free
Directions: Follow signs to city centre, then East Link
Toll Bridge, go over bridge, follow signs for RDS. Hotel
is on left.
Map ref: Ballsbridge 19 F1

Ice & slice? RAC's comprehensive
inspection means we even check drinks
are served the way you want.

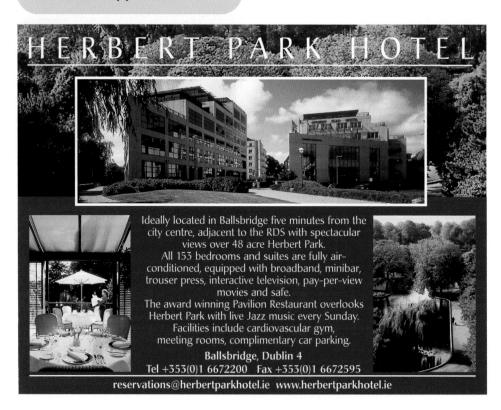

HERBERT PARK HOTEL

Ideally located in Ballsbridge five minutes from the
city centre, adjacent to the RDS with spectacular
views over 48 acre Herbert Park.
All 153 bedrooms and suites are fully air-
conditioned, equipped with broadband, minibar,
trouser press, interactive television, pay-per-view
movies and safe.
The award winning Pavilion Restaurant overlooks
Herbert Park with live Jazz music every Sunday.
Facilities include cardiovascular gym,
meeting rooms, complimentary car parking.
Ballsbridge, Dublin 4
Tel +353(0)1 6672200   Fax +353(0)1 6672595
reservations@herbertparkhotel.ie   www.herbertparkhotel.ie

Stillorgan Park Hotel

★★★★ ®
Stillorgan Road, Dublin 18
Tel: +353(0)1 2881621 Fax: +353(0)1 2831610
Email: reservations@stillorganpark.com
Web: www.stillorganpark.com

Superior 4-star hotel welcomes the corporate and
leisure guest to its beautifully inspired hotel. Boasting
165 luxuriously appointed suites, the elegant Purple
Sage restaurant, along with The White Pebble Spa,
complete with 7 treatment rooms.
Rooms: 165 all ensuite ❤❤ ◈
Pricing: Sgl €110–170 Dbl €130–190
Dinner available from €37.50
CC: Accepted
Room facilities: ▢ ☎ ◔ ◟ ❄
Access: ᴊ
Conference: 16 meeting rooms (Thtr 600 max),
24hr-delegate from €179, day-delegate from €55
Children: Welcome ᴛ
Licenses: ◁◈ ⑂
Leisure: Gym, Health spa
Parking: Off-street and free
Directions: Only minutes drive from City Centre. Less
than 3 miles Dun Laoghaire Port with several bus
routes including express coach to/from Dublin Airport.
Map ref: Dublin 19 F1

The Burlington Hotel
★★★★
Upper Leeson Street, Dublin 4
Tel: +353(0)1 6605222 Fax: +353(0)1 6608496
Email: bookings@jurysdoyle.com
Web: www.jurysdoyle.com

Rooms: 500 all ensuite ◈
Pricing: Sgl €152–342 Dbl €172–397
Dinner available from €29.40
CC: Accepted
Room facilities: ▢ ☎ ◔ ◟ Access: ᴊ

Conference: 24 meeting rooms (Thtr 1200 max),
24hr-delegate from €343, day-delegate from €86
Children: Welcome ᴛ
Licenses: ◁◈ ⑂
Leisure: Gym
Parking: Off-street and free
Directions: From airport take N1 into city centre. Then
go towards N11 southbound out of city centre. Hotel
located at start of N11.
Map ref: Dublin 19 F1

The Gresham
★★★★ ®®
23 Upper O'Connell Street, Dublin 1
Tel: +353(0)1 8746881 Fax: +353(0)1 8787175
Email: reservations@thegresham.com
Web: www.gresham-hotels.com

Good city centre location and a wonderful ambience
with large comfortable public areas. Two venues for
dining with the award-winning 'No. 23' restaurant.
Rooms are spacious and comfortable with good
facilities. Ideal for visiting Dublin.
Rooms: 289 all ensuite ❤❤ ◙ ◈
Pricing: Sgl €125–367 Dbl €155–400
Dinner available from €29.95
CC: Accepted
Room facilities: ▢ ☎ ◔ ◟
Access: ᴊ
Conference: 26 meeting rooms (Thtr 350 max),
24hr-delegate from €265, day-delegate from €78.75
Children: Welcome ᴛ
Licenses: ⑂
Leisure: Gym
Parking: Off-street
Directions: Situated on Dublin's main thoroughfare,
O'Connell Street.
Map ref: Dublin 19 F1

Republic of Ireland

Ashling Hotel — Best Western

★★★

Parkgate Street, Dublin 8
Tel: +353(0)1 6772324 Fax: +353(0)1 6793783
Email: info@ashlinghotel.ie
Web: www.ashlinghotel.ie
Seasonal closure: 22–27 December
Rooms: 150 all ensuite 🛁 🚭
Pricing: Dinner available from €25   CC: Accepted
Room facilities: 📺 ☎ ☕ Access: ♿
Conference: 11 meeting rooms (Thtr 200 max)
Children: Welcome 🍴 Dogs: Assistance dogs only
Licenses: ⚱ 👥 Parking: Off-street and free
Directions: Take city centre route and briefly follow
River Liffey westward. Take taxi or 'Airlink' bus from
airport. Hotel is across from Heuston Railway Station.
Map ref: Dublin 19 F1

Cassidy's Hotel

★★★🛎

Cavendish Row, Upper O'Connell Street, Dublin 1
Tel: +353(0)1 8780555 Fax: +353(0)1 8780687
Email: stay@cassidyshotel.com
Web: www.cassidyshotel.com
Seasonal closure: 24–27 December
Rooms: 88 all ensuite 🚭
Dinner available CC: Accepted
Room facilities: 📺 ☎ ☕ Access: ♿
Conference: 4 meeting rooms (Thtr 80 max)
Children: Welcome 🍴 Licenses: 👥
Parking: Off-street and free
Directions: Continue up O'Connell Street away from
the river. Cassidy's is located opposite the famous
Gate Theatre on Cavendish Row.
Map ref: Dublin 19 F1

Finnstown Country House Hotel

★★★★🛎🛎

Newcastle Road, Lucan, Co. Dublin
Tel: +353(0)1 601 0700 Fax: +353(0)1 628 1088
Email: manager@finnstown-hotel.ie
Web: www.finnstown-hotel.ie

One of County Dublin's finest country house hotels. Set
on 45 acres of private grounds it offers privacy, peace
and seclusion yet is only twenty minutes drive from the
bustling city centre of Dublin. If it's good old-fashioned
hospitality you're after – something the Irish are famous
for – great food and drink, a relaxed atmosphere and
stylish surroundings, you're in the right place.
Rooms: 77 all ensuite 🛁 🚭 🚭
Pricing: Sgl €45–85 Dbl €110–155
Dinner available from €46
CC: Accepted
Room facilities: 📺 ☎ ☕ 🕯
Conference: 7 meeting rooms (Thtr 300 max),
24hr-delegate from €230, day-delegate from €85
Children: Welcome 🍴
Dogs: Welcome
Licenses: ⚱ 👥
Leisure: Indoor pool, Gym, Tennis, Games room,
Snooker/billiards, Pitch and putt
Parking: Off-street and free
Directions: From Dublin, travel along South Quays,
passing Heuston Station. Continue on N4. At traffic
lights after Texaco garage, turn left. Hotel on right after
two roundabouts.
Map ref: Lucan 19 F1

Jurys Inn Christchurch

★★★

Christchurch Place, Dublin 8
Tel: +353(0)1 454 0000 Fax: +353(0)1 454 0012
Email: bookings@jurysdoyle.com
Web: www.jurysinns.com
Seasonal closure: 24-26 December

JURYS DOYLE
HOTELS

Rooms: 182 all ensuite 🛁 🚭
Pricing: Sgl €111.50–265.50 Dbl €111.50–265.50
Dinner available from €25–35
CC: Accepted
Room facilities: 📺 ☎ ☕ 🕯
Access: ♿
Children: Welcome 🍴
Licenses: 👥
Parking: Off-street
Directions: Located 10 km from airport. Follow signs to
city centre. Inn is located opposite Christchurch
Cathedral at the top of Dame Street.
Map ref: Dublin 19 F1

Jurys Inn Custom House

★★★

Custom House Quay, Dublin 1
Tel: +353(0)1 607 5000 Fax: +353(0)1 829 0400
Email: bookings@jurysdoyle.com
Web: www.jurysinns.com
Seasonal closure: Christmas

JURYS DOYLE
HOTELS

Rooms: 239 all ensuite 🛁 🚭

Pricing: Sgl €111.50–265.50 Dbl €111.50–265.50
Dinner available from €25 CC: Accepted
Room facilities: 🖵 ☎ 🖫 📠
Access: ㋡
Conference: 6 meeting rooms (Thtr 80 max),
24hr-delegate from €200, day-delegate from €59
Children: Welcome ㋡
Licenses: ⦙⦙⦙
Directions: Follow signs for city centre. Take left at
O'Connell Bridge. Inn is past the Custom House in the
I.F.S.C.
Map ref: Dublin 19 F1

Jurys Inn Parnell Street
★★★
Parnell Street, Dublin 1
Tel: +353(0)1 878 4900 Fax: +353(0)1 878 4999
Email: bookings@jurysdoyle.com
Web: www.jurysinns.com
Seasonal closure: 24-26 December

JURYS DOYLE
HOTELS

Rooms: 253 all ensuite 🐾 🚭
Pricing: Sgl €111.50–265.50 Dbl €111.50–265.50
Dinner available from €20
CC: Accepted
Room facilities: 🖵 ☎ 🖫 📠 ❋
Access: ㋡
Conference: 3 meeting rooms (Thtr 40 max),
24hr-delegate from €208, day-delegate from €62
Children: Welcome ㋡
Licenses: ⦙⦙⦙
Directions: Follow signs City Centre. Turn left at north
end of O'Connell Street. Hotel is on your left.
Map ref: Dublin 19 F1

Jurys Montrose Hotel
★★★
Stillorgan Road, Dublin 4
Tel: +353(0)1 269 3311 Fax: +353(0)1 269 1164
Email: bookings@jurysdoyle.com
Web: www.jurysdoyle.com

JURYS DOYLE
HOTELS

Rooms: 178 all ensuite 🚭
Pricing: Sgl €109–240 Dbl €123–284
Dinner available from €26.25 CC: Accepted
Room facilities: 🖵 ☎ 🖫 📠
Access: ㋡
Conference: 8 meeting rooms (Thtr 70 max),
24hr-delegate from €178.50, day-delegate from €52.50
Children: Welcome ㋡ ☕
Licenses: ⦙⦙⦙
Leisure: Beauty salon
Parking: Off-street and free
Directions: M50 follow signs for N11, cross toll bridge
along Coast Road. Left onto Merrion Road, right onto
Woodbine. Montrose on left.
Map ref: Dublin 19 F1

Lynch Green Isle Hotel
★★★
Newlands Cross, Dublin 22
Tel: +353(0)65 6823000 Fax: +353(0)65 6823759
Email: reservations@lynchotels.com
Web: www.lynchotels.com
Rooms: 232 (90 ensuite) 📠 🚭
Pricing: Dinner available from €30
CC: Accepted
Room facilities: 🖵 ☎ 🖫 📠
Access: ㋡
Conference: 43 meeting rooms (Thtr 250 max),
24hr-delegate from €180, day-delegate from €55
Children: Welcome ㋡
Licenses: ⚓ ⦙⦙⦙
Leisure: Indoor pool, Gym, Health spa, Beauty salon
Parking: Off-street and free
Directions: M50 southbound, onto N7 southbound.
Straight through lights at Newlands Cross, second left
marked Kingswood exit. Follow sign for Green Isle and
continue up Boot Road. Hotel on left.
Map ref: Dublin 19 F1

Marine Hotel
★★★ 🍴
Sutton Cross, Sutton, Dublin 13
Tel: +353(0)1 8390000 Fax: +353(0)1 8390442
Email: info@marinehotel.ie
Web: www.marinehotel.ie
Seasonal closure: Christmas
Rooms: 48 all ensuite 🚭
Pricing: Sgl €89–99 Dbl €105–165
Dinner available from €35
CC: Accepted
Room facilities: 🖵 ☎ 🖫 📠
Access: ㋡
Conference: 7 meeting rooms (Thtr 100 max),
24hr-delegate from €180, day-delegate from €55
Children: Welcome ㋡
Licenses: ⦙⦙⦙
Leisure: Indoor pool, Sauna, Steam room
Parking: Off-street and free
Directions: From O'Connell Bridge, turn onto Quays,
turning left at Liberty Hall, follow straight through
Fairview (R105) to Howth/Sutton.
Map ref: Sutton 19 F1

Sleep easy
Rest assured. Our
comprehensive
inspection process
includes checking
beds are comfortable.

Republic of Ireland

Mount Herbert Hotel

★★★

Herbert Road, Lansdowne Road, Ballsbridge, Dublin 4
Tel: +353(0)1 6684321 Fax: +353(0)1 6607077
Email: info@mountherberthotel.ie
Web: www.mountherberthotel.ie

Located in the Ballsbridge area and close to the city centre. Facilities include 180 modern bedrooms, Tritonville Bar with terrace and brasserie, business centre with Wi-Fi, private car park and picturesque gardens.
Rooms: 180 all ensuite
Pricing: Sgl €59–199 Dbl €79–199
Dinner available from €28.50
CC: Accepted
Room facilities:
Access:
Conference: 3 meeting rooms (Thtr 100 max)
Children: Welcome
Dogs: Assistance dogs only
Licenses:
Leisure: Complimentary use of local gym
Parking: Off-street and free
Directions: From city centre, Nassau Street at Trinity College along Merrion Square, Mount Street, Northumberland Road. At Lansdowne Road turn left. Cross DART line, pass rugby stadium, cross bridge.
Map ref: Ballsbridge 19 F1

North Star Hotel

★★★

Amien Street, Dublin 1
Tel: 08000 183127
Web: www.northstarhotel.ie
Rooms: 140 all ensuite
Pricing: Sgl €70–160 Dbl €80–180
Dinner available from €22
Room facilities:
Access:
Conference: 4 meeting rooms (Thtr 120 max)
Children: Welcome
Licenses:
Leisure: Gym, Sauna, Steam room
Parking: Off-street
Map ref: Dublin 19 F1

Temple Bar Hotel

★★★

Fleet Street, Dublin 2
Tel: +353(0)1 6773333 Fax: +353(0)1 6773088
Email: reservations@tbh.ie
Web: www.towerhotelgroup.com
Seasonal closure: 23–25 December
Rooms: 129 all ensuite
Pricing: Sgl €163 Dbl €210
Dinner available from €30
CC: Accepted
Room facilities:
Access:
Conference: 5 meeting rooms (Thtr 70 max)
Children: Welcome
Licenses:
Map ref: Dublin 19 F1

The Lucan Spa Hotel

★★★

Lucan, Co. Dublin
Tel: +353(0)1 6280494 Fax: +353(0)1 6280841
Email: info@lucanspahotel.ie
Web: www.lucanspahotel.ie
Seasonal closure: 25 December

Set in a quiet country setting, this Dublin hotel offers its guests a choice of 4 meeting rooms, 2 restaurants and 70 bedrooms, all equipped to 3 star standards.
Rooms: 70 all ensuite
Pricing: Sgl €60–150 Dbl €100–180
Dinner available from €27.50
CC: Accepted
Room facilities: Access:
Conference: 4 meeting rooms (Thtr 600 max)
Children: Welcome
Licenses:
Parking: Off-street and free
Directions: From Dublin City Centre, take N4 (heading West). 6 miles from City Centre. From Dublin Airport, take M50 (southbound). Exit after toll bridge (N4).
Map ref: Lucan 19 F1

The Parliament Hotel

 ★★★

Lord Edward Street, Temple Bar, Dublin
Tel: +353(0)16 708777 Fax: +353(0)16 708787
Email: parl@regencyhotels.com
Web: www.regencyhotels.com
Rooms: 63 all ensuite
Pricing: Sgl €80–160 Dbl €120–200
CC: Accepted
Room facilities: ▢ ☎ ☐ ☎
Access: |↨↑
Conference: 2 meeting rooms (Thtr 60 max)
Children: Welcome
Dogs: Assistance dogs only
Directions: Located in Temple Bar opposite Dublin
Castle, 2 minutes from Trinity College.
Map ref: Dublin 19 F1

White Sands Hotel

 ★★★

Coast Road, Portmarnock, Co. Dublin
Tel: +353(0)1 8666000 Fax: +353(0)1 8666006
Email: sandshotel@eircom.net or
info@whitesandshotel.ie
Web: www.whitesandshotel.ie
Seasonal closure: 24–25 December
Rooms: 58 all ensuite
Pricing: Sgl €80–125 Dbl €100–180
Dinner available from €25–30 CC: Accepted
Room facilities: ▢ ☎ ☐ ☎ Access: |↨↑
Conference: 2 meeting rooms (Thtr 100 max),
24hr-delegate from €100
Children: Welcome ♀
Dogs: Assistance dogs only
Licenses: ⬥ ♟
Parking: Off-street and free
Directions: Take Belfast road from Dublin airport. Right
at third roundabout for Malahide. Left at T-junction, left
through Malahide to Portmarnock. Hotel is on right
facing beach.
Map ref: Dublin 19 F1

Aberdeen Lodge

 ◆◆◆◆◆ ✕◤ ✧

53 Park Avenue, Ballsbridge, Dublin 4
Tel: +353(0)1 2838155 Fax: +353(0)1 2837877
Email: aberdeen@iol.ie
Web: www.halpinsprivatehotels.com
Rooms: 18 all ensuite
Pricing: Sgl €90–124 Dbl €109–149
CC: Accepted
Room facilities: ▢ ☎ ☐ ☎
Conference: 1 meeting room (Thtr 40 max),
24hr-delegate from €149, day-delegate from €64
Children: Welcome ♀
Licenses: ♟
Parking: Off-street and free
Directions: Minutes from city centre by DART or car.
Take Merrion Road towards Sydney Parade DART
station, then first left onto Park Avenue.
Map ref: Ballsbridge 19 F1

Glenogra

 ◆◆◆◆◆ ✕◤ ✧

64 Merrion Road, Ballsbridge, Dublin 4
Tel: +353(0)1 6683661 Fax: +353(0)1 6683698
Email: info@glenogra.com
Web: www.glenogra.com
Seasonal closure: Christmas to New Year

Glenogra is a beautiful guest house situated in the
heart of Ballsbridge just ten minutes from Dublin city
centre. High standards, dedication to excellence and
service to our guests makes Glenogra stand out as
one of Dublin's leading guest houses.
Rooms: 12 all ensuite
Pricing: Sgl €79–89 Dbl €109–119
CC: Accepted
Room facilities: ▢ ☎ ☐
Children: Welcome
Parking: Off-street and free
Directions: Situated opposite Four Seasons Hotel in
Ballsbridge on main route from Dun Laoghaire car
ferry.
Map ref: Ballsbridge 19 F1

Are the bells ringing?

Getting married? Congratulations!
Look for the wedding bells symbol
which shows hotels licensed for
civil ceremonies.

Republic of Ireland

Harrington Hall

◆◆◆◆◆ ✶⊠

70 Harcourt Street, Dublin 2
Tel: +353(0)1 4753497 Fax: +353(0)1 4754544
Email: harringtonhall@eircom.net
Web: www.harringtonhall.com

Harrington Hall is a large period property located close
to Dublin city centre. All rooms are very comfortable
and well designed with secure parking available.
Rooms: 28 all ensuite 🐾 🚭
Pricing: Sgl €116–140 Dbl €150–187.50
CC: Accepted
Room facilities:
Access: ⼮
Conference: 2 meeting rooms (Thtr 20 max)
Children: Welcome 🔞
Dogs: Assistance dogs only
Licenses: 🍶
Parking: Off-street and free
Directions: Follow signs to city centre, Harrington Hall
is on Harcourt Street, which enters south-west corner
of St Stephen's Green (attention: one-way).
Map ref: Dublin 19 F1

Merrion Hall

◆◆◆◆◆ ✶⊠ 🖐

54 Merrion Road, Ballsbridge, Dublin 4
Tel: +353(0)1 6681426 Fax: +353(0)1 6684280
Email: merrionhall@iol.ie
Web: www.halpinsprivatehotels.com
Rooms: 24 all ensuite 🐾 📋 🚭
Pricing: Sgl €99–149 Dbl €119–179
CC: Accepted
Room facilities:
Access: ⼮
Conference: 3 meeting rooms (Thtr 50 max),
24hr-delegate from €149, day-delegate from €64
Children: Welcome ⼮
Licenses: 🍶
Leisure: Health spa
Parking: Off-street and free
Directions: Located in Ballsbridge, close to city centre
on Merrion Road. Minutes from city centre by DART or
bus.
Map ref: Ballsbridge 19 F1

Pembroke Townhouse · `Little Gem`

◆◆◆◆◆ ✶⊠ 🖐

90 Pembroke Road, Ballsbridge, Dublin 4
Tel: +353(0)1 6600277 Fax: +353(0)1 6600291
Email: info@pembroketownhouse.ie
Web: www.pembroketownhouse.ie
Seasonal closure: 22 December to 1 January
Rooms: 48 all ensuite 🚭
Pricing: Sgl €90–185 Dbl €125–260
CC: Accepted
Room facilities: 📺 ☎ 🍵
Access: ⼮
Conference: 1 meeting room (Thtr 10 max)
Children: Welcome
Dogs: Assistance dogs only
Parking: Off-street and free
Directions: From city centre, cross O'Connell Bridge
towards Trinity College. Turn left at the front gates of
Trinity. Continue straight onto Merrion Square, over
canal and turn right just after petrol station on right.
Hotel is 10 doors up on the right.
Map ref: Ballsbridge 19 F1

Redbank Guesthouse & Restaurant

◆◆◆◆ ⓈⒶ

6-7 Church Street, Skerries, Co. Dublin
Tel: +353(0)1 8490439 Fax: +353(0)1 8491598
Email: info@redbank.ie
Web: www.redbank.ie
Seasonal closure: Restaurant 24–27 December

The Redbank Guesthouse is located in the small
seaside town of Skerries and a short drive from Dublin.
This popular restaurant and guest house offers fine
dining and very comfortable bedrooms.
Rooms: 18 all ensuite 🐾 🚭
Pricing: Sgl €75–85 Dbl €110–140
Dinner available from €45
CC: Accepted
Room facilities: 📺 ☎ 🍵 📞
Conference: 2 meeting rooms (Thtr 30 max)
Children: Welcome
Licenses: ⌚ 🍶
Parking: Off-street and free
Directions: 20 minutes off the N1 Dublin to Belfast
road. From the south, through Lusk village. From the
north, turn to left at Balbriggan and follow coast road.
Off new M1@Lissenhall Interchange and follow above.
Map ref: Skerries 17 E4

Baggot Court

92 Lower Baggot Street, Dublin 2
Tel: +353(0)1 6612819 Fax: +353(0)1 6610253
Email: baggot@indigo.ie
Web: www.baggotcourt.com
Seasonal closure: Christmas and New Year

A warm, friendly atmosphere awaits you in this
Georgian house, just a short stroll from the city centre.
We provide luxurious accommodation with a good
hearty breakfast.
Rooms: 11 all ensuite ⊛ CC: Accepted
Room facilities: ▢ ☎ ⊚
Children: Welcome 8yrs min age
Parking: Off-street and free
Directions: Located in the city centre, south of St
Stephen's Green on no. 10 bus route from O'Connell
Street.
Map ref: Dublin 19 F1

"Here!"

Need a pet friendly property?
Look out for 'Dogs welcome' in
our listings.

Charleville Lodge

268-272 North Circular Road, Phisborough, Dublin 7
Tel: +353(0)1 8386633 Fax: +353(0)1 8385854
Email: info@charlevillelodge.ie
Web: www.charlevillelodge.ie

Charleville Lodge (former home to Lord Charleville) is a
beautifully-restored terrace of Edwardian houses,
offering all the luxury expected from a large hotel,
whilst retaining the old-world charm.
Rooms: 30 all ensuite ⊛ ⊛
Pricing: Sgl €55–140 Dbl €70–250
CC: Accepted
Room facilities: ▢ ☎
Conference: 1 meeting room
Children: Welcome
Parking: Off-street and free
Directions: North from city centre (O'Connell Street) to
Phisborough, then take left fork at St. Peter's Church.
200 metres on the left; or take no.10 bus.
Map ref: Phisborough 19 F1

Eliza Lodge

23/24 Wellington Quay, Temple Bar, Dublin 2
Tel: +353(0)1 671 8044 Fax: +353(0)1 671 8362
Email: info@dublinlodge.com
Web: www.dublinlodge.com
Seasonal closure: 20 December to 3 January
Rooms: 18 all ensuite ⊛
Pricing: Sgl €76–95 Dbl €130–150
CC: Accepted
Room facilities: ▢ ☎ ⊚ ✳
Access: ⏏
Children: Welcome ⟩
Dogs: Assistance dogs only
Directions: Located at foot of Millennium Bridge,
second bridge after O'Connell Bridge. 25 minutes'
drive from Dublin Airport.
Map ref: Dublin 19 F1

Republic of Ireland

Kilronan House

◆◆◆◆ ✕ ☙

70 Adelaide Road, Dublin 2
Tel: +353(0)1 4755266 Fax: +353(0)1 4782841
Email: info@dublinn.com
Web: www.dublinn.com

This period property is located close to Dublin city
centre and close to many key tourist attractions. All
rooms are comfortable and a warm welcome is
guaranteed.
Rooms: 12 all ensuite ⚲ ⊗
Pricing: Sgl €45–85 Dbl €70–170
CC: Accepted
Room facilities: ▢ ☎ ☕
Children: Welcome
Dogs: Welcome
Parking: Off-street
Directions: Drive down St Stephen's Green east onto
Earlsfort Terrace. Proceed onto Adelaide Road. House
is on right-hand side.
Map ref: Dublin 19 F1

Lynam's Hotel

◆◆◆◆ ✕

63-64 O'Connell Street, Dublin 1
Tel: +353(0)1 8880886 Fax: +353(0)1 8880890
Email: lynamhtl@indigo.ie
Web: www.lynams-hotel.com
Seasonal closure: 22-26 December
Rooms: 42 all ensuite ⊗
Dinner available
CC: Accepted
Room facilities: ▢ ☎ ☕ ☎
Access:
Children: Welcome
Licenses: ♦♦♦
Map ref: Dublin 19 F1

Trinity Lodge   Little Gem

◆◆◆◆ ✕ ☙

12 South Frederick Street, Dublin 2
Tel: +353(0)1 6170900 Fax: +353(0)1 6170999
Email: trinitylodge@eircom.net
Web: www.trinitylodge.com
Seasonal closure: 22–27 December
.Rooms: 16 all ensuite ⚲ ⊗
Pricing: Sgl €110–150 Dbl €150–200
CC: Accepted
Room facilities: ▢ ☎ ☕ ☎
Children: Welcome
Directions: Trinity Lodge is in city centre, adjacent to
Trinity College off Nassau Street and two streets
parallel to Grafton Street.
Map ref: Dublin 19 F1

Egans House

◆◆◆

7 Iona Park, Glasnevin, Dublin 9
Tel: +353(0)18 303611 Fax: +353(0)18 303312
Email: info@eganshouse.com
Web: www.eganshouse.com
Rooms: 23 all ensuite ⚲ ⊗
Pricing: Sgl €49–75 Dbl €80–150
CC: Accepted
Room facilities: ▢ ☎ ☕ ☎
Children: Welcome
Licenses: ♦♦♦
Leisure: Lounge area with computer access, TV, VCR,
radio and piano
Parking: Off-street and free
Directions: 2km north of Dublin city centre, 9km to
Dublin airport and close to car ferry. Frequent buses,
10 minutes by taxi to city centre.
Map ref: Glasnevin 19 F1

Blakes Townhouse

◆ New for 2006

50 Merrion Road, Ballsbridge, Dublin 4
Tel: +353(0)1 6688324 Fax: +353(0)1 6684280
Email: blakestownhouse@iol.ie
Web: www.halpinsprivatehotels.com
Rooms: 13 all ensuite ⚲ ✍ ⊗
Pricing: Sgl €90–124 Dbl €109–149
CC: Accepted
Room facilities: ▢ ☎ ☕ ☎
Conference: 1 meeting room (Thtr 30 max),
24hr-delegate from €149, day-delegate from €69
Children: Welcome ♀
Licenses: ♦♦♦
Parking: Off-street
Directions: Located in Ballsbridge, close to city centre
on the Merrion Road. Minutes from city centre by
DART or bus.
Map ref: Ballsbridge 19 F1

Dun Laoghaire, Co. Dublin

Tara Hall

◆◆◆

24 Sandycove Road, Dun Laoghaire, Co. Dublin
Tel: +353(0)1 2805120 Fax: +353(0)1 2805120
Email: charcon@gofree.indigo.ie
Web: www.tara-hall.ie

A Regency-style house, ideally situated in Sandycove near the Joyce Tower and Dun Laoghaire Harbour. The dining room, which once hosted dances and readings by poet William Monk Gibbon, now offers breakfast with a selection from continental and cooked.
Rooms: 7 (6 ensuite) 🐾 Ⓢ
Pricing: Sgl €35–50 Dbl €70–80
CC: Accepted
Room facilities: 🖵 🍵
Children: Welcome
Dogs: Welcome
Parking: Off-street and free
Directions: Located on Sandycove Road. 5 minutes from Dun Laoghaire Ferry Port.
Map ref: Dun Laoghaire 19 F1

Dundalk, Co. Louth

Ballymascanlon House Hotel

★★★★ 🦌

Ballymascanlon, Dundalk, Co. Louth
Tel: +353(0)42 9358200 Fax: +353(0)42 9371598
Email: info@ballymascanlon.com
Web: www.ballymascanlon.com
Rooms: 90 all ensuite 🚭 Ⓢ
Dinner available
CC: Accepted
Room facilities: 🖵 ☎ 🍵 📞
Access: ⏣
Conference: 6 meeting rooms (Thtr 300 max)
Children: Welcome 🛉
Licenses: ⬙ ⏐⏐⏐
Leisure: Indoor pool, Gym, Health spa, Tennis, Golf
Parking: Off-street and free
Directions: Hotel is situated 2 miles north of Dundalk, off main Belfast Road (on Carlingford Road).
Map ref: Ballymascanlon 17 E3

Green Gates Bed & Breakfast

◆◆◆ 🦌

Dublin Road, Blackrock, Dundalk, Co. Louth
Tel: +353(0)42 9322047 Fax: +353(0)42 9322047
Email: orla@greengatesblackrock.com
Web: www.greengatesblackrock.com
Rooms: 4 all ensuite 🚭 Ⓢ
CC: Accepted
Room facilities: 🖵 🍵
Children: Welcome 🛉 ❄
Parking: Off-street and free
Directions: From Dublin, exit M1 at Dundalk. Turn right at Xerox traffic lights. Take second left after Fairways Hotel, second house on left.
Map ref: Blackrock 17 E3

Dundrum, Co. Tipperary

Dundrum House Hotel

★★★

Dundrum Near Cashel, Co. Tipperary
Tel: +353(0)62 71116 Fax: +353(0)62 71366
Email: dundrum@lol.ie
Web: www.dundrumhousehotel.com
Rooms: 86 all ensuite 🚭 📺
Dinner available CC: Accepted
Room facilities: 🖵 ☎ 📞 ❄
Access: ⏣
Conference: 6 meeting rooms (Thtr 400 max)
Children: Welcome 🛉
Licenses: ⬙
Leisure: Indoor pool, Gym, Beauty salon, Golf, Games room, Snooker/billiards
Parking: Off-street and free
Directions: Situated on the R505 to Dundrum 7 miles outside Cashel.
Map ref: Dundrum 19 D2

Dunfanaghy, Co. Donegal

Arnolds Hotel

★★★★ 🦌🦌

Dunfanaghy, Co. Donegal
Tel: +353(0)74 9136208 Fax: +353(0)74 9136352
Email: enquiries@arnoldshotel.com
Web: www.arnoldshotel.com
Seasonal closure: November to March
Rooms: 30 all ensuite 🚭 Ⓢ
Pricing: Sgl €89–125 Dbl €118–190
Dinner available from €40
CC: Accepted
Room facilities: 🖵 ☎ 🍵
Conference: 1 meeting room (Thtr 15 max)
Children: Welcome 🛉
Licenses: ⏐⏐⏐
Leisure: Riding
Parking: Off-street and free
Directions: Take N56 northwest from Letterkenny. After 23 miles, hotel is on left as you enter village.
Map ref: Dunfanaghy 16 C1

Dungarvan, Co. Waterford

The Castle Country House `Little Gem`

◆◆◆◆◆

Mill Street, Dungarvan, Co. Waterford
Tel: +353(0)58 68049 Fax: +353(0)58 68099
Email: castlefm@iol.ie
Web: www.castlecountryhouse.com
Seasonal closure: November to February
Rooms: 5 all ensuite
Dinner available
CC: Accepted
Room facilities:
Children: Welcome
Dogs: Welcome
Licenses:
Leisure: Fishing
Parking: Off-street and free
Directions: Located 15km off N25 on R671.
Map ref: Dungarvan 19 D3

Dunmore East, Co. Waterford

The Beach Guest House

◆◆◆◆

Lower Village, Dunmore East, Co. Waterford
Tel: +353(0)51 383316 Fax: +353(0)51 383319
Email: beachouse@eircom.net
Web: www.vizor.ie/beachouse
Rooms: 7 all ensuite
Pricing: Sgl €40–60 Dbl €70–90
CC: Accepted
Room facilities:
Children: Welcome 6yrs min age
Parking: Off-street and free
Directions: Take left after petrol station in the village,
drive to beach 300 metres, guest house is on left
facing the beach.
Map ref: Dunmore East 19 E3

Ennis, Co. Clare

The Mountshannon Hotel

★★

Mountshannon, Ennis, Co. Clare
Tel: +353(0)61 927162
Email: info@mountshannon-hotel.ie
Web: www.mountshannon-hotel.ie
Rooms: 16 all ensuite
Dinner available
CC: Accepted
Room facilities:
Conference: 1 meeting room (Thtr 200 max)
Children: Welcome
Licenses:
Leisure: Golf, Riding, Snooker/billiards, Pool table
Parking: Off-street and free
Directions: From Shannon Airport drive to Ennis. Take
the road signed for Tulla. Continue to Seariff, then 5
miles to Mountshannon.
Map ref: Mountshannon 18 C2

Ennistymon, Co. Clare

Grovemount House

◆◆◆◆

Lahinch Road, Ennistymon, Co. Clare
Tel: +353(0)65 7071431 Fax: +353(0)65 7071823
Email: grovemnt@gofree.indigo.ie
Web: www.grovemount.com
Seasonal closure: November to April
Rooms: 7 all ensuite
CC: Accepted
Room facilities:
Children: Welcome
Parking: Off-street
Directions: Take N85 from Ennis to Ennistymon, N67
from Ennistymon to Lahinch. Grovemount House is
situated on the outskirts of Ennistymon on the right.
Map ref: Ennistymon 18 B1

Faithlegg, Co. Waterford

Faithlegg House Hotel

★★★★★

Faithlegg, Co. Waterford
Tel: +353(0)51 382000 Fax: +353(0)51 382010
Email: reservations@fhh.ie
Web: www.towerhotelgroup.com
Seasonal closure: 22–26 December & January
Rooms: 82 all ensuite
Pricing: Sgl €199–260 Dbl €260–360
Dinner available from €50 CC: Accepted
Room facilities: Access:
Conference: 5 meeting rooms (Thtr 180 max)
Children: Welcome
Licenses:
Leisure: Indoor pool, Gym, Beauty salon, Tennis, Golf
Parking: Off-street and free
Map ref: Faithlegg 19 E3

Fermoy, Co. Cork

Ballyvolane House `Little Gem`

◆◆◆◆◆

Castlelyons, near Fermoy, Co. Cork
Tel: +353(0)25 36349 Fax: +353(0)25 36781
Email: ballyvol@iol.ie
Web: www.ballyvolanehouse.ie
Seasonal closure: 24-31 December
Rooms: 6 all ensuite
Pricing: Sgl €105–125 Dbl €150–190
Dinner available from €47.50 CC: Accepted
Room facilities:
Conference: 1 meeting room (Thtr 14 max),
24hr-delegate from €170, day-delegate from €85
Children: Welcome
Licenses:
Leisure: Fishing, Badminton, Croquet, Cycling, Walking
Parking: Off-street and free
Directions: From Cork, turn right off N8 at River Bride,
just before Rath Cormal (R628). Follow 4 House signs.
Map ref: Castlelyons 18 C3

Galway, Co. Galway

Ardilaun House Hotel Conference Centre and Leisure Club

★★★★ ⓡ

Taylors Hill, Galway, Co. Galway
Tel: +353(0)91 521433 Fax: +353(0)91 521546
Email: info@ardilaunhousehotel.ie
Web: www.ardilaunhousehotel.ie
Seasonal closure: 22–27 December
Rooms: 89 all ensuite ⌨ ⊗
Pricing: Sgl €90–140 Dbl €160–280
Dinner available from €29–39
CC: Accepted
Room facilities: ▢ ☎ ☕ ⅃
Access: ⌊↥
Conference: 8 meeting rooms (Thtr 400 max),
24hr-delegate from €140, day-delegate from €45
Children: Welcome ⍭ ⅋
Dogs: Welcome
Licenses: ⅏
Leisure: Indoor pool, Gym, Health spa, Beauty salon,
Games room, Snooker/billiards
Parking: Off-street and free
Directions: Approaching Galway take N6 to Galway
City West. Then follow signs for N59 Clifden and then
the N6 for Salthill. Taylor's Hill is enroute.
Map ref: Galway 18 C1

Galway Bay Hotel Conference & Leisure Centre

★★★★ ⓡ

The Promenade, Salthill, Galway, Co. Galway
Tel: +353(0)91 520520 Fax: +353(0)91 520530
Email: info@galwaybayhotel.net
Web: www.galwaybayhotel.net
Rooms: 153 all ensuite ⌨ ⊗
Pricing: Sgl €80–175 Dbl €160–280
Dinner available from €36–39
CC: Accepted
Room facilities: ▢ ☎ ☕ ⅃ ❄
Access: ⌊↥
Conference: 15 meeting rooms (Thtr 500 max)
Children: Welcome ⍭
Dogs: Assistance dogs only
Licenses: ⅏
Leisure: Indoor pool, Gym, Beauty salon
Parking: Off-street and free
Directions: Approaching Galway take N6 to Galway
City West. Then follow signs for N59 Clifden and the
N6 for Salthill.
Map ref: Galway 18 C1
See advert on this page

Glenlo Abbey Hotel

★★★★ ⓡⓡⓡ

Bushypark, Galway, Co. Galway
Tel: +353(0)91 526666 Fax: +353(0)91 527800
Email: info@glenloabbey.ie
Web: www.glenlo.com
Seasonal closure: Christmas
Rooms: 46 all ensuite ▱ ⊗
Pricing: Dinner available from €50
CC: Accepted
Room facilities: ▢ ☎ ⅃
Access: ⌊↥
Conference: 9 meeting rooms (Thtr 180 max)
Children: Welcome ⍭
Licenses: ⅏
Leisure: Golf, Fishing, Riding, Clay pigeon shooting
Parking: Off-street and free
Directions: Situated on the N59, 4km or 2½ miles from
Galway City Centre.
Map ref: Bushypark 18 C1
See advert on following page

Republic of Ireland

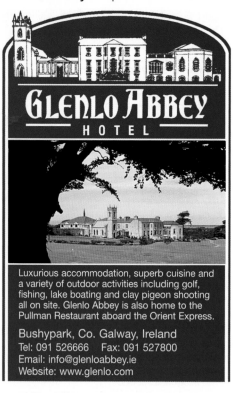

Luxurious accommodation, superb cuisine and a variety of outdoor activities including golf, fishing, lake boating and clay pigeon shooting all on site. Glenlo Abbey is also home to the Pullman Restaurant aboard the Orient Express.

Bushypark, Co. Galway, Ireland
Tel: 091 526666   Fax: 091 527800
Email: info@glenloabbey.ie
Website: www.glenlo.com

Park House Hotel

An oasis of luxury and calm situated in the city centre of Galway. Award-winning hotel and restaurant – "Hotel of the Year Ireland 2000 – Les Routiers". Park Room Restaurant – Bord Failte Awards of Excellence over many years. Les Routiers Plat d'Or 2000. Private, secure residents' car park.

Forster Street, Eyre Square, Galway
Tel: +353 91 564924   Fax: +353 91 569219
Email: parkhousehotel@eircom.net
www.parkhousehotel.ie

Park House Hotel

★★★★ ♫♫

Forster Street, Eyre Square, Galway, Co. Galway
Tel: +353(0)91 564924 Fax: +353(0)91 569219
Email: parkhousehotel@eircom.net
Web: www.parkhousehotel.ie
Seasonal closure: 24-26 December
Rooms: 84 all ensuite ♿
Pricing: Sgl €85–300 Dbl €125–300
Dinner available from €42.50
CC: Accepted
Room facilities: ▢ ☎ ☕ 🎿 ❄
Access: ⌴↑
Children: Welcome 🍴
Licenses: ♙♙♙
Parking: Off-street and free
Directions: Follow all signs for city centre. Hotel is situated on Forster Street, off Eyre Square. Car park is at rear of hotel.
Map ref: Galway 18 C1
See advert on this page

Imperial Hotel

★★★

Eyre Square, Galway, Co. Galway
Tel: +353(0)91 563033 Fax: +353(0)91 568410
Email: imperialhtl@hotmail.com
Web: www.imperialhotelgalway.ie

A bustling hotel in the centre of Galway City with modern, comfortable 3-star bedrooms, redecorated bar and restaurant. Located in the main shopping area, surrounded by a large choice of restaurants, pubs and quality shops. Five minutes walk from the new Galway Theatre, main bus and train terminals.
Rooms: 85 all ensuite
Pricing: Sgl €80–200 Dbl €120–210
Dinner available from €25–30
CC: Accepted
Room facilities: ▢ ☎ ☕
Access: ⌴↑
Children: Welcome
Licenses: ♙♙♙
Directions: On approaching Galway, follow signs for Galway City East and proceed to Eyre Square.
Map ref: Galway 18 C1

Jurys Inn Galway

★★★

Quay Street, Galway, Co. Galway
Tel: +353(0)91 566444 Fax: +353(0)91 568415
Email: bookings@jurysdoyle.com
Web: www.jurysinns.com
Seasonal closure: Christmas

Rooms: 130 all ensuite 🛏 🚭
Pricing: Sgl €90–261 Dbl €105–272
Dinner available from €25
CC: Accepted
Room facilities: 📺 ☎ 🍵 🔌
Access: ♿
Children: Welcome 12yrs min age 🍴
Licenses: 🍸
Parking: Off-street
Directions: Located 5 miles/8 km from Galway airport. Train station 5 minutes walk. Centrally located beside Spanish Arch and overlooking Galway Bay.
Map ref: Galway 18 C1

Almara House

♦♦♦♦ ⚜ 🍷

2 Merlin Gate, Merlin Park, Dublin Road, Galway, Co. Galway
Tel: +353(0)91 755345/+353(0)86 2451220 Fax: +353(0)91 771585
Email: matthewkiernan@eircom.net
Web: www.almarahouse.com
Seasonal closure: 1 week at Christmas
Rooms: 6 all ensuite 🚭
Pricing: Sgl €45–60 Dbl €70–90
CC: Accepted
Room facilities: 📺 🍵 🔌
Children: Welcome 🍴
Parking: Off-street and free
Directions: Located in city suburbs. Adjacent N6 (Dublin), N18 (Shannon), N17 (Sligo) junctions. Restaurants and pubs close by. Follow signs for Merlin Park.
Map ref: Galway 18 C1

Auburn House

♦♦♦ 🍷

1 Merlin Gate, Dublin Road, Galway, Co. Galway
Tel: +353(0)91 771018
Email: auburnhousegalway@eircom.net
Web: www.auburnhousegalway.com
Rooms: 5 (4 ensuite) 🚭
Pricing: Sgl €40–50 Dbl €70–90
CC: Accepted
Room facilities: 📺 🍵
Children: Welcome ☕
Parking: Off-street and free
Directions: At Martin roundabout take city east road for 2km to 50km/h limit. First left after shop. First house on left.
Map ref: Galway 18 C1

Gorey, Co. Wexford

Ashdown Park Hotel

★★★★ 🍷🍷

Coach Road, Gorey, Co. Wexford
Tel: +353(0)55 80500 Fax: +353(0)55 80777
Email: info@ashdownparkhotel.com
Web: www.ashdownparkhotel.com

On arrival at The Ashdown Park Hotel you will experience the grandeur of what we are about. Warm, friendly welcome, offering the very highest standard in food and service.
Rooms: 79 all ensuite 📠 🚭
Pricing: Sgl £85–120 Dbl £80–130
Dinner available from £39
CC: Accepted
Room facilities: 📺 ☎ 🍵 🔌
Access: ♿
Conference: 6 meeting rooms (Thtr 600 max), 24hr-delegate from £150, day-delegate from £40
Children: Welcome 🍴
Dogs: Assistance dogs only
Licenses: 🍸
Leisure: Indoor pool, Gym, Beauty salon
Parking: Off-street and free
Directions: M11/N11 southbound from Dublin to Gorey. Turn left before railway bridge, hotel on left.
Map ref: Gorey 19 F2

Marlfield House

★★★★ 🍷🍷🍷   Premier

Courtown Road, Gorey, Co. Wexford
Tel: +353(0)55 21124 Fax: +353(0)55 21572
Email: info@marlfieldhouse.ie
Web: www.marlfieldhouse.com
Seasonal closure: Mid December to January
Rooms: 20 all ensuite 📠 🚭
Dinner available
CC: Accepted
Room facilities: 📺 ☎
Conference: 2 meeting rooms (Thtr 20 max), 24hr-delegate from €250, day-delegate from €80
Children: Welcome 🍴 ☕
Dogs: Welcome
Licenses: 🍸
Leisure: Tennis
Parking: Off-street and free
Directions: Marlfield House is 1 mile outside Gorey on the Courtown Road R742.
Map ref: Gorey 19 F2

Republic of Ireland

Gougane Barra. Co. Cork

Gougane Barra Hotel

★★★

Gougane Barra, Ballingeary, Co. Cork
Tel: +353(0)26 47069 Fax: +353(0)26 47226
Email: gouganebarrahotel@eircom.net
Web: www.gouganebarra.com
Seasonal closure: 10 October to 15 April
Rooms: 25 all ensuite
Dinner available
CC: Accepted
Room facilities:
Children: Welcome
Licenses:
Directions: Gougane Barra is 1¼ miles (2km) from
main route (R584) which runs between Macroom and
Bantry.
Map ref: Gougane Barra 18 B4

Kenmare, Co. Kerry

Park Hotel Kenmare

★★★★ Premier

Kenmare, Co. Kerry
Tel: +353(0)64 41200 Fax: +353(0)64 41402
Email: info@parkkenmare.com
Web: www.parkkenmare.com
Seasonal closure: 30 November to 23 December,
4 January to 12 February
Rooms: 46 all ensuite
Pricing: Sgl €206–256 Dbl €166–385
Dinner available from €71
CC: Accepted
Room facilities:
Access:
Children: Welcome
Dogs: Welcome
Licenses:
Leisure: Outdoor pool, Gym, Health spa, Beauty salon,
Tennis, Golf, 12 seater cinema
Parking: Off-street and free
Directions: Located at the top of the town of Kenmare.
Map ref: Kenmare 18 B4

Sheen Falls Lodge

★★★★ Premier

Kenmare, Co. Kerry
Tel: +353(0)64 41600 Fax: +353(0)64 41386
Email: info@sheenfallslodge.ie
Web: www.sheenfallslodge.ie
Seasonal closure: January only
Rooms: 66 all ensuite
Pricing: Sgl €304–450 Dbl €320–475
Dinner available from €65
CC: Accepted
Room facilities:
Access:
Conference: 5 meeting rooms (Thtr 120 max)
Children: Welcome
Licenses:

Leisure: Indoor pool, Gym, Health spa, Beauty salon,
Tennis, Fishing, Riding, Games room, Snooker/billiards,
Library, Wine cellar, Vintage car rides, Walking,
Cycling, Bird watching
Parking: Off-street and free
Directions: From Kenmare, take N71 towards
Glengarriff. Turn left after suspension bridge. Sheen
Falls Lodge is on the left-hand side.
Map ref: Kenmare 18 B4

Kilkee, Co. Clare

Halpins Townhouse Hotel

◆◆◆◆

Erin Street, Kilkee, Co. Clare
Tel: +353(0)65 9056032 Fax: +353(0)65 9056317
Email: halpinshotel@iol.ie
Web: www.halpinsprivatehotels.com
Seasonal closure: December to February
Rooms: 12 all ensuite
Pricing: Sgl €55–75 Dbl €89–109
Dinner available from €25
CC: Accepted
Room facilities:
Conference: 1 meeting room (Thtr 40 max),
24hr-delegate from €129, day-delegate from €50
Children: Welcome
Licenses:
Parking: Off-street
Directions: Hotel is in the centre of Kilkee. Shannon
Airport 50-minute drive away on N67, Killimer Car
Ferry 10 miles away.
Map ref: Kilkee 18 B2

Kilkenny, Co. Kilkenny

Kilkenny River Court Hotel

★★★★

The Bridge, John Street, Kilkenny, Co. Kilkenny
Tel: +353(0)56 7723388 Fax: +353(0)56 7723389
Email: reservations@kilrivercourt.com
Web: www.kilrivercourt.com
Seasonal closure: 25–26 December
Rooms: 90 all ensuite
Pricing: Sgl €75–155 Dbl €90–210
Dinner available from €45
CC: Accepted
Room facilities:
Access:
Conference: 6 meeting rooms (Thtr 220 max),
24hr-delegate from €190, day-delegate from €40
Children: Welcome
Dogs: Assistance dogs only
Licenses:
Leisure: Indoor pool, Gym, Beauty salon
Parking: Off-street and free
Directions: Kilkenny Castle is a landmark: the hotel is
situated directly opposite across river. Entrance under
archways at bridge in city centre.
Map ref: Kilkenny 19 E2

Hotel Kilkenny

★★★

College Road, Kilkenny, Co. Kilkenny
Tel: +353(0)56 7762000 Fax: +353(0)56 7765984
Email: kilkenny@griffingroup.ie
Web: www.griffingroup.ie

A popular hotel located close to the historic town of Kilkenny. It offers comfortable accommodation and an excellent leisure complex. Ample and secure parking is provided and the hotel is situated close to the major road network.
Rooms: 103 all ensuite 🛏 🚭
Pricing: Sgl €85–140 Dbl €120–260
Dinner available from €40 CC: Accepted
Room facilities: 🖵 ☎ 🍵 ☕
Conference: 7 meeting rooms (Thtr 400 max),
24hr-delegate from €149.95, day-delegate from €36.95
Children: Welcome ♁ Licenses: ⅲ
Leisure: Indoor pool, Gym, Health spa, Beauty salon
Parking: Off-street and free
Directions: From all major routes, across the city's ringroad, hotel is located at Clonmel/Cork (N76) roundabout.
Map ref: Kilkenny 19 E2

Killarney, Co. Kerry

Cahernane House Hotel

Commended

★★★★ 🐾🐾🐾

Muckross Road, Killarney, Co. Kerry
Tel: +353(0)64 31895 Fax: +353(0)64 34340
Email: cahernane@eircom.net
Web: www.cahernane.com
Rooms: 38 all ensuite 🛏 🚭
Dinner available CC: Accepted
Room facilities: 🖵 ☎ 🍵 ☕ Access: ⅱ
Conference: 1 meeting room (Thtr 30 max)
Children: Welcome ♁ ☕ Licenses: ⅲ
Leisure: Tennis, Fishing, Snooker/billiards
Parking: Off-street
Directions: Outside Killarney town on the Kenmare road — N71. Map ref: Killarney 18 B3

Killarney Royal

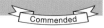
Commended

★★★★★ 🐾🐾

College Street, Killarney, Co. Kerry
Tel: +353(0)64 31853 Fax: +353(0)64 34001
Email: royalhot@iol.ie
Web: www.killarneyroyal.ie
Seasonal closure: 23–26 December
Rooms: 29 all ensuite 🛏 🚭
Pricing: Sgl €120–205 Dbl €190–320
Dinner available from €30–40
CC: Accepted
Room facilities: 🖵 ☎ ☕ ❄ Access: ⅱ
Conference: 3 meeting rooms (Thtr 50 max),
24hr-delegate from €190, day-delegate from €75
Children: Welcome ♁ Dogs: Welcome
Licenses: ⅲ
Parking: Off-street
Directions: Centre of Killarney across from the railway station.
Map ref: Killarney 18 B3

Muckross Park Hotel

★★★★★ 🐾🐾

Muckross Village, Killarney, Co. Kerry
Tel: +353(0)64 31938 Fax: +353(0)64 31965
Email: info@muckrosspark.com
Web: www.muckrosspark.com

The oldest Victorian hotel in Killarney, Muckross Park combines all the charm of a four-star Irish country house whilst providing guests with all the modern comforts. Complete with conference and meeting facilities, the recently launched International Well Being Luxury Spa, Gymnasium and the award-winning Molly Darcy's Traditional Irish Pub & Restaurant.
Rooms: 108 all ensuite 🛏 📺 🚭
Pricing: Sgl €120–280 Dbl €170–400
Dinner available from €45 CC: Accepted
Room facilities: 🖵 ☎ 🍵 ☕
Access: ⅱ
Conference: 4 meeting rooms (Thtr 400 max),
24hr-delegate from €150, day-delegate from €60
Children: Welcome ♁ ☕
Licenses: ♿ ⅲ
Leisure: Gym, Health spa
Parking: Off-street and free
Directions: Situated 4 km outside Killarney on the main Kenmare Road N71, adjacent to Killarney's World Famous National Park, Muckross House and Gardens.
Map ref: Muckross 18 B3

Republic of Ireland

Riverside Hotel

★★★★

Muckross Road, Killarney, Co. Kerry
Tel: +353(0)64 39200 Fax: +353(0)64 39202
Email: stay@riversidehotelkillarney.com
Web: www.riversidehotelkillarney.com
Rooms: 69 all ensuite ♨ ⊗
Pricing: Sgl €95–150 Dbl €130–250
Dinner available from €35
CC: Accepted
Room facilities: ▢ ☎ ☕ ✆
Access: |↓↑
Children: Welcome ㅐ
Licenses: ♦♦♦
Leisure: Beauty salon
Parking: Off-street and free
Directions: Follow signs for Killarney town centre and then for Muckross Road. Hotel is on the right, 1km from town centre.
Map ref: Killarney 18 B3
See advert on this page

Brook Lodge Hotel

★★★

High Street, Killarney, Co. Kerry
Tel: +353(0)64 31800 Fax: +353(0)64 35001
Map ref: Killarney 18 B3

Holiday Inn Killarney

★★★

Muckross Road, Killarney, Co. Kerry
Tel: +353(0)64 33000 Fax: +353(0)64 33001
Email: reservations@holidayinnkillarney.com
Web: www.holidayinnkillarney.com
Seasonal closure: Christmas Day
Rooms: 100 all ensuite ♨ ⊗
Pricing: Sgl €60–110 Dbl €100–180
Dinner available from €30
CC: Accepted
Room facilities: ▢ ☎ ☕ ✆ Access: |↓↑
Conference: 3 meeting rooms (Thtr 80 max), day-delegate from €45
Children: Welcome ㅐ ⚘
Licenses: ♦♦♦
Leisure: Indoor pool, Gym
Parking: Off-street and free
Directions: Follow signs for Killarney town centre, and then for Muckross Road; hotel is on the right 2 minutes' drive from the centre.
Map ref: Killarney 18 B3

Victoria House Hotel

★★★★

Muckross Road, Killarney, Co. Kerry
Tel: +353(0)64 35430 Fax: +353(0)64 35439
Map ref: Killarney 18 B3

Earls Court House `Little Gem`

♦♦♦♦♦ ⚒ ♞

Woodlawn Junction, Muckross Road,
Killarney, Co. Kerry
Tel: +353(0)64 34009 Fax: +353(0)64 34366
Email: info@killarney-earlscourt.ie
Web: www.killarney-earlscourt.ie
Seasonal closure: December to February
Rooms: 20 all ensuite ♨ ⊟ ⊗
CC: Accepted
Room facilities: ▢ ☎ ⊠ ✎ Access: ⬆
Children: Welcome ⊺ Dogs: Welcome
Licenses: ⦀
Parking: Off-street and free
Directions: Take Muckross Road from Killarney. At the
traffic light, take a left and Earls Court House is third
house on your left.
Map ref: Killarney 18 B3

Fairview Guest House `Little Gem`

♦♦♦♦♦ ⚒ ♞

College Street, Killarney, Co. Kerry
Tel: +353(0)64 34164 Fax: +353(0)64 71777
Email: info@fairviewkillarney.com
Web: www.fairviewkillarney.com
Rooms: 18 all ensuite ♨ ⊗
Pricing: Sgl €90–140 Dbl €90–195
CC: Accepted
Room facilities: ▢ ☎ ⊠ ✎ ❄
Children: Welcome ⊺
Parking: Off-street
Directions: Town centre Killarney located just off
College Street, Michael Collins' Place, Killarney.
Map ref: Killarney 18 B3

Foley's Townhouse

♦♦♦♦♦ ⚒

23 High Street, Killarney, Co. Kerry
Tel: +353(0)64 31217 Fax: +353(0)64 34683
Email: info@foleystownhouse.com
Web: www.foleystownhouse.com
Rooms: 28 all ensuite ⊗
Pricing: Sgl €70–80 Dbl €100–130
Dinner available from €20–45
CC: Accepted
Room facilities: ▢ ☎ ⊠ ✎ ❄
Children: Welcome Licenses: ⬙ ⦀
Parking: Off-street and free
Directions: Town centre location on right-hand side of
High Street (when travelling north, direction Tralee).
Map ref: Killarney 18 B3

Kathleens Country House

♦♦♦♦♦ ⚒ ♞

Madams Height, Tralee Road (N22), Lakes of Killarney,
Killarney, Co. Kerry
Tel: +353(0)64 32810 Fax: +353(0)64 32340
Email: info@kathleens.net
Web: www.kathleens.net
Seasonal closure: 1 November to 15 March

RAC/AA 5 diamonds, small hotel/guesthouse of the year.
17 superior rooms with large bathrooms, TV, tea and
coffee making facilities and telephones. Ideal golfing and
touring base. Owned and operated by Kathleen.
Rooms: 17 all ensuite ♨ ⊗
Pricing: Sgl €50–100 Dbl €100–140
CC: Accepted
Room facilities: ▢ ☎ ⊠ ✎
Children: Welcome 3yrs min age
Licenses: ⦀
Parking: Off-street and free
Directions: 1 mile north of Killarney Town in scenic
rural peaceful surrounds, accessible through N22.
Map ref: Lakes of Killarney 18 B3

Ashville Guest House

♦♦♦♦ ⚒ ♞

Rock Road, Killarney, Co. Kerry
Tel: +353(0)64 36405 Fax: +353(0)64 36778
Email: info@ashvillekillarney.com
Web: www.ashvillekillarney.com
Seasonal closure: November to February

A purpose built guest house just out of the town centre
within easy walking distance. It is both well appointed
throughout and comfortable and personally run by
caring owners.
Rooms: 12 all ensuite ♨ ⊗
Pricing: Sgl €50–90 Dbl €70–110
CC: Accepted
Room facilities: ▢ ☎ ⊠
Children: Welcome
Parking: Off-street and free
Directions: On the N22 from Cork and Tralee and from
Limerick on the N21. Two minutes walk from town
centre
Map ref: Killarney 18 B3

ARBUTUS HOTEL KILLARNEY

ARBUTUS HOTEL COLLEGE STREET KILLARNEY CO. KERRY
PHONE + 353 [0] 64 310 37 FAX + 353 [0] 64 340 33
stay@arbutuskillarney.com www.arbutuskillarney.com

The Arbutus Hotel and the Buckley family - at the heart of Killarney hospitality since 1926. Generations of visitors have enjoyed our personal introduction to the many attractions of the area whilst enjoying the warmth of a townhouse hotel where loving attention to detail is evident in home-cooked food, our original Buckley's Bar and the marvellous Celtic Deco design throughout.

Rates: B&B from €65 to €90
         2 B&B 1 Dinner from €150

Killarney Villa

◆◆◆◆ ✗ ✎

Cork/Mallow Road (N72), Killarney, Co. Kerry
Tel: +353(0)64 31878 Fax: +353(0)64 31878
Email: killarneyvilla@le-post.com
Web: www.killarneyvilla.com
Seasonal closure: November to April
Rooms: 6 all ensuite ✿ ⊛
Pricing: Sgl €30–40 Dbl €60–75
CC: Accepted
Room facilities: ☐ ☕
Children: Welcome 6yrs min age ☍
Dogs: Welcome
Parking: Off-street and free
Directions: Take N22 out of Killarney. Travel through two roundabouts on the Cork Mallow road for 1.3 miles. Take left at the Mallow N72 junction for 200 yards, to Killarney Villa on left.
Map ref: Villa 18 B3

Ross Castle Lodge

◆◆◆◆ ✗

Ross Road, Killarney, Co. Kerry
Tel: +353(0)64 36942 Fax: +353(0)64 36942
Email: rosscastlelodge@killarneyb-and-b.com
Web: www.killarneyb-and-b.com
Rooms: 4 all ensuite ⊛
Pricing: Sgl €50–60 Dbl €60–90
CC: Accepted
Room facilities: ☐ ☕
Parking: Off-street and free
Directions: 100 metres past Cineplex Cinema, turn right at Texaco garage. House is on left immediately after Ross Golf Club.
Map ref: Killarney 18 B3

The Arbutus Killarney

◆◆◆◆ ✗

College Street, Killarney Town Centre,
Killarney, Co. Kerry
Tel: +353(0)64 31037 Fax: +353(0)64 34033
Email: stay@arbutuskillarney.com
Web: www.arbutuskillarney.com
Seasonal closure: 8 December to 10 February
Rooms: 35 all ensuite ✿ ⊛
Pricing: Sgl €85–180 Dbl €130–210
CC: Accepted
Room facilities: ☐ ☎ ☕
Access: |↥↑
Children: Welcome ☍
Licenses: �
Parking: Off-street
Directions: At junction of Lewis Road and College Street, 3 minutes from bus and railway station, in Killarney town centre.
Map ref: Killarney 18 B3
See advert on this page

Kilmessan, Co. Meath

The Station House Hotel

★★★★

Kilmessan, Co. Meath
Tel: +353(0)46 9025239 Fax: +353(0)46 9025588
Email: info@thestationhousehotel.com
Web: www.thestationhousehotel.com
Rooms: 20 all ensuite
Pricing: Sgl €85–130 Dbl €130–220
Dinner available from €12.95–44.95
CC: Accepted
Room facilities:
Conference: 3 meeting rooms (Thtr 400 max),
24hr-delegate from €150, day-delegate from €75
Children: Welcome
Licenses:
Parking: Off-street and free
Directions: From Dublin N3 to Dunshaughlin, left at end
of village Y junction, turn right to Dunsany, right and
left in Dunsany to Kilmessan.
Map ref: Kilmessan 17 E4

Kiltimagh, Co. Mayo

Cill Aodain Hotel

★★

Main Street, Kiltimagh, Co. Mayo
Tel: +353(0)94 9381761 Fax: +353(0)94 9381838
Email: cillaodain@eircom.net
Web: www.irishcountryhotels.ie
Seasonal closure: 24-26 December
Rooms: 16 all ensuite
Pricing: Dinner available from €30
CC: Accepted
Room facilities:
Children: Welcome
Licenses:
Directions: 5 km off the Sligo Galway main road N17 or
turn off at Bohola on the N5, 10 minute drive.
Map ref: Kiltamagh 16 B3

Kinnity, Co. Offaly

Aaron House

◆◆◆◆

Kinnitty, Birr, Co. Offaly
Tel: +353(0)509 37040 Fax: +353(0)509 37040
Email: bgrimes@oceanfree.net
Web: www.aaron.house.ie
Rooms: 5 all ensuite
Pricing: Sgl €60 Dbl €75
CC: Accepted
Room facilities:
Children: Welcome
Parking: Off-street and free
Directions: 8 miles from Birr on the R241 beside
Kinnitty National School.
Map ref: Kinnity 19 D2

Kinsale, Co. Cork

Actons Hotel

★★★★

Pier Road, Kinsale, Co. Cork
Tel: +353(0)21 772135 Fax: +353(0)21 772231
Email: information@actonshotelkinsale.com
Web: www.actonshotelkinsale.com
Rooms: 73 all ensuite
Pricing: Sgl €100–175 Dbl €140–250
Dinner available from €37–45 CC: Accepted
Room facilities: Access:
Conference: 3 meeting rooms (Thtr 300 max),
24hr-delegate from €170, day-delegate from €40
Children: Welcome Dogs: Assistance dogs only
Licenses: Leisure: Indoor pool, Gym
Parking: Off-street and free
Directions: In town centre, 500 yards from yacht club
marina on the waterfront. Map ref: Kinsale 18 C4

Trident Hotel

★★★★

World's End, Kinsale, Co. Cork
Tel: +353(0)21 4779300 Fax: +353(0)21 4774173
Email: info@tridenthotel.com
Web: www.tridenthotel.com
Seasonal closure: Christmas

Situated right on the water's edge, the Trident offers
unrivalled views and award-winning cuisine.
Extensively redeveloped in 2005, it now boasts
executive rooms and luxury suites with spectacular
views and provides all the services expected from a
superior 4-star hotel.
Rooms: 75 all ensuite
Pricing: Sgl €95–250 Dbl €110–495
Dinner available from €25–50 CC: Accepted
Room facilities: Access:
Conference: 5 meeting rooms (Thtr 200 max),
24hr-delegate from €145, day-delegate from €38
Children: Welcome Licenses:
Leisure: Gym, Sauna, Steam room, Jacuzzi
Parking: Off-street and free
Directions: Take the R600 to Kinsale from Cork City.
The Trident is located at the end of Pier Road on the
waterfront.
Map ref: Kinsale 18 C4

Republic of Ireland

Friar's Lodge

♦♦♦♦♦ ⚹

Friar's Street, Kinsale, Cork, Co. Cork
Tel: +353(0)21 4777384 Fax: +353(0)21 4774363
Web: www.friars-lodge.com
Seasonal closure: 24-28 December

In the heart of picturesque Kinsale, famous for its
gourmet restaurants and character bars, the best of Irish
hospitality awaits at Friar's Lodge. Luxury five-diamond
accommodation in a bright, spacious, purpose-built
facility in the centre of town.
Rooms: 18 all ensuite 🦞 ⊗
Pricing: Sgl €50–80 Dbl €90–160
CC: Accepted
Room facilities: ▯ ☎ ▣ ⤵
Access: |↓↑
Children: Welcome
Dogs: Welcome
Licenses: ▦
Parking: Off-street and free
Directions: Cork to Kinsale. Follow signs for Airport.
Straight run from Airport to Kinsale (N71), Friar's Lodge
is next to parish church on Friar's Street.
Map ref: Cork 18 C4

Old Bank House

♦♦♦♦♦ ⚹ ⚘

11 Pearse Street, next to Post Office,
Kinsale, Co. Cork
Tel: +353(0)21 4774075 Fax: +353(0)21 4774296
Email: oldbank@indigo.ie
Web: www.oldbankhousekinsale.com
Seasonal closure: 4 days over Christmas.

A very comfortable stay is guaranteed at this popular
property. All individually designed bedrooms are of a
very high standard. Located in Kinsale town centre,
overlooking the harbour.
Rooms: 17 all ensuite ⊗
Pricing: Dbl €170–245
CC: Accepted
Room facilities: ▯ ☎
Access: |↓↑
Children: Welcome 10yrs min age
Licenses: ▦
Directions: On the right hand side at the start of
Kinsale Town. On R600 from Cork Airport, straight run
with no traffic lights and no roundabouts. 15 minutes.
Map ref: Kinsale 18 C4

Long Quay House

♦♦♦♦

Long Quay, Kinsale, Co. Cork
Tel: +353(0)21 4774563 Fax: +353(0)21 4773201
Email: longquayhouse@eircom.net
Web: www.longquayhousekinsale.com
Seasonal closure: mid November and December
Rooms: 7 all ensuite 🦞
Pricing: Sgl €60–85 Dbl €70–130
CC: Accepted
Room facilities: ▯ ☎ ▣
Children: Welcome
Dogs: Assistance dogs only
Directions: Take R600 from Cork to Kinsale. Hotel on
right as you enter Kinsale, just before supermarket and
Post Office.
Map ref: Kinsale 18 C4

Knock, Co. Mayo

Belmont Hotel

★★★★
Knock, Co. Mayo
Tel: +353(0)94 9388122 Fax: +353(0)94 9388532
Email: reception@belmonthotel.ie
Web: www.belmonthotel.ie
Rooms: 63 all ensuite 🐾 🛏 🚫
Pricing: Sgl €55–80 Dbl €90–140
Dinner available from €32–38
CC: Accepted Room facilities: 🖵 ☎ 🍵 ❄
Access: ⏸
Conference: 3 meeting rooms (Thtr 350 max)
Children: Welcome 🍴 🍼
Licenses: 🍷 ♨
Leisure: Gym, Health spa, Beauty salon,
Hydrotherapy bath
Parking: Off-street and free
Directions: Leaving Knock in the direction of Galway,
take a left turn and go 200 metres.
Map ref: Knock 16 B3

Knock House Hotel

★★★★
Ballyhaunis Road, Knock, Co. Mayo
Tel: +353(0)94 9388088 Fax: +353(0)94 9388044
Email: info@knockhousehotel.ie
Web: www.knockhousehotel.ie
Rooms: 68 all ensuite
Pricing: Sgl €63–93 Dbl €106–146
Dinner available from €38 CC: Accepted
Room facilities: 🖵 ☎ 🍵 Access: ⏸
Conference: 3 meeting rooms (Thtr 150 max)
Children: Welcome 🍴
Licenses: ♨ Parking: Off-street and free
Directions: Adjacent to Marian Shrine and Basilica on
Ballyhaunis Road, 200 metres from roundabout in
village, on the right-hand side.
Map ref: Knock 16 B3

Letterkenny, Co. Donegal

Silver Tassie Hotel

★★★★
Ramelton Road, Letterkenny, Co. Donegal
Tel: +353(0)74 9125619 Fax: +353(0)74 9124473
Email: silvertassie@eircom.net
Web: www.theblaneygroup.com
Rooms: 36 all ensuite 🐾 🚫
Pricing: Sgl €50–90 Dbl €70–140
Dinner available from €25 CC: Accepted
Room facilities: 🖵 ☎ 🍵 🔌 Access: ⏸
Conference: 4 meeting rooms (Thtr 350 max),
24hr-delegate from €95, day-delegate from €30
Children: Welcome 🍴 Dogs: Assistance dogs only
Licenses: 🍷 ♨ Parking: Off-street and free
Directions: At Port Bridge roundabout in Letterkenny
take third exit, R245. Keep straight for 3 miles. Hotel is
on left.
Map ref: Letterkenny 17 D1

Limerick, Co. Limerick

Lynch South Court Hotel

★★★★★
Raheen Roundabout, Adare Road,
Limerick, Co. Limerick
Tel: +353(0)65 6823000 Fax: +353(0)65 6823759
Email: reservations@lynchotels.com
Web: www.lynchotels.com
Rooms: 124 all ensuite 🚫
Pricing: Dinner available from €30
CC: Accepted
Room facilities: 🖵 ☎ 🍵 🔌
Access: ⏸
Conference: 10 meeting rooms (Thtr 1250 max),
24hr-delegate from €175, day-delegate from €50
Children: Welcome 🍴
Dogs: Assistance dogs only
Licenses: 🍷 ♨
Leisure: Gym
Parking: Off-street and free
Directions: Located on the outskirts of Limerick city, on
the N20 route, Cork/Kerry road. 20 minutes drive from
Shannon airport.
Map ref: Limerick 18 C2

Jurys Inn Limerick

★★★
Lower Mallow Street, Limerick, Co. Limerick
Tel: +353(0)61 207000 Fax: +353(0)61 400966
Email: jurysinnlimerick@jurysdoyle.com
Web: www.jurysinns.com
Seasonal closure: Christmas

Rooms: 151 all ensuite 🐾 🚫
Pricing: Sgl €100 Dbl €113
Dinner available from €20
CC: Accepted
Room facilities: 🖵 ☎ 🍵 🔌
Access: ⏸
Conference: 1 meeting room (Thtr 40 max)
Children: Welcome 12yrs min age 🍴
Licenses: ♨
Parking: Off-street
Directions: Located 15 miles/24 km from Shannon
International Airport. Colbert train station 1 mile/2 km.
Heart of the city on the banks of Shannon.
Map ref: Limerick 18 C2

"Stay!"

Need a pet friendly
property? Look out for
'Dogs welcome' in
our listings.

Republic of Ireland

Macroom, Co. Cork

Castle Hotel and Leisure Centre

★★★★ ⓡ

Main Street, Macroom, Co. Cork
Tel: +353(0)26 41074 Fax: +353(0)26 41505
Email: castlehotel@eircom.net
Web: www.castlehotel.ie
Seasonal closure: 25–27 December
Rooms: 60 all ensuite
Pricing: Sgl €89–110 Dbl €140–170
Dinner available from €35–37
CC: Accepted
Room facilities:
Access: ⌊↑
Conference: 3 meeting rooms (Thtr 200 max),
24hr-delegate from €75
Children: Welcome
Licenses:
Leisure: Indoor pool, Gym, Health spa, Steam room,
Kids playroom
Parking: Off-street and free
Directions: On the N22, 25 miles from Cork and 30
miles from Killarney.
Map ref: Macroom 18 B4

Mallow, Co. Cork

Springfort Hall Country House

★★★ ⓡ

Mallow, Co. Cork
Tel: +353(0)22 21278 Fax: +353(0)22 21557
Email: stay@springfort-hall.com
Web: www.springfort-hall.com
Seasonal closure: 23–28 December
Rooms: 49 all ensuite
Pricing: Sgl €85–110 Dbl €140–165
Dinner available from €43
CC: Accepted
Room facilities:
Conference: 5 meeting rooms (Thtr 360 max),
24hr-delegate from €135, day-delegate from €45
Children: Welcome
Licenses:
Parking: Off-street and free
Directions: From Cork, N20 to Newtwopothouse (5 km
outside Mallow). Right towards Doneraile, hotel on
right approx 1/2 mile. From Limerick, N20 through
Charleville and Buttevant to Newtwopothouse, left
towards Doneraile, on right 1/2 mile. From Dublin, N8 to
Mallow, N20 to Newtwopothouse. Turn right, 1/2 mile.
Map ref: Newtwopothouse 18 C3

Maynooth, Co. Kildare

Moyglare Manor Hotel

★★★★ ⓡⓡ

Maynooth, Co. Kildare
Tel: +353(0)1 6286351 Fax: +353(0)1 6285405
Email: info@moyglaremanor.ie
Web: www.moyglaremanor.ie
Seasonal closure: 24–26 December
Rooms: 16 all ensuite
Dinner available CC: Accepted
Room facilities:
Conference: 3 meeting rooms (Thtr 30 max),
24hr-delegate from €250
Children: Welcome 12yrs min age
Licenses: Parking: Off-street and free
Directions: Travelling west on N4/M4, take slip road for
Maynooth. Keep right at Catholic church to Moyglare
Road. Hotel is after 2 km. Map ref: Maynooth 19 E1

Midleton, Co. Cork

Ballymaloe House   Little Gem

◆◆◆◆◆ ⓡⓡ

Shanagarry, Midleton, Co. Cork
Tel: +353(0)21 4652531 Fax: +353(0)21 4652021
Email: res@ballymaloe.ie
Web: www.ballymaloe.ie
Seasonal closure: 23–26 December

Internationally famous for food and hospitality,
Ballymaloe House offers a relaxed environment to
celebrate special occasions with the family, small
business meetings or a special romantic break. 30
minutes drive from Cork airport.
Rooms: 33 all ensuite
Pricing: Dinner available from €60 CC: Accepted
Room facilities:
Conference: 3 meeting rooms (Thtr 30 max)
Children: Welcome Dogs: Assistance dogs only
Licenses: Leisure: Outdoor pool, Tennis, Golf
Parking: Off-street and free
Directions: From Cork, take N25 to Midleton, then the
Ballycotton Road via Cloyne (signposted from Midleton).
Map ref: Shanagarry 19 D4

Monasterevin, Co. Kildare

Hazel Hotel

Dublin Road, Monasterevin, Co. Kildare
Tel: +353(0)45 525373 Fax: +353(0)45 525810
Email: sales@hazelhotel.com
Web: www.hazelhotel.com
Seasonal closure: 24–25 December
Rooms: 24 all ensuite
Pricing: Sgl €70–140 Dbl €130–160
Dinner available from €35
CC: Accepted
Room facilities:
Conference: 4 meeting rooms
Children: Welcome
Parking: Off-street and free
Directions: The hotel is situated on the N7
Cork/Limerick road to the west of Monasterevin.
Map ref: Monasterevin 19 E1
See advert on this page

Relax & smell the coffee

Fresh coffee, chilled juices for breakfast.
RAC's team of qualified Inspectors
check them both.

Naas, Co. Kildare

Killashee House Hotel & Villa Spa

★★★★★ Excellent

Killcullen Road, Naas, Co. Kildare
Tel: +353(0)45 879277 Fax: +353(0)45 879266
Email: reservations@killasheehouse.com
Web: www.killasheehouse.com
Seasonal closure: 24-25 December
Rooms: 142 all ensuite
Pricing: Sgl €144–495 Dbl €198–495
Dinner available from €48.50
CC: Accepted
Room facilities:
Access:
Conference: 20 meeting rooms (Thtr 1000 max),
24hr-delegate from €195, day-delegate from €59
Children: Welcome
Licenses:
Leisure: Indoor pool, Gym, Health spa, Beauty salon
Parking: Off-street and free
Directions: 30 mins from Dublin on N7 to Naas then 1
mile along R448 Killcullen Road.
Map ref: Naas 19 E1
See advert on following page

Republic of Ireland

Harbour Hotel & Restaurant

★★

Limerick Road, Naas, Co. Kildare
Tel: +353(0)45 879145 Fax: +353(0)45 874002
Seasonal closure: Christmas to New Year
Rooms: 10 all ensuite ⊛
Pricing: Sgl €70–75 Dbl €100–110
Dinner available
CC: Accepted
Room facilities: 📺 ☎ 🛏
Licenses: 🍷 👯
Parking: Off-street
Map ref: Naas 19 E1

Ballinagappa Country House

◆◆◆◆◆

Clane, near Naas, Co. Kildare
Tel: +353(0)45 892087 Fax: +353(0)45 892087
Email: ballinagappahouse@eircom.net
Web: www.ballinagappa.com
Rooms: 3 (2 ensuite) ⊛
Room facilities: 📺 🛏 📞
Children: Welcome 🪑 ⊛
Dogs: Welcome
Parking: Off-street
Directions: From the N4, go towards Naas; Clane is 6½ miles. Take second right, and Ballinagappa is 1½ miles on the left.
Map ref: Clane 19 E1

Portlaoise, Co. Laois

The Heritage Hotel, Conference & Leisure Club

★★★★

Jessop Street, Portlaoise, Co. Laois
Tel: +353(0)502 78588 Fax: +353(0)502 78577
Email: info@theheritagehotel.com
Web: www.theheritagehotel.com
Seasonal closure: 23-27 December
Rooms: 110 all ensuite ⊛
Pricing: Sgl €170 Dbl €240
Dinner available
CC: Accepted
Room facilities: 📺 ☎ 🛏 📞
Access: 🚹
Conference: 14 meeting rooms (Thtr 500 max)
Children: Welcome 🪑
Licenses: 👯
Leisure: Indoor pool, Gym, Health spa, Beauty salon
Parking: Off-street and free
Directions: The Heritage Portlaoise is situated in the town centre, only 1 hour's drive from Dublin, 5 minutes off the M7 motorway to Cork and Limerick and 2 minutes walk from the main rail line to the south.
Map ref: Portlaoise 19 E2
See advert on this page

Portmagee, Co. Kerry

Moorings

◆◆◆◆

Portmagee Village, Co. Kerry
Tel: +353(0)66 9477108 Fax: +353(0)66 9477220
Email: moorings@iol.ie
Web: www.moorings.ie
Seasonal closure: November to February
Rooms: 14 all ensuite ⊛ CC: Accepted
Room facilities: ▢ ☎ ☺ ✆
Children: Welcome ☡ Licenses: ⬥ ⚹
Parking: Off-street and free
Directions: Follow the Ring of Kerry Road — Killarney
to Caherciveen. 3 miles outside Caherciveen, turn right
for Portmagee. Moorings is in the centre of the village.
Map ref: Portmagee 18 A3

Portumna, Co. Galway

Shannon Oaks Hotel and Country Club

★★★★ ⚲⚲

St Joseph's Road, Portumna, Co. Galway
Tel: +353(0)90 9741777 Fax: +353(0)90 9741357
Email: sales@shannonoaks.ie
Web: www.shannonoaks.ie
Rooms: 63 all ensuite ⬚ ⊛
Dinner available CC: Accepted
Room facilities: ▢ ☎ ☺ ✆ ✳ Access: ⇅
Conference: 3 meeting rooms, 24hr-delegate from €167
Children: Welcome ☡ ⚹ Licenses: ⬥ ⚹
Leisure: Indoor pool, Gym, Health spa, Beauty salon,
Tennis, Golf, Riding
Parking: Off-street and free
Directions: Shannon Oaks Hotel & Country Club is
located on St Joseph's Road in the village of
Portumna. Map ref: Portumna 19 D1

Rathmullan, Co. Donegal

Rathmullan House

★★★★ ⚲⚲⚲

Rathmullan, Letterkenny, Co. Donegal
Tel: +353(0)74 9158188 Fax: +353(0)74 9158200
Email: info@rathmullanhouse.com
Web: www.rathmullanhouse.com
Seasonal closure: 18-27 December

Time moves slowly in the mature, tranquil gardens that
slope down to the sea. Fine Georgian proportioned
lounges, elegantly furnished, beautifully appointed
bedrooms and restaurant offering seasonal organic
produce.
Rooms: 32 all ensuite ⚹ ⬚ ⊛
Pricing: Sgl €93.50–121 Dbl €187–286
Dinner available from €45–55
CC: Accepted
Room facilities: ▢ ☎ ☺ ✆
Conference: 1 meeting room (Thtr 80 max)
Children: Welcome ☡ ⚹
Dogs: Welcome
Licenses: ⚹
Leisure: Indoor pool, Beauty salon, Tennis
Parking: Off-street and free
Directions: N13 to Letterkenny, R245 to Ramelton. Go
over bridge and turn right to Rathmullan (R247). Hotel
north of village, gates on right.
Map ref: Letterkenny 17 D1

Riverstown, Co. Sligo

Coopershill House   `Little Gem`

◆◆◆◆◆ ⚲ ✕ ⚘

Riverstown, Co. Sligo
Tel: +353(0)719165108 Fax: +353 (0)719165466
Email: ohara@coopershill.com
Web: www.coopershill.com
Seasonal closure: 31 October to 1 April

This fine Georgian Mansion House provides very high
standards of guest accommodation and has been
home to seven generations of the O'Hara family. Built
in 1774, the public areas are both spacious and
comfortable, while fine dining can be enjoyed in the
evenings.
Rooms: 8 (7 ensuite) ⬚ ⊛
Pricing: Sgl €127–143 Dbl €216–248
Dinner available from €48
CC: Accepted
Room facilities: ☎ ☺
Children: Welcome ☡ ⚹
Leisure: Tennis, Fishing, Snooker/billiards
Parking: Off-street and free
Directions: Signed from Drumfin crossroads 19 km
south-east of Sligo en route N4 to Dublin.
Map ref: Riverstown 16 C3

Republic of Ireland

Roscommon, Co. Roscommon

Gleesons Town House and Restaurant

 ◆◆◆◆ℝ

Market Square, Roscommon, Co. Roscommon
Tel: +353(0)90 6626954 Fax: +353(0)90 6627425
Email: info@gleesonstownhouse.com
Web: www.gleesonstownhouse.com
Rooms: 19 all ensuite 🛏️ 🚭
Dinner available
CC: Accepted
Room facilities: 📺 ☎ 🍵 📞
Conference: 2 meeting rooms (Thtr 80 max)
Children: Welcome ♒ 🎠 Dogs: Welcome
Licenses: 🍷 🎎
Parking: Off-street and free
Directions: Town centre next door to tourist
office/county museum.
Map ref: Roscommon 16 C4
See advert on this page

Rosslare, Co. Wexford

Kelly's Resort Hotel

★★★★ ℝℝ

Rosslare, Co. Wexford
Tel: +353(0)53 32114 Fax: +353(0)53 32222
Email: kellyhot@iol.ie
Web: www.kellys.ie
Seasonal closure: 11 December to 17 February

Renowned resort hotel with fine food and wine.
Extensive leisure and beauty complex with superb new
spa facility. Special spring to autumn midweeks,
two-day weekends and five-day midweeks.
Rooms: 118 all ensuite 🛏️
Pricing: Sgl €75–100 Dbl €140–200
Dinner available from €42 CC: Accepted
Room facilities: 📺 ☎ 📞 Access: ♿
Children: Welcome ♒ 🎠 🎠 Licenses: 🎎
Leisure: Indoor pool, Gym, Health spa, Tennis,
Games room, Snooker/billiards, Thermal suite,
Sea water vitality pool, Rock Sauna,
Self-infused steam room, Rainforest,
Heated loungers, Hair salon, Croquet, Bowls
Parking: Off-street and free
Directions: From Dublin airport, take N11 to Rosslare,
signposted South-East (Gorey, Enniscorthy, Wexford,
Rosslare). The hotel is situated in Rosslare Strand.
Map ref: Rosslare 19 F3

Churchtown House   Little Gem

◆◆◆◆◆ ℝ 🍽️ 🐾

Tagoat, Rosslare, Co. Wexford
Tel: +353(0)53 32555 Fax: +353(0)52 32577
Email: info@churchtownhouse.com
Web: www.churchtownhouse.com
Seasonal closure: November to February
Rooms: 12 all ensuite 🚭
Pricing: Sgl €65–95 Dbl €120–180
Dinner available from €39.50
CC: Accepted
Room facilities: 📺 ☎
Children: Welcome
Licenses: 🎎
Parking: Off-street and free
Directions: Half a mile from the N25 at Tagoat. Turn
between pub and church onto R736 at Tagoat village.
Map ref: Tagoat 19 F3

Slane, Co. Meath

Conyngham Arms Hotel

★★★

Slane, Co. Meath
Tel: +353(0)41 9884444 Fax: +353(0)41 9824205
Email: enquiry@conynghamarms.com
Web: www.conynghamarms.com
Seasonal closure: 24-25 December
Rooms: 15 all ensuite 🛏️ 📠 🚭

Pricing: Sgl €55 Dbl €120
Dinner available from €18
CC: Accepted
Room facilities: 🖥 ☎ 🛏
Conference: 3 meeting rooms (Thtr 200 max),
24hr-delegate from €126, day-delegate from €55
Children: Welcome 7yrs min age 🍴
Licenses: 🍷 🍸
Parking: Off-street and free
Directions: Located in the manor village of Slane 30
minutes drive from Dublin and Dundalk, 10 minutes
from Drogheda and Navan.
Map ref: Slane 17 E4

Straffan, Co. Kildare

The K Club

★★★★★ 🍴🍴🍴  Premier
Straffan, Co. Kildare
Tel: +353(0)1 6017200 Fax: +353(0)1 6017297
Email: resortsales@kclub.ie
Web: www.kclub.ie
Rooms: 92 all ensuite 🛁 🍸 🚭
Pricing: Sgl €265–495 Dbl €265–495
Dinner available from €75
CC: Accepted
Room facilities: 🖥 ☎ 🛏
Access: ♿
Conference: 8 meeting rooms (Thtr 400 max)
Children: Welcome 🍴
Licenses: 🍸
Leisure: Indoor pool, Gym, Health spa, Beauty salon,
Golf, Fishing, Riding, Games room, Snooker/billiards
Parking: Off-street and free
Directions: Take N7 south to the Kill crossing, turn right
at traffic lights. Resort is 5 miles, well-signposted from
that point.
Map ref: Straffan 19 E1
See advert on this page

Barberstown Castle

★★★★ 🍴🍴
Straffan, Co. Kildare
Tel: +353(0)1 6288157 Fax: +353(0)1 6277027
Email: barberstowncastle@ireland.com
Web: www.barberstowncastle.ie
Rooms: 60 all ensuite 🍸 🚭
Dinner available
CC: Accepted
Room facilities: 🖥 ☎ 🛏
Conference: 4 meeting rooms (Thtr 200 max)
Children: Welcome 12yrs min age
Licenses: 🍷 🍸
Parking: Off-street and free
Directions: N4 west from Dublin — exit at Maynooth/
Straffan. N7 south from Dublin exit at 'Kill' junction.
Map ref: Straffan 19 E1

Tallaght, Co. Dublin

Plaza Hotel

★★★★

Belgard Road, Tallaght, Dublin 24
Tel: +353(0)1 4624200 Fax: +353(0)1 4624600
Email: sales@plazahotel.ie
Web: www.plazahotel.ie
Seasonal closure: 24–31 December

Located in south Dublin at the foothills of the Dublin
mountains, The Plaza caters for both business and
tourist visitors with many facilities, including two
restaurants, three bars, conference facilities, secure
parking, Wi-Fi internet access and several golf courses
nearby.
Rooms: 122 all ensuite 🚭
Pricing: Sgl €102.50–205 Dbl €102.50–205
Dinner available from €35 CC: Accepted
Room facilities: 🖵 ☎ 🖫 Access: ⬆
Conference: 11 meeting rooms (Thtr 220 max)
Children: Welcome ♀
Dogs: Assistance dogs only
Licenses: ⬦ ⁂
Parking: Off-street and free
Directions: From Dublin airport take M50 southbound
past tollbridge. Take exit for N81 (Blessington Road).
Follow N81 to Tallaght village. Hotel on right after
lights.
Map ref: Dublin 19 F1

Thomastown, Co. Kilkenny

Mount Juliet Conrad

★★★★★ ⓡⓡ   *Premier*

Thomastown, Co. Kilkenny
Tel: +353(0)56 777 3000 Fax: +353(0)56 777 3010
Email: mountjulietinfo@conradhotels.com
Web: www.ConradHotels.com
Rooms: 57 all ensuite ⧉ 🚭
Pricing: Sgl €162–667 Dbl €179–684
Dinner available from €45–66.5
CC: Accepted

Room facilities: 🖵 ☎ 🖫
Conference: 5 meeting rooms (Thtr 130 max),
24hr-delegate from €222, day-delegate from €65
Children: Welcome ♀ ⁑
Licenses: ⁂
Leisure: Indoor pool, Gym, Health spa, Tennis, Golf,
Fishing, Riding, Snooker/billiards, Clay target shooting,
Archery Parking: Off-street and free
Directions: Situated in the south-east of Ireland 75
miles from Dublin, 55 from Rosslare. Train services to
Thomastown; helipad on site.
Map ref: Thomastown 19 E3

Tralee, Co. Kerry

Ballygarry House

★★★★★ ⓡⓡ   *Excellent*

Killarney Road, Tralee, Co. Kerry
Tel: +353(0)66 7123322 Fax: +353(0)66 7127630
Email: info@ballygarryhouse.com
Web: www.ballygarryhouse.com
Seasonal closure: 20-26 December

Privately owned, well established 'old world charm',
set on six acres of landscaped gardens. Bedrooms,
tastefully furnished and equipped with every modern
convenience. Dining in Brooks Restaurant a very
pleasant experience. High standard of hospitality in a
relaxing environment. 'Aurora' health spa opens
February 2006.
Rooms: 46 all ensuite ⧉ ⧉ 🚭
Pricing: Sgl €120–190 Dbl €150–250
Dinner available from €35
CC: Accepted
Room facilities: 🖵 ☎ 🖫 🖫
Access: ⬆
Conference: 1 meeting room (Thtr 250 max)
Children: Welcome ♀ ⁑
Licenses: ⬦ ⁂
Leisure: Health spa, Beauty salon
Parking: Off-street and free
Directions: Ballygarry House is situated just off the
main Killarney to Tralee road 1½km from Tralee, 6km
from Kerry Airport.
Map ref: Tralee 18 B3

Tullow, Co. Carlow

Mount Wolseley Country Resort
★★★★★ ☕☕

Tullow, Co. Carlow
Tel: +353(0)59 915 1674 Fax: +353(0)59 915 2123
Map ref: Tullow 19 E2

Waterford, Co. Waterford

Granville Hotel
★★★★ ☕

Meagher Quay, Waterford, Co. Waterford
Tel: +353(0)51 305555 Fax: +353(0)51 305566
Email: stay@granville-hotel.ie
Web: www.granville-hotel.ie
Seasonal closure: 25–26 December
Rooms: 100 all ensuite 🍴 ⊗
Pricing: Sgl €85–145 Dbl €110–200
Dinner available from €27.50–400
CC: Accepted
Room facilities: ▢ ☎ 🍵 Access: |↕
Conference: 4 meeting rooms (Thtr 200 max),
24hr-delegate from €150, day-delegate from €35
Children: Welcome ♀
Licenses: ⟁ ⚎
Parking: Off-street
Directions: City centre, on the quay opposite
clocktower.
Map ref: Waterford 19 E3
See advert on this page

Dooley's Hotel
★★★ ☕

The Quay, Waterford, Co. Waterford
Tel: +353(0)51 873531 Fax: +353(0)51 870262
Email: hotel@dooleys-hotel.ie
Web: www.dooleys-hotel.ie
Rooms: 113 all ensuite 🍴 ▱ ⊗
Pricing: Sgl €70–130 Dbl €120–198
Dinner available from €28 CC: Accepted
Room facilities: ▢ ☎ 🍵 Access: |↕
Conference: 2 meeting rooms,
24hr-delegate from €143, day-delegate from €30.96
Children: Welcome ♀
Licenses: ⚎
Directions: Located in Waterford City on the quayside
overlooking the River Suir. Follow the N25 route to the
city centre.
Map ref: Waterford 19 E3

McEniff Ard Ri Hotel
★★★

Ferrybank, Waterford, Co. Waterford
Tel: +353(0)51 832111 Fax: +353(0)51 832863
Email: mairead_moroney@ardri.org
Web: www.ardri.org
Seasonal closure: Christmas
Rooms: 99 all ensuite ⊗
Pricing: Sgl €139–151 Dbl €169–197

City centre, Manor style hotel overlooking the
River Suir. This family-run hotel has been
charmingly restored and completely refurbished
retaining its 'Olde Worlde' charm and character.
One of Ireland's oldest hotels, owners Liam and
Ann Cusack vigorously pursue the Granville's long
tradition of hospitality, friendliness and comfort.

**Meagher Quay, Waterford,
Co. Waterford, Ireland**
Tel: +353(0)51 305555 Fax: +353(0)51 305566
Email: stay@granville-hotel.ie
Web: www.granville-hotel.ie

Dinner available from €30–45
CC: Accepted
Room facilities: ▢ ☎ 🍵 Access: |↕
Conference: 5 meeting rooms (Thtr 400 max)
Children: Welcome ♀ Dogs: Assistance dogs only
Licenses: ⟁ ⚎
Leisure: Indoor pool, Gym, Health spa, Tennis
Parking: Off-street and free
Directions: Follow sign city centre, drive along Quay,
over bridge, take second exit off roundabout. Hotel is
left side of dual carriageway.
Map ref: Waterford 19 E3

Tower Hotel
★★★ ☕

The Mall, Waterford, Co. Waterford
Tel: +353(0)51 862300 Fax: +353(0)51 870129
Email: reservations@thw.ie
Web: www.towerhotelgroup.com
Seasonal closure: 23–27 December
Rooms: 140 all ensuite 🍴
Pricing: Sgl €140–154 Dbl €199–237
Dinner available from €29 CC: Accepted
Room facilities: ▢ ☎ 🍵 Access: |↕
Conference: 7 meeting rooms (Thtr 450 max)
Children: Welcome ♀ Licenses: ⟁ ⚎
Leisure: Indoor pool, Gym, Health spa
Parking: Off-street and free
Map ref: Waterford 19 E3

Republic of Ireland

Westport, Co. Mayo

Hotel Westport

★★★★ ®

Newport Road, Westport, Co. Mayo
Tel: +353(0)98 25122 Fax: +353(0)98 26739
Email: reservations@hotelwestport.ie
Web: www.hotelwestport.ie
Rooms: 129 all ensuite 🛏 ⊗
Pricing: Sgl €90–140 Dbl €140–240
Dinner available from €36 CC: Accepted
Room facilities: ▢ ☎ 🍵 🔌 Access: ♿
Conference: 6 meeting rooms (Thtr 450 max)
Children: Welcome ♁ ⅛℃
Licenses: ♦♦♦
Leisure: Indoor pool, Gym
Parking: Off-street and free
Directions: Take N5 to Castlebar, N60 to Westport. At
end of Castlebar Street turn right before the bridge.
Turn right at lights and take immediate left at hotel
signpost. Follow to end of road.
Map ref: Westport 16 B3

Knockranny House Hotel

★★★★ ®®®

Knockranny, Westport, Co. Mayo
Tel: +353(0)98 28600 Fax: +353(0)98 28611
Email: info@khh.ie
Web: www.khh.ie
Seasonal closure: 22 to 27 December

Overlooking Westport, this luxurious Victorian hotel
boasts panoramic views of the spectacular local
scenery. The already excellent standards of service
and cuisine have now been augmented by the
wonderful Spa Salveo.
Rooms: 54 all ensuite 🍵 🛏 ⊗
Pricing: Sgl €130–180 Dbl €210–270
Dinner available from €47 CC: Accepted
Room facilities: ▢ ☎ 🍵 🔌 Access: ♿
Conference: 3 meeting rooms (Thtr 400 max),
24hr-delegate from €165, day-delegate from €50
Children: Welcome ♁ ⅛℃
Licenses: ♦♦♦
Leisure: Gym, Snooker/billiards, Destination spa
Parking: Off-street and free
Directions: The hotel is on your left as you enter
Westport on the main Dublin/Castlebar road (N5).
Map ref: Westport 16 B3

The Atlantic Coast Hotel

★★★★ ®®®

The Quay, Westport, Co. Mayo
Tel: +353(0)98 29000 Fax: +353(0)98 29111
Email: reservations@atlanticcoasthotel.com
Web: www.atlanticcoasthotel.com
Seasonal closure: 23–27 December
Rooms: 85 all ensuite 🍵 ⊗
Pricing: Sgl €70–155 Dbl €120–270
Dinner available from €36
CC: Accepted
Room facilities: ▢ ☎ 🍵 🔌
Access: ♿
Conference: 4 meeting rooms (Thtr 140 max)
Children: Welcome ♁ ⅛℃
Licenses: ⬧ ♦♦♦
Leisure: Indoor pool, Gym, Health spa, Beauty salon
Parking: Off-street and free
Directions: Located on Westport Harbour 1 mile from
Westport town on the Quay Road.
Map ref: Westport 16 B3

Augusta Lodge

◆◆◆◆ ⚡🍽

Golf Course Road, Westport, Co Mayo
Tel: +353(0)98 28900 Fax: +353(0)98 28995
Email: info@augustalodge.ie
Web: www.augustalodge.ie
Seasonal closure: 22 December to 26 December

Augusta Lodge is a family-run purpose built 4-diamond
guest house 5 minutes walk from Westport. All rooms
ensuite with DD telephone, satellite TV, hairdryer and
tea/coffee making facilities. A golfer's haven with
putting green on site. Liz and Dave will ensure your
stay is a memorable one.
Rooms: 10 all ensuite 🍵 ⊗
Pricing: Sgl €50–65 Dbl €80–100
CC: Accepted
Room facilities: ▢ ☎ 🍵
Children: Welcome ⅛℃
Leisure: Putting green
Parking: Off-street and free
Directions: N5 to Westport, Newport Road, left to golf
course road.
Map ref: Westport 16 B3

Wexford, Co. Wexford

Ferrycarrig Hotel

★★★★ ☏☏

Ferrycarrig Bridge, Wexford, Co. Wexford
Tel: +353(0)53 20999 Fax: +353(0)53 20982
Email: ferrycarrig@ferrycarrighotel.com
Web: www.ferrycarrighotel.ie

A well-established modern hotel that has been much extended and improved. It boasts light, comfortable rooms, good food, a friendly team of young staff and excellent leisure facilities.
Rooms: 102 all ensuite ✥ ☺
Pricing: Sgl €115–185 Dbl €130–1000
Dinner available from €40–55 CC: Accepted
Room facilities: ▢ ☎ ☕ ✎
Access: ⇅
Conference: 4 meeting rooms (Thtr 400 max)
Children: Welcome ☰ 🐎
Licenses: ⛉
Leisure: Indoor pool, Gym, Health spa, Beauty salon
Parking: Off-street and free
Directions: Travelling on N11 from Enniscorthy to Wexford town, hotel is 2 miles from Wexford on Enniscorthy Road, overlooking River Slaney estuary.
Map ref: Ferrycarrig Bridge 19 E3

Talbot Hotel

★★★★

On the Quay, Wexford, Co. Wexford
Tel: +353(0)53 22566 Fax: +353(0)53 23377
Email: sales@talbothotel.ie
Web: www.talbothotel.ie
Rooms: 109 all ensuite ✥ ☺
Pricing: Sgl €95–105 Dbl €150–170
Dinner available from €39 CC: Accepted
Room facilities: ▢ ☎ ☕ ✎ Access: ⇅
Conference: 9 meeting rooms (Thtr 400 max),
24hr-delegate from €165, day-delegate from €38
Children: Welcome ☰ 🐎
Licenses: ⛉
Leisure: Indoor pool, Gym, Beauty salon
Parking: Off-street and free
Directions: From Dublin and Rosslare, take N11, following signs for Wexford. The hotel is in the town centre, on the quay.
Map ref: Wexford 19 F3
See advert on this page

Cedar Lodge Hotel

★★★★ ☏☏

Carrigbyrne, Newbawn, New Ross, Co. Wexford
Tel: +353(0)51 428386 Fax: +353(0)51 428222
Email: cedarlodge@eircom.net
Web: www.prideofeirehotels.com
Seasonal closure: January

A very popular hotel situated close to the main Waterford road. All rooms are of a very high standard and a warm welcome is guaranteed.
Rooms: 28 all ensuite ☺
Pricing: Sgl €90–150 Dbl €150–200
Dinner available from €50–55
CC: Accepted
Room facilities: ▢ ☎ ☕ ❄
Children: Welcome ☰
Licenses: ⛉ ⛉
Parking: Off-street and free
Directions: On the N25 road between Wexford and New Ross.
Map ref: Carrigbyrne 19 E3

Whitford House Hotel
Health & Leisure Club

- Luxury Accommodation
- Exclusive Health & Leisure Club
- Footprints Award Winning Restaurant
  (live classical music)
- Forthside Bar/Bistro/Beer Garden
  – Dining Pub of the Year winner.
  - Park Room Conference Facilities
  - Kiddies Playground
  - 15 km from port on N25
    just off the Duncannon
    roundabout

New Line Road,
Wexford.
Tel 053 43444
Fax 053 46399
info@whitford.ie
www.whitford.ie

Whitford House Hotel
Health & Leisure Club

★★★ ®

New Line Road, Wexford, Co. Wexford
Tel: +353(0)53 43444 Fax: +353(0)53 46399
Email: info@whitford.ie
Web: www.whitford.ie
Seasonal closure: 23-28 December
Rooms: 36 all ensuite 🛁 Ⓢ
Pricing: Sgl €62–144 Dbl €100–217
Dinner available from €25–40
CC: Accepted
Room facilities: 🖳 ☎ 🍵 🐾
Conference: 4 meeting rooms (Thtr 40 max)
Children: Welcome 🍴 🌣
Licenses: 🎎
Leisure: Indoor pool, Gym, Beauty salon
Parking: Off-street and free
Directions: Situated 2 miles from Wexford Town, 10
miles from Rosslare Port, easy access to N11 and
N25.
Map ref: Wexford 19 F3
See advert on this page

Wicklow, Co. Wicklow

Marriott Druids Glen Hotel & Country Club

★★★★ ®®

Newtownmountkennedy, Co. Wicklow
Tel: +353(0)1 2870800 Fax: +353(0)1 2870801
Email: mhrs.dubgs.reservations@marriotthotels.com
Web: www.marriott.co.uk/dubgs
Rooms: 148 all ensuite 🛁 Ⓢ
Pricing: Sgl €132–200 Dbl €160–226
Dinner available from €35
CC: Accepted
Room facilities: 🖳 ☎ 🍵 🐾 ❄
Access: ♿
Conference: 7 meeting rooms
Children: Welcome 🍴 🌣
Licenses: 🔻 🎎
Leisure: Indoor pool, Gym, Health spa, Golf
Parking: Off-street and free
Directions: From Dublin take N11 southbound, pass
exits for Bray and Greystones, take right at sign for
Newtownmountkennedy, take first right off roundabout,
continue until T-junction, turn right. Hotel signposted
from here.
Map ref: Newtownmountkennedy 19 F2

Tinakilly House Hotel

★★★ ®®® Excellent

Rathnew, Wicklow, Co. Wicklow
Tel: +353(0)404 69274 Fax: +353(0)404 67806
Email: reservations@tinakilly.ie
Web: www.tinakilly.ie
Seasonal closure: 24-26 December
Rooms: 51 all ensuite 🗐
Pricing: Sgl €169–395 Dbl €216–668
Dinner available from €55
CC: Accepted
Room facilities: 🖳 ☎ 🍵
Access: ♿
Conference: 4 meeting rooms (Thtr 65 max)
Children: Welcome
Licenses: 🎎
Leisure: Tennis, 7 acres of gardens
Parking: Off-street and free
Directions: Take N11/M11 (Dublin-Wicklow-Wexford
road) to Rathnew village. At roundabout, follow R750
to Wicklow Town. Entrance is 500m from village.
Map ref: Rathnew 19 F2

Youghal, Co. Cork

Ahernes Seafood Restaurant & Accommodation

Little Gem

◆◆◆◆◆ ℞℞ ✖ ℟

163 North Main Street, Youghal, Co. Cork
Tel: +353(0)24 92424 Fax: +353(0)24 93633
Email: ahernes@eircom.net
Web: www.ahernes.com
Seasonal closure: 23-28 December

Ahernes is a very popular family run establishment located in Youghal town centre. All rooms are of a very high standard and very comfortable. Secure parking is available and the property is close to the major road network.

Rooms: 13 all ensuite ℠ ⊗
Pricing: Sgl €110–130 Dbl €220–240
Dinner available from €45–50
CC: Accepted
Room facilities: ⬚ ☎
Conference: 1 meeting room (Thtr 25 max),
24hr-delegate from €155
Children: Welcome � ℘
Licenses: ⟁ ⅲ
Parking: Off-street and free
Directions: On N25 between Cork and Waterford. From Waterford, take the sign for town centre — Ahernes on left on Main Street.
Map ref: Youghal 19 D4

The Gresham Metropole, Cork

Isle of Man

Point of Ayre

Rue Point

A10

Bride

Point Cranstal

Andreas

Jurby Head   Jurby

St Judes

Ramsey Bay

A14

A10   Sulby

Ramsey

A3   Tableland Point

Orrisdale Head   Ballaugh

A3   A18   Maughold Head

Kirkmichael

A4

SNAEFELL 2034' ▲

A14

St Germains

St Patrick's Isle

Injebreck

Bulgham Bay

Peel

A3   A18   Laxey

Contrary Head

A1

Laxey Bay

St Johns   Baldwin

Clay Head

A1

A3   Crosby

A2

Carran   Foxdale

A1   Onchan

The Niarbyl

Douglas   Douglas Bay

Niarbyl Bay

A27

Douglas Head

A2

Fleshwick Bay

Port Soderick

A5

Bradda Head   Ballabeg   Santon

Santon Head

Colby   Ballasalla

Port Erin

A5   IOM Ronaldsway   Derbyhaven

Poolvash Bay

Calf of Man

Port St Mary   Castletown   St Michael's Island

Spanish Head   Castletown Bay

Craigher Point   Langness Point

Note:
Dark blue dots represent the location of RAC-inspected accommodation

Isle of Man

Mount Murray Hotel and Country Club

★★★★★

Santon, Isle of Man, IM4 2HT
Tel: 01624 661111 Fax: 01624 611116
Email: hotel@mountmurray.com
Web: www.mountmurray.com

Situated in 200 acres of countryside, conveniently placed for airport, seaport, town. Restaurant, bars overlooking lake and golf course. Unrivalled health and fitness club with 18-hole golf course. Conference facilities.
Rooms: 90 all ensuite 🖨 🚭
Pricing: Sgl £63.50–98 Dbl £85.50–167
Dinner available from £22.95
CC: Accepted
Room facilities: 🖵 ☎ 🍵 🔌
Access: ♿
Conference: 6 meeting rooms (Thtr 300 max), 24hr-delegate from £131, day-delegate from £37.50
Children: Welcome 🐎
Licenses: 🍾
Leisure: Indoor pool, Gym, Health spa, Beauty salon, Tennis, Golf
Parking: Off-street and free
Directions: From airport take main road to Douglas. Turn left at Santon. Hotel is signposted.
Map ref: Santon 10 A4

Port Erin Royal Hotel

★★★

Promenade, Port Erin, Isle of Man, IM9 6LH
Tel: 01624 833116 Fax: 01624 835402
Email: rac@porterinhotels.com
Web: www.porterinhotels.com
Seasonal closure: December to January
Rooms: 79 all ensuite 🍵 🖨
Pricing: Sgl £34–56 Dbl £68–112
Dinner available from £18.95
CC: Accepted
Room facilities: 🖵 ☎ 🍵
Access: ♿

Children: Welcome 🐎 ☕
Dogs: Assistance dogs only
Licenses: 🍾
Leisure: Indoor pool, Games room, Snooker/billiards
Parking: Off-street and free
Directions: Take road signs from either the sea terminal or airport marked 'Port Erin and the South'. Hotel on the upper promenade facing the sea.
Map ref: Port Erin 10 A4

Port Erin Imperial Hotel

★★

Promenade, Port Erin, Isle of Man, IM9 6LH
Tel: 01624 832122 Fax: 01624 835402
Email: rac@porterinhotels.com
Web: www.porterinhotels.com
Seasonal closure: October to March
Rooms: 51 all ensuite 🍵
Dinner available
CC: Accepted
Room facilities: 🖵 ☎ 🍵
Access: ♿
Children: Welcome 🐎 ☕
Licenses: 🍾
Parking: Off-street and free
Directions: Take road signs from sea terminal or airport marked 'Port Erin and the South'. Hotel on upper promenade facing the sea.
Map ref: Port Erin 10 A4

Mount Murray Hotel and Country Club

Jersey

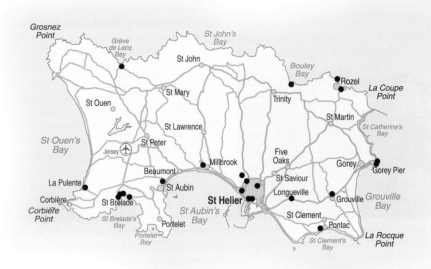

Award winners

To help you choose somewhere really special for your stay, we've listed here all RAC Award-winning properties in Jersey.

Gold Ribbon Award

Premier

		pg
Atlantic Hotel and Ocean Restaurant, St Brelade	★★★★	615
Chateau La Chaire, St Martin	★★★	617
Longueville Manor, St Saviour	★★★★	615

Longueville Manor, St Saviour

Jersey

Atlantic Hotel and Ocean Restaurant

★★★★★ ♍♍♍

Le Mont de la Pulente, St Brelade, Jersey, JE3 8HE
Tel: 01534 744101 Fax: 01534 744102
Email: info@theatlantichotel.com
Web: www.theatlantichotel.com
Seasonal closure: 2 January to 9 February

Award-winning luxury hotel with a reputation for friendly attentive service. In private local ownership since 1970. Superbly appointed guestrooms. Breathtaking ocean views. Member of Small Luxury Hotels of the World.
Rooms: 50 all ensuite
Pricing: Sgl £145–185 Dbl £190–550
Dinner available from £35–45 CC: Accepted
Room facilities: ☐ 🖥 ☎ ☕ ✎ Access: |↟
Conference: 2 meeting rooms (Thtr 60 max),
24hr-delegate from £175, day-delegate from £55
Children: Welcome ♿ ☕ Licenses: ⚜ ⛊
Leisure: Indoor pool, Outdoor pool, Gym, Tennis
Parking: Off-street
Directions: From the A13 take the B35 to Le Mont de la Pulente. Hotel sign is on the right.
Map ref: St Brelade 2 A2

Hotel La Place

★★★★ ♍♍

Route Du Coin, La Haule, St Brelade, Jersey, JE3 8BT
Tel: 01534 744261 Fax: 01534 745164
Email: reservations@hotellaplacejersey.com
Web: www.hotellaplacejersey.com

Located in the heart of the countryside, only a short walk from the picturesque St Aubin's Harbour and the golden sands of Beauport. Choose from our lounge, cocktail bar, poolside terrace or secluded courtyard, or explore the gardens.

Rooms: 42 all ensuite ♿ 🖥 ⊗
Pricing: Dinner available from £24.95
CC: Accepted
Room facilities: ☐ ☎ ☕
Conference: 2 meeting rooms (Thtr 100 max),
24hr-delegate from £130, day-delegate from £45
Children: Welcome ♿ ☕
Dogs: Welcome
Licenses: ⚜ ⛊
Leisure: Outdoor pool
Parking: Off-street and free
Directions: Approaching St Aubin from St Helier, at La Haule Manor turn right. Take second left then first right. 200 yards on right. Please contact hotel for further directions.
Map ref: St Brelade 2 A2

Longueville Manor

★★★★★ ♍♍♍

Longueville Road, St Saviour, Jersey, JE2 7WF
Tel: 01534 725501 Fax: 01534 731613
Email: info@longuevillemanor.com
Web: www.longuevillemanor.com

Stunning 13th Century Norman manor, set in a 16-acre wooded valley. Luxurious bedrooms, award-winning restaurant, and beautiful gardens. Member of Relais & Châteaux.
Rooms: 30 all ensuite ♿ 🖥
Pricing: Sgl £190–325 Dbl £230–500
Dinner available from £42
CC: Accepted
Room facilities: ☐ ☎ ✎
Access: |↟
Conference: 3 meeting rooms (Thtr 40 max),
24hr-delegate from £245, day-delegate from £60
Children: Welcome ♿ ☕
Dogs: Welcome
Licenses: ⚜ ⛊
Leisure: Outdoor pool, Tennis
Parking: Off-street and free
Directions: From Jersey airport, take A1 to St Helier and then A3 towards Gorey. Longueville Manor is situated approximately 1 mile on left.
Map ref: St Saviour 2 B2

Pomme d'Or Hotel

★★★★★ ☕☕

Liberation Square, St Helier, Jersey, JE1 3UF
Tel: 01534 880110 Fax: 01534 737781
Email: enquiries@pommedorhotel.com
Web: www.pommedorhotel.com

Jersey's best known hotel is ideally located at the heart of St Helier's shopping and financial district. The Pomme d'Or overlooks the island's marina and offers outstanding service.
Rooms: 143 all ensuite ☕ ⊗
Pricing: Sgl £74–165 Dbl £108–230
Dinner available from £18.95–25 CC: Accepted
Room facilities: ☐ ☎ ☕ ✎ ❄ Access: ⟊
Conference: 13 meeting rooms (Thtr 220 max), 24hr-delegate from £140, day-delegate from £36.50
Children: Welcome ⊼ ☕ Dogs: Assistance dogs only
Licenses: ⋔⋔⋔
Directions: A one-way system operates around the hotel and access to the square is available eastbound from La Route de la Liberation.
Map ref: St Helier 2 B2

St Brelade's Bay Hotel

★★★★★ ☕☕

St Brelade's Bay, Jersey, JE3 8EF
Tel: 01534 746141 Fax: 01534 747278
Email: info@stbreladesbayhotel.com
Web: www.stbreladesbayhotel.com
Seasonal closure: 10 October to 21 April

St Brelade's offers seven acres of award-winning gardens, two fresh water heated swimming pools, one especially for children, tennis courts, sauna, gymnasium, croquet and large play area. All bedrooms welcome you with a basket of fresh fruit. Two luxury penthouses available.
Rooms: 72 all ensuite ☕
Pricing: Sgl £75–114 Dbl £110–268
Dinner available from £20 CC: Accepted
Room facilities: ☐ ☎ ☕ ✎ Access: ⟊
Conference: 1 meeting room (Thtr 20 max), 24hr-delegate from £125, day-delegate from £35
Children: Welcome ⊼ ☕
Licenses: ⋔⋔⋔
Leisure: Outdoor pool, Gym, Tennis, Games room, Snooker/billiards, Sauna, Croquet
Parking: Off-street and free
Directions: Located in the southwest of the island.
Map ref: St Brelade's Bay 2 A2

Beau Couperon Hotel and Apartments

★★★★ ☕

Rozel Bay, St Martin, Jersey, JE3 6AN
Tel: 01534 865522 Fax: 01534 865332
Email: beaucouperon@southernhotels.com
Web: www.jerseyhols.com/beaucouperon
Seasonal closure: 1 November to 23 March
Rooms: 36 all ensuite ☕ ⊗
Pricing: Sgl £41.20–86.10 Dbl £82.40–114.80
Dinner available from £13.50–20 CC: Accepted
Room facilities: ☐ ☎ ☕
Children: Welcome ⊼
Dogs: Welcome
Licenses: ⋔⋔⋔
Leisure: Outdoor pool
Parking: Off-street and free
Directions: From St Helier, follow signs for St Martin. At St Martin's church turn right, directly followed by a left turn. Follow signs towards Rozel Bay.
Map ref: St Martin 2 A2

Beausite Hotel

★★★

Grouville Bay, Grouville, Jersey, JE3 9DJ
Tel: 01543 857577 Fax: 01543 857211
Email: beausite@jerseymail.co.uk
Web: www.southernhotels.com
Seasonal closure: November to February
Rooms: 76 all ensuite ☕
Pricing: Sgl £41–78 Dbl £68–106
Dinner available from £13.95
CC: Accepted
Room facilities: ☐ ☎ ☕
Children: Welcome ⊼
Dogs: Welcome
Licenses: ⟐ ⋔⋔⋔
Leisure: Indoor pool, Gym, Games room, Snooker/billiards
Parking: Off-street and free
Directions: Follow A1 east to the A17. At Georgetown take the A3 towards Gorey. The hotel is on the right at Grouville, after passing the Beachcombers Hotel.
Map ref: Grouville Bay 2 B2

Best Western Royal Hotel

★★★

David Place, St Helier, Jersey, JE2 4TD
Tel: 01534 726521 Fax: 01534 811046
Email: reservations@royalhoteljersey.com or
enquiries@royalhoteljersey.com
Web: www.royalhoteljersey.com
Rooms: 88 all ensuite 🛁 🎠 ⊗
Pricing: Sgl £55–65 Dbl £85–95
Dinner available from £16.95
CC: Accepted
Room facilities: 🖵 ☎ ☕ 🕯
Access: ♿
Conference: 6 meeting rooms (Thtr 400 max),
24hr-delegate from £125, day-delegate from £35
Children: Welcome 🍴
Licenses: ⚓ 🍾
Parking: Off-street and free
Directions: Follow signs for the ring road, then Rouge
Bouillon A14. Turn right at roundabout and right at
traffic lights into Midvale Road. Past two lights, hotel is
on left corner at lights.
Map ref: St Helier 2 B2

Chateau La Chaire

★★★ 🦢🦢🦢 Premier

Rozel, St Martin, Jersey, JE3 6AJ
Tel: 01534 863354 Fax: 01534 865137
Email: res@chateau-la-chaire.co.uk
Web: www.chateau-la-chaire.co.uk
Rooms: 14 all ensuite 🎠
Dinner available
CC: Accepted
Room facilities: 🖵 ☎ 🕯
Conference: 1 meeting room (Thtr 20 max)
Children: Welcome 7yrs min age
Licenses: ⚓ 🍾
Parking: Off-street and free
Directions: On entering Rozel from St Helier turn left by
the Rozel Bay Inn, Chateau La Chaire is 150 yards on
the right.
Map ref: St Martin 2 A2

Chateau Valeuse Hotel

★★★★🦢

St Brelade's Bay, Jersey, JE3 8EE
Tel: 01534 746281 Fax: 01534 747110
Email: chatval@itl.net
Web: www.chateauvaleuse.com
Seasonal closure: Mid October to mid April
Rooms: 34 all ensuite 🛁
CC: Accepted
Room facilities: 🖵 ☎ ☕
Children: Welcome 5yrs min age 🍴 ☕
Licenses: 🍾
Leisure: Outdoor pool Parking: Off-street
Directions: From airport south from harbour west to St
Brelade's Bay. Hotel up lane to Churchill Memorial
Park.
Map ref: St Brelade's Bay 2 A2

Hotel Savoy

★★★

Rouge Bouillon, St Helier, Jersey, JE2 3ZA
Tel: 01534 619916 Fax: 01534 506969
Email: enquiries@hotelsavoyjersey.com
Web: www.hotelsavoyjersey.com
Seasonal closure: December to January
Rooms: 59 all ensuite 🛁 ⊗
Pricing: Sgl £33 Dbl £60
Dinner available from £13.95
CC: Accepted
Room facilities: 🖵 ☎ ☕
Access: ♿
Conference: 1 meeting room (Thtr 40 max)
Children: Welcome 🍴 ☕
Licenses: 🍾
Leisure: Outdoor pool, Games room, Snooker/billiards
Parking: Off-street and free
Map ref: St Helier 2 B2

Moorings Hotel

★★★★🦢🦢

Gorey Pier, Gorey, Jersey, JE3 6EW
Tel: 01534 853633 Fax: 01534 857618
Email: reservations@themooringshotel.com
Web: www.themooringshotel.com

An intimate hotel providing an ideal venue for leisure or
business. The restaurant has captivated a blend of
classic cuisine with the best fish and shellfish. The Pier
Bar & Bistro leads to an alfresco terrace with views
across the harbour.
Rooms: 15 all ensuite 🛁
Pricing: Sgl £47–64 Dbl £94–128
Dinner available from £20.50
CC: Accepted
Room facilities: 🖵 ☎ ☕ 🕯
Conference: 1 meeting room (Thtr 20 max)
Children: Welcome 🍴 ☕
Licenses: 🍾
Directions: Situated on the east coast of the island,
near to golf club. 4 miles from town centre and 8 miles
from airport.
Map ref: Gorey 2 B2

Jersey

Pontac House Hotel

★★★

St Clement's Bay, St Clement's, Jersey, JE2 6SE
Tel: 01534 857771 Fax: 01534 857031
Email: info@pontachouse.com
Web: www.pontachouse.com
Seasonal closure: January to February
Rooms: 27 all ensuite
Pricing: Sgl £43–59 Dbl £38–108
Dinner available from £13.75–19
CC: Accepted
Room facilities: 🖵 ☎ 🍵
Children: Welcome ⻌ 🌣
Dogs: Welcome
Licenses: ⫙
Leisure: Outdoor pool, Games room
Parking: Off-street and free
Directions: From St Helier follow the A4 coast road to
Gorey, approximately 2½ miles. Entrance to hotel car
park is at the rear.
Map ref: St Clement's Bay 2 B2
See advert on this page

Revere Hotel

★★★

Kensington Place, St Helier, Jersey, JE2 3PA
Tel: 01534 611111 Fax: 01534 611116
Email: reservations@revere.co.uk
Web: www.revere.co.uk
Rooms: 58 (57 ensuite) 🛇 📠 🚫
Pricing: Sgl £40–68 Dbl £80–136
Dinner available from £18.50
CC: Accepted
Room facilities: 🖵 ☎ 🍵 ⟍
Conference: 1 meeting room (Thtr 16 max)
Children: Welcome ⻌ 🌣
Licenses: ⟁ ⫙
Leisure: Outdoor pool
Directions: 10 minutes from the airport by car, 10
minutes from the ferry terminal by foot. 3 minutes walk
from town centre, 2 minutes walk from beach.
Map ref: St Helier 2 B2

Royal Yacht

★★★

Weighbridge, St Helier, Jersey, JE2 3NF
Tel: 01534 720511 Fax: 01534 767729
Email: theroyalyacht@mail.com
Rooms: 43 all ensuite 🚫
Pricing: Dinner available
CC: Accepted
Room facilities: 🖵 ☎ 🍵
Access: ⎸↕
Conference: 4 meeting rooms (Thtr 80 max)
Children: Welcome ⻌
Licenses: ⟁ ⫙
Directions: Located in the heart of St Helier, walking
distance to all business houses. Four miles from
airport.
Map ref: St Helier 2 B2

The Water's Edge Hotel

★★★★

Bouley Bay, Jersey, JE3 5AS
Tel: 01534 862777 Fax: 01534 863645
Email: mail@watersedgehotel.co.je
Web: www.watersedgehotel.co.je
Seasonal closure: November to March

The Water's Edge Hotel is in a stunning location of
natural beauty and tranquility with breathtaking views
overlooking Bouley Bay.
Rooms: 50 all ensuite 🛇
Pricing: Sgl £40–61 Dbl £80–122
Dinner available from £21.50–50
CC: Accepted
Room facilities: 🖵 ☎ 🍵 Access: ⎸↕
Conference: 1 meeting room (Thtr 50 max),

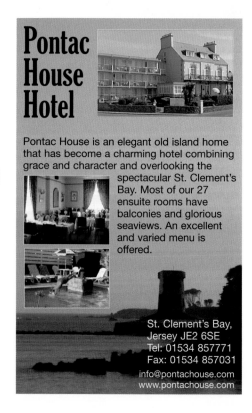

Pontac House Hotel

Pontac House is an elegant old island home
that has become a charming hotel combining
grace and character and overlooking the
spectacular St. Clement's
Bay. Most of our 27
ensuite rooms have
balconies and glorious
seaviews. An excellent
and varied menu is
offered.

St. Clement's Bay,
Jersey JE2 6SE
Tel: 01534 857771
Fax: 01534 857031
info@pontachouse.com
www.pontachouse.com

24hr-delegate from £72, day-delegate from £32
Children: Welcome ⼊ ℅
Dogs: Assistance dogs only
Licenses: Leisure: Dive centre
Parking: Off-street and free
Directions: 20 minutes' drive from the airport. Located on the north-east coast of the island in the parish of Trinity.
Map ref: Bouley Bay 2 B2

Windmills Hotel
★★★
Mont Gras d'Eau, St Brelade, Jersey, JE3 8ED
Tel: 01534 744201 Fax: 01534 744202
Email: info@windmillshotel.com
Web: www.windmillshotel.com
Seasonal closure: 8 October
Rooms: 40 all ensuite
Pricing: Sgl £47.50–69 Dbl £75–118
Dinner available from £15 CC: Accepted
Room facilities: 🖵 ☎ 🗃 🖦 Access: ⼁⼁⼁
Children: Welcome ⼊ ℅
Licenses: ⼁⼁⼁
Leisure: Outdoor pool, Gym, Health spa, Games room
Parking: Off-street and free
Directions: Head to St Brelade along A13. Turn down Mont Gras d'Eau, turn right next to Hotel Mirimar.
Map ref: St Brelade 2 A2

Beau Rivage Hotel
★★
St Brelade's Bay, St Brelade, Jersey, JE3 8EF
Tel: 01534 745983 Fax: 01534 747127
Email: beau@jerseyweb.demon.co.uk
Web: www.jersey.co.uk/hotels/beau
Seasonal closure: November to March

Most of the Beau Rivage's all ensuite bedrooms have fine sea views and many have balconies for enjoying Jersey's mild climate. A residents' bar opens onto a terrace and the golden sands of Jersey's most popular beach.
Rooms: 27 all ensuite
Pricing: Sgl £50–75 Dbl £66–140
Dinner available from £16–20
CC: Accepted
Room facilities: 🖵 ☎ 🗃
Access: ⼁⼁⼁
Children: Welcome ⼊ ℅
Licenses:
Leisure: Games room
Parking: Off-street and free
Directions: The hotel is located on the seaward side of the coast road, in the centre of St Brelade's Bay.
Map ref: St Brelade 2 A2

Dolphin Hotel
★★★🔔🔔
Gorey Pier, Gorey, Jersey, JE3 6EW
Tel: 01534 853370 Fax: 01534 855343
Email: dolphinhotel@jerseymail.co.uk
Web: www.adwebjersey.co.uk/tourism/hotels/dolphin
Rooms: 15 all ensuite
Pricing: Sgl £33–42 Dbl £66–84
Dinner available from £18.50–19.50
CC: Accepted
Room facilities: 🖵 ☎ 🗃 🖦
Conference: 1 meeting room (Thtr 20 max)
Children: Welcome ⼊ ℅
Licenses: ⼁⼁⼁
Directions: Situated underneath Mont Orgueil Castle, facing the harbour of Gorey Pier, 4 miles from town centre and 8 from the airport.
Map ref: Gorey 2 B2

Are the bells ringing?

Getting married? Congratulations! Look for the wedding bells symbol which shows hotels licensed for civil ceremonies.

Jersey

Millbrook House Hotel

◆◆◆◆

Rue de Trachy, Millbrook, St Helier, Jersey, JE2 3JN
Tel: 01534 733036 Fax: 01534 724317
Email: millbrook.house@jerseymail.co.uk
Web: www.millbrookhousehotel.com
Seasonal closure: 1 October to 30 April

Peace, quiet and character, where the air is clear and traditional values are maintained. 10 acres of grounds, car park, 27 ensuite rooms, memorable food and wines.
Rooms: 27 all ensuite ⊛
Pricing: Sgl £38.50–42.50 Dbl £77–85
Dinner available from £12
CC: Accepted
Room facilities: ☐ ☎ ☕
Access: |↓↑
Children: Welcome
Licenses: ▮▮▮
Leisure: Golf
Parking: Off-street and free
Directions: 1¹/₂ miles west from St Helier off A1.
Map ref: St Helier 2 B2

The big sleep

As part of our comprehensive inspection process, RAC Inspectors investigate the comfort of the beds.

Sarum Hotel

◆◆◆◆

19-21 New St John's Road, St Helier, Jersey, JE2 3LD
Tel: 01534 758163 Fax: 01534 731340
Email: sarum@jerseyweb.demon.co.uk
Web: www.jersey.co.uk/hotels/sarum

This budget hotel is conveniently located on the west side of St Helier, a 5 minute stroll from the beach and within easy walking distance of the town shopping precinct.
Rooms: 52 all ensuite ⊛
Pricing: Sgl £35–52 Dbl £50–74
CC: Accepted
Room facilities: ☐ ☎ ☕
Access: |↓↑
Children: Welcome
Licenses: ▮▮▮
Leisure: Outdoor pool, Games room
Parking: Off-street
Directions: On western side of St Helier, ¹/₂ mile from town centre. See our website for full directions.
Map ref: St Helier 2 B2

Hotel des Pierres

◆◆◆

Greve de Lecq Bay, St Ouen, Jersey, JE3 2DT
Tel: 01534 481858 Fax: 01534 485273
Email: despierres@jerseyhols.com
Web: www.jerseyhols.com/despierres
Seasonal closure: 15 December to 11 January
Rooms: 16 all ensuite ⊛ ⊛
Pricing: Sgl £33.50–39 Dbl £53–64
Dinner available from £11.50–14.50
CC: Accepted
Room facilities: ☐ ☕
Children: Welcome
Licenses: ▮▮▮
Leisure: Gym
Parking: Off-street and free
Directions: From Airport to St Peter on B36 at roundabout turn left onto A12 through St Ouen village. From harbour A1 to A2 to A1 to A12 to Beaumont Hill.
Map ref: St Ouen 2 A2

Guernsey & Sark

Guernsey

L'Ancresse Bay
Fort Doyle Point
Les Dicqs Peninsula
Grand Havre
Islet Village
Vale
Capelles
St Sampson
Cobo Bay
Belle Grève Bay
Vazon Bay
St George
Lihou Island
Perelle Bay
L'Erée Bay
Kings Mills
Catel
Rohais Village
St Peter Port
Havelet Bay
Rocquaine Bay
St Saviour
St Andrew
Les Hubits
St Peter
Guernsey
St Martin
Fermain Bay
Torteval
Forest
Moulin Huet Bay
Pleinmont Point
Icart Bay
Saints Bay
Jerbourg Point
Corbier Bay

Sark

Brecqhou Island
Petit Champ
Dixcart
Creux Harbour
Baleine Bay
Little Sark

Guernsey

St Pierre Park Hotel

★★★★

Rohais, St Peter Port, Guernsey, GY1 1FD
Tel: 01481 728282 Fax: 01481 712041
Email: info@stpierreparkhotel.com
Web: www.stpierreparkhotel.com
Rooms: 131 all ensuite
Pricing: Sgl £130 Dbl £170
Dinner available from £23.50 CC: Accepted
Room facilities: 🖵 ☎ 🗗 ✆ Access: ⅃ㅣㅣ
Conference: 12 meeting rooms (Thtr 200 max),
24hr-delegate from £160, day-delegate from £45
Children: Welcome
Licenses:
Leisure: Indoor pool, Gym, Health spa, Beauty salon,
Tennis, Golf, Snooker/billiards
Parking: Off-street and free
Directions: 10 minutes' drive from airport and harbour
front. Hire cars provide free maps.
Map ref: St Peter Port 2 A2

The Old Government House

★★★★

St Ann's Place, St Peter Port, Guernsey, GY1 4AZ
Tel: 01481 724921 Fax: 01481 724429
Email: ogh@theoghhotel.com
Web: www.theoghhotel.com
Rooms: 68 all ensuite
Dinner available CC: Accepted
Room facilities: 🖵 ☎ 🗗 ✆ Access: ⅃ㅣㅣ
Conference: 6 meeting rooms (Thtr 300 max)
Children: Welcome
Licenses:
Leisure: Outdoor pool, Gym, Health spa, Beauty salon
Parking: Off-street and free
Directions: The hotel is located off St Julian's Avenue
in St Ann's Place.
Map ref: St Peter Port 2 A2

Atlantique Hotel

★★★

Perelle Bay, St Saviours, Guernsey, GY7 9NA
Tel: 01481 264056 Fax: 01481 263800
Email: enquiries@perellebay.com
Web: www.perellebay.com
Seasonal closure: December only
Rooms: 23 all ensuite
Pricing: Sgl £45–85 Dbl £60–130
Dinner available from £22 CC: Accepted
Room facilities: 🖵 ☎ 🗗
Conference: 1 meeting room (Thtr 40 max)
Children: Welcome
Licenses:
Leisure: Outdoor pool
Parking: Off-street and free
Directions: Situated on the west coast. Turn right out
of airport. Continue until you reach the west coast.
Turn right and follow the coast for 1½ miles.
Map ref: St Saviour 2 B2

Best Western Hotel de Havelet

★★★★

Havelet, St Peter Port, Guernsey, GY1 1BA
Tel: 01481 722199 Fax: 01481 714057
Email: havelet@sarniahotels.com
Web: www.havelet.sarniahotels.com

This Georgian house enjoys a superb location on the
outskirts of St Peter Port. With its choice of
restaurants, attractive health suite and gardens,
De Havelet makes an excellent holiday base.
Rooms: 34 all ensuite
Pricing: Sgl £50–100 Dbl £82–140
Dinner available from £18.50
CC: Accepted
Room facilities: 🖵 ☎ 🗗 ✆
Conference: 1 meeting room (Thtr 30 max),
24hr-delegate from £120, day-delegate from £35
Children: Welcome
Licenses: Leisure: Indoor pool
Parking: Off-street and free
Directions: From the airport, turn left and follow signs
for St Peter Port. At bottom of Val de Terres Hill, turn
left up Havelet Hill (signposted). Hotel on right of hill.
Map ref: St Peter Port 2 A2

Green Acres Hotel

★★★

Les Hubits, St Martins, Guernsey, GY4 6LS
Tel: 01481 235711 Fax: 01481 235971
Email: greenacres@guernsey.net
Web: www.greenacreshotel.guernsey.net
Rooms: 43 all ensuite
Pricing: Sgl £30–60 Dbl £44–96
Dinner available from £15 CC: Accepted
Room facilities: 🖵 ☎ 🗗
Conference: 1 meeting room (Thtr 80 max),
24hr-delegate from £52.50, day-delegate from £23
Children: Welcome Dogs: Welcome
Licenses: Leisure: Outdoor pool, Free access to
local health suite
Parking: Off-street and free
Directions: Follow hotel signs from the three main
roads that surround Les Hubits area in the south-east
corner of Guernsey.
Map ref: St Martin 2 A2

Guernsey/Sark

Hotel Hougue du Pommier

★★★★♙♙

Hougue du Pommier Road, Castel, Guernsey, GY5 7FQ
Tel: 01481 256531 Fax: 01481 256260
Email: hotel@houguedupommier.guernsey.net
Web: www.hotelhouguedupommier.com
Rooms: 43 all ensuite ♙ ♙ ♙ ♙
Pricing: Sgl £40.50–99 Dbl £81–163
Dinner available from £22.95
CC: Accepted
Room facilities: ▢ ☎ ☕ ⌕
Conference: 1 meeting room (Thtr 25 max)
Children: Welcome �🏃 ⚙
Dogs: Welcome
Licenses: ⚏⚏⚏
Leisure: Outdoor pool
Parking: Off-street and free
Directions: From Cobo Bay, take the road inland to
Route de Hougue du Pommier. Ten minutes' drive from
St Peter Port and 20 minutes from the airport.
Map ref: Castel 2 A2
See advert on this page

La Trelade Hotel

★★★★♙

Forest Road, St Martins, Guernsey, GY4 6UB
Tel: 01481 235454 Fax: 01481 237855
Email: latrelade@guernsey.net
Web: www.latreladehotel.com
Rooms: 45 all ensuite ♙ ♙ ♙
Pricing: Sgl £70–80 Dbl £98–119
Dinner available from £20
CC: Accepted
Room facilities: ▢ ☎ ☕ ⌕
Access: ⛌⛌
Conference: 3 meeting rooms (Thtr 100 max)
Children: Welcome �🏃
Licenses: ⚏⚏⚏
Leisure: Indoor pool, Gym
Parking: Off-street and free
Directions: From airport turn left, hotel 1 mile. From
harbour, follow signs to airport through St Martins; 3
miles on left.
Map ref: St Martin 2 A2

Le Chalet Hotel

★★★★♙

Fermain Bay, St Martins, Guernsey, GY4 6SD
Tel: 01481 235716 Fax: 01481 235718
Email: chalet@sarniahotels.com
Web: www.chalet.sarniahotels.com
Seasonal closure: mid-October to mid-April

Idyllically nestling in wooded Fermain Valley, Le Chalet
is perfectly situated close to the picturesque bay and
coastal cliff walks. A courtesy bus operates into St
Peter Port.
Rooms: 41 all ensuite
Pricing: Sgl £45–80 Dbl £72–112
Dinner available from £18.50
CC: Accepted
Room facilities: ▢ ☎ ☕
Children: Welcome �🏃
Licenses: ⚏⚏⚏
Parking: Off-street and free
Directions: From Guernsey airport, turn left and follow
signs for St Martins and St Peter Port. After Sausmarez
Manor, follow signs for Fermain Bay and Le Chalet.
Map ref: St Martin 2 A2

Les Rocquettes Hotel

★★★

Les Gravees, St Peter Port, Guernsey, GY1 1RN
Tel: 01481 722146 Fax: 01481 714543
Email: rocquettes@sarniahotels.com
Web: www.rocquettes.sarniahotels.com

Conveniently located in St Peter Port, Les Rocquettes offers excellent leisure facilities, comfortable, well-equipped bedrooms and good food and service.
Rooms: 51 all ensuite ⊗
Pricing: Sgl £47–85 Dbl £76–126
Dinner available from £17
CC: Accepted
Room facilities: ▢ ☎ 🗗 ✆
Access: ⫯
Conference: 2 meeting rooms (Thtr 110 max), 24hr-delegate from £100, day-delegate from £25
Children: Welcome ♁
Licenses: ♦♦♦
Leisure: Indoor pool, Gym, Beauty salon
Parking: Off-street and free
Directions: From airport turn left. At 2nd traffic lights turn left. Straight on at next traffic lights and over roundabout. At 4th lights turn right. At filter turn left. At next filter turn left into Les Gravees. Hotel on right.
Map ref: St Peter Port 2 A2

Moores Hotel

★★★

Le Pollet, St Peter Port, Guernsey, GY1 1WH
Tel: 01481 724452 Fax: 01481 714037
Email: moores@sarniahotels.com
Web: www.moores.sarniahotels.com

Ideally located for business or leisure, Moores Hotel is in the heart of St Peter Port. The marinas and ferries to the smaller islands are just a stroll away.
Rooms: 49 all ensuite 🐾 ⊗

Pricing: Sgl £45–100 Dbl £80–122
Dinner available from £19
CC: Accepted
Room facilities: ▢ ☎ 🗗 ✆
Access: ⫯
Conference: 2 meeting rooms (Thtr 50 max), 24hr-delegate from £120, day-delegate from £35
Children: Welcome ♁
Licenses: ♦♦♦
Leisure: Gym
Directions: From airport follow signs to St Peter Port along sea front. On North Esplanade take left turn into Lower Pollet and continue to hotel on right.
Map ref: St Peter Port 2 A2

Peninsula Hotel

★★★

Les Dicqs, Vale, Guernsey, GY6 8JP
Tel: 01481 248400 Fax: 01481 248706
Email: peninsula@guernsey.net
Web: www.peninsulahotelguernsey.com
Rooms: 99 all ensuite ⊗
Dinner available
CC: Accepted
Room facilities: ▢ ☎ 🗗 ✆
Access: ⫯
Conference: 5 meeting rooms (Thtr 200 max)
Children: Welcome ♁
Licenses: ♦♦♦
Leisure: Outdoor pool
Parking: Off-street and free
Map ref: Vale 2 A2

Saints Bay Hotel & Restaurant

★★★

Icart Point, St Martins, Guernsey, GY4 6JG
Tel: 01481 238888 Fax: 01481 235558
Email: info@saintsbayhotel.com
Web: www.saintsbayhotel.com
Rooms: 35 all ensuite ⊗
Pricing: Sgl £20–74.50 Dbl £40–128
Dinner available from £12.50–18.50
CC: Accepted
Room facilities: ▢ ☎ 🗗
Children: Welcome ♁ ⋰
Dogs: Assistance dogs only
Licenses: ♦♦♦
Leisure: Outdoor pool
Parking: Off-street and free
Directions: The Saints Bay Hotel and Restaurant are located at Icart Point on the island's most southerly tip.
Map ref: St Martin 2 A2

The Duke of Richmond Hotel

★★★ ®

Cambridge Park, St Peter Port, Guernsey, GY1 1UY
Tel: 01481 726221 Fax: 01481 728945
Email: duke@guernsey.net
Web: www.dukeofrichmond.com

Conveniently situated and enjoying picturesque views
overlooking St Peter Port and the neighbouring
islands. This combined with traditional hospitality and
comfortable rooms make this hotel your perfect choice
when staying in Guernsey.
Rooms: 75 all ensuite ✈ ⊗
Pricing: Sgl £50–77.50 Dbl £75–125
Dinner available from £19.95
CC: Accepted
Room facilities: ☐ ☎ ☕ ⬟
Access: |↕|
Conference: 5 meeting rooms (Thtr 110 max),
day-delegate from £30
Children: Welcome 🍴
Licenses:
Leisure: Outdoor pool
Parking: Off-street and free
Directions: Located adjacent to Candie Gardens and
the Island's Beau Sejour conference and leisure centre.
Map ref: St Peter Port 2 A2

Grange Lodge Hotel

★★★ ®

The Grange, St Peter Port, Guernsey, GY1 1RQ
Tel: 01481 725161 Fax: 01481 724211
Email: receptionist@grange-lodge.hotel.freeserve.co.uk
Web: www.grange-lodge.hotel.freeserve.co.uk
Rooms: 30 all ensuite
Dinner available
CC: Accepted
Room facilities: ☐ ☎ ☕
Children: Welcome 🍴
Licenses: ⟨▲⟩
Leisure: Outdoor pool, Snooker/billiards
Parking: Off-street
Map ref: St Peter Port 2 A2

Dixcart Bay Hotel

★★

Sark, via Guernsey, GY9 0SD
Tel: 01481 832015 Fax: 01481 832164
Email: info@dixcartbayhotel.com
Web: www.dixcartbayhotel.com
Seasonal closure: November to February open for
advance bookings only

The haunt of Victor Hugo, Swinburne and Mervyn
Peake. Sark's oldest hotel offers comfortable
accommodation, good food, log fires and gentle
hospitality. In a world of its own, this converted farm
long house is surrounded by 40 acres of woodlands
leading to the sheltered bay of Dixcart.
Rooms: 15 all ensuite ✈
Pricing: Sgl £40–57.50 Dbl £80–115
Dinner available from £17
CC: Accepted
Room facilities: ☐ ☎ ☕ ⬟
Conference: 1 meeting room (Thtr 20 max)
Children: Welcome 🍴 🌐 Dogs: Welcome
Licenses:
Leisure: Fishing, Library, Chess table, Card table
Directions: From top of Harbour Hill take avenue
through centre of village. Turn left, following signs to
Dixcart Hotel.
Map ref: Sark 2 A2

Hotel Petit Champ

◆◆◆◆ ® ® ❦

Sark, Guernsey, GY9 0SF
Tel: 01481 832046 Fax: 01481 832469
Email: info@hotelpetitchamp.co.uk
Web: www.hotelpetitchamp.co.uk
Seasonal closure: October to Easter
Rooms: 10 all ensuite
Pricing: Sgl £43–52.50 Dbl £82–101
Dinner available from £19.95–20.25
CC: Accepted
Children: Welcome 6yrs min age 🍴
Licenses: ♦♦♦
Leisure: Outdoor pool, Putting green, Croquet lawn
Directions: Follow the signposted lane towards the sea
from the Methodist chapel.
Map ref: Sark 2 A2

Wherever you go, we'll be there too.

For instant breakdown cover and the reassurance RAC gives you, wherever in the UK you're travelling to, call

0800 550 550
quoting ref: Hotel

www.rac.co.uk

For Personal Finance, **Insurance**, BSM Lessons, **Injury Claims** and Windscreen Repairs call 08000 966 000

Gibraltar

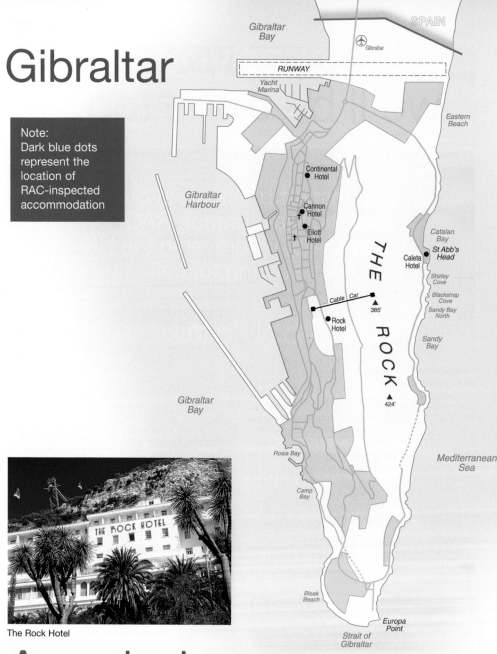

Note:
Dark blue dots represent the location of RAC-inspected accommodation

SPAIN

Gibraltar Bay

Gibraltar

RUNWAY

Yacht Marina

Gibraltar Harbour

Eastern Beach

Continental Hotel

Cannon Hotel

Eliott Hotel

Catalan Bay

St Abb's Head

Caleta Hotel

Shirley Cove

Blackstrap Cove

Cable Car

385'

Sandy Bay North

Rock Hotel

Sandy Bay

THE ROCK

424'

Gibraltar Bay

Rosia Bay

Mediterranean Sea

Camp Bay

Bleak Beach

Europa Point

Strait of Gibraltar

The Rock Hotel

Award winners

To help you choose somewhere really special for your stay, we've listed here the RAC Award-winning property in Gibraltar.

White Ribbon Award

Commended

pg

The Rock Hotel, Gibraltar ★★★★ 629

Gibraltar

Eliott Hotel

★★★★

2 Governor's Parade, Gibraltar
Tel: +350(0) 70500 Fax: +350(0) 70243
Email: eliott@gibnet.gi
Web: www.ocallaghanhotels.com

The elegant Eliott Hotel is situated on a quiet tree-lined square in the city centre. 118 rooms, ensuite bathrooms, conference facilities. 8th floor includes the rooftop restaurant, bar and pool, light gym and sauna, with views over Africa.
Rooms: 118 all ensuite
Pricing: Sgl £205–240 Dbl £231–270
Dinner available from £25–35
CC: Accepted
Room facilities: Access:
Conference: 5 meeting rooms (Thtr 180 max)
Children: Welcome
Licenses:
Leisure: Outdoor pool, Gym, Beauty salon
Parking: Off-street and free
Directions: From Airport, follow signs for city centre, turn left at 3rd set of traffic lights and follow signs for Eliott Hotel. Hotel is 10 minutes from Gibraltar Airport.

The Caleta Hotel

★★★★★

Sir Herbert Miles Road, PO Box 73, Gibraltar
Tel: +350 76501 Fax: +350 42143
Email: reservations@caletahotel.gi
Web: www.caletahotel.gi
Rooms: 160 all ensuite
Pricing: Dinner available from £18
CC: Accepted
Room facilities:
Access:
Conference: 5 meeting rooms (Thtr 210 max),
24hr-delegate from £130, day-delegate from £36
Children: Welcome
Licenses:
Leisure: Outdoor pool, Gym, Beauty salon, Games room
Parking: Off-street and free
Directions: Enter Frontier, cross runway, turn left at first roundabout. Follow road all the way to hotel. Hotel is on the left.

The Rock Hotel

★★★★★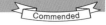

Europa Road, Gibraltar
Tel: +350(0) 73000 Fax: +350(0) 73513
Email: rockhotel@gibtelecom.net
Web: www.rockhotelgibraltar.com

The Rock Hotel perches majestically within the Rock with magnificent views across the bay, the Spanish mainland and Morocco's Rif Mountains. The hotel's restaurant boasts an eclectic cuisine with influences from Britain, Iberia and North Africa.
Rooms: 104 all ensuite
Pricing: Sgl £165 Dbl £165
Dinner available from £23.95 CC: Accepted
Room facilities: Access:
Conference: 3 meeting rooms (Thtr 100 max),
24hr-delegate from £135, day-delegate from £35
Children: Welcome Dogs: Welcome
Licenses:
Leisure: Outdoor pool, Beauty salon, Casino adjacent to hotel
Parking: Off-street and free
Directions: Follow Tourist Board signs from Frontier. Taxis are plentiful at airport and Frontier also. Hotel sits midway up Europa Road.
See advert on following page

The Continental Hotel

★★

1 Engineer Lane, Gibraltar
Tel: +350(0) 76900

Cannon Hotel

◆

9 Cannon Lane, Gibraltar
Tel: +350(0) 51711 Fax: +350(0) 51789
Web: www.cannonhotel.gi
Rooms: 18 (2 ensuite)
CC: Accepted
Children: Welcome Dogs: Welcome
Licenses:

Gibraltar

An oasis...

...in a busy world!

Bedrooms
104 bedrooms and suites in a colonial style all with a sea view

Conference facilities
Full upgraded conference facilities available for board meetings, training courses and presentations

Weddings
The Rock is an ideal wedding venue whether it be a small intimate wedding or large family gathering. We are also a recognised venue for civil marriages and ceremonies can now be conducted in various parts of the hotel

Banqueting
Weddings, banqueting, private dining or office parties catered for

Swimming pool
Outdoor swimming pool with pool side bar and pool side menu. We welcome private pool membership, our Lido Club, with private pool hire for parties and barbecues and children's parties

Restaurant
The restaurant has stunning views over the bay. Our "house" menu is excellent value for three courses including an aperitif Manzanilla, olives and coffee. A full à la carte menu along with a superb eclectic wine list is also available

Wisteria Terrace
The Wisteria Terrace for lunches, dinner, barbecues, afternoon teas, evening drinks and informal dining

Barbary Bar
Barbary Bar and terrace for a relaxing drink and, for the wine buff, a choice of nine wines by the glass

Lounges
Take a good old fashioned English tea in one of the spacious lounges

Orlando's Salon
For the best in hairdressing, facials, manicure, pedicure, tanning, waxing and a host of other beauty treatments

Europa Road, Gibraltar
Tel: (+350) 73000 Fax: (+350) 73513
E-mail: rockhotel@gibtelecom.net
Web site: www.rockhotelgibraltar.com

The Rock Hotel

Distance Chart

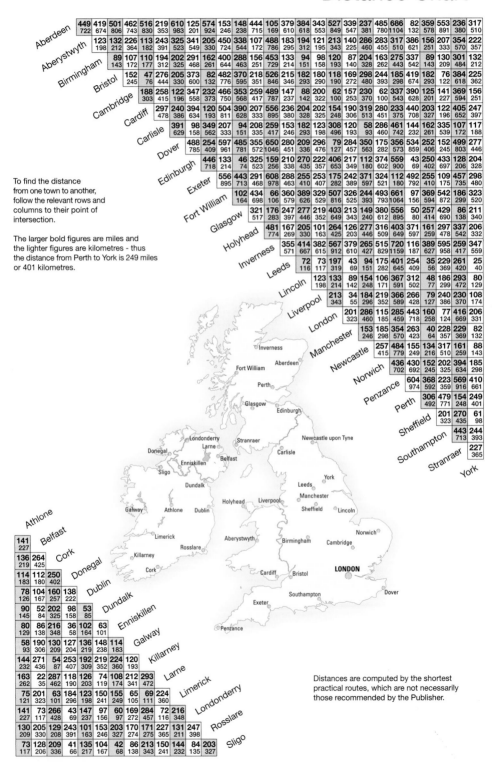

To find the distance from one town to another, follow the relevant rows and columns to their point of intersection.

The larger bold figures are miles and the lighter figures are kilometres - thus the distance from Perth to York is 249 miles or 401 kilometres.

Distances are computed by the shortest practical routes, which are not necessarily those recommended by the Publisher.

Key to Maps

ENGLAND & WALES
16 miles to 1 inch (approx)

SCOTLAND
21 miles to 1 inch (approx)

IRELAND
20 miles to 1 inch (approx)

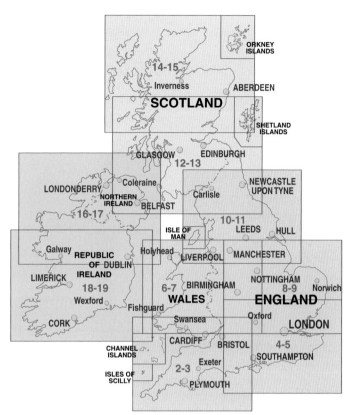

Legend

M5 — S — Service Area	Motorway	*EXMOOR* Regional Maps only	National Park
18 — 19 Restricted Full Access	Motorway with Junctions	*TAY* Regional Maps only	Forest Park
A303	Primary Route Dual Carriageway	*Gower* Regional Maps only	Area of Outstanding Natural Beauty
A39	Primary Route		National Boundary
A30	"A" Road		County or Unitary Boundary
B3153	"B" Road	DEVON	County or Unitary Name
✈ Exeter Ⓗ Penzance	Airport and Heliport	●	RAC Inspected property or properties

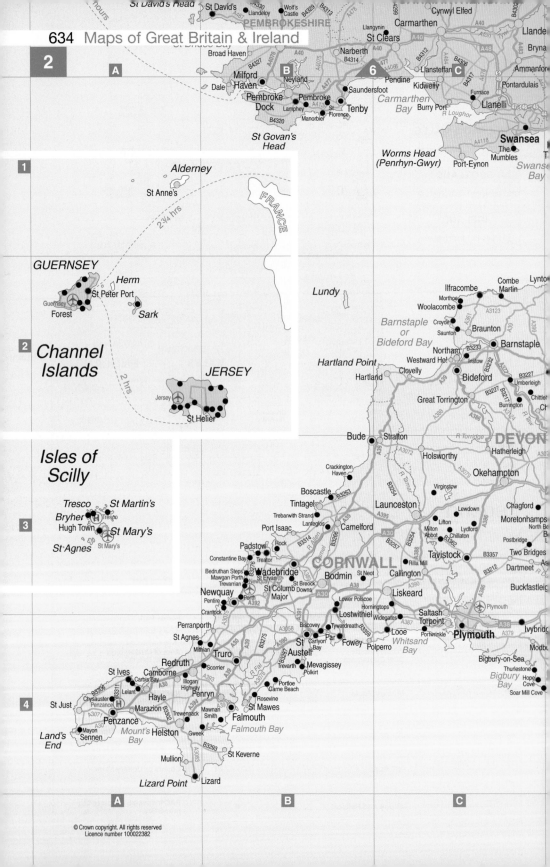

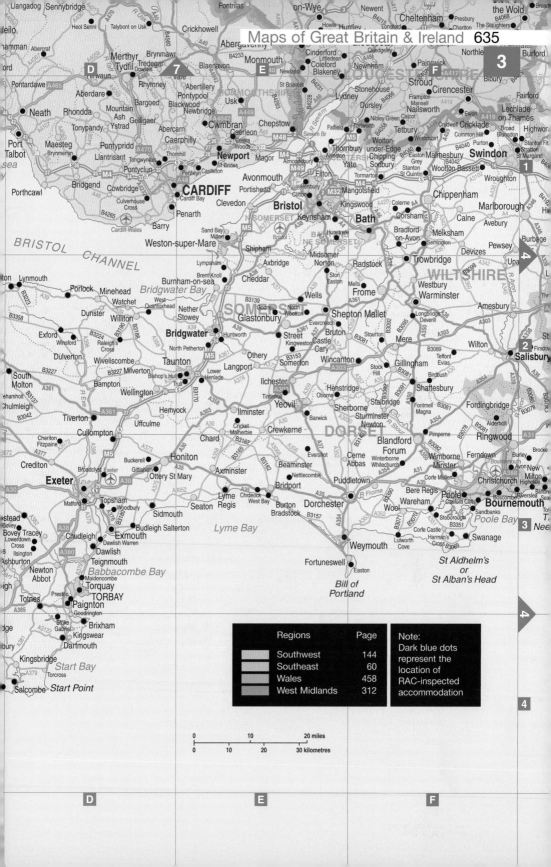

Regions	Page
Southwest	144
Southeast	60
Wales	458
West Midlands	312

Note:
Dark blue dots represent the location of RAC-inspected accommodation

0	10		20 miles
0	10	20	30 kilometres

Regions	Page
Southeast	60
Southwest	144
London	20
East Anglia	260
West Midlands	312
East Midlands	286

Note:
Dark blue dots
represent the
location of
RAC-inspected
accommodation

6

A   B   C

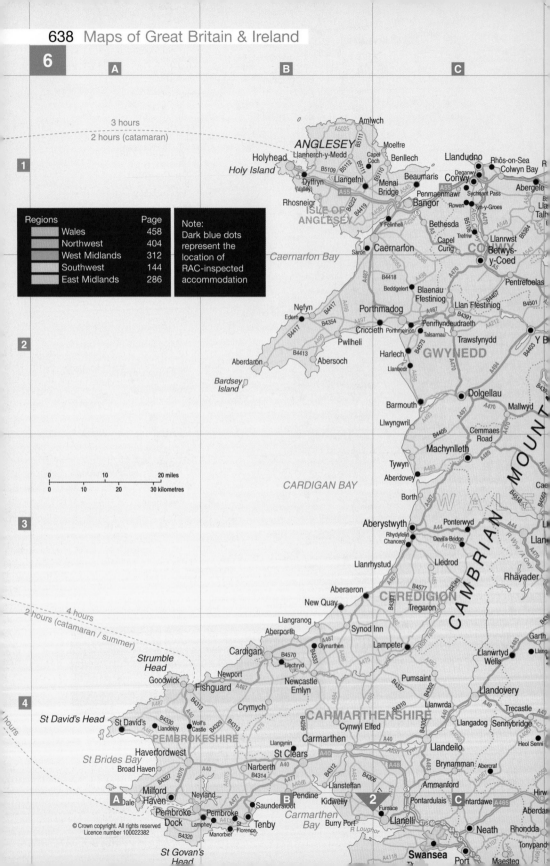

3 hours
2 hours (catamaran)

1

Amlwch
ANGLESEY
Holyhead
Holy Island
Llannerch-y-Medd
Moelfre
Capel
Coch
Benllech
Llandudno
Rhôs-on-Sea
Colwyn Bay
Dyffryn
(Valley)
Llangefni
Menai
Bridge
Beaumaris
Deganwy
Conwy
Sychnant Pass
Abergele
Lla
Tal
Rhosneigr
ISLE OF
ANGLESEY
Penmaenmawr
Bangor
Rowen
Tyn-y-Groes
Y Felinheli
Bethesda
Trefriw
Llanrwst
Caernarfon Bay
Saron
Caernarfon
Capel
Curig
Betwys-
y-Coed
CO

Regions	Page
Wales	458
Northwest	404
West Midlands	312
Southwest	144
East Midlands	286

Note:
Dark blue dots
represent the
location of
RAC-inspected
accommodation

Pentrefoelas

Beddgelert
Blaenau
Ffestiniog
Llan Ffestiniog

Nefyn
Edern
Porthmadog
Penrhyndeudraeth
Talsarnau
Trawsfynydd
Y B

2

Criccieth
Porthmeirion
Pwllheli
Harlech
Llanbedr
GWYNEDD

Aberdaron
Abersoch
Dolgellau
Mallwyd

Bardsey
Island
Barmouth

Llwyngwril
Cemmaes
Road

10   20 miles
10 20   30 kilometres

Machynlleth

Tywyn
Aberdovey

CARDIGAN BAY

Borth

Cae

W A L E

3

Aberystwyth
Ponterwyd
Rhydyfelin
Chancery
Devil's Bridge

Llanrhystud
Lledrod
Rhayader

CAMBRIAN MOUNT

Aberaeron
New Quay
Aberporth
CEREDIGION
Tregaron

Llangranog
Synod Inn

Cardigan
Llechryd
Llanwrtyd
Wells
Garth
Llang

4

Newport
Lampeter
Pumsaint
Llandovery
Trecastle

Goodwick
Fishguard
Newcastle
Emlyn
Crymych
CARMARTHENSHIRE
Llanwrda
Llangadog
Sennybridge

St David's Head
St David's
Landeloy
Wolf's
Castle
Cynwyl Elfed
Heol Senni

Haverfordwest
PEMBROKESHIRE
Llangynin
St Clears
Carmarthen
Llandeilo
Brynamman
Abercraf
Hirw

Broad Haven
Narberth
Llansteffan
Ammanford
Aberdar

Milford
Haven
Neyland
Pendine
Kidwelly
Pontardulais
Ontardawe
A465

Dale
Saundersfoot
Furnace
Llanelli

Pembroke
Dock
Lamphey
St
Florence
Tenby
Carmarthen
Bay
Burry Port
Neath
Rhondda

Manorbier
Swansea
Port
Tonypand

St Govan's
Head
Maestg

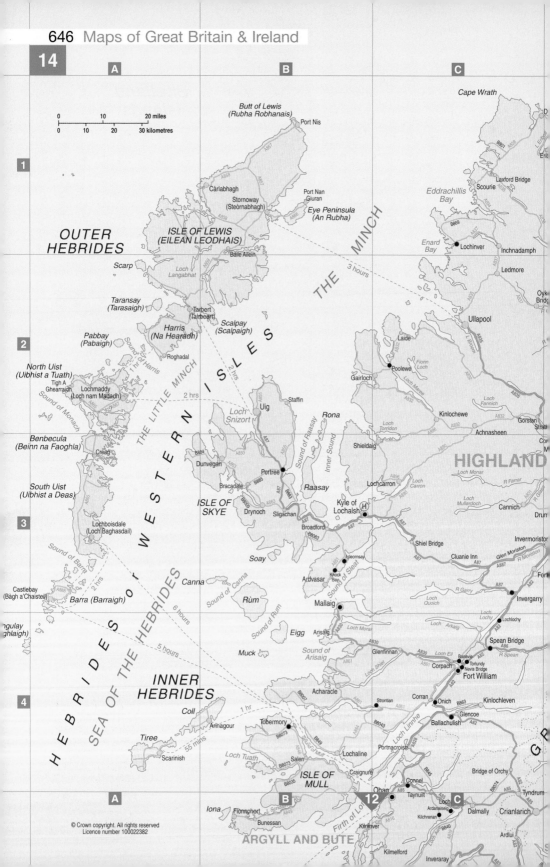

19

17

D | **E** | **F**

Region:

Republic
of Ireland
page 554

Note:
Dark blue dots
represent the
location of
RAC-inspected
accommodation

0   10   20 miles
0   10   20   30 kilometres

How the index works

```
                                                    location
                                            map number
                                          map grid reference
```

Abberley............................**7 E3**
   The Elms Hotel......315

```
                                          directory page reference
                                          hotel name
```

The index on the following pages alphabetically lists all of the locations shown on the gazetteer maps (pages 634-647) and London maps pages (20-23).

Where there is RAC accommodation at a location, the property name is listed and the property's directory page number and map reference shown. Please note, that there is not RAC accommodation at every location listed in this index, only at the locations where you see the property details listed.

The map number and grid reference is also displayed for each property within the main directory. This enables you to find a property's location on the gazetteer maps directly and without using the index.

Index to locations of Great Britain

Members
Look into bigger car insurance savings
Our new, 'Direct' approach means a more tailored quote for you

RAC Direct Insurance offers you:

✔ Extra discounts for RAC members

✔ Up to 70% no claims discount

✔ Windscreen repair or replacement

✔ Personal injury cover for you and your partner

✔ Optional courtesy car while yours is being repaired

✔ Optional cover for up to 90 days while you're driving anywhere in the EU.

Call now for bigger savings
0800 015 2284
Quoting ref RAC4
People behind people behind the wheel

RAC direct insurance

How the index works

location
map number
map grid reference

Ballycotton.............................19 D4
Bayview Hotel......563

directory page reference
hotel name

The index on the following pages alphabetically lists all of the locations shown on the gazetteer maps (pages 648-651).

Where there is RAC accommodation at a location, the property name is listed and the property's directory page number and map reference shown. Please note, that there is not RAC accommodation at every location listed in this index, only at the locations where you see the property details listed.

The map number and grid reference is also displayed for each property within the main directory. This enables you to find a property's location on the gazetteer maps directly and without using the index.

Index to locations of Ireland

Alphabetical Index to Accommodations

D

Alphabetical Index to Accommodations 691

To be avoided at all costs.

Call:1740*
from your mobile.

Call 1740 from your mobile for up to the minute news of tail-backs, bottlenecks and accidents on the road ahead.

always there

Notes

Notes

Notes

Notes